Fundamentals of Physics: A Senior Course

Fundamentals of Physics:
A Senior Course

David G. Martindale
Robert W. Heath
Philip C. Eastman

HEATH

D.C. Heath Canada Ltd.

Consumer and Corporate Affairs Canada has granted use of the National Symbol for Metric Conversion.

Canadian Cataloguing in Publication Data

Martindale, David G.
    Fundamentals of physics : A senior course

Includes index.
ISBN 0-669-95047-5

1. Physics.   I. Heath, Robert W.   II. Eastman, Philip, 1932–   III. Title.

QC21.2.M37 1986   530   C85-099930-8

Authors' acknowledgements

Producing a textbook on a subject of this magnitude cannot be the work solely of the authors, and we wish to thank the many people who have contributed to this book in various ways. The teachers who read all or part of the manuscript and offered many excellent comments and suggestions include William Konrad, Gunther Kamutzki, Bryan Kaufman, and Robert Squires. The senior administration at D.C. Heath Canada who approved the project and enthusiastically supported it at every stage were Robert Ross (President), Stephen Mills (former Vice-President), Martin Goldberg (Editor-in-Chief), and Susan Hall (former Managing Editor). The editorial assistance of Lana Kong was invaluable as well, when it came time to put the pieces together, not to mention ferreting out the photographs requested by the authors.

An extremely important aspect of any science textbook is both the quantity and quality of its illustrations and photographs. For their careful concern and creativity in the design and layout of this book, we especially thank Peter Maher and Nicholas Owocki of Newton Frank Arthur Inc.

A special word must be said about the editor of both this and our previous text. Tom Fairley was an outstanding editor, a fine gentleman, and a good friend, who, to our great regret, passed away during the early stages of the book. His work was most ably carried on by Bob Grundy and Lorraine Fairley.

Finally, we must salute our wives and children who, with patience and understanding, have encouraged us over the past five years, even though the project removed us from them for too many hours.

Design and illustration: NewtonFrankArthur Inc.

Cover photo: Four by Five Photography Inc.

Contents

12 Waves Travelling in One Dimension 446

13 Waves Travelling in Two Dimensions 482

Preface

For many students, *Fundamentals of Physics: A Senior Course* will be a continuation of *Fundamentals of Physics*, Heath, Macnaughton, and Martindale, D.C. Heath Canada, 1979, or a similar introductory course in high school physics. It is an algebra-based physics text that provides the prerequisite knowledge of the subject for university entrance. Although the Wave-Particle story-line is clearly visible, many other topics are included that are not found in the traditional PSSC approach to physics. More material is offered than could be covered in one school year, so it is expected that the teacher will select specific chapters and topics to meet the demands of the prescribed curriculum.

It has been the authors' intent to make the book readable and interesting, while at the same time providing a thorough examination of basic physical concepts. The book also includes applications that give insight into the relevance of physics in our modern, technological world. We hope that many students will be encouraged, thereby, to pursue the study of physics at university or college, whether they make it their major field of study, or take it as part of other professional training in such areas as engineering, medicine, or business.

The authors firmly believe that students learn physics best from their own experience, whether through laboratory investigation of physical principles or from the study and analysis of examples from everyday life. Accordingly, laboratory investigations have been provided at the end of most chapters, and nearly all the problems and examples are based on either life experience or examples in the physical world. As a rule, a topic begins with a concrete example that leads to a more formal and sometimes abstract summary of a physical principle.

Much attention is given to problem solving. When an equation has been developed, **Sample Problems** provide examples of the application of the physical principle. In some instances, alternate solutions are given. In every case, each step is clearly shown, including units, and the answer is stated to the correct number of significant digits. Additional comments that follow the solution, or are placed in the margin, emphasize the method of reasoning. Free-body diagrams are stressed, since skill in their use is very important for all students, especially those going on to study physics at university. The **Practice** problems that follow the sample problems are straightforward and of a similar nature. Second-order and multi-level problems, making use of the same concepts, are placed in the **Review** section at the end of each chapter. The review section is divided into two sub-sections: **Discussion** and **Problems**. The discussion questions can be answered by students working on their own or in class discussion. Some require research or work beyond the classroom, but most are based on the physical principles covered in the chapter. The problem questions ask for formal solutions and numerical answers. For the most part, they are arranged in the same order as the material in the text. Problems similar to those presented in the practice sections are followed by others of greater difficulty. The most difficult of all are located at the end of the review section. For every problem in the book, numerical answers are located near the questions for the student's convenience. In the case of practice problems, the answers are placed in brackets at the end of each problem, while for review problems they are listed in the margin on one of the final pages of the chapter. Full solutions for all problems, as well as sample results and hints for the investigations, are found in the teacher's guide, published separately. (Système International [SI] units are used throughout the text.)

One of the most useful techniques for solving problems in physics is the use of ratio and proportion. Because we believe this topic is important, we have included it in the first chapter of the book, and recommend that the contents of this chapter be covered, whether or not they are formally part of the curriculum.

Numerous examples are given in the text of different applications of physics. Marginal notes are used to record supplementary material, including the lives of some well-known scientists, secondary facts of interest, cross-references, and essential qualifications for statements made in the text. Throughout the text are more detailed articles on such physical applications as the G-suit, centripetal forces, laser light, xerography, and videodiscs.

The **Investigations** are designed to be done by students individually or in groups. In each case, the materials are listed and the steps numbered. Examples of the required charts are illustrated, and questions are asked which help form the basis for lab reports.

Seven **Appendices** are located at the end of the text. Most will be used only for reference, but Appendix F — Graphing Scientific Data — could be used as textual material. A full **Index** is located at the end of the book.

A physics textbook is probably one of the most difficult to publish free of error, but the responsibility for all errors lies, of course, with the authors. We welcome any corrections or comments.

D.G.M.   R.W.H.   P.C.E.

For our children:
Scott, Karen, and Kevin
David, Robbie, and Christopher
Gordon and Sidney

1 Measurement and Analysis

1.1 Introduction

"Using any reasonable definition of a scientist, we can say that between 80 and 90 percent of all the scientists that have ever lived are alive now. Now depending on what one measures and how, the crude size of science in manpower or in publications tends to double within a period of 10 to 15 years."

Derek de Solla Price, professor, history of science

Until the end of the 18th century, all scientific study, whether of plant and animal life or of non-living materials, was called natural philosophy. Knowledge had expanded to such an extent by that time that the study of material things was divided into two branches — the physical sciences for the study of non-living matter and the biological sciences for the study of living things.

By the end of the 19th century, the increase in knowledge of the physical sciences required that they be subdivided into two branches, physics and chemistry. There is a close relationship between these two branches. However, chemistry deals essentially with the interaction between different kinds of matter on a molecular scale, whereas physics is concerned mainly with the relationship between matter and energy.

Physics was broken down at first into broad areas of study such as mechanics, the properties of matter, waves, optics, electricity, and magnetism. As knowledge of the physical world expanded, particularly in the last 40 years, these divisions proved to be inadequate. Today, we find many further subdivisions for particular areas of study. These include, for example, solid-state physics, particle physics, nuclear physics, and plasma physics. At the same time, physics is fundamental to other branches of science, where we find subdivisions with such names as physical chemistry, optical chemistry, biophysics, geophysics, and astrophysics.

Physics involves, first, the measurement of certain properties of matter. These results are then analysed to determine any mathematical relationships between them. These relationships are usually described by means of equations, which is a convenient way of stating the laws that govern the physical world.

Once the laws of the universe and the equations that precisely express them are known, they can be used in the search for a fuller understanding of the world, and as an aid in building a better world for us to live in.

1.2 Fundamental Dimensions and Units

Many measurements in physics may be expressed in terms of fundamental quantities — length, mass, and time. Until recently, two systems of measurement were in common use around the world, the imperial system and the metric system. In 1960, a conference on weights and measures was held, involving representatives from most nations of the world. The participants decided to recommend that all countries use the same system of measurement — the metric system.

The metric system had taken various forms in the countries that had been using it. These were standardized and the number of units was reduced. The result is what is called the International System of Units (known in all countries as "SI", after the French name, Système International).

In SI, the base unit for length is the metre (m); for mass, the kilogram (kg); and for time, the second (s). Other units defined in terms of these base units are called derived units. A few examples of derived units are given in the margin. A complete list of the SI units is given in Appendix A.

Historically, the metric system used two systems of basic units. These were the "MKS" (metre, kilogram, second) system and "CGS" (centimetre, gram, second) system. Some scientists still refer to the SI units as MKS units.

Some SI-Derived Units

Quantity	Unit	Symbol
speed	metres per second	m/s
volume	cubic metre	m³
density	kilograms per cubic metre	kg/m³
force	kilogram metres per square second	kg·m/s²
pressure	newtons per square metre	N/m²

Some Metric Prefixes Used in This Course

Prefix	Abbreviation	Multiplier
giga-	G	× 10⁹
mega-	M	× 10⁶
kilo-	k	× 10³
centi-	c	× 10⁻²
milli-	m	× 10⁻³
micro-	μ	× 10⁻⁶
nano-	n	× 10⁻⁹

Length

The SI unit of length was originally defined as the distance, at 0°C, between two lines on a platinum-iridium bar that was kept in the International Office of Weights and Measures at Sèvres, near Paris, France. Copies of this bar were kept in most of the larger countries in the world. Metal bars, even finely constructed, can undergo

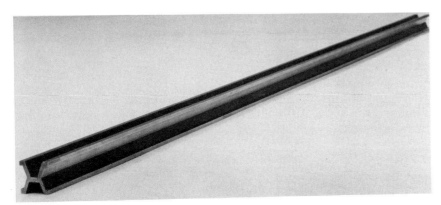

International prototype metre bar at Sèvres, France.

minute changes over a period of time. Modern science demanded more accuracy than could be given by the metal metre, and in 1960 it was decided to define the metre in terms of the wavelength of light, as follows: one metre is the length of 650 763.73 wavelengths of the orange-red spectral line emitted by krypton-86.

In 1983 the metre was redefined by the General Conference of Weights and Measures. Its length was defined as the distance that light travels in 1/299 792 458 s. This definition is based on the wave equation for light, $c = f\lambda$ (see Section 14.5), where the speed of light is given the exact value of 299 792 458 m/s. The latest standard was chosen not to alter the length of the metre as previously defined, but to express it with more precision. It is possible to measure frequencies with greater accuracy than wavelengths because of the precise definition of the second. This new definition is 10 000 times more precise than the previous krypton-based standard of length.

Other metric units of length were related to the metre by multiples or sub-multiples of 10, whereas multiples or sub-multiples of 1000 are generally preferred in SI. (Although the centimetre is not a preferred unit, it is acceptable for use in everyday applications.) Some of the multiples and sub-multiples of the metre are shown in the margin.

1 gigametre	= 1 Gm	= 10^9 m
1 megametre	= 1 Mm	= 10^6 m
1 kilometre	= 1 km	= 10^3 m
1 centimetre	= 1 cm	= 10^{-2} m
1 millimetre	= 1 mm	= 10^{-3} m
1 micrometre	= 1 μm	= 10^{-6} m
1 nanometre	= 1 nm	= 10^{-9} m

Mass

The mass of a body is a measure of the quantity of matter it contains. The basic SI unit of mass is the kilogram (kg). The standard kilogram is the mass of a certain cylindrical piece of platinum-iridium alloy kept at Sèvres. Some common multiples and sub-multiples and their relationships are:

$$1 \text{ t} = 1000 \text{ kg} \quad 10^3$$
$$1 \text{ g} = 10^{-3} \text{ kg}$$
$$1 \text{ mg} = 10^{-6} \text{ kg}$$
$$1 \text{ }\mu\text{g} = 10^{-9} \text{ kg}$$

The average rate of the Earth's spin has been decreasing very gradually for the last 400 million years, and in 1972 the world's timekeepers began adding a "leap second" to the length of each year. In 1981, this was changed to a leap second every 18 months. From the rate at which the Earth's rotation is decreasing, it is estimated that 400 million years ago a day lasted only about 20 h, and that in 500 million years a day will last 31 h.

Time

The Egyptians originated the first units of time. The Earth's rotation provided the standard — the solar day, which is the time from one high noon to the next. The day was divided into 24 equal segments, or hours, a division that has been used ever since. Each hour was divided into 60 min and each minute into 60 s. So the second was defined as 1/86 400 of a solar day.

This definition was adequate until this century, when more accurate timekeeping disclosed some inconsistencies. It was found that not all the days of the year are the same length. In fact, they can vary throughout the year by as much as seven minutes. The Earth's rotation is also slowing down, lengthening the average solar day by a small fraction of a second each year.

Because of this, it was decided to redefine the second in terms of the radiation emitted by a specific cesium atom, in what is called a cesium atomic clock. In this clock, cesium-133 electrons are excited into higher energy levels; then when these electrons fall and make the transition between two sharply defined energy levels, radiation of a certain frequency is emitted. Unlike astronomical observations, it is not subject to variation. Another advantage is that the frequency can be reproduced by a competent person anywhere on Earth or in space.

In 1967, the second was redefined as the interval of time representing 9 192 631 770 periods of radiation produced by a specific energy change in the cesium-133 atom. With a cesium atomic clock, time intervals can be measured with approximately 10 000 times the precision of astronomical methods.

A cesium atomic clock.

Practice

Express each of the following measurements in terms of the basic SI unit, e.g., 1.6 km = 1600 m.

(a) 0.56 km
(b)   75 cm
(c) 3224 mm
(d)   655 mm
(e)   961 μm

(f)   7564 g
(g) 0.056 t
(h)   252 g
(i)   52 μs
(j)   15 a (15 years)

(560 m, 0.75 m, 3.224 m, 0.655 m, 9.61×10^{-4} m, 7.564 kg, 56 kg, 2.52×10^{-4} kg, 5.2×10^{-5} s, 4.7×10^{8} s)

1.3 Scientific Notation — the Accuracy of Measured Quantities

Expressing the Accuracy of Measurements — Significant Digits

In physics, we measure many different physical quantities. No measured quantity is ever exact. There is always some error or uncertainty. The size of the error is determined both by the measuring device used and by the skill of the person using it. For example, if two students are measuring the frequency of a pendulum, one with an electronic stopwatch accurate to 1/1000 s, and the other with a wristwatch accurate to the nearest 1/2 s, their margins of error will differ because one measuring device is more accurate than the other. On the other hand, if both students are using the same electronic stopwatch, their measurements will probably again be different, because their reaction times will be different and one is more skilful or takes more care than the other.

The way in which a measured quantity is written down indicates not just the quantity but also its degree of accuracy. For example, if we measure the length of a desk and state it to be 1.638 m, we are indicating by the three measured digits to the right of the decimal point that we used a ruler that is accurate to the nearest 1/1000 of a metre. Digits that are obviously the result of careful measurement are called significant digits, or significant figures. The degree of accuracy of a measurement is shown by the number of significant digits it has.

While all non-zero digits are considered to be significant, it is not always easy to determine the number of significant digits when zeros occur in the measurement. For example, the distance from the Earth to the moon is commonly stated as 382 000 km. This number, as stated, is *probably* accurate only to the nearest 1000 km and thus has three significant digits (i.e., the 3, the 8, and the 2). The zeros merely indicate the position of the decimal point. Similarly, 0.000 536 cm contains only three significant digits.

However, zeros are sometimes significant. In each of the following cases there are four significant digits: 20.64 cm and 46.20 cm. In the second case, the zero indicates that the measurement is more accurate than 46.2 cm. Zeros after a decimal should not be added indiscriminately to a measured quantity, since each additional zero indicates a greater degree of accuracy.

Sometimes the nature of the measured quantity indicates the correct number of significant digits. For example, if a watch is used to measure 200 s, we know, since the watch has a sweep second hand, that the zeros are significant. Or, if a distance of 500 km is measured on a car's odometer, we can be fairly certain that the distance measured is accurate to the nearest kilometre, and thus to three significant digits. But, if no information is available, we must assume that the zeros are there only to place the decimal and are not significant. For example, 46 000 has only two significant digits.

A person with a wristwatch might reasonably be expected to measure time intervals to the nearest second.

$$1 \text{ s} = 0.017 \text{ min}$$
$$= 0.000 \ 28 \text{ h}$$

"MY GOODNESS, IT'S 12:15:0936420175. TIME FOR LUNCH."

Therefore, that person can measure such time intervals as these:

26 s

304 s

3.00 min

146.42 min

7.0006 h

A person with an ordinary stopwatch (1/10 s) can do better, and electronic stopwatches are accurate to 1/100 s.

0.01 s = 0.000 17 min

= 0.000 002 8 h

This means that a person with an electronic stopwatch can measure time intervals such as these:

11.23 s

4.0002 min

3.000 008 h

When we count objects, the number is exact. The degree of accuracy and the number of significant digits are not involved. For example, if we count the students in a class and get 32, we know that 32.2 or 31.9 are not possible answers. Only a whole-number answer is possible. Other examples of exact numbers are days in a month, swings of a pendulum, ticks from a recording timer, vibrations of a spring, electrons in an atom, and pennies in a dime.

Scientific Notation, or Standard Form

Trailing zeros in whole numbers can be confusing. For example, we said that 382 000 km, the distance to the moon, was *probably* accurate only to three significant digits, because when we give the number of kilometres as "382 000" we imply that we cannot be any more precise than that — presumably because we have no knowledge of the accuracy of the instruments and techniques that were used in making this measurement. In fact, the reading may be correct to the nearest 10 km rather than just the nearest 1000 km, but we cannot record that information by means of common notation. Unless we know differently, all trailing zeros in a whole number must be considered as place holders.

This problem is resolved by using what is called scientific notation, or standard form, which enables us to express very large and very small quantities in a form that is easily understood and conveys the number of significant digits. In scientific notation, the number is expressed by writing the correct number of significant digits with one non-zero digit to the left of the decimal point, and then multiplying the number by the appropriate power of 10 (positive or negative). Thus, if 382 000 km is accurate to the nearest 10 km, there are five significant digits, and the measurement should be expressed as 3.8200×10^5 km.

The number of electrons in a coulomb of charge is 6 242 000 000 000 000 000. This measurement is accurate only to four significant figures, but the degree of accuracy is not evident in the form in which it is recorded. In scientific notation it would be expressed as 6.242×10^{18}, which makes the number of significant digits quite clear. The mass of a proton is 0.000 000 000 000 000 000 000 000 001 672 kg. This measurement is known to be accurate to four significant digits, which is evident from the way it is written. But the form of the number is very inconvenient, and it is expressed in scientific notation as 1.672×10^{-27} kg.

Summary

- All counted quantities are exact.
- All measured quantities have some degree of error.
- All non-zero digits are significant; e.g., 259.67 has five significant digits.
- All zeros between non-zero digits and trailing zeros to the right of a decimal point are significant; e.g., 606 and 7.00 both have three significant digits.
- In whole numbers, all trailing zeros (those to the right of the last non-zero digit) are not considered to be significant unless, by inspection of the measured quantity, the number of significant digits can be assessed; e.g., 350 km on the odometer of a car would be assessed to have three significant digits.
- In decimal fractions smaller than 1, leading zeros (to the left of the first non-zero digit) are not significant; e.g., 0.003 68 has only three significant digits.
- In scientific notation, the number is expressed by writing the correct number of significant digits with one non-zero digit to the left of the decimal point, and then multiplying the number by the appropriate power of 10 (positive or negative).

Another convention sometimes used for scientific notation is that of writing all numbers as values between 0.1 and 1. Thus, 9 200 000 becomes 0.92×10^7. This convention is used in many computer systems.

Sample problems

1. How many significant digits are there in each of the following measured quantities?
   (a) 47.2 m $\hspace{5cm}$ (3)
   (b) 401.6 kg $\hspace{4.7cm}$ (4)

(c) 0.000 067 s   (2)
(d) 6.00 cm   (3)
(e) 46.03 m   (4)
(f) 0.000 000 000 68 m   (2)
(g) 0.07 m   (1)
2. Express each of the following numbers in scientific notation
   with the correct number of significant digits.
   *(a) 76 (7.6×10^1)
    (b) 0.60 (6.0×10^{-1})
    (c) 435 (4.35×10^2)
    (d) 5230 (four significant digits) (5.230×10^3)
    (e) 2 999 900 (five significant digits) (2.9999×10^6)
    (f) 0.000 16 (1.6×10^{-4})
    (g) 0.000 000 000 32 (3.2×10^{-10})
    (h) 760 (two significant figures) (7.6×10^2)
   *Scientific notation is optional for numbers between 1 and 100,
   except where the zeros preceding the decimal point create
   some uncertainty.

Practice

1. State the number of significant digits in each of the following.
   (a) 908   (b) 7.60   (c) 0.0050   (d) 0.010   (e) 760
   (f) 0.000 000 000 69   (g) 6.743
2. Express each of the following in scientific notation.
   (a) 6807   (b) 0.000 053   (c) 5200 (two significant digits)
   (d) 39 879 280 000 (seven significant digits)
   (e) 0.000 000 000 813   (f) 0.070 40
   (g) 40 000 000 000 (one significant digit)
   (h) 0.80   (i) 68
3. Express each of the following in common notation.
   (a) 7×10^1 (b) 5.2×10^3 (c) 8.3×10^9
   (d) 10.1×10^{-2} (e) 6.3868×10^3 (f) 4.086×10^{-3}
   (g) 6.3×10^2

Answers
1. (a) 3   (b) 3   (c) 2   (d) 2
   (e) 2   (f) 2   (g) 4
2. (a) 6.807×10^3 (b) 5.3×10^{-5}
   (c) 5.2×10^3 (d) $3.987 928 \times 10^{10}$
   (e) 8.13×10^{-10} (f) 7.040×10^{-2}
   (g) 4×10^{10} (h) 8.0×10^{-1}
   (i) 6.8×10
3. (a) 70   (b) 5200
   (c) 8 300 000 000   (d) 0.101
   (e) 638 680   (f) 0.004 086
   (g) 630

Calculations Involving Measured Quantities

Often in physics a measured quantity is combined mathematically with another measured quantity, using such operations as addition, subtraction, multiplication, division, or square root. It is important that the mathematical operations do not themselves appear to express accuracy that is not based on direct measurement. As a general rule, the results of the mathematical operations can be no more accurate than the *least* accurate direct measurement used in the calculation.

Addition and Subtraction

Suppose we have three measurements of length that are to be added together, e.g., 6.6 m, 18.74 m, and 0.766 m. Since the least precise measurement is 6.6 m (it is accurate to only the nearest 0.1 m), the sum cannot be expressed any more accurately than to the nearest 0.1 m. Thus the sum of 26.106 m has to be rounded off to 26.1 m. A similar procedure is followed in subtraction.

$$
\begin{array}{r}
6.6 \text{ m} \\
18.74 \text{ m} \\
\underline{0.766 \text{ m}} \\
26.106 \text{ m} \\
\text{or } 26.1 \text{ m}
\end{array}
$$

In rounding off to the correct number of significant digits, if the digit to be dropped is greater than 5, the next digit to the left is increased by 1. If the digit to be dropped is less than 5, the preceding digit remains the same. If the digit to be dropped is 5, the preceding digit is usually increased (see marginal note).

Rounding off is of particular importance when electronic calculators are being used. Even the simplest calculation may generate eight digits. It is important to understand when and how to round off, and to know the correct number of significant digits to use when rounding off.

It is a common misconception that the dividing line is 5, when a value expressed in scientific notation is being rounded off. The dividing line is $\sqrt{10}$, or 3.16. For example, $3.25 \times 10^4 \approx 10^5$, but $2.95 \times 10^4 \approx 10^4$. This is because the rounding off is to the closest integral power of ten.

Multiplication and Division

The area of a rectangle whose dimensions are given as 14.25 cm and 6.43 cm is (by multiplication) 91.6275 cm². The product appears to be much more accurate than the two measurements, though this obviously could not be so. In any measured quantity, the last digit is the least reliable, and any calculation that involves this least reliable digit will itself be unreliable.

If we examine the multiplication of these two numbers, we note that the digits 6275 in the product were obtained by calculations involving the last digit in each number. The degree of unreliability increases from left to right, so that the 6 is not as unreliable as the 2 and so on. Since for all measured quantities the last digit involves some degree of unreliability, the product may reasonably be rounded off and expressed as 91.6 cm². (The least reliable digits are printed in a different colour.)

$$
\begin{array}{r}
14.25 \\
6.43 \\
\hline
42.75 \\
570.0 \\
8550. \\
\hline
91.6275
\end{array}
$$

In general, the product of two or more measured quantities is only as accurate as the factor that has the fewest significant digits, regardless of the decimal point. This rule also holds for division, squaring, and square root.

In this case, 14.25 (four significant digits) times 6.43 (three significant digits) gives a product of 91.6 (three significant digits).

Sometimes a calculation is easier to perform if scientific notation is used. In the answer to the expression $7\ 640 \times \dfrac{0.006\ 50}{0.054}$, for example, there may be some difficulty in placing the decimal point correctly. If the numbers are expressed in scientific notation and the powers of 10 are moved to the right, the mathematical operations will be easier to perform and there should be no difficulty in determining the proper position of the decimal point.

$$10^n \times 10^m = 10^{n+m}$$
$$10^n \div 10^m = 10^{n-m}$$
$$(10^n)^m = 10^{nm}$$

$$
\begin{aligned}
\frac{7\ 640 \times 0.006\ 50}{0.054} &= \frac{(7.64 \times 10^3)(6.50 \times 10^{-3})}{5.4 \times 10^{-2}} \\
&= \frac{(7.64)(6.50)}{(5.4)} \times \frac{(10^3)(10^{-3})}{10^{-2}} \\
&= 9.1963 \times 10^2 \\
&= 9.2 \times 10^2 \quad \text{(correct to two significant digits)}
\end{aligned}
$$

Fundamentals of Physics: A Senior Course

Summary

- When adding or subtracting measured quantities, the answer should be expressed to the same number of decimal places as the *least* precise quantity used in the calculation.
- When multiplying, dividing, or finding the square root of measured quantities, the answer should have the same number of significant digits as the *least* precise quantity used in the calculation.

Sample problems

1. What is the sum of 15.35 g + 236.4 g + 0.645 g?

   15.35 g + 236.4 g + 0.645 g = 252.395 g, or 252.4 g

   Since the least precise measurement is 236.4 g, the answer can only be precise to 1/10 of a gram, or one decimal place. Thus the answer is rounded off to 252.4 g.

2. Perform the following operations to the correct number of significant digits.

   (a) 87.63 m − 54.1 m = 33.53 m, or 33.5 m (correct to one decimal place)

   (b) 65.6 × 0.62 = 40.672, or 41 (correct to two significant digits)

   (c) 452.6 ÷ 37.2 = 12.167, or 12.2 (correct to three significant digits)

   (d) 4.9 ÷ 2.2 = 2.227, or 2.2 (correct to two significant digits)

Practice

1. Perform the following mathematical operations, expressing the answers to the correct number of significant digits.

   (a) 463.66 + 29.2 + 0.17   (b) 426.66 − 39.2

   (c) (2.6)(42.2)   (d) (65)(0.041)(325)

   (e) (0.0060)(26)(55.1)   (f) $\dfrac{650}{4.0}$

   (g) $\dfrac{0.452}{0.012}$ (h) $\dfrac{(5.21)(0.45)}{0.0060}$

   (i) 3.5^2 (j) $\sqrt{4.9}$

2. Simplify each of the following, using scientific notation where appropriate.

   (a) $10^2 \times 10^1$ (b) $10^4 \times 10^2$ (c) $10^{-2} \times 10^5$

   (d) $10^{-6} \times 10^2$ (e) $10^2 \div 10^5$ (f) $10^4 \div 10^7$

   (g) $10^{-6} \div 10^2$ (h) $10^{-6} \div 10^{-7}$ (i) $(1.4 \times 10^2)(3 \times 10^1)$

   (j) $(3.5 \times 10^4)(2.0 \times 10^{-3})$ (k) $(5.0 \times 10^{-5})(4.00 \times 10^{-3})$

Answers

1. (a) 493.0   (b) 387.5
   (c) 1.1×10^2 (d) 8.7×10^2
   (e) 8.6   (f) 1.6×10^2
   (g) 38   (h) 3.9×10^3
   (i) 12   (j) 2.2
2. (a) 10^3 (b) 10^6
   (c) 10^3 (d) 10^{-4}
   (e) 10^{-3} (f) 10^{-3}
   (g) 10^{-8} (h) 10^1
   (i) 4×10^3 (j) 7.0×10^1, or 70
   (k) 2.0×10^{-7} (l) 1.7×10^4
   (m) 1.4×10^{-25} (n) 1.8×10^8
   (o) 3.33×10^{-17} (p) 8.3×10^{-5}
   (q) 6.0×10^2 (r) 4.1
3. 4.0×10^2 atoms
4. 1.1×10^{25} atoms

(l) $\dfrac{5.0 \times 10^7}{3.0 \times 10^3}$ (m) $\dfrac{6.63 \times 10^{-34}}{4.8 \times 10^{-9}}$

(n) $\dfrac{(5.0 \times 10^6)(7.0 \times 10^{-4})}{2.00 \times 10^{-5}}$ (o) $\dfrac{(6.63 \times 10^{-34})(3.00 \times 10^8)}{5.98 \times 10^{-9}}$

(p) $\dfrac{(0.534)(6.2 \times 10^{-3})}{4.0 \times 10^1}$ (q) $\dfrac{(360)(5.0 \times 10^{-4})}{0.000\ 30}$

(r) $\dfrac{(6.67 \times 10^{-11})(5.98 \times 10^{24})(50)}{(7.0 \times 10^7)^2}$

3. If a gold atom is considered to be a cube with sides 2.5×10^{-9} m, how many gold atoms could stack on top of one another in gold foil with a thickness of 1.0×10^{-7} m?

4. On the average, 1.0 kg of aluminum consists of 2.2×10^{25} atoms. How many atoms would there be in a block of aluminum 10 cm by 1.2 cm by 15.6 cm, if the density of aluminum is 2.7 g/cm³, or 2.7×10^3 kg/m³.

1.4 Rapid Estimation — Orders of Magnitude

It is often useful to be able to estimate the value for a quantity. This may be because you want to check a calculation quickly, to determine whether the decimal is properly placed or whether the numbers were entered properly in an electronic calculator. When an exact solution is not needed and/or an accurate calculation would take more time than it is worth, a rapid estimation will do.

Orders of magnitude of length within the universe, in metres. The numbers above the scale are powers of 10. The Earth is about halfway between the smallest and largest objects known to exist.

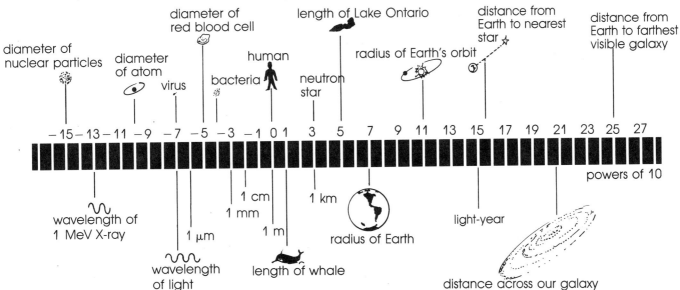

To make an "orders of magnitude" estimate, all numbers are rounded off to one significant digit plus its power of 10. After the calculation has been made, only one significant digit is retained. Some examples will illustrate how a rapid estimation is made.

Sample problems

1. Estimate the number of seconds in a year.

   number of seconds = (seconds/hour)(hours/day)(days/year)
   $$= (3600 \text{ s/h})(24 \text{ h/d})(365.25 \text{ d/a})$$
   $$\approx (4 \times 10^3)(2 \times 10)(4 \times 10^2)$$
   $$\approx 3 \times 10^7 \text{ s}$$

   The comparable answer to four significant figures is 3.156×10^7 s.

2. Estimate the volume of water in a round reservoir approximately 1 km in diameter, if the average depth of the water is 15 m.

   volume of water $= \pi r^2 h$
   $$\approx (3)(5 \times 10^2 \text{ m})^2(1 \times 10 \text{ m})$$
   $$\approx 75 \times 10^5$$
   $$\approx 8 \times 10^6 \text{ m}^3$$
   $$\approx 1 \times 10^7 \text{ m}^3$$

3. Approximately how many ping-pong balls with a radius of 1.8 cm could you put in a classroom whose dimensions are 18 m × 11 m × 4 m?

   volume of room $= (18 \text{ m})(11 \text{ m})(4 \text{ m})$
   $$\approx (2 \times 10)(1 \times 10)(4)$$
   $$\approx 8 \times 10^2 \text{ m}^3$$
   $$\approx 8 \times 10^8 \text{ cm}^3$$

   volume of one ping-pong ball $= 4/3 \ \pi r^3$
   $$\approx 4/3 \ (3)(2 \text{ cm})^3$$
   $$\approx 3 \times 10 \text{ cm}^3$$

   The estimated number of balls is $\dfrac{8 \times 10^8 \text{ cm}^3}{3 \times 10 \text{ cm}^3} \approx 3 \times 10^7$.

≈ means "equals approximately".

One light-year is the distance travelled by light in one year. The distances in outer space are so great that metre and kilometre units are too small to be practical. As well as the light-year, astronomers use the *astronomical unit*, 1.50×10^{11} m, and the *parsec*, 3.09×10^{16} m. None of these units are SI units.

Practice

1. Estimate the number of minutes in a human lifetime of 80 years. $(3 \times 10^7 \text{ min})$
2. Estimate the area of Canada in square kilometres, without using a calculator. $(2 \times 10^7 \text{ km}^2)$
3. The speed of light is 3.00×10^8 m/s. How many metres are there in a light-year? $(1 \times 10^{16} \text{ m})$

4. A gold atom is approximately 2.5×10^{-10} m in "diameter". Estimate the number of atoms in a cubic centimetre of gold. Assume that the gold atoms line up in rows. (3×10^{22})
5. How many cups of water are required to fill a typical bathtub? (3×10^3)

1.5 Expressing Error in Measurement

Observations and experiments constitute the basis of all natural science. But all observations and experiments involving numerical results are the result of measurements that contain some degree of error. From a practical standpoint, it is important to be able to estimate both the errors incurred in making measurements and the errors resulting from what is done with those measurements, because it is only then that we can safely use the conclusions drawn from the observations.

No matter how small the divisions on a measuring scale, there is a limit to the accuracy of any measurement made with it. Every measurement made on every scale has some unavoidable possibility of error, usually assumed to be one-half of the smallest division marked on the scale. The accuracy of calculations involving measured quantities is often indicated by a statement of the **possible error**.

Possible error can best be explained by an example. Using a metric ruler calibrated in centimetres and millimetres, you are asked to measure the length of a block of wood to the nearest millimetre. You do so and obtain the result of, say, 126 mm. Assuming that you read the numbers on the ruler correctly, the maximum possible error in your measurement is 0.5 mm. The possible error in the measurement would be indicated by 126 ± 0.5 mm.

Absolute error is the difference between the measured or observed value and the accepted value. The equation for absolute error is

absolute error = measured value − accepted value

Relative error is expressed as a percentage, and is usually called **percentage error**. It is calculated as follows:

$$\text{percentage error} = \frac{\text{absolute error}}{\text{accepted value}} \times 100\%$$

Sometimes, in an investigation, a calculation of a known value is being determined. For example, in an investigation to measure the acceleration due to gravity (see Section 5.14), the experimenter

The possible error in the measurement of the block may be expressed as a percentage error, as follows:
$$\frac{0.5 \text{ mm}}{126 \text{ mm}} \times 100\%$$
$$= 0.4\%$$
Note that the same possible error in a smaller block of wood, for example, a block 8.0 mm long, would give a larger percentage error:
$$\frac{0.5 \text{ mm}}{8.0 \text{ mm}} \times 100\% = 6\%$$

In everyday usage, "accuracy" and "precision" are used interchangeably, but in science it is important to make a distinction between them.

Accuracy refers to the closeness of a measurement to the accepted value for a specific quantity.

Precision is the degree of agreement among several measurements that have been made in the same way.

Target Shooting

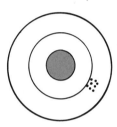

Good precision,
poor accuracy

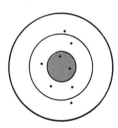

Poor precision,
average accuracy

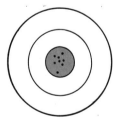

Good precision,
good accuracy

calculates a value of 9.5 m/s². Since the accepted value at the Earth's surface is known to be 9.8 m/s², the percentage error is calculated as follows:

$$\text{percentage error} = \frac{\text{absolute error}}{\text{accepted value}} \times 100\%$$

$$= \frac{\text{measured value} - \text{accepted value}}{\text{accepted value}} \times 100\%$$

$$= \frac{9.5\ \text{m/s}^2 - 9.8\ \text{m/s}^2}{9.8\ \text{m/s}^2} \times 100\%$$

$$= -3.1\%$$

The negative sign indicates that the measured value was less than the accepted value. A positive sign would indicate that the measured value was greater than the accepted value.

Sometimes, if two values of the same quantity are measured, it is useful to compare the precision of these values by calculating the percentage difference between them, as follows:

$$\frac{\text{percentage}}{\text{difference}} = \frac{\text{difference in measurements}}{\text{average measurement}} \times 100\%$$

For example, if two measurements of the acceleration due to gravity are 9.6 m/s² and 9.2 m/s², their percentage difference is calculated as follows:

$$\text{percentage difference} = \frac{0.4\ \text{m/s}^2}{9.4\ \text{m/s}^2} \times 100\%$$

$$= 4.3\%$$

Practice

1. A student measures the acceleration due to gravity and finds it to be 9.72 m/s². What is his percentage error, if the accepted value is 9.81 m/s²?   (−0.92%)

2. You estimate that the maximum possible error of an equal-arm balance is 0.01 g. What is the possible percentage error when you use this balance to measure each of the following masses?
   (a) 700 g   (b) 20 g   (c) 3 kg   (d) 1.0 g
   (0.001%, 0.05%, 0.0003%, 1%)

3. When determining Planck's constant (see Section 18.1), a student's measurements produce values of 5.78×10^{-34} J·s and 7.29×10^{-34} J·s. If the accepted value is 6.63×10^{-34} J·s, what is
   (a) the percentage difference for the measured values?
   (b) the percentage error for each value?
   (23%; −12.8%, 10.0%)

1.6 Measuring Short Time Intervals

One way to measure a motion so rapid that it is a blur to our eyes is to make a series of photographs of it at very short intervals, and analyse the photographs. Suppose we use a movie camera set to make 24 frames (individual pictures) per second, and we find that the motion we are interested in is completed in four frames. We know, then, that the motion took 1/6 s.

To "freeze" and measure an extremely fast motion, we use a stroboscope. Instead of a camera shutter opening and closing rapidly, brief (1/30 000 s) flashes of intense light are directed at the object to be photographed, in a darkened room. A camera with its shutter open will record an image each time the light flashes. With a still camera, one picture composed of a series of images is created. If a synchronized movie camera is used, a series of still pictures is obtained.

Illustrated below is a multiple-exposure photograph of a bouncing golf ball. The photograph was taken at a flash rate of 20 Hz, so the time between images was 1/20 s, or 0.05 s. By measuring the distance between successive images on the photograph, and scaling this measurement, the speed of the ball at various points in its path can be caculated. Also it is clear from the photograph how the ball's speed changed as it bounced.

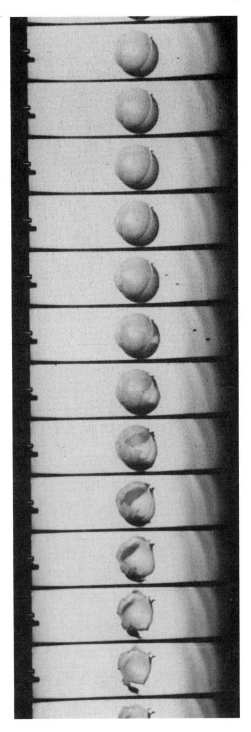

If the interval between flashes is known, it is possible to determine the time taken by the action photographed. For example, for the series of 13 photographs reproduced on the right, the flash rate was 4000 Hz, making each of the 12 intervals 1/4000 s. Therefore, the total time for a series of 13 pictures was 12/4000 s = 3/1000 s. By analysing frames 3, 4, and 5, we learn that the bullet took less than 1/2000 s to pass through the balloon. Also, the balloon collapsed in 10 frames, or 1/400 s. Such an analysis would not be possible without a stroboscope.

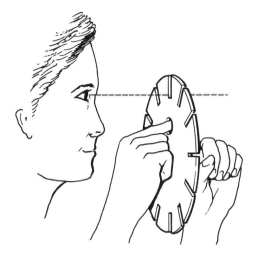

Note that frequency and period are reciprocals of each other. In other words, $f = \frac{1}{T}$ and $T = \frac{1}{f}$.

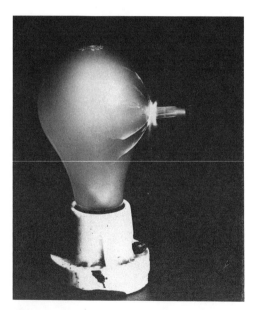

This high-speed photograph, of a thirty-calibre bullet penetrating a light bulb, was taken at a rate of less than one million flashes per second.

A typical laboratory stroboscope is constructed with a xenon flash tube that is electronically controlled to flash at a uniform rate, typically from 1 Hz to 250 Hz.

It is also possible to measure short intervals involved in periodic motion without using multiple-flash photography. In an alternative technique, a large disc with slits spaced at equal intervals around its circumference is used. The disc is designed to turn freely and may be hand-held. When the disc is positioned in front of the eye, as illustrated, the moving object is glimpsed each time an open slit passes in front of the eye, and only then.

To see how the hand stroboscope works, we will consider how it could be used to study the motion of a simple pendulum. When the pendulum is set in motion, it will swing back and forth at a regular rate. Its frequency will be the number of cycles, or complete back-and-forth swings, that it completes in one second.

For example, if the pendulum completes 20 cycles in 10 s, its frequency (f) is $\frac{20 \text{ cycles}}{10 \text{ s}} = 2.0$ Hz. The period (T) of a pendulum is the time for one cycle, in this case 0.50 s. If the motion of the pendulum is viewed through a strobe disc, the observer will get a glimpse of it only when an open slit lines up with the eye. If only one slit is open, the viewer will get only one "look" per rotation of the disc.

Suppose that we spin the stroboscope so that the single open slit goes around in exactly the same time that the pendulum takes to complete one cycle. The pendulum will appear to stand still, even though it is swinging. In this example, the time for one rotation of the strobe is exactly the same as the period of the pendulum. In other words, their periods are equal. If the stroboscope goes a little too slowly or too quickly, we will catch glimpses of the pendulum in slightly different positions of its cycle, and it will appear to be moving slowly. Thus, by adjusting the speed of the stroboscope to make the pendulum appear to stand still, we make their frequencies equal. By measuring the rotation rate of the strobe, we can determine the frequency, or period, of the pendulum. We can do this with any object executing a periodic motion.

The same technique can be used to measure the frequency, or period, of an object that is moving too fast to be measured directly. If more slits are opened, then there are more "looks" per rotation of the strobe. For example, if four equally spaced slits are open and the disc is rotated 10 times in 2.5 s, the rotational frequency of the disc is 4.0 Hz. But, the "look" frequency will be 16 Hz, which is four times faster. If the strobe, in this example, "stopped" a black mark on the edge of a turning rotator, the frequency of the rotator would be the same as the "look" frequency of the stroboscope,

16 Hz. This example illustrates the fact that a stroboscope can time events that are much shorter than the rotation time of the disc — as many times shorter as there are equally spaced slits in the disc.

Errors can easily be made with a stroboscope if it is not correctly used. For example, in the one-slit strobe, "stopping" the motion of the pendulum may occur every second or every third swing for each rotation of the disc. Similarly, when the speed of a rapidly rotating object is being measured with a multiple-slit strobe, the motion may be "stopped", but at a "look" rate that is a sub-multiple of the correct rate. On the other hand, if the strobe is rotated too quickly, the object, or a mark on an oscillating object, may be seen more than once in each cycle, and will therefore appear as a multiple image. In this case the strobe frequency is too high. How can we make sure that the hand stroboscope is being rotated at the correct "stopping" frequency? The following steps should be followed.

- Rotate the strobe disc, increasing the rate gradually until the motion is stopped.
- Since the highest rotation rate of the strobe that stops the object is the correct one, continue to increase the rate gradually through a series of "stopped" single images, until the object is "stopped" at more than one location. Then, gradually reduce the rotation rate until a "stopped" single image is again seen. This will be the highest rate that produces a single "stopped" image.
- Determine the rotational frequency of the strobe by measuring the time for 10 complete rotations.
- Multiply this rotational frequency by the number of open slits to obtain the "look" frequency. The highest "look" frequency is equal to the frequency of the oscillating object.

**frequency of oscillating object = highest "look" frequency
= highest strobe frequency × number of open slits**

A stroboscope, like any instrument, has its limitations. If the disc is moving too rapidly, it is possible that insufficient light will pass through each slit to allow the viewer to see clearly. An alternative is to illuminate the oscillating object with a multiple-flash strobe light. The technique is the same as that outlined above except that the frequency of the flashing light is adjusted until the highest "stopping" frequency is achieved. The "look" frequency is read directly from the scale on the strobe light to determine the frequency of the oscillating object. Most scientists, if they have a choice, will use the strobe light, but in some cases, such as the study of water waves, the hand strobe may have to be used (see Chapter 12).

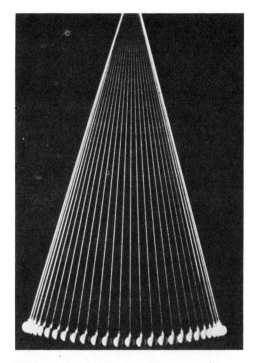

Strobe photo of a swinging pendulum.

The frequency of the object being studied is equal to the "look" frequency or any integral (whole number) multiple of it.

Sample problems

1. A single-slit hand strobe is rotated at a rate of 15 r (revolutions) in 10 s. If this "stops" a spinning object, what are its possible rotational frequencies? How would you isolate the correct frequency?

$$\text{strobe frequency} = \frac{15 \text{ cycles}}{10 \text{ s}} = 1.5 \text{ Hz}$$

The possible frequencies of the object are 1.5 Hz, 3.0 Hz, 4.5 Hz, etc., since the strobe may be producing a "look" in every cycle, every two cycles, every three cycles, etc. To isolate the correct frequency, the strobe frequency would have to be increased to the highest frequency at which a single image occurs.

2. A twelve-slit strobe disc is rotated at the highest stopping frequency for a vibrating object. The *strobe* is rotated at 4.0 Hz.
   (a) What is the period of the vibrating object?
   (b) If every second slit is covered with tape, how fast would the strobe now have to be rotated to "stop" the same object?

   (a) "look" frequency $= 12 \times 4.0$ Hz $= 48$ Hz
   $$T = \frac{1}{f} = \frac{1}{48 \text{ Hz}} = 0.021 \text{ s}$$
   (b) Since every second slit is taped up, only six are open. To achieve the same "look" frequency, the strobe would have to rotate to make $\quad 6 \times f = 48$ Hz
   $$f = 8.0 \text{ Hz}$$

Practice

1. (a) Find the periods corresponding to each of the following frequencies.
   (i) 100 Hz   (ii) 0.60 Hz   (iii) 2.0×10^3 Hz
                            (0.01 s, 1.7 s, 5.0×10^{-4} s)
   (b) Find the frequencies corresponding to each of the following periods.
   (i) 0.10 s   (ii) 0.02 s   (iii) 1.0 s
                           (10 Hz, 50 Hz, 1.0 Hz)
2. A disc stroboscope contains four open slits and is turned six times in 10 s. What is the interval between successive glimpses, seen through the stroboscope?   (0.42 s)
3. An eight-slit strobe is rotated 20 times in 9.0 s, "stopping" the waves in a ripple tank. How would you check to make sure that you are rotating the strobe at the highest "stopping" frequency? What is the frequency of the waves?   (18 Hz)
4. A twelve-slit strobe "stops" the rotation of an electric drill when

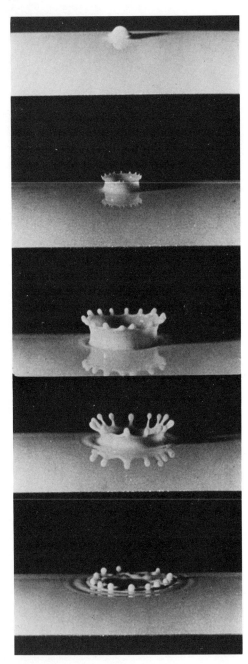

A series of strobe photos showing a drop of milk falling onto a thin layer of milk.

the strobe rotates 24 times in 10.0 s. If this is the highest "stopping" frequency, what is the rate of rotation of the drill, in revolutions per minute?   (1.73×10^3 r/min)

5. A ten-slit stroboscope was rotated at a constant rate for 20.0 s. It was used to determine that the period of a spinning motor shaft was 0.025 s. How many rotations did the stroboscope make during the 20 s interval?   (80)

6. A six-slit stroboscope is rotated at the highest "stopping" frequency of 2.5 Hz for the blade of a food processor.
    (a) What is the period of the processor blade?
    (b) If every second slit on the strobe is taped closed, how fast must the strobe be rotated in order to be at the highest "stopping" frequency for the same food processor blade?
                                     (0.067 s, 5.0 Hz)

1.7 Analysing Experimental Data — Proportioning Techniques

In physics, we seek to correlate things we observe, that is, to see how a change in one quantity affects the value of another quantity. For example, how does the elapsed time affect the distance a car travels? Or, what is the relationship between the speed of a falling ball and the air resistance opposing the ball's motion? Or, how does the distance separating two masses affect the force of gravity between them? The stating of such relationships in a concise form is central to the structure of physics. The statements themselves become the laws of physics.

The statement of how one quantity varies in relation to another is called a **proportionality** expression. Most of the relationships described in this text are relatively simple, being either direct or inverse variations (proportions). An example of a direct proportion is the relationship between the distance travelled from the starting position and the time, for an object travelling at a uniform speed. As seen in the chart, when the time doubles, the distance doubles; when the time triples, the distance triples; and so on.

time (s)	1	2	3	4	5	6	7
distance (m)	28	56	84	112	140	168	196

Mathematically, we say that distance is directly proportional to time, or

$$d \propto t$$

Above and below the chart are arrows indicating that d's multiplier and t's multiplier are equal for the same pairs of numbers. This means that, if $d \propto t$, then

$$d\text{'s multiplier} = t\text{'s multiplier}$$

In the case of an inverse proportion, for example, the relationship between the frequency (f) and period (T) of a vibrating object, the multipliers are reciprocals of each other.

frequency (Hz)	5	10	20	50	75	100
period (s)	0.2	0.1	0.05	0.02	0.013	0.01

In this case, the frequency's multiplier must be inverted to get the period's multiplier. If $f \propto \dfrac{1}{T}$, then

$$f\text{'s multiplier} = \text{the reciprocal of } T\text{'s multiplier}$$

When a scientist attempts to determine how one measurable physical quantity (y) varies with another (x), he usually performs an experiment in which all other variables that might affect y are kept constant, and then he measures values of y for various values of x. The experiment thus yields a table of values, or a set of ordered pairs, for y and x, such as those listed in the sample problems, below. The scientist uses such tables to determine the relationship between y and x, asking the question, "What must I do to x's multiplier to get y's multiplier?"

Sample problems

1.

y	x
250	3
750	9
2500	30
5000	60

y's multiplier = x's multiplier

∴ y ∝ x

2.

A	B
20	14
80	28
180	42
2000	140

×4   ×2

× 100   × 10

A's multiplier = B's multiplier squared

∴ A ∝ B²

3.

F	r
900	1
225	2
36	5
14	18
1	30

× 1/4   × 2

× 1/25   × 5

× 1/900   × 30

F's multiplier = the reciprocal of r's multiplier squared

$$\therefore F \propto \frac{1}{r^2}$$

Practice

Determine the proportion for each of the following tables of values.

A	B
2	100
8	200
50	500
200	1000

C	D
3	120
6	60
9	40
12	30

E	F
2	90
54	270
16	180
250	450

G	H
6	5
12	20
18	45
42	245

K	L
7	800
35	32
28	50
70	8

M	N
2	3
4	24
6	81
8	192

The examples used above involve easily calculated multipliers and ones that showed the relationship clearly. In practice, experimental results always involve some error, and the relationship may not be as obvious. In these cases, graphs can be used to determine the correct proportion.

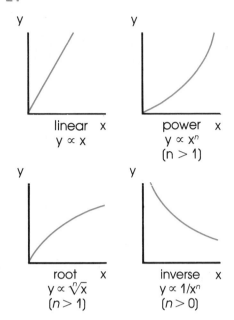

linear x
$y \propto x$

power x
$y \propto x^n$
$(n > 1)$

root x
$y \propto \sqrt[n]{x}$
$(n > 1)$

inverse x
$y \propto 1/x^n$
$(n > 0)$

First, plot y versus x. The variable on the left of the proportion is called the dependent variable, and it is usually plotted on the vertical axis. Four basic graph types are illustrated.

Note that the only graph that is a straight line and passes through zero is $y \propto x$. Thus, if when the experimental values are plotted they form a straight line through the origin, the proportion must be $y \propto x$. If the graph produced is any one of the other shapes, we can tell the general form of the proportion but we do not know the value of "n".

To determine the value of n, we can replot y versus some function of x that we choose. For example, if y versus x appears to be a power curve ($y \propto x^n$), we might try plotting y versus x^2 or y versus x^3. The correct choice will produce a linear graph for y versus the correct power of x. If, for example, a graph of y versus x^3 is a straight line through the origin, then $y \propto x^3$.

Unfortunately, this is a trial-and-error process, but we can often make an educated guess on the basis of the multipliers of the two variables or from our understanding of the physics underlying the investigation. In general, when y versus x^n makes a linear graph, $y \propto x^n$.

Sample problem

Given the table of experimental results below, find the relationship between a and b.

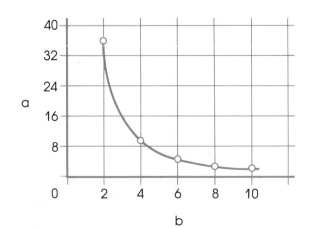

b	a
2.0	36
4.0	9.0
6.0	4.0
8.0	2.3
10	1.4

Plotting a graph of a versus b, we discover from its shape that a is inversely proportional to b^n ($a \propto \frac{1}{b^n}$).

Since $a \propto \frac{1}{b^n}$, we assume the simplest value of n, that is, $n = 1$, and set up a column of values of $\frac{1}{b}$. Then we plot a versus $\frac{1}{b}$.

We have limited our discussion here to relationships where the origin lies on the curve, since many of the relationships in physics, and most of those discussed in this text, have this condition. Relationships with a y-intercept are of the form $y = mx + b$, where m is the slope and b the intercept. Such a relationship will be encountered in Section 18.2.

$\frac{1}{b}$	a
0.50	36
0.25	9.0
0.17	4.0
0.13	2.3
0.10	1.4

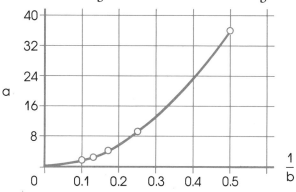

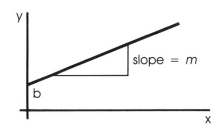

Since the plot of a versus $\frac{1}{b}$ does not produce a straight line, we set up a column of values for $\frac{1}{b^2}$ and plot a versus $\frac{1}{b^2}$. As illustrated below, this plot does produce a straight line, and thus $a \propto \frac{1}{b^2}$.

$\frac{1}{b^2}$	a
0.25	36
0.063	9.0
0.019	4.0
0.017	2.3
0.010	1.4

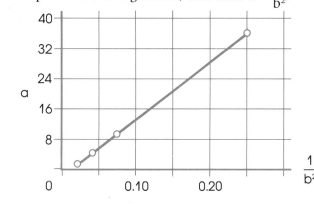

Practice
1. In the following table of results, determine the relationship between F and r, using graphical techniques.

r	1	1.2	1.8	2.4	3.0
F	10	6.9	3.1	1.7	1.1

2. A slider that starts from rest and slides down an inclined air track covers the distances d in the times t. Using graphical methods, determine the relationship between d and t.

t	0	0.8	1.0	1.2	1.4
d	0	12.8	20.0	28.8	39.2

3. An experiment is performed to find the relationship between two physical quantities, B and A. The following data is obtained.

A	100	64	49	36	25	16
B	1.99	1.59	1.39	1.19	1.00	0.80

Determine the relationship between B and A.

1.8 Using Proportioning Techniques in Physics

Forming Equations from a Proportion

Once the proportionality has been determined, the next step is usually to change it into an equation. This makes it possible to link the two quantities numerically. To form an equation from a proportion, simply replace the proportionality sign ($\propto$) by an equals sign ($=$) and a proportionality constant (usually "k").

Thus, $y \propto x^n$ becomes $y = kx^n$

The preferred method for determining the value of the proportionality constant is to find the slope of the straight-line graph relating the two variables. Suppose, for example, that it is found that two variables, F and v, are related by the proportionality statement $F \propto v^2$. A graph of F versus v^2 produces a straight line, as illustrated. The slope of the graph provides the numerical value of k, in this case 0.027 N/m^2/s^2. When substituted back into the general equation, it becomes $F = 0.027\, v^2$. This equation will be valid only for F in newtons and v in metres per second.

The units for k, N/m^2/s^2, can also be expressed as N·m^{-2}s^{-2}.

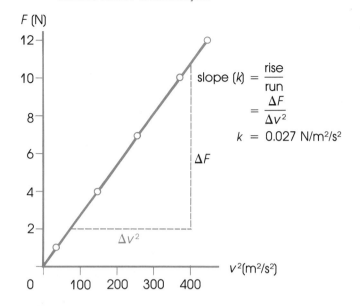

F(N)	v(m/s)	v²(m²/s²)
1.0	6.0	36
4.0	12.0	144
7.0	16.0	256
10.0	19.2	369
12.0	21.1	445

In mathematics, the value of the constant "k" is usually determined by substituting in only one ordered pair. This is a dangerous procedure in physics. All measured data contain error. The ordered pair substituted in the equation could possibly be the least precise pair of values. The resulting equation will not accurately describe the relationship between the two variables.

If it is not practical to draw a graph, an average, or "best", value for the proportionality constant may be calculated, using the pairs of values from the experimental data. For example, if $I \propto \frac{1}{d^2}$, then

$I = \frac{k}{d^2}$, or $k = Id^2$. If two measured values are $d = 3.0$ cm and $I = 10$ lx, then

$$k = Id^2$$
$$= (10 \text{ lx})(3.0 \text{ cm})^2$$
$$= 90 \text{ lx·cm}^2$$

This procedure is repeated for the other pairs of values, and an average value of k, for example, 92, is calculated. The resulting equation, $I = \frac{92}{d^2}$, is valid only for I in lx and d in cm, since these are the units that were used to calculate k. Some electronic calculators are programmed to do the above calculation or some other line-fitting method, displaying the average value of k as the slope of the graph.

The lux (lx) is the SI unit of illuminance.

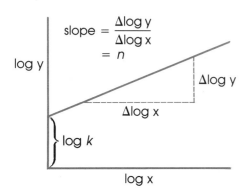

Note that the equation log y = log k + nlog x may be rewritten as log y = nlog x + log k, which is the same form as y = mx + b.

Using Logarithms to Determine an Equation

The general proportion, $y \propto x^n$, expressed as an equation, is $y = kx^n$. Taking the logarithm of each side of the equation, it may be rewritten as

$$\log y = \log k + n\log x$$

When the logs of the values of x and y are plotted in a graph of log y versus log x, a straight-line graph results, as illustrated. The slope of this graph is n, and the log y intercept is log k. The values of n and k are then substituted back into $y = kx^n$ to determine the equation.

Forming a Proportion from an Equation

The proportional relationship may be formed from an equation by working backwards from the equation. All numerical constants, and any variable that is held constant for the purpose of the problem, are replaced by a single constant, k. Then the equals sign and the constant, k, are replaced by the proportionality sign.

For example, one equation for centripetal acceleration (Section 3.9) is $a_c = \dfrac{4\pi^2 R}{T^2}$ or $4\pi^2 R \times \dfrac{1}{T^2}$

but $4\pi^2 R = $ a constant, k, if R is kept constant.

Therefore, $a_c = k \times \dfrac{1}{T^2}$

and $a_c \propto \dfrac{1}{T^2}$ (if R is held constant).

Similarly, $a_c \propto R$ (if T is held constant).

Solving Problems Using Proportioning Techniques

If the proportion relating two variables is known, many seemingly difficult problems can be solved easily, using proportioning techniques. A series of sample problems will illustrate different applications of these techniques.

Sample problems

1. The force of air resistance (F) on a moving body is related to the speed of the body (v) by the proportion $F \propto v^2$. If the speed triples, how many times greater is the force?

Since $F \propto v^2$
F's multiplier = v's multiplier squared
   $F' = F \times 3^2$
or $F' = 9F$ (F' means the new value of F)
   Thus, if the speed triples, the force increases by a factor of nine.

2. A cylindrical water tank holds 1.0×10^5 L of water. How much would it hold if all of its dimensions were doubled? The volume of a cylinder is given by
$$V = \pi r^2 h$$
   Since all of the linear dimensions (l) are doubled and π is a constant, the equation may be expressed as a proportionality, i.e., $V \propto l^3$.

> The same would be true for *any* shape of tank, as long as the shape did not change when the dimensions were scaled up or down.

$$V' = V \times 2^3$$
$$= (1.0 \times 10^5 \text{ L})(8)$$
$$V' = 8.0 \times 10^5 \text{ L}$$

3. The equation describing the displacement of a uniformly accelerating object starting from rest is $d = 0.5at^2$, where d is the displacement, a is the acceleration, and t is the time interval. An object travels 100 m in 10 s when its acceleration is 2.0 m/s². What is its displacement if the acceleration is 0.50 m/s² and the time interval is 40 s?

   $d_1 = 100$ m $a_1 = 2.0$ m/s² $t_1 = 10$ s
   $d_2 = ?$ $a_2 = 0.50$ m/s² $t_2 = 40$ s

   In this question, acceleration is multiplied by a factor of 1/4 and time is multiplied by a factor of 4.
   Since $d \propto at^2$ (from the equation $d = 0.5at^2$)
   a is multiplied by a factor of 1/4
   t is multiplied by a factor of 4 and
   t^2 is multiplied by a factor of 16
   so d_1 is multiplied by a factor of $1/4 \times 16 = 4$
   therefore $d_2 = d_1 \times 4$
   $$= 100 \text{ m} \times 4$$
   $$= 400 \text{ m}$$

Alternate Solution
   Since $d = 0.5at^2$, $d \propto at^2$
   therefore $\dfrac{d_1}{d_2} = \dfrac{a_1 t_1^2}{a_2 t_2^2}$
   $$\frac{100 \text{ m}}{d_2} = \frac{(2.0 \text{ m/s}^2)(10 \text{ s})^2}{(0.5 \text{ m/s}^2)(40 \text{ s})^2}$$
   $$d_2 = 400 \text{ m}$$

Practice

1. Express each of the following equations as proportions, using only the variables indicated.

   (a) $V = 4/3\pi r^3$; V and r

   (b) $F_c = \dfrac{mv^2}{R}$;   (i) F_c and v,   (ii) F_c and R

   (c) $F_g = \dfrac{Gm_1m_2}{R_2}$; (i) F_g and m_1,   (ii) F_g and R, where G is a constant

   (d) $K = \dfrac{R^3}{T^2}$; R and T, where K is a constant

2. Given the relationship $E \propto mv^2$:   (a) If E is 98 units when m is 4.0 units and v is 7.0 units, express the proportion as an equation.

   (b) What is the value of E when m is 10 units and v is 42 units?
   (8.8×10^3)

3.

x	0.2	0.4	0.6	0.8	1.0
y	200	50	22.2	12.5	8.0

   (a) Determine the proportion relating y and x.
   (b) Write an equation relating y and x.
   (c) If x = 0.55, what is y, predicted from (b)?   (26)

4. Two neighbours have swimming pools with identical shapes. One pool holds 2.0×10^4 L of water. How many litres will the second pool hold if all its dimensions are 1.6 times as large?
   $(8.2 \times 10^4 \text{ L})$

5. Given $F_c = \dfrac{mv^2}{R}$

   What is the effect on F_c of each of the following?
   (a) increasing m by a factor of 3
   (b) decreasing v to 1/3 of its former value
   (c) decreasing R to 1/4 of its former value
   (d) all of the above $(\times 3, \times 1/9, \times 4, \times 4/3)$

6. If $a \propto b^3$ and a = 4.0 when b = 3.5, what is a when b = 7.0?
   (32)

7. Given that $d \propto at^2$. If a = 2.0 m/s^2 and t = 4.0 when d = 32 m, what will be the value of d when a = 2.0 m/s^2 and t = 12 s?
   $(5.8 \times 10^2 \text{ m})$

8. Given that $p \propto q^3/r^2$, and that p = 400 when q = 5.0 and r = 3.0. Calculate the value of p when q = 15 and r = 5.0.
   (3.9×10^3)

1.9 Investigations

Investigation 1.1: Measuring Short Time Intervals

Problem:
How can a stroboscope be used to time rapidly moving objects?

Materials:
stopwatch
variable speed rotor, with a white disc and a black spot on the disc
12-slit strobe disc
electric bell with variable power supply
masking tape (small pieces for covering disc slits, as required)

Procedure:
1. Adjust the speed of the rotor so that you can easily follow the black spot on the disc as it rotates. Using a one-slit strobe, hold the stroboscope in front of your eye and rotate the strobe slowly while looking at the rotating disc. When the black spot appears "stopped", measure the time for 10 rotations of the strobe disc. Determine the frequency of the strobe disc. By direct observation, determine the frequency of the rotor. Compare the two frequencies. Also, compare the time required for one rotation of the hand stroboscope with that for one rotation of the black spot, when the motion appears "stopped".
2. Increase the rate of rotation of the black spot. Remove the tape from the slit of the stroboscope opposite the open one. Determine the highest frequency of the strobe required to "stop" the black spot. How can you tell that the black spot was "stopped" at its highest frequency?
3. Calculate the "look" frequency of the stroboscope. What is the frequency of the rotating black spot, measured without the stroboscope? Compare the answers you obtained by the two methods.
4. "Stop" the black spot in one position, using the two-slit strobe. Determine the frequency of the stroboscope. Calculate the "look" frequency of the strobe. What is the frequency of the rotating black spot? How can you check to make sure that this is the correct frequency?

5. Increase the rate of rotation of the black spot. Remove the tape from three equally spaced slits, and "stop" the rotation of the black spot. Determine the period of the stroboscope, and from this calculate the time for one rotation of the black spot.
6. Without changing the rate of rotation of the black spot, repeat the procedure, using four equally spaced slits. Compare your results for the period of the black spot.
7. Increase the speed of the rotor. Determine its frequency using both six- and twelve-slit stroboscopes.
8. Attach a clothes-pin to the clapper of the 1.5 V bell to decrease the frequency to a range that can be measured easily with a hand stroboscope. "Stop" the motion of the clothes-pin, using the four-slit hand stroboscope. Repeat with a six-slit stroboscope, and determine in each case the time for one vibration of the loaded clapper.
9. Remove the clothes-pin, and find the frequency and period of the electric clapper, using both a six- and a twelve-slit stroboscope.
10. If a multi-flash stroboscope is available, repeat steps 7 to 9.
11. Summarize the steps in a procedure you would use to determine the period of an oscillating object with **(a)** a hand stroboscope and **(b)** a multi-flash stroboscope.

Investigation 1.2: Analysing the Motion of a Pendulum

Problem:
What is the relationship between the length and the frequency of a simple pendulum?

Materials:
apparatus as illustrated
stopwatch

Procedure:
1. Attach a simple pendulum to a rigid support, with the centre of the bob about 100 cm below the pivot point. Measure the length of the pendulum from the pivot point to the centre of the bob. Pull the bob aside about 20° and release it. Using a stopwatch, determine the length of time, in seconds, required for 30 cycles.
2. Decrease the length of the pendulum from 100 cm, in steps of approximately 20 cm, to a final length of about 20 cm. Determine the frequency of the pendulum for each length.

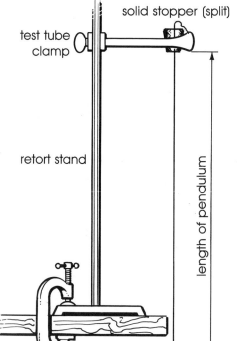

test tube clamp

solid stopper (split)

retort stand

length of pendulum

C clamp

bob

3. Plot a graph of pendulum frequency (f) against pendulum length (l). Describe the graph obtained. What happens to the frequency of the pendulum as the length is decreased? What relationship does this suggest might exist between f and l?
4. On the basis of your graph, suggest a proportionality statement, and replot the data in a form that results in a straight-line graph. Write the correct proportionality statement.
5. Determine the value of the proportionality constant needed to make an equation, and write the equation describing each of the following.
   (a) frequency and pendulum length
   (b) period and pendulum length
6. Using these equations, predict the frequency of a similar pendulum of length 140 cm. Show the calculations.
7. Do you think the amplitude of the pendulum's vibration has any effect on its frequency? Check your answer by doing a simple experiment with the same apparatus. Discuss.

Investigation 1.3: Analysing Experimental Data

Problem:
What is the relationship between the resistance, the length, and the diameter of an electrical conductor?

Experimental Data:
The data given below were recorded in an investigation to measure the electrical resistances of nichrome wires of various lengths and diameters.

Diameter (cm) \ Length (cm)	100	140	170	220
	Resistance (Ω)			
2.5×10^{-2}	15.7	22.0	26.8	34.7
4.0×10^{-2}	6.1	8.5	10.4	13.3
7.5×10^{-2}	1.9	2.5	3.0	3.9
12.5×10^{-2}	0.6	0.9	1.1	1.4

The unit of electrical resistance is the ohm. The symbol chosen for it is the Greek capital "O" — Ω (omega).

Procedure:
1. On graph 1 plot the resistance (R) in ohms versus the diameter (d) in centimetres for a piece of nichrome wire 100 cm long.
2. Using your graph, find, by interpolation, the values of R for diameters of 0.03 cm and 0.06 cm.

3. Using extrapolation, find the resistances when the diameters are 0.02 cm and 0.15 cm. Discuss the accuracy of your answers determined by extrapolation and the accuracy of those obtained by interpolation.

4. Analyse the shape of your graph, and write a proportionality statement relating R and d.

5. Choose a function of the diameter such that, when it is plotted against R, a straight line results. Proportioning techniques may be helpful (see Section 1.8). Plot graph 2 of R versus the "rearranged" data for d. Scale the resistance axis of the graph so that the maximum resistances for the other lengths can be plotted on the same graph later, in step 8.

6. When a straight line is achieved, write a proportionality statement relating R and d, for a constant length. Using the slope of the graph, write an equation for this proportion.

7. Using the equation, determine the resistance for a diameter of 0.06 cm. Compare your results with those determined in step 2.

8. Determine whether the same relationship between R and d holds for different lengths of the nichrome wire by plotting the remaining data on graph 2. Label each line according to its length. Describe the resulting family of lines.

9. Using graph 2, predict the relationship between R and l. On graph 3, plot R versus l for a constant diameter of 2.5×10^{-2} cm. If the line is extrapolated, does it pass through the origin? Explain.

10. Check to see if the relationship holds between R and l for $d = 7.50 \times 10^{-2}$ cm. Explain your procedure for checking.

11. Use graphs 2 and 3 in the following two ways to obtain the resistance (R) for $l = 200$ cm and $d = 5.00 \times 10^{-2}$ cm.

    (a) Using graph 2, interpolate the values of R for all four values of l plotted for $\dfrac{1}{d^2} = \dfrac{1}{(5.0 \times 10^{-2})^2} = 400$. On graph 4 plot R versus l for a constant diameter of 5.00×10^{-2} cm. By interpolation, find the value of R for $l = 200$ cm.

    (b) Using graph 3, interpolate the value of R, when $l = 200$ cm, for $d = 2.5 \times 10^{-2}$ cm. Plot this point on graph 2. Since the relationship between R and d has been established, we know that the graph line for a constant length of 200 cm will pass through the origin. Use this line, drawn on graph 2, to interpolate the value of R when $\dfrac{1}{d^2} = \dfrac{1}{(5.0 \times 10^{-2})^2} = 400$.

12. Combine the proportionality statements for R and d and R and l to form one statement relating R, d, and l. Express this as a general

equation, using values from the observation chart. Using the equation, determine the value of R for $d = 5.0 \times 10^{-2}$ cm and $l = 200$ cm. Compare your answer with those determined graphically in step 11. Which of the procedures is more accurate? Discuss.

13. A conductor with a length of 10 m and a diameter of 4.00×10^{-2} cm has a resistance of 2.1 Ω. Another conductor of the same material has a resistance of 0.78 Ω when its length is 15 m. Determine the diameter of the new conductor. Are the two conductors used in this step made of the same material as the conductors in the investigation? Explain your reasoning.

1.10 Review

Problems

1. Write each of the following numbers in scientific notation.
   (a) 27 600
   (b) 0.000 45
   (c) 538 000
   (d) 0.39×10^{-5}
   (e) 84×10^{-3}
   (f) 297×10^3
   (g) 0.043×10^{-6}
   (h) 0.689×10^{24}
   (i) 860.3×10^{-19}
   (j) 0.000 000 079 36

2. Express each of the following in scientific notation in the basic SI unit.
   (a) 5.00×10^6 mm
   (b) 6.000 km
   (c) 25 nm
   (d) 55.00 min
   (e) 55 MW
   (f) 2.61 kPa
   (g) 102 MHz
   (h) 159 GHz

3. The wavelength of red light is 6.5×10^{-7} m. How many wavelengths will fit along a line 1.0 cm long?

4. There are approximately 1.0×10^{11} stars in our galaxy. If the average mass of a star and its planets is 2.0×10^{30} kg, what is the approximate mass of our galaxy?

5. A thin film of rolled gold is used in Rutherford's scattering experiment (Chapter 19). If the average thickness of the film is 1.0×10^{-6} m and the diameter of a gold atom is 2.5×10^{-10} m, approximately how many gold atoms make up the thickness of the gold foil? Assume that the gold atoms are lined up in a straight line.

6. Electric current flows through a conductor at a rate of 2.50 C/s. If a coulomb is composed of 6.24×10^{18} electrons, how many electrons will flow through the conductor in 10.0 min?

A coulomb per second (C/s) is defined as an ampere.

7. Three steel sections have the following dimensions:

strip 1 l = 148.2 cm w = 3.0 cm
strip 2 l = 102 cm w = 1.29 cm
strip 3 l = 142.73 cm w = 5.891 cm

Each of the numbers shows the precision with which the measurements were made. Calculate the following, to the number of significant figures warranted by the information, and express your answer in scientific notation.
   (a) the total length of the strips joined end to end
   (b) the total width of the strips joined side to side
   (c) the area of strip 1
   (d) the ratio l/w for strip 3

8. If light travels at 3.00×10^8 m/s, estimate the number of kilometres to Proxima Centauri, the nearest star to our solar system, if it is located 4.3 light-years from the sun.

9. Estimate, in seconds, the time you spend in school each month.

10. Find the order of magnitude of the number of basketballs required to fill a sphere of radius 6.4×10^3 km (the approximate radius of the Earth).

11. The total number of protons in the known universe is estimated to be about 10^{81}, and the radius of a proton is about 10^{-15} m. What is the order of magnitude of the radius of the sphere that would contain all of these protons if they were tightly packed together? Give your answer in metres. (SIN '71)

12. A spherical tank 30 m in diameter is full of water. Estimate the mass of the water (density of water = 1000 kg/m³).

13. The speed of sound was measured. Two values were calculated, 328 m/s and 336 m/s. The actual value was 342 m/s. Determine the percentage difference for the measured values and the percentage error for each.

14. A student makes a movie with a Super-8 camera that can take pictures at different speeds. He wants to slow down the action to one-quarter normal speed, when the final film is projected on the screen at 18 pictures/s. At what speed will he set the camera to achieve the desired result?

15. In film animation, frames are created one at a time. If an animated film is projected at 24 frames/s, how many pictures must be created for a 10 min cartoon?

16. The time required for a flower to open completely is 3.00 d. The opening of the flower is to be photographed by time-lapse photography, to make a 30 s film projected at 24 frames/s. What should be the time interval between photographs?

17. A flying mosquito can beat its wings 1000 times/s.
   (a) How many times do the wings move in a minute?

Problems labelled (SIN '00) are based on questions used in the annual Sir Isaac Newton (SIN) Scholarship Test. Further information about this contest is available in the Teacher's Manual.

   (b) What is the minimum period at which a strobe may flash
        to "stop" the wing motion?
18. A camera takes pictures of a rotating disc at the rate of
    24 frames/s. A section of the resulting film is shown below.
    (a) If the disc is moving counterclockwise, what is its minimum
         frequency?
    (b) If the disc is moving clockwise, what is its minimum fre-
         quency?

19. A rotating bicycle wheel with a single white mark on its tire
    was observed by a student with a four-slit hand stroboscope
    disc. At the highest "stopping" frequency, the student had to
    turn the strobe 25 times in 10 s. What was the period of ro-
    tation of the bicycle wheel?
20. A rotating spinning wheel with one dot on it appears "stopped"
    through a five-slit stroboscope rotating 16 times in 30 s. What
    are two possible rotational frequencies of the wheel?
21. A 12-slit stroboscope has a frequency of 2.0 Hz. If a vibrating
    bell clapper viewed through it appears as illustrated, what is
    the minimum frequency of the bell clapper?
22. A spot on a rotating shaft is viewed through an eight-slit stro-
    boscope. The maximum frequency of rotation of the strobe for
    which the motion of the spot appears "stopped" is 40 r in 10 s.

    (a) What is the frequency of the shaft?
    (b) What is the period of rotation of the shaft?
23. In an investigation, a hand stroboscope with 12 open slits was
    used to "stop" the motion of a bell clapper. The time required
    for 20 rotations of the strobe was 4.0 s. This was the highest
    stopping frequency.
    (a) What was the period of the clapper?
    (b) What other strobe frequency would stop this motion?
24. A standard 60 cycle fluorescent light goes "out" every time
    the AC voltage passes through zero. A $33\frac{1}{3}$ r/min record-player
    disc can have its speed checked by the stroboscopic action of
    such a light on a series of equally spaced marks around its rim.
    What is the smallest number of marks that will permit a viewer
    to see the same pattern for the moving disc that would be seen
    for a stationary disc? (SIN '69)

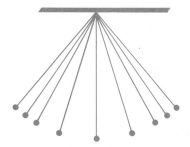

25. A strobe light is set to a flashing rate of 600 flashes/min and is used to make a multi-flash photograph of a swinging pendulum for one-half of a cycle. The resulting picture is shown. Estimate the period of the pendulum.

26. In each of the following cases, determine the relation that best describes the data and that would produce a linear graph.

(a)

Y	X
22.7	482.3
46.3	240.7
67.1	163.8
90.0	119.6

(b)

B	A
17.3	23.2
35.0	93.6
50.9	210.0
169.8	2298.0

(c)

N	M
5.3	173.5
21.7	351.5
127.4	847.4
527.9	1748.5

27. Here are three sets of experimental measurements. Find the relationship between each pair of variables.

(a)

v	F
20	10
28	20
40	40
48	60

(b)

R	F
0.1	1.0
0.2	0.25
0.3	0.11
0.4	0.04

(c)

T	R
7.6×10^6	5.8×10^{10}
30×10^6	15×10^{10}
380×10^6	78×10^{10}
930×10^6	143×10^{10}

28. An experiment produced the set of values shown below for separation (d) and energy (E). A graph was drawn of E versus d.

Separation, d (cm)	Energy, E (J)
2.2	16.2
4.4	8.2
6.1	5.4
11.1	3.2

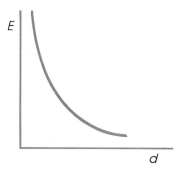

Determine an equation relating E and d. Explain how you obtained it.

29. When a mass is placed on the free end of a board, the end is deflected downward. The following table shows the downward deflection (d) corresponding to various lengths of board, as measured in an experiment. Each deflection was produced by the same mass.

Length of board (l)	Downward deflection (d)
(m)	(cm)
1.0	0.4
2.0	3.2
3.0	10.8
4.0	25.6
5.0	50.0

(a) Determine the relationship between d and l.
(b) Determine an equation relating d and l.
(c) Predict the deflection of the board when the length is 2.5 m, and when it is 6.0 m.

30. It can be shown that the kinetic energy E_k of a moving car is proportional to the square of its velocity, i.e., $E_k \propto v^2$. At 90 km/h, a certain car's E_k is measured as 400 units.
(a) What is the car's E_k at 270 km/h?
(b) What is the car's E_k at 45 km/h?
(c) What is the car's velocity when its E_k is 16 units?

31. The resistance (R) of 1000 m of nichrome wire is tabulated for various diameters (d). From the following table, determine the mathematical equation relating electrical resistance and the diameter of a conductor.

d	0.01	0.02	0.03	0.04	0.05
R	130	33	14	8.1	5.0

32. Measurements are made of the resistance (R) and the power consumption (P) of a tungsten filament lamp, with the following results.

Power (P), in watts	2.2	5.7	12.3	27.1	52.9
Resistance (R), in ohms	1.6	2.0	2.4	2.9	3.4

Show that the relationship between P and R is of the form $P = aR^n$, and find the values of n and a. (Note that the resistance (R) is the "cold" resistance and may vary as the filament heats up.)

33. The extra power required to overcome the drag produced on a car with its windows open is given by the relationship $P = cv^n$, where P is the extra power and v is the velocity of the car. The following table gives values measured for a late model car.

Numerical Answers to Review Problems

1. (a) 2.76×10^5 (b) 4.5×10^4
   (c) 5.38×10^5 (d) 3.9×10^{-6}
   (e) 8.4×10^{-2} (f) 2.97×10^5
   (g) 4.3×10^{-8} (h) 6.89×10^{23}
   (i) 8.603×10^{-17} (j) 7.936×10^{-8}
2. (a) 5.00×10^3 m (b) 6.000×10^3 m
   (c) 2.5×10^{-8} m (d) 3.3×10^3 s
   (e) 5.5×10^7 W (f) 2.61×10^3 Pa
   (g) 1.02×10^8 Hz (h) 1.59×10^{11} Hz
3. 1.5×10^4 wavelengths
4. 2.0×10^{41} kg
5. 4.0×10^3 atoms
6. 9.36×10^{21} electrons
7. (a) 393 cm (b) 10.2 cm
   (c) 4.4×10^2 cm² (d) 24.23
8. 4×10^{13} km
9. 5×10^5 s
10. 10^{23} basketballs
11. 10^{12} m
12. 2×10^6 kg
13. 2.4%, −4.1%, −1.8%
14. 72 frames/s
15. 1.44×10^4 pictures
16. 6.0 min
17. (a) 6.0×10^4 times (b) 1.0×10^{-3} s
18. (a) 3.0 Hz (b) 21 Hz
19. 0.10 s
20. 2.7 Hz, 5.4 Hz
21. 12 Hz
22. (a) 32 Hz (b) 0.013 s
23. (a) 0.017 s (b) 2.5 Hz, 1.25 Hz
24. 216 marks
25. 1.6 s
29. (a) $d \propto L^3$ (b) $d = 0.40 L^3$
   (c) 6.3 cm, 86 cm
30. (a) 3.6×10^3 units
   (b) 1.0×10^2 units (c) 18 km/h
31. $R = \dfrac{1.3 \times 10^{-2}}{d^2}$
32. 0.31, 4.2
33. 2.1×10^{-6}, 3
34. (a) 3.0 m (b) 1.0 m, 3.0 m
35. 64 busts
36. 60 mm

velocity (km/h)	32	64	96.5	129	161
extra power (kW)	0.069	0.55	1.89	4.50	8.76

Determine the values of c and n.

34. The intensity of the light that falls on a certain area from a point source of light is inversely proportional to the square of the distance from the source to the area.
   (a) How far must a screen be placed from the source to have an intensity four times what it had when it was placed 6.0 m from the source?
   (b) Two identical light sources are placed 4.0 m apart. At a point between the two sources, their intensities are measured and found to be in a ratio of 9 to 1. How far is each source from the point of measurement?

35. In a last-ditch attempt to increase their budget, physicists at a university cast small solid bronze busts of their chairperson for sale to students as doorstops, bootracks, paperweights, boat anchors, etc. One order, in suspiciously familiar handwriting, came in for a bust that would be identical except for scale: it was to stand four times as tall as the standard model. How many of the small busts did the physicists have to melt down to cast this big one? (SIN '77)

36. Marshmallows are said to obey Boyle's Law (volume × pressure at constant temperature is constant). A supply of such ideal marshmallows was shipped to a remote planet (αβ–soup, to be exact) at the far end of the galaxy, where the atmospheric pressure is only one-eighth of that on Earth, but the temperature is the same. The marshmallows were cylinders 24 mm high and 30 mm in diameter on Earth. What would their diameter be on αβ–soup, assuming uniform change? Answer in millimetres. (SIN '78)

How an Electronic Digital Watch Works

An electronic digital watch uses the oscillations of a quartz crystal to produce accurate time. The quartz crystal oscillates at a frequency of 32 768 Hz. Battery-powered microcircuits in an electronic "chip", inside the watch, cut the pulses in half fifteen times, consecutively, to arrive at intervals of one second. In a digital stopwatch, pulses from the fifth division divide the frequency of 1024 Hz electronically by tens, to arrive at approximate 10ths and 100ths of a second.

The watch's digital display is controlled by the same electronic chip. Just below the glass surface of the watch is a polarizing film (see diagram). Below that, millions of microscopic liquid crystals float between a grid of electrodes. When the electrodes are charged, an electric field is created (Section 15.4), and the crystals line up in opposition to the surface-polarizing film. Cross polarization results (Section 14.8) that effectively eliminates most light reflected from the mirrored surface at the bottom of the display. Dark areas are thus produced that form the digits in the display. Since the display depends on reflected light, a battery-operated light is sometimes mounted next to the digital display so that it can be read in low-light conditions. A similar display is used in many electronic calculators.

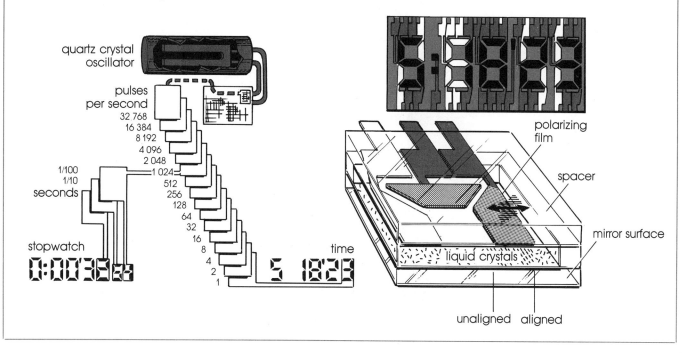

2 Motion in a Straight Line

2.1 Position and Displacement

A new generation of guided, non-contact, "flying trains", using magnetic levitation and propulsion, could revolutionize interurban rapid transit. "MagLev" vehicles of this type can travel at speeds of up to 300 km/h, floating 1 cm above a straight concrete guideway, or track.

At 20:00 one evening, a speeding MagLev vehicle passed the 18 km sign on its way into town. It had been moving at a steady speed of 180 km/h along a straight guideway, in an easterly direction. At the sign, it began a gradual deceleration, eventually stopping at the station to pick up some passengers. The time was exactly 20:12. Twelve minutes later it started up again, accelerating down the guideway at a steady rate until it passed the 20 km sign on the other side of the station at 20:42. From this point, the vehicle continued its eastward journey at a uniform velocity of 200 km/h.

This description of the motion of a MagLev vehicle has been recounted in terms of the vehicle's position, time, velocity, and acceleration. The whys and hows of its motion were not revealed. This was a kinematic description of the vehicle's motion.

Kinematics is the branch of physics that deals with the description of the motion of objects without reference to the forces or agents causing the motion. The branch that deals with both the motion of bodies and the forces that produce it is **dynamics**. Chapters 2 and 3 concern kinematics. The study of dynamics begins in Chapter 4.

You will have noted that the MagLev vehicle travelled along a straight guideway. All motion discussed in this chapter will stay "on the track". That is, the description of motion will be limited to what occurs in a straight line. In Chapter 3, motions will get "off the track", so to speak, and motion will be described in two-dimensional space, in a plane.

For an accurate description of the motion of an object, it is necessary to have a point of reference and a direction. In the example described above, the station was chosen as the reference point and all measurements were made in relation to that fixed point.

The straight track is used in the same way that a number line is used in mathematics. Motion in one direction is positive, motion in the other direction is negative. It does not matter which way is chosen as positive and which as negative, but following the

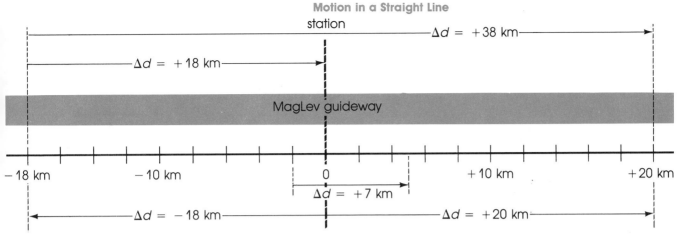

mathematical convention right is usually designated as positive and left as negative.

The positions of the vehicle on either side of the station may be described as −18 km and +20 km, respectively. The plus and minus signs indicate the directions relative to the zero point (the station), and the figures describe the distances from the zero point. If the vehicle moves from −18 km to 0 km, we can say that it has had a displacement of +18 km, since it has moved a distance of 18 km in the positive direction. A change of position from 0 km to +18 km would also be a displacement of +18 km. If the vehicle moved from 0 km to −18 km, its displacement would be −18 km. **Displacement**, then, describes both the magnitude of the change in position and the direction of that change.

The Greek letter delta, written as Δ (Greek capital D), is used to represent "change of", "increase of", "decrease of", "difference", or "interval". Thus, Δt means an interval of time, Δv means a change in velocity, and Δd means a change in position of an object, or, more simply, a displacement.

In physics, quantities such as position and displacement that have a magnitude, a unit, and a direction are called "vector quantities", or simply **vectors**. Those that have only a magnitude and a unit are called **scalars**. Many scalars, such as time, mass, and length, will already be familiar to you. Vectors, such as position and displacement, will become familiar as you progress through the study of mechanics.

Vector quantities may be represented graphically as arrows of varying length, according to a chosen scale, and pointing in the direction of the vector quantity. For example, a displacement of 8.0 km due east may be represented as follows:

Scale: 1 cm = 2.0 km

When a vector quantity is described in writing, the symbol has an arrow above it, and the direction is given after the unit, in square brackets. A displacement of 8.0 km due east is written as follows:

$$\Delta \vec{d} = 8.0 \text{ km[E]}$$

To describe the magnitude of a vector quantity only, ignoring the direction, write,

$$|\Delta \vec{d}| = 8.0 \text{ km}$$

The symbol $|\Delta \vec{d}|$ means the absolute value of the displacement. Specifically, in the case of a change in position, we can express the displacement as follows:

$$\Delta \vec{d} = \vec{d_2} - \vec{d_1}$$

where $\vec{d_1}$ is the initial position

$\vec{d_2}$ is the final position

$\Delta \vec{d}$ is the displacement

Often, when describing vector quantities, the vector notation is cumbersome and unnecessary. When the direction of motion is obvious and does not change, the vector notation may be omitted for the sake of simplicity. In this chapter, all motion is in a straight line, so that vector notation will be omitted. Vectors in the direction of motion will be assumed to be positive, and those in the opposite direction negative.

In the description of the MagLev vehicle's motion, it was stated that the vehicle travelled from -18 km to 0 and eventually on to $+20$ km. Using the above equation, its displacement would be calculated as follows:

$$\Delta d = d_2 - d_1 = [+20 - (-18)] \text{ km} = +38 \text{ km}$$

$|\Delta \vec{d}| = |\vec{d_2} - \vec{d_1}|$

$|\Delta \vec{d}|$ represents the distance, that is, the magnitude of the displacement, without any indication of the direction.

If the vehicle had moved from -2 km to $+5$ km, its displacement would have been

$$\Delta d = d_2 - d_1 = [+5 - (-2)]\ km = +7\ km$$

In Chapter 3 and later, when the direction of motion changes, it will be necessary to reintroduce vector notation. For purposes of simplicity, in this book, vector notation will be used only when the direction of vector quantities changes or is significant to an understanding of a physical situation or problem.

Practice

1. State the displacement of each of the following changes in position (refer to the diagram on page 43, if necessary).
    (a) -8 km to -2 km
    (b) $+2$ km to -8 km
    (c) 0 km to $+8$ km
    (d) -8 km to $+20$ km
    (e) $+8$ km to -8 km
            $(+6$ km, -10 km, $+8$ km, $+28$ km, -16 km$)$
2. The symbol "Δ" has other uses. Find the change in each of the following.
    (a) The temperature falls from $+10°C$ to $-20°C$. Find Δt.
    (b) The value of a stock increases from $\$12.00$ to $\$17.50$. Find $\Delta \$$.
    (c) A person on a diet goes from 60 kg to 55 kg. Express Δm.
    (d) A ball falls from a point $+20$ m above the ground into a hole -10 m deep. Find Δd.
            $(-30°C, +\$5.50, -5$ kg, -30 m$)$

2.2 Uniform Velocity

You are driving a car in a straight line, at a steady speed of 80 km/h. Using a stopwatch, you drop small paper bags of flour out of the window at 5 s intervals. You leave behind a series of equally spaced "splashes" of flour on the ground. When you pull a ticker tape through a vibrating timer at a uniform speed, equally spaced dots are recorded on the tape. Both cases leave evidence of uniform velocity. There have been equal displacements in equal intervals of time. The photograph shows a stroboscopic picture of a puck moving on an air table with uniform velocity.

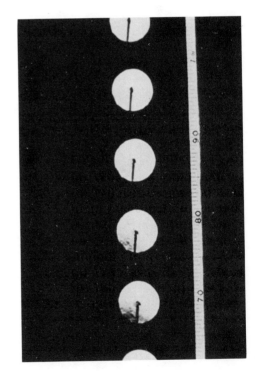

A strobe photo of an air puck moving at a uniform velocity. The puck has nearly equal displacements in equal time intervals.

Uniform velocity may be described mathematically as follows.

$$\vec{v} = \frac{\Delta \vec{d}}{\Delta t}$$

where $\vec{v}$ is the uniform velocity

$\Delta \vec{d}$ is the displacement

Δt is the time interval

This equation is very limited. It can only be used for velocities that do not change. This is an exception, not the rule, in everyday life. It is difficult, for example, to operate an automobile at a constant velocity. Nevertheless, we find it useful to make approximations and to assume that a velocity is uniform even if it does vary slightly. When it does change slightly, the equation gives us an average velocity (see Section 2.4).

Once again, since we are dealing only with motion in a straight line, the vector notation may be omitted from this equation if the direction remains the same and is understood from the context of the problem. For example, if a car travels with a uniform velocity of 80 km/h towards the north for 2.5 h, we can calculate its displacement as follows.

$$v = \frac{\Delta d}{\Delta t} \quad \text{or} \quad \Delta d = v \Delta t$$

$$= (80 \text{ km/h})(2.5 \text{ h})$$
$$= 200 \text{ km, towards the north}$$
$$= 200 \text{ km[N]}$$

Note that the direction of the displacement is the same as that of the uniform velocity. This is always true. It is also important to remember that the time interval is always positive. Time only goes one way — unfortunately!

50 km towards the north may be written as 50 km[N]. Square brackets are usually reserved for directions.

In some situations, it is useful to use a negative interval of time to describe an event in the past. Physicists usually choose the origin for time as the beginning of a particular sequence of events, thus avoiding negative time intervals.

Practice

1. What is the uniform velocity of an airplane that flies 602 m[E] in 2.50 s? Express your answer in metres per second and kilometres per hour.   (241 m/s[E], 867 km/h[E])

2. The tine on a tuning fork moves 1.0 mm to the right in 4.0×10^{-3} s. What is the uniform velocity of the tine in metres per second?   (0.25 m/s[right])

3. An electron travels at a uniform velocity of 1.30×10^5 m/s. How much time is required for a displacement of 1.00 m?   (7.69×10^{-6} s)

4. A spaceship travelled at a uniform velocity of 3.2×10^4 km/h for 2.7 d. What was the displacement of the spaceship?   (2.1×10^6 km)

2.3 Position-Time Graphs

In physics, graphs are often used to describe the motion of objects. The position-versus-time (*d-t*) graph for the train described in Section 2.1 is illustrated.

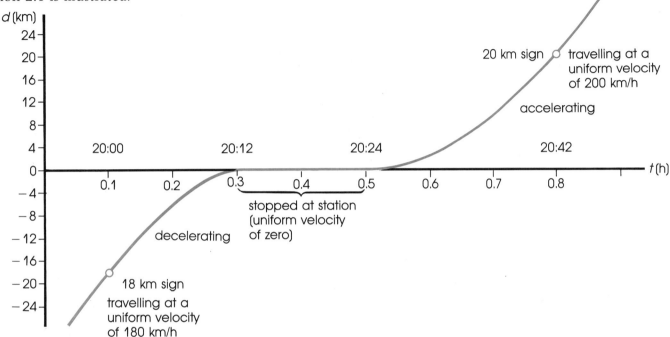

On the graph are labelled the various types of motion executed by the train. The first and last sections are straight-line segments representing uniform velocities. This is what should be expected, since it is only for a straight line that equal changes in position correspond to equal changes in time. Thus, whenever a straight line is found on a position-time graph, uniform velocity is being described.

Some examples of uniform velocity on *d-t* graphs are illustrated.

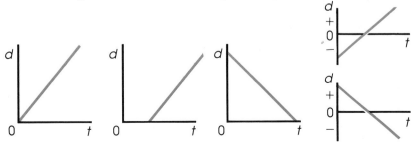

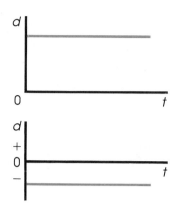

Refer back to the *d-t* graph for the MagLev vehicle (page 47), and note that between 0.3 h and 0.5 h the vehicle was stopped. Since there was no change in position, there was no displacement. When the displacement is zero, the *d-t* graph is always a straight line parallel to the time axis. Other examples are illustrated.

In a *d-t* graph, if the velocity is not constant, the graph is not a straight line. When the vehicle was accelerating or decelerating, the velocity was changing. This was indicated by a smooth curved line in these two segments.

The value $\Delta d/\Delta t$ is represented on a *d-t* graph by the value of the slope. For example, if an object moves from d_1 to d_2 in a time interval Δt, as illustrated, the value of the slope of the line is equal to the velocity of the object.

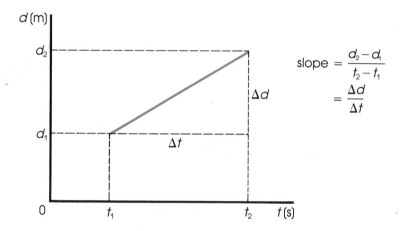

$$\text{slope} = \frac{d_2 - d_1}{t_2 - t_1}$$

$$= \frac{\Delta d}{\Delta t}$$

Velocity is given by the slope of a position-time graph.

$$v = \frac{\Delta d}{\Delta t} = \text{slope of } d\text{-}t \text{ graph}$$

Note that, since the velocity can have a positive or a negative value, the slopes can also have positive or negative values. A positive value of velocity represents motion in a forward direction; a negative value of velocity represents backward motion.

Sample problem

Carefully examine the following position-time graph. Find the velocity in each section.

	A	B	C	D	E	F
Δd(m)	6.0	0	-16.0	0	6.0	4.0
Δt(s)	2.0	4.0	4.0	2.0	1.0	4.5
v(m/s)	3.0	0	-4.0	0	6.0	0.89

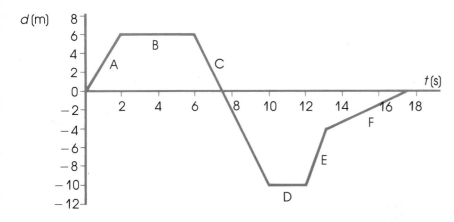

Practice

Find the velocity in each section of the following position-time graph. $(-2.5$ m/s, 0, 10 m/s, -3.8 m/s, 0, 8.8 m/s)

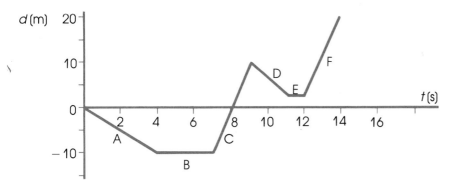

2.4 Average Velocity

Average velocity involves the total displacement and the total time required for the displacement as follows:

$$v_{av} = \frac{\Delta d}{\Delta t}$$

where Δd is the total displacement
Δt is the time interval
v_{av} is the average velocity

When the velocity is uniform, the average velocity and the velocity over any short interval of time will have the same value. On the other hand, when the velocity changes, the average velocity and the velocity over a short time interval will usually not be the same. For example, if a car travels 1.0 km through a town at 50 km/h and then out into the countryside for 1.0 km at 100 km/h, on a straight road, its average velocity is:

total displacement $\Delta d = 1.0 \text{ km} + 1.0 \text{ km} = 2.0 \text{ km}$

$$\text{total time } \Delta t = \frac{1.0 \text{ km}}{50 \text{ km/h}} + \frac{1.0 \text{ km}}{100 \text{ km/h}}$$
$$= 0.020 \text{ h} + 0.010 \text{ h}$$
$$= 0.030 \text{ h}$$

$$v_{av} = \frac{\Delta d}{\Delta t}$$
$$= \frac{2.0 \text{ km}}{0.030 \text{ h}}$$
$$= 66.6 \text{ km/h}, \quad \text{or } 67 \text{ km/h}$$

Note that the answer is not the average of the velocities, i.e., 75 km/h. Average velocity is the total displacement divided by the total time.

A *d-t* graph for the motion of the car described above is illustrated. Note that the average velocity is the slope of the line constructed between the initial and final positions of the car.

Average velocity is given by the slope of the line joining two points on a position-time graph.

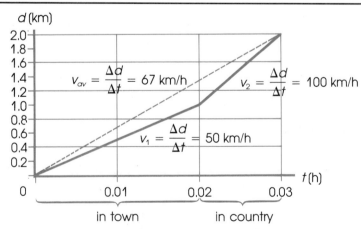

Sample problems

1. A person walks 5.0 km towards the east in 2.00 h, then 1.5 km towards the west in 0.50 h, and finally 10.0 km towards the east again in 2.25 h. What is the person's average velocity?

   Assume that vectors in the easterly direction are $(+)$, and those in the westerly direction are $(-)$.

   total displacement $\Delta d = \Delta d_1 + \Delta d_2 + \Delta d_3$
   $$= +5.0 \text{ km} + (-1.5 \text{ km}) + (+10.0 \text{ km})$$
   $$= +13.5 \text{ km}$$
   total time $\Delta t = 2.00 \text{ h} + 0.50 \text{ h} + 2.25 \text{ h}$
   $$= 4.75 \text{ h}$$
   $$v_{av} = \frac{\Delta d}{\Delta t}$$
   $$= \frac{+13.5 \text{ km}}{4.75 \text{ h}}$$
   $$= +2.8 \text{ km/h}$$
   which, since it is positive, represents an average velocity towards the east.

2. A car is driven for 1.00 h with a velocity of 100 km/h towards the south, then for 0.50 h with a velocity of 50 km/h towards the north, and finally for 0.75 h with a velocity of 80 km/h towards the south. Find the car's average velocity.

   Let [N] be positive $(+)$.
   $$\Delta d_1 = v_1 \Delta t_1 = (-100 \text{ km/h})(1.00 \text{ h}) = -100 \text{ km}$$
   $$\Delta d_2 = v_2 \Delta t_2 = (50 \text{ km/h})(0.50 \text{ h}) = 25 \text{ km}$$
   $$\Delta d_3 = v_3 \Delta t_3 = (-80 \text{ km/h})(0.75 \text{ h}) = -60 \text{ km}$$
   $$\Delta d = \Delta d_1 + \Delta d_2 + \Delta d_3$$
   $$= -100 \text{ km} + 25 \text{ km} + (-60 \text{ km})$$
   $$= -135 \text{ km}$$
   $$\Delta t = \Delta t_1 + \Delta t_2 + \Delta t_3$$
   $$\Delta t = 1.00 \text{ h} + 0.50 \text{ h} + 0.75 \text{ h} = 2.25 \text{ h}$$
   Therefore $v_{av} = \frac{\Delta d}{\Delta t}$
   $$= \frac{-135 \text{ km}}{2.25 \text{ h}}$$
   $$= -60 \text{ km/h, or } 60 \text{ km/h[S]}$$

3. Find the average velocities for the intervals AB and BC.

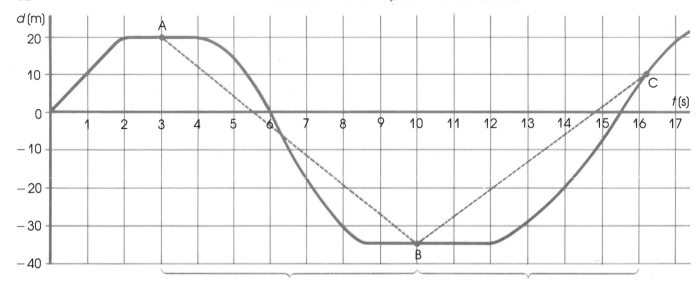

$$v_{av} = \frac{\Delta d}{\Delta t}$$

Interval AB

$$\text{slope} = \frac{d_2 - d_1}{t_2 - t_1} = \frac{d_B - d_A}{t_B - t_A}$$

$$= \frac{(-35 - 20) \text{ m}}{(10.0 - 3.0) \text{ s}}$$

$$= \frac{-55 \text{ m}}{7.0 \text{ s}} = -7.9 \text{ m/s}$$

Interval BC

$$v_{av} = \frac{\Delta d}{\Delta t}$$

$$\text{slope} = \frac{d_2 - d_1}{t_2 - t_1} = \frac{d_C - d_B}{t_C - t_B}$$

$$= \frac{[10 - (-35)] \text{ m}}{(16.3 - 10.0) \text{ s}}$$

$$= \frac{45 \text{ m}}{6.3 \text{ s}} = 7.1 \text{ m/s}$$

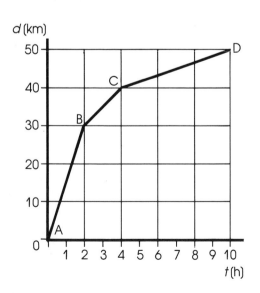

Practice

1. A hockey player's slapshot averages 51.5 m/s on its flight from the blue line to the goal, 20 m away. How long does the puck take to reach the goal? (0.39 s)

2. A rally driver completes three consecutive sections of a straight rally course as follows: section 1 (10 km) in 7.50 min, section 2 (18 km) in 14.40 min, and section 3 (9.8 km) in 5.80 min. What was the average velocity for the three sections? (Assume no stop between sections.) (82 km/h)

3. Using the graph, determine the average velocity for these intervals: (a) AB, (b) AD, (c) BD.

   (15 km/h, 5.0 km/h, 2.5 km/h)

4. Using the graph for sample problem 3 (top of page), determine the average velocity for each of the following sections.
   (a) $t = 0$ s to $t = 2$ s (b) $t = 6$ s to $t = 12$ s
   (c) $t = 6$ s to $t = 15.5$ s (10 m/s, −5.8 m/s, 0)

2.5 Instantaneous Velocity

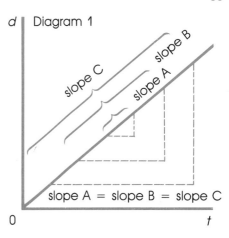

d | Diagram 1

slope C   slope A   slope B

slope A = slope B = slope C

0   t

As mentioned in the previous section, in a time interval where the velocity is uniform, the velocity at any instant, or instantaneous velocity (v_{inst}), has the same value as the average velocity. As may be seen in diagram 1, the average velocity, as determined by the slope, is the same for both large and small time intervals.

However, if the graph is not a straight line, the velocity is not uniform and the value of the instantaneous velocity (v_{inst}) changes from point to point. This is indicated in diagram 2 by a changing slope. To determine the instantaneous velocity, the slope of the d-t graph must be determined at one point of time. This appears to be an impossible task, since an instant in time means that the time interval decreases, or approaches the value of zero.

In diagram 2, note that, when the average velocity is taken over a smaller interval of time (slope A), the value for the average velocity is a more reliable approximation of instantaneous velocity (at the point P) than for larger time intervals. If we take an average velocity over an even smaller interval of time, the approximation will be even better. We are finding the average velocity for an extremely small interval of time, an interval that approaches zero. This is expressed mathematically as follows:

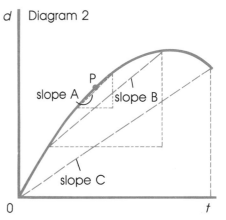

d | Diagram 2

slope A   P   slope B

slope C

0   t

$$v_{inst} = \lim_{\Delta t \to 0} \frac{\Delta d}{\Delta t}$$

This segment is too small to measure accurately, but, if the line is extended on either side, it approximates a tangent at the point where the instantaneous velocity is being determined. To make calculations of the slope easier, we usually extend the tangent line until it intersects grid lines, as shown in the example.

Instantaneous velocity is given by the slope of the tangent to a position-time graph.

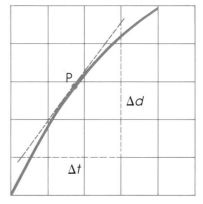

P

Δd

Δt

v_{inst} = slope of tangent at P

$$= \frac{\Delta d}{\Delta t}$$

Sample problem

On the following position-time graph, find the instantaneous velocities at points A, B, and C by finding the slope of the tangent to the graph at each of the points.

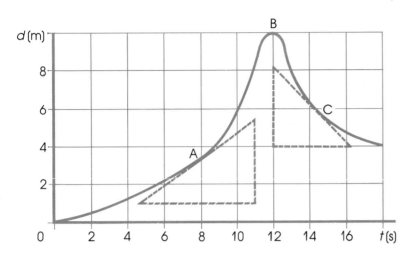

For point A: $v = \dfrac{\Delta d}{\Delta t} = \dfrac{5.5 \text{ m} - 1.0 \text{ m}}{11 \text{ s} - 4.3 \text{ s}}$

$= \dfrac{4.5 \text{ m}}{6.7 \text{ s}}$

$= 0.67 \text{ m/s}$

For point B: $v = \dfrac{\Delta d}{\Delta t}$

$= \dfrac{0 \text{ m}}{10 \text{ s}}$

$= 0 \text{ m/s}$

For point C: $v = \dfrac{\Delta d}{\Delta t} = \dfrac{4.0 \text{ m} - 8.0 \text{ m}}{16.1 \text{ s} - 12.1 \text{ s}}$

$= \dfrac{-4.0 \text{ m}}{4.0 \text{ s}}$

$= -1.0 \text{ m/s}$

Practice

Using the graph, determine each of the following.
(a) the average velocity for the first 2.5 s
(b) the average velocity for the interval 2.5 to 7.5 s
(c) the instantaneous velocity at the points A, B, and C
(d) the times at which the instantaneous velocity is approximately zero

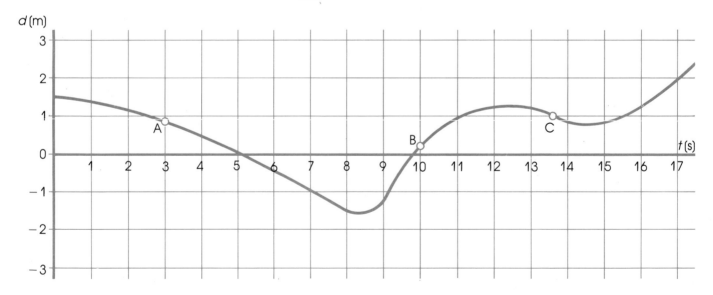

2.6 Velocity-Time Graphs

With a position-versus-time graph, the velocities for various intervals or instants can be determined by using a series of slopes. As an example, consider the position-time graph below. In sections A, E, and I there is no change in position. Hence the velocity is zero in each of these intervals. Another way of looking at it is that the slope of the *d-t* graph in these sections is zero. In sections C and G the slope of the *d-t* graph is constant, producing straight lines parallel to the time axis in the velocity-time (*v-t*) graph, the second of the graphs.

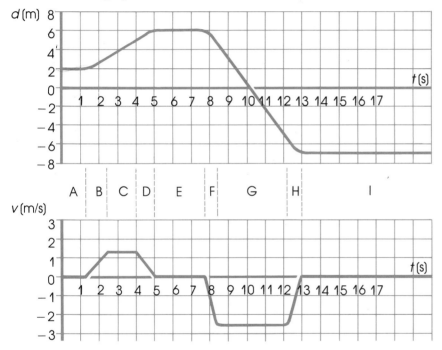

In section G, the slope of the *d-t* graph is negative, making the velocity on the *v-t* graph negative. In sections B, D, F, and H of the *d-t* curve, the slope is changing, indicating that the velocity is changing. Acceleration is occurring in these sections.

Acceleration is defined as the rate of change of velocity. Constant acceleration on a *v-t* graph appears as a sloping straight line. The slope of the *v-t* graph may be positive, or negative, or zero, making the acceleration positive, or negative, or zero.

The basic types of *v-t* graphs are summarized in a series of diagrams.

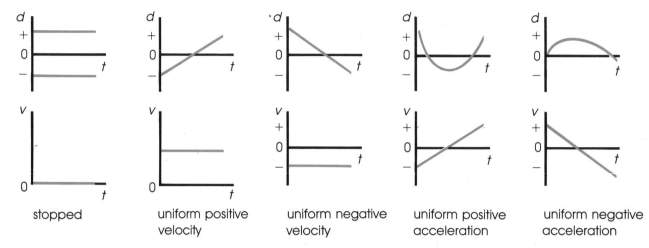

stopped | uniform positive velocity | uniform negative velocity | uniform positive acceleration | uniform negative acceleration

In summary, then, to produce a *v-t* graph from a *d-t* graph, a series of slopes is taken from the *d-t* graph and these values are plotted on the *v-t* graph. To produce a *d-t* graph from a *v-t* graph requires a different technique, which will be examined in the next section.

Practice

The following graph is that of an object moving in a straight line. East is considered as the positive direction.

(a) Determine the position of the object after 7.0 s.

(b) The graph shows five distinct sections. Briefly, and in general terms, describe the motion of the object in each of these sections.

(c) Considering the whole journey, calculate the average velocity.

(d) Find the instantaneous velocity at $t = 13$ s.

(e) Using an appropriate scale, draw a velocity-time graph from the position-time graph.   ((a) − 10 m, (c) 1.3 m/s, (d) 1.3 m/s)

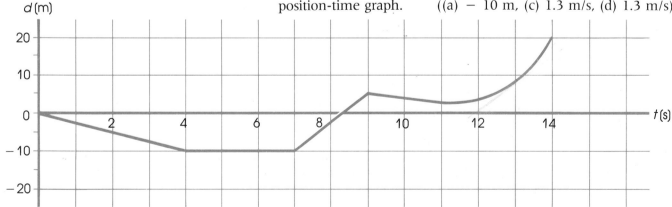

2.7 Position-Time Graphs from Velocity-Time Graphs

If an object's velocity is uniform, the displacement is calculated by using the relationship $\Delta d = v\Delta t$. The $v\text{-}t$ graph of this motion is a straight line parallel to the time axis.

An object travelling at 10 m/s for 5.0 s has a displacement of 50 m. On the graph, this is represented by the area under the $v\text{-}t$ graph for the interval $t = 0$ s to $t = 5$ s.

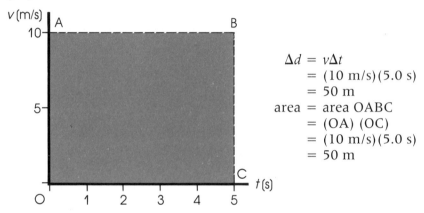

$$\begin{aligned} \Delta d &= v\Delta t \\ &= (10 \text{ m/s})(5.0 \text{ s}) \\ &= 50 \text{ m} \\ \text{area} &= \text{area OABC} \\ &= (OA)(OC) \\ &= (10 \text{ m/s})(5.0 \text{ s}) \\ &= 50 \text{ m} \end{aligned}$$

For objects whose velocity changes uniformly, the $v\text{-}t$ graph is sloping. In the example shown, the velocity changes from 4 m/s to 12 m/s in 4.0 s. Even in situations like this, when the velocity changes during the time interval, it is still meaningful to do a calculation of the area under the curve. For example, when the velocity changes from 4 m/s to 12 m/s in 4.0 s, the total time interval may be thought of as a large number of very small sub-intervals, in each of which the velocity is essentially constant.

For any one of these sub-intervals, the displacement is given by the area of the long narrow rectangle under the "step". The total area under all of the steps in the curve is a good approximation of the total displacement. If we take a larger number of smaller sub-intervals, the steps become even narrower and the step-curve becomes an even closer approximation of the actual graph. Thus the area under the graph becomes equivalent to the total displacement during the interval. This result is important because it is valid for all cases, whatever the shape of the $v\text{-}t$ graph.

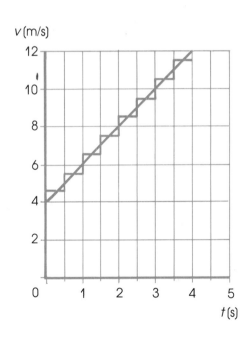

The displacement in any interval is given by the area under the $v\text{-}t$ graph for that interval.

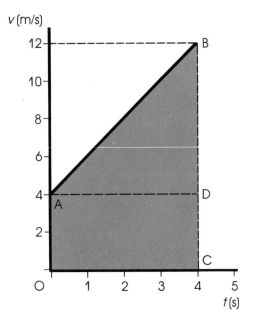

Returning to the original graph for uniformly changing velocity, the displacement is equal to the area under the graph between $t = 0$ and $t = 4$ s. For this example, the area may be calculated either by finding the area of the trapezium or by adding together the areas of the triangle and the rectangle formed under the v-t graph.

$$\Delta d = \text{area ABCO}$$
$$= \text{area ABD} + \text{area ADCO}$$
$$= \frac{1}{2}(4.0 \text{ s})(8.0 \text{ m/s}) + (4.0 \text{ m/s})(4.0 \text{ s})$$
$$= 16 \text{ m} + 16 \text{ m}$$
$$= 32 \text{ m}$$

$$\text{or} \quad \Delta d = \text{area of trapezium ABCO}$$
$$= \frac{1}{2}(\text{OA} + \text{CB})(\text{OC})$$
$$= \frac{1}{2}(4.0 \text{ m/s} + 12 \text{ m/s})(4.0 \text{ s})$$
$$= 32 \text{ m}$$

In some cases where the motion varies, a series of areas may be added together to find the total displacement (see illustration). Note that areas above the time axis are positive and areas below the time axis are negative. The sign must be considered when determining the total displacement. It should be emphasized that, in all cases, the area is calculated using the units given on the axes of the graph. No direct measurements are made.

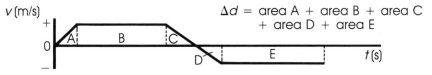

$$\Delta d = \text{area A} + \text{area B} + \text{area C} + \text{area D} + \text{area E}$$

Areas D and E are negative displacements, because the velocities are negative.

When the motion is even less uniform, other techniques are necessary to determine the area under the v-t graph.

One approach is to isolate larger areas that form rectangles and triangles, and find their areas. Then count the number of squares in the remaining areas. For partial squares, estimate the area of each and add them together, expressing the total to the nearest number number of whole squares (see illustration on the next page). Then find the total number of whole and partial squares. Finally, multiply the total number of squares by the value of one square (using the scale of the graph). The sum of the areas of the squares and the other regular-shaped areas approximates the total displacement.

Another method available for the accurate determination of area, even when the equation is not known, involves the use of a device called a *planimeter*.

area of shaded sections (one square = 0.50 s × 0.50 m/s = 0.25 m)
$$= 11 \text{ full squares} + 6.5 \text{ partial squares}$$
$$= 17.5 \text{ full squares}$$
$$= (17.5)(0.25 \text{ m}) = 4.4 \text{ m}$$

Δd = area under the curve
$$= \text{area I} + \text{area II} + \text{area III} + \text{area of the shaded sections}$$
$$= (2.0 \text{ m/s})(6.0 \text{ s}) + (2.5 \text{ m/s})(4.0 \text{ s}) + (1.0 \text{ m/s})(2.0 \text{ s}) + 4.4 \text{ m}$$
$$= 12 \text{ m} + 10 \text{ m} + 2 \text{ m} + 4.4 \text{ m}$$
$$= 28.4 \text{ m} = 28 \text{ m}$$

The accuracy of the approximation will improve if smaller squares are used. To produce a very accurate value for the displacement, integral calculus may be used, provided the equation of the line on the v-t graph is known. You may wish to review this section of the text later, if you are taking a parallel course in calculus.

It is important to remember that, to draw a d-t graph on the basis of information derived from a v-t graph, the displacement (Δd) must be added to the initial position (d_1) to locate the final position (d_2) on the d-t graph.

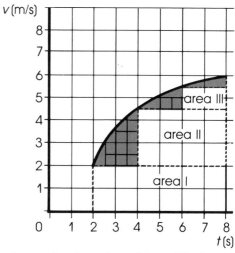

Where a is a function of b, and both vary, the area under the curve is equal to $\int a\,db$ instead of the product ab. This will become more apparent when calculus is studied.

Practice

1. This graph describes the motion of an object moving in a straight line. At the beginning it is going east. From the graph determine each of the following.
   (a) the object's displacement in the first 3.0 s
   (b) the object's displacement between $t = 3.0$ s and $t = 5.0$ s
   (c) the total displacement of the object in 14 s
   (d) the average velocity of the object from $t = 0$ to $t = 8.0$ s
   (e) the d-t graph; use it to check your answers to parts (a) to (d)
                           (200 m[E], 0, 0, 17.5 m/s [E])
2. Use this graph of the motion of a car to find the total displacement (north is positive).   (150 m[N])

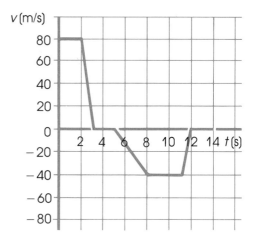

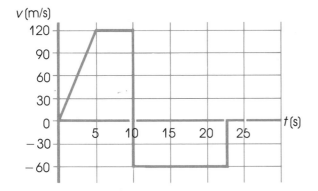

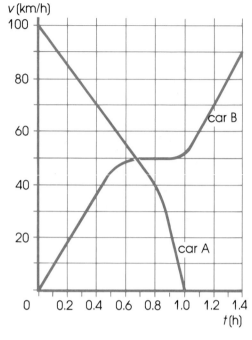

3. This graph illustrates the motion of two cars travelling due north. Assuming that both cars were at the same position at $t = 0$, answer the following questions.
   (a) At what time do both cars have the same velocity?
   (b) At $t = 0.4$ h, which car is ahead and by how much?
   (c) At $t = 1.0$ h, what is the distance separating the two cars?

   (0.68 h; A, 26 km; 25 km)

4. From the v-t graph below, determine the total displacement of the object in the first 12 s.   (505 m)

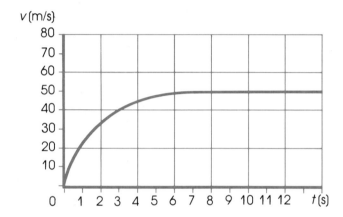

2.8 Acceleration

As mentioned in Section 2.6, acceleration is defined as the rate of change of velocity. Thus, acceleration is a vector quantity and is expressed mathematically as follows:

$$\vec{a} = \frac{\Delta \vec{v}}{\Delta t} \quad \text{or} \quad \vec{a} = \frac{\vec{v_2} - \vec{v_1}}{\Delta t}$$

where $\vec{a}$ is the acceleration

$\Delta \vec{v}$ is the change in velocity

$\vec{v_1}$ is the initial velocity

$\vec{v_2}$ is the final velocity

Δt is the time interval for the acceleration

Once again, although acceleration is a vector quantity, in straight-line motion the vector notation may be omitted, by relying on the plus and minus sign convention used previously.

Just as the slope of a position-time graph gives the rate of change of the displacement, the slope of a velocity-time graph gives the rate of change of velocity, that is, the acceleration. If the rate of change of velocity is uniform, the velocity-time graph will be a sloping straight line, as shown. The slope of the *v-t* graph gives the acceleration.

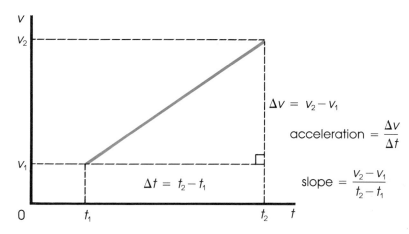

$$\Delta v = v_2 - v_1$$

$$acceleration = \frac{\Delta v}{\Delta t}$$

$$\Delta t = t_2 - t_1$$

$$slope = \frac{v_2 - v_1}{t_2 - t_1}$$

Other examples of uniform acceleration are illustrated below. Note that, if the slope is negative, the acceleration is negative.

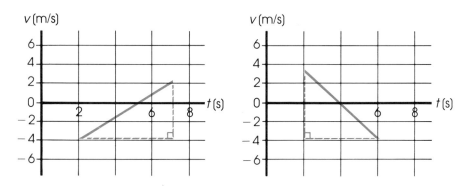

Sample problems

The graphs above represent the acceleration of two objects. Determine the acceleration of each object.

acceleration = slope of v-t graph   acceleration = slope of v-t graph

$$a = \frac{\Delta v}{\Delta t} = \frac{v_2 - v_1}{t_2 - t_1}$$ $$a = \frac{\Delta v}{\Delta t} = \frac{v_2 - v_1}{t_2 - t_1}$$

$$= \frac{2.0 \text{ m/s} - (-4.0 \text{ m/s})}{7.0 \text{ s} - 2.0 \text{ s}}$$ $$= \frac{-4.0 \text{ m/s} - 3.0 \text{ m/s}}{6.0 \text{ s} - 2.0 \text{ s}}$$

$$= \frac{6.0 \text{ m/s}}{5.0 \text{ s}} = 1.2 \text{ m/s/s}$$ $$= \frac{-7.0 \text{ m/s}}{4.0 \text{ s}} = -1.8 \text{ m/s/s}$$

$$= 1.2 \text{ m/s}^2$$ $$= -1.8 \text{ m/s}^2$$

Note that the unit for acceleration, m/s/s, is abbreviated and written as m/s².

Practice
From this graph determine the acceleration for each interval, using the slopes.   (2.0 m/s², 0, −1.8 m/s², 0, 1.0 m/s²)

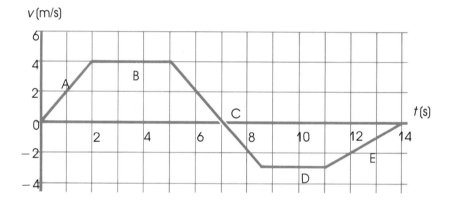

2.9 Uniform Acceleration

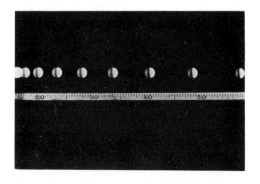

In Section 2.2, the relationship $v = \Delta d/\Delta t$ was useful, provided the velocity was uniform. Similarly, the relationship $a = \Delta v/\Delta t$ is useful, as long as we recognize that it is only valid when the acceleration is uniform. If the value of the acceleration varies, we cannot use this relationship over any extended interval of time.

In physics, there are many situations in which the acceleration is uniform. Two examples are the acceleration due to gravity and the acceleration of charged particles in uniform electric fields. Five examples of how the relationship $a = \dfrac{\Delta v}{\Delta t}$ can be used are given next.

Sample problems

1. A car accelerates uniformly from 10 m/s to 30 m/s in 10 s. What is its acceleration?

$$a = \frac{\Delta v}{\Delta t} = \frac{(v_2 - v_1)}{\Delta t}$$
$$= \frac{(30 \text{ m/s} - 10 \text{ m/s})}{10 \text{ s}}$$
$$= \frac{20 \text{ m/s}}{10 \text{ s}} = 2.0 \text{ m/s}^2$$

2. A ball thrown straight up in the air has an initial velocity of 40 m/s and final velocity of zero, 4.0 s later. Find the acceleration of the ball.

When the direction of the motion is not specified, it is necessary to designate one direction as positive and the other negative. In cases involving motion near the surface of the Earth, it is customary to define up as positive and down as negative.

$$a = \frac{(v_2 - v_1)}{\Delta t}$$
$$= \frac{0 \text{ m/s} - (+40 \text{ m/s})}{4.0 \text{ s}} = -10 \text{ m/s}^2$$

The negative sign in the acceleration indicates that the final velocity is less than the initial velocity. As the ball moves up, its speed is decreasing. This situation is sometimes called deceleration, but, as this example illustrates, deceleration may also be considered as a negative acceleration.

The word deceleration is discouraged in physics, because beginning students assume incorrectly that all negative values of acceleration are decelerations.

A negative value of acceleration can mean one of these two things:

1. The object moves in the original (positive) direction with a decreasing speed (commonly called deceleration).
2. The object moves in the opposite (negative) direction with an increasing speed. (It makes no sense to call this a deceleration.)

Which of the two conditions exists depends on the situation. In sample problem 2, negative acceleration occurs because of the first condition. On the other hand, if the same ball is allowed to fall freely, it will move down with an increasing speed, also exhibiting negative acceleration, since we defined up as positive.

3. A car decelerates at 2.0 m/s². If the car's initial velocity is 40 m/s(E), what is its final velocity 3.5 s later?

For motion in a straight line, the motion can occur in only two directions. Thus, it is usually more convenient to define one direction as positive and the other negative. Either of the following solutions is correct, but the second solution is usually the preferred one.

Solution 1

$$a = \frac{(v_2 - v_1)}{\Delta t}$$

or $v_2 = v_1 + a\Delta t$

$$= 40 \text{ m/s[E]} + (2 \text{ m/s}^2[\text{W}])(3.5 \text{ s})$$
$$= 40 \text{ m/s[E]} + 7 \text{ m/s[W]}$$
$$= 33 \text{ m/s[E]}$$

Solution 2

Choosing directions so that east is positive $(+)$ and west is negative $(-)$,

$v_2 = v_1 + a\Delta t$

$$= 40 \text{ m/s} + (-2 \text{ m/s}^2)(3.5 \text{ s})$$
$$= 40 \text{ m/s} - 7.0 \text{ m/s}$$
$$= +33 \text{ m/s, or } 33 \text{ m/s[E]}$$

4. A ball is rolled up a slope with an initial velocity of 6.0 m/s. The ball experiences an acceleration of -2.0 m/s^2. What is its velocity after **(a)** 2.0 s, **(b)** 3.0 s, and **(c)** 4.0 s?

   Choosing directions so that up the slope is positive and down the slope is negative,

   (a) $v_2 = v_1 + a\Delta t$
   $$= 6.0 \text{ m/s} + (-2.0 \text{ m/s}^2)(2.0 \text{ s})$$
   $$= 6.0 \text{ m/s} - 4.0 \text{ m/s}$$
   $$= +2.0 \text{ m/s, or } 2.0 \text{ m/s[up the slope]}$$

   (b) $v_2 = v_1 + a\Delta t$
   $$= 6.0 \text{ m/s} + (-2.0 \text{ m/s}^2)(3.0 \text{ s})$$
   $$= 0 \text{ m/s, i.e., it is momentarily stopped}$$

   (c) $v_2 = v_1 + a\Delta t$
   $$= 6.0 \text{ m/s} + (-2.0 \text{ m/s}^2)(4.0 \text{ s})$$
   $$= -2.0 \text{ m/s, or } 2.0 \text{ m/s[down the slope]}$$

5. A gun shoots a bullet vertically upward with a velocity of 1200 m/s. How long will it take for the bullet to have a velocity of 600 m/s on its way back down to Earth, if the bullet experiences an acceleration of $10.0 \text{ m/s}^2[\text{down}]$?

   Choosing up as positive and down as negative,

   $$a = \frac{v_2 - v_1}{\Delta t}, \text{ or } \Delta t = \frac{v_2 - v_1}{a}$$

   $$= \frac{-600 \text{ m/s} - (+1200 \text{ m/s})}{-10 \text{ m/s}^2}$$

$$= \frac{-1800 \text{ m/s}}{-10 \text{ m/s}^2}$$
$$\Delta t = +180 \text{ s}$$

Note that Δt has a positive value in this example. If Δt is negative, a mistake has been made in one or more of the quantities.

Practice

1. A dragster accelerates uniformly from rest to 56 m/s in 3.7 s. What is its acceleration?   (15 m/s²)
2. A car accelerates at -2.0 m/s². If its initial velocity is 24 m/s, to the east, what will its velocity be 8.0 s later?   (8.0 m/s[E])
3. A ball is thrown vertically into the air with a velocity of 30 m/s[up]. If the acceleration due to gravity is 10 m/s²[down], what will its velocity be after (a) 2.0 s, and (b) 4.0 s?
                        (10 m/s[up], 10 m/s[down])
4. An arrow is shot straight up into the air at 40 m/s. As it falls back to Earth, acceleration due to gravity is 10 m/s²[down], and the final velocity is 40 m/s. How long does it take the arrow to come back to the ground?   (8.0 s)
5. A steel ball, starting from rest, rolls down one slope and up another. It takes 2.5 s to reach the bottom of the first slope, at which point its speed is 5.0 m/s. If the magnitude of the acceleration on the second slope is exactly one-half that on the first slope, how long will it take for the ball to come to a stop on the second slope?   (5.0 s)

2.10 Average Acceleration

Average velocity involves the total displacement and the total time. Similarly, average acceleration (a_{av}) involves the total velocity change and the time required for that change.

$$\mathbf{a_{av}} = \frac{\Delta v}{\Delta t}$$

where a_{av} is the average acceleration
Δv is the change in velocity
Δt is the time interval

When the acceleration is uniform, the average acceleration and the instantaneous acceleration have the same value, since the slope of the v-t graph is constant during the interval. If the slope of the v-t graph changes during the interval, the average acceleration and the instantaneous acceleration do not have the same value.

To find the average acceleration from a v-t graph, calculate the slope for the time interval concerned. In some cases, the average acceleration may not be useful, particularly if the velocity has changed in an irregular way.

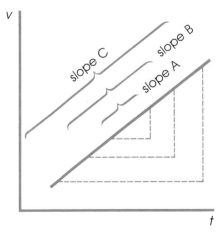

slope A = slope B = slope C

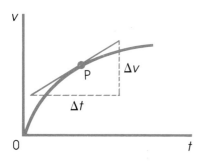

$$a_{inst} = \lim_{\Delta t \to 0} \frac{\Delta v}{\Delta t}$$

$$= \text{slope of tangent at P}$$

2.11 Instantaneous Acceleration

To determine the instantaneous acceleration when the velocity-time graph is not a straight line, a procedure similar to that used for the instantaneous velocity is followed. The instantaneous acceleration is given by the slope of the tangent to the velocity-time graph at a specific time (see illustration). This is stated mathematically as:

$$a_{\text{inst}} = \lim_{\Delta t \to 0} \frac{\Delta v}{\Delta t}$$

where a_{inst} is the instantaneous acceleration
Δv is the velocity change
Δt is the time interval

Sample problem

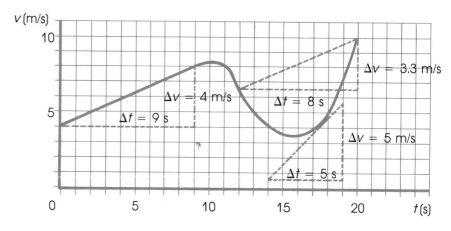

Remember that a tangent forms a right angle with a radius of a circle. One convenient way to draw an accurate tangent is to first draw a straight line through the desired point, approximating a radius of the circle. Then, draw the tangent at right angles to this artificial radius line.

On the velocity-time graph illustrated, determine each of the following.
(a) the acceleration at any instant during the first 9.0 s
(b) the average acceleration between $t = 12$ s and $t = 20$ s
(c) the instantaneous acceleration at $t = 17.5$ s

(a) The acceleration in the first 9.0 s is constant.

Its value is: $a = \dfrac{\Delta v}{\Delta t} = \dfrac{(8.0-4.0) \text{ m/s}}{(9.0-0) \text{ s}} = \dfrac{4.0 \text{ m/s}}{9.0 \text{ s}} = 0.44 \text{ m/s}^2$

(b) $a_{av} = \dfrac{\Delta v}{\Delta t} = \dfrac{(10.0-6.5) \text{ m/s}}{(20.0-12.0) \text{ s}} = \dfrac{3.5 \text{ m/s}}{8.0 \text{ s}} = 0.44 \text{ m/s}^2$

(c) The instantaneous acceleration at $t = 17.5$ s is the slope of the
tangent at $t = 17.5$ s.

$$a_{inst} = \lim_{\Delta t \to 0} \frac{\Delta v}{\Delta t} = \frac{(5.7-0.7) \text{ m/s}}{(19.0-14.0) \text{ s}} = \frac{5.0 \text{ m/s}}{5.0 \text{ s}} = 1.0 \text{ m/s}^2$$

Practice

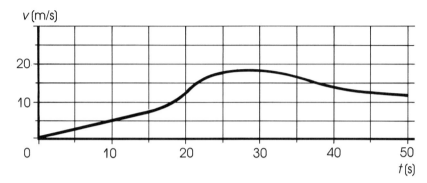

From this velocity-time graph, determine each of the following.
(a) the acceleration at any instant in the first 12 s
(b) the instantaneous acceleration at (i) $t = 25$ s and (ii) $t = 40$ s
(c) the average acceleration for the intervals (i) $t = 0$ to $t = 25$ s
   and (ii) $t = 30$ s to $t = 50$ s
   (0.50 m/s²; 0.57 m/s², −0.38 m/s²; 0.70 m/s², −0.30 m/s²)

2.12 Acceleration-Time Graphs

By finding the instantaneous acceleration at different times, an acceleration-time graph can be plotted, as illustrated below.

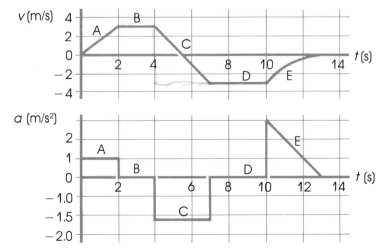

A tangent may also be drawn with the help of a mirror. Place the mirror on the curve at the point desired. Adjust the mirror so that the real curve merges smoothly with its image in the mirror. (The mirror will be perpendicular to the curve at that point.) A line drawn perpendicular to the mirror edge will be parallel to a tangent drawn to the curve.

In cases where the acceleration varies, for example, in rockets, the slope of the *a-t* graph is taken, to find the rate of change of acceleration. This is known as the "jerk", and it is defined as jerk = $\Delta a/\Delta t$. The unit for jerk is m/s³.

Note that, in sections B and D, the object has a uniform velocity. Thus, the slope of the *v-t* graph and therefore the acceleration for that interval is zero. In sections A and C the acceleration is uniform, whereas in section E the acceleration is non-uniform. In most of the cases we will study, the acceleration is uniform, and acceleration-time graphs are made up of a series of straight lines parallel to the time axis.

We saw earlier that the area between a velocity-time curve and the time axis gives the displacement of an object. Similarly, the area between an acceleration-time curve and the time axis gives the velocity change during that interval, as illustrated.

The change in velocity in any interval is given by the area under the *a-t* graph for that interval.

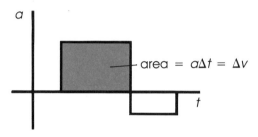

This area gives only the velocity change (Δv), and it is necessary to know the initial velocity (v_1) in order to determine the final velocity (v_2) from an acceleration-time curve. As before, areas below the time axis are negative, corresponding to a decrease of velocity.

Transitions between *d-t* graphs and *v-t* graphs use techniques similar to those used for transitions between *v-t* graphs and *a-t* graphs. Thus, it is useful to summarize all the possible transitions, as follows:

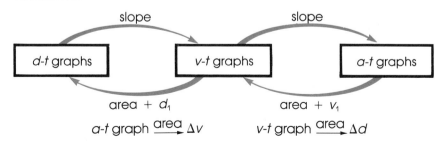

Note that the most useful graph is the *v-t* graph. Its slope gives the object's acceleration and its area gives the object's displacement, in any interval.

Sample problem

Given the information on the *v-t* graph in the margin, draw the corresponding *d-t* and *a-t* graphs for the interval from $t=0$ to $t=20$ s. (Assume that $d_1 = 0$.)

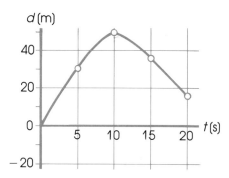

Practice

From the *v-t* graph below, draw the corresponding *d-t* graph and *a-t* graph. (Assume that $d_1 = 0$.)

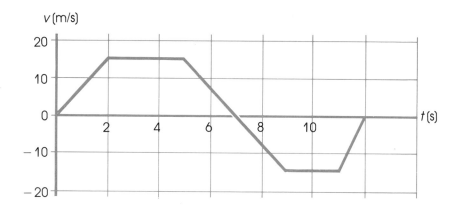

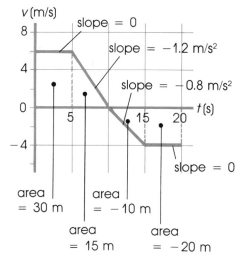

2.13 Useful Equations for Uniform Acceleration

As discussed in Section 2.9, uniform acceleration is defined by the equation $a = \dfrac{\Delta v}{\Delta t}$. The *v-t* graph for an interval of uniform acceleration is shown on the next page.

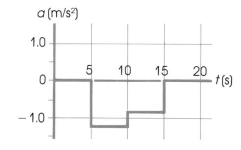

Since acceleration = slope of *v-t* graph

$$a = \frac{\Delta v}{\Delta t} = \frac{v_2 - v_1}{\Delta t}$$

which may be rewritten as:

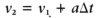

$$v_2 = v_1 + a\Delta t \qquad \textbf{Equation 1}$$

To find the displacement, the area under the v-t graph is determined. This area may be calculated these three ways, each method resulting in an equation:

(a) *Area of a trapezium*

$$\text{area of trapezium} = \frac{1}{2}(\text{sum of the parallel sides})(\text{height})$$

$$= \frac{1}{2}(v_1 + v_2)(\Delta t)$$

$$\Delta d = \frac{(v_1 + v_2)}{2}\Delta t \qquad \textbf{Equation 2(a)}$$

This equation can also be expressed as:

$$\Delta d = v_{av}\Delta t \qquad \textbf{Equation 2(b)}$$

(b) *Area of a rectangle + area of a triangle*

$$\text{total area} = \text{area of rectangle} + \text{area of triangle}$$

$$\Delta d = v_1\Delta t + \frac{1}{2}\Delta v(\Delta t)$$

$$\text{but} \quad \Delta v = a\Delta t,$$

$$\text{so} \quad \frac{1}{2}\Delta v(\Delta t) = \frac{1}{2}(a\Delta t)(\Delta t), \text{ or } \frac{1}{2}a(\Delta t)^2$$

$$\Delta d = v_1\Delta t + \frac{1}{2}a(\Delta t)^2 \qquad \textbf{Equation 3}$$

(c) *Area of a rectangle − area of a triangle*

$$\text{displacement} = \text{area of large rectangle} - \text{area of triangle}$$

$$\Delta d = v_2\Delta t - \frac{1}{2}a(\Delta t)^2 \qquad \textbf{Equation 4}$$

A fifth equation can be obtained from the first and third equations, as follows:

From Equation 1, $v_2 = v_1 + a\Delta t$

Squaring both sides of the equation,

$$(v_2)^2 = (v_1 + a\Delta t)^2$$

$$v_2{}^2 = v_1{}^2 + 2av_1\Delta t + a^2(\Delta t)^2$$

Taking a factor of $2a$ from the last two terms in the expression, we obtain

$$v_2{}^2 = v_1{}^2 + 2a(v_1\Delta t + \frac{1}{2}a(\Delta t)^2)$$

But the term in brackets is Equation 3.

$$v_2{}^2 = v_1{}^2 + 2a\Delta d \qquad \textbf{Equation 5}$$

The choice of a particular equation will depend on the information given in the problem. One way to attack problems of this type is to start by writing down what is known. Then determine what is the unknown quantity. Then select the equation that includes both the known and the unknown quantities. Finally, substitute the values and calculate the answer.

These equations may be used to solve a wide variety of problems involving uniform acceleration. To gain competence in their use, experience is neccessary. For practice, see the problems that follow and those in the review section at the end of the chapter.

Sample problems

1. A ball rolls down a hill with a constant acceleration of 2.0 m/s². If the ball starts from rest, (a) what is its velocity at the end of 4.0 s? (b) How far did the ball move?

$$a = 2.0 \text{ m/s}^2 \qquad v_2 = ?$$
$$v_1 = 0 \text{ (rest)} \qquad \Delta d = ?$$
$$\Delta t = 4.0 \text{ s}$$

(a)
$$v_2 = v_1 + a\Delta t$$
$$= 0 + (2.0 \text{ m/s}^2)(4.0 \text{ s})$$
$$= 8.0 \text{ m/s}$$

(b)
$$\Delta d = v_1 \Delta t + \frac{1}{2}a(\Delta t)^2$$
$$= 0 + \frac{1}{2}(2.0 \text{ m/s}^2)(4.0 \text{ s})^2$$
$$= 16 \text{ m}$$

2. An electron is accelerated uniformly from rest to a velocity of 2.0×10^7 m/s. (a) If the electron travelled 0.10 m while it was being accelerated, what was its acceleration? (b) How long did the electron take to attain its final velocity?

$$v_1 = 0 \qquad a = ?$$
$$v_2 = 2.0 \times 10^7 \text{ m/s} \quad \Delta t = ?$$
$$\Delta d = 0.10 \text{ m}$$

(a)
$$v_2^2 = v_1^2 + 2a\Delta d$$
$$(2.0 \times 10^7 \text{ m/s})^2 = 0^2 + 2a(0.10 \text{ m})$$
$$a = 2.0 \times 10^{15} \text{ m/s}^2$$

(b)
$$\Delta d = \left(\frac{v_1 + v_2}{2}\right)\Delta t$$

or $\quad \Delta t = \dfrac{2\Delta d}{v_1 + v_2}$

$$= \frac{(2)(0.10 \text{ m})}{0 \text{ m/s} + 2.0 \times 10^7 \text{ m/s}}$$

$$= 1.0 \times 10^{-8} \text{ s}$$

alternatively $\quad \Delta v = a\Delta t$

$$\Delta t = \frac{2.0 \times 10^7 \text{ m/s}}{2.0 \times 10^{15} \text{ m/s}^2}$$

$$= 1.0 \times 10^{-8} \text{ s}$$

3. During a 30.0 s interval, the velocity of a rocket increased from 200 m/s to 500 m/s. What was the displacement of the rocket during this time interval?

$$\Delta t = 30.0 \text{ s}$$
$$v_1 = 200 \text{ m/s}$$
$$v_2 = 500 \text{ m/s}$$

$$\Delta d = \left(\frac{v_1 + v_2}{2}\right)\Delta t$$

$$= \left(\frac{200 \text{ m/s} + 500 \text{ m/s}}{2}\right)30.0 \text{ s}$$

$$= 10\ 500 \text{ m, or } 1.05 \times 10^4 \text{ m}$$

4. A bullet that is shot vertically into the air has an initial velocity of 500 m/s. The acceleration due to gravity is 10 m/s²[down].
(a) How long does it take before the bullet stops rising?
(b) How high does the bullet go?

Choosing up as positive and down as negative,
$$v_1 = 500 \text{ m/s}$$
$$a_g = -10 \text{ m/s}^2$$
$$v_2 = 0$$

(a)
$$\Delta t = \frac{(v_2 - v_1)}{a_g}$$

$$= \frac{0 \text{ m/s} - 500 \text{ m/s}}{-10 \text{ m/s}^2}$$

$$= 50 \text{ s}$$

(b) *Solution 1* *Solution 2*

$$\Delta d = \left(\frac{v_1 + v_2}{2}\right)\Delta t \qquad \Delta d = v_1\Delta t + \frac{1}{2}a_g(\Delta t)^2$$

$$= \left(\frac{500 \text{ m/s} + 0}{2}\right)(50 \text{ s}) \qquad = 500 \text{ m/s}(50 \text{ s}) + \frac{1}{2}(-10 \text{ m/s}^2)(50 \text{ s})^2$$

$$= 12\ 500 \text{ m} \qquad\qquad = 25\ 000 \text{ m} - 12\ 500 \text{ m}$$

$$= 1.3 \times 10^4 \text{ m} \qquad\quad = 12\ 500 \text{ m}$$

$$\qquad\qquad\qquad\qquad\quad = 1.3 \times 10^4 \text{ m}$$

5. A balloon is ascending at the rate of 9.0 m/s and has reached a height of 80 m above the ground when it releases a package. How long does the package take to reach the ground? ($a_g = 10 \text{ m/s}^2[\text{down}]$)

Choosing up as positive and down as negative,
$$v_1 = 9.0 \text{ m/s}$$
$$\Delta d = -80 \text{ m}$$
$$a_g = -10 \text{ m/s}^2$$

$$\Delta d = v_1\Delta t + \frac{1}{2}a_g(\Delta t)^2$$

$$-80 \text{ m} = (9.0 \text{ m/s})\Delta t + \frac{1}{2}(-10 \text{ m/s}^2)(\Delta t)^2$$

$$5\Delta t^2 - 9.0\Delta t - 80 = 0, \text{ or } (\Delta t - 5)(5\Delta t + 16) = 0$$
$$\Delta t = 5.0 \text{ s, or } \Delta t = -3.2 \text{ s}$$
Since time must be positive,
$$t = 5.0 \text{ s}$$

Practice
1. A skier starts down a slope 0.50 km long at a velocity of 4.0 m/s. If he accelerates at a constant rate of 2.0 m/s², find his velocity at the bottom of the slope. (45 m/s)
2. Pressing on the brake pedal slows a car down from a velocity of 35 m/s to 20 m/s in 8.0 s. Assuming that the acceleration is uniform, what is the displacement of the car? (2.2×10^2 m)
3. A sports car starts from rest and has a uniform acceleration of 1.2 m/s². (a) What is its velocity after 30 s? (b) How far does it go in that time? (36 m/s, 5.4×10^2 m)
4. An object dropped from a balloon descending at 4.0 m/s lands on the ground 10 s later. What was the altitude of the balloon at the moment the object was dropped? (Use $a_g = 10 \text{ m/s}^2[\text{down}]$.) ($5.4 \times 10^2$ m)

Canadian Olympic gold medal winner, Linda Thom

5. A ball thrown vertically upward returns to the ground 6.0 s later. **(a)** How many seconds did the ball take to reach its highest point? **(b)** How high did the ball go? **(c)** With what velocity did it hit the ground? (Use $a_g = 10$ m/s²[down].)

(3.0 s, 45 m, 30 m/s [down])

6. A bullet leaves the muzzle of a gun with a velocity of 400 m/s. The length of the gun barrel is 0.50 m. **(a)** Assuming that the bullet is uniformly accelerated, what is its average velocity inside the barrel? **(b)** How long is the bullet in the gun after being fired?

$(2.0 \times 10^2$ m/s, 2.5×10^{-3} s)

2.14 Investigations

Investigation 2.1: Uniform Acceleration

Problem:

What type of motion is experienced by a cart rolling down an incline?

Materials:

ticker-tape timer
2.0 m ticker tape
cart
masking tape
bricks
ramp 2.0 m long

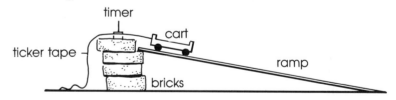

Procedure:

1. Set up the apparatus illustrated. One end of the ramp should be at least 20 cm higher than the other. Make sure that the wheels on the cart are "free wheeling" and that the ramp is clean.

2. Arrange for your partner to stop the speeding cart at the bottom of the ramp. Start the timer and release the cart.

3. Select a suitable unit of time for the investigation. For example, if the timer has a period of 1/60 s, then six dots on the tape represent 0.10 s, a convenient unit of time.

4. Draw a line across the tape through the first clear dot located on the end of the tape where the motion began. Draw a line through every sixth dot all the way along the tape, as illustrated.

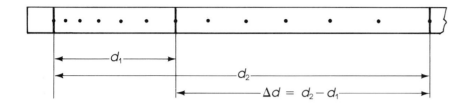

5. Set up an observations chart similar to the one illustrated.

Time $t(s)$	Position d (cm)	Displacement Δd (cm)	Av. velocity v_{av} (cm/s)	Inst. velocity $v_{inst.}$ (cm/s)	Acceleration a (m/s²)
0.00	0	0	0	0	0
0.10					
0.20					

6. Measure the distance, in centimetres, from the first dot to the end of each marked time interval. Record this data in the position column.
7. Plot a graph of position versus time. What type of motion was the cart undergoing? How can you tell by the shape of the d-t graph?
8. Calculate the average velocity for each 0.10 s time interval, recording the results in the average velocity column. The average velocity represents the slope of the position-time graph half-way in time for each time interval, i.e., at 0.050 s. Enter the values in your chart.
9. On the position-time graph, determine the instantaneous velocity at 0.10 s intervals, starting with $t = 0.15$ s. This will involve determining the slope of the tangent to the position-time graph at each of the indicated times. Enter the values in your chart.
10. Compare the values of average velocity and instantaneous velocity for each time interval. What conclusion can you draw?
11. Plot a graph of average velocity versus time. Remember to plot the points at the midpoints in time, i.e., at 0.05 s, 0.15 s, 0.25 s, etc.
12. Draw the best straight line through the plotted points and determine the slope. What does the slope represent?
13. Calculate the area under the velocity-versus-time graph. Compare this value with the displacement measured on the tape

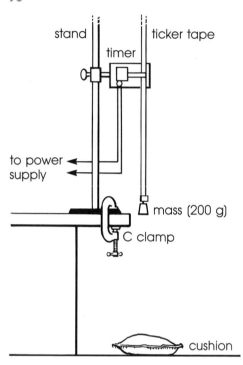

stand | ticker tape

timer

to power supply

mass (200 g)

C clamp

cushion

from $t = 0$ to the last time interval on the tape by calculating the percentage difference.

14. Using either the table or the graph, determine the instantaneous acceleration for each time interval. Plot a graph of acceleration versus time.

15. In many cases the average-velocity-versus-time graph does not pass through zero. If this is so in your tape, briefly suggest some reasons why.

Investigation 2.2: Acceleration Due to Gravity

Problem:
What type of motion is experienced by a freely falling mass?

Materials:
See diagram.

Procedure:
1. Clamp the timer in a vertical position 2.0 m above the floor. Thread 2.0 m of ticker tape through the timer. Make sure it does not have any kinks or folds in it that would interfere with its free movement through the timer.

2. Attach a 200 g mass to the lower end of the tape, using masking tape.

3. Start the timer, then release the 200 g mass. Make sure the mass will miss all obstacles as it falls.

4. Repeat steps 2 and 3, this time using a 0.5 kg mass.

5. Mark off each tape in six-dot intervals.

6. Construct a chart for each tape with these headings: time, displacement, average velocity.

7. Plot a graph of average velocity versus time and find the average acceleration for each tape. Compare the values.

8. Is the acceleration due to gravity uniform? Explain your answer, using evidence from your investigation.

9. The accepted value for a freely falling object is 980 cm/s². Determine the percentage error for each of the masses. What factors could have produced the error?

10. Using the data from your investigation, determine whether mass affects the acceleration due to gravity.

Investigation 2.3: Position, Velocity, and Acceleration

Problem:
How can we describe the motion of an object, using position-time, velocity-time, and acceleration-time graphs?

Materials:
ticker-tape timer
2.0 m ticker tape
cart
masking tape

Procedure:
1. Set up the apparatus illustrated, making sure that the surface is level. Thread approximately 2.0 m of tape through the timer, attaching it to the cart with masking tape.
2. Start the timer. Place your hand on the cart and accelerate it steadily to a uniform velocity. The tape should record approximately one-half accelerated motion and one-half uniform velocity. It is advisable to make a few practice runs before making your final tape.
3. Prepare a chart similar to the one used in the first investigation, omitting the column for instantaneous velocity.
4. Use the same procedure as in the first investigation to mark off suitable time intervals, of perhaps 0.10 s. Measure both the position from start for each time and the displacement for each time interval. Record the data in your chart.
5. Plot a position-time graph.
6. On the position-time graph, find the slope of the line joining the first and last times on the graph. What does this slope represent? In the second half of the graph, locate a relatively straight section of the graph and find its slope. What does this slope represent?
7. By noting changes in the slope of the *d-t* graph, describe the motion of the cart.
8. Calculate the average velocity for each 0.10 s time interval, recording the results in the average velocity column. The average velocity represents the slope of the position-time graph half-way in time for each time interval, i.e., at 0.050 s.
9. Plot an average velocity-time graph using the values calculated in the table with the times of: 0.05 s, 0.15 s, 0.25 s, etc.
10. In the first half of the graph, locate a relatively straight section and find its slope. What does this slope represent?
11. Compare the values on the average velocity-time graph with your predictions made in step 7. Were they correct?

12. Calculate the total displacement of the cart during the first 10 intervals of time by the method of area under the curve. Compare your result with that achieved by direct measurement.

13. Using the average velocity-time graph, describe the acceleration of the cart.

14. Calculate the average slope of the velocity-time graph for each time interval. To do this, first calculate Δv, the difference between successive values of the average velocity. Then, divide by Δt (0.10 s). This average slope is the average acceleration, half-way, in time, between the values of the average velocity from which it was calculated. Thus the average acceleration occurs at the original time intervals, i.e., 0.1 s, 0.2 s, etc.

15. Plot a graph of average acceleration versus time. Compare the values on the average acceleration-time graph with your predictions in step 13. Were they correct?

Investigation 2.4: Non-Uniform Acceleration

Problem:
What type of motion is exhibited by an object experiencing an increasing force?

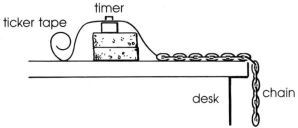

Materials:
ticker-tape timer
2.0 m ticker tape
clamp
1.0 m chain

Procedure:
1. Set up the apparatus illustrated.
2. Pull the chain over the edge until it begins to fall by itself. Start the timer.
3. Examine the tape carefully, using only the section where the chain is falling, before it hits the floor.
4. Divide the tape into appropriate time intervals, perhaps of 0.10 s, and record your data in an observation chart. Plot a graph of average velocity versus time.
5. Join the first and last points on your graph and calculate the slope of this straight line. What does the slope represent?
6. Using the tangent method, find the instantaneous accelerations at the midpoint time interval. Plot a graph of acceleration versus time, using the instantaneous acceleration values.
7. Find the slope of the acceleration-time graph. What does this slope represent?

2.15 Review

Discussion

1. What do the five equations for uniform acceleration reduce to in each of the following cases?
   (a) the object travels with a uniform velocity
   (b) the object starts from rest
2. List 10 careers related to the study or monitoring of motion.
3. "Faster transportation is not always better transportation." Select a specific land or air mode of transportation and write a short essay on this topic. Your discussion should include cost, comfort, convenience, safety, and energy consumption.

Problems

(For problems involving the acceleration due to gravity, use the value $a_g = g = 9.8$ m/s^2, unless otherwise instructed.)

4. An airplane travels from Calgary to Toronto in 4 h 20 min. Find the average speed if the distance between the two cities is 4330 km.
5. An executive jet cruises at 700 km/h. If the winds are light, it consumes kerosene at the rate of 38.0 L/min. If the jet's fuel tanks contain 6840 L when full, what is its maximum range?
6. An earthquake created a succession of giant water waves, called tsunamis, off the coast of Japan. The waves travelled at an average velocity of 800 km/h. If the distance from the source of the quake to the northern coast of Australia was 8200 km, how long did it take the first wave to reach the Australian coast?
7. A British Concorde (BC) and a French Concorde (FC) flew in opposite directions around the world, a distance of 40 000 km. The BC covered half of its flight distance at a supersonic speed of 2500 km/h and the other half at a subsonic speed of 1000 km/h. The FC spent half of its flight time at 2500 km/h and the other half at 1000 km/h. Which Concorde completed the trip first, and by how many hours did it beat the other? (SIN '76)
8. Using this graph of the motion of a car travelling in a straight line, determine each of the following.
   (a) the velocity of the car in each of the intervals
   (b) the average velocity of the car for the whole trip

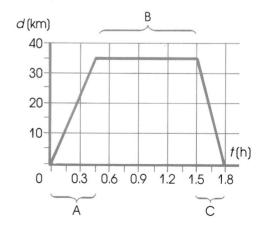

9. A train travels 58 km at an average velocity of 77 km/h[E], waits for 5.0 min at a station, and then runs for half an hour at an average velocity of 64 km/h[E]. Find (a) the total displacement of the train, and (b) the average velocity for the whole trip.

10. (a) Which sections of this graph represent (i) uniform velocity, (ii) the object at rest, and (iii) acceleration?
    (b) What is the average velocity in the intervals (i) t = 0 s to t = 5.0 s and (ii) t = 15 s to t = 20 s?
    (c) What is the instantaneous velocity at (i) t = 3.0 s, (ii) t = 24 s, and (iii) t = 8.0 s?

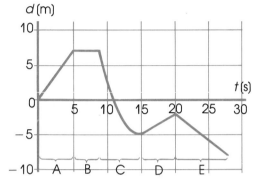

11. A cart, starting from rest, slides down an inclined air-track and passes certain positions (d) in the time shown (t). Using graphing techniques, show that the cart travels with uniform acceleration, and determine the value of the acceleration in m/s².

d (cm)	0	12.8	20.0	28.8	39.2	51.2	64.8
t (s)	0	0.8	1.0	1.2	1.4	1.6	1.8

12. A balloonist jumped from a balloon at an altitude of 23 300 m and fell with an unopened parachute for 178 s. The balloonist was travelling at 62.6 m/s when the parachute opened.
    (a) What was the average acceleration?
    (b) Why was the value of the average acceleration less than that for gravity?

13. An electric train initially moving at 25 km/h accelerates to 35 km/h in 20 s. Find its average acceleration in m/s².

14. A rocketship in space moves with a constant acceleration of 9.8 m/s². If it starts from rest, how long will it take to reach a velocity one-tenth that of light (v_{light} = 3.00 × 10⁸ m/s)?

15. A plane travelling at 200 km/h[N] accelerates at the rate of 5.0 km/h/s[N] for 1.0 min. What is its final velocity?

16. A train travelling at 100 km/h slows down with a uniform deceleration of 0.60 m/s². How long does it take to stop?

17. A motorist travelling at 90 km/h applies his brakes and comes to rest with uniform deceleration in 20 s. Calculate the acceleration in m/s².

18. The v-t graph on the next page represents the motion of a car. Assume that north is positive.
    (a) In which interval(s) is the velocity uniform?
    (b) In which interval(s) is the acceleration uniform?
    (c) How far has the car travelled after (i) 11 s and (ii) 25 s?
    (d) How far did the car travel in the 13th second?

(e) What is the acceleration (i) in the first 5.0 s and (ii) from
   $t = 11$ s to $t = 14$ s?
(f) What is the instantaneous acceleration at (i) t = 12.5 s
   and (ii) t = 22 s?

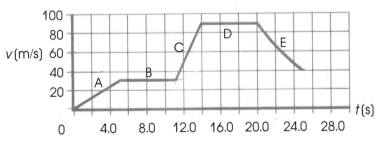

19. A car accelerates uniformly from rest at the rate of 2.0 m/s²
   for 6.0 s. It then maintains a constant velocity for 0.50 min.
   Finally, the brakes are applied, and the vehicle slows down at
   a uniform rate and comes to rest in 5.0 s. Find (a) the maximum velocity of the car and (b) the total displacement.

20. This is the v-t graph for the previous problem. Find the total
   displacement, using graphing techniques.

21. A ball rolls along the floor, up a sloping board, and then back
   down the board and across the floor again. The graph below
   represents this motion.
   (a) At what time is the ball at its highest point?
   (b) What was the acceleration when the ball was (i) rolling up
      the board, (ii) rolling down the board, and (iii) at rest at
      the top point?
   (c) How far up the board did the ball go?
   (d) What was the total displacement of the ball over the 9.0 s
      trip?

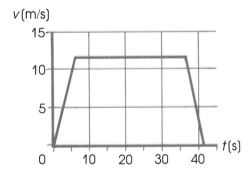

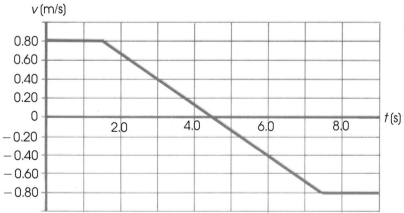

a) find area under two curves

A_ ½ . 4×40

d = 8m.

b) $\frac{v_1+v_2}{2} \cdot t$

$\left(\frac{22+30}{2}\right) \cdot 4$

= 6.4

∴ B is larger

b) .6 h

$Av = \frac{\Delta d}{\Delta t}$ find area

= $\frac{8 + 8}{.6}$

= $\frac{16}{.6}$

= 26.6

c) find slope

$\frac{20 - 30}{.5}$

= -20.

d) $d = \frac{\Delta v}{\Delta t}$

$\frac{-(40-60)}{.7-.4}$

$\frac{20}{.3}$

= 66.7

22. Two trains, A and B, are on separate, parallel tracks. Initially, train B is beside train A and passing it. The graph describes their motions. Using the graph, answer the following questions:
- (a) At $t = 0.40$ h, which train is ahead, and by how much?
- (b) What is the average velocity of train A during the first 36 min?
- (c) What is the instantaneous acceleration of train B at $t = 0.30$ h?
- (d) What is the average acceleration of train A from $t = 0.40$ h to $t = 0.70$ h?
- (e) Draw position-time and acceleration-time graphs for both train A and train B.

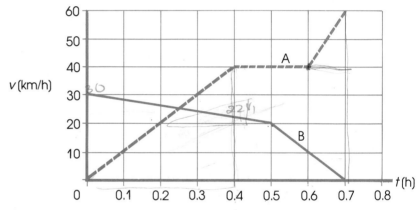

23. This graph describes the motion of a car.
- (a) What is the instantaneous acceleration at (i) $t = 3.0$ s, (ii) $t = 7.0$ s, and (iii) $t = 11.0$ s?
- (b) How far does the car travel in the first (i) 5.0 s, (ii) 9.0 s, and (iii) 13.0 s?

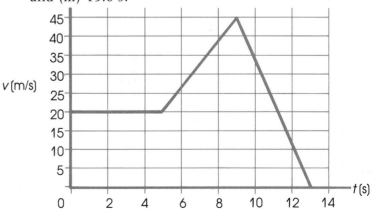

24. Here is a *v-t* graph of two cars, A and B. At $t = 0$ s, A and B pass each other.
 (a) Determine the acceleration of B during the final 3.0 s.
 (b) Find the distance between A and B at $t = 5.0$ s.
 (c) Find the average velocity of A in the first 5.0 s.
 (d) Find the instantaneous acceleration of A at $t = 7.0$ s.
 (e) Plot an acceleration-time graph for both A and B on the same sheet of graph paper. Assume that any changes in acceleration occur instantaneously.

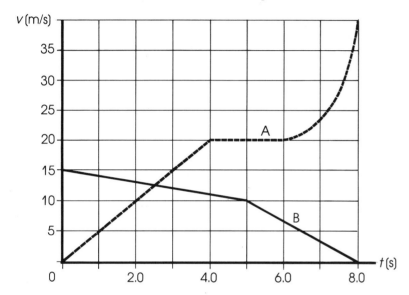

25. At $t = 0$, a stationary police car is passed by a speeding sports car. This occurs on a straight highway. Their subsequent velocities are shown in a *v-t* graph. Use the graph to solve the following problems.

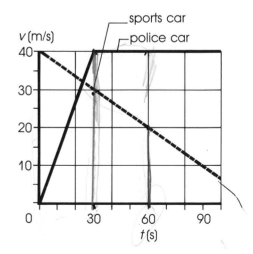

 (a) Prove that the police car overtakes the sports car when $t = 60$ s.
 (b) Determine the average velocity at which the police car travels during this 60 s time interval.
 (c) Find the distance between the two cars when $t = 30$ s.
 (d) Find the acceleration of the sports car when $t = 30$ s.
26. The Easter bunny runs along a straight and narrow path with a constant speed of 25 m/s. He passes a sleeping tortoise, which immediately starts to chase the bunny with a constant acceleration of 3.0×10^{-3} m/s². How long does it take the tortoise to catch the bunny? (Answer in hours.) (SIN '80)
27. The graph on the next page describes the motion of a capsule carried on a rocket fired vertically upward. The rocket ejected

the capsule at its highest point. The capsule fell freely with the rocket until its parachute opened at $t = 300$ s.

(a) At what time did the rocket reach its highest altitude?

(b) What was the maximum altitude of the rocket?

(c) What was the acceleration of the rocket during (i) the first stage, and (ii) the second stage?

(d) What was the average acceleration of the capsule during the interval $t = 100$ s to $t = 300$ s?

(e) What was happening during the period $t = 300$ s to $t = 400$ s?

(f) What was the terminal velocity of the capsule just before "splashdown"?

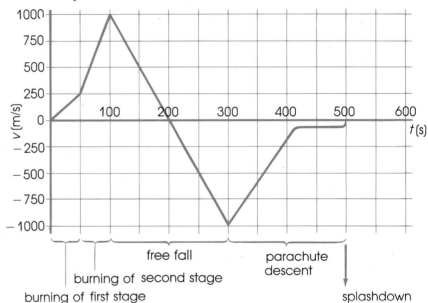

28. At the instant when the traffic light turns green, an automobile starts with a constant acceleration of 1.8 m/s². At the same instant a truck travelling with a constant speed of 8.5 m/s overtakes and passes the automobile. (a) How far beyond the starting point will the automobile overtake the truck? (b) How fast will the car be travelling at that instant?

29. A subway train starts from rest at a station and accelerates at the rate of 2.0 m/s² for 10 s. It runs at a constant speed for 30 s, and then decelerates at 2.4 m/s² until it stops at the next station. Find the total distance between the stations and the average speed of the train.

30. An airplane taking off from an airfield has a run of 370 m. If it starts from rest, moves with constant acceleration, and makes the run in 30 s, with what velocity, in kilometres per hour, does it take off?

31. A bobsled has a constant acceleration of 2.0 m/s², starting from rest.
    (a) How fast is it going after 5.0 s?
    (b) How far has it travelled in 5.0 s?
    (c) What is its average velocity in the first 5.0 s?
    (d) How far has it travelled by the time its speed has reached 40 m/s?

32. While driving her car, Mrs. Jones sees an obstruction in the road. It takes her 0.80 s to react and put her foot on the brake. Her car is travelling at 25 m/s.
    (a) How far will the car travel before she puts her foot on the brake?
    (b) If, when the brake is applied, the car decelerates at a uniform rate of 9.3 m/s², what is the total displacement of the car?

33. A boy in a wagon starts down a hill 90 m long with an initial velocity of 1.2 m/s, reaching the bottom of the hill in 0.50 min. Calculate his acceleration (assumed to be uniform) and his velocity at the bottom of the hill.

34. An object starts from rest and accelerates at 3.0 m/s² for 4.0 s. Its velocity remains constant for 7.0 s, and it finally comes to rest with uniform deceleration after another 5.0 s. Find (a) the displacement for each stage of the motion and (b) the average velocity over the whole time interval.

35. A Formula One car accelerates from rest uniformly at 2.40 m/s² for 15.0 s, then moves with a uniform velocity for 200 s, and finally decelerates uniformly at 3.60 m/s² until it comes to a stop. How long will the car be in motion, how far will it travel, and what will be its average speed?

36. A turtle is moving with a constant acceleration along a straight ditch. He starts his stopwatch as he passes a fence post and notes that it takes him 10 s to reach a pine tree 10 m farther along the ditch. As he passes the pine tree, his speed is 1.2 m/s. How far was he from the fence post when he started from rest? (SIN '76)

37. A meson, a subatomic particle having a mass 250 times that of an electron, is shot with a constant speed of 5.00×10^6 m/s into a region where an electric field causes a deceleration of 1.25×10^{14} m/s². (a) How far does the meson travel before coming to rest? (b) How long does it take the meson to come to rest?

Numerical Answers to Review Problems

 4. 1.00×10^3 km/h
 5. 2.10×10^3 km
 6. 10.3 h
 7. BC by 5.1 h
 8. (a) 78 km/h, 0, -1.2×10^2 km/h
    (b) 0
 9. (a) 90 km (b) 68 km/h[E]
10. (b) 1.4 m/s, 0.60 m/s
    (c) 1.4 m/s, -0.75 m/s, 0
12. (a) 0.352 m/s²
13. 0.14 m/s²
14. 3.1×10^6 s
15. 5.0×10^2 km/h[N]
16. 46 s
17. -1.3 m/s²
18. (c) 2.6×10^2 m, 1.3×10^3 m
    (d) 60 m (e) 6.0 m/s², 20 m/s²
    (f) 20 m/s², -10 m/s²
19. (a) 12 m/s (b) 4.3×10^2 m
20. 4.3×10^2 m
21. (a) 4.5 s (b) -0.27 m/s², -0.27 m/s², -0.27 m/s² (c) 1.2 m (d) 0
22. (a) B ahead by 2.4 km (b) 27 km/h
    (c) -20 km/h² (d) 67 km/h²
23. (a) 0, 6.3 m/s², -11 m/s²
    (b) 100 m, 230 m, 320 m

38. A rocket-driven sled running on a straight, level track is used to investigate the physiological effects of rapid accelerations on humans. One such sled can attain a velocity of 1600 km/h in 1.8 s, starting from rest.
    (a) Assuming that the acceleration is uniform, what is its value in m/s²?
    (b) Express the acceleration in (a) in terms of g, where $g = 9.8$ m/s².
    (c) Under the last 2.00 km of the track there is a trough of water. The "brakes" of the rocket consist of a scoop that displaces water from the trough, stopping the sled. Assuming that the sled stops at the end of the trough, what is the deceleration of the sled, expressed in terms of g?

39. An electron with an initial velocity of 1.0×10^4 m/s enters a region 1.0 cm long where it is electrically accelerated. It emerges with a velocity of 4.2×10^6 m/s. What was its acceleration, assuming that it was constant? (Such a process occurs in the electron gun in a cathode-ray tube, used in television receivers and oscilloscopes.)

40. Suppose that you are called by a lawyer to give advice concerning the physics involved in one of her cases. The question is whether a driver was exceeding the speed limit of 50 km/h before he made an emergency stop, with brakes locked and wheels sliding. The length of the skid marks on the road was 5.85 m. A police officer made the reasonable assumption that the maximum deceleration would not exceed that of gravity. On the basis of the evidence, was the driver exceeding the speed limit before the brakes were applied?

41. Two trains, one travelling at 100 km/h and the other at 128 km/h, are headed towards one another along a straight, level track. When the trains are 1.2 km apart, each engineer simultaneously sees the other's train and applies the brakes. Both trains have equal, constant decelerations of 0.9 m/s². Will there be a collision?

42. A bullet is fired straight up with a muzzle velocity of 460 m/s. How long will it take it to reach its highest point and how high will that be? (The air resistance may be neglected.)

43. A stone is thrown straight down from the top of a cliff with an initial velocity of 6.0 m/s. It reaches the bottom in 3.0 s. How high is the cliff?

44. (a) With what speed must a ball be thrown vertically upward in order to rise to a height of 16 m?
    (b) How long will that same ball be in the air?

45. A ball is thrown vertically upward from a window at 10 m/s.

25. (b) 30 m/s (c) 450 m (d) -0.33 m/s²
26. 4.6 h
27. (a) 200 s (b) 8.8×10^4 m (c) 5.0 m/s², 15 m/s² (d) -10 m/s² (f) -50 m/s
28. (a) 80 m (b) 17 m/s
29. 7.8×10^2 m, 16 m/s
30. 89 km/h
31. (a) 10 m/s (b) 25 m (c) 5.0 m/s (d) 4.0×10^2 m
32. (a) 20 m (b) 54 m
33. 0.12 m/s², 4.8 m/s
34. (a) 24 m, 84 m, 30 m (b) 8.6 m/s
35. 225 s, 7.7×10^3 m, 34 m/s
36. 8.0 m
37. (a) 0.100 m, (b) 4.00×10^{-8} s
38. (a) 2.5×10^2 m/s² (b) $25\,g$ (c) $-5.0\,g$
39. 8.8×10^{14} m/s²
41. No; 0.1 km apart when stopped
42. 47 s, 1.1×10^4 m
43. 62 m
44. (a) 18 m/s (b) 1.8 s
45. 73 m
46. (a) 98 m/s (b) 2.6×10^3 m (c) 8.0 m/s (d) 224 s (e) 3.3 m
47. 12 m/s
48. 89 m/s
50. 3.9 s

It hits the ground 5.0 s later. What is the height of the window from the ground?

46. A parachutist jumps from a height of 3.1×10^3 m and falls freely for 10 s. She then opens her parachute, and for the next 20 s slows down with an acceleration of -4.5 m/s^2. After that, she falls the rest of the distance to the ground at a uniform velocity.

    (a) What is her velocity just before the parachute opens?
    (b) At what altitude does the parachute open?
    (c) What is the velocity of the parachutist, just before she strikes the ground?
    (d) Calculate the time required for the whole descent.
    (e) From what height would she have to fall freely in order to strike the ground with the same velocity as she does when wearing a parachute? (This is how parachutists are trained.)

47. A stone is dropped into the water from a bridge 44 m above the water. Another stone is thrown vertically downward 1.0 s after the first was dropped. Both stones strike the water at the same time. What was the initial velocity of the second stone?

48. A student is determined to test the law of gravity for himself. He walks off a skyscraper 320 m high, stopwatch in hand, and starts his free fall (zero initial velocity). Five seconds later, Superman arrives at the scene and dives off the roof to save the student. What must Superman's initial velocity be in order to catch the student just before the student reaches the ground? (Assume that Superman's acceleration is that of any freely falling body, i.e., $g = 9.8$ m/s^2.)

49. A convertible with its top down drove towards the entrance of an underground garage with a velocity of 24 km/h. A window cleaner on a scaffold directly above the entrance accidentally kicked a bucket of water off a moving scaffold. The scaffold at that moment was 9.0 m vertically higher than the top of the car and the car was 12 m from the entrance. The scaffold was moving up at 1.5 m/s. Did the driver get wet?

50. An efficient parcel service wants to speed up its deliveries by dropping parcels into moving trucks. An employee is positioned on an overpass directly above a straight, level road to drop the parcels into the trucks at just the right time. One day, a delivery truck starts from rest and drives along the road with a constant acceleration of $1/2\ g$. A package is released at the correct instant to land in the truck. If the overpass was 30 m above the truck and the truck started from a position 100 m from the point of impact, how long after the truck started did the employee wait before dropping the parcel? (SIN '78)

3 Motion in a Plane

3.1 Vectors in Two-dimensional Space

In Chapter 2, the discussion of motion was limited to objects that move in a straight line. The direction in which the objects were moving was either evident from the description or it did not matter. The objects never veered, or moved in a different direction. In the words used earlier, they stayed on the track''.

As a result, we were able to omit the vector notation when using vector quantities to describe straight-line motion, without any loss in understanding. There were some instances in which the object stopped and reversed its direction, but we were able to describe this type of motion adequately by assigning positive and negative values to the quantities describing it. Negative values of displacement and velocity were used to represent motion in the opposite direction.

However, in real life very few objects move back and forth in a straight line. A delivery truck moves in one direction for a short time but then turns and moves in another direction, and it continues to do this as it moves from street to street. Similarly, a racing car speeding around an oval track has two stretches of straight-line motion but must also make two semicircular turns in every lap. To describe fully motion in which the direction changes, we must take such changes into account, and we do this by considering the vector nature of the quantities that describe motion.

This involves using the vector notation described in Section 2.1. A symbol representing a vector quantity is written with an arrow above it, and the direction of the vector is given in square brackets, following the magnitude and the unit. The definitions of displacement, velocity, and acceleration in Chapter 2 were given in vector terms, even though all the motions studied in that chapter were straight-line motions, and it would have sufficed to assign positive or negative values to each quantity, indicating its forward or backward direction.

In this chapter, we will examine the true vector nature of quantities like those introduced in Chapter 2, and use these quantities to describe motion in two dimensions, in a plane. This could, of course, be extended to cover three-dimensional motion in space.

3.2 Displacement as a Vector Quantity

In Section 2.1 it was explained that the length and direction of the straight line joining an object's initial and final positions is called its displacement. This definition holds true whether the object moves in a straight line from A to B,

Directions that are not exact compass points are written this way:

Scale:
1 cm = 2.0 km

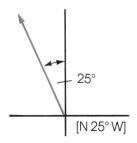

and described this way: "north, 25 degrees towards the west".

or in a series of several straight-line segments from A to B,

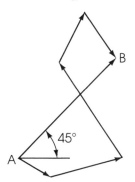

or along a smooth, curving path from A to B.

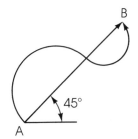

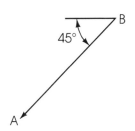

In all three cases, the displacement is 7.5 km[NE], even though the actual path taken and the total distance travelled are different. Also, if the trip is reversed, beginning at B and arriving, by any path, at A, the displacement is reversed. It is 7.5 km[SW].

Note that displacements of 7.5 km[NE] and 7.5 km[SW] are not the same. They are equal in magnitude but opposite in direction.

The displacement from Quebec City to Montreal is 250 km[W41°S]. The displacement from Baltimore, Maryland, to Charlottesville, Virginia, is 250 km[W41°S]. Since each displacement has the same magnitude (250 km) and the same direction ([W41°S]), they are the same vectors. Vectors with the same magnitude and direction are identical, even though their starting positions are different.

The actual displacement between any two points may be determined by drawing a scale diagram with a ruler and a protractor, or by using simple trigonometry. The following example illustrates this.

Sample problem

Find the displacement of an airplane that flies 5.0 km due east and then turns and flies 7.0 km due north.

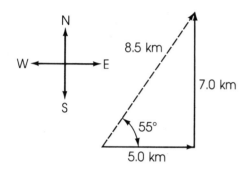

Scale Drawing Solution:
Using a scale of 1 cm = 2.0 km and with directions as indicated, a scale diagram of the plane's motion is drawn.

Using a ruler and the scale, the magnitude of the plane's displacement is found to be 8.5 km. Using the protractor and measuring the angle between the plane's displacement and due east, its direction is found to be [E55°N].

$$\text{Thus, } \Delta \vec{d} = 8.5 \text{ km[E55°N]}$$

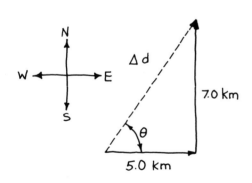

Mathematical Solution:
Draw a rough sketch representing the plane's motion. Using the Pythagorean Theorem to find the magnitude of its displacement, we have

$$|\Delta \vec{d}|^2 = (5.0 \text{ km})^2 + (7.0 \text{ km})^2$$
$$= 25 \text{ km}^2 + 49 \text{ km}^2$$
$$= 74 \text{ km}^2$$

$$|\Delta \vec{d}| = 8.6 \text{ km}$$

Also, if we call the angle between the plane's displacement and due east θ, we have

$$\tan \theta = \frac{7.0 \text{ km}}{5.0 \text{ km}}$$
$$= 1.4$$
$$\theta = 54°$$

$$\text{Thus, } \Delta \vec{d} = 8.6 \text{ km[E54°N]}$$

In most examples, the graphical method can produce an answer as accurate as the mathematical method, if sufficient care is taken. In the sample problems in this chapter, both mathematical and graphical solutions will be given.

3.3 Velocity as a Vector Quantity

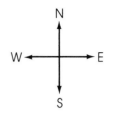

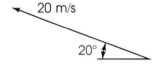

In Section 3.1, a racing car moving around an oval track was described as an object whose direction of motion is changing. Even if its speed remained constant, the car was at one moment moving south, and a few moments later moving east. To describe its motion fully, we combine together its speed and the direction in which it is moving at any instant, and we call this its velocity, a vector quantity.

It is necessary now to distinguish between velocity and speed. Speed is the rate of change of distance with time, without regard to direction. Velocity is the rate of change of displacement with time, and it includes an expression of direction. The average speed and the average velocity for any interval may be quite different. However, instantaneous speed and instantaneous velocity are always numerically equal, even for motion along a curved path. Speed is represented by the symbol v and velocity is represented by the symbol $\vec{v}$.

A velocity of 20 m/s[W20°N] could be represented by an arrow drawn to scale in the appropriate direction, as illustrated.

Thus, a car moving in a circle at a constant speed of 20 m/s has the velocity vectors shown in the diagram, at various times during each lap.

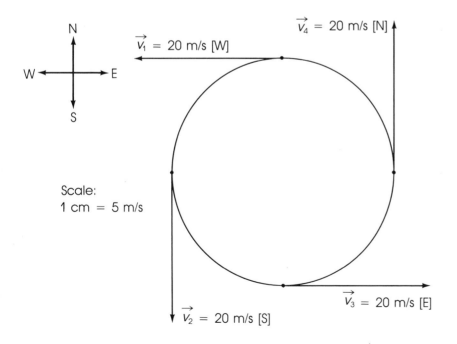

Because of their vector nature, both average velocity and instantaneous velocity require definitions that are slightly more general than those given in Chapter 2 for straight-line motion. These definitions are as follows:

In this text, whenever $\vec{v}$ is written without a subscript it will be taken to mean instantaneous velocity. Average velocity will be written as $\vec{v}_{av}$.

$$\vec{v}_{av} = \frac{\Delta \vec{d}}{\Delta t}$$

$$\vec{v}_{inst} = \lim_{\Delta t \to 0} \frac{\Delta \vec{d}}{\Delta t}$$

where $\Delta \vec{d}$ is the displacement of an object during the time interval Δt.

In effect, instantaneous velocity is just the instantaneous speed at any point, together with the direction in which the object is moving at the time. A sample problem will help to clarify this.

Sample problem

A clock has a second hand that is 12 cm long. Find each of the following.
(a) the average speed of the tip of the second hand
(b) its instantaneous velocity as it passes the 6 and the 9 on the clock face
(c) its average velocity in moving from the 3 to the 12 on the clock face

The circumference of a circle is $2\pi r$.

(a) The tip of the second hand makes one complete revolution in 60 s.

$$
\begin{aligned}
v_{av} &= \frac{\Delta d}{\Delta t} \\
&= \frac{2\pi \,(12 \text{ cm})}{60 \text{ s}} \\
&= 1.3 \text{ cm/s}
\end{aligned}
$$

(b) Since the speed is constant, $|\vec{v}| = v = 1.3$ cm/s

Therefore, $\vec{v}_6 = 1.3$ cm/s[left]

$\vec{v}_9 = 1.3$ cm/s[up]

(c) The displacement of the tip of the second hand in moving from the 3 to the 12 may be found from the following diagram:

Mathematical Solution: *Graphical Solution:*

$$|\overrightarrow{\Delta d}|^2 = (12 \text{ cm})^2 + (12 \text{ cm})^2$$
$$= 288 \text{ cm}^2$$

$$|\overrightarrow{\Delta d}| = \sqrt{288 \text{ cm}^2}$$
$$= 17 \text{ cm}$$

(the direction of $\overrightarrow{\Delta d}$ is up 45° to the left)

$$\overrightarrow{\Delta d} = 17 \text{ cm[left 45° up]}$$

Therefore, $\overrightarrow{v}_{av} = \dfrac{\overrightarrow{\Delta d}}{\Delta t}$

$$= \dfrac{17 \text{ cm[left 45° up]}}{45 \text{ s}}$$
$$= 0.38 \text{ cm/s[left 45° up]}$$

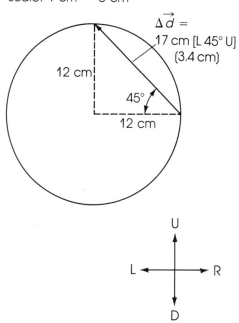

Scale: 1 cm = 5 cm

$\overrightarrow{\Delta d} =$ 17 cm [L 45° U] (3.4 cm)

12 cm

45°

12 cm

Practice

1. A police cruiser chasing a speeding motorist travelled 60 km[S], then 35 km[NE], and finally 50 km[W].
   (a) Calculate the total displacement of the cruiser.
   (b) If the chase took 1.3 h, what was the cruiser's (i) average speed and (ii) average velocity, for the trip.
   (43 km[S36°W]; 1.1 × 10² km/h, 33 km/h[36°W])

2. An express bus travels directly from A-town to B-ville. A local bus also links these two towns, but it goes west 30 km from A-town to C-city, then 30 km south to D-ville, and finally 12 km west to E-town and 30 km northeast to B-ville.
   (a) What is the shortest distance from A-town to B-ville?
   (b) In what direction does the express bus travel?
   (c) If the express bus takes 0.45 h to go from A-town to B-ville, and the local bus takes 3.0 h, calculate the average speed and the average velocity for each bus.
   (23 km, [W24°S];
   51 km/h, 51 km/h[W24°S]; 34 km/h, 7.7 km/h[W24°S])

3. A hiker walks 10.0 km[NE], 5.0 km[W], and then 2.0 km[S] in 2.5 h.
   (a) What is the hiker's displacement?
   (b) In what direction must the hiker set out, in order to return by the most direct route to the starting point?
   (c) If the hiker walks at a constant speed for the entire trip and returns by the most direct route, how long will the total walk take?   (5.5 km[E68°N], [S22°W], 3.3 h)

3.4 The Addition and Subtraction of Vectors

In arithmetic, 2 + 2 always equals 4. When adding vectors, $\vec{2}$ + $\vec{2}$ can have any result between 0 and $\vec{4}$, depending on the relative directions. With vectors, the rules for adding and subtracting can produce some surprising results.

In Chapter 2, displacements in a straight line were simply added arithmetically when they were in the same direction, or one was subtracted from the other when the directions were opposite. The addition and subtraction of displacements, or any other vector quantities, cannot be accomplished by such simple algebraic operations when they are not in the same, or opposite, directions.

To add vector quantities, the arrows representing the vectors are joined tip-to-tail, and the vector representing their sum joins the tail of the first vector to the tip of the last vector added.

The sum of $\vec{A}$ and $\vec{B}$, the vector $\vec{A}$ + $\vec{B}$, is given by this vector diagram:

In drawing vector diagrams, the vectors may be moved around on the page, as long as their lengths and directions are not altered. In this diagram, shifting vectors $\vec{A}$ and $\vec{B}$ so that they are joined tip-to-tail does not change the value of either.

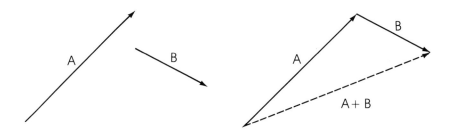

Note that, when the two vectors are added in the reverse order, their sum is the same. Mathematically, we say that vector addition is commutative.

A mathematical operation is commutative if the order in which it is performed has no effect on the result. Since $\vec{A}$ + $\vec{B}$ and $\vec{B}$ + $\vec{A}$ are the same vector, vector addition is commutative.

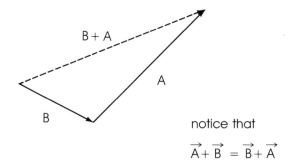

notice that

$$\vec{A} + \vec{B} = \vec{B} + \vec{A}$$

If more than two vectors are to be added, the vectors are successively joined, tip-to-tail, so that the vector representing their sum joins the tail of the first vector to the tip of the last vector to be added.

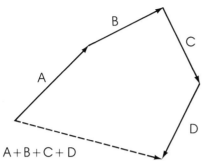

A+B+C+D

To subtract one vector from another, add the negative of the one to be subtracted. The vector $-\vec{B}$ is just the vector $\vec{B}$ with its direction reversed. Thus, to find $\vec{A} - \vec{B}$, we simply add $\vec{A}$ and $-\vec{B}$, as shown graphically:

In this text, $\overrightarrow{-B}$ and $-\vec{B}$ will be taken to represent the same thing: a vector of the same magnitude as $\vec{B}$ but in the opposite direction.

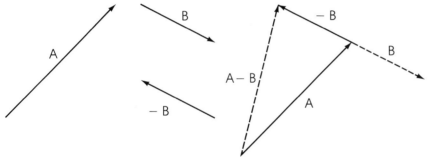

To find the difference between two vectors, it is often simpler to draw the two vectors from the same point. The vectors to be subtracted are drawn with their tails together. Their difference is found by joining the tip of the second vector to the tip of the first vector. Using the same example as before:

Note that the result, $\vec{A} - \vec{B}$, is the same as when we added $\vec{A}$ and $-\vec{B}$.

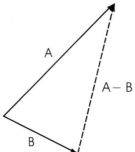

To add vectors, join them tip-to-tail; to subtract vectors, join them tail-to-tail.

The equivalence of these two methods of subtracting vectors may be shown easily by this parallelogram of vectors:

Remember, opposite sides of a parallelogram are equal in length and parallel to each other.

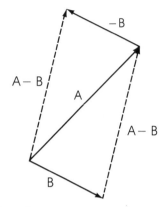

This is not a "new" rule for subtracting vectors, just a geometric representation of the same process, as may be seen in the parallellogram of vectors.

What is the result when vectors are subtracted in the reverse order?

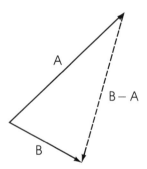

As you can see, the subtraction of vectors is not commutative. $\vec{A} - \vec{B}$ is not the same as $\vec{B} - \vec{A}$. In fact, $\vec{A} - \vec{B}$ and $\vec{B} - \vec{A}$ are equal in magnitude but opposite in direction. They are different vectors.

Note that the tip of the difference vector, $\vec{B} - \vec{A}$, is pointing towards the tip of the vector $\vec{B}$, which is the first term in the expression $\vec{B} - \vec{A}$. Similarly, in the difference vector, $\vec{A} - \vec{B}$, the tip points towards the tip of vector $\vec{A}$. This is a good way to remember the direction of the difference vector in a vector subtraction operation.

The actual magnitude and direction of the vectors representing the sums and differences in these cases may be determined using either a vector scale diagram or simple trigonometry.

Practice

1. For each of the following, copy the vectors into your notebook and perform the vector operation indicated, to find either the sum or the difference vector.

(a) Determine $\vec{A} + \vec{B}$

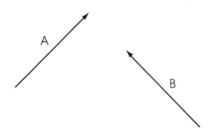

(b) Determine $\vec{D} - \vec{C}$

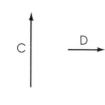

(c) Determine $\vec{E} - \vec{F}$

(d) Determine $\vec{v}_2 - \vec{v}_1$

2. A plane's velocity changes from 200 km/h[N] to 300 km/h [N30°W]. Find the change in velocity, $\Delta \vec{v}$. (Hint: $\Delta \vec{v} = \vec{v}_2 - \vec{v}_1$)
   (155 km/h[N70°W])

3. A car travelling at 15 m/s[N] executes a gradual turn, so that it then moves at 18 m/s[E]. What is the car's change in velocity?
   (23 m/s[E40°S])

4. A plane is flying at 100 m/s[E]. The pilot changes its velocity by 30 m/s[E30°N]. What is the plane's final velocity?
   (126 m/s[E6°N])

3.5 The Multiplication of a Vector by a Scalar

It is often necessary to multiply a vector quantity by a scalar quantity. For example, the displacement $\Delta \vec{d}$ of an object moving at a constant velocity $\vec{v}$ for a time Δt is given by the product of the vector $\vec{v}$ and the scalar Δt: $\Delta \vec{d} = \vec{v} \Delta t$.

In general, the product of a scalar k and a vector $\vec{A}$ is a vector whose magnitude is $k|\vec{A}|$, whose units are the product of the units of k and $\vec{A}$, and whose direction is that of the vector $\vec{A}$. Division of a vector $\vec{A}$ by a scalar k is treated as if it were multiplication by the scalar $1/k$.

Graphically, the product is a vector parallel to $\vec{A}$, but k times as long.

Vectors may be multiplied together in two distinct ways. The vector dot product, written as $\vec{A} \cdot \vec{B}$, produces a result that is not a vector, but a scalar quantity whose magnitude is AB cos θ, where θ is the angle between $\vec{A}$ and $\vec{B}$. The vector cross product, written $\vec{A} \times \vec{B}$, produces a result that is a vector of magnitude AB sin θ, in a direction perpendicular to the plane of $\vec{A}$ and $\vec{B}$, given by a right-hand rule. The vector dot product will be used in Chapter 8.

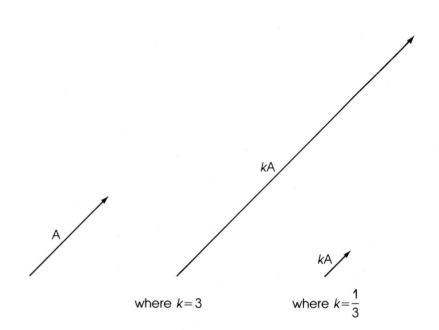

where $k=3$ where $k=\dfrac{1}{3}$

Practice

1. The vector $\vec{B}$ is illustrated. Draw the following vectors, to the same scale.

    (a) 2 $\vec{B}$

    (b) 10 $\vec{B}$

    (c) $\frac{1}{2}\vec{B}$

    (d) $-3\ \vec{B}$

2. A car travels at 20 m/s[N35°E] for 3.0 s. Draw its velocity vector, and then, using scalar multiplication, draw the vector representing its displacement during this time interval.

3.6 The Components of a Vector

Section 3.4 showed that the sum of any two vectors can be determined by drawing the vectors, joined tip-to-tail. The vector representing their sum joins the tail of the first to the tip of the second.

It is valuable to consider the reverse operation. Can we find two vectors, $\vec{A}$ and $\vec{B}$, whose sum is a given vector, $\vec{C}$? A possible solution is shown.

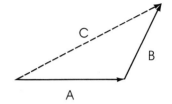

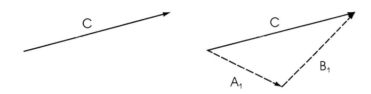

It is not difficult to see that there are a great many possible solutions to this problem. In fact, a solution is provided by any pair of vectors that, together with the vector $\vec{C}$, form the sides of a closed triangle.

Even if we specify that the vectors $\vec{A}$ and $\vec{B}$ must be perpendicular to each other, there are still many solutions.

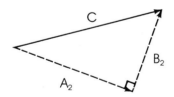

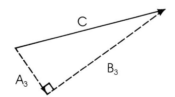

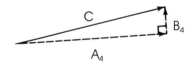

But if we further insist that one of these two perpendicular vectors lies in a predetermined direction, there is only one solution.

No other pair of vectors, perpendicular to each other and with one pointing in the specified direction, can be added to give the vector $\vec{C}$.

When two vectors, $\vec{A}$ and $\vec{B}$, add to produce a third vector, $\vec{C}$, we say that $\vec{A}$ and $\vec{B}$ are components of $\vec{C}$. A vector may have

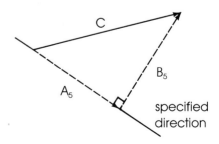

any number of components, but most problems involving motion in a plane may be solved by considering only one pair of components. When these component vectors are perpendicular to each other, they are called **orthogonal** or **rectangular components**.

Any vector in a plane may be resolved into two rectangular components. The most commonly chosen sets of directions, north-south-east-west and up-down-left-right, may be represented by the directions of the X and Y axes of a Cartesian plane.

Thus, any vector, $\vec{A}$, has X and Y components, $\vec{A}_x$ and $\vec{A}_y$, as shown:

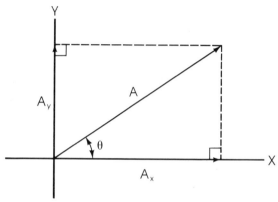

The magnitudes of the components $\vec{A}_x$ and $\vec{A}_y$ may be determined by using a scale diagram, or by trigonometry, using θ as the angle between $\vec{A}$ and the X-axis.

$$\frac{|\vec{A}_y|}{|\vec{A}|} = \sin\theta, \text{ and } \frac{|\vec{A}_x|}{|\vec{A}|} = \cos\theta$$

$$|\vec{A}_y| = |\vec{A}|\sin\theta \qquad |\vec{A}_x| = |\vec{A}|\cos\theta$$

Vectors that are perpendicular to each other are said to be mutually independent. That is, neither of them has a component in the direction of the other. Thus, they act independently of each other. A swimmer swimming due north through the water in a river with an easterly current takes the same time to reach the far shore as he would if there were no current. All the current does is push him sideways as he crosses. His swimming and the current are mutually independent. The easterly velocity of the water over the Earth has no effect on the northerly velocity of the swimmer through the water. Of course, his path with respect to the Earth is affected.

Sample problem

The displacement of an airplane from its starting point is 100 km[E30°N]. Determine the components of its displacement in the easterly and northerly directions.

Mathematical Solution: *Graphical Solution:*

$$|\Delta \vec{d}_x| = |\Delta \vec{d}| \cos \theta$$
$$= 100 \text{ km (cos } 30°)$$
$$= 100 \text{ km (0.8660)}$$
$$= 86.6 \text{ km}$$

$$|\Delta \vec{d}_y| = |\Delta \vec{d}| \sin \theta$$
$$= 100 \text{ km (sin } 30°)$$
$$= 100 \text{ km (0.5000)}$$
$$= 50.0 \text{ km}$$

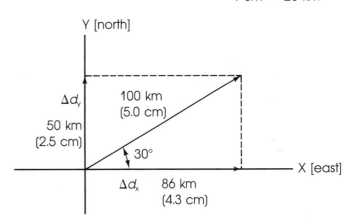

Scale:
1 cm = 20 km

Therefore, the components of a displacement of 100 km[E30°N] are 86.6 km[E] and 50.0 km[N].

Conversely, the magnitude and direction of any vector may be determined from a knowledge of its components in the following manner.

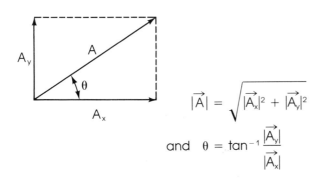

$$|\vec{A}| = \sqrt{|\vec{A}_x|^2 + |\vec{A}_y|^2}$$

and $\theta = \tan^{-1} \dfrac{|\vec{A}_y|}{|\vec{A}_x|}$

Sample problem

The easterly and northerly components of a car's velocity are 24 m/s and 30 m/s, respectively. In what direction and with what speed is the car moving? In other words, what is the car's velocity?

Graphical Solution:

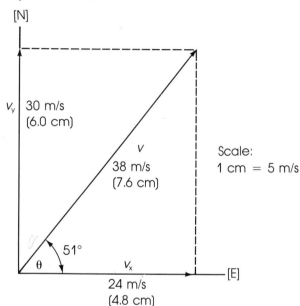

Scale:
1 cm = 5 m/s

Mathematical Solution:

$$\tan \theta = \frac{|\vec{v_y}|}{|\vec{v_x}|}$$
$$= \frac{30 \text{ m/s}}{24 \text{ m/s}}$$
$$= 1.25$$
$$\theta = 51°$$

$$|\vec{v}|^2 = |\vec{v_x}|^2 + |\vec{v_y}|^2$$
$$= (24 \text{ m/s})^2 + (30 \text{ m/s})^2$$
$$= 576 \text{ m}^2/\text{s}^2 + 900 \text{ m}^2/\text{s}^2$$
$$= 1476 \text{ m}^2/\text{s}^2$$

$$|\vec{v}| = \sqrt{1476 \text{ m}^2/\text{s}^2}$$
$$= 38 \text{ m/s}$$

Therefore, the car is moving in a direction 51° to the north of due east, with a speed of 38 m/s ($\vec{v}$ = 38 m/s [E51°N]).

Practice

1. A boat sails in a straight line 20 km[N30°E]. What are the components of its displacement to the north and east?
   (17 km[N], 10 km[E])
2. A cannon fires a cannonball with a speed of 100 m/s at an angle of 20° above the horizontal. What are the horizontal and vertical components of the initial velocity of the cannonball?
   (94 m/s[H], 34 m/s[V])
3. A girl swims at 3.0 m/s across a swimming pool at an angle of 30° to the side of the pool, as shown. What are the components of her swimming velocity in each of the following directions?
   (a) across the pool
   (b) along the pool's edge
   (1.5 m/s[across], 2.6 m/s[along])

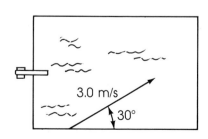

4. An airplane is climbing at an angle of 15° to the horizon, with the sun directly overhead. Its shadow is observed to be moving across the ground at 200 km/h.
   (a) What is the actual air speed of the plane?
   (b) How long does it take to increase the airplane's altitude by 1000 m?

   (207 km/h, 1.9×10^{-2} h or 1.1 min)

5. A football player is running at a constant speed in a straight line up the field at an angle of 15° to the sidelines. The coach notices that it takes the player 4.0 s to get from the 25 m line to the goal line. How fast is the player running?   (6.5 m/s)

3.7 Relative Motion and Frames of Reference

We have been studying vectors in order to describe exactly how an object moves from one position to another. A woman standing on a railway platform watching a train pull away would have no difficulty in describing the motion of a friend sitting in one of the train's coaches. As the passenger's displacement increases, the woman could measure this displacement at two points in time and determine the average velocity with which the passenger is moving away. The passenger, on the other hand, might not consider herself to be moving at all. Perhaps she sees herself at rest in her seat. Although she knows better, she might even think of herself as being at rest and her friend on the platform, and the rest of the world as well, as moving backward. If the train had no windows, she would have no visual clues to guide her.

The two women give different discriptions of the same motion. The explanation for this is that they are viewing the motion from different frames of reference. The woman on the platform sees the passenger getting farther away while everything else around her is at rest. The passenger sees all the seats and the other people on the train staying in their same relative positions, while the woman at the station recedes into the distance. Motion is described differently, depending on the frame of reference of the observer.

This same confusion arises whenever an object is moving relative to some frame of reference which, itself, is in motion. Some examples are a person swimming through moving water, a bird flying through a gust of wind, and an object that has been thrown from a moving vehicle. In each of these cases, the velocity of the moving object, in relation to the frame of reference of the Earth, is determined by means of vectors. A few sample problems will illustrate this.

Fundamentals of Physics: A Senior Course

Sample problem 1

The airspeed of a small plane is 200 km/h. The wind speed is 50.0 km/h from the west. Determine the velocity of the plane relative to the ground if the pilot keeps the plane pointing in each of the following directions.

(a) [E]

Note that a west wind is a wind that blows *from* the west, so that its velocity vector points east.

(b) [W]

(c) [N]

(d) [N40°E]

Velocities in this type of problem may be written with two subscripts. The pre-subscript denotes the object that is moving. The post-subscript denotes the frame of reference with respect to which it is moving.

$\vec{_pV_g}$ is the velocity of the *plane* with respect to the *ground*

$\vec{_pV_a}$ is the velocity of the *plane* with respect to the *air*

$\vec{_aV_g}$ is the velocity of the *air* with respect to the *ground*

In problems such as this, a simple chain rule relates the velocities.

$$\vec{_pV_g} = \vec{_pV_a} + \vec{_aV_g}$$

Graphical Solution:

Mathematical Solution:

(a) Scale:
1 cm = 25 km/h

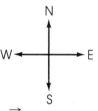

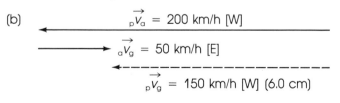

$\vec{_pV_a}$ = 200 km/h [E] (8.0 cm) $\vec{_aV_g}$ = 50 km/h [E] (2.0 cm)

$\vec{_pV_g}$ = 250 km/h [E] (10.0 cm)

(b) $\vec{_pV_a}$ = 200 km/h [W]

$\vec{_aV_g}$ = 50 km/h [E]

$\vec{_pV_g}$ = 150 km/h [W] (6.0 cm)

$$\vec{_pV_g} = \vec{_pV_a} + \vec{_aV_g}$$
$$= 200 \text{ km/h[E]} + 50 \text{ km/h[E]}$$
$$= 250 \text{ km/h[E]}$$

$$\vec{_pV_g} = \vec{_pV_a} + \vec{_aV_g}$$
$$= 200 \text{ km/h[W]} + 50 \text{ km/h[E]}$$
$$= 200 \text{ km/h[W]} - 50 \text{ km/h[W]}$$
$$= 150 \text{ km/h[W]}$$

Mathematical Solution: *Graphical Solution:*

(c) Using the Pythagorean Theorem:

$$|_p\vec{v}_g|^2 = |_p\vec{v}_a|^2 + |_a\vec{v}_g|^2$$
$$= (200 \text{ km/h})^2 + (50 \text{ km/h})^2$$
$$= 42\ 500 \text{ km}^2/\text{h}^2$$

$$|_p\vec{v}_g| = \sqrt{42\ 500 \text{ km}^2/\text{h}^2}$$
$$= 206 \text{ km/h}$$

$$\tan \theta = \frac{|_a\vec{v}_g|}{|_p\vec{v}_a|}$$

$$= \frac{50 \text{ km/h}}{200 \text{ km/h}}$$
$$= 0.25$$
$$\theta = 14°$$

therefore $_p\vec{v}_g = 206 \text{ km/h}[\text{N}14°\text{E}]$

(d) Using the cosine law:

$$|_p\vec{v}_g|^2 = |_p\vec{v}_a|^2 + |_a\vec{v}_g|^2 - 2|_p\vec{v}_a|\,|_a\vec{v}_g| \cos \phi$$
$$= (200)^2 + (50)^2 - 2(200)(50)\cos 130°$$
$$= 40\ 000 + 2500 - 20\ 000(-0.6293)$$
$$= 42\ 500 + 12\ 586$$
$$= 55\ 086$$

$$|_p\vec{v}_g| = 235 \text{ km/h}$$

Using the sine law:

$$\frac{\sin \theta}{|_a\vec{v}_g|} = \frac{\sin \phi}{|_p\vec{v}_g|}$$

$$\sin \theta = \frac{(50 \text{ km/h})(0.7660)}{235 \text{ km/h}}$$
$$= 0.1630$$
$$\theta = 9°$$

therefore $_p\vec{v}_g = 235 \text{ km/h}[\text{N}49°\text{E}]$

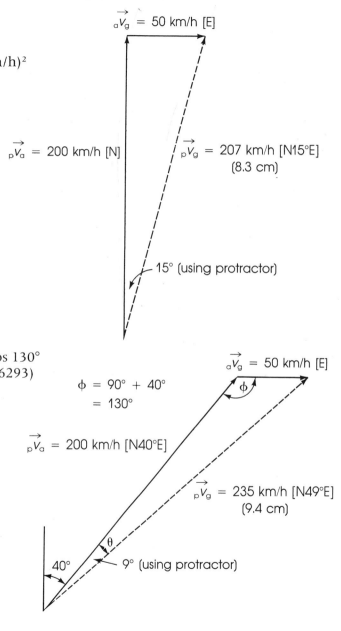

$_a\vec{v}_g = 50 \text{ km/h [E]}$

$_p\vec{v}_a = 200 \text{ km/h [N]}$

$_p\vec{v}_g = 207 \text{ km/h [N15°E]}$
(8.3 cm)

15° (using protractor)

$\phi = 90° + 40°$
$= 130°$

$_a\vec{v}_g = 50 \text{ km/h [E]}$

$_p\vec{v}_a = 200 \text{ km/h [N40°E]}$

$_p\vec{v}_g = 235 \text{ km/h [N49°E]}$
(9.4 cm)

40°   9° (using protractor)

This type of vector problem may also be solved by adding components of the velocity vectors, in the x (east-west) and y (north-south) directions. Part (d) is particularly interesting.

$$(_pv_a)_x = 200 \sin 40° \text{ km/h} = 200(0.6428) \text{ km/h} = 128 \text{ km/h}$$
$$(_pv_a)_y = 200 \cos 40° \text{ km/h} = 200(0.7660) \text{ km/h} = 153 \text{ km/h}$$
$$(_av_g)_x = 50 \text{ km/h}$$
$$(_av_g)_y = 0$$

$$_p\vec{v}_g = {}_p\vec{v}_a + {}_a\vec{v}_g$$

Taking components in the x-direction,

$$(_pv_g)_x = (_pv_a)_x + (_av_g)_x$$
$$= 128 \text{ km/h} + 50 \text{ km/h}$$
$$= 178 \text{ km/h}$$

Taking components in the y-direction,

$$(_pv_g)_y = (_pv_a)_y + (_av_g)_y$$
$$= 153 \text{ km/h} + 0$$
$$= 153 \text{ km/h}$$

When relative velocities, doubly subscripted, are added, a type of chain rule for subscripts is evident:

$$_a\vec{v}_d = {}_a\vec{v}_b + {}_b\vec{v}_c + {}_c\vec{v}_d$$

This rule could be used to find the resultant velocity, regardless of how many different frames of reference are involved in the problem.

so that
$$|_p\vec{v}_g| = \sqrt{(_pv_g)_x^2 + (_pv_g)_y^2}$$
$$= \sqrt{(178 \text{ km/h})^2 + (153 \text{ km/h})^2}$$
$$= 235 \text{ km/h}$$

and
$$\theta = \tan^{-1}\frac{(_pv_g)_y}{(_pv_g)_x}$$
$$= \tan^{-1}\frac{153 \text{ km/h}}{178 \text{ km/h}}$$
$$= \tan^{-1} 0.8596$$
$$= 41°$$

therefore
$$_p\vec{v}_g = 235 \text{ km/h[E41°N]}$$

Sample problem 2

A swimmer can swim at a speed of 1.80 m/s in still water. If the current in a river 200 m wide is 1.00 m/s[E], and the swimmer starts on the south bank and swims so that she is always headed directly across the river, determine each of the following.
(a) the swimmer's resultant velocity, relative to the river bank
(b) how long she will take to reach the far shore
(c) how far downstream she will land (from the point opposite her starting point)

(a) The swimmer's velocity relative to the river bank (ground), $_s\vec{v}_g$, is the vector sum of her velocity relative to the water, $_s\vec{v}_w$, and the velocity of the water relative to the ground, $_w\vec{v}_g$.

$$_s\vec{v}_g = _s\vec{v}_w + _w\vec{v}_g$$

Mathematical Solution:

$$|_s\vec{v}_g|^2 = |_s\vec{v}_w|^2 + |_w\vec{v}_g|^2$$
$$= (1.80 \text{ m/s})^2 + (1.00 \text{ m/s})^2$$
$$= 4.24 \text{ m}^2/\text{s}^2$$

$$|_s\vec{v}_g| = 2.06 \text{ m/s}$$

$$\tan \theta = \frac{|_w\vec{v}_g|}{|_s\vec{v}_w|}$$
$$= \frac{1.00 \text{ m/s}}{1.80 \text{ m/s}}$$
$$= 0.5555$$
$$\theta = 29°$$

Graphical Solution:

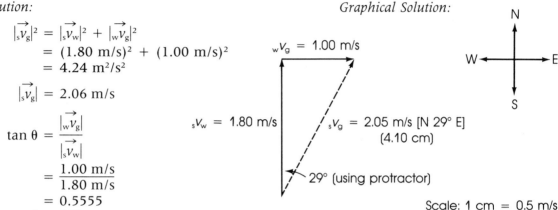

The swimmer's resultant velocity is 2.06 m/s[N29°E] relative to the river bank.

(b) The time required to cross the river is the same in still water as in water with a current, because the water velocity and the swimmer's velocity are at right angles to each other, and are therefore mutually independent. That is, the water velocity (current) has no component in the direction of the swimmer's velocity; therefore, it neither aids nor hinders her in crossing the river. What it does do is cause her to move downstream as she crosses.

We know that $\Delta_s\vec{d}_g = _s\vec{v}_g \Delta t$. Then, taking components in the y-direction,

$$\Delta t = \frac{(\Delta_s \vec{d}_g)_y}{(_s\vec{v}_g)_y}$$
$$= \frac{200 \text{ m}}{1.80 \text{ m/s}}$$
$$= 111 \text{ s}$$

(c) Again, the swimmer's downstream velocity is independent of her swimming velocity, since it has no component in the downstream or upstream direction. As a result, she will move downstream at the same rate whether she is swimming across the river, or simply floating.

Now, taking components in the x-direction,

$$(\Delta_s \vec{d}_g)_x = (_s\vec{V}_g)_x \, \Delta t$$
$$= (1.00 \text{ m/s})(111 \text{ s})$$
$$= 111 \text{ m[E]}$$

In planning ahead, a factor that is more significant than the velocity a pilot or swimmer acquires in the presence of a wind or current is the velocity the airplane or the person must maintain in order to arrive at a predetermined destination. Again, the techniques of vector analysis allow us to solve such basic navigational problems.

Sample problem 3

A swimmer on the south shore of a river wishes to swim to a dock due north of his starting point. His maximum swimming speed in still water is 4.0 km/h, and there is a current in the river flowing at 2.5 km/h towards the west.

(a) In what direction must he set out and continue swimming through the water?

(b) If the river is 2.0 km wide, how long does it take him to make the crossing?

(a) The swimmer's velocity relative to the ground, $_s\vec{V}_g$, is the vector sum of his swimming velocity relative to the water, $_s\vec{V}_w$, plus the velocity of the water relative to the ground, $_w\vec{V}_g$.

$$_s\vec{V}_g = {_s\vec{V}_w} + {_w\vec{V}_g}$$

This equation may be rewritten, as an expression for $_s\vec{V}_w$ as:

$$_s\vec{V}_w = {_s\vec{V}_g} - {_w\vec{V}_g}$$

In order to reach a point due north of his starting point, the swimmer must swim so that the direction of $_s\vec{V}_g$ is due north.

Graphical Solution:

Scale:
1 cm = 1 km/h

direction of $\vec{V}_g$

arc, of radius 4.0 cm

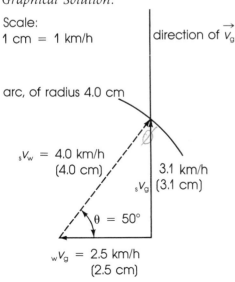

$_sV_w$ = 4.0 km/h
(4.0 cm)

3.1 km/h
$_sV_g$ (3.1 cm)

$\theta = 50°$

$_wV_g$ = 2.5 km/h
(2.5 cm)

Mathematical Solution:

$$\sin \phi = \frac{|_w\vec{V}_g|}{|_s\vec{V}_w|}$$
$$= \frac{2.5 \text{ km/h}}{4.0 \text{ km/h}}$$
$$= 0.6250$$
$$\phi = 40°$$

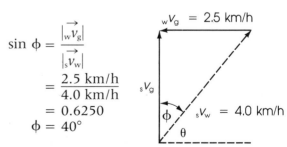

$_wV_g$ = 2.5 km/h

$_sV_g$

ϕ

$_sV_w$ = 4.0 km/h

θ

He must point himself in the direction [N40°E].

(b) It is his velocity relative to the ground, $_s\vec{v}_g$, that determines how long it will take him to cross the river.

From the scale diagram,

$$_s\vec{v}_g = 3.1 \text{ km/h[N]}$$

since the scaled vector is 3.1 cm long.

Using the Pythagorean Theorem,

$$|_s\vec{v}_g|^2 = |_s\vec{v}_w|^2 - |_w\vec{v}_g|^2$$
$$= (4.0 \text{ km/h})^2 - (2.5 \text{ km/h})^2$$
$$= 9.75 \text{ km}^2/\text{h}^2$$

$$|_s\vec{v}_g| = 3.1 \text{ km/h}$$

Therefore, $\Delta t = \dfrac{\Delta(_s\vec{d}_g)_N}{(_s\vec{v}_g)_N}$

$$= \frac{2.0 \text{ km}}{3.1 \text{ km/h}}$$
$$= 0.65 \text{ h, or } 39 \text{ min}$$

Practice

1. The pilot of a light plane heads due north at an air speed of 400 km/h. A wind is blowing from the west at 60 km/h.
   (a) What is the plane's velocity with respect to the ground?
   (b) How far off course would the plane be after 2.5 h, if the pilot had hoped to travel due north but had forgotten to check the wind velocity?
   (405 km/h[N8.5°E], 150 km[E])

2. A canoeist paddles "north" across a river at 3.0 m/s. (The canoe is always kept pointed at right angles to the river.) The river is flowing east at 4.0 m/s and is 100 m wide.
   (a) What is the velocity of the canoe relative to the river bank?
   (b) Calculate the time required to cross the river.
   (c) How far downstream is the landing point from the starting point?
   (5.0 m/s[N53°E], 33 s, 133 m)

3. A pilot wishes to make a flight of 300 km[NE] in 45 min. On checking with the meteorological office, she finds that there will be a wind of 80 km/h from the north for the entire flight. What heading and airspeed must she use for the flight?
   ([E52°N], 460 km/h)

4. A quarterback is running across the field, parallel to the line of scrimmage, at a constant speed of 2.5 m/s, when he spots an open, stationary receiver straight downfield from him (i.e., in a line parallel to the sidelines). If he can throw the football at a speed of 8.0 m/s, relative to himself, at what angle, relative to the sidelines, must he throw it in order to hit the receiver? How far downfield was the receiver, if the pass took 3.0 s to reach him?
   (18°, 23 m)

Navigators have exact meanings for many of the terms we use in relative velocity problems. Some of them are:
heading: the direction in which the vehicle is aimed, either through the air, for a plane, or through the water, for a boat.
course (or track): the path, with respect to the ground along which a vehicle moves.

In navigation, directions are all taken clockwise from due north. For example, a heading of 180° is due south, and a heading of 120° is the same as [E30°S].

3.8 Acceleration as a Vector

In Chapter 2, acceleration was defined as the rate of change of velocity. The vector nature of velocity requires vector definitions of both average acceleration and instantaneous acceleration that are slightly more general than those given in Chapter 2. These definitions of acceleration are as follows:

As with velocity, whenever acceleration, $\vec{a}$, is written without a subscript it is taken to mean instantaneous acceleration.

$$\vec{a}_{av} = \frac{\Delta \vec{v}}{\Delta t}$$

$$\vec{a}_{inst} = \lim_{\Delta t \to 0} \frac{\Delta \vec{v}}{\Delta t}$$

Chapter 2 dealt only with motion in a straight line: only the magnitude or sign of an object's velocity changed. It was shown that an object has a positive acceleration in its direction of motion when its velocity increases, and a negative value when its velocity decreases. When an object is free to move in two dimensions in a plane, its velocity can change in magnitude or direction, or both. What differences will this make in the way we calculate velocity changes and accelerations?

An object, such as a racing car, moving along a curved path with a changing speed, is a good example of this type of motion. A diagram shows the path of such an object, and its velocity vectors at two points along the path.

In moving from position 1 to position 2, the car has changed its direction and increased its speed.

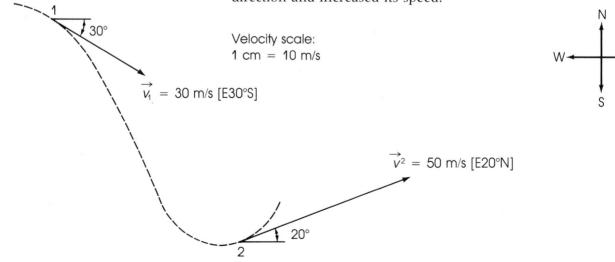

30°

Velocity scale:
1 cm = 10 m/s

$\vec{v_1}$ = 30 m/s [E30°S]

$\vec{v2}$ = 50 m/s [E20°N]

20°

N
W — E
S

To find its change in velocity, $\Delta \vec{v}$, we make use of the relationship $\Delta \vec{v} = \vec{v_2} - \vec{v_1}$, and this vector diagram.

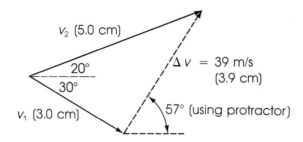

v_2 (5.0 cm)

20°

30°

v_1 (3.0 cm)

$\Delta v = 39$ m/s
(3.9 cm)

57° (using protractor)

If the car took 5.0 s to move from position 1 to position 2, we may calculate its average acceleration during the interval as follows:

$$\vec{a}_{av} = \frac{\Delta \vec{v}}{\Delta t}$$

$$= \frac{39 \text{ m/s[E57°N]}}{5.0 \text{ s}}$$

$$= 7.8 \text{ m/s}^2\text{[E57°N]}$$

It is significant that the car does have an acceleration during this interval of motion and that the average acceleration is in the same direction as the car's velocity change, $\Delta \vec{v}$.

Practice

Copy each of the following vector diagrams into your notebook and determine the missing quantity in each case.

1. Find $\Delta \vec{v}$.

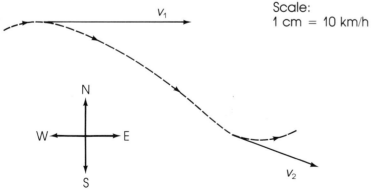

v_1

Scale:
1 cm = 10 km/h

N

W

E

S

v_2

2. Find $\vec{v_2}$.

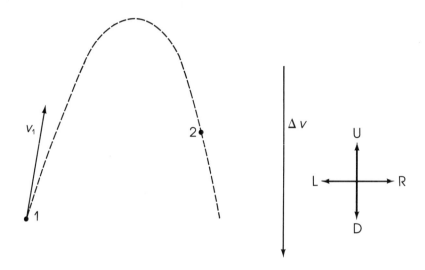

3. Find $\vec{v_1}$.

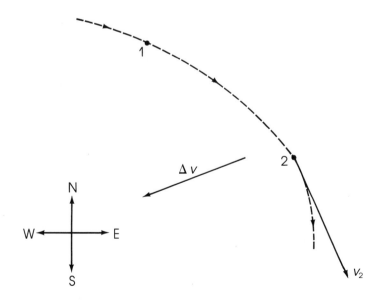

4. Points 1, 2, and 3 occur 1.0 s apart. Knowing that $\Delta \vec{v} = \vec{a}\Delta t$, find and draw vectors $\vec{v_2}$ and $\vec{v_3}$.

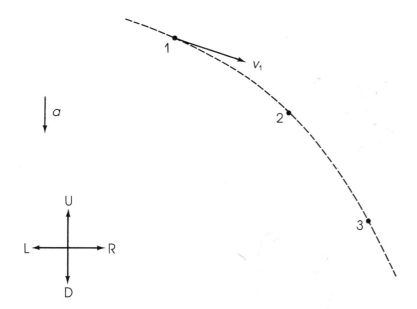

5. A helicopter travelling horizontally at 150 km/h[E] executes a gradual turn, and eventually is moving at 120 km/h[S]. If the turn takes 50 s to complete, what is the average acceleration of the helicopter? (3.8 km/h/s[S51°W])

6. A hockey puck hits the boards with a velocity of 10 m/s at an angle of 20° to the boards. It is deflected with a velocity of 8.0 m/s at 24° to the boards. If the time of impact is 0.03 s, what is the average acceleration of the puck?
   (2.3 × 10² m/s² out from the boards at an angle of 107°)

3.9 Uniform Circular Motion

This section deals with motion in which only the direction changes: motion in a circle and at a constant speed. The magnitude of the object's velocity remains constant, but its direction changes continuously as it moves along a circular path.

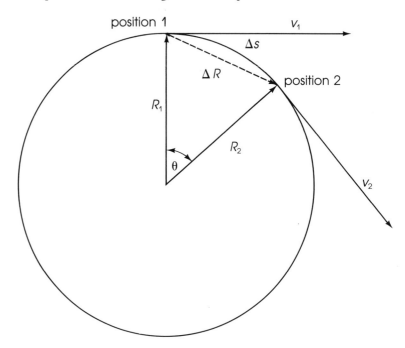

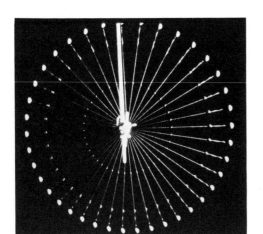

A strobe photo of an object moving in a circle at a constant speed has images that are equally spaced, in both time and position.

In the time interval Δt (see the diagram), as the object moves from position 1 to position 2, its velocity vector changes from $\vec{v_1}$ to $\vec{v_2}$ while its displacement from the centre of the circle (position vector $\vec{R}$) rotates through an angle θ, from $\vec{R_1}$ to $\vec{R_2}$.

To find the average acceleration in this interval,

$$\vec{a}_{av} = \frac{\Delta \vec{v}}{\Delta t}$$

$$= \frac{\vec{v_2} - \vec{v_1}}{\Delta t}$$

To determine $\Delta \vec{v}$, draw the scale diagram on the next page.

Note that the angle θ, between $\vec{v_1}$ and $\vec{v_2}$, is the same as the angle between $\vec{R}_1$ and $\vec{R}_2$ in the previous diagram.

During the interval, the object undergoes a change in velocity (given by $\Delta\vec{v}$) and hence an acceleration. The acceleration is in the same direction as $\Delta\vec{v}$, not in the direction of either $\vec{v}_1$ or $\vec{v}_2$.

To find the instantaneous acceleration of the object at any point, we make use of the definition

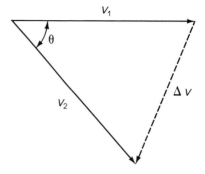

$$\vec{a}_{\text{inst}} = \lim_{\Delta t \to 0}\frac{\Delta\vec{v}}{\Delta t}$$

To evaluate this limit, we must allow the interval considered previously to become progressively smaller. Position 2 becomes very close to position 1, θ becomes very small, and Δt approaches zero. To see what effect this limiting process has on the value of $\Delta\vec{v}$, we compare the vector diagram already drawn for $\Delta\vec{v}$ with a similar diagram that may be drawn to find $\Delta\vec{R}$:

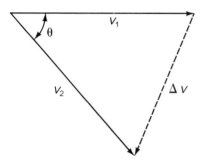 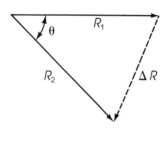

Mathematically, these two isosceles triangles are similar; therefore, the magnitudes of their corresponding sides are proportional.

If we write $|\vec{v}_1| = |\vec{v}_2| = v$, $|\vec{R}_1| = |\vec{R}_2| = R$, $|\Delta\vec{R}| = \Delta R$, and $|\Delta\vec{v}| = \Delta v$

$$\text{then} \quad \frac{\Delta R}{R} = \frac{\Delta v}{v}$$

$$\text{or} \quad \Delta v = \frac{v}{R}\Delta R$$

Then, substituting this value for Δv into the equation for $\vec{a}_{\text{inst}}$,

$$\vec{a}_{\text{inst}} = \lim_{\Delta t \to 0}\frac{\Delta\vec{v}}{\Delta t}$$

$$\text{or } a_{\text{inst}} = \lim_{\Delta t \to 0}\frac{v\Delta R}{R\Delta t}$$

$$= \frac{v}{R}\lim_{\Delta t \to 0}\frac{\Delta R}{\Delta t}$$

since v and R are constant in magnitude and do not change as the time interval shrinks.

But, as $\Delta t \rightarrow 0$, ΔR approaches Δs, the arc of the circular path during the interval. Since Δs is the actual distance the object travels in the interval Δt, at speed v, then $\Delta s = v\Delta t$.

Thus, as $\Delta t \rightarrow 0$, $\dfrac{\Delta R}{\Delta t} \rightarrow \dfrac{v\Delta t}{\Delta t} \rightarrow v$

In the limit,

$$a_{\text{inst}} = \frac{v}{R}\,(v)$$
$$= \frac{v^2}{R}$$

The equation above gives only the magnitude of the acceleration of an object moving in a circle at constant speed. To determine the direction of this acceleration, let us suppose that, at any point, $\vec{a}$ makes an angle, θ, with $\vec{v}$, as shown:

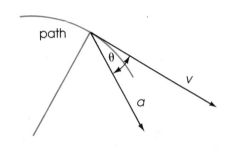

We can resolve $\vec{a}$ into two perpendicular components, $\vec{a_1}$, parallel to $\vec{v}$, and $\vec{a_2}$, perpendicular to $\vec{v}$.

In Chapter 2 it was shown that, for an object with a constant speed, the acceleration in the direction of motion is zero. Thus, since $\vec{v}$ is constant in magnitude, $\vec{a_1}$ must be zero.

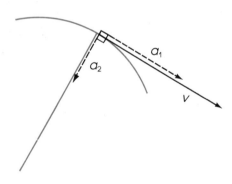

But, $|\vec{a_1}| = |\vec{a}|\cos\theta$

$0 = |\vec{a}|\cos\theta$

Then, $\cos\theta = 0$

and $\theta = 90°$

Thus, the angle between $\vec{a}$ and $\vec{v}$ for an object moving in a circle at constant speed is 90°; $\vec{a}$ is perpendicular to $\vec{v}$ and always points towards the centre of the circle. For that reason, it is called the **centripetal acceleration**.

We use the symbol "a_c" to represent the centripetal acceleration of an object moving in a circular path at a constant speed. The subscript "c" serves to remind us of the vector nature of centripetal acceleration, and that its direction is continuously changing but is always towards the centre of the circular path.

Therefore,

$$a_c = \frac{v^2}{R}$$

The name "centripetal" comes from the Greek expression for "centre-seeking".

Since the direction is always understood, it is not necessary to use the vector notation in centripetal motion equations.

Sample problems

1. A car turns a circular curve with a speed of 20 m/s. If the radius of the curve is 100 m, what is the centripetal acceleration of the car?

$$a_c = \frac{v^2}{R}$$
$$= \frac{(20 \text{ m/s})^2}{(100 \text{ m})}$$
$$= 4.0 \text{ m/s}^2$$

2. A ball on a string swings in a horizontal circle of radius 2.0 m. If its centripetal acceleration is 15 m/s², what is the speed of the ball?

$$a_c = \frac{v^2}{R}$$
$$\text{Therefore, } v = \sqrt{a_c R}$$
$$= \sqrt{(15 \text{ m/s}^2)(2.0 \text{ m})}$$
$$= 5.5 \text{ m/s}$$

For many objects moving at a constant speed in a circular path, it is the period, or frequency, of the circular motion that is known, rather than the speed.

Since $v = \frac{\Delta d}{\Delta t}$, and Δd is the circumference of the circle, then $v = \frac{2\pi R}{T}$, where T is the period of motion (Δt for one circumference of the circle).

$$\text{Therefore, } a_c = \frac{v^2}{R}$$
$$= \frac{(2\pi R/T)^2}{R}$$

$$a_c = \frac{4\pi^2 R}{T^2}$$

Alternatively, since period and frequency are related by the equation $T = \frac{1}{f}$, we can write

$$a_c = 4\pi^2 R f^2$$

These are not new results, in any sense, but different expressions for $\frac{v^2}{R}$ that are useful in certain applications.

Sample problems

1. What is the centripetal acceleration of a stone being whirled in a circle, at the end of a 1.5 m string, on a smooth sheet of ice, with a frequency of 1.25 Hz?

$$a_c = 4\pi^2 R f^2$$
$$= 4\pi^2 (1.5 \text{ m})(1.25 \text{ Hz})^2$$
$$= 92.5 \text{ m/s}^2, \text{ or } 93 \text{ m/s}^2$$

2. The planet Mercury moves in an approximately circular path around the sun at an average distance of 5.8×10^{10} m, accelerating centripetally at 0.04 m/s². What is its period of revolution around the sun?

$$a_c = \frac{4\pi^2 R}{T^2}$$

$$\text{thus, } T^2 = \frac{4\pi^2 R}{a_c}$$

$$= \frac{4\pi^2 (5.8 \times 10^{10} \text{ m})}{0.04 \text{ m/s}^2}$$

$$= 5.7 \times 10^{13} \text{ s}^2$$

$$\text{or } T = \sqrt{5.7 \times 10^{13} \text{ s}^2}$$

$$= 7.6 \times 10^6 \text{ s, or approximately 88 d on Earth}$$

Practice

1. What is the centripetal acceleration of a locomotive that travels around a circular curve of radius 250 m at a constant speed of 70 km/h?   (1.5 m/s²)
2. What is the centripetal acceleration of a small girl standing at the outer edge of a carousel 4.0 m in diameter, which makes one complete rotation in 6.0 s?   (2.2 m/s²)
3. Patrons on the midway ride called the Rotor stand with their backs against the wall of a revolving cylinder, while the floor drops away from beneath them. To keep from falling, they require a centripetal acceleration of about 25 m/s². If the rotor has a diameter of 5.0 m, with what minimum frequency does it revolve? (The vertical force required to support their weight is supplied by friction with the wall.)   (0.50 Hz)
4. An airplane flies in a horizontal circle of radius 500 m. If its centripetal acceleration is 20 m/s², how long does it take to complete the circle?   (31 s)

3.10 The Motion of a Projectile

A projectile is an object moving freely, under the influence of gravity alone. The motion of a projectile provides an interesting example of acceleration and change in velocity. The strobe photo shows the position of a ball rolled horizontally off a table, at equal time intervals 1/20 s apart. Horizontal and vertical lines have been drawn at each position of the ball to show its horizontal and vertical displacements in each time interval. Note that the ball travels equal horizontal distances in equal time intervals, but the vertical distance travelled increases with each time interval. We will study the reasons for this motion in Chapter 5. For now, we can determine the instantaneous velocity of the ball at each recorded point by using the technique outlined below, involving the ball's constant horizontal component of velocity.

We know that the instantaneous velocity at any point will lie in the direction of the tangent to the path at that point. The instantaneous velocity may be resolved into a horizontal component (which is constant) and a vertical component (which is increasing in magnitude).

We can make use of our knowledge of vector components from Section 3.6 to determine the instantaneous velocity at any point. If the constant horizontal component of velocity is drawn at a point, a vertical projection from the tip of this component will meet the tangent to the path at the tip of the actual instantaneous velocity vector.

For example, to determine the instantaneous velocity at point 4, first draw the horizontal component of the velocity at point 4. Its magnitude is proportional to the horizontal distance between two consecutive images of the ball. Next, draw the tangent to the curve at point 4, and project a vertical line down from the tip of the horizontal velocity component to meet this tangent. The point at which this projection meets the tangent represents the tip of the instantaneous velocity vector at point 4. The same procedure may be used to determine the instantaneous velocity vector at each point along the projectile's path, i.e., $\vec{v}_1$, $\vec{v}_2$, $\vec{v}_3$, $\vec{v}_4$, $\vec{v}_5$, and $\vec{v}_6$.

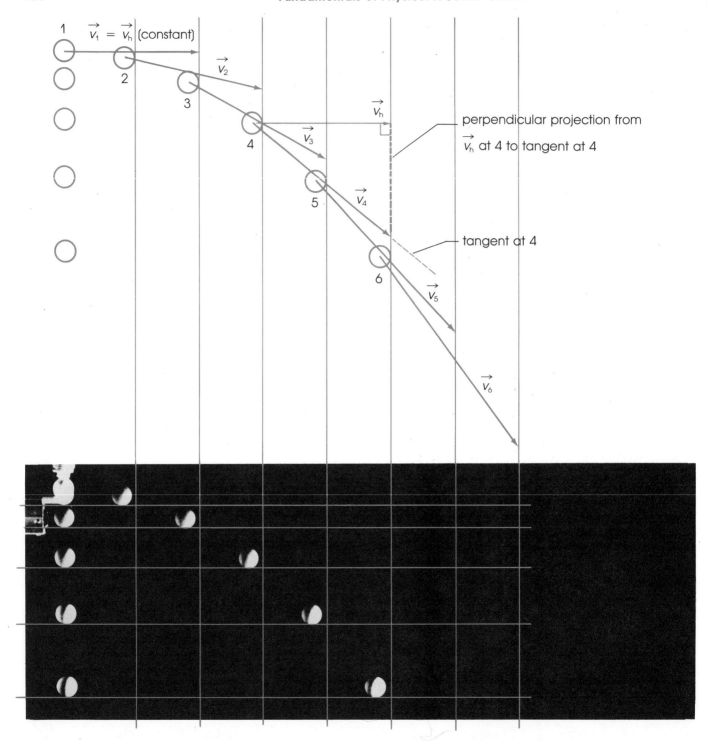

All of these instantaneous velocity vectors may be drawn from the same point, using a scale diagram, as shown.

For each of the five intervals, $\Delta \vec{v}$ may be found, using the vector subtraction diagrams farther down the page.

Note that the result is the same for each interval: $\Delta \vec{v}$ is constant in magnitude and direction. As the projectile moves along its curved path, its speed increases and its direction changes in such a way that the change in velocity in each interval, and hence the acceleration, is constant and always points straight down.

This constant downward acceleration is caused by gravity, and is called the acceleration due to gravity. In Chapter 2, it was mentioned that the downward acceleration of a freely falling object is 9.8 m/s². In Chapter 5, projectile motion will be examined more closely, and it will be shown that projectiles also have a constant downward acceleration of 9.8 m/s².

3.11 Review

Discussion

1. One car travels east at 100 km/h and another travels north at 100 km/h. Are their velocities equal? Are their speeds equal?
2. Give examples of several objects whose velocity is zero when their acceleration is not.
3. Every car has an odometer and a speedometer. Do these devices measure a vector quantity or a scalar quantity? How could the speedometer be modified to show velocity?
4. What is the average velocity of a runner who completes one lap of a 400 m track in 75 s? Discuss.
5. Why do airplanes usually take off and land into the wind?
6. How can a car moving at a uniform speed be accelerating at the same time?
7. A baseball player running to first base sometimes jumps for the base at the last moment. Is this a good idea? Discuss.
8. Two balls at the ends of two strings are moving at the same speed in circular paths. Compare their centripetal accelerations if one string is three times as long as the other.
9. In what directions are two vectors that, when added, give the largest possible resultant? The smallest possible resultant?
10. How are velocity vectors added when there are more than two velocities involved? As an example, a person is walking across the aisle of an airplane that is flying through the air that is blowing over the ground.

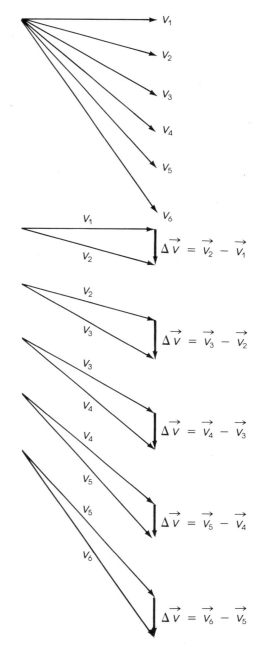

11. A sports car moves through a curve (not necessarily circular) at a constant speed. What is the direction of the instantaneous acceleration at every point in the curve?

12. Describe the ways in which the sum of three vectors, $\vec{X}$, $\vec{Y}$, and $\vec{Z}$, may be determined.

Problems

13. A train moving at a constant speed of 100 km/h travels east for 40 min, then 30° east of north for 20 min, and finally west for 30 min. What is the train's average velocity for the trip?

14. A man walks 600 m[E47°N], then 500 m[N38°W], then 300 m[W29°S], and finally 400 m[S13°E]. Find his resultant displacement.

15. A snowmobile is being driven across a frozen lake. $\vec{v_1}$ and $\vec{v_2}$ in the diagram represent its velocity vectors at two instants 3.0 s apart. The scale is 1 cm = 5.0 m/s. Copy these vectors into your notebook, and use an accurate vector diagram to determine $\Delta \vec{v}$. What is the average acceleration of the snowmobile?

16. This diagram shows a racing car's position at three equally spaced points in time. It also shows the car's instantaneous velocity vectors at points 1 and 2. If the acceleration of the car is uniform, determine, using an accurate vector diagram, the instantaneous velocity of the car at point 3. Scale: 1 cm = 5.0 m/s.

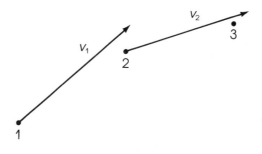

17. The current in a river moves at 2.0 m/s[S]. How fast and in what direction must a swimmer move through the water in order to have a resultant velocity relative to the river bank of
    (a) 3.6 m/s[S]?
    (b) 3.6 m/s[N]?
    (c) 3.6 m/s[E]?
18. A boat sails 8.0 km[S10°E] through still water. What are the components of its displacement in each of the following directions?
    (a) [S]
    (b) [E]
    (c) [S20°E]
    (d) [E10°N]
19. A helicopter rises with a uniform speed of 30 m/s at an angle of 50° to the horizontal.
    (a) What are the vertical and horizontal components of its velocity?
    (b) How long will it take to reach an altitude of 1.00 km?
    (c) What horizontal distance will it have covered by that time?
20. A ball is thrown from the top of a building with a speed of 20 m/s and at a downward angle of 30° to the horizontal, as shown. What are the horizontal and vertical components of the ball's initial velocity?

21. A boat travelling at 3.0 m/s through the water keeps its bow pointing north across a stream that flows west at 5.0 m/s. What is the resultant velocity of the boat with respect to the shore?
22. A dog walks at 1.6 m/s on the deck of a boat that is travelling north at 7.6 m/s with respect to the water.
    (a) What is the velocity of the dog with respect to the water if it walks towards the bow?
    (b) What is the velocity of the dog with respect to the water if it walks towards the stern?
    (c) What is the velocity of the dog with respect to the water if it walks towards the east rail, at right angles to the boat's keel?
23. An airplane maintains a heading due west at an air speed of 900 km/h. It is flying through a hurricane with winds of 300 km/h, from the northeast.

(a) In which direction is the plane moving relative to the ground?

(b) What is the plane's ground speed?

(c) How long would it take the plane to fly from one city to another 500 km away, along the path in (a)?

24. Two boathouses are located on a river, 1.0 km apart on the same shore. Two men make round trips from one boathouse to the other, and back. One man paddles a canoe at a velocity of 4.0 km/h relative to the water, and the other walks along the shore at a constant velocity of 4.0 km/h. The current in the river is 2.0 km/h in the starting direction of the canoeist.

(a) How much sooner than the walker does the canoeist reach the second boathouse?

(b) How long does it take each to make the round trip?

25. A 70 m wide river flows at 0.80 m/s. A girl swims across it at 1.4 m/s relative to the water.

(a) What is the least time she requires to cross the river?

(b) How far downstream will she be when she lands on the opposite shore?

(c) At what angle to the shore would she have to aim, in order to arrive at a point directly opposite the starting point?

(d) How long would the trip in part (c) take?

26. An ocean liner is steaming at 18 km/h due south. A passenger strolling on the deck walks towards the rear of the ship at 3.0 m/s. After walking for 12 s, he turns right and walks at the same speed towards the rail, 15 m from his turning point.

(a) What is his velocity, relative to the water, while walking towards the rear? While walking towards the rail?

(b) Draw a scale vector diagram, or make a sketch and use the mathematical approach, to determine his resultant displacement relative to the water at the end of his walk.

27. A newspaper boy throws papers sideways onto the porches of his customers while riding his bicycle along the sidewalk. The sidewalk is 15 m in front of the porches. The boy throws the papers at a horizontal speed of 6.0 m/s relative to himself, and rides the bicycle at a speed of 4.0 m/s relative to the sidewalk.

(a) With what horizontal speed do the papers actually travel relative to the ground?

(b) How far in advance of a porch should the boy throw a paper, so that it lands on target?

(c) If he waits until he is directly opposite a porch, at what horizontal angle with respect to the sidewalk will he have to throw the paper, to hit the porch?

28. A pilot maintains a heading due west with an air speed of 240 km/h. After flying for 30 min, he finds himself over a town

that he knows is 150 km west and 40 km south of his starting point.

(a) What is the wind velocity, in magnitude and direction?

(b) What heading should he now maintain, with the same air speed, to follow a course due west from the town?

29. The navigator of an airplane plans a flight from one airport to another 1200 km away, in a direction 30° east of north. The weather office informs him of a prevailing wind from the west, of 80 km/h. The pilot wants to maintain an air speed of 300 km/h.

(a) What heading should the navigator give the pilot?

(b) How long will the flight take?

(c) How much time did the wind save?

30. A train has a speed of 20 km/h. Raindrops falling against its side windows make traces inclined at 30° to the vertical. We ignore air turbulence and there is no wind.

(a) What is the horizontal component of a raindrop's velocity with respect to the Earth? With respect to the train?

(b) What is the velocity of the raindrop with respect to the Earth? With respect to the train?

31. An airplane flying at a constant speed of 1000 km/h executes a slow, level turn that changes its direction from west to east. If the turn takes 80 s, calculate the plane's average acceleration.

32. A car, moving initially at 32 km/h[N], turns a corner and continues at 32 km/h[W]. The turn takes 3.0 s to complete. Find (a) the change in velocity and (b) the average acceleration during the turn.

33. A traditional watch has a second hand 1.5 cm long, from centre to tip.

(a) What is the speed of the tip of the second hand?

(b) What is the velocity of the tip at 15 s? at 45 s? at 60 s?

(c) What is its change in velocity between 30 s and 45 s?

(d) What is its average acceleration during the same interval?

34. A puck sliding across the ice at 20 m/s[E] is struck by a stick and moves at 30 m/s, at an angle of 120° to its original path. Find its change in velocity.

35. A batter strikes a baseball moving horizontally towards him at 15 m/s. The ball leaves the bat horizontally at 24 m/s, 40° to the left of a line from the plate to the pitcher. The ball is in contact with the bat for 0.01 s. Determine

(a) the change in velocity of the ball.

(b) its average acceleration while being hit by the bat.

36. A racing car starts into a circular portion of a Grand Prix course at 200 km/h[E], travelling in a clockwise direction. By the time

it is headed due south, its speed has increased to 240 km/h. (a) If this took 12.0 s, find the average acceleration during the turn. (b) Estimate the radius of the curve.

37. A car, travelling at 25 m/s around a circular curve, has a centripetal acceleration of 8.3 m/s². What is the radius of the curve?

38. What is the centripetal acceleration of a point on the rim of a bicycle wheel of radius 0.25 m, if the bicycle's speed is 5.0 m/s? (HINT: Take the acceleration relative to the bicycle frame.)

39. The moon, an Earth satellite with a period of about 27.3 d and a nearly circular orbit, has a centripetal acceleration of 2.7×10^{-3} m/s². What is the average distance from the Earth to the moon?

40. What is the centripetal acceleration due to the daily rotation of an object at the Earth's equator if the equatorial radius is 6.4×10^{6} m?

41. A biophysicist is able to separate very small subcellular particles, using an analytic ultracentrifuge. The physicist must determine the amount of acceleration provided by the centrifuge at various speeds and radii. (1 g of acceleration is equal to the acceleration due to gravity, i.e., about 9.8 m/s².) Calculate the number of gs of acceleration at 8.4 cm from the centre of the centrifuge when it is spinning at 60 000 r/min.

42. A person walks up a stalled escalator in a department store in 90 s. When standing still on the same escalator in motion, he is carried up in 60 s. How much time would it take him to walk up the moving escalator? Could he walk down the escalator while it was moving up? If so, how long would that take? (SIN '70)

43. A slightly disoriented homing pigeon flies the following course at a constant speed of 15 m/s:
    (i)   800 m, 37° east of north,
    (ii)   300 m due west, and
    (iii) 400 m, 37° south of east.
    A crow flies in a straight line (as the crow flies) between the starting and finishing points. At what speed must the crow fly, if the birds leave and arrive together? (SIN '72)

44. A power boat travels down the St. Lawrence River from Montreal to Quebec City, at full throttle. The trip takes 3.0 h. The boat then heads back to Montreal, again at full throttle. This time, the trip takes 15 h. With no gas left, the boat now drifts with a steady current back to Quebec City. How long does the third trip take? (SIN '73)

45. Snoopy is flying his plane, the Sopwith Camel, in search of the Red Baron. He flies with a constant speed of 120 km/h relative to the air, and makes instantaneous turns, when necessary. He follows a perfectly square path on the ground, using north-south and east-west roads as a guide for each of the 60 km sides. On a day when there is a steady 60 km/h wind blowing diagonally across the square (say from the northeast) how long does the trip take? (SIN '77)

46. A sunbather, drifting downstream on a raft, dives off the raft just as it passes under a bridge and swims against the current for 15 min. She then turns and swims downstream, making the same total effort and overtaking the raft when it is 1.0 km downstream from the bridge. What is the speed of the current in the river? (SIN '75)

47. Two boys are at point X on one side of a river, 40 m wide and having a current of 1.0 m/s, flowing as shown. Simultaneously, they dive into the water in an attempt to reach point Y, directly opposite X. Both swim at 2.0 m/s relative to the water, but one directs himself so that his net motion corresponds to XY, while the other keeps his body perpendicular to the current and consequently lands at point Z. After landing, he runs along the shore to point Y at a speed of 6.0 m/s. Which boy arrives at Y first, and by how much time does he beat the other? (SIN '79)

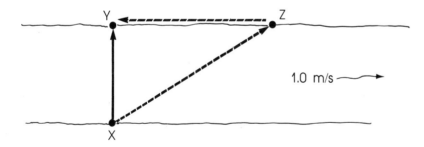

Numerical Answers to Review Problems

13. 30 km/h[E40°N]
14. 306 m[N13°W]
15. 5.1 m/s²[E24°S]
16. 18 m/s[E13°S]
17. (a) 1.6 m/s[S] (b) 5.6 m/s[N]
   (c) 4.1 m/s[E29°N]
18. (a) 7.9 km (b) 1.4 km (c) 7.9 km
   (d) 0
19. (a) 23 m/s, 19 m/s (b) 43 s
   (c) 8.3 × 10² m
20. 17 m/s, − 10 m/s
21. 5.8 m/s[W31°N]
22. (a) 9.2 m/s[N] (b) 6.0 m/s[N]
   (c) 7.8 m/s[N12°E]
23. (a) [W11°S] (b) 1132 km/h
   (c) 0.44 h or 27 min
24. (a) 5.0 min (b) 40 min, 30 min
25. (a) 50 s (b) 40 m (c) 55° (d) 61 s
26. (a) 2.0 m/s[S], 5.8 m/s[S31°W]
   (b) 51 m[S17°W]
27. (a) 7.2 m/s (b) 10 m (c) 48°
28. (a) 100 km/h[S37°W] (b) [W19°N]
29. (a) [N17°E] (b) 3.6 h (c) 0.40 h
30. (a) 0, − 20 km/h
   (b) 35 km/h [down], 40 km/h
   [down 30° back]
31. 25 km/h/s[E]
32. (a) 45 km/h[SW] (b) 15 km/h/s[SW]
33. (a) 0.16 cm/s
   (b) 0.16 cm/s[D], 0.16 cm/s[U],
   0.16 cm/s[R] (c) 0.23 cm/s [U45°R]
   (d) 1.5 × 10⁻² cm/s²[U45°R]
34. 44 m/s[W37°S]
35. (a) 37 m/s[25°L of pitcher]
   (b) 3.7 × 10³ m/s²[25°L of pitcher]
36. (a) 26 km/h/s[S40°W] (b) 5.2 × 10² m
37. 75 m
38. 1.0 × 10² m/s²
39. 3.8 × 10⁸ m
40. 3.4 × 10⁻² m/s²
41. 3.4 × 10⁵ gs
42. 36 s, no
43. 6.4 m/s
44. 7.5 h
45. 2.5 h
46. 2.0 km/h
47. straight across, by 0.2 s

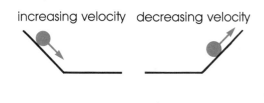

Aristotle

4 Newton's Laws of Motion

4.1 Kinematics and Dynamics

The first three chapters have dealt with the description of motion. Measurements and calculations of displacement, velocity, and acceleration make possible a complete description of the way an object moves from one point to another, whether in a straight line or along a curved path. This branch of physics, dealing with the description of motion, is called kinematics, from the Greek word "kinema", meaning motion.

Once we are able to observe and describe motion completely, some more fundamental questions arise. What causes objects to move the way they do? Why do some objects speed up while some slow down and others remain at rest or keep moving at a steady speed? Also, what must occur to make a moving object change its direction? The branch of physics that deals with the causes of motion is called dynamics, from the Greek word "dynamis", meaning power. Kinematics and dynamics, together, form the larger branch of physics known as **mechanics**, the study of motion.

4.2 Galileo Looks at Force and Motion

People have been curious about the causes of motion for over 2000 years, but a systematic approach to dynamics began only during the time of Galileo Galilei (1564-1642) and Isaac Newton (1642-1727).

The Greeks, about the time of Aristotle (384-322 BC), observed that, in everyday situations, it requires a continuous pushing or pulling to keep an object such as a rolling stone moving. When the pushing or pulling is no longer applied, the stone comes to rest. The early Greek law of motion was simple: a constant force was required to produce a constant velocity. If the force was increased, the object moved faster. If the force was decreased, the object moved more slowly. If the force was removed, the object stopped.

These statements seem logical, but they are incorrect. Nevertheless, the assumptions they were based on endured for nearly 2000 years, until the great Italian physicist Galileo explained the relationship between force and motion more accurately. Galileo devised two simple thought experiments about motion on inclined planes to explain his theory.

increasing velocity   decreasing velocity

constant velocity

In his first thought experiment, he reasoned that since a ball rolling down a slope speeds up and a ball rolling up a slope slows down, then a ball rolling across a horizontal (non-sloping) surface neither slows down nor speeds up but continues to move with a constant velocity, indefinitely.

Galileo did, of course, observe that a ball rolling along a horizontal surface eventually stops, but he assumed correctly that the ball was being slowed down by friction, or "resistance", as he called it.

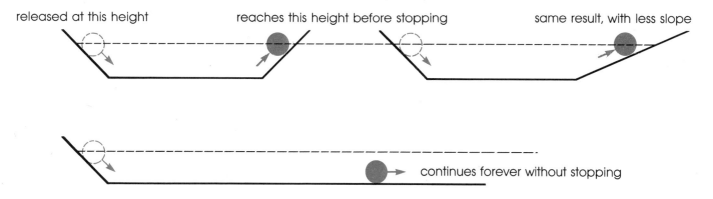

released at this height   reaches this height before stopping   same result, with less slope

continues forever without stopping

In his second thought experiment, Galileo reasoned that if the slope of the rising plane was decreased to make it less steep than the descending slope, the ball would roll farther along this slope, stopping when it reached the height from which it was released on the first slope (see diagram). The fact that the ball did not quite reach that height he attributed, once again, to friction. He concluded, logically, that if the slope of the second plane was zero, the ball, once rolling, would continue forever with no loss of speed, in an attempt to reach its original height.

This reasoning showed great imagination. After all, there is no such thing as a frictionless surface. Also, it was in direct conflict with Aristotelian physics, which enjoyed general acceptance at the time. In contrast with previous beliefs, Galileo argued that it is just as "natural" for an object to move with a constant speed as it is for it to be at rest.

Many of the so-called disagreements between Galileo and Aristotle are due to differences in their use of language, i.e., their different interpretation of the same word or phrase. For example, Galileo identified friction as a force while Aristotle considered it to be "natural" and therefore not a force.

4.3 Newton's Law of Inertia (Newton's First Law)

Galileo published his ideas about motion in the early years of the 17th century, and they became accepted by scientists all over Europe almost immediately (see Section 7.6). Isaac Newton summarized his own work and that of Galileo in his book *Principia Mathematica*, published in 1687. Newton described what Galileo had discovered about inertia much the way Galileo had described it; and because it was included with Newton's other laws of motion it is often referred to as Newton's First Law. It may be stated in either of these ways:

When no external, unbalanced force acts on an object, its velocity remains constant.

or

If no net force acts on an object, it maintains its state of rest or its constant speed in a straight line.

This famous and important law has several significant implications, which must be clearly understood:

- An external force is required to change the velocity of an object. Internal forces have no effect on an object's motion. For example, the driver pushing on the dashboard of his car does not cause the car's velocity to change.
- The external force must be unbalanced; that is, two equal opposing forces acting on an object will not change its velocity. For the object's velocity to change, the vector sum of the applied forces on the object must be different than zero.
- Objects at rest remain at rest unless acted upon by an external unbalanced force. For example, a ball on a horizontal floor will remain at rest forever, unless someone gives it a push.
- Moving objects continue to move in a straight line at a constant speed, unless acted upon by an external unbalanced force. For example, a car moving into a flat icy curve will tend to continue in a straight line, off the side of the road.

The ability of an object to resist changes in its state of motion is a fundamental property of all matter. Newton called this property "inertia". Because of inertia, a moving object tends to remain in motion in a straight line at a constant speed, and a stationary object tends to remain at rest.

There are many everyday examples of objects resisting a change in their motion, due to inertia, including the following.

Aristotle's description of motion was abandoned primarily because it was not as simple as Galileo's and Newton's: it required more assumptions and divided motion into more categories, each with its own description.

- When a car stops suddenly, a passenger in the front seat (not wearing a seat belt) continues to move forward (due to the passenger's inertia) and collides with the car's windshield.

- A magician pulls a smooth tablecloth quickly out from under a place-setting of expensive china. Due to their inertia, the dishes remain at rest where they were, and are not broken.

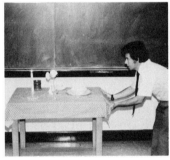

- If a coin is balanced on a horizontal playing card on a finger, and the card is then flipped away, the coin, because of its inertia, will remain at rest on the finger.

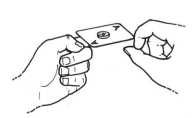

How a Snowmobile Moves

The snowmobile, a common sight in rural areas of countries with snowy winter climates, was invented by a Canadian, Armand Bombardier, in the 1930s. It operates by making use of many principles of physics, in particular Newton's Laws.

A gasoline engine drives a flywheel connected to sprockets that cause a large, oval-shaped, rubber "track" to rotate. The snowmobile sits with a sizable portion of this track in contact with the snow. In spite of the considerable mass of the snowmobile and its riders, the large area of the track decreases the snowmobile's pressure on the snow to a small enough value that it doesn't sink in appreciably.

As the track begins to rotate, towards the rear along the bottom of the machine, ridges perpendicular to the direction of motion dig into the snow, and push backward on it. Newton's Third Law states that the snow then pushes forward on the track, with an equal reaction force, causing the machine to accelerate forward. The harder the track pushes back, the greater the forward reaction force of the snow on it, and hence on the machine. Of course, when the frictional force of the snow on the machine is equal to the reaction force caused by the rotating track, the machine continues to move with a constant speed.

- If a mallet strikes one of a stack of stationary wooden discs, only the disc that was struck will move. The rest of the stack, because of its inertia, will remain at rest horizontally.

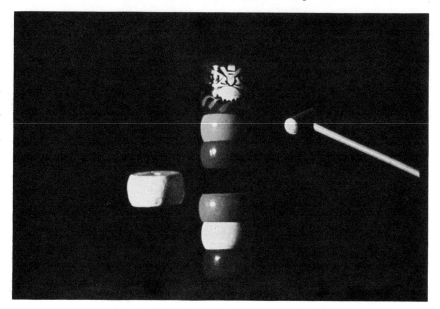

- It is more difficult to get a stalled car moving by pushing it than it is to keep it moving once it has started to coast along. Also, it is difficult to stop a stalled car that is coasting by pushing backwards on it. The car's inertia makes it difficult to move when stopped, and difficult to stop, when moving.

The amount of inertia an object possesses is related to its mass. In fact, an object's mass is a measure of its inertia, and vice versa. Section 4.4 will explain how to measure an object's mass by determining its ability to resist changes in its motion.

4.4 Newton's Law of Motion (Newton's Second Law)

Newton's Law of Inertia describes exactly how an object moves in the absence of any external unbalanced force — it moves with a constant velocity. It seems logical to assume, then, that when an external force is applied to an object its velocity changes. Is there a direct and simple relationship between the force applied to an object and the change in velocity that results?

Experiments can be devised to measure the change in velocity produced by various forces acting on different masses. Using experimental evidence such as that provided by investigations similar to the one at the end of this chapter, we can draw the following conclusions.

When an external, unbalanced force acts on an object, the object accelerates. The acceleration is in the same direction as the net force acting on the object.

The acceleration varies directly with the net force applied.
The acceleration varies inversely with the mass of the object.

These three statements embody what is called Newton's Law of Motion, or Newton's Second Law. Mathematically, the relationships between force, $\vec{F}$, mass, m, and acceleration, $\vec{a}$, may be written as:

$$\vec{a} \propto \vec{F} \qquad \text{if } m \text{ is constant}$$

$$\text{and} \qquad \vec{a} \propto \frac{1}{m} \qquad \text{if } \vec{F} \text{ is constant}$$

Combining these two proportionality statements, we have

$$\vec{a} \propto \frac{\vec{F}}{m}$$

or, inserting a proportionality constant, k, to produce an equation,

$$\vec{a} = k\frac{\vec{F}}{m}$$

which is more commonly written as

$$k\vec{F} = m\vec{a}$$

In SI units, mass is measured in kilograms and acceleration in metres per second per second. Up to this point, we have not needed to measure force, but we must do that now. The SI unit of force that is used in physics is the force needed to cause a mass of 1 kg to have an acceleration of 1 m/s². This amount of force is called a newton (1 N). If we substitute these values in the equation, we get

$$k\,(1\text{ N}) = (1\text{ kg})(1\text{ m/s}^2)$$

$$\text{or} \qquad k = 1\,\frac{\text{kg}\cdot\text{m/s}^2}{\text{N}}$$

Since, using these units for $\vec{F}$, m, and $\vec{a}$, the value of k will always be 1, it may be omitted from the equation. Thus, Newton's Law of Motion may be stated, mathematically, as:

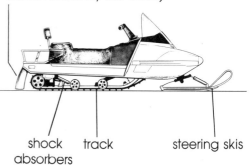

snow deflector
(protects those following from snow thrown back by the track)

shock absorbers   track   steering skis

The snowmobile is only one of many examples of the application of the laws of physics to the betterment of our quality of life.

The elegance of Newton's laws of motion lies in the fact that they apply universally, from the motion of the galaxies to that of subatomic particles.

$$\vec{F} = m\vec{a}$$

where $\vec{F}$ is the external, unbalanced force acting on an object (often called the "net" force, or the vector sum of all the forces acting), in newtons.

m is the mass of the object, in kilograms.

$\vec{a}$ is the acceleration of the object in the direction of the net force, in metres per second per second.

Also, the SI unit of force, the newton (N), is defined as follows:

1 N is the force that, when applied to a mass of 1 kg, produces an acceleration of 1 m/s².

$$1 \text{ N} = 1 \text{ kg·m/s}^2$$

It is interesting to note that Newton's First Law is just a special case of Newton's Second Law; when $\vec{F} = 0$, $\vec{a} = 0$; therefore $\vec{v}$ is constant. Newton's Second Law makes it possible to determine an object's mass by measuring its "accelerability", or the amount of force required to produce a given acceleration of the object. When mass is determined in this way, it is called "inertial mass". For example, if a force of 12 N causes an object to accelerate at 2.0 m/s², the object's inertial mass is

Can you see how the spin cycle in an automatic washer makes use of Newton's laws to separate much of the water from wet clothes?

$$m = \frac{\vec{F}}{\vec{a}}$$

$$= \frac{12 \text{ N}}{2.0 \text{ m/s}^2}$$

$$= 6.0 \text{ kg}$$

Chapter 5 will introduce another way of measuring an object's mass.

The only situation in nature in which there is only one force acting on an object is when an object is falling freely through a vacuum. In all other situations, more than one force is acting. For example, an object being accelerated across a horizontal, frictionless surface has three forces acting on it:

● the downward force of gravity on the object, $\vec{F}_g$

● the upward, supporting force of the surface, $\vec{F}_N$ or normal force

● the applied, horizontal, accelerating force, $\vec{F}_a$

In order to visualize how several forces acting simultaneously on an object can affect its motion, we may draw a **free-body diagram** of the object. There are a few simple rules to remember when drawing free-body diagrams:

- Draw a sketch of the object, completely removed from its physical surroundings.
- Represent each of the forces that are acting on the object in its physical surroundings by a force vector, showing the direction of each force and its magnitude.
- Do *not* include forces exerted on the surroundings by the object.
- Use the rules for vector addition to determine the net force acting on the object, in order to determine its acceleration. (Sometimes it is helpful to deal with specific components of the vectors in the equation $\vec{F} = m\vec{a}$.)

A free-body diagram of the object mentioned on the previous page would appear as shown.

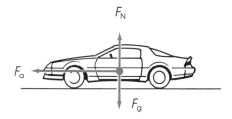

In cases such as this, $\vec{F_g}$ and $\vec{F_N}$ are equal in magnitude; their sum is zero, and the net force on the object, and hence its acceleration, is horizontal.

Three other typical free-body diagrams of familiar situations are illustrated.

An object sliding down an inclined plane: (a) smooth (b) with friction

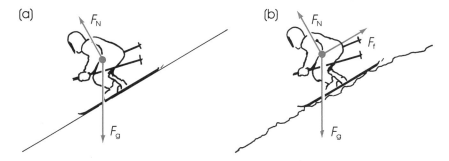

An object pulled across a rough horizontal surface by an applied force inclined at an angle to the horizontal

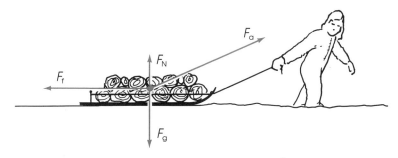

An object moving in a circular path at the end of a string

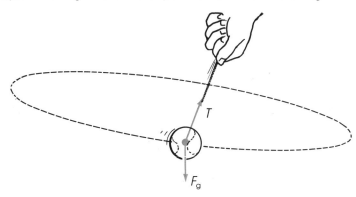

Sample problems

1. An object with a mass of 15 kg rests on a frictionless horizontal plane and is acted upon by a horizontal force of 30 N.
   (a) What is its acceleration?
   (b) How far will it move in 10 s?
   (c) What will be its velocity after 10 s?

   (a) Using Newton's Second Law,

   $$\vec{a} = \frac{\vec{F}_{net}}{m}$$

   $$= \frac{30 \text{ N}}{15 \text{ kg}}$$

   $= 2.0 \text{ m/s}^2$ in the direction of the applied horizontal force

   (b) Since the acceleration is constant, the equations of uniformly accelerated motion, from Chapter 2, may be used to describe its motion.

   $$\Delta \vec{d} = \vec{v}_1 \Delta t + \frac{1}{2} \vec{a} (\Delta t)^2$$

   $$= (0 \text{ m/s})(10 \text{ s}) + \frac{1}{2}(2.0 \text{ m/s}^2)(10 \text{ s})^2$$

   $$= 0 \text{ m} + 100 \text{ m}$$

   $= 100 \text{ m}$ in the direction of the applied horizontal force

   (c) $\vec{v}_2 = \vec{v}_1 + \vec{a}\Delta t$

   $$= 0 \text{ m/s} + (2.0 \text{ m/s}^2)(10 \text{ s})$$

   $= 20 \text{ m/s}$ in the direction of the applied horizontal force

2. A car with a mass of 1000 kg is moving in a straight line at a constant speed of 30 m/s. It is brought to rest in 25 s. What constant force is acting to stop the car?

Again, using the equations of uniformly accelerated motion to determine the car's acceleration (and choosing positive as the car's direction of motion),

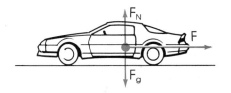

$$\vec{a} = \frac{\vec{\Delta v}}{\Delta t} = \frac{\vec{v_2} - \vec{v_1}}{\Delta t}$$

$$= \frac{0 \text{ m/s} - 30 \text{ m/s}}{25 \text{ s}}$$

$$= -1.2 \text{ m/s}^2$$

which represents a deceleration in the direction of motion of the car, as well as an acceleration in the opposite direction.

Then, applying Newton's Second Law,

$$\vec{F} = m\vec{a}$$

$$= (1000 \text{ kg})(-1.2 \text{ m/s}^2)$$

$$= -1200 \text{ N in the direction of motion of the car}$$

Note that, in this case, the force acting on the car is negative. A deceleration, or negative acceleration, is caused by a force in a direction opposite to the direction of motion, often called an "opposing force".

3. A baby carriage with a mass of 50 kg is being pushed along a rough sidewalk with an applied horizontal force of 200 N, and it has a constant velocity of 3.0 m/s.
   (a) What other horizontal force is acting on the carriage, and what is the magnitude of that force?
   (b) What value of applied horizontal force would be required to accelerate the carriage from rest to 7.0 m/s in 2.0 s?

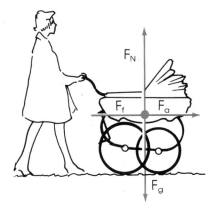

(a) The baby carriage is being pushed along a "rough" sidewalk; therefore, there must be some frictional force that is opposing its motion, between its wheels and the concrete. However, since the carriage is moving with a constant velocity (zero acceleration), according to Newton's Second Law the net force acting on it must be zero. Thus, the other force acting on the carriage is the force of friction, and its value is 200 N in the direction opposite to the carriage's motion.

(b) If we choose the direction of motion as positive, we may omit vector notation for this one-dimensional problem. The acceleration of the carriage is given by

$$a = \frac{v_2 - v_1}{\Delta t}$$

$$= \frac{7.0 \text{ m/s} - 0 \text{ m/s}}{2.0 \text{ s}}$$

$$= 3.5 \text{ m/s}^2$$

The net horizontal force in the direction of this acceleration is
$$F_{net} = F_a + F_f$$
$$= F_a - 200 \text{ N}$$
But, according to Newton's Second Law,
$$F_{net} = ma$$
$$= (50 \text{ kg})(3.5 \text{ m/s}^2)$$
$$= 175 \text{ N}$$
Therefore,
$$F_a - 200 \text{ N} = 175 \text{ N}$$
$$F_a = 375 \text{ N, or } 3.8 \times 10^2 \text{ N}$$

Practice

1. (a) What is the net force required to give an automobile of mass 1600 kg an acceleration of 4.5 m/s²?
   (b) What is the acceleration of a wagon of mass 20 kg if a horizontal force of 64 N is applied to it (ignore friction)?
   (c) What is the mass of a block of iron if a net force of 240 N causes it to accelerate across a smooth horizontal surface at 2.5 m/s²?   (7.2×10^3 N, 3.2 m/s², 96 kg)

2. A 1.0 kg toy car is moving across a smooth floor with a velocity of 5.0 m/s. An unbalanced force of 2.0 N acts on the car for 4.0 s. Determine the velocity of the car at the end of the interval in each of the following cases.
   (a) if the force acts in the direction of motion of the car
   (b) if the force acts in the opposite direction to the motion of the car   (13 m/s, -3.0 m/s)

3. An electron has a mass of 9.1×10^{-31} kg. Between the electrodes of a cathode-ray tube, it moves a distance of 4.0 mm, accelerated by a net electrical force of 5.6×10^{-15} N. Assuming that it started from rest, find its acceleration and its final velocity.   (6.2×10^{15} m/s², 7.0×10^6 m/s)

4. A bullet of mass 20 g strikes a fixed block of wood at a speed of 320 m/s. The bullet embeds itself in the block of wood, penetrating to a depth of 6.0 cm. Calculate the average net force acting on the bullet while it is being brought to rest.   (1.7×10^4 N)

5. A 0.50 kg skateboard is at rest on a rough, level floor on which two lines have been drawn 1.0 m apart. A constant horizontal force is applied to the skateboard at the beginning of the interval, and is removed at the end. The skateboard takes 8.5 s to travel the 1.0 m distance, and it then coasts for another 1.25 m before coming to rest. Calculate the force applied to the skateboard, and also the constant frictional force opposing its motion.   (2.6×10^{-2} N, 1.2×10^{-2} N)

4.5 The Vector Nature of Newton's Second Law

Newton's Second Law is a vector relationship, in that it states: "An object accelerates *in the direction* of the net force acting on it." In Section 4.4, the force acting to accelerate an object was always either in the object's direction of motion (so that its velocity increased but its direction remained the same) or in the opposite direction (so that its velocity decreased but its direction remained the same or was reversed). In what way will the velocity of a moving object change, if a force acts on it in a direction other than its direction of motion? Three sample problems are given next, to illustrate this.

Many areas in the fields of engineering and technology require a complete understanding of the relationship between force and motion. Even nontechnical areas of everyday life, such as moving on a slippery slope, can be explained.

Sample problem 1

A small boy pulls his wagon, of mass 24 kg, giving it a horizontal acceleration of 1.5 m/s². If the wagon's handle makes an angle of 40° with the ground while the boy is pulling on it, and there is a frictional force of 6.0 N opposing the wagon's motion, with what force is he pulling on the handle of the wagon?

The wagon will accelerate horizontally along the ground. To determine the force causing this acceleration, we should resolve the applied force, $\vec{F}$, into two rectangular components: $\vec{F_h}$ parallel to the ground, and $\vec{F_v}$ perpendicular to the ground.

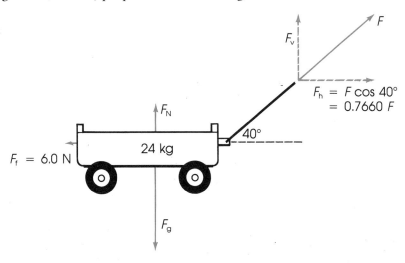

F

F_v

$F_h = F \cos 40°$
$\quad = 0.7660\ F$

40°

F_N

24 kg

$F_f = 6.0\ N$

F_g

The net force in the direction of motion of the wagon is given by

$$\vec{F}_{net} = \vec{F}_h + \vec{F}_f$$
$$= (0.7660\ F - 6.0)\ N$$

It is this value of force that gives the wagon a horizontal acceleration of 1.5 m/s².

$$\text{Since}\quad \vec{F}_{net} = m\vec{a}$$
$$(0.7660\ F - 6.0)\ N = (24\ kg)(1.5\ m/s^2)$$
$$= 36\ N$$
$$\text{Therefore,}\quad 0.7660\ F = 36\ N + 6.0\ N$$
$$F = \frac{42\ N}{0.7660}$$
$$= 54.8\ N,\ \text{or } 55\ N$$

Thus, the force applied by the boy to the wagon's handle is 55 N, at an angle of 40° up from the horizontal.

It is also interesting to note here that, since the wagon did not accelerate in the vertical direction (that is, it remained on the horizontal plane), the net force in the vertical direction must be zero.

$$\text{That is,}\quad \vec{F}_N + \vec{F}_v + \vec{F}_g = 0$$

Sample problem 2

Two girls are trying to pull a 20 kg toboggan out of a deep snow drift that provides an opposing force of 8.0 N. They are using ropes attached to the toboggan and parallel to the ground. The forces exerted by the girls, and the directions in which they pull on the ropes are shown, from above, in this diagram:

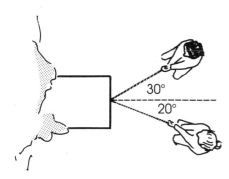

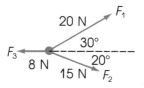

Find the acceleration of the toboggan, at the instant it starts to move.

According to Newton's Second Law, the force accelerating the toboggan is the net force acting on it externally. To find this *net force*, the three individual forces, $\vec{F}_1$, $\vec{F}_2$, and $\vec{F}_3$ must be added vectorially. The following scale diagram (or trigonometry) may be used.

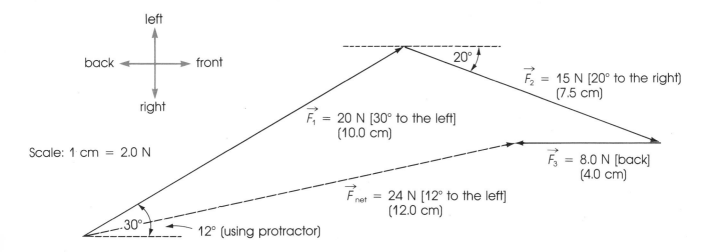

left

back ← → front

right

$\vec{F_2}$ = 15 N [20° to the right)
(7.5 cm)

$\vec{F_1}$ = 20 N [30° to the left]
(10.0 cm)

Scale: 1 cm = 2.0 N

$\vec{F_3}$ = 8.0 N [back]
(4.0 cm)

$\vec{F}_{net}$ = 24 N [12° to the left]
(12.0 cm)

30°

12° (using protractor)

20°

Therefore, the net force acting to accelerate the toboggan is

$$\vec{F}_{net} = 24 \text{ N}[12° \text{ to the left}]$$

$$\text{Then,} \quad \vec{a} = \frac{\vec{F}_{net}}{m}$$

$$= \frac{24 \text{ N}[12° \text{ to the left}]}{20 \text{ kg}}$$

$$= 1.2 \text{ m/s}^2 \text{ [12° to the left]}$$

Therefore, the instantaneous acceleration of the toboggan is 1.2 m/s² at an angle of 12° to the left of straight ahead.

Sample problem 3

A 40 kg wind-sled is gliding across a frozen lake with a constant velocity of 12 m/s[E], when a gust of wind from the southwest exerts a constant force of 100 N on its sails for 3.0 s. With what velocity will the sled be moving after the wind has subsided? Assume that there are no frictional forces in any direction.

Using Newton's Second Law,

$$\vec{a} = \frac{\vec{F}_{net}}{m}$$

$$= \frac{100 \text{ N[NE]}}{40 \text{ kg}}$$

$$= 2.5 \text{ m/s}^2\text{[NE]}$$

Note that the acceleration of the sled is in the same direction as the force acting on the sled.

But, we know that $\vec{a} = \dfrac{\Delta \vec{v}}{\Delta t}$ for an interval of uniform acceleration

$$\text{Therefore, } \Delta \vec{v} = \vec{a}\,\Delta t$$
$$= (2.5 \text{ m/s}^2[\text{NE}])(3.0 \text{ s})$$
$$= 7.5 \text{ m/s}[\text{NE}]$$

Also, the change in velocity is in the same direction as the force.

$$\text{However, } \Delta \vec{v} = \vec{v_2} - \vec{v_1}$$

$$\text{Therefore, } \vec{v_2} = \vec{v_1} + \Delta \vec{v}$$

Since $\vec{v_1}$ and $\Delta \vec{v}$ are vectors whose directions are not the same, this addition must be performed vectorially. The scale vector diagram or trigonometry may be used to find $\vec{v_2}$.

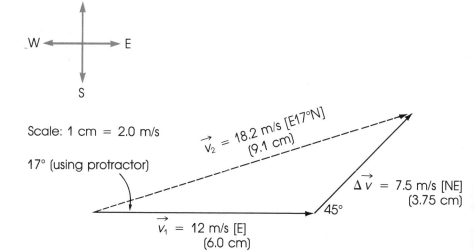

Thus, the final velocity of the wind-sled is 18 m/s[E17°N].

In all of these sample problems illustrating the vector nature of Newton's Second Law, there are three important points to remember:

● The direction of an object's acceleration, not necessarily its motion, is the same as the direction of the net force acting on the object.

● When more than one external force is acting on an object, the

Ingenious application of the laws of motion to the development of increasingly sophisticated machinery has reduced the need for physical labour, giving people more time for leisure activities.

object accelerates in the direction of the net force; this net force may be determined by the vector addition of all the individual forces that are acting on the object.

- When other forces acting on an object allow it to move only in a certain direction, then it is the net force in that direction that causes the acceleration.

Practice

1. Forces of 100 N[N] and 80 N[W] act simultaneously on an object of mass 10 kg. What is the acceleration of the object?

(13 m/s²[N39°W])

2. Forces of 2.0 N and 1.0 N act on an object of mass 5.0 kg, as shown in the diagram.

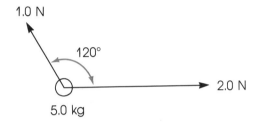

(a) Calculate the net force acting on the object.
(b) What is the acceleration of the object?

(1.7 N[E31°N], 0.34 m/s²[E31°N])

3. An empty railway flatcar of mass 15 000 kg is being pulled along a smooth, horizontal track by a tractor travelling on a road parallel to the track. The rope joining the tractor and the flatcar makes an angle of 25° with the track.

(a) If the acceleration of the flatcar is 0.80 m/s², what is the force exerted by the rope on the flatcar?
(b) Why does the flatcar have no sideways acceleration? A sideways force is exerted by the rope!

(1.3 × 10⁴ N[25° to track])

4. A block of mass 2.0 kg is placed on a smooth plane, inclined to the horizontal at an angle of 15°. The force of gravity, acting straight down on the block, is 20 N.

(a) What is the acceleration of the block down the plane?
(b) How far up the plane was the block released, if it took 1.5 s to reach the bottom after it was released from rest?

(2.6 m/s², 2.9 m)

5. A speedboat is pulling two water skiers, using two ropes attached to the back of the boat. Each rope makes an angle of 30° on either side of the boat's axis. The force exerted by each rope is 400 N. If the boat is moving in a straight line at constant speed, what force must it be exerting to keep the pair of skiers moving?

(693 N)

4.6 Newton's Third Law

When a balloon is blown up and then released, air rushing from the open nozzle causes the balloon to move off in the opposite direction. A skater, standing at the side of a skating rink, pushes against the boards and, as a result, glides off in the other direction, towards the centre of the ice. A soldier places a rifle against his shoulder and pulls the trigger. As the bullet speeds from the muzzle, the rifle is driven backward into the soldier's shoulder in a violent recoil.

These familiar situations are examples of a phenomenon that Newton summarized in his work on motion. We now call it Newton's Third Law of Motion:

For every action force, there exists a reaction force that is equal in magnitude but opposite in direction.

In simpler terms, this law means that whenever one object exerts a force on another object, the second object simultaneously exerts an equal force back on the first object, but in the opposite direction. For example, when a skater pushes against the boards of the rink (action force), the boards push back on the skater with an equal force but in the opposite direction (reaction force). This force causes the skater to move in the opposite direction from the one in which she originally pushed. Mathematically, we can write:

$$\vec{F}_{\text{skater-on-boards}} = -\vec{F}_{\text{boards-on-skater}}$$
$$\text{(action force)} \qquad \text{(reaction force)}$$

Similarly, the reaction force of a bullet backward on the rifle causes the rifle to move backward into the soldier's shoulder, and the reaction force of the air pushing on the inner surface of the rubber balloon causes it to move in the opposite direction to that of the escaping air.

In each of these cases, it is the reaction force that causes the described motion. No force in nature exists without its equal and opposite reaction force.

Practice

1. State the reaction force for each of the following forces.
   (a) the southward force of a field goal kicker's toe on a football
   (b) the backward force of a jogger's shoe on the ground
   (c) the downward force of a book on a desk
   (d) the backward force of a jet's engines on its exhaust gases
   (e) the backward pull of a swimmer's hands on the water in the butterfly stroke.

2. A beginning physics student, confused by a seeming contradiction in Newton's laws, asks her teacher the following question: "If, for every force there is an equal and opposite reaction force, then all forces in nature come in equal and opposite pairs, and are therefore balanced. Thus, since there can never be such a thing as an unbalanced force, how can any object ever accelerate?"

   Explain the fault in this common misconception.

3. A fireman at the scene of a fire is holding a heavy hose out of which water is gushing. To keep his balance, he often has to lean. Which way does he lean, forward or backward, and why?

4. A squirrel with an armful of nuts is sliding helplessly across a flat, icy roof, getting dangerously close to the edge. He understands Newton's Third Law, and is able to save himself. Explain how he does it.

5. A rocket carrying the Space Shuttle blasts off from the Kennedy Space Center. In which of the following positions will it have a greater acceleration, assuming that the engines exert a constant force?
   (a) at ground level
   (b) 50 m above ground level
   Explain your answer.

A very important application of Newton's Third Law is in rocket propulsion. Rockets burn fuel and eject the exhaust gases backward at high speeds. In doing so, the rocket's engines must exert large forces backward on these gases. The equal and opposite force of the exhaust gases on the rocket causes the rocket to accelerate forward. As a result, rockets can accelerate in empty space; they do not "push against" the atmosphere, as is often thought.

Space vehicles can manoeuvre in empty space simply by firing small rockets in the direction opposite to that in which they wish to accelerate. Of course, they would have to fire another rocket in the forward direction to eliminate the new velocity and establish final position.

When more than one object is being accelerated, Newton's Third Law must be used to determine how the applied force affects each of the accelerating objects.

Sample problem

A pull toy consists of three carts joined together by two short strings and with a longer string, for pulling, attached to the front cart. If a child pulls the toy with a horizontal force of 6.0 N, what force must each of the short strings be able to withstand?

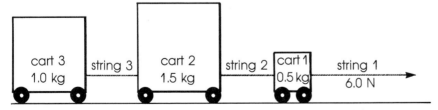

The total mass being accelerated is 3.0 kg, distributed among the three carts as indicated in the diagram. The net external force is 6.0 N, as shown. Assume vectors to the right are positive.

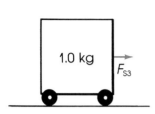

Therefore,
$$\vec{a} = \frac{\vec{F}_{net}}{m_{total}}$$
$$= \frac{6.0\ N}{3.0\ kg}$$
$$= 2.0\ m/s^2 \text{ for each cart}$$

Consider cart 3 first, since it has only the force of string 3 pulling on it.

Using Newton's Second Law

$$\vec{F}_{s3} = m_3 \vec{a}_3$$
$$= (1.0\ kg)(2.0\ m/s^2)$$
$$= 2.0\ N$$

This is the value of the force with which string 3 pulls forward on cart 3, as well as the force with which cart 3 pulls backward on string 3. It is also the force with which string 3 pulls backward on cart 2. It is usually called the tension in the string.

Now consider cart 2, with string 2 pulling forward on it and string 3 pulling backward on it, as shown. Let the force with which string 2 pulls forward on it be $\vec{F}_{s2}$.

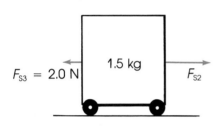

$$\vec{F}_{net} = \vec{F}_{s2} + \vec{F}_{s3}$$
$$= F_{s2} + (-2.0\ N) \text{ since } \vec{F}_{s3} \text{ is in the opposite}$$
$$\text{direction to the motio}$$
$$\text{but } \vec{F}_{net} = m\vec{a}$$
$$= (1.5\ kg)(2.0\ m/s^2)$$
$$= 3.0\ N$$
$$\text{therefore } F_{s2} - 2.0\ N = 3.0\ N$$
$$F_{s2} = 5.0\ N$$

As a final check, calculate the inertial mass of cart 1. String 1 pulls forward on it with a force of 6.0 N, while string 2 pulls backward on it with a force of 5.0 N, as shown.

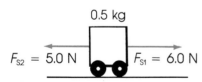

$$\vec{F}_{net} = \vec{F}_{s1} + \vec{F}_{s2}$$
$$= 6.0\ N + (-5.0\ N)$$
$$= 1.0\ N$$
$$m = \frac{F_{net}}{a}$$
$$= \frac{1.0\ N}{2.0\ m/s^2}$$
$$= 0.5\ kg$$

This is the value given originally for the mass of the first cart. Therefore, the first string must be able to withstand a force of 6.0 N, the second 5.0 N, and the third 2.0 N.

Practice

1. Two girls, one of mass 40 kg and the other of mass 60 kg, are standing side by side in the middle of a frozen pond. One pushes the other with a force of 360 N for 0.10 s. The ice is essentially frictionless.
   (a) What is each girl's acceleration?
   (b) What velocity will each girl acquire in the 0.10 s that the force is acting?
   (c) How far will each girl move during the same time period?
   (9.0 m/s², − 6.0 m/s²; 0.90 m/s, − 0.60 m/s; 4.5 × 10⁻² m, − 3.0 × 10⁻² m)

2. Two crates, of mass 12.0 kg and 20.0 kg, respectively, are pushed across a smooth floor together, the 20 kg crate in front of the 12 kg crate. Their acceleration is 1.75 m/s². Calculate each of the following.
   (a) the force applied to push the crates
   (b) the action-reaction forces between the two crates
   (56.0 N, 35.0 N)
   Recalculate (a) and (b) if the relative positions of the two crates are reversed.

3. A locomotive with a mass of 2.0 × 10⁴ kg accelerates from rest to a velocity of 2.0 m/s in 5.0 s. If it is pulling a train of 20 cars, each of mass 1.0 × 10⁴ kg, what is the force in the coupling at each of the following points?
   (a) between the locomotive and the first car
   (b) between the 10th car and the 11th car
   (8.0 × 10⁴ N, 4.0 × 10⁴ N)

4. Three small children of mass 20.0 kg, 24.0 kg, and 16.0 kg, respectively, hold hands, as shown, and are pulled across a smooth frozen pond by a larger boy on skates, who pulls a horizontal rope being held by the first child. The skater pulls on the rope with a force of 135 N. Calculate each of the following.
   (a) the acceleration of the skater
   (b) the force with which each pair of children must hold hands, to ensure that the chain is not broken
   (2.25 m/s²; 90.0 N, 36.0 N)

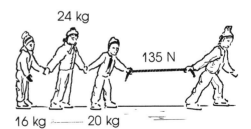

4.7 Investigations

Investigation 4.1: Newton's Second Law

Problem:
What is the relationship between an object's mass, its acceleration, and the net force applied to it?

Materials:
dynamics cart
2 additional masses (such as bricks) that have approximately the
  same mass as the cart
3 large, identical elastic bands
metre stick (notched at one end)
recording timer
supply of ticker tape for recording timer
spring scale (calibrated in newtons)

Procedure:

1. Clamp the recording timer at one end of a long, level table.
2. Loop one end of one of the elastic bands around a hook on the dynamics cart, and loop the other end in the notch at the end of the metre stick. Practise accelerating the cart across the table by pushing on the metre stick with a steady force, so that the stretched elastic band actually pulls the cart (see illustration). A constant stretching of the elastic band will indicate that you are exerting a constant force on the metre stick. After several practice runs, select an amount of stretching of the elastic band that you can comfortably maintain; use this amount of stretching, and hence this amount of force, throughout this experiment.

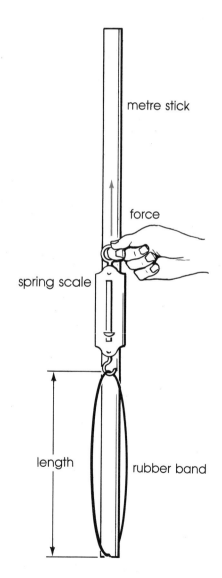

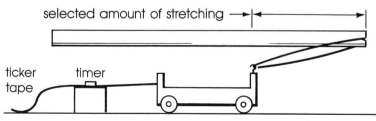

3. With one end of the elastic band hooked in the notch on the metre stick, pull the other end out to the previously selected length, using the spring scale. Measure and record, in newtons, the amount of force required to stretch the elastic band to this length.

Part A: The relationship between acceleration and force, with mass constant

4. Attach a piece of ticker tape to the back end of the cart and feed it through the timer. Position the cart in front of the timer, with the free end of the ticker tape hanging loose over the edge of the table.

5. Loop the stretched elastic band over the cart and the metre stick, as you did in the practice runs, and have your partner hold the cart to keep it from moving. Make sure that the elastic band is stretched to the selected length.

6. On a signal, have your partner start the timer and then release the cart. Accelerate the cart the full length of the table, pushing on the metre stick and maintaining the elastic band at the selected length.

7. Repeat the entire procedure, using first two and then three stretched elastic bands in parallel to accelerate the cart. Ensure that the elastic bands are always stretched to exactly the selected length during the run. Label and save each of the three ticker tapes for later analysis.

Part B: The relationship between acceleration and mass, with force constant

8. Again, repeat the entire procedure, using a constant force of two stretched bands, accelerating the cart first with one brick on it and then with two bricks on it. Label and save these tapes for later analysis.

Calculations:

1. Analyse each of the five tapes to determine the acceleration of the cart (and bricks). Use the procedure given in investigations 2.1 and 2.2 to plot a velocity-time graph from each tape, and then determine the average acceleration by finding the slope of the velocity-time graph.

2. Record all of the measured and calculated data in a chart similar to the one that follows.

    Mass of cart = _____ kg   Mass of each brick = _____ kg
    Force required to stretch one band to selected length = _____ N

	Mass being accelerated		Force causing acceleration		Average acceleration (from ticker tape)
		(kg)		(N)	(m/s²)
Part A:	cart		1 elastic		
	cart		2 elastics		
	cart		3 elastics		
Part B:	*cart		2 elastics		
	cart + 1 brick		2 elastics		
	cart + 2 bricks		2 elastics		

*Note that this line is a repeat of the second tape in part A.

3. Using the results of part A, plot a graph of force ($\vec{F}$) versus acceleration ($\vec{a}$) for one cart. Plot $\vec{a}$ horizontally. From your graph, determine the slope of the curve. What does this slope represent?

4. Using the results of part B, plot a graph of mass m versus acceleration $\vec{a}$, plotting m horizontally. Describe the type of relationship between $\vec{a}$ and m that is indicated by this graph. Redraw the graph, this time plotting $\vec{a}$ versus $\frac{1}{m}$. Determine the slope of this graph. What does this slope represent?

5. Using all of the results from both parts, draw a graph of $\frac{\vec{F}}{m}$ versus $\vec{a}$, plotting $\frac{\vec{F}}{m}$ horizontally. What is the slope of this graph?

Questions:

1. By observing the graph of $\vec{a}$ versus $\vec{F}$ for a constant mass of one cart, state the relationship between the force applied to an object and the object's acceleration.

2. By observing the graph of $\vec{a}$ versus m for a constant force of two stretched bands, state the relationship between the mass of an object and its acceleration.

3. What is the slope of the graph of $\vec{a}$ versus $\frac{\vec{F}}{m}$? From this graph and a knowledge of its slope, state the relationship between $\vec{F}$, m, and $\vec{a}$.

4. The graph of $\vec{a}$ versus $\vec{F}$ should pass through the origin, indicating that when no force is exerted on an object the object does not accelerate. Many graphs of $\vec{a}$ versus $\vec{F}$ do not pass

through the origin, but appear as shown in the diagram. Explain why this is so, and state the significance of the point where the graph intersects the $\vec{F}$ axis.

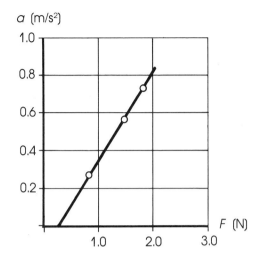

4.8 Review

Discussion

1. In an air hockey game, the discs float on a thin layer of air flowing from a large number of equally spaced holes in the table. Friction is reduced to a minimum. Explain the motions of a "puck" during a typical game, using Newton's three laws.
2. Whiplash injuries are common in automobile accidents where the victim's car is struck from behind. Explain how Newton's Laws apply in this situation and how injuries can be reduced by considering these laws in car seat design.
3. Why does a child on a toboggan fall backward when the toboggan is given a sharp tug?
4. If you get to your feet in a canoe and move towards the front, the canoe moves in the opposite direction. Explain why.
5. Why does your toe hurt when you kick a football?
6. Why must an object at rest have either no force or a minimum of two forces acting on it?
7. "Should car seat belts and air bags be mandatory?" Discuss this topic in 400 words or less, including in your discussion the related physics, the social and economic benefits to society, and the issue of human rights.

Problems

8. A 3.0 kg toy is pulled by a force of 24 N. If the toy starts from rest, how far will it travel in the first 5.0 s?
9. A 40 kg sprinter starts from rest and 2.0 s later is running at a speed of 8.0 m/s. What is the average net horizontal force acting on her? What exerts this force?
10. An 8.0 g bullet travelling at 400 m/s passes through a heavy block of wood in 4.0×10^{-4} s, emerging with a velocity of 100 m/s. Ignore any motion of the wood.
    (a) With what average force did the wood oppose the motion of the bullet?
    (b) How thick is the block of wood?

Most modern car seat belts have an "inertial" mechanism that allows the passenger freedom of movement under normal conditions but holds the belt tightly in place during extreme deceleration. Can you suggest how this mechanism might work? Perhaps you could take a belt apart to discover its secret; but make sure you put it back together.

Many track and field events involve Newton's Third Law. A high jumper extends her contracted leg muscles to push down as hard as possible on the ground. The ground exerts an equal force in the opposite direction on her, causing her to accelerate up and over the bar. What other track and field events make use of the reaction to the force exerted by the athlete?

Numerical Answers to Review Problems

8. 1.0×10^2 m
9. 1.6×10^2 N[F]
10. (a) -6.0×10^3 N[F] (b) 1.0×10^{-1} m
11. 9.0×10^2 N[F]
12. yes, by 3.0 m
13. 44 kg
14. (a) 6.3 m/s[F] (b) 1.1 s
15. 1.3 m/s²[F]
17. 2.5 m/s²[F]
18. 29°
19. 1.4 m/s² [E5.6°S]
20. 2.0×10^2N, 2.0×10^2N, -6.7 m/s²
21. (a) 3.2×10^2 m (b) 4 000 N
22. (a) 5.0 kg (b) friction force of 0.60 N

11. A 0.22 calibre rifle shoots a bullet of mass 1.8 g with a muzzle velocity of 500 m/s. If the barrel is 25 cm long, what is the average force exerted on the bullet while it is in the barrel?

12. A motorist has a reaction time of 0.60 s. (Reaction time is the interval between seeing a danger and applying the brakes.) While driving at 72 km/h, he sees a child run suddenly onto the road, 40 m in front of his car. If the mass of the car is 1000 kg and the average horizontal force supplied during braking is 8000 N, will he be able to stop in time to avoid hitting the child?

13. A child's wagon experiences a frictional force of 73 N whenever it is in motion, regardless of the load it is carrying. An applied horizontal force of 128 N causes the wagon to accelerate at 5.0 m/s². The same applied force, with a child on the wagon, causes it to accelerate at 1.0 m/s². What is the mass of the child?

14. A sled of 6.0 kg mass is moving along a smooth, horizontal ice surface with a velocity of v_0. A force of 36 N is applied to the sled in its direction of motion, increasing its velocity to $2\,v_0$ while it moves 10 m. Find (a) the sled's original velocity, v_0, and (b) the length of time that the force acted.

15. A net force of 8.0 N gives a mass m_1 an acceleration of 2.0 m/s² and a mass m_2 an acceleration of 4.0 m/s². What acceleration would the force give the two masses if they were fastened together?

16. The graph shows the velocity of a 5.0 kg radio-controlled toy car, moving in a straight line, as a function of time. Plot a force-time graph for the car.

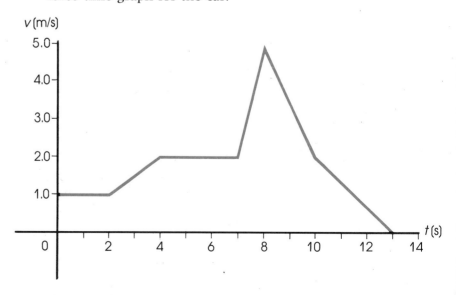

17. A gardener pushes down along the handle of a lawn mower of 20 kg mass with a force of 150 N. The handle makes an angle of 60° with the ground. Calculate the instantaneous acceleration of the mower if the frictional force between its wheels and the ground at that instant is 25 N.

18. A man drags a package across the floor with a force of a 40 N, as shown. The mass of the package is 10 kg. If the acceleration of the package is 3.5 m/s², and friction can be neglected, at what angle to the horizontal does the man pull?

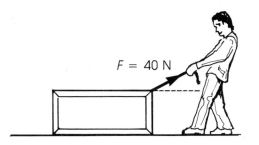

19. Two girls pull a sled across a field of snow, as shown in the diagram. A third girl pulls backward with a 2.0 N force. If the mass of the sled is 10 kg, determine its instantaneous acceleration.

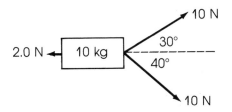

20. A boy with a mass of 30 kg pulls a cart with a mass of 100 kg towards himself by a rope. With what force does he have to pull on the rope to accelerate the cart at 2.0 m/s²? With what force must his feet push on the ground to keep him from moving towards the cart? If there is no friction between his feet and the ground, what is his acceleration?

21. A plane takes off from a level runway with two gliders in tow, one behind the other. The first glider has a mass of 1600 kg and the second a mass of 800 kg. The frictional drag may be assumed as constant and equal to 2000 N on each glider. The towrope between the first glider and the plane can withstand a tension of 10 000 N.

    (a) If a velocity of 40 m/s is required for takeoff, how long a runway is needed?

    (b) How strong must the towrope between the two gliders be?

22. A cart is pulled in each of several trials, with a different number of stretched elastic bands. A constant acceleration is observed in each trial. The graph shows acceleration versus force exerted by the stretched bands.

    (a) What is the mass of the cart?

    (b) An extrapolation of the graph does not pass through the origin. What does this indicate?

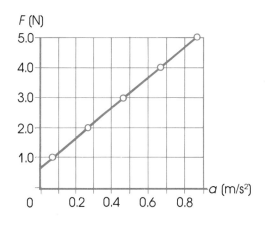

5 Motion Near the Earth's Surface

5.1 Gravitational Forces

The gravitational force field surrounding the Earth.

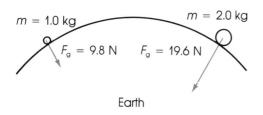

In the case of gravitational force fields, the forces are always attractive, never repulsive.

Based on our knowledge of Newton's Laws of Motion and our everyday experience, we assume that when a body is accelerating a force must be present to cause the acceleration. In most cases, up to now, we have dealt with forces that are in direct contact with the object being accelerated. But the forces need not be "contact" forces. They can be forces "acting at a distance", such as magnetic, electrical, nuclear, and gravitational forces. Newton's laws hold for all forces, whether "contact" or "non-contact".

When a ball is dropped from the top of a building it accelerates downward at approximately 9.8 m/s². Since it accelerates, a force must be acting on it. The force is the gravitational force of the Earth. We use the symbol F_g for the gravitational force. Near the Earth, the magnitude of this force is relatively constant for a given object, varying only by approximately 2%. (See chart on next page.) An object having a mass of 1.0 kg will experience a gravitational force of 9.8 N at the Earth's surface. We call the ratio of gravitational force to mass the **gravitational field constant**, and represent it by the symbol "g". Thus, the value of g is 9.8 N/kg at the Earth's surface, with the gravitational force always acting towards the centre of the Earth.

We say there is a field of gravitational force surrounding the Earth. The strength of the gravitational force field at any point is equal to the force it exerts on a 1 kg mass at that point. In other words, near the Earth's surface the gravitational field strength is 9.8 N/kg, always towards the centre of the Earth. We represent it as a vector.

If a mass is released near the Earth, the gravitational force causes the mass to accelerate in a straight line towards the centre of the Earth, as illustrated. The arrows represent the magnitude and direction of the force field.

For a mass of 1.0 kg the force of gravity is 9.8 N. For a mass of 2.0 kg the force of gravity would be 19.6 N, as illustrated.

To determine the gravitational force on any object we simply multiply the mass of the object by the gravitational field constant as follows:

$$\vec{F}_g = m\vec{g}$$

where $\vec{F}_g$ is the force of gravity, in newtons
   m is the mass, in kilograms

   $\vec{g}$ is the gravitational field constant,
   in newtons per kilogram
   The subscript g will remind us that this force always acts towards
the centre of the Earth.

Latitude (°)	g^* (N/kg)	Distance to centre (km)*
0 (equator)	9.7805	6378
15	9.7839	6377
30	9.7934	6373
45	9.8063	6367
60	9.8192	6362
75	9.8287	6358
90 (North Pole)	9.8322	6357

*all measurements made at sea level

Sample problem

What is the force of gravity acting on a 1000 kg car resting on the
Earth?

$$\vec{F}_g = m\vec{g}$$
$$= (1000 \text{ kg})(9.8 \text{ N/kg})$$
$$= 9.8 \times 10^3 \text{ N[down]}$$

Location	Latitude (°)	g at sea level (N/kg)	Altitude (m)	g (N/kg)
Toronto	44	9.8054	162	9.8049
Mt. Everest	28	9.7919	8848	9.7647
Dead Sea	32	9.7950	−397	9.7962

Practice
1. What is the force of gravity at the Earth's surface on
    (a) a 50 kg girl, and
    (b) a 100 g bullet?
                                    $(4.9 \times 10^2 \text{ N}, 0.98 \text{ N})$
2. If the gravitational field constant on the surface of the moon
    is 1.6 N/kg, what is the force of gravity on the two masses in
    the previous question, if they are on the surface of the moon?
                                    (80 N, 0.16 N)

Planet	g	Relative to Earth (Earth = 1)
Mercury	3.52 N/kg	0.36
Venus	8.52 N/kg	0.87
Mars	3.72 N/kg	0.38
Earth	9.81 N/kg	1.00
Jupiter	26.10 N/kg	2.66
Saturn	11.07 N/kg	1.12
Uranus	10.49 N/kg	1.07
Neptune	13.80 N/kg	1.40
Pluto	0.31 N/kg	0.032
Moon	1.61 N/kg	0.16

5.2 Weight

The term "weight" is used in everyday conversation as if it were
the same thing as mass. In physics, we define weight as the gravitational force acting on a mass. Since weight is a force, its units
will be force units, i.e., newtons, and it will be a vector quantity.

$$\text{weight} = \vec{F}_g$$
$$\vec{F}_g = m\vec{g}$$

Mass never changes. Weight varies
with g.

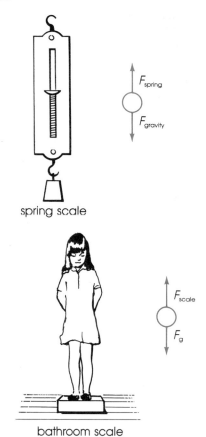

spring scale

bathroom scale

Again, since $\vec{g}$ always acts in the same direction, it is acceptable to omit the vector notation.

The weight of a 60 kg girl at the Earth's surface will be the force of gravity acting on a mass of 60 kg, or 588 N (60 kg × 9.8 N/kg). As long as a force of gravity is present, an object has weight. Whether you are sitting, standing, flying, falling, or even orbiting the Earth in a space vehicle, you have weight, since the force of gravity is present. One place where you would have no weight is interstellar space, where you would be so far removed from other objects that the force of gravity would approach zero.

Weight is often measured using a spring scale. The object whose weight is being measured is pulled down by the force of gravity until the upward force of the spring is equal to the gravitational force pulling down. The value of the force exerted by the spring, indicated by the pointer, is thus a measure of the weight of the object. Even though the two forces are in opposite directions, they are equal in magnitude and sum to zero.

In a similar way, if you stand on a bathroom scale, the pointer indicates the upward force exerted on you by the scale. This force is equal in magnitude but in the opposite direction to the force of gravity on your mass.

Now let us assume, for the sake of argument, that you are standing on a bathroom scale in an elevator. When the elevator is at rest, the force of the scale's springs is equal in magnitude to the force of gravity acting on you. On the other hand, if the elevator cable suddenly snaps and the elevator falls freely, the needle of the scale will soon read zero, indicating that there is no force exerted on you by the scale. You might say, "I'm weightless", which would be technically wrong. Your weight has not changed. The force of gravity is still there. All that has happened is that your weight is no longer supported by an external force — the scale — and you are accelerating downward.

Sample problem

A 75 kg man stands in an elevator. What will be the force the elevator exerts on him when (a) the elevator is at rest, (b) the elevator is moving upward with a uniform acceleration of 2.0 m/s², and (c) the elevator is moving downward with a uniform acceleration of 2.0 m/s²?

In each case, draw a free-body diagram of the man. Only two forces will act on him; the force of gravity (F_g) downward and the force of the elevator (F_e) upward. F_g will always be

If the man is standing on a bathroom scale, the answers to (a), (b), and (c) will be the actual scale readings, assuming that the scale is calibrated in newtons.

$$\vec{F}_g = m\vec{g}$$
$$= (75 \text{ kg})(9.8 \text{ N/kg[down]})$$
$$= 735 \text{ N [down]}$$

The value of $\vec{F}_e$ will change.

(a) $\vec{F}_{net} = \vec{F}_e + \vec{F}_g = m\vec{a}$

But both the elevator and the man are at rest, so $\vec{a} = 0$.

$$\vec{F}_e + \vec{F}_g = 0$$
$$\text{or} \quad \vec{F}_e = -\vec{F}_g$$

Taking vertical components, with up as positive,
$$F_e = -(-735 \text{ N}) = 735 \text{ N}$$

$$\text{or} \quad \vec{F}_e = 735 \text{ N [up]}$$

In other words, the force of the elevator on the man is equal but opposite in direction to the force of gravity on the man.

(b) If the elevator is accelerating upward at 2.0 m/s², so is the man. Thus, the net force will be in the same direction as the acceleration, that is, upward.

$$\vec{F}_{net} = \vec{F}_e + \vec{F}_g = m\vec{a}$$
$$\vec{F}_e = m\vec{a} - \vec{F}_g$$

Taking vertical components,
$$F_e = (75 \text{ kg})(2.0 \text{ m/s}^2) - (-735 \text{ N})$$
$$= 150 \text{ N} + 735 \text{ N}$$
$$= 885 \text{ N}$$

$$\text{or } \vec{F}_e = 8.9 \times 10^2 \text{ N [up]}$$

(c) When the elevator is accelerating downward, the net force on the man is downward as well.

$$\vec{F}_{net} = \vec{F}_e + \vec{F}_g = m\vec{a}$$
$$\vec{F}_e = m\vec{a} - \vec{F}_g$$

. Taking vertical components,
$$F_e = (75 \text{ kg})(-2.0 \text{ m/s}^2) - (-735 \text{ N})$$
$$= -150 \text{ N} + 735 \text{ N}$$
$$= 585 \text{ N}$$

$$\text{or } \vec{F}_e = 5.9 \times 10^2 \text{ N [up]}$$

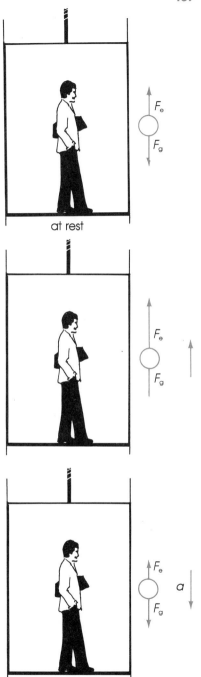

The fact that the tension is the same throughout the length of the string is a direct result of the first assumption. In the free-body diagram, T_1 and T_2 are the tension forces at each end of the string. When Newton's Second Law is applied to the string,

$$\vec{F}_{net} = \vec{T}_1 + \vec{T}_2 = m\vec{a}$$

But $m = 0$, since the string is massless.

Therefore $\vec{T}_1 + \vec{T}_2 = 0$

and $\vec{T}_i = -\vec{T}_2$

or $T_1 = T_2$

Practice

1. A passenger in an elevator has a mass of 100 kg. Calculate the force, in newtons, exerted on the passenger by the elevator, if the elevator is (a) at rest, (b) moving with an upward acceleration of 30 cm/s², (c) moving with a downward acceleration of 15 cm/s², (d) moving upward with a uniform velocity of 15 cm/s, and (e) falling freely (the cable breaks).

   (980 N[up], 1010 N[up], 965 N[up], 980 N[up], 0 N)

2. An elevator, complete with contents, has a mass of 2000 kg. By drawing free-body diagrams and by performing the necessary calculations, determine the value of T (the tension in the elevator cable) when (a) the elevator is at rest, (b) the elevator is moving upward at a constant velocity of 2.0 m/s, (c) the elevator is moving downward at a constant velocity of 2.0 m/s, (d) the elevator is accelerating upward at 1.0 m/s², and (e) the elevator is accelerating downward at 1.0 m/s².

   (2.0 × 10⁴ N, 2.0 × 10⁴ N, 2.0 × 10⁴ N, 2.2 × 10⁴ N, 1.8 × 10⁴ N)

3. A man measures the acceleration of an elevator by using a spring balance. He fastens the scale to the roof, and suspends a mass from it. If the scale reads 98 N when the elevator is at rest, and 93 N when the elevator is moving, (a) what is the acceleration of the elevator? (b) in which direction is the elevator accelerating?   (0.50 m/s², down)

5.3 Strings, Pulleys, and Gravity

There are many situations where the gravitational force acting on one object indirectly produces motion in another object. In some cases, a falling object is connected to another object by a light string or rope passing over a nearly frictionless pulley.

To understand this type of motion, we make the following assumptions about strings and pulleys:

- Strings are considered to have negligible mass and are capable of exerting only "pulling" forces on objects to which they are attached (tension forces).
- Strings transmit forces undiminished: the tension force in a string is the same throughout its length.
- A frictionless pulley changes the direction of a string without diminishing its tension.
- Strings are assumed not to stretch.

A few sample problems will illustrate how these assumptions are applied in problems involving strings and pulleys.

Sample problems

1. A 2.0 kg mass, placed on a smooth, level table, is attached by a light string passing over a frictionless pulley to a 5.0 kg mass hanging freely over the edge of the table, as illustrated. Calculate (a) the tension in the string, and (b) the acceleration of the 2.0 kg mass.

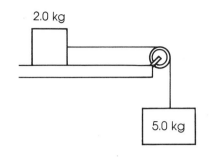

The 2.0 kg mass will accelerate to the right at the same rate at which the 5.0 kg mass accelerates downward. If we let the tension force in the string be T, the free-body diagrams for the masses are as shown.

Since the masses will move at right angles to one another, for the sake of simplification the normal sign convention and vector notation have not been used in this solution.

(a) Using Newton's Law of Motion,

$$a_1 = \frac{F_{net}}{m_1} \qquad\qquad a_2 = \frac{F_{net}}{m_2}$$

$$= \frac{T}{2.0 \text{ kg}} \qquad\qquad = \frac{49 \text{ N} - T}{5.0 \text{ kg}}$$

but
$$a_1 = a_2$$

therefore
$$\frac{T}{2.0 \text{ kg}} = \frac{49 \text{ N} - T}{5.0 \text{ kg}}$$

$$5.0\,T = 98 \text{N} - 2.0\,T$$

$$T = 14 \text{ N}$$

(b)
$$a_1 = \frac{T}{m_1} = a_2$$

$$= \frac{14 \text{ N}}{2.0 \text{ kg}}$$

$$= 7.0 \text{ m/s}^2$$

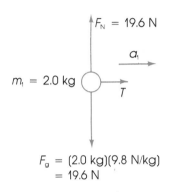

Alternate Solution:

Although the foregoing solution is preferred, there is a shorter solution to this problem, which follows. This is a one-dimensional problem if we take positive motion along the string directed to the right above the pulley and downward below the pulley. The only external accelerating force in these directions is the force of gravity acting downward on the 5.0 kg mass.

$$F_g = mg$$

$$= (5.0 \text{ kg})(9.8 \text{ N/kg})$$

$$= 49 \text{ N}$$

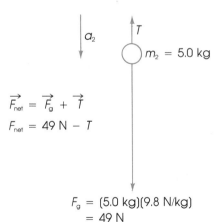

The total mass being accelerated is 2.0 kg + 5.0 kg = 7.0 kg

$$a = \frac{F_{net}}{m_{total}}$$

$$= \frac{49 \text{ N}}{7.0 \text{ kg}}$$

$$= 7.0 \text{ m/s}^2$$

Considering the 5.0 kg mass only, the net force causing it to accelerate downward is given by

$$F_{net} = ma$$

$$= (5.0 \text{ kg})(7.0 \text{ m/s}^2)$$

$$= 35 \text{ N}$$

To find the tension, we analyse the net forces on the 5.0 kg mass.

$$\vec{F}_{net} = \vec{F}_g + \vec{T}$$

$$35 \text{ N} = 49 \text{ N} - T$$

$$T = 14 \text{ N}$$

The tension can also be determined by considering the 2.0 kg mass (m_1).

$$T = F_{net}$$

$$= m_1 a$$

$$= (2.0 \text{ kg})(7.0 \text{ m/s}^2)$$

$$= 14 \text{ N}$$

The only reason that this alternate solution is valid is that all the other external forces acting on the string and pulley are at right angles to the axis of the string.

$m_1 = 1.5$ kg

$m_2 = 3.0$ kg

a_1

T

F_g

$F_{g_1} = (1.5 \text{ kg})(9.8 \text{ N/kg})$
$= 14.7$ N

T

a_2

$F_{g_2} = (3.0 \text{ kg})(9.8 \text{ N/kg})$
$= 29.4$ N

F_g

2. Two spheres of masses 1.5 kg and 3.0 kg are tied together by a light string looped over a frictionless pulley. They are allowed to hang freely. What will be the acceleration of each mass? Assume that up is positive and down is negative.

For m_1
the net force on m_1 is

$$\vec{F}_{net} = \vec{T} + \vec{F}_g$$

$$F_{net} = T - 14.7 \text{ N}$$

The acceleration of m_1 is

$$\vec{a} = \frac{\vec{F}_{net}}{m_1}$$

$$a = \frac{T - 14.7 \text{ N}}{1.5 \text{ kg}}$$

For m_2
the net force on m_2 is

$$\vec{F}_{net} = \vec{T} + \vec{F}_g$$

$$F_{net} = T - 29.4 \text{ N}$$

The acceleration of m_2 is

$$\vec{a} = \frac{\vec{F}_{net}}{m_2}$$

$$a = \frac{T - 29.4\ N}{3.0\ kg}$$

The accelerations of the masses have the same magnitude, but opposite directions.

Thus $\quad \dfrac{T - 14.7\ N}{1.5\ kg} = -\left(\dfrac{T - 29.4\ N}{3.0\ kg}\right)$

$$= \frac{29.4\ N - T}{3.0\ kg}$$

$$T = 19.6\ N$$

The acceleration of each mass is the same. Substituting for m_1 the acceleration is

$$a = \frac{T - 14.7\ N}{1.5\ kg}$$

$$= 3.3\ m/s^2$$

If we had initially assumed that m_1 accelerated downward, we would find that $a_1 = -3.3\ m/s^2$. Try it!

Practice

1. A 5.0 kg mass rests on a level, frictionless table, attached to a 3.0 kg mass by a light string that passes over a frictionless pulley. Calculate the tension in the string when the masses are released.
(18 N)

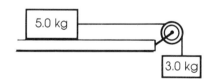

2. A 40 kg block on a level, frictionless table is connected to a 15 kg mass by a rope passing over a frictionless pulley. What will be the acceleration of the 15 kg mass when it is released?
($2.7\ m/s^2$)

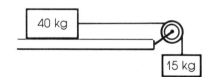

3. A 3.0 kg mass is attached to a 5.0 kg mass by a strong string that passes over a frictionless pulley. When the masses are allowed to hang freely, what will be (a) the acceleration of the masses, and (b) the magnitude of the tension in the string?
($2.4\ m/s^2$, 37 N)

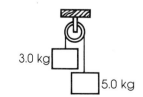

5.4 Friction

In earlier chapters of this book it was convenient to assume that objects moved over frictionless surfaces. But now, since friction acts to oppose motion, we must examine the effects of frictional force between two surfaces, where one surface moves over the other.

One factor that affects the magnitude of a frictional force is the nature of the surfaces in contact. Even the smoothest looking surface appears quite irregular when viewed through a microscope. When one such surface slides over another similar surface, the various projections from the two surfaces catch one another, opposing the sliding motion. On the other hand, if very smooth surfaces slide over one another, for example, two pieces of glass, the molecules in one piece act on those in the other, creating forces of cohesion. This tends to hold the two pieces together, and likewise opposes the sliding motion.

For any given pair of surfaces, the force of friction always acts opposite to the direction of motion or attempted motion. It was Leonardo da Vinci who discovered that the force of friction along a horizontal surface is directly proportional to the weight of an object resting on it. Nowadays, we say that the force of friction is directly proportional to the normal force (F_N) between the two surfaces. (The normal force is the force that one body exerts on another, and vice versa, perpendicular to the common surface of contact.)

Stated mathematically:

$$F_f \propto F_N$$

$$\text{or } F_f = \mu F_N$$

where: F_f is the force of friction, in newtons

F_N is the normal force, in newtons

μ is the constant of proportionality, called the coefficient of friction. It has no units.

The value of the coefficient of friction (μ) depends only on the nature of the two surfaces in contact. It does not depend on the speed with which the surfaces move over one another, nor is it affected by the extent of the area in contact. Measured values of coefficients of friction for a variety of surfaces are given in the following table.

Coefficients of Friction*

Surface	Coefficient of static friction (μ_s)	Coefficient of kinetic friction (μ_k)
oak on oak, dry	0.40	0.30
waxed hickory on dry snow	0.22	0.18
steel on steel, dry	0.60	0.41
lubricated	0.15	0.12
steel on ice		0.010
rubber on asphalt, dry		1.07
wet		0.95
rubber on concrete, dry		1.02
wet		0.97
rubber on ice		0.005

* Values are approximate and intended as a guide only.

The value for the coefficient of friction also depends on whether we are dealing with static ("at rest") friction or kinetic ("moving") friction. The coefficient of static friction (μ_s) is used when describing the maximum frictional force that must be overcome just to start an object sliding over a specific surface. Once the object is moving, the frictional force required to maintain motion usually decreases. As a result, the values for the coefficient of kinetic friction (μ_k) are lower than those for static friction.

Static frictional forces exist only when there is an external force acting on an object. When there is no external force, the force of static friction is zero. Thus the force of static friction can have any value from zero up to $\mu_s F_N$. Kinetic friction has only the value given by $\mu_k F_N$. To summarize:

$$\text{Static friction} \quad F_f \leq \mu_s F_N$$
$$\text{Kinetic friction} \quad F_f = \mu_k F_N$$

Static friction is discussed in more detail in Section 6.2.

Sample problems

1. A horizontal force of 50 N is required to pull an 8.0 kg block of aluminum at a uniform velocity across a horizontal wooden desk. What is the coefficient of kinetic friction?

Since the acceleration is zero, $F_f = F = 50$ N; also, $F_N = F_g$

$$\mu_k = \frac{F_f}{F_N}$$

$$= \frac{F_f}{mg} = \frac{50 \text{ N}}{(8.0 \text{ kg})(9.8 \text{ N/kg})}$$

$$= 0.64$$

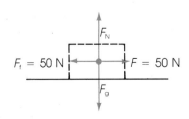

Static friction is used because the tire surface is not moving relative to the road.

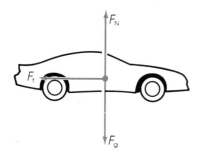

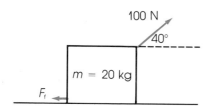

2. The driver of a 2000 kg car applies the brakes on a dry concrete roadway. Calculate the force of friction between the tires and the road surface (use table on page 163).

$$F_f = \mu_k F_N$$
$$= 1.02 \ (2000 \text{ kg})(9.8 \text{ N/kg})$$
$$= 2.0 \times 10^4 \text{ N}$$

(Of course, this force is divided among the four wheels of the car.)

3. A 20 kg box is dragged across a level floor with a force of 100 N. The force is applied at an angle of 40° above the horizontal. If the coefficient of kinetic friction is 0.32, what is the acceleration of the box?

Draw a free-body diagram of the box. Four forces act on it. $\vec{F}_N$ is the normal force of the table, acting up. $\vec{F}_g$ is the gravitational force acting down. $\vec{F}_f$ is the friction opposing the motion of the box, and $\vec{F}$ is the applied force of 100 N.

$$\vec{F}_g = m\vec{g}$$
$$= (20 \text{ kg})(9.8 \text{ N/kg})$$
$$= 196 \text{ N[down]}$$

The applied force of 100 N has both horizontal and vertical components, as follows:

$$\vec{F}_v = (100 \text{ N})(\sin 40°) = (100 \text{ N})(0.643) = 64 \text{ N[up]}$$

$$\vec{F}_h = (100 \text{ N})(\cos 40°) = (100 \text{ N})(0.766) = 77 \text{ N[to the right]}$$

Now $\vec{F}_{net} = \vec{F}_N + \vec{F}_g + \vec{F}_f + \vec{F} = m\vec{a}$

Taking vertical components,

$$F_{v_{net}} = F_N - F_g + 0 + F_v = ma_v.$$

But $a_v = 0$, since F_v is less than F_g.

Thus $0 = F_N - 196 \text{ N} + 64 \text{ N}$
$$F_N = 132 \text{ N}$$

As a result, the force of friction is

$$F_f = \mu_k F_N$$
$$= (0.32)(132 \text{ N})$$
$$= 42 \text{ N}$$

The net horizontal force on the box is

$$\vec{F}_{h_{net}} = \vec{F}_h + \vec{F}_f$$
$$= 77 \text{ N} - 42 \text{ N}$$
$$= 35 \text{ N}$$

Therefore, the horizontal acceleration of the box is

$$a_h = \frac{F_{h_{net}}}{m}$$
$$= \frac{35 \text{ N}}{20 \text{ kg}}$$
$$= 1.8 \text{ m/s}^2$$

4. A boy on a toboggan is sliding down a snow-covered hillside. The boy and toboggan together have a mass of 50 kg, and the slope is at an angle of 30° to the horizontal. Find the boy's acceleration (a) if there is no friction, and (b) if the coefficient of kinetic friction is 0.15.

(a) Since there is no friction, the only force exerted by the slope is perpendicular to itself, that is, the normal force (F_N). Since there is no acceleration perpendicular to the slope, $F_N = mg \cos 30°$ (see diagram), and the net force down the slope is

$$F = mg \sin 30°$$
$$\text{but } F = ma;$$
$$\text{therefore } ma = mg \sin 30°$$
$$\text{or } a = g \sin 30°$$
$$= 9.8 \text{ m/s}^2(0.50)$$
$$= 4.9 \text{ m/s}^2$$

(a)

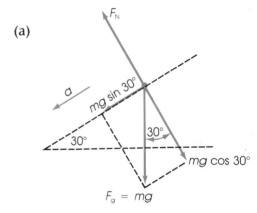

Note that the mass divides out, and thus the acceleration down the slope does *not* depend on the mass.

(b) As in the previous example, the hillside exerts a normal force on the toboggan, that is, $F_N = mg \cos 30°$. However, in this case, the hillside also exerts a frictional force, that is, $F_f = \mu_k F_N$.

$$\vec{F}_{net} = \vec{F}_{down\ slope} + \vec{F}_f$$
$$F_{net} = mg \sin 30° - \mu_k F_N$$
$$\text{but } F_{net} = ma, \text{ and } F_N = mg \cos 30°$$
$$\text{therefore } ma = mg \sin 30° - \mu_k mg \cos 30°$$
$$\text{or } a = g \sin 30° - \mu_k g \cos 30°$$
$$= (9.8 \text{ m/s}^2)(0.500) - (0.15)(9.8 \text{ m/s}^2)(0.866)$$
$$= 4.9 \text{ m/s}^2 - 1.3 \text{ m/s}^2$$
$$= 3.6 \text{ m/s}^2$$

(b)

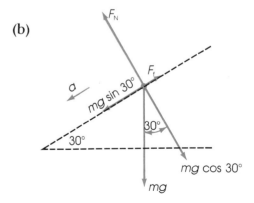

Down the slope is positive, up the slope is negative.

Practice

In the following questions, kinetic friction is implied unless otherwise stated.

1. It takes a 50 N horizontal force to pull a 20 kg object along the ground at a constant velocity. What is the coefficient of friction?

(0.26)

2. If the coefficient of friction is 0.30, how much horizontal force is needed to pull a mass of 15 kg across a level board at a uniform velocity?   (44 N)
3. A cart with a mass of 2.0 kg is pulled across a level desk by a horizontal force of 4.0 N. If the coefficient of kinetic friction is 0.12, what is the acceleration of the cart?   (0.83 m/s²)
4. A girl pushes a light snow shovel at a uniform velocity across a sidewalk. If the handle of the shovel is inclined at 55° to the horizontal and she pushes along the handle with a force of 100 N, what is the force of friction? What is the coefficient of kinetic friction?   (57 N, 0.70)
5. A 10 kg block of ice slides down a ramp 20 m long, inclined at 10° to the horizontal.
   (a) If the ramp is frictionless, what is the acceleration of the block of ice?
   (b) If the coefficient of kinetic friction is 0.10, how long will it take the block to slide down the ramp, if it starts from rest?
                                                              (1.7 m/s², 7.6 s)
6. A skier has just begun descending a 20° slope. Assuming that the coefficient of kinetic friction is 0.10, calculate (a) the acceleration of the skier, and (b) his final velocity after 8.0 s.
                                                              (2.4 m/s², 19 m/s)
7. The coefficient of friction between the 40 kg block and the surface in question 2, page 161, is 0.35. What is the new acceleration of the 15 kg mass?   (0.18 m/s²)

5.5 Inertial and Gravitational Mass

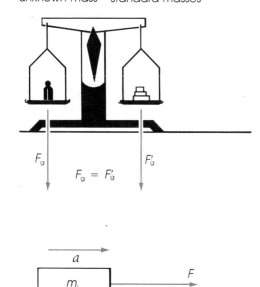

unknown mass   standard masses

F_g F_g'

$F_g = F_g'$

a

m_i F

To measure the mass of an object, the common procedure is to place the object and a standard mass or masses on a balance. The measurement consists of comparing two gravitational forces, one on the object, the other on the standard mass or set of masses. Although the forces of gravity may vary from place to place, the two masses will balance anywhere, since the forces of gravity on either side balance. The mass measured by using the force of gravity in this way is called the **gravitational mass** (m_g).

The mass could also be measured using Newton's Second Law. In this case, we are measuring, in a sense, the "accelerability" of the object, or its **inertial mass** (m_i). As mentioned in the previous chapter (Section 4.3), we can compare inertial masses in an acceleration experiment by pulling each mass along a horizontal surface, measuring the force and the acceleration, and then calculating the mass, using $m_i = \dfrac{F}{a}$.

What is the relationship between gravitational and inertial mass? It has been found experimentally that the two masses are equivalent. This extremely important fact forms one basis for Einstein's General Theory of Relativity, which is known as the **Principle of Equivalence.** In other words, the inertial mass and the gravitational mass of an object have exactly the same value, the only difference being how the mass was determined. Because of the equivalence of inertial and gravitational mass, a measurement of gravitational mass gives us the inertial mass. We do not normally make a distinction between them and, instead, use the term ''mass'' to refer to either one.

5.6 Free Fall

Galileo is particularly remembered for his work on the acceleration of falling bodies. The legend has it that Galileo ascended to the top of the leaning tower of Pisa and simultaneously released two iron spheres of different masses. They both reached the ground at exactly the same time. This was contrary to an assertion by Aristotle, that had been accepted for centuries, that larger masses fall faster. Aristotle had observed that a feather falls more slowly than a stone, but we now know that the air resistance on the feather had not been considered in this argument. When air resistance is eliminated, both feather and stone will fall with the same rate of acceleration. This was first demonstrated by Robert Boyle, shortly after Galileo's death. Using his newly developed air pump, he removed the air from a long tube containing a lead ball and a feather. With the air removed and the tube inverted, both fell at exactly the same rate. This reinforced Galileo's conclusion that all objects, whatever their mass, accelerate at the same rate under free fall near the Earth's surface.

We can now better understand Galileo's experiment with falling objects, using our knowledge of both Newton's Second Law and gravitational forces. If an object accelerates, Newton's Second Law expresses the relationship between the net force and the resulting acceleration as follows:

$$\vec{F}_{net} = m\vec{a}$$

If the air resistance is assumed to be zero, then the net force causing the acceleration is the force of gravity, i.e., $\vec{F}_{net} = \vec{F}_g$, and the resulting acceleration is the acceleration due to gravity, i.e., $\vec{a} = \vec{a}_g$. Thus we can write:

$$\vec{F}_g = m\vec{a}_g$$

Galileo Galilei (1564-1642)

Galileo argued that this experiment did not prove the case either way! You get the same results whether the Earth is at rest or is moving at a constant velocity.

This equation can be rewritten as:

$$\vec{a}_g = \frac{\vec{F}_g}{m}$$

or $\vec{a}_g \propto \vec{F}_g$ where m is constant

Since the gravitational field is relatively constant near the Earth's surface, the value of F_g does not vary for a particular mass and, thus, neither will the value of a_g.

The relationship between a_g and g can be derived by rearranging the two equations as follows:

$$F_{net} = ma_g$$
$$\text{but} \quad F_{net} = F_g$$
$$ma_g = mg$$
$$\text{or} \quad a_g = g$$

In other words, the acceleration due to gravity (a_g) and the gravitational field constant (g) are equal in value. Thus, if the gravitational field is uniform, as it is near the Earth's surface, the acceleration due to gravity is uniform, just as Galileo predicted. Mass is not a factor.

Sample problem

The gravitational field constant at the moon's surface is 1.6 N/kg. A moon rock is dropped from a height of 10 m. How long will it take to reach the surface of the moon?

Since g for the moon is 1.6 N/kg, on the moon a_g will be 1.6 m/s^2.

$$\Delta d = v_1 t + \frac{1}{2}a(\Delta t)^2$$

and $\Delta d = \frac{1}{2}a_g(\Delta t)^2$ since $v_1 = 0$

or $\Delta t = \sqrt{\dfrac{2\,\Delta d}{a_g}}$

$$= \sqrt{\frac{2(10\text{ m})}{1.6\text{ m/s}^2}}$$

$$= 3.5\text{ s}$$

Units

$a_g = $ m/s^2

$g = $ N/kg

$= \dfrac{\text{(kg) (m/s}^2)}{\text{kg}}$

$= $ m/s^2

Chart of Gravitational Fields of Force Relative to Earth (Earth = 1)

Planet	g	a_g	$\dfrac{g_P}{g_E}$
Mercury	3.52 N/kg	3.52 m/s^2	0.36
Venus	8.52 N/kg	8.52 m/s^2	0.87
Mars	3.72 N/kg	3.72 m/s^2	0.38
Earth	9.81 N/kg	9.81 m/s^2	1.00
Jupiter	26.10 N/kg	26.10 m/s^2	2.66
Saturn	11.07 N/kg	11.07 m/s^2	1.12
Uranus	10.49 N/kg	10.49 m/s^2	1.07
Neptune	13.80 N/kg	13.80 m/s^2	1.40
Pluto	0.31 N/kg	0.31 m/s^2	0.032
Moon	1.61 N/kg	1.61 m/s^2	0.16

Practice
1. The gravitational field constant 150 km above the Earth's surface is 9.5 N/kg. What is (a) the force of gravity on a 60 kg astronaut at this altitude, and (b) what will be the final velocity of a rock if it falls freely at this altitude for 10 s, starting at rest?
(5.7 × 10² N, 95 m/s)
2. An astronaut finds that the force of gravity on his 70.0 kg mass is 1.83 × 10³ N on a certain planet. What is the gravitational acceleration at the surface of this planet? Which planet might it be? (See the chart on the previous page.) (26.1 m/s²)

5.7 Free Fall and Air Resistance

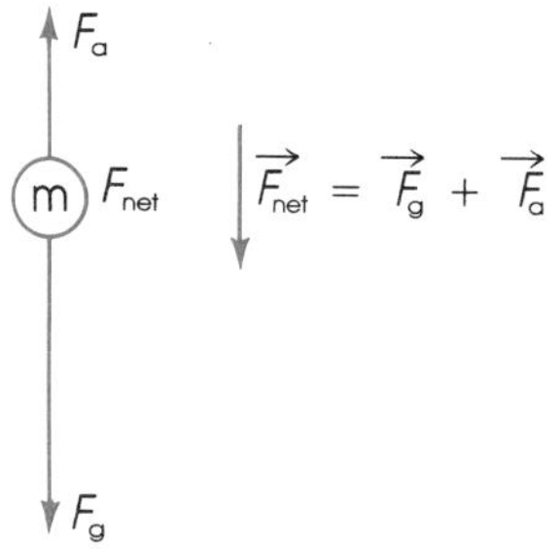

If a billiard ball and a styrofoam ball are dropped simultaneously, the styrofoam ball will quickly lag behind the billiard ball. Air resistance creates this difference. As was discussed in Chapter 1, the force of air resistance varies directly as the square of the velocity, or $F_a \alpha v^2$. Indeed, if the billiard ball falls far enough, it too will reach a uniform velocity because of air resistance.

As the velocity of a freely falling object increases, the air resistance increases. The net force causing the acceleration of the object is made up of two components, the force of gravity downward and the air resistance upward. (Friction always opposes the motion of an object.)

As long as $F_g > F_a$, then $F_{net} > 0$, and a downward acceleration will occur. But, as the value of F_a increases, the magnitude of F_{net} will decrease, thus decreasing the acceleration. Eventually, when $F_a = F_g$, the net force on the object is zero, and acceleration ceases. We say that the object has then reached its **terminal velocity**. The value of the terminal velocity will vary. It is quite a bit slower for the styrofoam ball than it is for the billiard ball.

Although the surface of the styrofoam ball is different from that of the billiard ball, this is not the major factor affecting the terminal velocity of the ball. In fact, at low speeds, the air resistance on each ball will be similar. Their masses are vastly different and, as seen in the diagram, the net force downward on the billiard ball is much greater than that on the styrofoam ball.

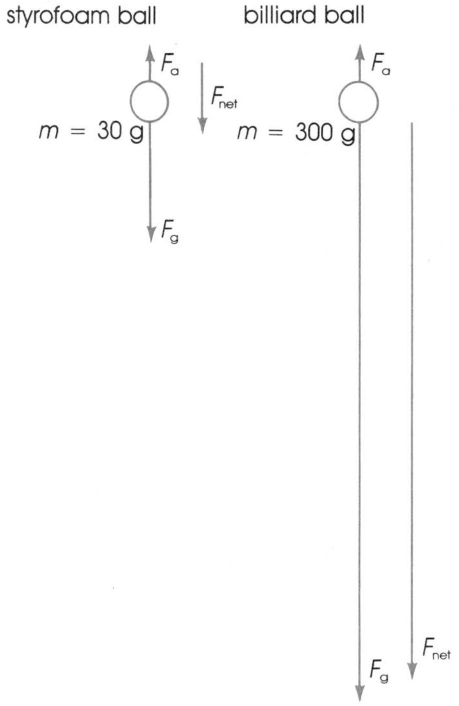

$$\vec{F}_{net} = \vec{F}_g + \vec{F}_a$$

styrofoam ball

$m = 30$ g

billiard ball

$m = 300$ g

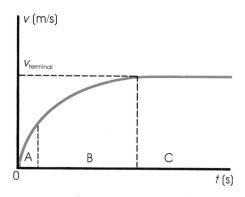

A parachutist jumping from an airplane also has a terminal velocity. Before the parachute opens, she is said to be in free fall. If a *v-t* graph of her motion is drawn, it will have the appearance illustrated.

In section A, air resistance is negligible, making $F_{net} = F_g$. This results in a constant slope on the *v-t* graph.

In section B, air resistance increases, resulting in a decreasing net force and a decreasing rate of acceleration. Thus, the graph is curved in this section.

In section C, the air resistance has increased to the point where $F_a = F_g$, and the net force on the parachutist is zero. No acceleration occurs (slope = 0), and she falls at a constant velocity (her terminal velocity).

When the sports parachutist is falling at her terminal velocity, approximately 200 km/h, she can change this velocity by increasing or decreasing her surface area (by changing the position of her arms and legs). When her parachute opens, the air resistance suddenly increases, and $F_a > F_g$, decelerating her to a slower terminal velocity (typically 3.0 to 4.3 m/s). At this point, $F_a = F_g$ again.

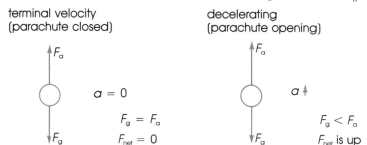

Sample problem

The graph on the next page shows the relationship between the force of air resistance and the velocity of a falling 1.0 kg steel ball. What is the instantaneous acceleration of the ball when it is travelling downward at 10.3 m/s?

$$\vec{F_g} = m\vec{g}$$
$$= 1.0 \text{ kg } (9.8 \text{ N/kg [down]})$$
$$= 9.8 \text{ N [down]}$$

At $v = 10.3$ m/s, the force of air resistance is 3.0 N [up] (see graph).

$$\vec{F}_{net} = \vec{F_g} + \vec{F_a} = 9.8 \text{ N} - 3.0 \text{ N} = 6.8 \text{ N [down]}$$
$$\vec{F}_{net} = m\vec{a}$$

or $\vec{a} = \dfrac{\vec{F}_{net}}{m}$

$\qquad = \dfrac{6.8 \text{ N}}{1.0 \text{ kg}}$

$\qquad = 6.8 \text{ m/s}^2[\text{down}]$

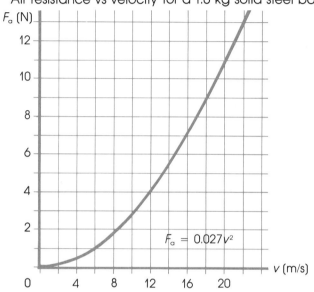

Air resistance vs velocity for a 1.0 kg solid steel ball

$F_a = 0.027v^2$

Canadian parachutist Kathy Cox won the World Championship in spot landing in 1980.

Practice

Using the above graph, answer the following questions.
1. What is the acceleration when the ball is falling at 8.0 m/s?
2. What is the terminal velocity of the steel ball?
3. If the steel ball is fired vertically downward at 22 m/s, what will be its initial acceleration?

$\qquad\qquad$ (8.0 m/s² [down], 19 m/s, 3.2 m/s² [up])

5.8 Two-Dimensional Motion in the Earth's Gravitational Field

If a rock is thrown horizontally from the top of a cliff, it follows a curved path. This curved path is the result of two independent motions, a horizontal motion with a uniform velocity and a vertical motion with a uniform acceleration, due to gravity. The independence of these two motions is shown in the photograph on the next page and was described in Section 3.10.

At one time of interest only to aeronautical engineers, aerodynamics is now important to automotive designers as well. Reducing drag is probably the most obvious of a number of strategies aimed at cutting gasoline consumption, because it is changing the appearance of the cars we drive.

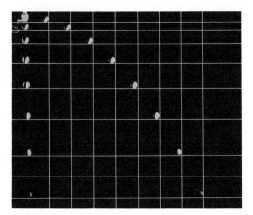

The two balls in this photograph were released simultaneously, but the right-hand ball was projected horizontally. The strobe light "stopped" the motion of each ball after equal intervals of time. A grid has been superimposed to make analysis more convenient. Notice that both balls fall by the same vertical displacement in each time interval, and that the displacement increases vertically in successive equal intervals of time. Note also that the projected ball travels the same horizontal displacement in each time interval. The independent horizontal and vertical motions combine to produce a curved path that is called the **trajectory** of the projectile. The curve of the trajectory forms a parabola.

As shown in the photograph, the two balls reached the lowest point at exactly the same time, even though one was projected horizontally. This is true of all horizontally projected objects. The time required to reach the lowest point, usually the ground, is exactly the same whenever they fall freely, with or without a horizontal velocity. This is because the initial vertical velocity is zero.

Sample problems

1. A rock is thrown horizontally at 10.0 m/s from the top of a cliff 122.5 m high.
   (a) How long does the rock take to reach the ground?
   (b) What is the horizontal displacement of the rock?

   (a) The time required for the projected rock to reach the ground is equal to the time it would take it to fall straight down. The time required to fall vertically is determined as follows. Assume that up is positive and down is negative.

   $$\Delta d = v_1 \Delta t + \frac{1}{2} a (\Delta t)^2$$

   $$-122.5 \text{ m} = 0(\Delta t) + \frac{1}{2}(-9.8 \text{ m/s}^2)(\Delta t)^2$$

   $$\Delta t = 5.0 \text{ s} \qquad \text{(The negative solution has no meaning in this question.)}$$

   (b) The motion in the horizontal direction is uniform.
   $$\text{Thus, } \Delta d = v \Delta t$$
   $$= (10 \text{ m/s})(5.0 \text{ s})$$
   $$= 50 \text{ m}$$

2. A ball is thrown from the top of a building with a horizontal velocity of 20 m/s. It hits level ground 80 m from the face of the building. How high is the building?

   Assuming that the horizontal motion is uniform,

$$\Delta t = \frac{\Delta d}{v}$$

$$= \frac{80 \text{ m}}{20 \text{ m/s}} = 4.0 \text{ s}$$

For the vertical motion, assuming up is positive,

$$\Delta d = v_1 \Delta t + \frac{1}{2} a_g (\Delta t)^2$$

$$= 0 + \frac{1}{2}(-9.8 \text{ m/s}^2)(4.0 \text{ s})^2$$

$$\vec{\Delta d} = -78.4 \text{ m, or } 78 \text{ m[down]}$$

3. A helicopter is rising vertically at a uniform velocity of 14.7 m/s. When it is 196 m from the ground, a ball is projected from it with a horizontal velocity of 8.5 m/s with respect to the helicopter. Calculate (a) when the ball will reach the ground, (b) where it will hit the ground, and (c) what its velocity will be when it hits the ground.

(a) Consider first the vertical component of the ball's motion. Vertically, up is positive, down is negative.

$$\Delta d_v = v_1 \Delta t + \frac{1}{2} a_g (\Delta t)^2$$

When the ball strikes the ground, $\Delta d_v = -196$ m.

$$-196 \text{ m} = (14.7 \text{ m/s})\Delta t + \frac{1}{2}(-9.8 \text{ m/s}^2)(\Delta t)^2$$

$$4.9(\Delta t)^2 - 14.7\Delta t - 196 = 0$$

$$(\Delta t)^2 - 3.0\Delta t - 40 = 0$$

$$(\Delta t - 8.0)(\Delta t + 5.0) = 0$$

The solutions of the equation are

$$\Delta t = 8.0 \text{ s or } \Delta t = -5.0 \text{ s}$$

The time taken to reach the ground is 8.0 s, since the negative solution has no meaning in this problem.

(b) Now consider the horizontal component, to find where the ball will land after 8.0 s.

$$\Delta d_h = \Delta v_h \Delta t$$

$$= (8.5 \text{ m/s})(8.0 \text{ s})$$

$$= 68 \text{ m from a point directly below the}$$
$$\text{vertically rising helicopter.}$$

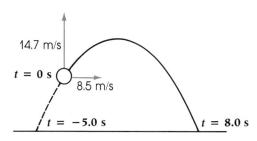

The negative answer does have some meaning. It represents the time at which a ball with the same trajectory would have left the ground.

(c) The vertical component of the velocity is

$$\vec{v_2} = \vec{v_1} + \vec{a_g}\Delta t$$

$$= 14.7 \text{ m/s} + (-9.8 \text{ m/s}^2)(8.0 \text{ s})$$

$$= -63.7 \text{ m/s}$$

$$= 64 \text{ m/s[down]}$$

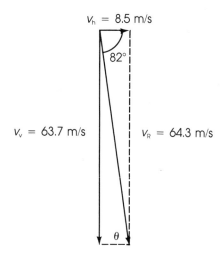

The horizontal component of the velocity is 8.5 m/s. Therefore the resultant velocity is the vector sum of the vertical and horizontal components as follows:

$$\vec{v}_R = \vec{v}_h + \vec{v}_v$$ where $\vec{v}_R$ = resultant velocity

$$|\vec{v}_R| = \sqrt{v_h^2 + v_v^2}$$ $\vec{v}_h$ = horizontal velocity

$$|\vec{v}_R| = \sqrt{(63.7 \text{ m/s})^2 + (8.5 \text{ m/s})^2}$$ $\vec{v}_v$ = vertical velocity

$$= 64.3 \text{ m/s}$$

$$\tan \theta = \frac{63.7 \text{ m/s}}{8.5 \text{ m/s}} = 7.49$$

$$\theta = 82°$$

Therefore the velocity of impact is 64 m/s [82° below the horizontal].

Practice

1. A stone thrown horizontally from the top of a tall building takes 7.56 s to reach the street. How high is the building?　(280 m)
2. A bullet is projected horizontally at 300 m/s from a height of 1.5 m. Ignoring air resistance, calculate how far it travels horizontally before it hits the ground. (Assume that the ground is level.)　$(1.7 \times 10^2$ m)
3. A ball projected horizontally from a ceiling height of 3.0 m hits the floor 4.0 m "down range". Calculate (a) its time of flight, and (b) its horizontal velocity.　(0.78 s, 5.1 m/s)
4. An object is projected horizontally with a velocity of 30 m/s. It takes 4.0 s to reach the ground. Neglecting air resistance, determine (a) the height at which the object was projected, and (b) the magnitude of the resultant velocity, just before the object strikes the ground.　(78 m, 49 m/s)
5. A bomber in level flight, flying at 92.0 m/s, releases a bomb at a height of 1950 m.
   (a) How long is it before the bomb strikes the Earth?
   (b) How far does it travel horizontally?
   (c) What are the horizontal and vertical components of its velocity when it strikes?
   (d) What is its velocity of impact?
   　　　(19.9 s; 1.84×10^3 m; 92.0 m/s, 195 m/s;
   　　　216 m/s [64.7° below the horizontal])
6. A cannonball shot horizontally from the top of a cliff with an initial velocity of 425 m/s is aimed towards a schooner on the ocean below. If the cliff is 78 m above the ocean surface, calculate the following: (a) the time for the cannonball to reach the water, (b) the horizontal displacement of the cannonball,

and (c) the velocity of the cannonball just before it strikes the water.

(4.0 s, 1.7×10^3 m, 4.3×10^2 m/s[5.3° to the horizontal])

7. A balloon is rising at a vertical velocity of 4.9 m/s. At the same time, it is drifting horizontally with a velocity of 1.6 m/s. If a bottle is released from the balloon when it is 9.8 m above the ground, determine (a) the time it takes for the bottle to reach the ground, and (b) the horizontal displacement of the bottle from the balloon.   (2.0 s, 0 m)

5.9 Analysing Projectile Motion

As noted in the previous section, the trajectory of an object projected in the Earth's gravitational field of force takes the shape of a parabola. More precise knowledge about the path of a projectile can be derived by applying some mathematics to this type of motion.

For a projectile launched horizontally and accelerating vertically, we already know the following equations:

(1) $\Delta d_h = v_h \Delta t$ where Δd_h represents the horizontal displacement and v_h represents the horizontal velocity

(2) $\Delta d_v = \frac{1}{2} a_g (\Delta t)^2$ where Δd_v represents the vertical displacement

From equation 1, for Δt we get

$$\Delta t = \frac{\Delta d_h}{v_h}$$

Substituting in equation 2, we get

$$\Delta d_v = \frac{1}{2} a_g (\Delta t)^2$$

$$= \frac{1}{2} a_g \left(\frac{\Delta d_h}{v_h} \right)^2$$

Using this equation, the vertical displacement can be derived provided the horizontal displacement is known, and vice versa. Such specialized equations may be useful in specific situations, but should not be memorized. They can be developed quickly when needed.

In the above equation, the number $\frac{1}{2}$, the uniform acceleration of gravity (a_g), and the initial horizontal velocity (v_h) are all constants. The only variables are Δd_v and Δd_h. Thus it can be seen that the vertical displacement is directly proportional to the square of

The mathematical equation for a projectile takes the form of $y = kx^2$, where k is a constant.

the horizontal displacement. In other words, the equation is that of a parabola.

$$\Delta d_v = \frac{a_g}{2v_h^2}(\Delta d_h)^2$$

or $\Delta d_v = k(\Delta d_h)^2$ where k is the propor-

or $\Delta d_v \propto (\Delta d_h)^2$ tionality constant

Thus, when a projectile goes twice as far horizontally, it falls four times as far vertically. This can be verified in an experiment similar to the one shown in the photograph on page 172 (the projected ball).

But a projectile does not necessarily have just a *horizontal* initial velocity. A ball thrown at an angle to the ground will also travel along a parabolic trajectory. If we break its initial velocity down into horizontal and vertical components we get

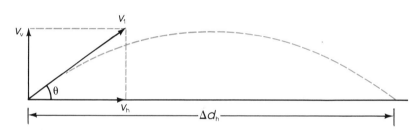

(1) $v_h = v_1 \cos \theta$

(2) $v_v = v_1 \sin \theta$

where θ is the angle of projection.

Using these components, we can derive an equation for the horizontal range of a projectile (Δd_h). (We have dispensed with the vector notation in this derivation.)

Horizontal motion $\Delta d_h = v_h \Delta t = v_1 \Delta t \cos \theta$ (3)

Vertical motion $\Delta d_v = v_v \Delta t + \frac{1}{2} a_g (\Delta t)^2$

but $a_g = -g$

therefore $\Delta d_v = v_1 \Delta t \sin \theta + \frac{1}{2}(-g)(\Delta t)^2$

$$\Delta d_v = v_1 \Delta t \sin \theta - \frac{1}{2} g (\Delta t)^2 \qquad (4)$$

These equations give the horizontal and vertical displacement in any time interval, measured from the instant the ball is thrown. At the specific time when the ball hits the ground, $\Delta d_v = 0$. (Remember that the ball was launched from the ground.)

Substituting in equation 4,

$$0 = v_1 \Delta t \sin \theta - \frac{1}{2}g(\Delta t)^2$$

or $\frac{1}{2}g(\Delta t)^2 = v_1 \Delta t \sin \theta$

Simplifying and solving for Δt, we obtain

$$\frac{1}{2}g\Delta t = v_1 \sin \theta$$

$$\Delta t = \frac{2v_1 \sin \theta}{g} \tag{5}$$

This equation gives the time of flight for any projectile arriving back at its original level.

Substituting in equation 3, we can find the range for such a projectile as follows:

$$\Delta d_h = v_1 \Delta t \cos \theta$$

$$= v_1 \left(\frac{2v_1 \sin \theta}{g}\right) \cos \theta$$

$$= \frac{v_1^2}{g} 2 \sin \theta \cos \theta$$

but $2 \sin \theta \cos \theta = \sin 2\theta$

therefore $\Delta d_h = \dfrac{v_1^2 \sin 2\theta}{g}$ \tag{6}

This equation can be used to find the horizontal range of a projectile that returns to the same level from which it was launched, provided the angle of projection (θ) and the initial velocity (v_1) are known. This relationship was the basis of tables compiled and used in both world wars to aim artillery shells, although corrections had to be made for air resistance and other effects.

It should be noted that the maximum range occurs with an angle of elevation of 45°. This is because the maximum value of $\sin 2\theta$ is 1 (when $2\theta = 90°$ in the equation, the value of θ that gives the maximum range is 45°). Note that, except for $\theta = 45°$, there are two possible elevations for each range. This phenomenon is illustrated in the diagram below.

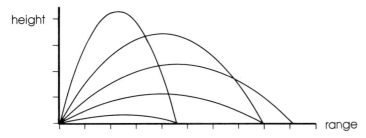

The Physics of the Fastball

Once pitched, a baseball's flight is subject to three forces: gravity, air resistance, and lift. The lift force can deflect the ball up or down, left or right, depending on how the pitcher throws it. The ball's spin disturbs the flow of air around the ball, increasing the air pressure on one side of it. Top spin produces a downward deflection that makes the pitch drop faster than it would as a result of gravity alone. A ball with backspin — a good fastball has a fair amount of backspin — will experience an upward lift and will not drop as fast as it would otherwise. If the pitcher spins the ball in the horizontal or some other plane, a curve or other breaking pitch is unleashed. Most players firmly believe that a fastball can rise in flight. They are so used to seeing the ball's curved trajectory, created by gravity, that the flight looks straight to them. As explained in the discussion of projectiles, it only looks as if the ball rises. Actually, it just doesn't fall as fast.

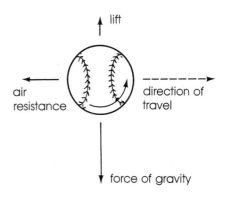

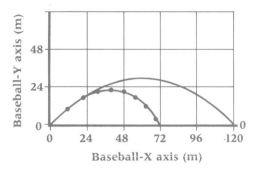

A baseball hit at an angle of 45° to the horizontal will land 120 m from home plate if its initial velocity is 34.3 m/s. This is the result if air resistance, or drag, is ignored. The reality is that its range is only 71.4 m when air resistance is included in the calculation. Both trajectories are plotted in the graph. The circles in the lower curve show the positions of the ball at 0.5 s intervals, and by counting we see that the ball stays in the air for just over 4.0 s.

A simple example of a projectile is an object that is fired horizontally and then falls freely. To see what happens in such a case, get two pennies and balance one of them on the edge of a desk. Place the other nearby, and then flick it with your finger, so that it shoots off the table, just grazing the first one on the way past. The idea is to get one penny simply to fall off the table while the other is shot off horizontally. What do you hear as the pennies hit the floor?

In this discussion of projectile motion, there have been a number of simplifying assumptions. Some of these are: (1) the effect of air resistance has been ignored, (2) the acceleration due to gravity has been considered to be constant, (3) the Earth has been assumed to be flat, and (4) the projectile has been considered to have remained in the same vertical plane throughout its flight. In reality, none of these assumptions is valid. For example, near the Earth's surface, the effect of air resistance will cause the path of a projectile to turn downward, thus shortening its range. For a rocket projected from one point to another on the Earth's surface, air resistance, gravity, and vertical plane all change during its flight. Also, the rocket is launched from a moving platform, the Earth, and the Earth's curvature cannot be ignored. More elaborate equations can be derived, which include all of these factors. This has been done by space scientists and engineers to determine the paths of rockets, both near the Earth's surface and in outer space. Because the calculations required are so laborious and must be done so quickly, small computers on board the rocket are used. It was the necessity of doing such calculations in the 1960s and 1970s that accelerated the growth of microelectronics and resulted in the computer technology we benefit from today.

Sample problem

A gun shoots a bullet at 1200 m/s at an angle of 60° above the horizontal. Neglecting air resistance, determine (a) its time of flight, and (b) its range.

(a) $$\Delta t = \frac{2v_1 \sin \theta}{g} \qquad \text{(equation 5)}$$

$$= \frac{2(1200 \text{ m/s})(\sin 60°)}{9.8 \text{ m/s}^2}$$

$$= 212 \text{ s}$$

(b) $$\Delta d_h = v_1 \Delta t \cos \theta \qquad \text{(equation 3)}$$

$$= (1200 \text{ m/s})(212 \text{ s})(\cos 60°)$$

$$= 1.3 \times 10^5 \text{ m}$$

This horizontal displacement is much higher than the actual range would be in practice, since air resistance has been ignored in the calculation, even at the high speeds involved.

Practice

1. A cannonball is fired with a velocity of 100 m/s at 25° above the horizontal. Determine how far away it lands on level ground.

$$(7.8 \times 10^2 \text{ m})$$

2. If a baseball player throws a ball at 35.0 m/s, what is its maximum range?   (125 m)
3. A player kicks a soccer ball towards the goalkeeper, but at an angle of 37° to the horizontal and with an initial speed of 14.7 m/s. The goalkeeper stands 26.0 m from the kicker. Where will the ball land relative to the goalkeeper?   (4.8 m short)
4. In problem 3, the goalkeeper watches the ball until it reaches maximum height, then runs at constant speed to just intercept it at ground level. How fast must he run?   (5.3 m/s)

5.10 Centripetal Acceleration and Centripetal Forces

If you whirl a heavy ball at the end of a string, on a horizontal surface such as the floor, the ball traces out a circular path. If the string breaks, the ball will travel in a straight line in the direction it was going at the time it was released (Newton's First Law). It will not go straight out as some may predict.

As we discussed in Section 3.9, the acceleration vector is perpendicular to the velocity vector at any point. This acceleration was called the centripetal acceleration (a_c) because it acted towards the centre of the circular path of the object.

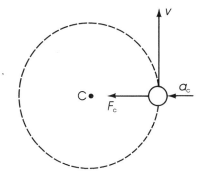

According to Newton's Law of Motion, this acceleration must be caused by a net force acting on the object, in the direction of the acceleration. In the illustration, the force of the string on the ball acts towards the centre, at right angles to the velocity vector. This force is called the **centripetal force** ($\vec{F_c}$) and can be determined from the relationship

$$\vec{F_c} = m\vec{a_c}$$

This is simply another application of Newton's Second Law. The term centripetal indicates the effect of the force.

Note that the centripetal force is in no way different from other forces causing acceleration. Centripetal forces, like other forces, are pushes and pulls exerted by strings and rods, or arise from forces that act at a distance, whether gravitational, electric, or magnetic. Centripetal forces produce a change in the direction of the velocity of the body on which they act, rather than a change in the magnitude of this velocity. This makes centripetal forces unique, since most forces produce a change in the magnitude of the velocity, with or without a change in its direction.

Since centripetal force and centripetal acceleration always act towards the centre of the circular path, their direction is understood and, hence, vector notation may be omitted. In Section 3.9 we derived expressions for centripetal acceleration. These can now be used to calculate the centripetal forces that give rise to centripetal acceleration.

Given, that $F_c = ma_c$, and realizing that

$$a_c = \frac{v^2}{R}$$

$$= \frac{4\pi^2 R}{T^2}$$

$$= 4\pi^2 R f^2$$

$$F_c = \frac{mv^2}{R} = \frac{4\pi^2 mR}{T^2} = 4\pi^2 mR f^2$$

Note that the radius is the denominator in the first expression of the force equation. The necessary force will be small, at a particular velocity, if R is very large. It is easier to follow a curve of large radius than of small radius. On the other hand, if you try to turn, say, a bicycle, in a tight turn, you may skid. In this case R is very small, so the force required is very large. If the force required is greater than the maximum frictional forces, skidding occurs.

Sample Problems

1. A 1000 kg car enters a level curve at 20 m/s. If the curve has a radius of 80 m, what centripetal force must be supplied by friction to keep the car from skidding?

$$F_c = \frac{mv^2}{R}$$

$$= \frac{1000 \text{ kg } (20 \text{ m/s})^2}{80 \text{ m}}$$

$$= 5.0 \times 10^3 \text{ N}$$

A frictional force of 5.0×10^3 N exerted by the road on the tires, directed towards the centre of the curve, keeps the car in the curve. Note that the weight of the car is at right angles to this centripetal force and thus has no direct effect on the motion of the car through the curve. Note also that the normal force is 9.8×10^3 N, so that the coefficient of friction must be at least $\frac{5.0 \times 10^3 \text{N}}{9.8 \times 10^3 \text{N}} = 0.51$, to supply the required F_c. In winter-

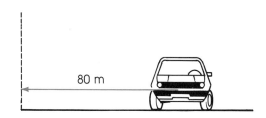

time, ice and snow reduce the value of the coefficient of static friction between the tires and the road, reducing the available centripetal force keeping the car in an icy curve. The results are disastrous. The car is unable to follow the curve and slides off the road.

2. A 1000 kg car travels around a frictionless, banked curve having a radius of 80 m. If the banking is 20° to the horizontal, at what specific speed must the car travel to maintain a constant radius?

Draw a free-body diagram of the car. There are only two forces acting on it, $\vec{F}_g$ and $\vec{F}_N$. The centripetal acceleration (a_c) is horizontal, as shown. The force of gravity on the car, $\vec{F}_g$, acts straight down. The force of the road on the car, at right angles to the road surface, is the normal force, F_N. It is the horizontal component of this normal force, in the direction of the centre of the curve, that supplies the only centripetal force on the car (the slope is frictionless in this question). The value of the normal force is calculated as follows, since there is no vertical acceleration:

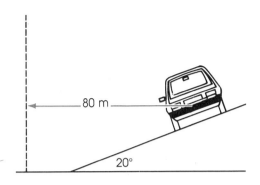

$$F_N \cos \theta = mg$$

which gives
$$F_N = \frac{mg}{\cos \theta}$$
$$= \frac{(1000 \text{ kg})(9.8 \text{ N/kg})}{\cos 20°}$$
$$= \frac{(1000 \text{ kg})(9.8 \text{ N/kg})}{0.9397}$$
$$= 1.04 \times 10^4 \text{ N}$$

The centripetal force is the horizontal component of this normal force, as follows:

$$F_c = F_N \sin \theta$$
$$= (1.04 \times 10^4 \text{ N})(\sin 20°)$$
$$= (1.04 \times 10^4 \text{ N})(0.3420)$$
$$= 3.57 \times 10^3 \text{ N}$$

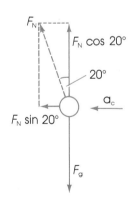

but $F_c = \dfrac{mv^2}{R}$, so $v^2 = \dfrac{RF_c}{m}$
$$= \frac{(80 \text{ m})(3.57 \times 10^3 \text{ N})}{(1000 \text{ kg})}$$
$$= 2.86 \times 10^2 \text{ (m/s)}^2$$
$$v = \sqrt{2.86 \times 10^2} \text{ m/s}$$
$$= 17 \text{ m/s}$$

If the car goes faster, it will slide up the banking. If it goes more slowly, it will slide down.

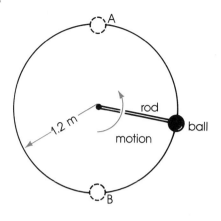

3. A 3.5 kg steel ball is swung at a constant speed in a vertical circle of radius 1.2 m, on the end of a light, rigid steel rod, as illustrated. If the ball has a frequency of 1.0 Hz, calculate the tension in the rod due to the mass at the top (A) and at the bottom (B) positions.

The ball is acted on by gravity and the rod. The ball has a constant centripetal acceleration, so there must be a constant centripetal force, F_c, directed towards the centre.

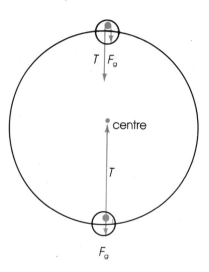

At the bottom, where the two forces act in opposite directions,
$$\vec{F}_c = \vec{T} + \vec{F}_g$$
or $\vec{T} = \vec{F}_c - \vec{F}_g$

Taking vertical components,
$$T = 4\pi^2 mRf^2 - (-mg)$$
$$= 4\pi^2(3.5 \text{ kg})(1.2 \text{ m})(1.0 \text{ Hz})^2 + (3.5 \text{ kg})(9.8 \text{ N/kg})$$
$$= 165.6 \text{ N} + 34.3 \text{ N}$$
$$= 2.0 \times 10^2 \text{ N}$$

This is the maximum value for the tension in the rod, pulling up.

At the top, where the two forces act downward,
$$\vec{F}_c = \vec{T} + \vec{F}_g$$
or $\vec{T} = \vec{F}_c - \vec{F}_g$

Taking vertical components,

$$-T = -4\pi^2\, mRf^2 - (-mg)$$
$$= -4\pi^2(3.5 \text{ kg})(1.2 \text{ m})(1.0 \text{ Hz})^2 + (3.5 \text{ kg})(9.8 \text{ N/kg})$$
$$= -165.6 \text{ N} + 34.3 \text{ N}$$
$$= -1.3 \times 10^2 \text{ N}$$
$$T = 1.3 \times 10^2 \text{ N}$$

This is the minimum value for the tension in the rod, pulling down.

Alternate Solution:

At the bottom, the rod must support the ball's weight as well as provide the centripetal force necessary to make it move in a circle.

$$\therefore T = F_c + F_g$$
$$= 4\pi^2 mRf^2 + mg$$
$$= 2.0 \times 10^2 \text{ N}$$

At the top, the ball's weight provides part of the centripetal force; the rod provides the rest.

$$\therefore T = F_c - F_g$$
$$= 4\pi^2 mRf^2 - mg$$
$$= 1.3 \times 10^2 \text{ N}$$

In this example, if the steel ball is rotated on a rod at a constant speed, it is interesting to note that, at any speed, the difference between the tension at the top and the tension at the bottom is always twice the force of gravity on the ball. This can be shown as follows:

$$\text{at the top, } T_{top} = F_c - mg$$
$$\text{at the bottom, } T_{bottom} = F_c + mg$$
$$\text{therefore, } T_{bottom} - T_{top} = 2\,mg$$

Practice

1. A 2.00 kg stone is whirled in a circle by a rope 4.00 m long, completing 5 revolutions in 2.00 s. Calculate the tension in the rope if the stone is rotated horizontally on a smooth frictionless surface. $(1.97 \times 10^3 \text{ N})$

2. A stone of mass 1.00 kg is attached to one end of a string 1.00 m long, of breaking strength 500 N, and is whirled in a horizontal circle on a frictionless table top. The other end of the string is kept fixed. Find the maximum speed the stone can attain without breaking the string.   (22.4 m/s)

3. A plane is flying in a vertical loop of 1500 m radius. At what speed is the plane flying at the top of the loop, if the vertical force exerted by the air on the plane is zero at this point?
                     (121 m/s, or 436 km/h)

4. The pilot of an airplane, which has been diving at a speed of 540 km/h, pulls out of the dive at constant speed.
   (a) What is the minimum radius of the plane's circular path in order that the acceleration of the pilot at the lowest point will not exceed 7 g?
   (b) What force is applied on an 80 kg pilot by the plane seat at the lowest point of the pull-out? $(328 \text{ m}, 6.3 \times 10^3 \text{ N})$

184

Applications of Centripetal Motion

When the Round-Up at the Canadian National Exhibition spins horizontally, the patrons feel "pushed" against the outside of the circular cage. Actually, the outside wall exerts a centripetal force on each person, keeping all of them in a circular path. When the rotor is moved to the vertical position, this force is sufficient to keep them in place as long as the rotation rate is maintained.

Cream is separated from milk in a dairy centrifuge by passing the milk over a series of plates that are rotating at over 6000 r/min. The milk, having more inertial mass than the cream, goes to the outside of the centrifuge, where it is collected. The cream is collected closer to the centre.

The banking of curves can reduce skidding because the normal force of the road on the car will have a component towards the centre of the curve (see page 181 for diagram).

As the cars move through the corkscrew curves in the Dragon Fyre at Canada's Wonderland, the centripetal force of the track on the cars is sufficient to keep them on the rails, even when upside down. As a safety precaution, the cars have wheels on both sides of the tubular rail and the patrons are strapped into their seats.

This centrifuge is used by NASA to test an astronaut's ability to withstand the large forces that are present when the space shuttle is launched or re-enters the Earth's atmosphere. By whirling the astronaut in a chamber at the end of the rotating arm, the centripetal force exerted on the astronaut can be increased to many times the force of gravity.

Blood cells are separated from blood plasma in a hospital centrifuge. When the test tube containing blood is rotated horizontally at high speeds, the blood cells move to the bottom of the test tube, leaving the blood plasma behind.

The G-Suit

When high-speed aircraft were introduced in the late 1930s, the lives of pilots were endangered by "blacking out": the effect of centripetal g forces in high-speed turns. In the middle of a turn, a pilot could experience a force of 7 g, seven times the normal pull of gravity. Blood would tend to "pool" in the pilot's legs and feet, and could not be pumped back to the brain. The resulting temporary loss of consciousness could cause the plane to crash.

Sir Frederick Banting, one of the discoverers of insulin, and the head of the Banting Institute at the University of Toronto, was asked for his help in solving this problem. He turned to Dr. Wilbur Franks (1901-1986), a professor engaged in medical research who, he was sure, would understand the nature of the problem. When Franks had used a high-speed centrifuge in cancer research, high g forces constantly shattered the test tubes placed inside it. When he floated small tubes inside larger ones, however, not a single one broke under identical centripetal forces. It became obvious to him that the same principle might be used to protect the human body.

Franks began conducting experiments using live mice. At high centripetal accelerations, their unprotected bodies were destroyed; enveloped by liquid, all of them survived. He devised a rubber suit that surrounded the human body with a thin film of water. In theory, this fluid would automatically exert counter pressure during high g centripetal acceleration.

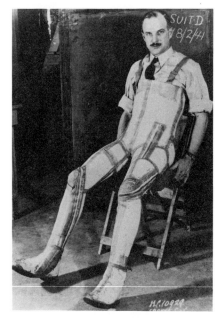

Dr. Franks insisted that he be the one to test the first suit. In the test flight, an RCAF Fleet Finch biplane climbed to an altitude of 2.7 km and then went into a steep dive at maximum speed. At the bottom of the dive the pilot pulled out and the g force registered 7.7. The pilot went blind, temporarily, but Franks was unaffected.

Franks joined the RCAF as a medical officer, and the "Franks Flying Suit" was tested in a Spitfire fighter under simulated combat conditions. It was a success, and Banting persuaded the government to provide funds to build a human-size centrifuge for final testing. By 1941, the Fleet Air Arm was using the suit in England, providing allied pilots with an extra advantage in combat. The Franks Flying Suit (later called a G-suit) remained one of the best-kept secrets of the war until as late as 1944.

Since the end of World War II, G-suits have become standard equipment for fighter pilots throughout the world. A sophisticated version is now being used by NASA space-shuttle astronauts so they can survive the large g forces encountered on blast-off and re-entry.

In honour of his work, Wilbur Franks received the Eric Liljencrantz Award "for outstanding research in aerospace medicine" and the U.S. Legion of Merit. Also, he was made an Officer of the Order of the British Empire and a member of the Canadian Aviation Hall of Fame.

5.11 Frames of Reference

In Chapter 3 we noted that all motion is relative and that our description of it depends on the frame of reference used. It is common to use a fixed frame of reference, usually the Earth. That is, we consider the Earth to be fixed, and the motions of other objects are measured relative to this fixed frame of reference.

If a stone is dropped from a tower, without a horizontal velocity, it falls vertically down with no horizontal displacement. But the Earth is rotating at uniform velocity, as is the tower. One could argue that the falling stone should not land vertically below, because the tower is in motion. It was this argument that was used by Galileo's critics to justify their belief that the Earth was fixed and that the heavens rotated around the Earth. Galileo argued, as we have seen in our discussion of projectiles, that the stone has the same horizontal velocity at the top of a tower as it has at the bottom, even though the vertical velocity of the stone increases. (The horizontal and vertical velocities are mutually independent.) Therefore, no matter what the constant velocity of the Earth, the stone will land at the foot of the tower.

Similarly, if a ball is dropped from the mast of a moving ship, it falls directly to the deck below, with no relative horizontal displacement. Or, if we throw a ball vertically up inside a car moving at uniform velocity, the ball falls directly back into our hand. We get the same results whether the boat or the car is at rest or is moving at uniform velocity.

From these and other observations, a generalization can be made. Newton's Law of Motion holds equally well whether the frame of reference is moving at a uniform velocity or is at rest. This generalization is called the **Galilean Relativity Principle.**

Sometimes our observations seem wrong because we have been confused about the frame of reference we are in. For example, we stop our car at a stoplight, adjacent to another car. Suddenly, we observe that we are rolling backward, so we slam on the brakes only to find, to our surprise, that our car was at rest. What happened? Actually, the other car had been slowly moving forward. Relative to the other car, we appeared to be moving backward. Relative to the Earth (a fixed frame of reference), we were at rest. Momentarily, we had used the other car as our frame of reference, assuming that it was still at rest when, in fact, it was not.

If a girl riding in the back of a truck travelling at a uniform velocity throws a ball vertically into the air, she will observe that the ball goes straight up and down, if air resistance is ignored. To

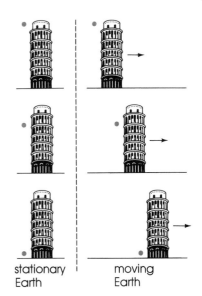

stationary Earth   moving Earth

Galileo's argument was that the falling stone continues to share the Earth's motion: an observer on Earth cannot tell, by watching the stone, whether or not the Earth moves.

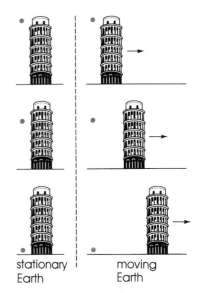

stationary Earth   moving Earth

Galileo's critics argued that a dropped stone would be left behind by a moving Earth, landing beyond the foot of the tower.

an observer standing at the side of the road, the path of the ball will be a parabola, as illustrated. What is observed depends upon the frame of reference in which the observation is made.

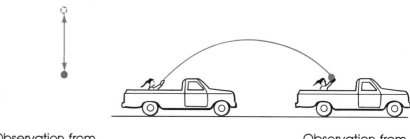

Observation from
the moving frame
of reference

Observation from
the fixed frame of
reference

Two airplanes are flying side by side in the same direction, plane A at an air velocity of 300 km/h, plane B at 250 km/h. From within plane B's frame of reference, plane A is pulling away at 50 km/h. From within plane A's frame of reference, plane B is falling behind at the rate of 50 km/h. Neither plane A nor plane B can determine its own velocity by observing the other plane; all either one can determine by such observation is its velocity relative to the other plane.

These examples illustrate that velocity measurements vary because they depend on the frame of reference used. You might argue that absolute measurements could be made if some absolute fixed frame of reference could be found. But there are no absolute frames of reference. The Earth, which is commonly used as a fixed frame of reference, rotates on its axis. It is also moving around the sun, and the sun is moving in our galaxy, and the galaxies are moving, and so on. There can be no such thing as the "absolute" velocity of an object — all measured velocities are relative.

Although velocity varies, other measured quantities such as force, mass, acceleration, and time interval can have the same value when measured from different reference frames, so long as the frames move with a constant velocity with respect to one another. Moreover, the relationships between such quantities are found to be the same. Since Newton's Law of Motion concerns the relationship between force, acceleration, and mass, Newton's Law of Motion holds both in frames of reference at rest and in those moving at uniform velocity. Since Newton's Law holds, these frames of reference are referred to as **Newtonian or inertial frames of reference.** Frames of reference that are accelerating are not inertial frames, and we should not expect Newton's laws to hold in them.

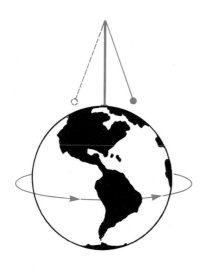

A Foucault pendulum located at the North Pole: the pendulum swings in nearly straight-line motion while the Earth rotates beneath it. To a man standing at the pole, the plane of the pendulum's motion appears to rotate.

Let us say a ball is placed on the floor of a bus. When the bus is at rest or moving with uniform velocity, the ball remains at rest on the floor. If the bus accelerates forward, in a straight line, the ball rolls straight backward. If the bus decelerates in a straight line, the ball rolls straight forward. If the bus turns a corner at uniform speed, the ball will move sideways.

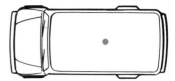

Bus at rest or moving with a uniform velocity

In the first case, the bus is an inertial frame of reference, and the ball remains at rest relative to it. But in the last three cases, the ball moves. It would be natural to assume that if there is an acceleration there must be a force on the ball. In fact, there is none.

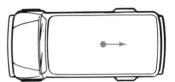

Bus accelerating forward

When the bus changed velocity, whether accelerating, decelerating, or travelling in a circular path, the ball was observed in an accelerating frame of reference. Newton's laws do not apply in **accelerating frames of reference**. Since we are so familiar with inertial frames of reference, we are tempted to assume that there must be forces present whenever we observe accelerated motions, and we invent fictitious forces to explain these motions. A common example of such a fictitious force is the **centrifugal force**.

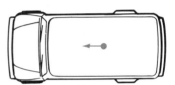

Bus accelerating backward

When travelling in a car at a uniform speed around a curve, you suddenly feel that you are being "pulled" across the seat towards the outer side of the car. You may assume that a "centrifugal" force is present, to explain this, since this would be the case in an inertial frame of reference. But you are making observations in an accelerating frame of reference, the car. What is actually happening is this: the frictional forces exerted on you by the car seat are not sufficient to provide the centripetal force necessary to keep you travelling in the same curve as the car. So you continue to move in a straight line, relative to the Earth, but slide across the seat, relative to the car.

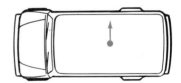

Bus turning to the left

To summarize, then, Newton's laws apply in inertial frames, but they do not apply in accelerated frames. Since the Earth is actually accelerating as it rotates about its axis, it is technically not an inertial system. However, the errors introduced by applying Newton's laws at the surface of the Earth are so small that we do not notice them experimentally. For all practical purposes, therefore, we consider the Earth to be an inertial system, where the Newtonian laws of motion can be used.

During the past ninety years, we have become aware that there are other instances where Newton's laws of motion do not work. This was not discovered earlier because it is only in recent times that we have been able to accelerate small particles to very high velocities.

In 1905, Einstein suggested one reason for such discrepancies. He predicted that a body's mass will increase as the velocity of the body increases. But, if the mass of a body is not constant, Newton's Second Law, as we know it, does not apply, because it was developed for objects with a constant mass. This increase in mass is negligible except when the velocity of the body approaches that of light. This is why no serious error is encountered when we use Newton's Second Law at ordinary velocities.

Einstein also predicted that both the length of an object and the time interval between two particular events will have different values when measured by moving observers. Again, these effects become significant only when the relative motion approaches the velocity of light.

Einstein developed the Special Theory of Relativity, a more general theory of motion that works for all velocities. At ordinary velocities, this theory gives the same results as Newton's Second Law. Einstein's theory is a good example of the development of theories in physics. The successful aspects of an old theory are often included as a special case of a newer and more general theory. Einstein's Special Theory of Relativity is described more fully in Chapter 17.

Newton began his thinking by using the work of Galileo. Einstein took Newton's laws of motion and enhanced them, in turn. In the future, as more information becomes available, Einstein's Theory of Relativity may also have to be revised and expanded. This is how the theories of science progress.

5.12 Investigations

Investigation 5.1: Acceleration of a Freely Falling Ball Bearing

Problem:
What is the acceleration due to gravity of a spherical mass?

Materials:
millimetre ruler
ball bearing (13 mm), painted white
Polaroid type camera on a tripod
metre stick
strobe light

Procedure:

Note — If the equipment is not available, omit steps 1 to 4 and use the accompanying photograph for your analysis.

1. Set up the apparatus as illustrated. Actual dimensions may vary slightly to produce the best results.
2. Set the strobe frequency at approximately 20 Hz.
3. Turn out the room lights, open the camera shutter, and drop the ball bearing. When it hits the floor, close the shutter.
4. Develop the picture. Make sure that at least 10 clear images of the ball bearing have been created on the film. If not, adjust the frequency of the strobe light and/or camera aperture, and repeat step 3.
5. Using the metre stick in the photograph, determine the scale of the photograph.
6. Measure the displacement for each time interval, recording your results in a chart.
7. Determine the period of the strobe and thus the time interval between images of the ball bearing on the film. Add these results to your chart.
8. Determine the average velocity for each time interval.
9. Plot a graph of average velocity versus time, and from the slope, determine the acceleration due to gravity.

Questions:

1. What is the experimental error of your measurement?
2. Could you use a ping-pong ball in this investigation? Explain your answer.

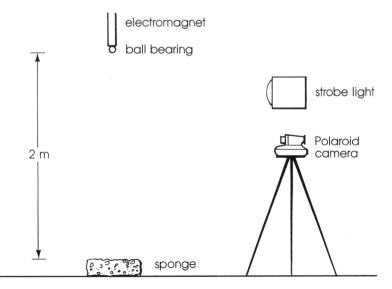

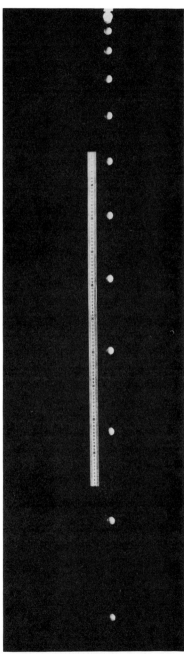

A strobe photograph of a falling ball bearing. The time between flashes is 0.0595 s. A metre stick is included to show the scale of the photograph.

Investigation 5.2: Centripetal Force

Problem:
What is the relationship between the centripetal force and the frequency, speed, mass, and radius of a rotating object?

Materials:
2 small rubber balls
28 steel washers
2 alligator clips (mass of one clip = mass of one washer)
1.5 m of fishing line or strong cord
reinforced glass tube with smooth ends
metre ruler

Procedure:

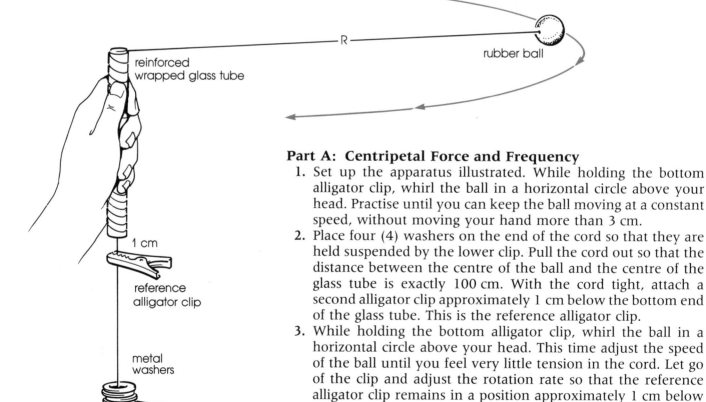

Part A: Centripetal Force and Frequency

1. Set up the apparatus illustrated. While holding the bottom alligator clip, whirl the ball in a horizontal circle above your head. Practise until you can keep the ball moving at a constant speed, without moving your hand more than 3 cm.

2. Place four (4) washers on the end of the cord so that they are held suspended by the lower clip. Pull the cord out so that the distance between the centre of the ball and the centre of the glass tube is exactly 100 cm. With the cord tight, attach a second alligator clip approximately 1 cm below the bottom end of the glass tube. This is the reference alligator clip.

3. While holding the bottom alligator clip, whirl the ball in a horizontal circle above your head. This time adjust the speed of the ball until you feel very little tension in the cord. Let go of the clip and adjust the rotation rate so that the reference alligator clip remains in a position approximately 1 cm below the glass tube. Have your partner determine the time for a definite number of rotations, say 15.

4. Set up the chart illustrated below.

Number of units of force	Number of rotations	Time (s)	Frequency (Hz)
6			
10			
14			

5. Repeat this procedure, adding four washers each time until a total of 28 washers and 2 alligator clips, or 30 units of force, create the centripetal force on the whirling ball.
6. Complete your observation chart by calculating the frequency. Note that if the centripetal force were zero, the number of rotations would be zero.
7. Plot a graph of force versus frequency. Using graphical techniques, determine the relationship between the centripetal force and the frequency. Write a proportionality statement for this relationship, and determine the constant of proportionality.
8. Using this equation, determine the force (in washers) required to maintain a ball of the same mass in a circular path of 1.0 m, with a frequency of 6 Hz.

Part B: Centripetal Force and Mass
9. Add one ball to the ball already on the end of the cord, effectively doubling the mass.
10. Place 10 washers on the string. Since the 2 alligator clips have a mass similar to 2 washers, the centripetal force has been doubled when compared to the total centripetal force of 6 washers in steps 2 and 3. Make sure that the reference alligator clip is replaced so that the distance from the tube to the balls is still 1.00 m.
11. Whirl the two balls, and vary the rotation rate until the reference alligator clip moves up to approximately 1 cm from the bottom of the glass tube. Determine the time for a definite number of rotations, say 10, and calculate the frequency.
12. Compare this frequency with the frequency in steps 2 and 3. Based on this information, what conclusion can you make about the relationship between the centripetal force and the mass, if both radius and frequency are kept constant?

Part C: Centripetal Force and Radius
13. Attach 10 washers to the end of the cord. This creates a centripetal force of 12 units (10 washers + 2 alligator clips). Attach the reference alligator clip so that the radius of rotation is now 0.50 m. Rotate one ball at a constant rate as you did previously,

It should be noted that in this investigation the radius of rotation is only an approximation, particularly at lower frequencies of rotation. As seen in the diagram, the radius (R) only approaches the length of the string (L) when θ approaches 0. The actual value for R is given by

$$R = L \cos \theta$$

However, the actual value for the centripetal force is given by the horizontal component of the tension (T).

$$F_c = T \cos \theta$$

These two effects exactly compensate, as follows:

$$F_c = 4\pi^2\, mRf^2$$
$$T \cos \theta = 4\pi^2\, m(L \cos \theta)\, f^2$$
$$T = 4\pi^2\, mLf^2$$

Note that the cos θs divide out and the tension in the string and the length of the string can be used for F_c and R, respectively.

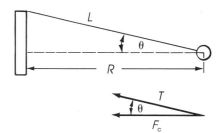

maintaining the reference clip approximately 1 cm below the glass tube. Record the time for a given number of rotations, say 10.

14. Set up an observations chart, similar to the one illustrated. Calculate the frequency and the frequency squared.

Radius (m)	Number of rotations	Time (s)	Frequency (Hz)	Frequency² (Hz²)
0.50				
0.75				
1.00				
1.25				

15. Repeat for radii of 0.75 m, 1.00 m, and 1.25 m.

16. Plot a graph of centripetal force (F_c) versus frequency squared (f^2). The graph should pass through the origin; in other words, $F_c = 0$ when $f^2 = 0$. Using the origin and the above data, we can determine four values of f^2 for a constant centripetal force of 12 units. Plot four curves of F_c versus f^2 on the same graph, one for each radius (see illustration).

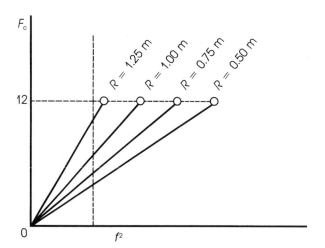

17. Draw a line parallel to the centripetal force axis, cutting each of the curves. Using interpolation, find for each radius the force required for a constant frequency (f^2 = constant).

18. Plot a graph of force (F_c) versus radius (R). Using the graph, determine the relationship between F_c and R.

19. To summarize, write a proportionality statement for (a) F_c and m, (b) F_c and f, and (c) F_c and R. Combine these into one proportionality statement relating F_c, m, f, and R.

5.13 Review

Discussion

1. How would you find the mass of an object in interstellar space, where the force of gravity approaches zero?
2. Why is it usually incorrect to say that an astronaut is "weightless" as he moves in orbit above the Earth?
3. A girl hopes to meet her boyfriend by sliding down a rope, made of nylon stockings, from her second story bedroom window. The stockings will break if the tension in them exceeds 400 N. The mass of the girl is 60 kg. Describe how she should slide down the rope so that she will land in the arms of her beloved at a minimum velocity.
4. What effect does the rotation of the Earth have on the apparent force of gravity on a man standing (a) at the equator and (b) at the North Pole?
5. A baseball is thrown vertically into the air. If there were no air resistance to be considered, it should return to its original position with the same speed as it had when thrown. But, given that air resistance is a factor, how will this affect its speed? Explain your reasoning.
6. In a disaster film, an elevator full of people falls freely when the cable snaps. In the film, the people are shown pressed upward against the ceiling. Is this good physics? Explain.
7. Future space stations may be designed like a giant wheel rotating about a central axis. The astronauts would live along the circumference of this structure. How would such a structure simulate gravity?
8. You wish to shoot a rocket to a point due north of your present position. In what direction should you aim the rocket if you are in the Northern Hemisphere? in the Southern Hemisphere?
9. A car being driven along a mountain road proceeds through an "S" curve. The first part of the curve has twice the radius of the second (reverse) part. How does the centripetal force acting on the car in the first part compare with that acting on the car in the second part? If the car doubles its speed, what changes occur in the size of the centripetal force acting on the car as it traverses each part of the curve?
10. A ball rolls off a horizontal table with a horizontal speed of 2 m/s. Stroboscopic photographs of the motion of the ball are taken from the three positions A, B, and C.

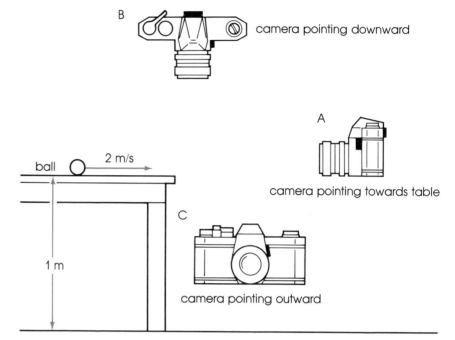

In position A, the camera is in front of the table with the ball rolling towards it. In position B, the camera is above the edge of the table. In position C, the camera is to one side of the table at right angles to the plane of the ball's path. Sketch the picture you would expect to obtain in each of the three positions.

11. A white disc is placed near the outside edge of a phonograph turntable that is rotating at $33\frac{1}{3}$ r/min. The turntable is on a cart moving at a constant velocity. The disc is illuminated by a strobe light flashing at a constant frequency. Draw a sketch showing the white disc as viewed from a fixed point above the path of the moving cart. Assume several strobe flashes per turntable rotation. Consider various speeds for the cart.

12. Very rapid circular motion, particularly of machinery near human beings, presents a serious safety hazard. Describe in three examples — one each from your home, the family automobile, and a family member's place of work — the hazard itself, the related physics, and the precautions and/or protection required.

13. Centrifuges assist analysts in determing the components of many substances and separating them out. Describe two applications in the following areas: blood analysis, research into DNA or proteins, dairy products, and minerals.

Problems

14. What would be the force of gravity on a 60.0 kg astronaut if she could stand on the surface of (a) Mars, (b) Uranus, (c) Pluto? (See chart on page 155.)

15. A horizontal force is applied to a 2.0 kg block, moving on a level table. A force that is one-quarter the force of gravity on the block is required to move it at a constant velocity. Calculate the force necessary to accelerate the moving block from rest to a speed of 3.0 m/s in 4.0 s.

16. A space traveller has landed on the surface of an unknown planet similar to Earth. He drops a small lead ball from the top of his space ship and finds it takes 3.0 s to reach the ground, 18 m below. If the force of gravity on the astronaut is 710 N on Earth, how much will it be on the planet? (SIN '69)

17. An aerospace scientist has designed a rocket with a mass of 1.0×10^3 kg. He wants it to accelerate straight up with an initial acceleration of 21 m/s^2. What thrust must the rocket engine develop?

18. A rocket of mass 1.0×10^3 kg is being fired to a height of 5.0×10^3 m. The rocket engine shuts off when the rocket reaches a height of 1.0×10^3 m, and the rocket coasts up to 5.0×10^3 m.
    (a) Draw a free-body diagram to show the forces acting on the rocket
        (i) while the engine is on, and
        (ii) after the engine shuts off.
    (b) What velocity must the rocket have at the 1.0×10^3 m point to enable it to reach 5.0×10^3 m?
    (c) What acceleration did the rocket experience while the engine was on? off?
    (d) What force did the rocket engine exert on the rocket?

19. An exceptional vertical jump from rest would raise a person 0.80 m off the ground. To do this, what constant force would a 70.0 kg person have to exert against the ground? Assume the person lowers himself by 0.20 m prior to jumping and remains in a standing position while in the air.

20. A 0.10 g spider is descending on a strand that supports it with a force of 5.6×10^{-4} N. What is the acceleration of the spider? Ignore the factor of air resistance.

21. A 5000 kg helicopter accelerates upward at 0.50 m/s^2 while lifting a 2000 kg car.
    (a) What is the lift force exerted by the air on the rotors?
    (b) What is the tension in the cable that connects the car to the helicopter?

22. Jane wishes to quickly scale a slender vine to visit Tarzan in his treetop hut. The vine is known to safely support the combined weight of Tarzan, Jane, and Cheeta. Tarzan has twice the mass of Jane, who has twice the mass of Cheeta. If the vine is 60 m long, what minimum time should Jane allow for the climb? (SIN '75)

23. A boy pushing a 20 kg lawn mower exerts a force of 100 N along the handle. If the handle is elevated 37° to the horizontal, determine
    (a) the component of the applied force that pushes the lawn mower forward,
    (b) the acceleration of the lawn mower, if the frictional force is 60 N,
    (c) the component of the applied force that pushes the lawn mower vertically towards the ground,
    (d) the gravitational force exerted on the mower,
    (e) the total downward force of the mower on the ground, when pushed,
    (f) the normal force exerted on the mower by the ground, and
    (g) the effective coefficient of kinetic friction.

24. An 80 kg man is standing in an elevator on a set of spring scales calibrated in newtons. Suppose the elevator accelerates downward at 3.0 m/s². What reading will the scales have?

25. An empty elevator of mass 2.7×10^3 kg is pulled upward by a cable at an acceleration of 1.2 m/s². (a) What is the tension in the cable? (b) What would the tension be if the elevator were accelerating downward at 1.2 m/s²? (c) Does the direction of motion of the elevator matter in (a) and (b)?

26. A fish hangs from a spring scale supported from the roof of an elevator. (a) If the elevator has an upward acceleration of 1.2 m/s² and the scale reads 200 N, what is the true force of gravity on the fish? (b) Under what circumstances will the scale read 150 N? (c) What will the scale read if the elevator cable breaks?

27. For each of the following systems:
    (i) draw a free-body diagram for each mass,
    (ii) find the tension in the string(s),
    (iii) find the rate at which the masses will accelerate, and
    (iv) calculate how far each mass will move in 2.0 s, if the system starts from rest.
    (Assume that both the surfaces and the pulleys are frictionless.)

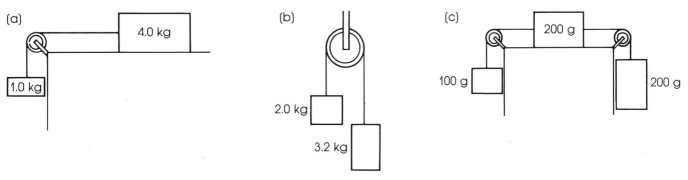

28. Two masses are connected by a light cord over a frictionless pulley, as illustrated. If the coefficient of kinetic friction is 0.18, what is (a) the acceleration of the system and (b) the tension in the cord? Assume that the system starts to move. (c) For what values of μ_s will it not start?

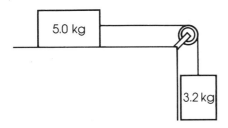

29. What is the acceleration of the system illustrated, if the coefficient of kinetic friction is 0.20? Assume that it starts.

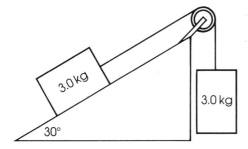

30. Tarzan (mass 100 kg) holds one end of an ideal vine (infinitely strong, completely flexible, but having zero mass). The vine runs horizontally to the edge of a cliff, then vertically to where Jane (mass 50 kg) is hanging on, above a river filled with hungry crocodiles. A sudden sleet storm has removed all friction. Assuming that Tarzan hangs on, what is his acceleration towards the cliff edge? (SIN '78)

31. An engineer designs a jet boat with a mass of 6.0×10^2 kg. The force of water resistance is given by $F_r = 1.8 \, v^2$. (F_r is the resistance in N, and v is the speed in m/s.)
    (a) What thrust (force) must the engine develop to enable the boat to reach a speed of 40 m/s?
    (b) What is the maximum acceleration the boat can achieve with this thrust?

32. A 70 kg hockey player coasts along the ice on steel skates. If the coefficient of kinetic friction is 0.010, (a) what is the force of friction? (b) How long will it take him to coast to a stop, if he is travelling at 1.0 m/s?

33. A 10 kg box is pulled across a level floor, where the coefficient of kinetic friction is 0.35. What horizontal force is required for an acceleration of 2.0 m/s²?

34. A small 10 kg cardboard box is thrown across a level floor. It slides a distance of 6.0 m, stopping in 2.2 s. Determine the coefficient of friction between the box and the floor.

35. A 0.5 kg wooden block is placed on top of a 1.0 kg wooden block. The coefficient of static friction between the two blocks is 0.35. The coefficient of kinetic friction between the lower block and the level table is 0.20. What is the maximum horizontal force that can be applied to the lower block without the upper block slipping?

36. A boy pulls a 50 kg crate across a level floor with a force of 200 N. If the force acts at an angle of 30° up from the horizontal, and the coefficient of kinetic friction is 0.30, determine
    (a) the normal force exerted on the crate by the floor,
    (b) the horizontal frictional force exerted on the crate by the floor,
    (c) the acceleration of the crate.

37. A can of pop is given a shove. It slides across a table, eventually coming to a stop. If its initial velocity is 2.0 m/s, and the coefficient of kinetic friction between the two surfaces is 0.30, how far will it travel across the table?

38. A skier skiing downhill reaches the bottom of a hollow with a velocity of 20 m/s, and then coasts up a hill with a 30° slope. If the coefficient of kinetic friction is 0.10, how far up the slope will she travel before she stops?

39. A multi-flash, stroboscopic photograph is taken of a freely-falling polystyrene ball. The flash rate of the stroboscope is 20 Hz. The resulting photograph is one-fifth actual size.
    (a) What is the time interval between pictures?
    (b) Calculate the average speed of the ball between each flash, in metres per second.

(c) Calculate
   (i) the increase in speed between successive ball positions and
   (ii) the acceleration between successive ball positions.
(d) Explain why the acceleration appears to decrease as the ball falls.

40. What force must a track star exert on a shot put of mass 5.0 kg to accelerate it from rest to a velocity of 6.0 m/s[up] while pushing it through a vertical distance of 80 cm? How long will it rise after leaving the shot-putter's hand?

41. A robber jumps from an apartment window 5.0 m high. When he strikes the ground below, he bends his knees so that his torso decelerates over an approximate distance of 0.70 m. If the mass of his torso (excluding his legs) is 50 kg, find
(a) his velocity just before his feet strike the ground, and
(b) the force exerted on his torso by his legs during the deceleration.

42. A ball is thrown horizontally from a window at 10 m/s and hits the ground 5.0 s later. What is the height of the window and how far from the base of the building does the ball hit?

43. A cannon is fired at 30° above the horizontal with a velocity of 200 m/s from the edge of a cliff 125 m high. Calculate where the cannonball lands on the level plain below.

44. A shell is fired horizontally from a powerful gun, located 44 m above a horizontal plane, with a muzzle speed of 245 m/s.
(a) How long does the shell remain in the air?
(b) What is its range?
(c) What is the magnitude of the vertical component of its velocity as it strikes the target?

45. A bomber, diving at an angle of 53° with the vertical, releases a bomb at an altitude of 730 m. The bomb hits the ground 5.0 s after being released.
(a) What was the velocity of the bomber?
(b) How far did the bomb travel horizontally during its flight?
(c) What were the horizontal and vertical components of its velocity just before striking the ground?

46. A driver, accelerating too quickly on a horizontal bridge, skids, crashes through the bridge railing, and lands in the river 20.0 m below the level of the bridge roadway. The police find that the car is not vertically below the break in the railing, but is 53.6 m beyond it horizontally.
(a) Determine the speed of the car before the crash, in km/h.

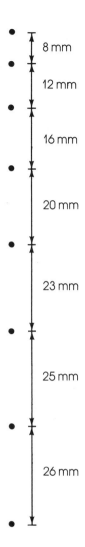

Numerical Answers to Review Problems

14. (a) 223 N (b) 629 N (c) 18.6 N
15. 6.4 N
16. 2.9×10^2 N
17. 3.1×10^4 N
18. (b) 2.8×10^2 m/s
    (c) 39 m/s², 9.8 m/s² (d) 4.9×10^4 N
19. 3.4×10^3 N
20. 4.2 m/s²[down]
21. (a) 7.2×10^4 N[up]
    (b) 2.1×10^4 N[up]
22. 2.2 s
23. (a) 80 N (b) 1.0 m/s² (c) 60 N
    (d) 2.0×10^2 N (e) 2.6×10^2 N
    (f) 2.6×10^2 N (g) 0.23
24. 544 N
25. (a) 3.0×10^4 N (b) 2.3×10^4 N
26. (a) 1.8×10^2 N (b) 1.5 m/s²[down]
    (c) 0
27. (a) (ii) 7.8 N (iii) 2.0 m/s² (iv) 1.4 m
    (b) (ii) 24 N (iii) 2.3 m/s² (iv) 1.6 m
    (c) (ii) 1.2 N, 1.6 N (iii) 2.0 m/s²
    (iv) 1.4 m
28. (a) 2.8 m/s² (b) 23 N (c) ≥ 0.46
29. 1.6 m/s²
30. 3.3 m/s²
31. (a) 2.9×10^3 N (b) 4.8 m/s²
32. (a) 6.9 N (b) 10 s
33. 54 N
34. 0.26
35. 8.1 N
36. (a) 3.9×10^2 N (b) 1.2×10^2 N
    (c) 1.1 m/s²
37. 1.0 m
38. 75 m
39. (a) 0.050 s
    (b) 0.80 m/s, 1.2 m/s, 1.6 m/s,
    2.0 m/s, 2.3 m/s, 2.5 m/s, 2.6 m/s
    (c) (i) 0.40 m/s, 0.40 m/s, 0.40 m/s,
    0.30 m/s, 0.20 m/s, 0.10 m/s
    (ii) 8.0 m/s², 8.0 m/s², 8.0 m/s²,
    6.0 m/s², 4.0 m/s², 2.0 m/s²
40. 1.6×10^2 N, 0.61 s
41. (a) 9.9 m/s (b) 3.5×10^3 N
42. 1.2×10^2 m, 50 m
43. 3.3×10^3 m
44. (a) 3.0 s (b) 7.4×10^2 m (c) 29 m/s
45. (a) 2.0×10^2 m/s (b) 8.0×10^2 m
    (c) 1.6×10^2 m/s, 1.71×10^2 m/s
46. (a) 26.5 m/s
47. (a) 42.9 s (b) 15.4 km

(b) What properties of falling bodies did you assume in making your calculation in (a)?

(c) State whether your answer in (a) is an overestimate or an underestimate, and why.

47. An artillery gun is fired so that its shell has a vertical component of velocity of 210 m/s and a horizontal component of 360 m/s. If the target is at the same level as the gun, and air friction is neglected,
    (a) how long will the shell stay in the air?
    (b) how far down-range will the shell hit the target?

48. A baseball, thrown from shortstop position to first base, travels 32 m horizontally, rises 3.0 m, and falls 3.0 m. Find the initial velocity of the ball.

49. If you can hurl a ball so that its initial speed is 30 m/s, what is the widest river you can throw it across?

50. A player kicks a football with an initial velocity of 15 m/s at an angle of 42° above the horizontal. A second player standing at a distance of 30 m from the first, in the direction of the kick, starts running to meet the ball at the instant it is kicked. How fast must he run in order to catch the ball before it hits the ground?

51. A rifle with a muzzle velocity of 460 m/s shoots a bullet at a small target 800 m away at the same height. At what angle above the horizontal must the gun be aimed so that the bullet will hit the target?

52. You have determined the following results when doing an investigation. Using proportioning techniques, find the new value for the centripetal force.

Before	*After*
mass = 1 ball	mass = 3 balls
radius = 0.75 m	radius = 1.50 m
frequency = 1.5 Hz	frequency = 3.0 Hz
centripetal force = 8.0 units	centripetal force = ? units

53. A 200 g ball on the end of a string is rotated in a horizontal circle of radius 10.0 m. The ball completes 10 rotations in 5.0 s. What is the centripetal force of the string on the ball?

54. In the Bohr model of the hydrogen atom, the electron revolves around the nucleus. If the radius of the orbit is 5.3×10^{-11} m and the electron makes 6.6×10^{15} r/s, find
    (a) the acceleration of the electron and
    (b) the centripetal force acting on the electron. (This force is due to the attraction between the positively charged nucleus and the negatively charged electron.) The mass of the electron is 9.1×10^{-31} kg.

55. A string pendulum 1.12 m long has a bob with a mass of 200 g.
   (a) What is the tension in the string when the pendulum is at rest?
   (b) What is the tension at the bottom of the swing, if the pendulum is moving at 1.2 m/s?

56. When you whirl a ball on a cord in a vertical circle, you find a critical speed at the top for which the tension in the cord is zero. This is because the force of gravity on the object itself supplies the necessary centripetal force. How slowly can you swing a 2.5 kg ball like this so that it will just follow a circle with a radius of 1.5 m?

57. An object of mass 3.0 kg is whirled around in a vertical circle of radius 1.3 m with a constant velocity of 6.0 m/s. Calculate the maximum and minimum tension in the string.

58. Snoopy is flying his vintage war plane in a "loop the loop" path chasing the Red Baron. His instruments tell him the plane is level (at the bottom of the loop) and travelling with a speed of 180 km/h. He is sitting on a set of bathroom scales, and notes that they read four times the normal force of gravity on him. What is the radius of the loop? Answer in metres. (SIN '75)

59. An Australian bushman hunts kangaroos with the following weapon, a heavy rock tied to one end of a light vine of length 2 m. He holds the other end above his head, at a point 2 m above ground level, and swings the rock in a horizontal circle. The cunning kangaroo has observed that the vine always breaks when the angle θ (measured between the vine and the vertical) reaches 60°. At what minimum distance from the hunter can the kangaroo stand with no danger of a direct hit? (SIN '72)

60. A pendulum of mass 1.0 kg is suspended from the roof of a car travelling on a level road. An observer in the car notices that the pendulum string makes an angle of 10° with the vertical. What is the acceleration of the car?

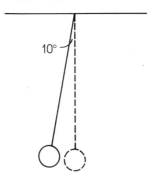

48. 22 m/s [21° to the horizontal]
49. 92 m
50. 3.6 m/s
51. 1.1°
52. 192 units
53. 3.2 × 10² N
54. (a) 9.1 × 10²² m/s² (b) 8.3 × 10⁻⁸ N
55. (a) 1.96 N (b) 2.2 N
56. 3.8 m/s
57. 1.1 × 10² N, 54 N
58. 85 m
59. 3.0 m
60. 1.8 m/s²

6 Bodies in Equilibrium

Statics is the branch of physics dealing with conditions in which bodies are kept at rest by the actions of forces. The words *static* (from the Latin for "at rest") and *equilibrium* (from the Latin for "equal forces") describe the forces acting in such a way that the net force on an object is zero. A body in equilibrium and at rest is said to be in **static equilibrium**, whereas a body moving with uniform velocity is said to be in **dynamic equilibrium**. The conditions for dynamic equilibrium were studied in Chapters 4 and 5. In this chapter we will concentrate on static equilibrium.

We experience the conditions for static equilibrium from earliest childhood. When a child stands up for the first time, the upward forces of the floor on her feet combine with the downward force of gravity to keep her body in a steady state, at rest, at least for a few moments. When a child piles up blocks or books, she learns what will remain stable and what will not. Most things around us, whether naturally occurring or made by human hands, are in a state of static equilibrium: an apple on a tree, snow on a roof, a boulder perched on a mountain slope, the house that shelters us, the bridge under our feet, or a ladder resting against the wall.

The knowledge gained from a study of statics is fundamental for architects and engineers. They must be able to calculate the stresses in the structural members of a building or a bridge. Any material will break or buckle if too much force is applied to it. A building can collapse under a heavy snow load, or a bridge can fall into a river, even under its own weight.

The Quebec Bridge collapse of 1907, which killed seventy-five workers, was blamed on an "error in judgement" by engineers.

In this chapter we will be primarily concerned with calculating the forces acting on bodies in equilibrium. We will begin by discussing the forces acting on small-point objects, where the mass and size are not considered. Next we will examine static equilibrium in the real world, where an object's weight, size, and shape must be considered. Later we will discuss the factors that determine the stability of an object, and how forces acting on an object produce stress and strain. Finally we will apply our knowledge of static equilibrium to applications in building construction and in the human body.

6.1 Equilibrium in Small Objects

Small objects are the easiest to analyse, because all forces on them tend to act at essentially the same point. Large objects can be treated in an identical fashion if all the forces are considered to act through a single point called the **centre of mass**. The centre of mass for a uniform, regular object, such as a sphere or brick, is simply the geometric centre. The centre of mass for irregular objects like bridges, cars, and humans will be discussed later in the chapter.

In order for an object to be in equilibrium, the vector sum of all the forces acting on it must be zero. As discussed in Chapters 3 and 4, this also implies that because of the vector nature of forces, the net force component in any direction that we choose must be zero. Some examples will illustrate this concept.

Forces that act at a common point are said to be concurrent.

Sample problems

1. Several children are playing on the smooth, frictionless, level floor of a nursery. They hold strings tied to a small toy truck, which they pull horizontally. Barbara(B) pulls with a force of 16 N [east], Scott(S) pulls with a force of 19 N [west]. With what force must Kevin(K) pull to keep the truck in equilibrium, horizontally?

To begin, we draw a free-body diagram of the truck. Since the truck is a small object, all the forces will be considered to act at the centre of mass.

$\vec{F}_S$, $\vec{F}_B$, and $\vec{F}_K$ are the forces applied by the three strings. $\vec{F}_g$ and $\vec{F}_N$ are the gravitational force and normal floor force, respectively. Since the truck is in static equilibrium, the vector sum of the forces must add to zero; that is,

$$\vec{F}_{net} = \vec{F}_N + \vec{F}_g + \vec{F}_B + \vec{F}_K + \vec{F}_S = 0$$

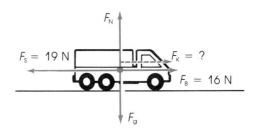

We will take the components of this vector equation in the easterly direction. It is helpful to also include the zero components, so that we do not forget any components. If east is taken as positive, then the vector equation becomes, for easterly components,

$$0 + 0 + 16\text{ N} + F_K - 19\text{ N} = 0$$
$$\text{and } F_K = 19\text{ N} - 16\text{ N}$$
$$= 3\text{ N}$$

Thus, Kevin exerts a force of 3 N [east].

It should be noted that the physical result would be the same if the components were taken in the westerly direction. Also, taking the vertical component of $\vec{F}_{net} = 0$ tells us only that $F_g = F_N$, which is not useful in this problem. In fact, since the vertical components in a sense cancel out one another, we can forget them, if we wish, and use only the horizontal components.

2. A few minutes later the children are pulling the truck in a different way. Barbara pulls with a force of 16 N [east] and Kevin pulls with a force of 12 N [north]. What force must Scott now apply to maintain static equilibrium?

First, draw the free-body diagram of the truck as seen from above. The vertical forces can be ignored.

There are three possible solutions for this problem. All are equally valid, although usually the component solution is easiest to use when more than two vectors are involved.

Solution 1: Vector Scale Diagram

For equilibrium, $\vec{F}_{net} = 0$; also, $\vec{F}_{net} = \vec{F}_K + \vec{F}_B + \vec{F}_S$.

The scaled vectors $\vec{F}_K$ and $\vec{F}_B$ are added head to tail, as illustrated. Then $\vec{F}_S$ is the vector running from the head of $\vec{F}_B$ to the tail of $\vec{F}_K$ so that $\vec{F}_K + \vec{F}_B + \vec{F}_S = 0$.

Thus, $\vec{F}_S = 20$ N [W37°S] by scaling, and measuring the angle θ.

Solution 2: Trigonometric

$$F_S = \sqrt{F_K{}^2 + F_B{}^2}$$
$$= \sqrt{(12\text{ N})^2 + (16\text{ N})^2}$$
$$= 20\text{ N}$$
$$\theta = \tan^{-1}\frac{12\text{ N}}{16\text{ N}} = 37°$$

Thus, $\vec{F}_S = 20$ N [W37°S].

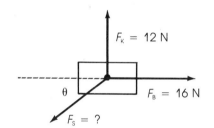

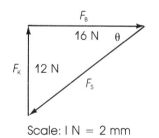

Scale: I N = 2 mm

Solution 3: Using Components

The components of $\vec{F}_S$ in the west and south directions are $\vec{F}_{Sw}$ and $\vec{F}_{Ss}$, as illustrated in the free-body diagram.

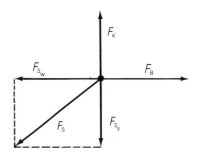

$$\vec{F}_{net} = 0$$

$$\vec{F}_{net} = \vec{F}_K + \vec{F}_B + \vec{F}_S = 0$$

Taking the easterly components,

$$0 = 0 + 16\,\text{N} - F_{Sw} = 0$$

Thus, $\qquad F_{Sw} = 16\,\text{N, or } \vec{F}_{Sw} = 16\,\text{N [west].}$

It should be noted that the component of $\vec{F}_K$ in the easterly direction is zero, since north is at 90° to east.

Similarly, taking northerly components,

$$0 = 12\,\text{N} + 0 - F_{Ss} = 0$$

Thus, $\qquad F_{Ss} = 12\,\text{N, or } \vec{F}_{Ss} = 12\,\text{N [south].}$

Since $\vec{F}_S$ has components of 16 N [west] and 12 N [south], the magnitude of $\vec{F}_S$ is

$$F_S = \sqrt{16^2 + 12^2}$$
$$= 20\,\text{N}$$

and its direction is given by

$$\theta = \tan^{-1}\frac{12}{16} = 37°.$$

Therefore, the required force is 20 N [W37°S].

3. A clothes-line is attached to high poles 10.0 m apart. A pulley, allowed to roll freely on the line, has a 30 kg mass hanging from it. Find the tension in each half of the clothes-line if the sag at the centre is 0.40 m as shown.

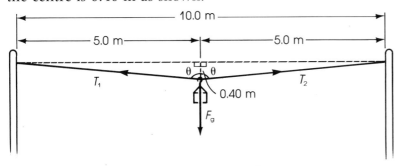

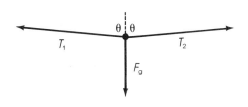

Draw a free-body diagram of the pulley and mass in static equilibrium. Three forces act on the pulley. The magnitude of the force of gravity on the 30 kg mass will be

$$F = mg$$
$$= (30 \text{ kg}) (9.8 \text{ N/kg})$$
$$= 294 \text{ N}$$

For equilibrium, $\vec{F}_{net} = 0$, and $\vec{F}_{net} = \vec{F}_g + \vec{T}_1 + \vec{T}_2 = 0$

Taking vertical components, the vector equation becomes

$$F_{net} = - F_g + T_1 \cos \theta + T_2 \cos \theta = 0$$

But $T_1 = T_2$ and, using the dimensions in the diagram,

$$\theta = \tan^{-1} \frac{5.0 \text{ m}}{0.40 \text{ m}} = 85.4°$$

Thus, $-294 \text{ N} + 2T_1 (\cos 85.4°) = 0$

and $T_1 = 1833 \text{ N}$

Therefore, $T_1 = T_2 = 1.8 \times 10^3 \text{ N}$

The horizontal components of the vector equation give

$$0 = T_2 \sin \theta - T_1 \sin \theta + 0$$

therefore $T_1 = T_2$

In both cases the tension force acting on the pulley is along the rope towards each pole.

Practice

1. Forces as given below are acting on a common point. Using two different solutions for each combination of forces, find the additional force required to maintain static equilibrium.
   (a) 160 N [east], 120 N [west];
   (b) 200 N [east], 160 N [north];
   (c) 100 N [N45°E], 150 N [W];
   (d) 6.0 N [N30°E], 10.0 N [N45°W], 12.0 N [W10°S].

   (40 N [E], 256 N [W39°S], 106 N [E42°S], 19.2 N [S57°E])

2.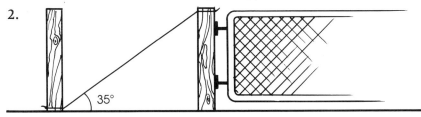

A guy wire attached to the top of a gate post is anchored to the bottom of the next post, as illustrated. Assuming that the gate post does not move, what are the horizontal and vertical components of the force exerted on the top of the post by the guy wire, if the tension in the wire is 500 N?

(410 N[left], 286 N[down])

3.

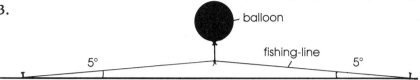

A helium balloon is attached to the middle of a light fishing-line anchored at both ends, as illustrated. If the upward force of the balloon is 0.05 N, find the tension in the fishing-line.

(0.29 N)

4.

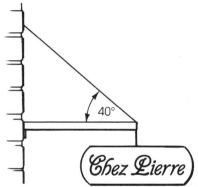

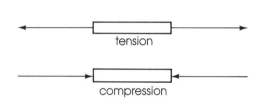

The sign for Pierre's restaurant has a mass of 82 kg. It is held out from the wall by a light horizontal steel rod, which supports no weight, and a wire at 40° to the horizontal, as illustrated. Find the tension in the wire and the compression in the steel rod. (1.3 × 10³ N, 9.6 × 10² N)

5.

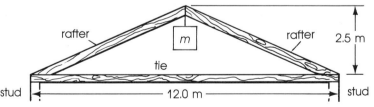

A simple roof truss is composed of two rafters and a horizontal tie, held together by one single pin at each vertex. If a 100 kg mass is hung from the apex of the rafters, as illustrated, what is

(a) the additional compression in each rafter,
(b) the additional tension in the tie, and
(c) the additional compression in each stud?

(1.3 × 10³ N, 1.2 × 10³ N, 4.9 × 10² N)

When considering trusses and other similar structures in this chapter, we use simple pin joints at the ends, so that the truss members will be in tension or compression. A pin cannot transmit a torque from one member to another. In practice, the joints will usually have more than one pin, and the analysis may be more complex.

6.2 Static Friction

So far we have not taken friction into account, but it is part of many practical applications involving static equilibrium. In the previous chapter, static friction was described as the maximum frictional force that must be overcome in order to just start an object moving over a specific surface. It was also emphasized that frictional forces always act in a direction opposite to that of the applied force. The mathematical relationship for static friction is:

$$F_S \leq \mu_s F_N$$

where F_S is the force of static friction on the object
μ_s is the coefficient of static friction
F_N is the normal force of the surface on the object
It should be recalled that a static frictional force acts in the plane of the surface, and only exists when there is an external, opposite force on the object in question. The values of static frictional force lie between zero (no force) and a maximum value given by $\mu_s F_N$.

The examples of friction in the previous chapter also involved kinetic friction. Since with static equilibrium the object is at rest, we need only deal with static friction here. Some examples will illustrate the use of static friction in equilibrium problems.

Sample problems

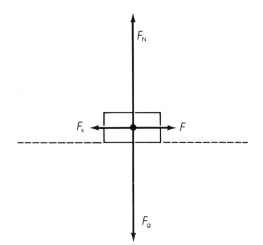

1. A horizontal pull is being exerted on a 10 kg box with a string. If the coefficient of static friction is 0.40, what is the maximum force in the string just before the box moves?

There are four forces acting on the box, as illustrated in the free-body diagram for maximum F just before slipping. Since the box is in equilibrium, $\vec{F}_{net} = 0$, and $\vec{F}_{net} = \vec{F} + \vec{F}_g + \vec{F}_S + \vec{F}_N = 0$.

Taking horizontal components to the right, the vector equation becomes
$$F + 0 - F_S + 0 = 0$$
or
$$F = F_S$$

Taking vertical components, with up as positive, the vector equation becomes
$$0 - F_g + 0 + F_N = 0$$
or
$$F_N = F_g$$
but
$$F_S = \mu_s F_N \text{ and } F_g = mg$$
Thus,
$$F = F_s = \mu_s\, mg$$
$$= 0.40 \ (10 \text{ kg}) \ (9.8 \text{ N/kg})$$
$$= 39.2 \text{ N, or } 39 \text{ N}$$

2. A 1.0 kg block is placed on an adjustable ramp. To what maximum angle can the ramp be raised before the block just begins to slide, if the coefficient of friction is 0.40?

First, draw the free-body diagram at the maximum angle (θ) just before slippage. There are three forces acting on the block. The force of gravity ($\vec{F_g}$), the normal force of the ramp on the block ($\vec{F_N}$), and the force of friction ($\vec{F_s}$). Note that normal force is always at 90° to the surface, even when the surface is tilted.

Since the block is in equilibrium,

$$\vec{F}_{net} = 0, \text{ and } \vec{F}_{net} = \vec{F_g} + \vec{F_s} + \vec{F_N} = 0$$

Taking components parallel to the ramp and making up positive, we obtain

$$-F_g \sin\theta + F_s + 0 = 0$$

or

$$F_s = F_g \sin\theta$$

Taking components normal to the ramp, and again making up positive, we obtain

$$-F_g \cos\theta + 0 + F_N = 0$$

or

$$F_N = F_g \cos\theta$$

Thus,

$$\frac{F_s}{F_N} = \mu = \frac{F_g \sin\theta}{F_g \cos\theta} = \tan\theta$$

so

$$\tan\theta = 0.40$$

and

$$\theta = \tan^{-1} 0.40 = 22°$$

Therefore the ramp must be elevated 22° to the horizontal in order for the block to begin to slide down it.

3. A 0.50 kg block of cheese sits on a level table, as shown. The coefficient of static friction is 0.60. Three strings are tied together in a knot at K. Kc is horizontal and fastened to the cheese. Kw angles up to the wall at 30° to the horizontal. Km hangs vertically, supporting a mouse. What is the maximum mass of the mouse, if the cheese and the mouse remain in equilibrium?

As seen in the diagram, the components of the force of gravity on the mass (mg) are $mg \sin\theta$, down the slope, and $mg \cos\theta$, perpendicular to the slope. But $F_s = mg \sin\theta$ and $F_N = mg \cos\theta$. Therefore, since

$$\mu = F_s/F_N$$
$$= \frac{mg \sin\theta}{mg \cos\theta}$$
$$\mu = \tan\theta$$

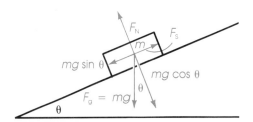

When the mass and the slope are made of the same material, θ is called the *angle of repose*. The angle of repose is used in geology. For example, the angle of repose for dry clay is 45°. For wet clay it is 17°. As a result, when there are heavy rains in the mountains, there are usually mud slides. (Ask your geography teacher about the famous Frank Slide in Alberta, which occurred in 1903.)

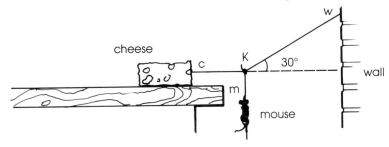

Focus your attention on the knot at K, and draw a free-body diagram for the limiting case just before slippage. The three forces shown are the tensions in the three strings. Since the

cheese

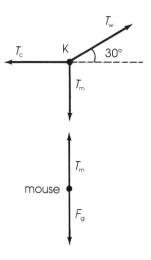

mouse

knot is in equilibrium, we know that
$$\vec{F}_{net} = \vec{T}_c + \vec{T}_w + \vec{T}_m = 0$$
Taking horizontal components, with right as positive, this vector equation gives us
$$-T_c + T_w \cos 30° = 0$$
or $T_c = T_w \cos 30°$
but $T_c = F_s = \mu_s F_N = \mu_s \, mg$
$$= 0.60 \, (0.50 \text{ kg}) \, (9.8 \text{ N/kg})$$
$$= 2.94 \text{ N}$$
Thus, $2.94 \text{ N} = T_w \cos 30°$
and $T_w = 3.39 \text{ N}$
Taking vertical components, with up as positive, gives us
$$0 + T_w \sin 30° - T_m = 0$$
or $T_m = T_w \sin 30°$
$$= (3.39 \text{ N}) \, (\sin 30°)$$
$$= 1.7 \text{ N}$$
Since $T_m = F_g$, the force of gravity on the mouse is 1.7 N, and its mass would be
$$F = mg$$
$$1.7 \text{ N} = m \, (9.8 \text{ N/kg})$$
$$m = 0.17 \text{ kg}$$

Practice

1. A flat rock with a mass of 20 kg rests on a rough horizontal plane. If the coefficient of friction is 0.22, find the least force required to just move the rock, if the force acts (a) horizontally, (b) at an angle of 37° above the horizontal, and (c) at an angle of 37° below the horizontal.   (43 N, 46 N, 65 N)

2.

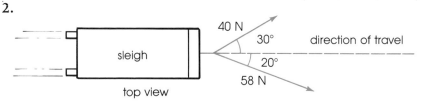

top view

Three children are playing in the snow with a sleigh. One child exerts a maximum force of 40 N and another 58 N, on ropes, to just get the sleigh to move with the third child seated in it. The angles the horizontal ropes make with the direction of travel are 30° and 20°, respectively. If the combined mass of the seated child and the sleigh is 75 kg, and the sleigh moves in a straight line, what is the coefficient of friction between the sleigh and the snow?   (0.12)

3.

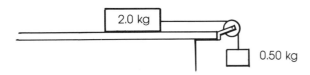

A 2.0 kg wooden block is attached to a 0.50 kg mass by a string passing through a frictionless pulley, as illustrated.

(a) If the mass of 0.50 kg provides the minimum force required to just get the block to move, what is the coefficient of friction?

(b)

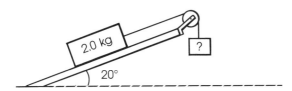

When we say the minimum force required to move something, we really mean the maximum force before static equilibrium is lost.

If the same plane surface is now inclined 20° to the horizontal, what minimum mass, attached to the string, will just get the block moving?   (0.25, 1.2 kg)

4. A 2.5 kg block rests on a plane inclined at 15° to the horizontal. If the coefficient of static friction for the surface is 0.30, will the block slide down the plane?   (no)

6.3 Static Equilibrium in Large Bodies — Torque

We have seen that an object can only be in equilibrium if the sum of all the forces acting on it is zero. However, this is not a sufficient condition, as a simple example will show.

Two children are pulling a log across the ice. Their ropes are attached one to each end of the log, and they are moving in a northerly direction with the log parallel to the ropes. After stopping for a rest, one child decides to go west and pulls with a force of 75 N due west. The other child disagrees, and pulls with a force of 75 N due east.

Now it is clear that the net force acting on the log will be zero. But it is equally clear that the log will not remain in its initial position but will rotate, with one end moving west and the other end east. This result does not violate the conditions for static equilibrium since the log's centre of mass is the pivot point, and this remains at rest. It does, however, show that we need more than

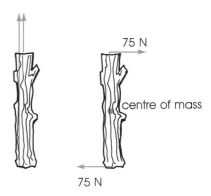

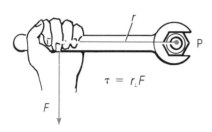

$$\tau = r_\perp F$$

To distinguish the units for torque and moment from those for work (Chapter 9), the unit newton metre (N·m) is used for torque and the joule is used for work, although they are dimensionally equal.

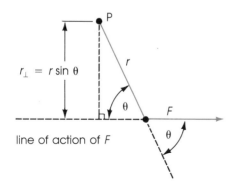

$r_\perp = r \sin \theta$

line of action of F

$\vec{F}_{net} = 0$ for static equilibrium in normal-size objects.

When we study the equilibrium of normal, large-size objects, the forces involved may not pass through a common point, as they do for small objects. We must also take the twisting or turning effect of each force into account. This twisting effect is called **torque**, or the **moment of the force**. If you have ever turned a screwdriver, twisted the lid from a bottle, tightened a nut with a wrench, or parked a car in a tight spot, you will know what torque is.

Suppose you are loosening a stubborn nut under a bicycle seat. First you fit a long-handled wrench on the nut and apply a force to the handle. It does not take long to learn that for the maximum effect you must pull as hard as you can on the end of the wrench, and in a direction perpendicular to the handle. All three factors are important: the size of the force, the point of application, and the direction in which the force is applied.

We will use the diagram to give a definition of torque suitable for two-dimensional problems, where all forces lie in one plane. A force (F) lying in the plane of the paper produces a torque about a point P, which is equal in magnitude to the applied force multiplied by the perpendicular distance ($r_\perp$) between the point of rotation P and the line of action of the force. As is true for many definitions in physics, torque is most easily expressed as a mathematical equation, as follows:

$$\tau = r_\perp F$$

where τ is the torque

      F is the applied force

      $r_\perp$ is the perpendicular distance between the point of rotation and the line of action of the applied force

The unit of torque is the newton metre (N·m) and the symbol usually used for it is τ, the Greek letter "tau". The force (F) must be expressed in newtons (N) and the perpendicular distance ($r_\perp$) in metres (m).

In circumstances where the applied force is not perpendicular to the length of the device applying the torque, $r_\perp$ will be less than r. As seen in the diagram, the value of $r_\perp$ will be determined by the value of $r \sin \theta$. The torque will be greatest when $\theta = 90°$ and $\sin \theta = 1$, and zero when $\theta = 0$ or $180°$. A more general expression for torque can be expressed as follows:

$$\tau = rF\sin \theta$$

In general, torque is a vector, but in this text we concentrate only on applications in which the forces are all in one plane. This means that we only have to keep track of the rotational direction of the twist. In the diagram on page 214, the twist, or turning effect, is counterclockwise, and we arbitrarily call this **positive torque**. If the wrench handle were flipped over to the right and the force still pulled down, the twist would be clockwise, and the torque would be negative.

When two or more torques act simultaneously on an object, each will tend to rotate the object about a given axis. For static equilibrium, **the sum of the counterclockwise torques about any point is equal to the sum of the clockwise torques**. This is called the **Principle of Torques**, but it is also referred to as the **Principle of Moments** or, simply, the **Law of the Lever**.

We now have two fundamental conditions that must be satisfied if any object, large or small, is to remain in static equilibrium, namely:

$\vec{F}_{net} = 0$, **that is, the total force acting on a rigid object is zero, no matter what direction is chosen.**

$\vec{\tau}_{net} = 0$, **that is, the total torque acting on a rigid object is zero, about any chosen axis of rotation.**

These conditions apply equally to toy trucks or skyscrapers. A few sample problems will illustrate these principles.

Sample problems

1. A cyclist applies a downward force of 65 N on the pedal of her bicycle, as illustrated. Find the torque for each position.

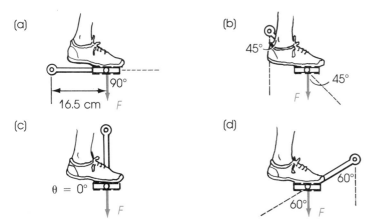

(a) 90° 16.5 cm *F*

(b) 45° 45° *F*

(c) θ = 0° *F*

(d) 60° 60° *F*

Note that torque can also be written as $\tau = rF_\perp$, where $F_\perp = F\sin\theta$, resulting in the same expression, i.e., $\tau = rF\sin\theta$.

The convention for the direction of torque appears to be backwards, since a clockwise rotation is negative. The convention comes from the definition of an angle in mathematics. In trigonometry the angles are considered to be positive when measured in a counterclockwise direction and negative in the clockwise direction.

A couple occurs when a pair of equal and opposite forces act on the same object along parallel lines of action. Two examples are the rotation of a lunch counter seat and the turning of a car steering wheel, in each case by using two hands, as shown. Couples do not exert a net force on the object, but they do exert a net torque. It is not possible to find a net force to replace a couple: a couple can only be balanced by an equal and opposite couple. The torque produced by a couple is independent of the pivot point chosen.

Torque is the product of two vectors, $\vec{r}$, the displacement from the point of rotation to the point of application of the force, and $\vec{F}$, the applied force. As will be discussed in Chapter 16, one product of two vectors is a vector cross-product, and torque would be written as

$$\vec{\tau} = \vec{r} \times \vec{F}$$

From the definition of a cross-product, $\vec{\tau}$ is perpendicular to the plane defined by $\vec{r}$ and $\vec{F}$. The direction of $\vec{\tau}$ can be determined by using the right-hand rule, as follows:

(a) put the two vectors $\vec{r}$ and $\vec{F}$ tail-to-tail;
(b) point the fingers of the right hand in the direction of $\vec{r}$;
(c) rotate your wrist so that the palm points towards $\vec{F}$;
(d) your thumb now points in the direction of $\vec{\tau}$.

The diagram illustrates the use of the right-hand rule.

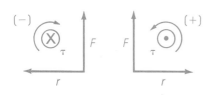

ⓧ into page

ⓞ out of page

(a) $\tau = rF\sin\theta$
$= (0.165 \text{ m})(65 \text{ N})(\sin 90°)$
$= 10.7 \text{ N·m, or } 11 \text{ N·m [clockwise]}$

(b) $\tau = rF\sin\theta$
$= (0.165 \text{ m})(65 \text{ N})(\sin 45°)$
$= 7.6 \text{ N·m [clockwise]}$

(c) $\tau = rF\sin\theta$
$= (0.165 \text{ m})(65 \text{ N})(\sin 0°)$
$= 0$

(d) $\tau = rF\sin\theta$
$= (0.165 \text{ m})(65 \text{ N})(\sin 60°)$
$= 9.3 \text{ N·m [counterclockwise]}$

2. Two children sit on a teeter-totter made from a uniform, 15.3 kg plank that rests on a frictionless pivot at its centre. A 35.7 kg girl sits at the left end, 1.8 m from the point of rotation. A 56.1 kg boy moves back and forth at the right end until the teeter-totter stays balanced horizontally.
(a) Where does he finally sit?
(b) What is the upward force of the pivot on the plank?

Even though this is a simple problem, we should use a systematic approach to it in order to build good habits for more complex problems. First, draw a free-body diagram of the plank. Four external forces act on it, as illustrated.

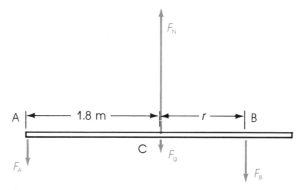

$\vec{F}_A$ and $\vec{F}_B$ are the downward forces exerted on the plank by the children at A and B. $\vec{F}_g$ is the downward force exerted on the plank by the pull of gravity, acting at the plank's centre of mass. $\vec{F}_N$ is the upward force exerted on the plank by the pivot at C. Now the condition $\vec{\tau}_{net} = 0$ can be applied about any convenient point. The natural pivot is at the point C. Four forces each contribute to the torque, but $\vec{F}_N$ and $\vec{F}_g$ will each contribute zero torque because they pass through C and hence have a value of r that is equal to zero.

The three forces due to gravity will be:
$$F_A = m_A g = (35.7 \text{ kg})(9.8 \text{ N/kg}) = 350 \text{ N}$$
$$F_g = m\, g = (15.3 \text{ kg})(9.8 \text{ N/kg}) = 150 \text{ N}$$
$$F_B = m_B g = (56.1 \text{ kg})(9.8 \text{ N/kg}) = 550 \text{ N}$$

(a) The torque from F_A will be
$$\tau_A = r_\perp F$$
$$= (1.8 \text{ m})(350 \text{ N})$$
$$= 630 \text{ N·m}$$

$$\overrightarrow{\tau_A} = 630 \text{ N·m counterclockwise, or } +630 \text{ N·m}$$

Similarly, the torque from F_B is
$$\tau_B = r\,(550 \text{ N})$$

$$\overrightarrow{\tau_B} = -r\,(550 \text{ N}) \text{ (the negative sign means clockwise)}$$

Since the plank is in equilibrium, the total torque at C is zero. That is,

$$\overrightarrow{\tau}_{\text{net}} = \overrightarrow{\tau_A} + \overrightarrow{\tau_B} = 0$$

or
$$0 = +630 \text{ N·m} - r\,(550 \text{ N})$$
and
$$r_\perp = 1.146 \text{ m, or } 1.1 \text{ m}$$

Therefore, the boy must sit 1.1 m to the right of the centre pivot to balance the teeter-totter.

(b) There are several ways to solve for F_N, the upward force of the pivot on the plank. First, since the plank is in static equilibrium, the sum of the vertical components of the forces is zero. That is,

$$\overrightarrow{F}_{\text{net}} = \overrightarrow{F_N} + \overrightarrow{F_A} + \overrightarrow{F_B} + \overrightarrow{F_g} = 0$$
$$0 = F_N - 350 \text{ N} - 550 \text{ N} - 150 \text{ N}$$

Thus
$$F_N = 1.1 \times 10^3 \text{ N}$$

The answer could also be obtained by finding the net torque about A or B, as shown below.

Torque about A

$$\overrightarrow{\tau}_{\text{net}} = \overrightarrow{\tau_A} + \overrightarrow{\tau_N} + \overrightarrow{\tau_g} + \overrightarrow{\tau_B} = 0$$
$$0 = 0 + (1.8 \text{ m})\, F_N - (1.8 \text{ m})(150 \text{ N}) -$$
$$(1.8 \text{ m} + 1.15 \text{ m})(550 \text{ N})$$
$$F_N = 1.1 \times 10^3 \text{N}$$

Torque about B

$$\overrightarrow{\tau}_{\text{net}} = \overrightarrow{\tau_B} + \overrightarrow{\tau_N} + \overrightarrow{\tau_g} + \overrightarrow{\tau_A} = 0$$
$$= 0 - (1.15 \text{ m})\, F_N + (1.15 \text{ m})(150 \text{ N}) +$$
$$(1.8 \text{ m} + 1.15 \text{ m})(350 \text{ N})$$
$$F_N = 1.1 \times 10^3 \text{ N}$$

3. A 16.3 kg flagpole is located on the outside face of a building. It is free to pivot on a horizontal hinge pin at P, and is held up by a cable AB, as illustrated. A 38.8 kg monkey hangs from the outer end of the pole. All dimensions and angles are given in the diagram. Calculate the tension in the cable AB, and also the vertical and horizontal components of the force exerted on the pole by the hinge pin at P.

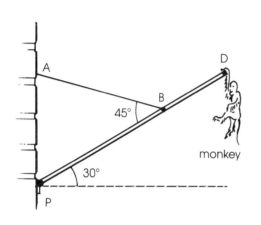

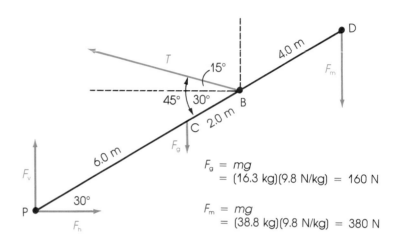

$$F_g = mg$$
$$= (16.3 \text{ kg})(9.8 \text{ N/kg}) = 160 \text{ N}$$

$$F_m = mg$$
$$= (38.8 \text{ kg})(9.8 \text{ N/kg}) = 380 \text{ N}$$

First, draw a free-body diagram of the flagpole. The force of gravity pulls down on the pole and the monkey with the forces shown. The cable pulls with an unknown tension T. The directions of the components of the hinge force are less apparent. F_h is horizontal, out from the wall. Drawing F_v upward is only a guess at this stage. Taking P as the point of rotation, the total torque will be zero, and we can solve for the tension as follows:

$$0 = (0)F_h + (0)F_v - (6.0 \text{ m})(\sin 60°)(160 \text{ N})$$
$$- (12.0 \text{ m})(\sin 60°)(380 \text{ N}) + (8.0 \text{ m})(\sin 45°)T$$
$$0 = -831.4 \text{ N·m} - 3949 \text{ N·m} + (8.0 \text{ m})(\sin 45°)T$$
$$T = 845 \text{ N, or } 8.5 \times 10^2 \text{ N}$$

Now, $\vec{F}_{net} = 0$, since the flagpole is in equilibrium; taking vertical components upward gives

$$0 = F_v + T\sin 15° - 160 \text{ N} - 380 \text{ N}$$
$$= F_v + 845 \text{ N} (\sin 15°) - 540 \text{ N}$$
$$F_v = 320 \text{ N}$$

Since F_v is positive, the force is upward. We guessed right!

Finally, taking horizontal components of $\vec{F}_{net} = 0$ gives

$$0 = F_h + 0 + 0 - T\cos 15°$$

and $\qquad F_h = T\cos 15°$

but $\qquad\qquad T = 845$ N

Therefore $\qquad F_h = (845 \text{ N})\cos 15°$

$\qquad\qquad\qquad = 816$ N

Thus, the cable tension is 8.5×10^2 N, while the hinge pin pushes outward with a force of 8.2×10^2 N and pushes upward with a force of 3.2×10^2 N.

Practice

1. Calculate the torque of each force about the corresponding point P. $\qquad$ (75 N·m, 26 N·m, 13 N·m, 0)

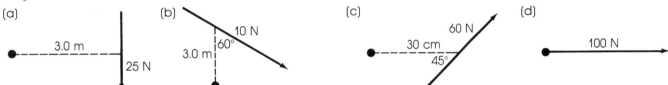

2. A uniform, 12.0 m long girder has a mass of 500 kg. It rests, unattached, on a concrete slab with one end overhanging the edge by 5.5 m. How far can an 80 kg man walk out on the girder before it tips? $\qquad$ (3.1 m)

3. A short-wave aerial is attached to the top of a mast 20 m high, and exerts a force of 600 N on the top of the mast (see diagram). The mast is supported by a guy wire running to the ground from a point 6.0 m below the top of the mast, inclined 60° to the horizontal. The mast is pivoted on a hinge pin at its base. Determine the tension in the guy wire. $\qquad$ (1.7×10^3 N)

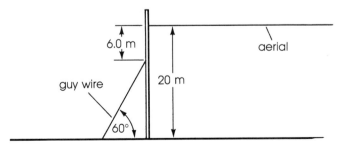

4. A 41 kg trapdoor, 1.2 m long, is supported by a hinge at A and a sloping rope at B. Find the tension in the rope and the vertical and horizontal reactions of the hinge if the rope is just about to open the trap door. $\qquad$ (2.2×10^2 N; 93 N, 2.0×10^2 N)

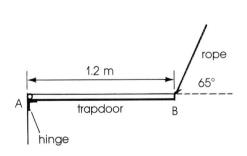

5. A 40 kg plank 6.0 m long is supported by sawhorses A and B, as shown. A 60 kg crate is placed on the plank, 2.0 m from B. (a) Find the reaction forces at A and B.

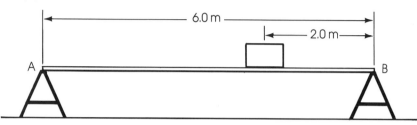

(b) If the box and sawhorse B are moved as illustrated, find the reaction forces at A and B.

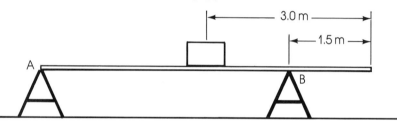

$(3.9 \times 10^2$ N, 5.9×10^2 N; 3.3×10^2 N, 6.5×10^2 N)

6. A 3.0 m diving board with a mass of 26 kg is fastened securely at two points A and B, as illustrated. If a 46 kg diver stands 0.50 m from the end, find the forces at A and B.

$(2.5 \times 10^3$ N [down], 3.2×10^3 N [up])

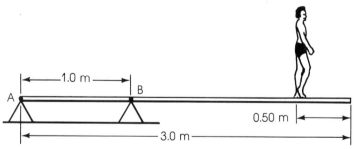

7. A 12.0 m ladder, whose mass is 20 kg, is leaning against a wall, with its base 6.0 m from the wall and at a slope of 60° to the floor. Because both the wall and the floor are frictionless, a rope is tied horizontally 0.50 m from the bottom of the ladder to the wall. A 72 kg plasterer climbs three-quarters of the way up the ladder and stops. What is the tension in the rope and what are the reactive forces at the wall and the floor?

$(3.8 \times 10^2$ N; 3.8×10^2 N, 9.0×10^2 N)

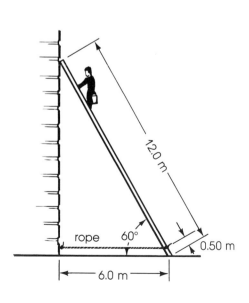

6.4 Centre of Gravity

The statement "All objects, large and small, are attracted to the Earth by the force of gravity" makes no reference to the point of application of this force. An object can be considered to be made up of a large number of tiny, equal particles, each of which is pulled to the Earth. For example, the Earth's pull on a rock consists of a large number of equal, parallel forces, each acting on the particles that make up the rock. These forces will have a vertical resultant force downward, equal to the sum of the individual forces acting on the particles. The net force downward is, of course, the force of gravity of the rock. This net downward force will act through a point called the **centre of gravity** (c.g.). The centre of gravity of a body is defined as the point of application of the resultant force representing the force of gravity on the object. The use of the concept of centre of gravity simplifies the physics of both static and moving objects.

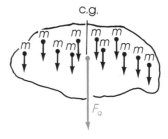

Centre of gravity

The centre of gravity of a particular object can be found in a number of ways. For example, if a ruler is in balance on a fingertip, the centre of gravity of the ruler is directly above the fingertip. For long, narrow objects such as rulers, teeter-totters, planks, billiard cues, etc., the centre of gravity is directly above the point of support when the object is balanced. The particles on either side of the balance point each have torque, but the net torque is zero, since the object does not rotate. A similar method can be used to find the centre of gravity of a flat plate. A more accurate method is to suspend the object from two or more points, in turn, as illustrated. Since it hangs freely from each point, the centre of gravity must lie on the vertical plumb line in each case; so the point of intersection of two or more plumb lines is the centre of gravity.

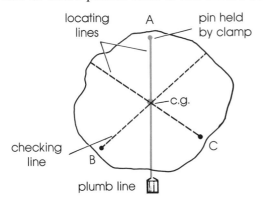

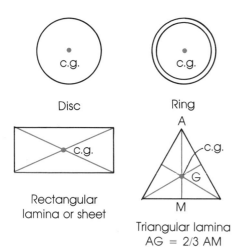

Disc

Ring

Rectangular
lamina or sheet

Triangular lamina
AG = 2/3 AM

For objects with uniform composition, the centre of gravity can be determined geometrically. For example, the centre of gravity of a solid cylinder lies at the midpoint of the cylinder's axis. This is also true of a hollow cylinder, such as a pipe. In the case of a triangular plate, the centre of gravity is two-thirds of the distance along a median from a vertex; and for a uniform, solid cone it is on the axis, three-quarters of the distance from the apex to the base.

We talked earlier about the centre of mass of an object. What is the difference between the centre of mass and the centre of gravity? If a uniform rod is placed on a frictionless surface and struck by a force near its end, it will rotate as it accelerates. On the other hand, if it is struck at its centre it will accelerate without rotation. The **centre of mass** of an object may be defined as the point at which a single applied force produces acceleration, but no rotation. In the case of the rod, the centre of gravity and the centre of mass are in the same position. This is true for the majority of objects. Except for objects of astronomical size, or objects in locations where gravitational forces change rapidly with position, the centre of gravity and the centre of mass are identical, and we will treat them as such.

For non-uniform objects, we also find the balance point, experimentally or by calculation. A sample problem will illustrate.

Sample problem

Weight, of course, is just the gravitational force exerted on a mass.

A cheerleader's baton consists of a 4.0 cm diameter sphere weighing 3.6 N and an 8.0 cm diameter sphere weighing 18 N, joined by a thin tube whose weight is 4.4 N and whose length is 86 cm. Calculate the centre of gravity.

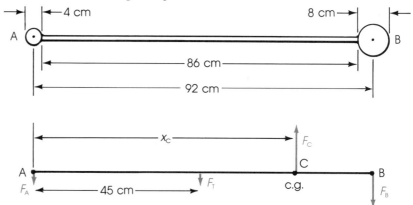

You should recognize that the baton presents a problem similar to the teeter-totter problem in the previous section. Draw a free-body diagram of the baton balanced at the unknown point C. By symmetry, the centres of mass for each sphere and for the tube must be at their respective geometric centres, so we know where the three forces, $\vec{F}_A$, $\vec{F}_T$, and $\vec{F}_B$, act. The only other force, $\vec{F}_c$, is at the point of support, acting at the centre of gravity. In the free-body diagram, x_C represents the unknown distance of the centre of gravity from the centre of the smaller sphere.

Applying $\vec{F}_{net} = 0$ in the vertical direction gives

$$\vec{F}_{net} = \vec{F}_A + \vec{F}_T + \vec{F}_C + \vec{F}_B = 0$$
$$0 = -3.6 \text{ N} - 4.4 \text{ N} + F_c - 18 \text{ N}$$
$$F_c = 26 \text{ N}$$

Taking A as the point of rotation, $\vec{\tau}_{net} = 0$, since the baton is balanced in equilibrium. Therefore

$$\vec{\tau}_{net} = \vec{\tau}_A + \vec{\tau}_T + \vec{\tau}_C + \vec{\tau}_B = 0$$
$$0 = (0 \text{ m})(3.6 \text{ N}) - (0.45 \text{ m})(4.4 \text{ N})$$
$$+ x_C (26 \text{ N}) - (0.92 \text{ m})(18 \text{ N})$$
$$x_C = 0.713 \text{ m, or 71 cm}$$

The centre of gravity is located 71 cm from A.

Practice

1. A 12 kg plank has four concrete blocks placed on it, as illustrated. If each block has a mass of 10 kg and a width of 24 cm, where is the centre of gravity of the system, located from the left end? (0.83 m)

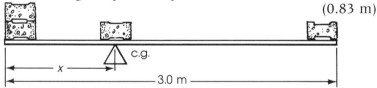

2. The centre of gravity of a person may be located by the arrangement shown in the diagram. Assuming the scales to be adjusted to zero with the plank alone, locate the centre of gravity of the person. (1.2 m)

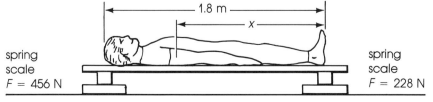

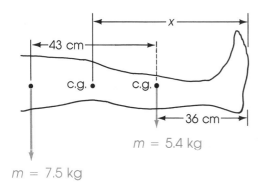

43 cm

x

c.g.

c.g.

36 cm

m = 5.4 kg

m = 7.5 kg

3. Locate the centre of gravity of an extended leg relative to the sole of the foot, given the locations of the centres of gravity of the upper and lower leg, as shown in the diagram.   (0.40 m)

4. A cylindrical steel rod of radius 2.0 cm and length 40 cm is turned down on a lathe to one-half of its radius for a distance of 30 cm from one end. Find the centre of gravity, measured from the thicker end (density of steel $= 7.89 \times 10^3$ kg/m³).
(0.14 m)

5. A 60 kg woman bends 90° forward from the waist, keeping her legs vertical. The centre of gravity for her upper body is located 70 cm from her hips. If two-thirds of her mass is in her upper body, how far forward from the line of her legs is her new centre of gravity?   (0.47 m)

6.5 Stable, Unstable, and Neutral Equilibrium

Designers of ships or cars must take stability into account. Ships, which undergo considerable rolling and pitching in high seas, can turn over and sink. A car travelling around a corner too fast also has a tendency to overturn. Objects such as these must be designed so that they have stable equilibrium under most conditions.

The stability of an object depends on the position of its centre of gravity and the torque its weight exerts. To illustrate this concept, let us examine the behaviour of a wooden cone placed on a tabletop. A cone cannot be made to stand on its apex, except momentarily. The slightest vibration or draft will cause it to tip slightly. The force of gravity, F_g, will then exert a torque of $x \cdot F_g$ about the apex, causing the cone to tip further and topple over. A cone placed on its apex is said to be in **unstable equilibrium**. Note that the centre of gravity becomes lower if the cone is slightly tipped.

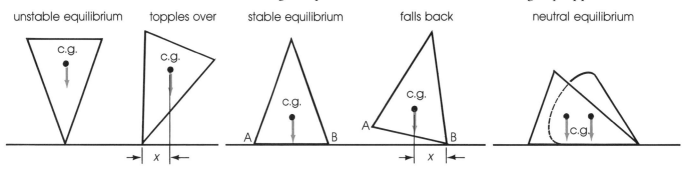

unstable equilibrium   topples over   stable equilibrium   falls back   neutral equilibrium

When the same cone is placed on its base, it exhibits **stable equilibrium**. If tilted to one side B, even through a fairly large angle, the vertical line originating at the centre of gravity will still fall inside the base AB. As a result, the force of gravity on the cone will have a torque $x \cdot F_g$ about the point of contact, which acts to bring the cone back to its original vertical position. Note that the centre of gravity of the cone rises when it is slightly tipped.

If the same cone is rolled on its side on the table, the vertical line from the centre of gravity continues to pass through the line of reaction of the table on the cone. The force of gravity exerts no torque on the cone, and its centre of gravity remains at the same height even when the cone is rolling. The cone exhibits **neutral equilibrium** in this position. Another example of neutral equilibrium is a ball resting or rolling on a smooth, horizontal surface.

In summary, it is the torque of the force of gravity, acting at the centre of gravity, that affects the stability of an object. The position of the centre of gravity, relative to the reaction force of the surface on the object, determines whether the object exhibits stable equilibrium, unstable equilibrium, or neutral equilibrium. If the vertical line from the centre of gravity of an object lies within the base of the body, the body is *stable*, even when slightly tipped. If the vertical line lies outside the base, the body is *unstable* with even slight tipping. If the vertical line runs through the point of reaction of the supporting surface on the object, and the object's centre of gravity maintains the same vertical position, the object exhibits *neutral equilibrium*.

From what has been said, it can be seen that the risk of unstable equilibrium increases as the height of the centre of gravity of an object increases or its base narrows. This is because the vertical line through the centre of gravity is more likely to fall outside the base when the object is tipped through a small angle. The nearer the centre of gravity is to the ground and the wider the base, the more stable the object is likely to be.

For this reason, a car or truck turning a sharp corner at high speed may become unstable if its centre of gravity is high (see diagram); racing cars are built with their centres of gravity low and their wheels far apart. Football players, at the line, crouch down, lowering their centre of gravity and broadening their stance, thus increasing their stability.

For a cornering automobile, things are not quite as simple as is stated. The car has centripetal acceleration, which should be taken into account. However, the conclusion is still correct.

unstable

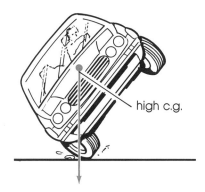

high c.g.

stable

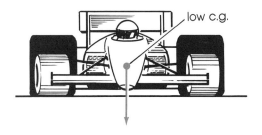

low c.g.

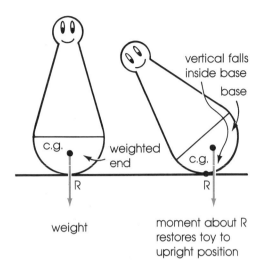

weight

moment about R
restores toy to
upright position

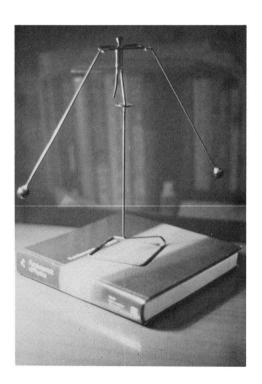

Some objects are constructed in such a way that they are always in stable equilibrium. For example, a child's inflated plastic punchball is given a heavy spherical base, usually weighted with sand. No matter how far the punchball is tipped to one side, the vertical from the centre of gravity passes on the side opposite the point of contact of the base (see diagram). This gives the punchball a restoring torque and twists it back upright. Other toys, and curios, are designed according to the same concept so that an object can be balanced on a stand (see photograph). In these cases, the centre of gravity is at, or even below, the base of the object, and thus the object is always stable. Objects such as Bunsen burners and table lamps are designed with heavy bases to make them stable. The astronaut suits used on the moon had weighted shoes to increase the astronauts' stability.

Stability is also increased by making the base larger. The CN Tower, for example, has a broad base but tapers to a narrow mast at the top. Humans are more stable with their feet apart than together: if someone shoves you, your automatic reaction is to increase the distance between your feet. Try it!

The principles of stability apply to animals as well. An animal with four legs is analogous to a table with four legs. If a table is tipped up far enough, so that its centre of gravity falls outside the base of its legs, the table will tip over. If a table has short legs, its centre of gravity will be low and it will be more stable. It can also be tipped to a greater angle. In the same way, animals with relatively short legs, such as the cat or squirrel, have more stability than animals with longer legs, such as the horse or antelope.

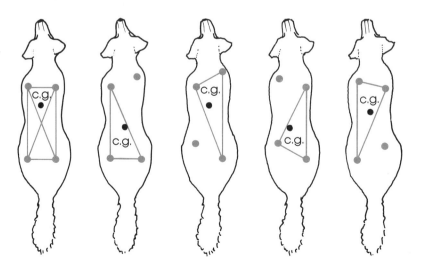

A dog remains stable when it lifts one of its legs, so long as its centre of gravity lies within the triangle formed by the other three legs. When a dog runs, there will be brief periods of instability when only two of its feet are on the ground at a time. Usually this is counteracted when the other two feet touch the ground; but this is a problem of dynamics, not statics.

As discussed earlier, when the vertical line from the centre of gravity of an object lies outside its base, an object is unstable and will tip over. The critical position for beginning to tip is called the **critical tipping angle**. This is the position when the centre of gravity is directly above the pivot point. Using the principles of static equilibrium, it is possible to calculate the critical tipping angle for both uniform and non-uniform objects.

Sample problems

1. What is the tipping angle for a 2.0 kg brick, 6.0 cm by 12.0 cm by 20 cm, when it is placed on end?

Since the brick is a uniform object, its centre of gravity will be located at its geometric centre. Also, at the critical tipping angle, the centre of gravity will be directly above the edge P, as illustrated.

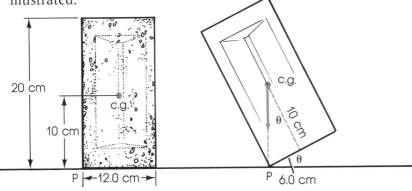

Given the dimensions in the diagram, it follows that

$$\tan \theta = \frac{6.0 \text{ cm}}{10 \text{ cm}}$$
$$\theta = 31°$$

Note that the mass of the object has no effect on the value of the tipping angle. The only important criteria are the dimensions of the object and the location of the centre of gravity. Of course, θ would be different if we tipped the brick on another edge.

2. The CN Tower, opened in Toronto in 1976, is still the tallest free-standing structure in the world. Made of reinforced concrete, it soars 553.2 m from the base of the tower to the highest antenna on its communication mast. A massive foundation plunges an additional 16.7 m below the base, to solid rock. The foundation has threefold symmetry, with the three corners lying on a circle of radius 55.0 m. The total tower mass is 1.18×10^8 kg, and the centre of gravity is located about 75 m above the bottom of the foundation. For the purposes of the problem given below, do not consider the effects of the earth and rock around the foundation, but assume the tower and foundation to be resting on horizontal bedrock.

(a) The Goodyear blimp fastens a cable to the uppermost tip of the tower, and pulls horizontally so that the tower pivots on two corners of the foundation. So long as nothing bends, breaks, or slides, what tension is needed to just start the tower tipping? Convert your answer to a fraction of the tower's mass.

(b) Suppose the blimp succeeds in starting the tower tipping, and carefully pulls it over to balance at the critical tipping angle: calculate this angle.

(a) The centre of gravity of the tower will be directly above the centre of the foundation, which is located one-half the circle radius from the pivot line (see diagram).

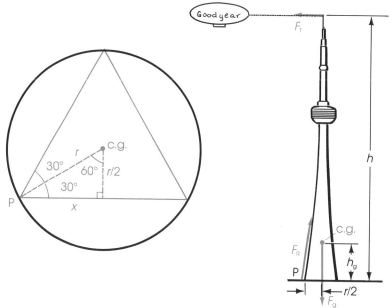

$\vec{F_T}$ is the cable tension pulling horizontally. $\vec{F_R}$ is the reaction force on the pivot edge P. $\vec{F_g}$ is the weight of the tower, h is the height of the top of the tower above bedrock, h_g is the height of the centre of gravity above bedrock, and r is the radius of the foundation circle. There are three forces acting on the tower, namely, the force of gravity ($\vec{F_g}$) acting at the centre of gravity, the reaction force ($\vec{F_R}$) of the bedrock on the pivot edge P, and the tension ($\vec{F_T}$) of the blimp cable at the top of the tower.

For equilibrium, the net torque about the edge P must be zero.

That is,

$$\vec{\tau}_{net} = \vec{\tau}_R + \vec{\tau}_g + \vec{\tau}_T = 0$$
$$0 = 0 - r/2\, F_g + h\, F_T$$
$$F_T = \frac{r\,(mg)}{2h}$$
$$= \frac{(55.0\text{ m})\,(1.18 \times 10^8\text{ kg})\,(9.8\text{ N/kg})}{2(570\text{ m})}$$
$$= 5.6 \times 10^7\text{ N}$$

This is a large force, but it is only about 5% of the force of gravity on the tower, as seen below.

$$\frac{5.6 \times 10^7\text{ N}}{(1.18 \times 10^8\text{ kg})\,(9.8\text{ N/kg})} \times 100\% = 5.0\%$$

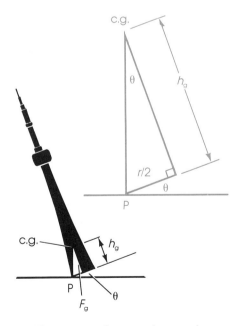

(b) The critical angle will occur when the centre of gravity of the tower is vertically above the supporting edge, as illustrated.

At the critical tipping angle,
$$\tan \theta = \frac{r/2}{h_g}$$
$$= \frac{(55.0\text{ m})}{2(75\text{ m})}$$
$$= 0.367$$

Therefore $\theta = 20.1°$

Thus, the tower will fall back to its upright position if the tipping angle is less than 20°.

Note: The upper diagram is an enlargement of the lower diagram.

Practice

1. For the brick in Sample problem 1, find the critical tipping angle for rotation about an edge if
   (a) it is standing on its side, or
   (b) it is standing on its face.   (27°, 63°)
2. What is the critical tipping angle for the table illustrated?
                                                      (43°)
3. A triangular steel sheet, with equal sides of 10 cm, is pushed at its peak. If the triangle is pushed parallel to its base, what angle will the base of the triangle make with the horizontal when it just begins to tip over?   (60°)

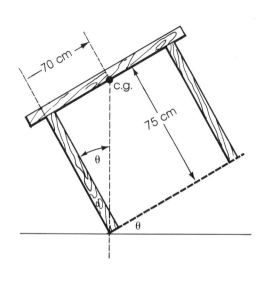

6.6 Hooke's Law

In the earlier sections of this chapter we calculated the forces acting on objects in equilibrium. For the remainder of the chapter we will study the effects of these forces on the objects themselves. This is an important study, because only by knowing the effects of the forces can we determine whether they are great enough to cause an object to break, or fracture, or even be noticeably deformed. This knowledge is critical to architects and engineers when they design a house or tall building, and specifically to engineers when they establish the safety of a building, bridge, or airplane.

When forces are applied to an object, the dimensions of the object tend to change. For example, if opposite forces are applied to both ends of a spring, it stretches or compresses. When the forces are removed, the spring returns to its original length. If an object returns to its original dimensions after the applied force is removed, we say that the object is **elastic**.

The British scientist Robert Hooke was one of the first to study the elasticity of matter. In 1678, he published his now famous statement of Hooke's Law.

The amount of deformation of an elastic object is proportional to the forces applied to deform it.

To begin with, we will study Hooke's Law as it applies to a simple, coiled spring, fixed at one end and either stretched or compressed by an applied force at the other end. We will call the deformation of the spring x; i.e., x is the amount by which it is stretched or compressed from its normal length. A graph of F versus x has the form shown.

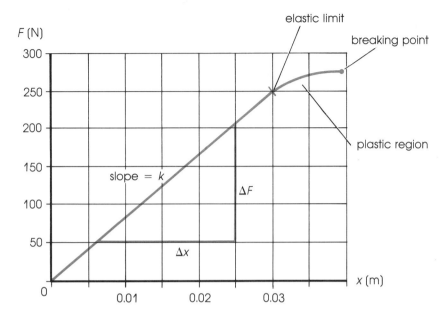

Note that the *F-x* graph is a straight line up to a point called the elastic limit of the spring. If the spring is deformed beyond this limit, the graph is no longer linear, and the spring may not return to its original shape after the force is removed. In fact, if deformed too far beyond the elastic limit, the spring may permanently stretch or fracture.

For the linear portion of the graph (sometimes called the "Hooke's Law region"), its constant slope, *k*, is given by

$$k = \text{rise/run} = F/x$$

and the equation relating force and deformation (extension or compression) is

---

$$F = kx$$

---

where *F* is the force exerted on the deformed spring, in newtons

      x is the amount of deformation of the spring, in metres

      k is the force constant of the spring, in newtons per metre

We can distinguish between compressions of the spring and extensions of it by adopting a simple sign convention. When the spring is compressed, both *x* and *F* are negative (−); when the spring is stretched, both *x* and *F* are positive (+). Notice that the force exerted on the spring and the deformation of the spring are in the same direction, making *k* always positive.

For the spring whose *F-x* graph is shown above,

$$k = \frac{\Delta F}{\Delta x}$$
$$= \frac{165 \text{ N} - 80 \text{ N}}{0.02 \text{ m} - 0.01 \text{ m}}$$
$$= \frac{85 \text{ N}}{0.01 \text{ m}}$$
$$= 8.5 \times 10^3 \text{ N/m}$$

Sample problem

A spring whose force constant is 48 N/m has a 0.25 kg mass suspended from it. What is the extension of the spring?

If the spring obeys Hooke's Law,
$$F = kx$$
$$\text{therefore } x = F/k$$
$$\text{but } F = mg$$
$$= (0.25 \text{ kg}) (9.8 \text{ N kg})$$
$$= 2.4 \text{ N}$$
$$\text{Therefore } x = \frac{2.4 \text{ N}}{48 \text{ N/m}}$$
$$= 0.050 \text{ m, or } 5.0 \text{ cm}$$

Practice

1. What force is necessary to stretch a spring whose force constant is 120 N/m by an amount of 30 cm?   (36 N)
2. A spring with a force constant of 600 N/m is used in a scale for weighing fish. What is the mass of a fish that stretches the spring 7.5 cm from its normal length?   (4.6 kg)
3. A spring in a pogo stick is compressed 12 cm when a 40 kg boy stands on the stick. What is the force constant for the pogo stick spring?   (3.3×10^3 N/m)
4. The force applied to a dynamics cart is measured with a stretched spring. What is the acceleration of a 2.0 kg cart on a flat, frictionless surface if pulled by a spring with a force constant of 40 N/m, stretched by a constant amount of 8.0 cm?
                    (1.6 m/s^2)

6.7 Young's Modulus — Stress and Strain

The amount of extension or elongation of a spring, or in fact any elastic object, depends on a number of other factors as well as the applied force. For example, if we have two springs made of the same material, with the same diameter and acted upon by the same applied force, we find that the longer of the two springs will stretch farther. The elongation is directly proportional to the length of the elastic object. On the other hand, if two steel springs are identical in length, but have different diameters, we find that, for identical forces applied to each, the elongation is inversely proportional to the cross-sectional area. And, as you might expect, springs of identical dimensions, made of different materials, for example, brass and steel, will have different extensions for the same force.

Summarizing the four factors mathematically, we have
- $\Delta L \propto L$ where ΔL is the extension or compression and L is the original length
- $\Delta L \propto 1/A$ where A is the area of the cross-section
- $\Delta L \propto K$ where K is a constant for the material
- $\Delta L \propto F$ where F is the applied force (Hooke's Law)

Combining the proportions, we obtain

$$\Delta L \propto \frac{KFL}{A}$$

This relationship was first derived by the brilliant English scientist Thomas Young (1773-1829), in 1807. (Young is more famous for his work in optics and waves, as will be seen in Chapter 14.)

To change this proportionality statement into an equation, a constant is required. The factor in the relationship that does not vary with geometry or force is the material. The constant of proportionality for the material is called the **elastic modulus** or **Young's Modulus**, and is given the symbol E. It has become the practice to express the constant of proportionality as $1/E$. As a result, the Young's Modulus equation can be stated as

$$\Delta L = \left(\frac{1}{E}\right)\left(\frac{FL}{A}\right)$$

or

$$E = \frac{F/A}{\Delta L/L}$$

This equation is much more useful than Hooke's Law, because it incorporates all of the factors that affect the extension of an object. A table that gives the values of Young's Modulus for various materials is provided on page 234. Note that units for Young's Modulus are N/m^2. These units are the same as those for pressure (force per unit area). The metric unit for pressure is the pascal (Pa). It is acceptable to express Young's Modulus in pascals or newtons per metre squared. To simplify problem solving, it is preferable to use the latter.

Actually, it is the cross-sectional area for a solid material. For a coil spring, it would be the area of the wire itself.

Elastic Moduli of Various Substances

Material	Elastic modulus $E(\text{N/m}^2)$	Shear modulus $G(\text{N/m}^2)$	Bulk modulus $B(\text{N/m}^2)$
Solids			
Aluminum	7.0×10^{10}	2.5×10^{10}	7.0×10^{10}
Bone (limb)	1.5×10^{10}	8.0×10^{10}	
Brass	9.0×10^{10}	3.5×10^{10}	7.5×10^{10}
Brick	1.4×10^{10}		
Copper	11×10^{10}	3.8×10^{10}	12×10^{10}
Concrete	2.0×10^{10}		
Glass	5.7×10^{10}	2.4×10^{10}	4.0×10^{10}
Granite	4.5×10^{10}		
Iron (cast)	10×10^{10}	6.0×10^{10}	12×10^{10}
Marble	5.0×10^{10}		
Nylon	0.5×10^{10}		
Steel	20×10^{10}	8.2×10^{10}	15×10^{10}
Wood (pine)			
(perpendicular to grain)	0.1×10^{10}		
(parallel to grain)	1.0×10^{10}		
Liquids			
Alcohol (ethyl)			1.0×10^{10}
Glycerin			4.5×10^{10}
Mercury			2.6×10^{10}
Water			2.3×10^{10}

In the Young's Modulus equation, the numerator and denominator are given special names. Force per unit area is known as **stress** and the ratio of the change in length to the original length is called **strain**. That is,

$$\text{stress} = \frac{\text{force}}{\text{area}} = \frac{F}{A} \qquad \text{strain} = \frac{\text{change in length}}{\text{original length}} = \frac{\Delta L}{L}$$

Substituting in the Young's Modulus Equation, we obtain

$$E = \frac{F/A}{\Delta L/L} = \frac{\text{stress}}{\text{strain}}$$

As can be seen from the relationship, since E is a constant, strain is directly proportional to stress.

There are three possible types of stress on an object — tension, compression, and shear. A stretched spring, or a guitar string, is said to be under tension or **tensile stress**. With tensile stress, forces act outward to cause an increase in length. On the other hand if the forces act inward on the ends of the object, causing its length to decrease, we say that there is compression or **compressive stress**. Any column that supports a weight, such as the concrete column under a highway bridge or the marble column in an ancient Greek temple, is under compressive stress. The Young's Modulus constant for a given material is usually the same for both tension and compression.

When there is tension or compression, the forces usually act along the length of the object. For an object under **shear stress**, however, the forces act across its opposite faces. For example, if the top cover of a textbook resting on a desk is pushed with a force parallel to the surface of the desk, the shape of the book changes, although the dimensions do not. There is angular deformation. We say that the textbook is under shear stress.

When Young's equation is used for shear stress, the constant of proportionality is called G, the **shear modulus**. Its value is usually smaller than the value of the elastic modulus, and is given by the following relationship.

$$G = \frac{F/A}{\Delta L/L}$$

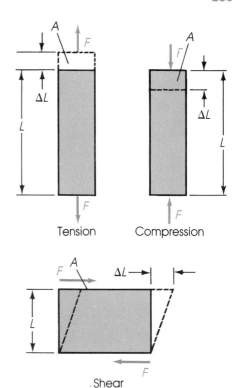

Tension   Compression

Shear

When an object is under too much stress, it may break or fracture. The maximum tensile force per unit area that an object can withstand is called its **tensile strength**. The values of tensile strength given in the chart are only representative values. The actual values can vary, and are affected by such factors as temperature and the molecular and crystalline structure of the material. As a result,

Ultimate Strengths of Materials (Force/Area)

Material	Tensile strength (N/m²)	Compressive strength (N/m²)	Shear strength (N/m²)
Iron, cast	1.7×10^8	5.5×10^8	1.7×10^8
Steel	5.0×10^8	5.0×10^8	2.5×10^8
Brass	2.5×10^8	2.5×10^8	2.0×10^8
Aluminum	2.0×10^8	2.0×10^8	2.0×10^8
Concrete	0.02×10^8	0.20×10^8	0.02×10^8
Brick		0.35×10^8	
Marble		0.8×10^8	
Granite		1.7×10^8	
Wood (pine)			
(parallel to grain)	0.40×10^8	0.35×10^8	0.05×10^8
(perpendicular to grain)		0.10×10^8	
Nylon	5.0×10^8		
Human bone (limb)	1.3×10^8	1.7×10^8	

these values are used only as a guide when designing a structure or device. Usually a safety factor of three to five times smaller for the value of the tensile strength is used, in order to build in a good margin of safety, but sometimes the weight and cost penalty is too high for this approach.

The Young's Modulus equation is used primarily for solids. When applied to fluids (liquids and gases), the equation is altered. If the object placed under pressure is a fluid, its volume is compressed (Boyle's Law). **Pressure** in a fluid is defined as force per unit area. This is the equivalent of stress. With solids, ΔL is proportional to L; the volume relationship is similar. That is, ΔV is proportional to V (the original volume) for a specific change in pressure (ΔP).

The Young's Modulus equivalent for fluids is called the **bulk modulus** (B), and is written as

$$B = \frac{-\Delta F/A}{\Delta V/V} = \frac{-\Delta P}{\Delta V/V}$$

where B is the bulk modulus constant.

The negative sign is included to make B positive. ΔV is always negative if ΔP is positive. The table on page 234 gives values of the bulk modulus for various fluids.

Sample problems

1. A 1.0 m steel guitar string has a diameter of 0.20 cm. What is the value of the tension in the string if it stretches 0.20 cm when tightened?

$$d = 0.20 \text{ cm} = 2.0 \times 10^{-3} \text{ m} \quad r = 1.0 \times 10^{-3} \text{ m}$$

$$A = \pi r^2$$
$$= \pi (1.0 \times 10^{-3})^2$$

$$E = \frac{F/A}{\Delta L/L}$$

$$\text{or } F = \frac{E \Delta L A}{L}$$

$$= \frac{(2.0 \times 10^{11} \text{ N/m}^2) (2.0 \times 10^{-3} \text{ m}) (\pi (1.0 \times 10^{-3})^2 \text{ m}^2)}{1.0 \text{ m}}$$

$$= 1.3 \times 10^3 \text{ N}$$

2. How much mass would have to be suspended on a vertical copper wire with a diameter of 0.30 cm to cause its length to increase by 0.20%?

$r = 1.5 \times 10^{-3}$ m

$A = \pi r^2$
$= \pi (1.5 \times 10^{-3} \text{ m})^2$
$= 7.07 \times 10^{-6} \text{ m}^2$

$F = \dfrac{E \Delta L A}{L}$

$= \dfrac{\Delta L E A}{L}$ $\qquad \left(\dfrac{\Delta L}{L} = 0.0020 = 2.0 \times 10^{-3} \right)$
$= (2.0 \times 10^{-3})(11 \times 10^{10} \text{ N/m}^2)(7.07 \times 10^{-6} \text{ m}^2)$
$= 1.56 \times 10^3$ N

$m = \dfrac{F}{g}$

$= \dfrac{1.56 \times 10^3 \text{ N}}{9.8 \text{ N/kg}} = 159$ kg, or 1.6×10^2 kg

3. A lighting engineer is designing a large chandelier for the lobby of a concert hall. The chandelier has a mass of 750 kg and is to be supported by a single steel cable. Assuming a safety factor of 5, what is the minimum diameter of the cable (steel tensile strength $= 5.0 \times 10^8$ N/m²)?

For a safety factor of 5,

tensile strength $= \dfrac{5.0 \times 10^8 \text{ N/m}^2}{5} = 1.0 \times 10^8$ N/m²

$F_g = mg$
$= (750 \text{ kg}) (9.8 \text{ N/kg})$
$= 7.35 \times 10^3$ N

$A = \dfrac{F}{\text{stress}}$

$= \dfrac{7.35 \times 10^3 \text{ N}}{1.0 \times 10^8 \text{ N/m}^2}$

$= 7.35 \times 10^{-5} \text{ m}^2$

$A = \pi r^2$, or $r = \sqrt{A/\pi}$

$= \sqrt{\dfrac{7.35 \times 10^{-5} \text{ m}^2}{\pi}}$

$= 4.84 \times 10^{-3}$ m

$\therefore d = 2r$
$= 2 \times 4.84 \times 10^{-3}$ m
$= 9.7 \times 10^{-3}$ m, or 0.97 cm

Practice

1. A marble column supporting a load of 1.0×10^5 kg has a diameter of 0.5 m.
   (a) What is the stress in the column?
   (b) What is the strain in the column?
   (c) If the column is 12 m high, how much will it be compressed?

   $(5.0 \times 10^6 \text{ N/m}^2, 1.0 \times 10^{-4}, 1.2 \times 10^{-3} \text{ m})$

2. An aluminum wire 1.0 m long is elongated 0.02 cm when under stress. If a brass wire with an identical diameter were used to support the same load, what would its initial length have been for it to have had the same extension?   (1.3 m)

3. How much will a 40 m steel elevator cable stretch if its diameter is 2.0 cm and it is supporting a static load of 1.5×10^4 N?

   $(9.6 \times 10^{-3} \text{ m})$

4. A 50 cm long rod with a diameter of 1.0 cm is used to support a load of 100 N along its length. As a result, the rod is compressed 9.1×10^{-3} mm. What is the Young's Modulus of the rod? What is the material? $(7.0 \times 10^{10} \text{ N/m}^2, \text{aluminum})$

5. A rectangular steel column 2.5 m long, with a cross-sectional area of 2.7×10^{-4} m², is used vertically to support a sagging floor. If the column supports a load of 5.5×10^3 kg, how much is it compressed? $(2.5 \times 10^{-3} \text{ m})$

6. A steel cable supports a 3000 kg elevator. Allowing for a safety factor of 4, calculate the diameter of the cable required if the maximum acceleration is 1.0 m/s². $(1.8 \times 10^{-2} \text{ m})$

6.8 Stress and Strain in Building Construction

The application of the principles of static equilibrium to the design and construction of buildings is a very important part of the education of architects, construction technologists, engineers, and others. A knowledge of how to use these principles is fundamental to the work they do daily. The competent, precise use of this knowledge protects the lives of the people constructing the buildings that have been designed, and the people who will later occupy them.

Historically, the first architectural innovation was the post-and-beam. This type of construction is found in the ancient buildings of Egypt, Greece, China, England, and other parts of the world. It was limited to small spans, because the only materials available were stone, such as marble, and timber. When a load is placed on a beam, the beam bends, as illustrated. The top part of the beam is in compression and the bottom part in tension. Since stone is

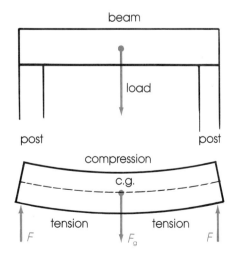

weak in tension, the spans of ancient beams were limited, and the columns had to be closely spaced, as seen in the photograph of a Greek temple.

The next major development in construction technology was the arch, first used by the Romans. Because of the arrangement of the stones in an arch, the stress is primarily compressive. The stones push against each other, to support large loads such as occur in a

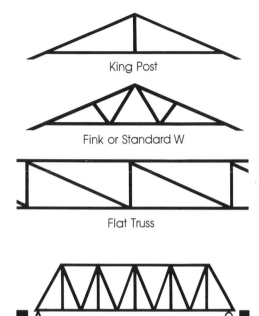

King Post

Fink or Standard W

Flat Truss

Trusses in a bridge

bridge, a triumphal arch, or a cathedral. The load is transferred along the arch to the vertical supports. Because these supports transfer horizontal as well as vertical forces, they must be very large, and/or the supporting walls have to be buttressed, as shown in the photograph of the Gothic cathedral on page 239.

When iron and steel came into use in 19th century construction, longer spans were possible, since these materials had much greater tensile strengths than earlier materials. But still the length of span was limited, because the longer the span, the deeper the beam had to be. This problem was solved by conceiving the truss, which distributes a given amount of material in a very efficient manner.

The simplest truss is a triangle composed of three bars (or pieces of lumber) called members, which are pinned (joined) together at their ends. A simple truss is used to support the roofs of houses and other narrow structures. For greater spans, such as in flat roofs and bridges, many triangles are combined to form the trusses, as can be seen in the series of illustrations. The connections in metal trusses can be made by bolting or welding; in wooden structures, bolting and nailing are used. In long spans, such as in bridges, provision must be made for movement of the structure, caused by large loads and thermal expansion and contraction. Rollers, rockers, or sliding plates under one end or both ends of the structure permit such movement.

The Eiffel tower contains many trusses.

The design of truss members is governed by the position and size of the loads on the truss. For example, the load from a roof is exerted on the top members of a truss, whereas in a bridge the load may be carried by either the top or bottom members. This leads to many different designs, depending on the particular application. In all of the designs, the truss spreads the load over all its members, some being placed under compression and some under tension. If the truss is made of steel, there are likely to be few problems, because steel has high tensile and compressive strengths. However, individual members must be designed so as to prevent buckling under compression. Wooden trusses of comparable size to steel trusses cannot carry comparable loads, because wood is not as strong as steel (see table on page 235 for a comparison of tensile and compressive strengths of wood and steel). The strength of the wooden trusses one sees in an arena or barn may have been increased by "tensioning" the trusses. For example, steel bars or cables are run along both sides of the bottom main member, to which they are firmly attached at one end. At the other end of the member, the cables or bars are placed under tension, by use of a jack or threaded bolts, and secured in the tensioned state. This compresses the wood, for increased strength, and also increases the tensile capacity of a member made of a material more suited to act in compression. The concept is most commonly used today with concrete.

Concrete is strong in compression but weak in tension. As a result, it is very suitable for vertical, supporting walls and foundations, where the structure is under compression. On the other hand, its use for beams is limited, since its resistance to tension is comparatively low.

The simplest method of strengthening concrete is to place steel rods in the forms before the concrete is poured and sets. Steel rods reinforce a concrete member by increasing its tensile strength. Such reinforcing also counters the cracking caused in concrete by thermal expansion and contraction.

The term reinforced concrete is not a precise term, since it is the concrete member that is reinforced — not the concrete itself. A more correct term is ferro-concrete.

In 1888, a patent was issued for **prestressed concrete**. The concept is as follows. Instead of reinforcing the tensile zone of a concrete beam, the beam is compressed (before any external load is applied). Then, when the beam is loaded in performance, no tension will be induced in the concrete until this precompression has been overcome. When designing a prestressed concrete member, an amount of precompression is calculated that will result in little or no tension in the concrete under working conditions. Precompression is created by running separate wires, cables, steel rods, or wire ropes through the form for the concrete. The cables are sometimes put under tension before the concrete is poured into the form. In this case, after the concrete has set, the concrete member is under compression, which increases its strength. At other times in certain large structures, such as a bridge or the CN Tower, the cables are run through ducts in the concrete. After the concrete has set, each cable is anchored at one end, and tension is induced in the cable by a screw at the other end. When the cable is tightened to a predetermined tension, it is anchored at the screw end and the concrete member is then under compression. This is called **post-stressed concrete**, since the tension is applied after the concrete has set. In both cases, the tension in the member is carried by the steel.

Steel rods "reinforce" concrete.

These hydraulically operated jacks post-stress the concrete structure.

In construction of large storage tanks, nuclear power vessels, silos, and similar structures, the concrete is prestressed by running a continuous helix of tension wire around the wall of the structure as it is erected. After the wire is put under tension and anchored, it is covered by a waterproof barrier of mortar to prevent rusting. This waterproofing is an important procedure for all containment structures. If water is allowed to get at reinforcing steel, the steel will rust. When steel rusts, it expands, fracturing the concrete and weakening the structure. The use of salt on roadways during winter has accelerated this process, and has required the reconstruction of many concrete bridges and parking garages in northern climates.

6.9 Static Equilibrium in the Human Body

The three parts of the human body responsible for physical movement are the muscles, the tendons, and the bones. Muscle cells are arranged in long fibres that generate contractive forces as they decrease in length and increase in width. Although there are three types of muscles, it is only the skeletal muscles that are under conscious control. These are the muscles that produce the motion of the body. The tendons transfer the tensile forces of these muscles to the bones, often over long distances. For example, the muscles that operate the fingers are located not in the hand, but in the forearm. The tendons under the skin of the back of the hand transfer the tensile forces from the wrist to the fingers.

Bones support the body and maintain its shape. They must be stiff, and strong in both compression and tension. As well, they act as levers, converting the pulls of the muscles into both pushes and pulls. Bones are composites, having properties similar to reinforced concrete. They are made up of two components. Calcium crystals (hydroxyapatite) act like concrete, carrying high compressive loads though they are weak in tension. Tensile load is carried by long strings of collagen fibres, which act like the steel in reinforced concrete. The combination is strong in both compression and tension. In comparison, the tensile strength of human bone (limb) is 1.3×10^8 N/m^2, whereas that of iron is 1.7×10^8 N/m^2.

Bones are not solid throughout. Usually the outer surface is solid, but the central region is either a spongy network of bone or is hollow. (The hollow section usually contains bone marrow, the material that produces red blood cells.) This hollow or spongy structure does not reduce the bone's tensile or compressive strengths; in fact, because it is hollow, it is much stronger in resisting torsion and bending than a solid bone of the same mass would be.

For most normal activities, the bones are strong enough to avoid fracture. However, accidents often apply large forces that exceed the tensile, compressive, or shear strengths of a bone, and fracture occurs. The forces causing the fracture can be tensile, compressive, shearing, or a combination of these. The various types of common fractures are illustrated.

The techniques used to calculate the forces acting on bodies in equilibrium can be applied to the bones and muscles of the human body. Generally, a muscle runs from one bone to another, attached to each at a point called an **insertion.** The bones are connected at a joint that provides flexibility of movement. These joints include the elbow, the shoulder, the hip, the foot, and the knee. A series

An infant's bones consist mainly of collagen. As a result, they are easily bent but not easily broken. In the prime of life, the balance of hydroxyapatite and collagen is perfect, giving both strength and flexibility. In old age, some of the calcium is reabsorbed from the hydroxyapatite, and the collagen loses its flexibility, making the bones more brittle and more easily broken.

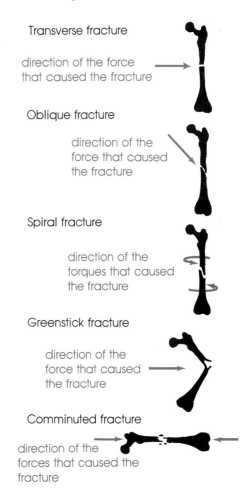

Transverse fracture

direction of the force that caused the fracture

Oblique fracture

direction of the force that caused the fracture

Spiral fracture

direction of the torques that caused the fracture

Greenstick fracture

direction of the force that caused the fracture

Comminuted fracture

direction of the forces that caused the fracture

of sample problems and their solutions will demonstrate the principles of static equilibrium as it applies in selected parts of the human body.

The Elbow

Since muscles only exert tension, two muscles are required to raise and lower the forearm. The triceps muscle runs from the upper end of the ulna bone, in the forearm, to the shoulder (scapula). When it contracts, the arm straightens out. The biceps muscle is connected to the shoulder and to the radius bone in the forearm. When it contracts, the arm bends at the elbow. The humerus bone forms a joint with the radius and ulna bones. The joint acts like a hinge, permitting one degree of freedom at the elbow.

The forearm is much like a lever, with the elbow joint acting as a fulcrum. When the forearm is perpendicular to the upper arm, the torque of the triceps muscle opposes the torque of the biceps muscle, as illustrated. When the hand is supporting a mass, only the biceps muscle exerts an upward force. A sample problem will illustrate the forces that act at a typical human elbow joint.

Sample problem

A 10 kg mass is held in a hand, as illustrated. The mass of the forearm is 2.0 kg, and its centre of gravity is located 14 cm from the joint. The biceps muscle is attached to the radius bone at 4.0 cm from the joint, and the mass is 32 cm from the joint.

(a) Find the tension in the biceps muscle.

(b) Find the tension in the biceps muscle if the forearm forms an angle of 45° with the horizontal.

(c) What is the reaction force of the radius on the humerus, at the joint, when the forearm is outstretched, as in (a)?

(a) First we draw a free-body diagram of the mass and forearm, in which the tension in the biceps muscle is $\vec{F}_B$, the force of gravity on the forearm is $\vec{F}_g$, the force of gravity on the mass is $\vec{F}_w$, and the force exerted on the radius bone by the humerus bone is $\vec{F}_H$.

The net torque about P will be zero, that is,

$$\vec{\tau}_{net} = \vec{\tau}_B + \vec{\tau}_g + \vec{\tau}_W + \vec{\tau}_H = 0$$

$0 = (0.040 \text{ m}) F_B - (0.14 \text{ m}) (2.0 \text{ kg}) (9.8 \text{ N/kg})$
$\quad - (0.32 \text{ m}) (10 \text{ kg}) (9.8 \text{ N/kg}) + 0$

$0 = (0.040 \text{ m}) F_B - 2.74 \text{ N·m} - 31.4 \text{ N·m}$

$F_B = 854 \text{ N, or } 8.5 \times 10^2 \text{ N}$

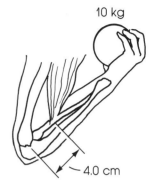

10 kg

4.0 cm

(b) When the elbow forms an angle of 45°, the forces act at 45° to the forearm, as illustrated. The torque equation in (a) will be the same, except that each factor will be multiplied by sin 45°. The result will be the same — a tension in the biceps muscle of 8.5×10^2 N. It follows that the tension in the biceps muscle will be the same for all angles of the elbow, when the same mass is held.

(c) Refer again to either free-body diagram. The net force on the forearm is zero, since there is equilibrium; that is,

$$\vec{F}_{net} = \vec{F}_H + \vec{F}_B + \vec{F}_g + \vec{F}_W = 0$$

Take vertical components, with up as positive.

$0 = - F_H + 844 \text{ N} - 19.6 \text{ N} - 98 \text{ N}$

$F_H = +726 \text{ N, or } 7.3 \times 10^2 \text{ N}$

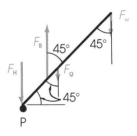

The humerus bone pushes down on the forearm at the elbow.

Note that the stresses in muscles, tendons, and joints are quite large, even during mild activity. In the sample problem, the tension in the biceps muscle was over eight times the force of gravity on the object lifted, and the force on the joint was over seven times that force. This is true of most skeletal muscles and joints. If mild activity produces forces so large, it follows that strenuous activities in such sports as tennis, football, field hockey, track and field, and weight lifting can produce damaging forces if care is not taken.

The Knee

The knee joint forms at the junction of the shinbone (tibia) and the thighbone (femur). The joint is covered on top by the kneecap (patella), and the quadriceps tendons run from the muscles in the upper leg to inserts on the tibia.

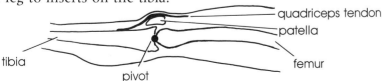

quadriceps tendon
patella
tibia
femur
pivot

Sample problem

The lower leg of a seated person is held straight out, as illustrated. The mass of the lower leg is 4.5 kg, and the line of action of the quadriceps tendon is 4.0 cm from the pivot point at the knee. Estimate the tension in the quadriceps tendon if we assume that the centre of gravity of the lower leg and foot is located at the midpoint of these two.

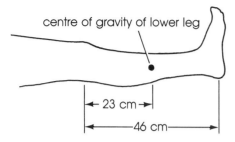
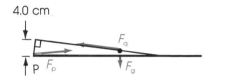

Draw a free-body diagram of the lower leg. Three forces act on it: $\vec{F_g}$, $\vec{F_q}$, and $\vec{F_p}$.

Taking the knee joint as the pivot, the net torque at P will be zero; that is,

$$\vec{\tau}_{net} = \vec{\tau}_g + \vec{\tau}_q + \vec{\tau}_P = 0$$
$$0 = -(0.23\ m)(4.5\ kg)(9.8\ N/kg) + (0.040\ m)F_q + 0$$
$$F_q = 253\ N, \text{ or } 2.5 \times 10^2\ N$$

Note that the force of the muscle is over five times the force of gravity on the leg and that when the leg is straight an equal force is acting directly on the joint!

The Human Foot

When a person stands on his or her toes, the foot acts like a lever. The Achilles tendon pulls upward, and the tibia exerts a downward force on the joint at the ankle. At the toes, the reaction force of the ground pushes upward with a force equal to the body weight carried by that leg. Standing on one's toes is a natural part of walking or running. As the mass of the body is transferred from foot to foot, the forces on the foot and ankle are quite large, as seen in the following sample problem.

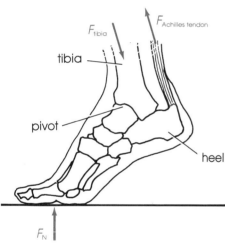

Sample problem

A 70 kg woman stands on her toes and then transfers her weight to one foot. Find the tension in her Achilles tendon, and the force exerted by her tibia on her ankle.

Draw a free-body diagram of the foot. Three forces act on it, as shown.

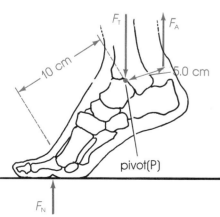

The net torque is zero at the pivot point P. Therefore,

$$\vec{\tau}_{net} = \vec{\tau}_N + \vec{\tau}_A + \vec{\tau}_T = 0$$
$$0 = (0.10\ m)(70\ kg)(9.8\ N/kg) - (0.050\ m)\ F_A + 0$$
$$F_A = 1372\ N, \text{ or } 1.4 \times 10^3\ N$$

Since the net force is zero for static equilibrium, taking up as positive,

$$\vec{F}_{net} = \vec{F}_N + \vec{F}_A + \vec{F}_T = 0$$
$$0 = (70 \text{ kg})(9.8 \text{ N/kg}) + 1372 \text{ N} - F_T$$
$$F_T = 2058 \text{ N, or } 2.1 \times 10^3 \text{ N}$$

The Spine

The spine consists of a series of vertebrae, which support the trunk of the body and protect the spinal nerve that runs down the middle of the spine. Not being a solid bone, the spine can easily be damaged by excessive forces. Many people are afflicted with lower back pain that resulted from poor positioning of the spine when they were lifting or carrying heavy objects.

Let us suppose that a father lifts his child, whose mass is 30.6 kg. Since the father's upper body mass is 40.8 kg, his spine must support a total force of 700 N. In a good lifting position, as illustrated, the spine is in compression. The force exerted by the spine is essentially equal and opposite in direction to the combined force of gravity on the child and the father's upper body. The spine is quite capable of supporting this force of 700 N. But in a poor lifting position, the forces, and the stresses and strains on the spine, are quite different.

When the body is bent over, it is held in position primarily by the erector spinae, the two muscle groups that run down both sides of the back from the neck to the pelvis. In a sense, the spine acts like the boom of a crane, the erector spinae forming the cables holding up the boom. The lowest vertebra of the spinal column (fifth lumbar vertebra) acts as the pivot when the back is in a bending position. The force on this lowest vertebra is transmitted from the sacral bone at the base of the spine through fluid-filled intervertebral discs. If the discs experience extreme forces, they can become perforated or crushed, or they may slip out of position (commonly called a slipped disc). In all cases, the result is extreme pain and immobility. What then are the forces involved when the same father lifts the child in a poor lifting position?

Sample problem

The father is bending over so that his back is at 25° to the horizontal. The combined force of gravity on his upper body and the child is considered to act at his shoulders, 70 cm from the lowest vertebra

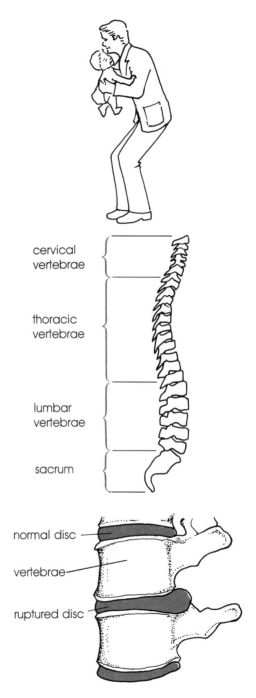

cervical vertebrae

thoracic vertebrae

lumbar vertebrae

sacrum

normal disc

vertebrae

ruptured disc

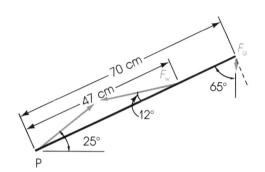

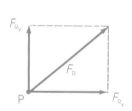

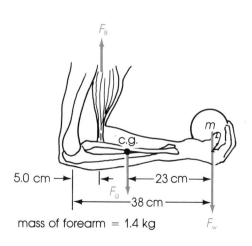

(the pivot point). The force exerted by the erector spinae muscles acts at 12° to the axis of the spine, and the point of attachment of the muscles is 47 cm from the lowest vertebra.

(a) Calculate the tension in the erector spinae muscles.

(b) Determine the magnitude of the force on the lowest vertebra.

(a) Draw a free-body diagram of the spine. Three forces act on it. Using the torque relationship at the bottom of the spine,

$$\vec{\tau}_{net} = \vec{\tau}_w + \vec{\tau}_g + \vec{\tau}_R = 0$$
$$0 = +\ (0.47\ \text{m})\ (\sin 12°)F_w - (0.70\ \text{m})\ (\sin 65°)$$
$$(700\ \text{N}) + 0$$
$$F_w = 4544\ \text{N, or } 4.5 \times 10^3\ \text{N}$$

Thus, the tension in the muscles is 4.5×10^3 N.

(b) To find the force on the bottom vertebra, we must first find the components of the force in the X and Y directions.

$$\vec{F}_{net} = 0 = \vec{F}_R + \vec{F}_w + \vec{F}_g$$
$$0 = F_{R_x} - F_w \cos (90° - 12° - 65°) + F_g \cos 90°$$
$$F_{R_x} = (4544\ \text{N})\ (\cos 13°) + 0$$
$$= 4428\ \text{N}$$

and
$$0 = F_{R_y} - F_w \cos (65° + 12°) - F_g$$
$$F_{R_y} = (4544\ \text{N})\ (\cos 77°) - 700\ \text{N}$$
$$= 1722\ \text{N}$$
$$F_R = \sqrt{F_{R_x}{}^2 + F_{R_y}{}^2}$$
$$= \sqrt{(4428\ \text{N})^2 + (1722\ \text{N})^2}$$
$$= 4751\ \text{N, or } 4.8 \times 10^3\ \text{N}$$

The force on the lowest vertebra in this problem is more than 11 times the force of gravity on the upper body of the person doing the lifting. This is not an extreme example. With such large forces acting on the discs between the lower vertebrae, it is not surprising that many people suffer lower back pain at some time in their lives. For a weight lifter, the lifting position is extremely important. Notice that the weight lifter does not bend over, but lifts straight up. No wonder!

Practice

1. Given the dimensions on the diagram of the forearm holding a mass of 5.4 kg, find
   (a) the tension in the biceps muscle and
   (b) the reactive force of the radius on the humerus, at the joint.
   (4.4×10^2 N, 3.8×10^2 N)

mass of forearm = 1.4 kg

2. During knee exercises, a mass is attached to the foot, as illustrated. Find the torque exerted on the knee joint by the leg and mass, if the mass of the lower leg and foot is 5.4 kg.

(19 N·m)

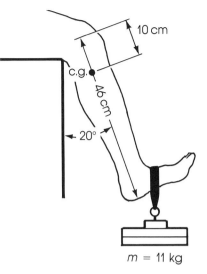

m = 11 kg

3. The father described in the sample problem on page 247 is doing his morning exercises and bends over so that his upper body is at 90° to his legs. In this case, the spinae muscles act at an angle of 9° to the axis of the spine. Determine the tension in the spinae muscles when he holds himself in this position, and the magnitude of the force on the lowest vertebra.

(3.8×10^2 N, 3.8×10^2 N)

4. Find the tension in the quadriceps tendon for the situation shown, assuming that the weight of the leg is ignored.

(1.5×10^3 N)

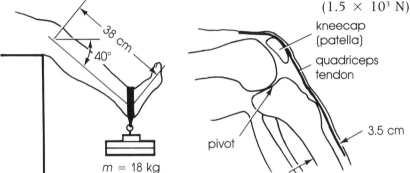

m = 18 kg

kneecap (patella)

quadriceps tendon

pivot

3.5 cm

5. The deltoid muscle raises the upper arm to a horizontal position, as illustrated in the diagram. If the mass of the arm is 4.1 kg and its centre of gravity is considered to act 36 cm from the shoulder joint, find
   (a) the tension in the deltoid muscle,
   (b) the components R_x and R_y of the force exerted by the shoulder joint, and
   (c) the magnitude of the resultant force on the shoulder joint.

(3.1×10^2 N; 2.7×10^2 N, 56 N; 2.8×10^2 N)

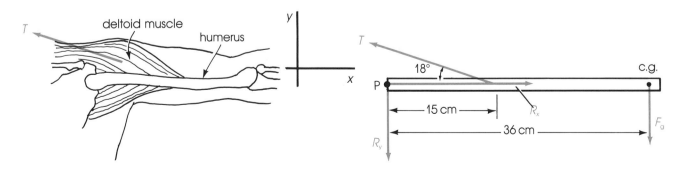

6.10 Investigations

Investigation 6.1: Equilibrium of Forces

Problem:
What is the first condition for static equilibrium?

Materials:
3 small pulleys
3 hangers plus masses
string
circular protractor

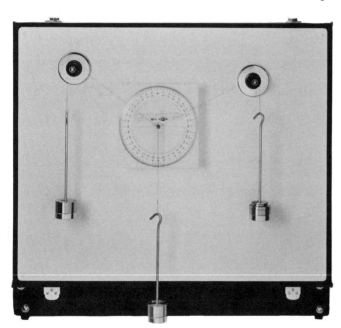
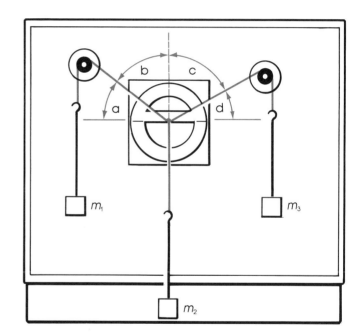

Procedure:
1. Tie one end of each of three pieces of string together (at a point).
2. Using two of the pulleys, make a "Y" out of the strings, and hang the three masses as illustrated. Adjust the masses and the pulleys until the "Y" remains at rest.
3. Place a circular protractor behind the junction of the "Y" so that its centre is behind the point where the three strings meet. Rotate the protractor until one of its axes (0, 90°, 180°, or 270°) is behind the vertical string.

4. Record the values of m_1, m_2, and m_3, and the values of the angles a, b, c, and d.
5. Find the vertical components of the forces produced in the sloping portions of string by m_1 and m_3, then compare their sum with the force produced by m_2.
6. Find the horizontal components of the sloping forces and compare them.
7. Vary the values and angles of m_1 and m_3, keeping m_2 vertical. Repeat steps 2 to 6.
8. Hold the third pulley against the string attached to m_2, so that the string is no longer vertical.
9. Find the vertical components of the three sloping forces, and determine the vector sum of the components.
10. Find the horizontal components of the three forces and their vector sum.
11. Repeat steps 8 to 10 for different values and angles of the forces.
12. State the first condition for static equilibrium.

Investigation 6.2: Principle of Torques

Problem:
What is the second condition for static equilibrium?

Materials:
metre ruler
several hangers plus masses from 100 g to 500 g
string
2 pulleys
spring scale (0-50 N)
pivot clamp

Procedure:
1. Hang the ruler from its midpoint so that it balances horizontally.
2. Hang unequal masses m_1 and m_2 from string loops on either side of the pivot, and adjust the distances d_1 and d_2 so that the ruler once more comes to rest horizontally.

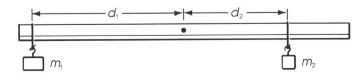

3. Calculate the torques of m_1 and m_2 about the pivot, then compare them.

4. Repeat the investigation with the same apparatus, only use sufficient string at the m_1 location to pass over a pulley, so that the line of action of the force from m_1 is not at right angles to the ruler. Hang m_2 to correspond (see diagram). Determine the torques of m_1 and m_2 about the pivot, then compare them. (Attach the string loop to the ruler with tape to prevent slipping.)

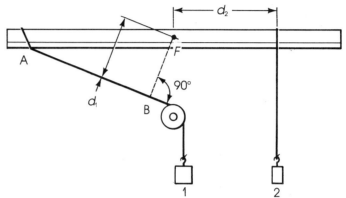

5. Using the same ruler, set up the apparatus illustrated. Adjust the values of the masses and/or their positions until there is a mid-range reading on the scale, and the ruler is balanced horizontally.

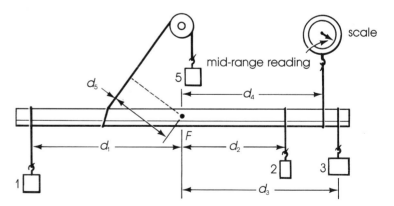

6. Calculate the torques of each of the five forces about the pivot, and compare the sum of the counterclockwise torques with the sum of the clockwise torques.

7. Repeat steps 5 and 6 with different masses and positions.

8. State the second condition for static equilibrium.

Investigation 6.3: Hooke's Law and the Elastic Limit

Problem:
    (a) What is the relationship between the load and extension for copper wire?
    (b) What is the elastic limit for copper wire?

Materials:
2 lengths of copper wire (approximately 50 cm long; diameter 0.45 mm)
centimetre and vernier scales
set of 200 g masses
safety glasses

SAFETY GLASSES MUST BE WORN AT ALL TIMES IN THIS INVESTIGATION.

Procedure:
1. Suspend the two wires vertically from a rigid support.
2. Attach the centimetre and vernier scales near the bottoms of the wires and load the left-hand reference wire with a 200 g mass to pull it straight.
3. Add a mass of 200 g to the other wire, and record the vernier reading.
4. Place a piece of rubber foam or other cushioning device beneath the apparatus to check the fall of the masses when the wire reaches its breaking point (at approximately 4 kg of load).
5. Add masses to the right-hand wire in steps of 200 g, to a total of 1200 g, recording the vernier reading each time. Enter the results in a table of observations, with headings of "load" and "extension".
6. Add further masses in 400 g steps, until failure occurs at approximately 4 kg total load, noting any physical changes in the wire as the masses are added. These readings should also be entered in the table of observations. Stand as far from the apparatus as possible when loading it to more than 2 kg, since a wire end could whip about when the wire breaks.
7. Plot a graph of load versus extension. Mark the following on the graph: region of elasticity, plastic region, elastic limit, yield point, and breaking point.
8. Find the slope of the graph for the region of elasticity.
9. Using Hooke's Law, determine the constant for your copper wire.
10. Determine the value for the elastic limit of this particular copper wire.

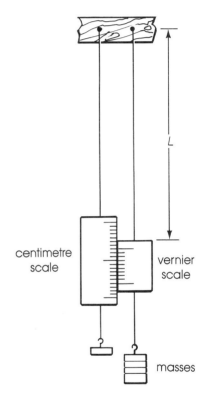

Investigation 6.4: Young's Modulus for a Wire

Problem:
What is Young's Modulus for steel wire?

Materials:
two 3.0 m lengths of steel wire
heavy mass (greater than 5 kg)
kilogram masses to 14 kg
metre ruler
centimetre and vernier scales
micrometer
safety glasses

SAFETY GLASSES MUST BE WORN AT ALL TIMES IN THIS INVESTIGATION.

Procedure:
1. Suspend both steel wires from the ceiling or some other high, strong support.
2. Attach the centimetre and vernier scales to the wires, as in the previous investigation.
3. Using a micrometer, measure the diameter of the wire under test (the right-hand wire) in two directions at three well-separated places.
4. Measure the length of this wire from the ceiling to the top of the vernier scale.
5. To remove any kinks in the wire to which the centimetre scale is attached, hang the heavy mass on it.
6. Add masses to the wire you are testing, in 2 kg steps, beginning with 2 kg and ending with 12 kg. Note the scale readings for each mass addition. (It may be necessary to load and unload the wire a few times for each reading.)
7. Remove the masses in steps of 2 kg, recording the readings each time. If the readings are much different from those for loading, the investigation should be repeated with different wires, or with all kinks removed.
8. Record your observations in a table.
9. Draw a graph of load versus extension. Find the slope.
10. Calculate Young's Modulus for your steel wire.
11. Obtain the value of Young's Modulus for this steel wire from your instructor. Calculate your percentage error.
12. List the sources of experimental error in the investigation.

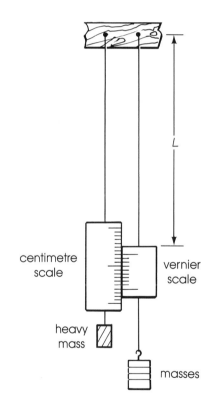

centimetre scale

vernier scale

heavy mass

masses

L

The wire used to support the centimetre scale is made of the same material as the wire being tested, to eliminate errors due to temperature. Thermal expansion affects both wires equally, therefore no relative change occurs.

6.11 Review

Discussion

1. Which is most likely to break when loaded with wet laundry, a clothes-line with a sag or one tightly stretched? Why?
2. One way to pull a car out of the mud is to tightly stretch a rope between the car and a tree, as illustrated. If you pull sideways at the middle of the rope, the pull on the car will be several times greater than your applied force on the rope. Why?
3. In most sports, athletic shoes should have a high coefficient of friction, so that one can stop and turn quickly. In what sports would this be a disadvantage?
4. When a person carries a heavy mass, such as a pail of water, the centre of gravity of the loaded person shifts towards the mass. What actions are taken by the person to maintain stability? Explain why they work.
5. Why is it easier to pick up a long pole at its centre of gravity than to lift it horizontally from one end?
6. Why do people take very short steps on slippery surfaces?
7. Empty ships returning to port are usually loaded with ballast. In the past, rocks were used, but water is usually used nowadays. Why is ballast added?
8. In what position of the arm is its pulling force greatest — when the lower arm is perpendicular to the upper arm, or when it is partially or fully extended? Why?

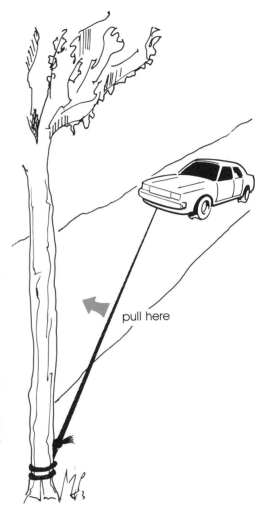

pull here

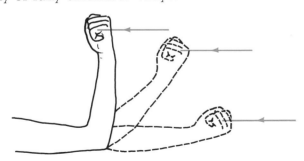

9. Why do high heels greatly increase the danger of ankle injury?
10. Why do car wheels that are out of alignment cause unnecessary wear and tear?
11. Many careers involve work with static forces, equilibrium, and elasticity. List at least five such careers in each of the following fields: construction, medicine, furniture making, athletics.

Problems

12. Find the resultant of the following concurrent forces:
    (a) 20 N [W] and 16N [N30°W].
    (b) 1200 N [N65°E], 800 N [E15°S], 1000 N [S30°W].
13. A pioneer farmer hitches a horse and an ox to a stump in order to remove it from a field. The horse pulls with a force of 1.2×10^4 N [W], while the ox pulls with a force of 1.6×10^4 N [W30°N]. What is the resultant force on the stump?
14. If the coefficient of friction between your running shoes and the gym floor is 0.80, how fast could you run around a circle with a radius of 2.0 m?
15. You are wearing shoes that have a coefficient of friction on rock of 0.70. On how steep a rock slope could you stand without slipping?
16. An arrow is drawn back against a bowstring with a force of 280 N. If the arrow makes an angle of 55° with the string above and below the arrow, find the tension in the string.
17. A guy wire makes an angle of 55° with the ground, and applies a force of 1600 N to the top of a vertical clothes-line pole. Find the vertical and horizontal components of the force exerted on the pole by the wire.
18. A tennis net is supported at each end by a steel post, as illustrated. If the maximum tension in the net rope is 800 N and the angles are as shown, calculate the tension in the guy wire and the compression in the steel post. (Assume a hinge pin at the base of each post).
19. A patient is in neck traction with skull calipers, as illustrated. Find the maximum value of the suspended mass that will cause no tension or other force in the neck, given that the mass of the head is 4.2 kg and the coefficient of friction between the bed and the head is 0.20.

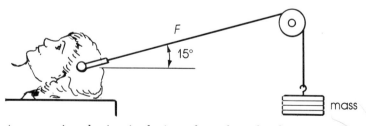

20. An exercise device is designed so that the force gets larger as the distance from the face of the support increases. As seen in the diagram, two pulleys, a mass, and a rope are used. Find the force needed to hold the movable pulley 0.50 m, 1.00 m, and 1.50 m from the wall.

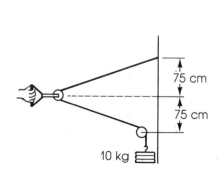

21. A 0.60 g spider hangs on its thread from the branch of a tree. A horizontal wind blows the spider and the thread to an angle of 35° from the vertical. Find the force of the wind on the spider and the tension in the thread.

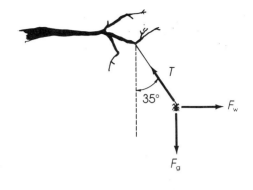

22. To keep Robin from being captured, Batman tosses him out of a third-storey window, knowing that a 17.0 m rope hangs slack between hooks of equal height on adjacent buildings 13.0 m apart. Robin grabs the rope and hangs on at a point 5.0 m from one end. Assuming that Robin's mass is 45.0 kg and the rope withstands the initial impulse, what is the tension in each part of the rope when equilibrium is established?

23. The Russell traction apparatus is used for a fractured femur. When the femur is healing, the muscles of the upper leg tend to pull the two sections of the femur together, which could result in a shortened leg after healing. The Russell apparatus provides a force parallel to the femur that prevents contraction of the femur. The sling supports the weight of the lower leg.

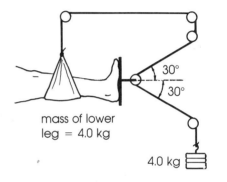

mass of lower leg = 4.0 kg

4.0 kg

   (a) Find the magnitude and direction of the horizontal force on the leg, i.e., the sole of the foot.
   (b) To adjust the size of this force, the angles at the pulley on the foot can be changed. Would the angles be made larger or smaller, to decrease the force on the leg? Explain your reasoning.
   (c) Why are the angles kept equal, as shown?

24. The tendons pull on the bones of the lower leg with a total force of 100 N, as illustrated. What torque is exerted on the leg by the tendons alone?

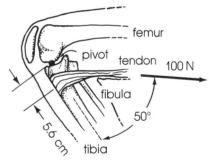

25. Two children balance on a seesaw. One, with a mass of 30 kg, is seated 2.0 m from the pivot. The other is seated 2.5 m from the pivot. What is the mass of the second child?

26. Find the tension in the bicycle chain shown. The bottom is slack.

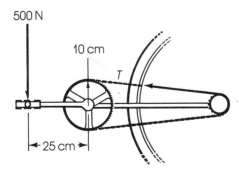

500 N

10 cm

T

25 cm

27. What total vertical force is required to lift the handles of the loaded wheelbarrow illustrated in the diagram?

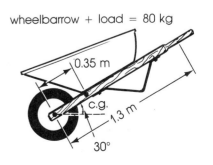

wheelbarrow + load = 80 kg

0.35 m

c.g.

1.3 m

30°

28. A marcher in a parade holds a flag at an angle of 60°. What force must the hand provide perpendicular to the pole?

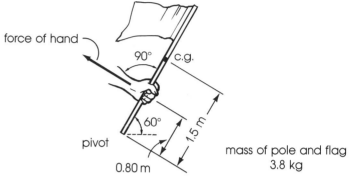

force of hand

90°   c.g.

60°

pivot

0.80 m   1.5 m

mass of pole and flag
3.8 kg

29. A pole-vaulter runs down the track at constant velocity, carrying a 6.0 m pole with a mass of 4.0 kg. Assuming that the centre of gravity of the pole is located at its midpoint, and the vaulter's hands are placed 1.0 m apart, find
    (a) the vertical force of each hand on the pole when the pole is carried horizontally, and

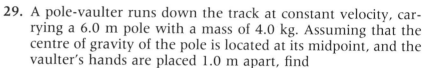

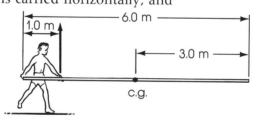

6.0 m

1.0 m

3.0 m

c.g.

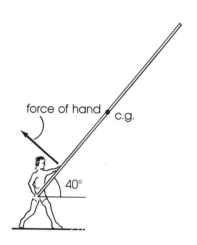

force of hand   c.g.

40°

    (b) the force on the pole-vaulter's upper hand during the high carry if it is perpendicular to the pole, as shown.

30. An oar is held by a rower at 0.35 m from the oarlock. The oar makes contact with the water at an average of 1.3 m from the oarlock. If the force applied by the rower on the oar is 80 N, what is
    (a) the force of the oar on the water, and
    (b) the force on the oarlock?

0.35 m

1.3 m

31. Calculate the force at the hands and toes of a 58 kg athlete holding a push-up position.

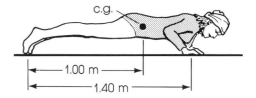

c.g.

1.00 m

1.40 m

32. Three men, 4.0 m apart as illustrated, are carrying a heavy load on a pole. Two are at one end of the pole and the third is at the other end. Where should the load be placed so that each man gives equal support?

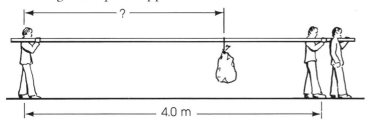

?

4.0 m

33. A designer wishes to construct a mobile (as shown in the diagram) using strings and light rods (of negligible mass). If the mass of the figure on the bottom left is 125 g, what are the required masses of the other figures so that the rods are horizontal?

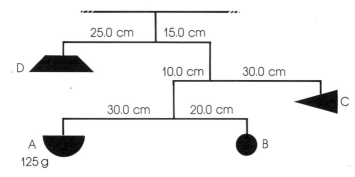

25.0 cm   15.0 cm

.D

10.0 cm   30.0 cm

30.0 cm   20.0 cm

C

A
125 g

B

34. The diagram shows a forearm supporting a shot put whose mass is 5.44 kg. Using the dimensions on the diagram, find the force exerted by the biceps and the force on the elbow joint.

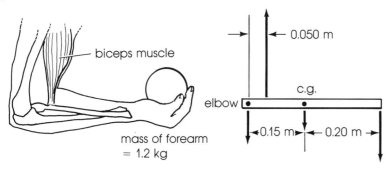

biceps muscle

0.050 m

c.g.

elbow

mass of forearm
= 1.2 kg

0.15 m   0.20 m

35. A 5.0 m diving board with a mass of 30 kg is supported at X and Y. Calculate the forces at X and Y when a 50 kg diver stands at the outer end of the board.

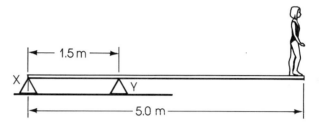

36. Two painters, Mike and Ned, have been lowered over the side of a ship on an 8.0 m plank supported by two ropes P and Q. The distance relationships are shown on the diagram, and the masses are as follows: Mike 60 kg, Ned 80 kg, and the plank 40 kg. Find the tensions in the two ropes.

37. A light, hinged rod and cable support a load, as shown. If the maximum tension the cable can withstand is 1.5×10^3 N, what is the maximum mass of the load?

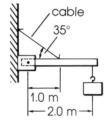

38. To make larger pictures, an enlarger can be moved to the edge of a table so that the image is projected onto the floor, as shown.

　(a) What is the minimum mass required on the base at point A to keep the enlarger from tipping off the table?

　(b) With this mass in place, what will be the reaction force at B?

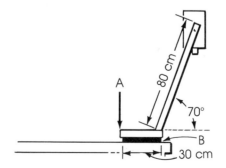

mass of base = 2.0 kg
mass of support = 2.0 kg
mass of enlarger = 6.0 kg

39. A 6.0 m ladder with a mass of 12.5 kg leans against a smooth wall at an angle of 50° to the horizontal. If the coefficient of static friction between the ladder and the ground is 0.40, how far up the ladder can a 70 kg woman climb before the ladder starts to slip?

40. Using the data found in the sample problem on page 248, determine the tension in the back muscles if the father bends over holding the child, so that his back is 40° to the horizontal and the muscles pull at 10° to the axis of his spine.

41. The Earth and moon are 3.8×10^8 m apart, and their masses are 6.0×10^{24} kg and 7.3×10^{22} kg, respectively. Where, approximately, is the centre of gravity (relative to the Earth) of the Earth-moon system?

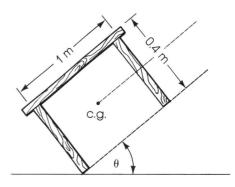

42. The four-legged table shown has a mass of 30 kg. Assuming that the legs are massless and the table does not slide, at what angle will it tip over?

43. A tall water glass with a mass of 300 g is about to be pushed (horizontally at its rim) across a table. The glass has a base 1.8 cm in diameter and is 6.0 cm tall. If the coefficient of friction with the table surface is 0.20, determine whether the glass will slide or tip.

44. A 50 kg high wire artist carries a weighted pole, as illustrated. Her centre of gravity is 80 cm above the high wire, and the two 23 kg masses are located 120 cm vertically below the wire. Find the vertical location of the centre of gravity of the walker and the weighted pole, relative to the high wire. Is this a case of stable or unstable equilibrium?

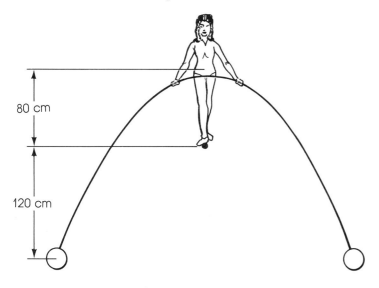

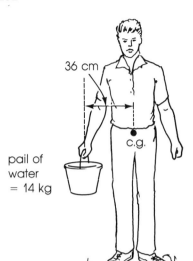

36 cm

c.g.

pail of
water
= 14 kg

45. Find the minimum lateral shift in position of the centre of gravity of a standing man, whose mass is 80 kg, when he is carrying a 14 kg pail of water. Assume that he wishes to have an equal load on each foot. How is this shift in his centre of gravity accomplished?

46. In a Hooke's Law experiment, a force of 160 N produces a stretch of 8.00 cm in a spring. What is the spring constant?

47. A 100 N force stretches a spring from 12 cm to 14 cm. What will be the length of the spring when a force of 500 N is applied, assuming that the spring remains within its elastic limit?

48. A copper wire 2.0 m long and 2.0×10^{-3} m in diameter is suspended from a solid support. A mass of 10 kg is hung from the bottom of the wire. What will be the stress and strain in the wire?

49. A rectangular steel bar 5.00 m long, with a cross-sectional area of 1.3×10^{-3} m², supports a mass of 1500 kg. How much is the bar stretched?

50. A wire 0.80 mm in diameter and 1.8 m long was stretched 1.3 mm by a force of 18 N. Find Young's Modulus for the wire.

51. A 48 cm long leg bone, with a cross-sectional area of 5.0 cm², supports a load one-half the force of gravity on a 65 kg person. What is the compression experienced by the leg bone?

52. A brass rod has a diameter of 5.0 mm. What force will stretch it by 0.02% of its length?

53. If the stress produced in stretching a 3.0 m wire is 4.00×10^6 N/m² from an applied force of 60 N, what is the cross-sectional area of the wire? How much will the wire stretch if Young's Modulus for the wire is 1.5×10^{11} N/m²?

54. A load of 250 kg is supported by two steel cables, as shown in the diagram.
(a) Find the tensions in the cables.
(b) If both cables have a diameter of 2.0 mm, how much does each cable stretch?

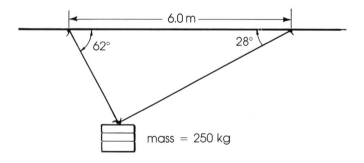

6.0 m

62°   28°

mass = 250 kg

55. A 50 kg traffic light is suspended above an intersection by a continuous steel cable, as illustrated. The cable has a diameter of 1.0 cm, and the light is depressed 12° below the horizontal. What is the fractional increase in the length of the cable due to the mass of the traffic light?

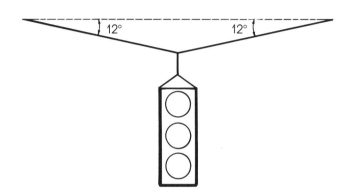

56. Two aluminum plates are joined together by an aluminum rivet with a diameter of 3.0 mm. If the maximum shear stress for aluminum is 1.5×10^8 N/m², how much force will have to be applied to one of the plates to shear through the rivet?

57. The radius bone in a forearm has an average effective cross-sectional area of 1.33×10^{-4} m². How much compressive force can it withstand before fracturing?

58. A solar-heated house has an uneven pitch, as shown. If a 250 kg tank of water is suspended from the apex, find the extra compressive force in each rafter.

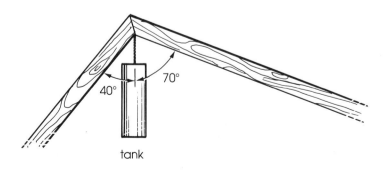

tank

Numerical Answers to Review Problems

12. (a) 32 N [W26°N]
    (b) 1.5×10^3 N [E23°S]
13. 2.7×10^4 N [W17°N]
14. 4.0 m/s
15. 35°
16. 2.4×10^2 N
17. 1.3×10^3 N, 9.2×10^2 N
18. 1.2×10^3 N, 1.1×10^3 N
19. 0.82 kg
20. 1.1×10^2 N, 1.6×10^2 N, 1.8×10^2 N
21. 4.1×10^{-3} N, 7.2×10^{-3} N
22. 1.5×10^2 N, 3.6×10^2 N
23. 68 N [horizontal]
24. 4.3 N·m
25. 24 kg
26. 1.3×10^3 N
27. 2.1×10^2 N
28. 35 N
29. (a) 78 N [down], 1.2×10^2 N [up]
    (b) 90 N [up]
30. (a) 22 N (b) 1.0×10^2 N
31. 4.1×10^2 N, 1.6×10^2 N
32. 2.7 m
33. B: 188 g, C: 104 g, D: 250 g
34. 4.1×10^2 N, 3.4×10^2 N
35. 1.3×10^3 N [down], 2.1×10^3 N [up]
36. 1.1×10^3 N, 6.4×10^2 N
37. 44 kg
38. (a) 5.4 kg (b) 1.5×10^2 N
39. 3.2 m from the top
40. 4.6×10^3 N
41. 4.6×10^6 m
42. 51°
43. tip
44. 16 cm below, stable
45. 5.4 cm
46. 2.0×10^3 N/m
47. 22 cm
48. 3.1×10^7 N/m², 2.8×10^{-4}
49. 2.8×10^{-4} m
50. 5.0×10^{10} N/m²
51. 2.0×10^{-5} m
52. 3.5×10^2 N
53. 1.5×10^{-5} m², 8.0×10^{-5} m
54. (a) 1.2×10^3 N, 2.1×10^3 N
    (b) 9.7×10^{-3} m, 9.7×10^{-3} m
55. 7.5×10^{-5}
56. 1.1×10^3 N
57. 1.7×10^4 N
58. 2.5×10^3 N, 1.7×10^3 N

7 Planetary Mechanics

7.1 Introduction

Since the time of the ancient Greeks, more than twenty-five centuries ago, two distinct types of motion have been central to our understanding of the universe. One is the motion of objects on the Earth — terrestrial motion. The other is the motion of objects in the heavens — celestial motion. Until the work of Copernicus, Kepler, Galileo, and Newton, these two types of motion were considered to be completely separate.

Our present view of the universe has developed step by step, one idea based on another, beginning with the theories and ideas of the ancients. As was discussed in Section 5.6, it is quite natural for us to draw incorrect conclusions if we work within a particular frame of reference. This same Earth-frame view led to many of the misconceptions of the ancients.

If you look up at the stars at night, for example, you will notice that they seem to be arranged on a large inverted bowl. This is why the ancient Greeks pictured them as fixed on the inside of a large rotating sphere. The permanence of the groupings of stars, or "constellations", led to their being named: Virgo, Sagittarius, etc. These groups appeared to move slowly across the heavens as the celestial sphere rotated.

At the same time, a number of star-like objects were observed, which moved with respect to the "fixed stars". Five of these nomadic objects were later named for Roman gods – Mercury, Venus, Mars, Jupiter, and Saturn — and were called planets (from the Greek word "planētēs", meaning wanderer). The planets and the fixed groupings of stars became part of the religion of the time, and astrology was born.

The fixed stars, as well as the sun and moon, seemed to move from east to west, and the whole celestial sphere completed one rotation in approximately twenty-four hours. Because the moon moved more slowly than the stars, it appeared to move eastward with respect to them. The motion of the planets among the stars is more irregular than that of the sun and moon, but it, too, is in an easterly direction with respect to the stars. An exception, for the planets, is an occasional periodic westerly motion, referred to as a "retrogression" (see diagram on page 265).

This time-lapse photograph shows the apparent circular motion of stars about the pole star.

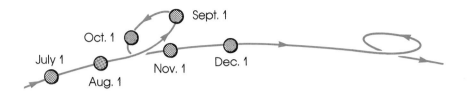

The path of the planet Mars among the stars over the course of several months, showing retrogression for various dates

These observations of the heavenly bodies made by ancient astronomers can still be made today, but we are not satisfied with simply observing. We want to understand what is behind our observations. We try to determine what kind of order or unifying principle explains and can predict them. In this effort, we create models or theories to explain our observations. This procedure is common to all the sciences, not just physics.

7.2 Early Theories of the Universe

As far back as the 6th and 7th centuries B.C., Greek philosophers, including Thales and Pythagoras, proposed that the heavens were composed of eight concentric, transparent spheres, as illustrated.

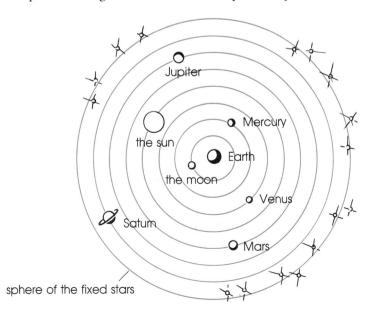

sphere of the fixed stars

Pythagoras (582-497 B.C.) is one of the most famous of the early Greek philosophers. Indeed, he is supposed to have originated the word "philosopher". Today we remember him mostly because of the Pythagorean theorem and his other work in mathematics; for example, the concept of the irrational number. His greatest scientific work was in the study of sound. Much of the work done by Pythagoras and his followers is difficult to isolate because the Pythagoreans were a secret, mystic group who kept their work from outsiders.

Thales (640-546 B.C.) was considered by later Greeks to have been the founder of Greek science, mathematics, and philosophy. He predicted an eclipse, thereby stopping a battle, studied magnetism, and proposed that all matter is made of fundamental elements.

The universe as conceived by early astronomers consisted of eight concentric spheres rotating about the Earth.

Aristotle (384-322 B.C.), a student of Plato, was a successful teacher, philosopher, and scientist. His most important scientific work was done in biology, where he classified over five hundred species and arranged them into hierarchies. He was not a good mathematician, but he founded a system of logic that stood without change for 1900 years. In fact, his logic was so convincing that it provided the intellectual basis for the notion of celestial spheres and the theory that Earth and Heaven were subject to two different sets of natural laws. Using the same logical approach, he "proved" that heavy objects fall faster than light ones and that a force is necessary for all motion. Because of the power of his logic, physics went virtually unchallenged up to the time of Newton, and was known as "Aristotelian physics". After Newton it was known as "Newtonian physics".

Ptolemy (127-151 A.D.) is less important for his own work than for synthesizing or bringing together the work of those who went before him. He drew principally on the work of Hipparchus (190?-120? B.C.) to form his theory of the universe, commonly called the Ptolemaic System.

Each sphere rotated on a different axis and at a different rate, but all were centred about the Earth. This **geocentric**, or Earth-centred, view of the universe persisted, with minor modifications, for over 2000 years.

The two greatest philosophers of Greek civilization, Plato and Artistotle, with their followers, contributed further detail to this concept of the universe. Plato and his students raised to the level of dogma the idea that the heavenly bodies must move in perfect circles. They could not conceive that the orbits of planets might be oval-shaped. This was a natural development of a philosophy largely concerned with form and perfection. To accommodate the idea of perfect motion in a circle, and at the same time explain the retrograde motion of the planets, Aristotelians devised a complicated system of fifty-four spheres that accounted for many of the observed motions of the heavenly bodies. This system still did not solve all the problems, however.

A model developed by the Aristotelians had spheres within spheres, rotating about the Earth as centre.

The geocentric view of the universe reached its peak in the work of Ptolemy, who made extensive astronomical observations in Alexandria. On the basis of these, he revised the geocentric model by proposing that the planets, the sun, and the moon moved in combinations of simple circles, with one pattern superimposed on another. This, he believed, accounted for the retrograde motion of the planets (see diagram next page). With some modifying, he produced a system that accurately gave both the past and future positions of planets. Although Ptolemy's theory did not agree perfectly with his observations, it was close enough that no one doubted it was basically correct. Indeed, no essential changes were made in it until Copernicus proposed a sun-centred, or **heliocentric**, view of the universe 1300 years later.

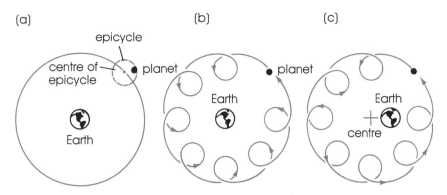

Aristarchus of Samos (310-230? B.C.) suggested a heliocentric model based on his observations of the relative distances of the sun and moon. His views were too revolutionary to be accepted by his contemporaries. In fact, his book on the subject did not survive, and we know of his work only because it was mentioned in the writings of Archimedes.

(a) An attempt to explain the retrograde motion of planets with the concept of an epicycle — a small circle turning about a centre, which itself moves on a larger circle: (b) the net motion of a planet would thus be a series of loops. (c) Ptolemy proposed that the Earth was not at the centre of the universe but, rather, a certain distance from it.

7.3 Copernican Concept of the Heavens

Nicolaus Copernicus (1473-1543) was a Polish mathematician, astronomer, doctor, and church official to whom it occurred that the tables of planetary position could be more easily calculated if it were assumed that the sun, not the Earth, was the centre of the universe. According to Copernicus, the Earth was just one of the planets, each revolving around the sun. Further, he reasoned, the Earth rotated on its own axis once a day, giving rise to the apparent daily motion of the sun, moon, and stars. He also proposed that the moon rotated around the Earth.

Copernicus was not the first to conceive of a heliocentric system, but the idea had always been rejected before. However, his was the time of the Renaissance, of Leonardo da Vinci Michelangelo, and Columbus — a time when new ideas could fall on more fertile ground. His theory better predicted the motion of planets than did the Ptolemaic theory. In particular, the calendar year was explained more simply by the Copernican system. Secondly, the puzzling, retrograde motion of the planets did not present a problem in his system. Nevertheless, opposition to the Copernican system was widespread, especially from the Christian Church, which held to the view that the Earth was the centre of the universe. One hundred years later, Galileo was put on trial by the church for supporting the Copernican theory.

Nicolaus Copernicus

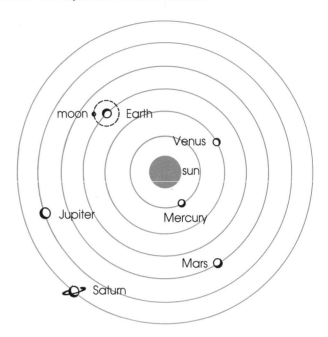

Copernicus's Polish name was
Nicholaus Koppernigk.

The publication of Copernicus' book
was placed in the hands of a Lutheran
minister. Since Luther had opposed the
theory, the minister added a preface
declaring that the book was not a
description of facts but a method of
computing planetary tables. This
weakened the effect of the book and
damaged the credibility of the theory
until Kepler's book was published in
1609, over fifty years later.

Copernicus described his system in a book, but for years hesitated
to publish it. Nevertheless, a summary of his ideas was prepared
in a manuscript, and this circulated among Europe's scholars, creating
considerable interest and enthusiasm. Finally, at the urging of his
friends, Copernicus permitted publication of his entire book, pru-
dently dedicating it to the Pope. The book was published in 1543,
four weeks before Copernicus died, and was an immediate success.

The Copernican theory is a landmark in the history of science.
It began the scientific revolution that dethroned Greek science and
set humankind on a new pathway to knowledge. In the work of
Isaac Newton, 150 years later, this revolution reached its climax
and fulfilment.

7.4 The Contributions of Tycho Brahe and Johann Kepler

*"This fool wants to turn the whole art
of astronomy upside down."*
                    Martin Luther on Copernicus

Tycho Brahe (1546-1601), a Dane, was the last and possibly the
greatest of the naked-eye astronomers. Brahe made his mark in
1572, with the publication of a book describing a new star. This
star grew to be brighter than Venus and remained visible for a year
and a half before fading.

Brahe's book established the name "nova" for all exploding stars. More importantly, it put to rest the Greek notion that the heavens were perfect and unchanging. He showed by the accuracy of his measuring methods that, although the new star was too far away for its distance to be measured, it was certainly farther from the Earth than was the sun.

The King of Denmark decided to be Brahe's patron. He built him an elegant observatory on the island of Hveen, near Elsinore (made famous by Shakespeare's *Hamlet*), not far from Copenhagen. Brahe constructed a large device called a quadrant, with which to view the sky. His instruments were so precise that he could measure the angular position of a star to an accuracy of 1/1000 of a degree. For more than twenty years, he plotted the paths of the planets.

When, in 1577, a great comet appeared in the sky, Brahe's parallax studies showed that this object had an orbit that must be elongated rather than circular. The comet could not exhibit such behaviour unless celestial spheres did not exist, a possibility that went against Brahe's own beliefs. He was basically a very conservative astronomer, who would not abandon the Greek notion that the Earth was the centre of the universe.

Because of Brahe's amazingly accurate observations, it became possible to bring the calendar into line with astronomical measurement. The result was the Gregorian Calendar, published in 1582 under the sponsorship of Pope Gregory XIII. It was quickly accepted by the Catholic nations, but only slowly by Protestant and Greek Orthodox countries. Today, it is universally accepted, except where religious ritual or tradition demands the use of older calendars such as the Julian and Chinese.

In 1597, Brahe lost his patron in Denmark and, at the invitation of Emperor Rudolf II, settled in Prague, Czechoslovakia. Here he made possibly his greatest discovery, in the brilliant young German mathematician he chose as his assistant — Johann Kepler (1571-1630). He gave Kepler his carefully accumulated observations, and assigned him the job of preparing tables of planetary motion. When Brahe died in 1601, Kepler inherited this invaluable data, including Brahe's observations of the motion of the planet Mars.

Born in southwest Germany, Kepler had been greatly influenced by the work of the Greeks and spent a great deal of time trying to devise systems with which to improve on the Ptolemaic view of the universe. But no matter how he tried, using Brahe's data, he could not find a system of perfect circles that worked. Finally, in 1595, he stopped investigations focused on the celestial spheres and, instead, searched for some non-circular curve that would suit. First, he tried an egg-shaped oval, then he settled on the ellipse.

Tycho Brahe's troubles in life were usually of his own making. He was arrogant, conceited, and quarrelsome. When he was only 19, he fought a foolish duel in which his nose was cut off; he had to wear a false nose of metal for the rest of his life.

Tycho Brahe

Using Brahe's observations of the planet Mars, Kepler found that its motion fitted an elliptical orbit with a high degree of accuracy. He later found that the orbits of the other known planets could also be drawn as ellipses, with the sun at one of the foci. This he announced in a book published in 1609. The motion of the planets in ellipses became known as Kepler's First Law. The book also contained the explanation of another important planetary relationship, now known as Kepler's Second Law: The line connecting a planet and the sun will sweep out equal areas in equal times, as the planet moves along its orbital path.

Kepler's Second Law results from the conservation of angular momentum of the planet about the sun.

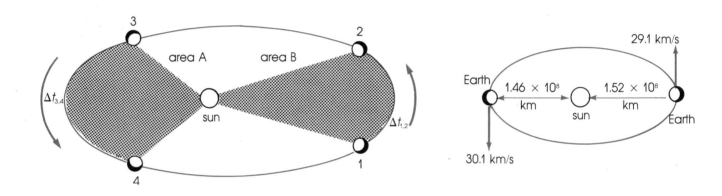

As illustrated in the diagram, for equal time intervals $\Delta t_{1,2} = \Delta t_{3,4}$, the areas swept out by the line between the sun and a planet are equal (Area A = Area B). This means that the closer a planet is to the sun, the faster it will move, and it will move in a predictable way.

Kepler's ellipses put an end to Greek astronomy. The long-established concept of celestial spheres and perfectly circular motion had been destroyed. Kepler's scheme of the solar system has been followed by astronomers and scientists ever since, without significant change.

With the elimination of the idea of celestial spheres, some other cause had to be found to explain the fact that the planets remained in their orbits. Kepler realized that the sun somehow controlled the motion of the planets, but he was unable to explain how it did this. It was left to Newton, fifty years later, to provide a satisfactory answer.

Kepler published a second book, in 1619. This book was verbose and rambling, and preoccupied with mysticism. Still, it contained

Kepler's view of the universe was restricted to the solar system. The stars, he thought, were all located in a thin layer, approximately 1.5 km thick, somewhere beyond the solar system.

Kepler's manuscripts have been preserved, and are now in the Pulkovo Observatory in the USSR.

what is now called Kepler's Third Law, which stated: The square of the orbital period of a planet is proportional to the cube of its mean distance from the sun.

This can be expressed mathematically as

$$\frac{R^3}{T^2} = K$$

where R is the mean radius of the orbit of the planet, T is the period of rotation about the sun, and K is a constant, usually referred to as Kepler's constant.

Kepler's three laws can be summarized as follows:

1. **The planets move about the sun in elliptical orbits, with the sun at one focus of the ellipses.**
2. **The straight line joining the sun and a given planet sweeps out equal areas in equal intervals of time.**
3. **The square of the period of revolution of a planet about the sun is proportional to the cube of its mean distance from the sun.**

The following table provides some accurate information about our solar system. Using the values for the mean orbital radius and the period of each planet, the ratio of R^3/T^2 has been calculated in the last column. Note that, using modern measurements, the value is a constant for the solar orbits, as predicted by Kepler in his Third Law.

Johann Kepler

The Solar System

Object	Mass (kg)	Radius of object (m)	Period of rotation on axis (s)	Mean radius of orbit (m)	Period of revolution of orbit (s)	Kepler constant R^3/T^2 (m³/s²)
sun	1.98×10^{30}	6.95×10^8	2.14×10^6	—	—	—
Mercury	3.28×10^{23}	2.57×10^6	5.05×10^6	5.79×10^{10}	7.60×10^6	3.35×10^{18}
Venus	4.83×10^{24}	6.31×10^6	2.1×10^7	1.08×10^{11}	1.94×10^7	3.35×10^{18}
Earth	5.98×10^{24}	6.38×10^6	8.61×10^4	1.49×10^{11}	3.16×10^7	3.35×10^{18}
Mars	6.37×10^{23}	3.43×10^6	8.85×10^4	2.28×10^{11}	5.94×10^7	3.35×10^{18}
Jupiter	1.90×10^{27}	7.18×10^7	3.54×10^4	7.78×10^{11}	3.74×10^8	3.35×10^{18}
Saturn	5.67×10^{26}	6.03×10^7	3.60×10^4	1.43×10^{12}	9.30×10^8	3.35×10^{18}
Uranus	8.80×10^{25}	2.67×10^7	3.88×10^4	2.87×10^{12}	2.66×10^9	3.34×10^{18}
Neptune	1.03×10^{26}	2.48×10^7	5.69×10^6	4.50×10^{12}	5.20×10^9	3.37×10^{18}
Pluto	6×10^{23}	3×10^6	5.51×10^5	5.9×10^{12}	7.82×10^9	3.36×10^{18}
moon	7.34×10^{22}	1.74×10^6	2.36×10^6	3.8×10^8	2.36×10^6	—

Note that the Earth's period of rotation on its axis is 8.61 × 10⁴ s, which is 23 h 55 min, 5 min less than the 24 h we would expect. This is why there are 364.25 d in a year, and leap years are necessary. The period of rotation of the Earth is called the *sidereal day*.

Sample Problem

An asteroid has a period of 8.1×10^7 s. What is its mean radius of orbit around the sun?

$$\frac{R^3}{T^2} = K, \qquad \text{or } R = \sqrt[3]{T^2 K}$$

$$= \sqrt[3]{(8.1 \times 10^7 \text{ s})^2 (3.35 \times 10^{18} \text{ m}^3/\text{s}^2)}$$

$$= 2.8 \times 10^{11} \text{ m}$$

Practice

1. A planet's mean distance from the sun is 2.0×10^{11} m. What is its orbital period? $(4.9 \times 10^7 \text{ s})$
2. If a small planet were discovered whose orbital period was twice that of the Earth, how many times farther from the sun would this planet be? (1.6 times)
3. Using the data from the table, determine the Kepler constant for any satellite of the Earth. (Note: The moon is a satellite of the Earth.) $(9.9 \times 10^{12} \text{ m}^3/\text{s}^2)$

7.5 Galileo Defends the Copernican System

Galileo was born in Pisa, February 15, 1564, and died in Arcetri (near Florence), January 8, 1642.

Kepler had greatly amplified the heliocentric view of the heavens, yet the controversy between the heliocentric and the geocentric systems was not over. Through the work of Galileo Galilei (1564-1642), the Copernican system received both its strongest support and, because the church rejected his work, its most powerful challenge.

Galileo was the son of an Italian nobleman of low rank. He was initially trained in medicine but then became interested in mathematics. He also composed music. He was a true Renaissance man, with many talents. One of the first to use the telescope, Galileo made several important discoveries, including four of the moons of Jupiter and the presence of many more stars in the sky than were previously envisaged. He also discovered that the moon was irregular in shape, and had mountains and craters, and that the sun had spots. He announced his discoveries in a periodical he called *Sidereus Nuncius (Starry Messenger)*.

At the University of Padua, Galileo was a brilliant lecturer who students flocked to hear, infuriating his colleagues. His caustic wit made many people look foolish and created bitter enemies for him, some of them, unfortunately, in positions of influence and authority.

As long as Galileo treated the Copernican theory as a working hypothesis and not as established dogma, he was left largely alone. Even so, he managed to provoke his fellow professors, originally at the University of Pisa and later at the University of Padua. In

1632 he published a book entitled *Dialogue on the Two Chief World Systems*, a defence of the Copernican system. The dialogue involved three characters, one of which was a rather simple-minded defender of the geocentric view. Unfortunately, the Pope was persuaded by Galileo's enemies that this character was a caricature of himself. As a result, Galileo was immediately summoned by the Inquisition, whose function was to defend the church against heretical teachings. Although he was well respected and had many friends in high places, he was put on trial.

Galileo was seventy years old at the time and was well aware of the power of the Inquisition. The threat of torture was enough to make him confess that his teachings were wrong. His recantation satisfied the Inquisition, and he was released to spend the remainder of his life under house arrest. Nevertheless, the defence of the heliocentric model had been made, and the Copernican view of the universe was firmly established.

After the trial, Galileo summarized his discoveries related to the motion of objects on the Earth, and published them in the book *Dialogues Concerning Two New Sciences*. This book contained Galileo's greatest contribution to the history of science. Concise and factual, his publications initiated a new style of writing for scientific books and reports. At the same time, his method of observation, measurement, calculation, conclusion, and generalization with regard to a law or principle provided a standard for scientific investigation. Some of his thoughts concerning gravity, uniform motion, and acceleration are presented in earlier chapters of this textbook. His work, along with that of Kepler and Copernicus, provided the basis for the work of Isaac Newton, probably one of the greatest scientists ever to have lived.

The rejection of the Copernican system was not restricted to Catholic believers. The Protestant reformers Martin Luther and John Calvin also denounced the theory. However, some church leaders (the Jesuits, for example) accepted and taught the Copernican system. Galileo's arrogance must bear some of the blame for the extent of the conflict.

The final degradation accorded Galileo by the church was its refusal to allow his body to be buried in consecrated ground. His works were denied to Roman Catholics for over 200 years, and it was only in 1979 that the church began the process of clearing the name of Galileo for its adherents.

As the English physicist Lord Rutherford, one of the pioneers of modern atomic theory, said: "It is not in the nature of things for any one man to make a sudden, violent discovery; science goes step by step, and every man depends upon the work of his predecessors . . . Scientists are not dependent on the ideas of a single man, but on the combined wisdom of thousands of men."

7.6 Sir Isaac Newton

Newton was born on Christmas Day, 1642, the same year in which Galileo died. At school, he was a strange boy with few friends. Although curious about the world around him, he was rather slow in his studies until his teens. When he was about fifteen, his mother removed him from school to help on her farm. Luckily, an uncle detected some brilliance in the boy and urged that he be sent to Cambridge. Newton graduated from that university in 1665, after majoring in mathematics. The plague hit England in that year, and Newton returned to his mother's farm for two years, safe from its threat. It was here, at the age of twenty-two, that he did some of his best thinking.

Newton as a young man

The story of Newton's reaction to the apple falling has been thought by many to be a legend or myth but, according to his own words, it is true.

Newton originally calculated the moon's rate of fall by determining how much weaker the Earth's gravitational force would be at the moon than it was at the Earth's surface. He found that his calculated figure was only seven-eighths of the actual value. He was terribly disappointed, and put aside the problem for fifteen years. Probably, the value he had used for the Earth's radius was too small, and also he had not been sure that he was right to take his distance from the centre of the Earth. When he returned to the problem, accurate measurements of the Earth's radius by Picard, and his own work in calculus, resolved these difficulties. The calculation worked out perfectly.

He had already worked out the binomial theorem in mathematics; he now began the work that was later to become the area of mathematics called calculus. Perhaps while watching an apple fall to the ground, he began to wonder if the force that accelerated the fall of the apple might also be the one responsible for maintaining the curved path of the moon's orbit. This resulted in his proposal that the rate of acceleration due to gravity at the Earth's surface was proportional to the Earth's gravitational force on the moon, and that the latter was inversely proportional to the square of the distance from the Earth to the moon — the Inverse Square Law for Gravitational Force. Here is Newton's own account of the discovery:

> The same year I began to think of gravity extending to ye orb of the Moon, and . . . from Kepler's Rule [Kepler's third law] . . . I deduced that the forces which keep the Planets in their Orbs must [vary] reciprocally as the square of their distances from the centres about which they revolve: and thereby compared the force requisite to keep the Moon in her Orb with the force of gravity at the surface of the earth, and found them to answer pretty nearly. All this was in the two plague years of 1665 and 1666, for in those days I was in the prime of my age for invention, and minded Mathematicks and Philosophy more than at any time since.

Using modern values, we can follow the calculation of Newton and verify that the force of gravity does indeed obey the Inverse Square Law.

The centre of the moon is 3.8×10^8 m from the centre of the Earth. An object at the Earth's surface is 6.38×10^6 m from the centre of the Earth. Therefore, the ratio of their distances from the Earth's centre is

$$\frac{3.8 \times 10^8 \text{ m}}{6.38 \times 10^6 \text{ m}} = \frac{60}{1}$$

Newton predicted that the value of the Earth's gravitational field strength (g) at the distance away of the moon, which causes the centripetal acceleration of the moon towards the Earth, would be $1/60^2$, or $1/3600$ of the gravitational acceleration at the Earth's surface.

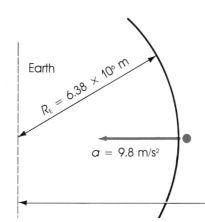

Earth

$R_E = 6.38 \times 10^6$ m

$a = 9.8$ m/s^2

$a = 2.7 \times 10^{-3}$ m/s^2

moon

$d_m = 3.8 \times 10^8$ m

$$\frac{F_{\text{moon}}}{F_{\text{Earth's surface}}} = \frac{a_{\text{moon}}}{a_{\text{Earth's surface}}} = \frac{R_E^{\,2}}{d_m^{\,2}}$$

$$\frac{a_{\text{moon}}}{9.8 \text{ m/s}^2} = \frac{1^2}{60^2}$$

$$a_{\text{moon}} = 2.7 \times 10^{-3} \text{ m/s}^2$$

But what is the actual centripetal acceleration of the moon in its nearly circular orbit around the Earth? Using the data in the table on page 271, the magnitude of the moon's acceleration towards the Earth is

$$a_c = \frac{4\pi^2 R}{T^2}$$

$$= \frac{4\pi^2(3.8 \times 10^8 \text{ m})}{(2.36 \times 10^6 \text{ s})^2}$$

$$= 2.7 \times 10^{-3} \text{ m/s}^2$$

Newton's prediction was correct. Since the acceleration is directly proportional to the net force, the force of gravity must also vary inversely as the square of the distance between the centres of the two objects. Stated mathematically:

Since $a_g \propto \dfrac{1}{R^2}$

and $F_g \propto a_g$

therefore, $F_g \propto \dfrac{1}{R^2}$ where F_g is the force of gravity
R is the distance between
the centres of the two objects

"Discovery consists of seeing what everybody has seen and thinking what nobody has thought."

Albert von Szent-Györgyi

Distance to the centre of the Earth (Earth radii)	Force of gravity on a 92 kg mass (N)
1	900
2	225
3	100
4	56
5	36
6	25
7	18
8	14
10	9
30	1

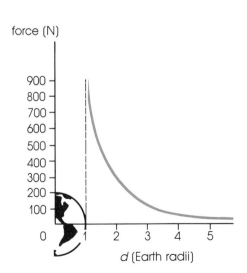

The force of gravity on a 92 kg object at various distances from the Earth

The years for approaches of Halley's
comet this century are 1910 and 1985.

7.7 The Law of Universal Gravitation

In 1684, Edmund Halley, the English astronomer who first plotted
the path of what is now known as Halley's comet, came to Newton
and asked him how the planets would move if the force of gravity
weakened in proportion to the square of the distance from the sun.
Newton replied at once, "They travel in ellipses." Halley asked how
he knew this. "Why," he replied "I have calculated it."

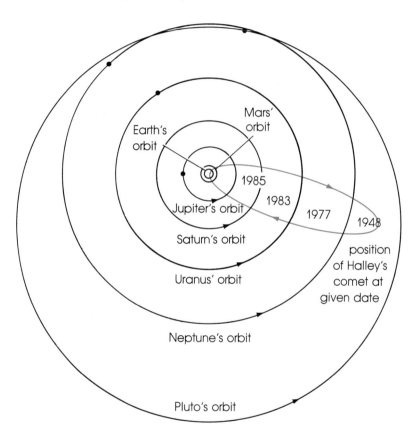

Ancient Romans called comets "hairy
stars" and considered them evil. In
1456, Pope Calixtus III is believed to
have excommunicated Halley's comet
as an agent of the devil.

Newton repeated the calculation he had made eighteen years
before on his mother's farm, this time with newer data, and this
time the result was correct. In the three years that he took to prove
his assertion that the Inverse Square Law for the force of gravity
was consistent with elliptical planetary motion, he summarized and
codified a set of laws that describe beautifully the motion both of
objects on the Earth and objects in the heavens. This work, pub-

lished as *Philosophiae Naturalis Principia Mathematica* (*Mathematical Principles of Natural Philosophy*) in 1687, caused a sensation, and continues to be considered the greatest scientific book ever published.

In it, Newton condensed Galileo's work in his First Law and summarized the effects of forces on objects in his Second and Third Laws (see Chapter 4). With these three laws and his Inverse Square Law for the force of gravity, he showed that the force of gravity was universal. It applied to any bodies that had mass, and it varied inversely as the square of the distance between them. The equation that resulted is known as the Law of Universal Gravitation. Newton's calculations require the use of calculus, but we can illustrate how Newton reached these conclusions if we use proportioning techniques.

For a planet moving at a uniform speed in a circle, the centripetal force is

$$F_c = \frac{4\pi^2 mR}{T^2}$$

From Kepler's Third Law,

$$\frac{R^3}{T^2} = K, \text{ or } T^2 = \frac{R^3}{K}$$

Substituting for T^2 in the first equation, we can express the force on the planet as

$$F = \frac{4\pi^2 mR}{(R^3/K)}$$
$$\text{from which } F = \frac{4\pi^2 Km}{R^2}$$
$$\text{or } F = (4\pi^2 K)\frac{m}{R^2}$$

Since the expression $(4\pi^2 K)$ is a constant, the force of gravitational attraction on the planet is directly proportional to the mass of the planet and inversely proportional to the square of its distance from the sun.

As shown in Section 7.4, Kepler's constant is the same for any object circling the sun, but it would have a different and smaller value for a satellite of the Earth (see problem 3, page 272). Newton suggested that the reason the value of K is smaller for an Earth satellite than it is for a satellite of the sun is that the mass of the Earth is smaller than the mass of the sun. In other words, Kepler's constant is proportional to the mass of the object exerting the force of attraction at the centre of the orbit. In the equation

Newton's book was published only with difficulty, because the Royal Society was short of funds and because of the intense animosity between Newton and Robert Hooke (see page 372), the president of the Royal Society. Fortunately, Halley, who was a man of means, agreed to cover the expenses of the publication.

Newton's deduction for the famous Inverse Square Law for the force of gravity was as follows, using modern mathematical notation:
For any object moving in a circle,

$$a = \frac{v^2}{R} \text{ (1)}$$

The gravitational force is inversely proportional to distance, that is,

$$F \propto \frac{1}{R^n} \text{ (2), where } n \text{ is a whole}$$

number > 0
From (1), $v^2 \propto aR$
But $F \propto a$ (Newton's Second Law)
therefore $v^2 \propto FR$ (3)
But $v = \frac{2\pi R}{T}$, or $v \propto \frac{R}{T}$ and $v^2 \propto \frac{R^2}{T^2}$ (4)

Combining (3) and (4), $FR \propto \frac{R^2}{T^2}$

or $F \propto \frac{R}{T^2}$

Combining this relationship with (2),

$$\frac{R}{T^2} \propto \frac{1}{R^n}$$

In other words, $\frac{R^{n+1}}{T^2} = \text{constant}$,

but $\frac{R^3}{T^2} = \text{constant}$ (Kepler's Third Law)
therefore $n = 2$, and substituting back into (2),

$$F \propto \frac{1}{R^2}$$

$$F_c = 4\pi^2 K \, m/R^2$$

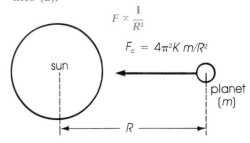

Newton in later life

$F = (4\pi^2 K)\dfrac{m}{R^2}$, the expression $(4\pi^2 K)$ is directly proportional to the mass of the sun.

Stated mathematically,

$\qquad 4\pi^2 K_s \propto m_s \qquad$ where m_s is the mass of the sun

$\qquad\qquad\qquad\qquad\qquad K_s$ is the Kepler constant for

$\qquad\qquad\qquad\qquad\qquad\qquad$ objects orbiting the sun

This would also be true for an Earth-centred system.

That is, $4\pi^2 K_E \propto m_E \qquad$ where m_E is the mass of the Earth

$\qquad\qquad\qquad\qquad\qquad K_E$ is the Kepler constant for

$\qquad\qquad\qquad\qquad\qquad\qquad$ objects orbiting the Earth

Since these relationships are valid both for a sun-centred system and an Earth-centred system, the constant of proportionality, G, will be the same for both systems.

That is, $\qquad 4\pi^2 K_s = Gm_s \quad$ where G is the universal

and $\qquad\quad 4\pi^2 K_E = Gm_E \quad$ gravitational constant

Substituting back into the original expression, we have

$$F = (4\pi^2 K_s)\frac{m}{R^2} = \frac{Gm_s m}{R^2}$$

$$F = (4\pi^2 K_E)\frac{m}{R^2} = \frac{Gm_E m}{R^2}$$

Newton's remarkable extension of this was to say that, if it applies to the sun and its planets, and to the Earth and its moon, then it should apply to any body in the universe that has mass. For any two masses located a distance d apart, the forces with which they attract one another would be calculated as follows:

$$F_{1-2} = \frac{Gm_1 m_2}{d^2}$$

$$F_{2-1} = \frac{Gm_2 m_1}{d^2}$$

The two forces are equal in magnitude although they are opposite in direction (Newton's Third Law).

We can summarize Newton's Law of Universal Gravitation as follows:

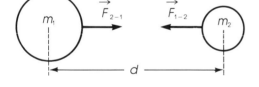

Any two bodies attract each other with forces proportional to the mass of each and inversely proportional to the square of the distance between them.

$$F = \frac{Gm_1 m_2}{d^2}$$

---

where G is the Universal Gravitational Constant.

In 1798, the British scientist Henry Cavendish, using the apparatus illustrated in the margin, succeeded in measuring the gravitational attraction between two small spheres hung on a rod approximately 2 m long, and two larger spheres mounted independently. Using this equipment, he calculated the value of G to be 6.67×10^{-11} N·m²/kg². His experiment showed that gravitational force exists even for relatively small objects and, by establishing the value of the constant of proportionality (G), he made it possible to use the Law of Universal Gravitation in calculations.

Isaac Newton was respected and honoured in his lifetime. He was elected president of the Royal Society in 1703, and re-elected every year until his death. He was made Warden of the Royal Mint, and knighted by Queen Anne in 1705. He died in 1727, and was buried in Westminster Abbey among England's other illustrious heroes. The British poet Alexander Pope wrote of him:

> Nature and Nature's laws lay hid in night:
> God said, Let Newton be! and all was light.

Newton's brilliant work dominated science for well over two centuries. His proof of the existence of exact laws in physics suggested to many thinkers in the 18th and 19th centuries that similar laws might be found in other fields of thought. This view of the natural world was slowly absorbed into the general culture, and the so-called "Age of Reason" was, in part, its outcome. It was believed that there existed a precise set of natural laws, which only needed to be discovered. These laws would predict and explain behaviour and its outcomes in such diverse fields as history, politics, ethics, and psychology. This view was carried to extremes in many cases; nevertheless, it did introduce a more analytical and scientific approach in other fields of knowledge. By the turn of the 20th century, scientific investigation showed that nature was not as exact and predictable as everyone had believed. In Chapter 19, we will be forced to deal with probabilities and estimations, and we will see that the tiny physical world of the atom does not obey strict, predictable laws. These scientific discoveries, in particular the work of Albert Einstein, have had an effect on human thought in other fields as well, where they have also tempered a strict deterministic view.

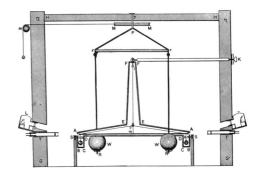

This is the sketch of the Cavendish apparatus that appeared in Cavendish's original paper. The two large masses are labelled W and the small masses x. Note that the whole device is mounted in a large case G, with outside controls to move the weights and adjust the horizontal rod. Scales at A near the ends of the rod were illuminated by the lamps L and observed through the telescope T. (Below is a simplified diagram.)

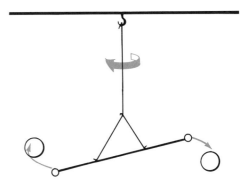

Newton was denied promotion at Cambridge University because he was a Unitarian.

"Determinism" is the belief that every event is the inevitable result of conditions that precede it, and that human beings do not have free will.

Sample problems

1. What is the gravitational attraction between two basketballs, each with a mass of 0.65 kg, that are 1.0 m apart?

$$F = \frac{Gm_1m_2}{d^2}$$

$$= \frac{(6.67 \times 10^{-11} \text{ N·m}^2/\text{kg}^2)(0.65 \text{ kg})(0.65 \text{ kg})}{(1.0 \text{ m})^2}$$

$$= 2.8 \times 10^{-11} \text{ N}$$

2. The force of gravity on a spacecraft some distance from the Earth is 900 N. What will be the force of gravity on a spacecraft with twice the mass, at a distance from the Earth's centre that is one-quarter as far?

The ratio of the masses is $\frac{m_1}{m_2} = \frac{1}{2}$

therefore the ratio of the forces due to mass alone is

$$\frac{F_1}{F_2} = \frac{m_1}{m_2} = \frac{1}{2}, \text{ or } F_2 = 2F_1$$

The ratio of the distances is $\frac{d_1}{d_2} = \frac{1}{1/4} = 4$

therefore the ratio of the forces due to distance alone is

$$\frac{F_1}{F_2} = \frac{d_2^2}{d_1^2} = \frac{1^2}{4^2}, \text{ or } F_2 = 4^2 F_1$$

Thus, the new force will be

$$F_2 = (2)(4^2)F_1$$
$$= (32)(900 \text{ N})$$
$$= 2.9 \times 10^4 \text{ N}$$

Alternate solution

$$F \alpha \frac{m}{d^2}$$

thus
$$\frac{F_2}{F_1} = \frac{m_2/d_2^2}{m_1/d_1^2}$$

$$= \frac{m_2 d_1^2}{m_1 d_2^2}$$

$$= \frac{m_2}{m_1}\left(\frac{d_1}{d_2}\right)^2$$

$$= \frac{2}{1}\left(\frac{4}{1}\right)^2$$

thus $F_2 = 2(4)^2 F_1$, or $2.9 \times 10^4 \text{ N}$

Practice

1. What is the force of gravitational attraction between two 1.8×10^8 kg supertankers moored so that their centres are located 94 m apart? $\qquad$ $(2.4 \times 10^2 \text{ N})$

2. A woman standing on the surface of the Earth, 6.38×10^6 m from its centre, has a mass of 50.0 kg. If the mass of the Earth is 5.98×10^{24} kg, what is the force of gravity on the woman? $\qquad$ $(4.9 \times 10^2 \text{ N})$

3. The force of gravitational attraction between two masses is 36 N. What will be the force if one mass is doubled and the distance between them is tripled? $\qquad$ (8.0 N)

4. Mars has a radius 0.54 times that of the Earth and a mass 0.11 times that of the Earth. If the force of gravity on your mass is 600 N on Earth, what will it be on Mars? $\qquad$ $(2.3 \times 10^2 \text{ N})$

5. The planet Jupiter has a mass of 1.9×10^{27} kg and a radius of 7.2×10^7 m. Calculate the acceleration due to gravity on Jupiter. $\qquad$ (24 m/s^2)

> "Newton was not the first of the age of reason. He was the last of the magicians, the last of the Babylonians and Sumerians, the last great mind which looked out on the visible and intellectual world with the same eyes as those who began to build our intellectual inheritance rather less than 10 000 years ago."
>
> *John Maynard Keynes*

7.8 Newton's Law of Universal Gravitation Applied in Space

Since Newton's Law of Universal Gravitation is applicable anywhere in the universe, immediately upon its appearance astronomers, mathematicians, and physicists used it to calculate the behaviour of objects far from the Earth, as well as to explain the effects of heavenly bodies on the Earth. It was first applied by Newton when he calculated the highly elliptical orbit of Halley's comet, allowing Halley to determine the comet's period and to predict its arrival near the sun every seventy-five years.

It was also Newton who first predicted that an artificial satellite could be put into orbit around the Earth. He imagined a large cannon firing cannonballs horizontally at greater and greater speeds (see diagram). At first they fall quickly to the ground, but as their speed increases they go farther and farther. Eventually, a critical speed is reached and a ball curves into an orbit, perpetually "falling" towards the Earth but never landing.

Newton used his Third Law and the Law of Universal Gravitation to explain the ocean tides: The Earth exerts a force on the moon that keeps it in orbit, but the moon exerts an equal and opposite force on the Earth. This attraction is most evident on the areas of the Earth's surface that are free to move — the oceans. The water

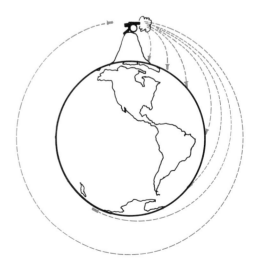

Dr Helen Hogg (1904–   ) has written a weekly column on astronomy for the *Toronto Star* for over twenty-five years. Chiefly, however, Dr. Hogg is recognized as the world authority on the properties of variable stars found in globular clusters (groups of stars that are very close together).

Born and educated in the United States, she graduated from Radcliffe College in 1931 with a Ph.D. in astronomy, one of the first women to do so. She married Dr. Frank Hogg, and together they went to work at the Dominion Observatory in Victoria, British Columbia. There they began a program of observing globular clusters. Later they moved to the David Dunlap Observatory, near Toronto, Ontario, where they continued this work. Dr. Helen Hogg has written over one hundred papers on the subject. She has been president of the Royal Canadian Institute and the Royal Astronomical Society of Canada, as well as program director for astronomy at the National Science Foundation in Washington.

Dr. Hogg has three children and seven grandchildren. In her retirement, she continues with research and writing. She has expressed disappointment that the percentage of women entering astronomy remains slight compared to the number of men.

in the part of the ocean facing towards the moon (point A) is attracted by a stronger than normal force, raising the water level on that side and creating a high tide. Simultaneously, a high tide occurs on the opposite side of the Earth (at point C).

This happens because the force of the moon on the water is smaller than normal on the far side of the Earth and, in a sense, the water is "left behind" because there is less force on it than on the Earth as a whole. As illustrated in the diagram, low tides occur at points B and D. As the Earth turns, the bulges of water remain relatively fixed in relation to the moon. In the Earth's frame of reference, the tides move to create a series of regularly spaced high and low tides at each point on the surface of the Earth.

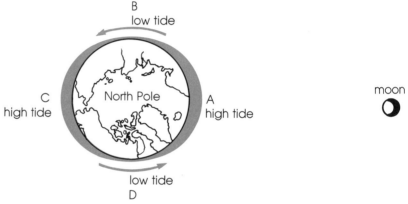

Because there is friction between the solid Earth and the moving water, and because the sun also exerts a gravitational force on the ocean water, the high tides do not correspond precisely to the time when the moon is directly overhead. These factors also affect the height of the tides. For example, the highest tides occur when the sun, moon, and Earth are lined up. These are called the **spring tides**. When the sun, moon, and Earth form a right angle, the effects of the sun and moon tend to reduce one another and the tides are minimized. These are called **neap tides**.

With a daily period for the rotating Earth, a lunar monthly period for the orbiting moon, and a yearly period for the orbiting Earth, it is not surprising that high and low tides occur at different times each day. In fact, tide tables must be prepared for each specific location on the Earth.

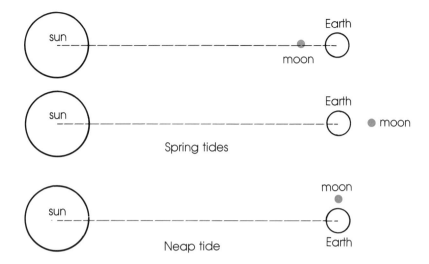

Newton's Laws have also been used to locate two hitherto unknown planets in our solar system. Usually the distance between adjacent planets is so great that the force of gravity exerted on one planet by another is very small compared with the effect of the sun in relation to the same planet. Nevertheless, small deviations in the elliptical planetary orbit do occur. These are called **perturbations**. Such perturbations led to the discovery of the planet Neptune.

The orbit of Uranus did not follow a perfect ellipse, and its perturbations could not be explained by the effects of the known planets. In the 1850s, careful calculations using Newton's Law of Universal Gravitation indicated that the deviations in the orbit of Uranus could be accounted for if there were an unknown planet beyond Uranus. The position of this planet was calculated and then, when telescopes were focused on this region of the sky, the planet Neptune was located. Similar but much smaller perturbations in Neptune's orbit led to the discovery of Pluto in 1930.

The mass of a planet can be calculated by observing the motions of a satellite around it. One of the original reasons for establishing artificial Earth satellites was to get a better value for the mass of the Earth. An example will illustrate how this is done.

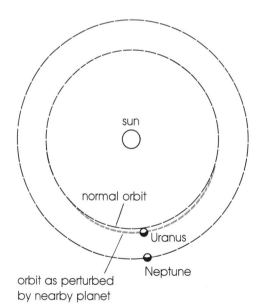

Sample problem

A satellite circles the Earth at an average altitude of 760 km, with a period of 100 min. Calculate the mass of the Earth.

The force of gravitational attraction provides the centripetal force necessary to hold the satellite in orbit around the Earth. Thus, there are two expressions for this force:

$$F_c = \frac{4\pi^2 m_{sat} R}{T^2} \quad \text{and} \quad F_g = \frac{Gm_E m_{sat}}{R^2}$$

but $$F_c = F_g \text{ (for a circular orbit)}$$

or $$\frac{4\pi^2 m_{sat} R}{T^2} = \frac{Gm_E m_{sat}}{R^2}$$

Simplifying, $$m_E = \frac{4\pi^2 R^3}{GT^2}$$

The radius of orbit of the satellite = R_E + altitude
$$= 6.38 \times 10^6 \text{ m} + 7.60 \times 10^5 \text{ m}$$
$$= 7.14 \times 10^6 \text{ m}$$

$$m_E = \frac{4\pi^2 (7.14 \times 10^6 \text{ m})^3}{(6.67 \times 10^{-11} \text{ N·m}^2/\text{kg}^2)(6.00 \times 10^3 \text{ s})^2}$$

$$= 5.98 \times 10^{24} \text{ kg}$$

Note that the mass of the satellite is not a factor.

Practice

1. An astronomer observes the planet Jupiter and finds that the period of its moon Io is 1.5×10^5 s. If this moon has an average radius of orbit about Jupiter of 4.2×10^8 m, what is the mass of Jupiter, using these measurements?   (1.9×10^{27} kg)

2. A lunar lander is to be placed in orbit around the moon at a mean altitude of 100 km. What will be the period of the lunar lander? (For reference, see the table on page 271.)
(7.09×10^3 s)

3. Communications satellites are placed in orbit so that they remain stationary relative to a specific area on the Earth's surface. They are given the name **synchronous satellites** because, to maintain such a position, their period as they orbit must be the same as the Earth's.

What is the height of such a satellite measured from **(a)** the centre of the Earth, and **(b)** the surface of the Earth?
(4.2×10^7 m, 3.6×10^7 m)

Is There a Tenth Planet?

When astronomers studied the planet Pluto, they determined that it weighed only one-quarter as much as our own moon, and yet, to explain the observed gravitational effects on Uranus and Neptune, Pluto should have had a mass 1000 times greater than that. This discovery led to speculation that Pluto may once have been a satellite of some other planet, most likely Neptune, and that another, still undiscovered planet caused Pluto to be flung away from Neptune into its own orbit. The planet also affected the orbits of Neptune's other moons. Astronomers affectionately called this tenth planet "Humphrey".

Careful calculations based on this theory cannot pinpoint the planet's location, but can at least narrow it down to a specific region of the sky. However, since Humphrey will be like Pluto, too distant to display the telltale, disc-like shape of a planet, how can it be detected?

This can be accomplished by using a telescope to photograph a large area of the sky twice, separated by an interval of a day or two, under conditions as similar as possible both times. The two photographic plates can then be compared, either electronically, using computer analysis, or by alternately projecting images from both plates onto a screen. Any missing planet moving relative to the fixed background of stars can be spotted.

Humphrey's orbit, if it exists, would be very elongated and have a period of approximately 800 years. This makes it difficult to predict when Humphrey will be seen, but this much is known: something very strange is happening to the orbits of Uranus and Neptune, and astronomers strongly believe that Humphrey, the elusive tenth planet, is to blame.

"I know not what I may appear to the world, but to myself I seem to have been only like a boy playing on the sea-shore, and diverting myself in now and then finding a smoother pebble or a prettier shell than ordinary, whilst the great ocean of truth lay all undiscovered before me."

Sir Isaac Newton.

"The essence of science lies not in discovering facts but in discovering new ways of thinking about them."

W.L. Bragg, The History of Science

7.9 Review

Discussion

1. Between March 21 and September 21 there are three days more than between September 21 and March 21. These two dates are the spring and fall equinoxes, when the days and nights are of equal length. Between the equinoxes, the Earth moves 180° around its orbit with respect to the sun. Using Kepler's Laws, explain clearly how you can determine the part of the year during which the Earth is closer to the sun.

2. The force of gravity on a 60 kg woman is 588 N. The woman also exerts a gravitational force on the Earth. How large a force is this?

3. The force of attraction between m_1 and m_2 is 26 N. What will this force become if m_2 is tripled and the distance between it and m_1 is halved?

4. The force of gravity between two masses was 14 N when they were 10 m apart. The distance between them was changed and the force became 56 N. How far apart were they then?

5. The force of gravity between A and B is 100 N. When the mass of B is doubled and the distance between it and A is halved, what is the new force?

6. If the moon's mass were suddenly to double, what effect would this change have on the moon's orbit, and how would such a change affect the Earth? (Assume that the velocity of the moon remains unchanged.)

7. At what height, expressed in Earth radii, will an astronaut have a true weight that is one-half his weight on the Earth's surface?

8. What keeps the space shuttle and other space vehicles and satellites in their orbits around the Earth?

9. What changes would have to be made in the speed of a space vehicle to enable it to increase or decrease the size of its circular orbit around the Earth?

The asteroids or minor planets are thousands of small bodies that revolve around the sun, mainly between the orbits of Mars and Jupiter. Most are invisible to the human eye. The largest, Ceres, is approximately 770 km in diameter, although most are less than 80 km across. The combined mass of all the asteroids is not greater than 5% of the mass of the moon.

Problems

10. (a) Calculate the Kepler constants by determining the R^3/T^2 values for each of the planet systems listed in the chart on page 287.
    (b) Using a graph, determine whether there is a mathematical relationship between the K values and the masses of the planets.

Natural Satellites in the Solar System*

Planet	Mass ($m_E = 1$)	Satellite	Orbital radius ($\times 10^3$ km)	Period (d)
Earth	1.00	Moon	384.4	27.322
Mars	0.107	Phobos	9.38	0.319
		Deimos	23.46	1.262
Jupiter	318	Thebe	221.9	0.675
		Io	421.6	1.769
		Europa	670.9	3.551
		Elara	11 737	259.7
Saturn	95.2	Janis	151.47	0.695
		Mimas	185.54	0.942
		Calypso	294.67	1.888
Uranus	14.6	Miranda	129.4	1.414
		Ariel	191.0	2.520
		Oberon	583.5	13.463
Neptune	1.72	Triton	355.3	5.877
		Nereid	5 510	360.21
Pluto	0.002	Charon	19.7	6.387

*"Planetary Satellites: An Update", *Sky and Telescope*, November 1983.

The period of Phobos is less than one-third of the period of Mars' rotation in the same direction. (In contrast, the moon's period is 27.3 d and the Earth's period of rotation on its axis is 1 d.) No other known natural satellite in the solar system revolves in an interval shorter than the rotation of its primary.

    (c) If the graph shows that there is a systematic relationship, express the relationship as a mathematical equation.

11. An asteroid has a mean radius of orbit of 4.8×10^{11} m. What will be its orbital period around the sun?

12. A spy satellite is located one Earth radius above the surface of the Earth. What is its period of revolution?

13. Mars has two moons, Phobos and Deimos (Fear and Panic, the companions of Mars, the god of war). Deimos has a period of 30 h 18 min and a mean distance from the centre of Mars of 2.3×10^4 km. If the period of Phobos is 7 h 39 min, what mean distance is it from the centre of Mars?

14. Obtain the value of g at the surface of the Earth by using the motion of the moon. Assume that the moon's period around the Earth is 27 d 8 h and the radius of its orbit is 60.1 times the radius of the Earth. (Radius of Earth $= 6.38 \times 10^6$ m.)

15. Calculate the gravitational force of attraction between two objects of masses 900 g and 400 g, respectively, placed with their centres 30 cm apart.

16. Calculate the gravitational attraction between a proton of mass 1.67×10^{-27} kg and an electron of mass 9.11×10^{-31} kg if they are 5×10^{-11} m apart (as they are in a normal hydrogen atom).

17. At a certain point between the Earth and the moon the total gravitational force exerted on an object by the Earth and the

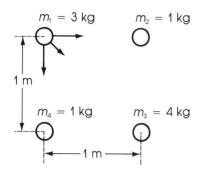

moon is zero. If the Earth-moon distance is 3.84×10^5 km and the moon has 1.2% of the mass of the Earth, where is this point located? Are there any other such points?

18. Four masses are located on a plane as illustrated. What is the magnitude of the net gravitational force on mass 1 due to the other three masses?

19. Find the acceleration of a falling object on Mars, given that the radius of Mars is one-half that of Earth and the mass of Mars is one-eighth that of Earth.

20. The planet Saturn has a mass of 5.67×10^{26} kg and a radius of 6.3×10^7 m. Calculate the acceleration due to gravity on Saturn. How much will the gravitational force be on a 60 kg man there?

21. What is the acceleration due to gravity on (a) Venus, (b) Pluto, and (c) the moon? (See page 271.)

22. A projectile will orbit the Earth at a low altitude if it is fired with such a velocity that its weight is equal to the centripetal force necessary for a circular orbit equal to the radius of the Earth.
    (a) Assuming that the projectile does not hit any mountains and there is no air resistance, calculate the necessary velocity.
    (b) Would there be any advantage if the projectile were launched in an equatorial orbit as opposed to a polar orbit?

23. It can be assumed that the Earth, to a good approximation, moves in a circular orbit about the sun. Using only the data for the Earth's orbit from the table on page 271, determine (a) the speed of the Earth and (b) the mass of the sun.

24. An Earth satellite travels in a circular orbit of radius four times the Earth's radius. Calculate its acceleration in m/s^2.

25. As an indication of the size of the sun's gravitational pull on the Earth, carry out the rough calculations that follow. Suppose that the sun's gravitational attraction could be replaced by a steel wire running from the sun to the Earth, with the wire's tension holding the Earth in its orbit. (Good steel has a breaking stress of 5.0×10^8 N/m^2 of cross-sectional area.)
    (a) Calculate very approximately the cross-sectional area of the wire that could just hold the Earth in its orbit.
    (b) Calculate approximately the corresponding wire diameter.

26. By looking at distant galaxies, astronomers have concluded that our solar system is circling the centre of our galaxy. The hub of this galaxy is located about 2.7×10^{20} m from our sun, and our sun circles the centre about every 200 million years. We assume that our sun is attracted by a large number of stars at the hub of our galaxy, and that the sun is kept in orbit by the gravitational attraction of these stars.

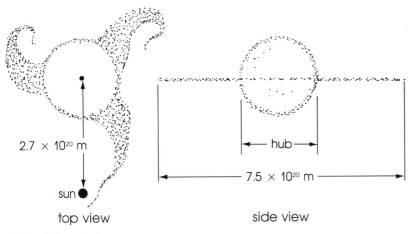

2.7×10^{20} m

sun ●

top view

← hub →

7.5×10^{20} m

side view

Milky Way Galaxy

Numerical Answers to Review Problems
   2. **588 N**
   3. **156 N**
   4. **5.0 m**
   5. **800 N**
   7. **$(\sqrt{2} - 1)R_E$**
  10. (c) $R = \sqrt[3]{7.6 \times 10^{13}mT^2}$
  11. **1.8×10^8 s**
  12. **1.5×10^4 s**
  13. **9.2×10^6 m**
  15. **2.7×10^{-10} N**
  16. **4.0×10^{-47} N**
  17. **3.4×10^8 m from the Earth**
  18. **6.8×10^{-10} N**
  19. **4.9 m/s²**
  20. **9.5 m/s², 5.7×10^2 N**
  21. **(a) 8.09 m/s² (b) 4.4 m/s² (c) 1.62 m/s²**
  22. **7.9×10^3 m/s**
  23. **(a) 2.96×10^4 m/s (b) 1.5×10^{30} kg**
  24. **6.1×10^{-2} m/s²**
  25. **(a) 3.56×10^{22} m² (b) 9.5×10^6 m**
  26. **(a) 2.9×10^{41} kg (b) 1.5×10^{11} stars**
  27. **(a) 9.5×10^6 m (b) 2.0×10^{25} kg**
  28. **2.8×10^7 s**

(a) Calculate the total mass of the stars at the hub of our galaxy.

(b) Calculate the approximate number of such stars that are the size of our sun (2.0×10^{30} kg).

27. You are on a strange planet. You note that the stars do not rise and set but circle around in planes parallel to the horizon.

(a) You set out on a journey that takes you in a straight line (really a great circle) for 1.5×10^4 km, and find that the stars now rise and set perpendicular to the horizon. What is the radius of the planet? (SIN '74)

(b) You drop a stone from a height of 2.0 m and measure the time the stone takes to fall to the ground, which is 0.52 s. What is the mass of the planet?

28. A certain "double star" consists of two identical stars, each with a mass of 3.0×10^{30} kg, separated by a distance of 2.0×10^{11} m, measured between their centres. These stars spin around a common centre like a giant dumbbell. How long does it take to complete one cycle? (Express the answer in seconds.) (SIN '70)

8 Momentum

8.1 Momentum and Motion

If someone tossed you a shot of the sort used in shot putting, you would get out of the way — quickly! But you would have no hesitation about reaching out to catch a rubber ball. What are the properties of the hurtling shot that make you avoid it? One is its velocity. A shot at rest would be of no concern. The other is its mass. Having a greater mass, a shot is a greater threat than a ball, even though the two may be moving at the same speed. On the other hand, if the ball were shot at you from a gun, it too would be a serious threat.

Newton combined a moving object's mass and its velocity in an expression that he called "quantity of motion". We now call this quantity **momentum**, and give it the symbol $\vec{p}$.

The momentum of a moving object is given by the equation

$$\vec{p} = m\vec{v}$$

where $\vec{p}$ is the object's momentum, in kilogram metres per second

m is its mass, in kilograms

$\vec{v}$ is its velocity, in metres per second

Momentum is a vector quantity whose direction is always the same as that of the velocity. The unit of momentum, kilogram metres per second (kg·m/s), is a derived unit, and has no special name.

Sample problem

What is the momentum of a 1000 kg car moving at 15 m/s[E]?

$$\vec{p} = m\vec{v}$$
$$= (1000 \text{ kg})(15 \text{ m/s[E]})$$
$$= 1.5 \times 10^4 \text{ kg·m/s[E]}$$

Practice

1. Calculate the momentum of each of the following objects:
   (a) a 0.50 kg ball thrown upward with a velocity of 30 m/s
   (b) a 2000 kg railway car moving south at 10 m/s
   (c) an electron of mass 9.1×10^{-31} kg, moving at a velocity of 1.0×10^7 m/s

(d) the Earth, of mass 6.0×10^{24} kg, moving along its solar orbit with a velocity of 3.0×10^4 m/s
(15 kg·m/s[upward], 2.0×10^4 kg·m/s[S], 9.1×10^{-24} kg·m/s[forward], 1.8×10^{29} kg·m/s[forward])

2. The momentum of a 7.3 kg shot is 22 kg·m/s[forward]. What is its velocity? (3.0 m/s[forward])

3. A bullet travelling at 900 m/s has a momentum of 4.5 kg·m/s. What is its mass? (0.0050 kg, or 5.0 g)

8.2 Impulse and Momentum

In Chapter 4 it was shown that an object acted upon by an external unbalanced force accelerates in the direction of the net force, and that the relationship between its mass, acceleration, and the force acting on it is expressed by the equation $\vec{F} = m\vec{a}$ (Newton's Second Law). In fact, Newton's original thinking was not in terms of an object's acceleration. He stated that the rate of change of momentum of an object is proportional to the net force applied, and that the change in momentum and the net force are in the same direction.

$$\vec{F} = \frac{\Delta \vec{p}}{\Delta t}$$

where $\Delta \vec{p}$ represents the change in momentum of the object.

This equation may be rewritten as

$$\vec{F}\Delta t = \Delta \vec{p}$$

This form of the equation can be quite useful. For example, when a golf ball is about to be hit by a club, the ball has zero momentum. After contact, it has a momentum in the same direction as the force of the club upon it. Similarly, if a force is applied to a moving tennis ball that already has momentum, the force could increase the ball's momentum, decrease its momentum, or change its direction.

How much the momentum changes depends on two factors: the magnitude of the force exerted on the object, and the length of time for which the force acts. Whenever there is an impact or collision between objects, the product $\vec{F}\Delta t$ has great significance. This product is given the name "impulse".

$$\text{impulse} = \vec{F}\Delta t$$

where $\vec{F}$ is the net force acting on an object, in newtons
Δt is the time for which the force acts, in seconds

In simple problems involving momentum, the direction of the moving object is often not stated. Usually, the direction is not significant to the understanding of the problem and we assume it is just "forward".

The symbol $\vec{J}$ is often used to represent impulse. Then,

$$\vec{J} = \vec{F}\Delta t = \Delta \vec{p}.$$

The unit for impulse is the newton second (N·s), and impulse is a vector quantity whose direction is the same as the direction of the net force causing the impulse.

The expression on page 291 may be used to calculate the impulse of a force only when the force remains constant during the time for which it is applied. If the magnitude of $\vec{F}$ changes uniformly during Δt, the expression $\vec{F}_{av}\Delta t$ may be used to calculate the impulse. These two cases are shown graphically below. In each case, the area under the F-t graph represents the impulse of the force.

Constant force

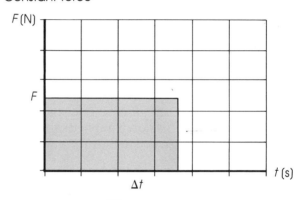

$$\text{impulse} = \vec{F}\Delta t$$
$$= \text{area of shaded rectangle under } F \text{ vs } t \text{ graph}$$

Uniformly changing force

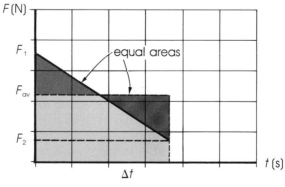

$$\text{impulse} = \vec{F}_{av}\Delta t$$
$$= \left(\frac{F_1 + F_2}{2}\right)\Delta t$$
$$= \text{area of shaded rectangle (enclosed by dotted line)}$$
$$= \text{area under graph of } F \text{ vs } t, \text{ during time interval } \Delta t$$

In many situations, the force applied to an object changes non-linearly during its time of application. Suppose the graph below represents the variation in the magnitude of $\vec{F}$ with t.

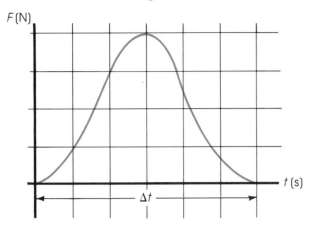

This *F-t* graph would be similar to the one you would expect when a tennis racket hits a ball, or when a billiard ball bounces off a rubber cushion.

How can impulse be determined in a case such as this? We can use the same technique that was used in Section 2.7 to determine the distance travelled in a time Δt when the velocity varied within that time interval. The time interval Δt may be thought of as n sub-intervals, each of duration $\Delta t/n$. During each of these sub-intervals, the force acting may be assumed to be constant, and may be approximated by the average force during that sub-interval. In this way, the F vs t graph would appear as a step-curve, shown below.

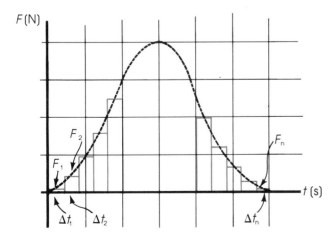

For those familiar with integral calculus, the area under the curve is represented by the integral $\int_{t_1}^{t_2} F\,dt$.

(If $\vec{F}$ changes direction as well as magnitude, then things get even more complicated.)

Then, as before, the total impulse may be calculated as

$$\text{impulse} = F_1\Delta t_1 + F_2\Delta t_2 + \ldots + F_n\Delta t_n$$
$$= \text{area under step 1} + \text{area under step 2} + \ldots$$
$$+ \text{area under step } n$$
$$= \text{total area under the step-curve during } \Delta t$$

If the number of sub-intervals, n, is increased, the steps become even smaller, and the step-curve becomes an even closer approximation of the real curve. In the limit, as $n \to \infty$, the step-curve becomes the real curve, and

impulse = area under F vs t graph, during the time interval Δt

Sample problems

1. What is the impulse given to a golf ball by a club if they are in contact for 0.0050 s, during which the club exerts an average force of 500 N on the ball?

$$\text{impulse} = \vec{F}_{av}\Delta t$$
$$= (500 \text{ N})(0.0050 \text{ s})$$
$$= 2.5 \text{ N·s[forward]}$$

2. The graph below approximates the force applied to a tennis ball by a racket during the time they are in contact.

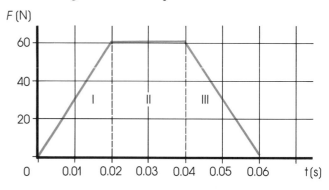

What impulse does the ball receive from the racket?

$$\text{impulse} = \text{area under } \vec{F} \text{ vs } t \text{ graph during } \Delta t$$
$$= \text{area triangle I} + \text{area rectangle II} + \text{area triangle III}$$
$$= \frac{1}{2}(0.02 \text{ s})(60 \text{ N}) + (0.02 \text{ s})(60 \text{ N}) + \frac{1}{2}(0.02 \text{ s})(60 \text{ N})$$
$$= 2.4 \text{ N·s[forward]}$$

Practice
1. What impulse is exerted in each of the following cases?
    (a) a force of 25 N[E] on a dynamics cart for 3.2 s
    (b) a hockey stick exerting a force of 120 N on a puck during the 0.05 s they are in contact
    (c) the Earth pulling down on a 12 kg rock during the 3.0 s it takes to fall from a cliff
    (d) a billiard ball bouncing off a cushion, if the force-time graph of the collision appears as below

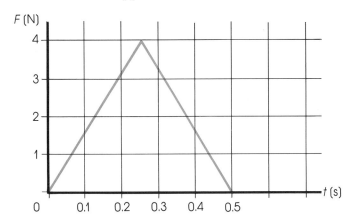

    (e) a collison between a toy car and a brick wall, if the force-time graph of the collision appears as below

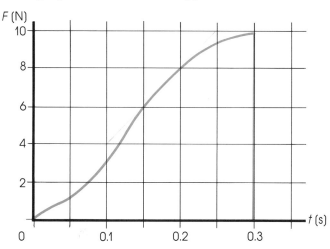

(80 N·s[E], 6 N·s[forward], 3.5 × 10² N·s[down],
1 N·s[opposite ball's original motion],
1.5 N·s[opposite car's original motion])

Newton's original statement of his Second Law, $\vec{F} = \dfrac{\Delta \vec{p}}{\Delta t}$, is actually more general than the more familiar form, $\vec{F} = m\vec{a}$, since it includes cases where the mass changes. An example of such a case is an ascending rocket. As the rocket rises, it loses mass as it burns fuel for propulsion.

The equation developed earlier in this section is very convenient for dealing with situations in which two or more objects interact and exert forces on each other. Keep in mind that Newton's Second Law may be written in the following form for one of the masses.

$$\vec{F}\Delta t = \Delta \vec{p}$$
$$= \vec{p_2} - \vec{p_1}$$
$$= m\vec{v_2} - m\vec{v_1}$$
$$= m\Delta\vec{v} \qquad \text{if } m \text{ remains constant}$$

The expression $m\vec{v_2} - m\vec{v_1}$ represents the difference between the momentum before and the momentum after the two objects interact, in other words, the change in momentum ($\Delta\vec{p}$) as a result of the collision or interaction. Thus,

$$\vec{F}\Delta t = \Delta \vec{p} = m\vec{v_2} - m\vec{v_1}$$

A few sample problems will show how this equation may be applied in situations where objects collide or interact.

Sample problems

1. What velocity will a 40 kg child sitting on a 40 kg wagon acquire if pushed from rest by a force of 75 N for 2.0 s?

$$\vec{F}\Delta t = m\Delta\vec{v}$$
$$= m\vec{v_2} - m\vec{v_1} \qquad \text{since } m \text{ is constant}$$
$$= m\vec{v_2} \qquad \text{since } \vec{v_1} = 0$$

Therefore $\vec{v_2} = \dfrac{\vec{F}\Delta t}{m}$

$$= \dfrac{(75 \text{ N})(2.0 \text{ s})}{80 \text{ kg}}$$

$$= 1.9 \text{ m/s [in the direction of } \vec{F}]$$

2. What average force will stop a 1000 kg car in 1.5 s, if the car is moving at 22 m/s?

$$\vec{F}\Delta t = m\vec{v_2} - m\vec{v_1}$$

Therefore $\vec{F} = \dfrac{m\vec{v_2} - m\vec{v_1}}{\Delta t}$

$$= \frac{(1000 \text{ kg})(0 \text{ m/s}) - (1000 \text{ kg})(22 \text{ m/s})}{1.5 \text{ s}}$$

$$= \frac{-22\,000 \text{ kg·m/s}}{1.5 \text{ s}}$$

$$= -1.5 \times 10^4 \text{ N[in the direction of motion]}$$

The negative sign indicates that the direction of the force is opposite to that of the car's initial velocity. This force could also be expressed as 1.5×10^4 N[backward].

In situations where the colliding or interacting objects move in a straight line, the vector notation for momentum and impulse may be omitted. As before, directions forward and backward can be indicated by using + and − signs. Even so, it is essential to remember that not all interactions are one-dimensional and that the vector property of momentum and impulse is very important.

Practice

1. A billiard ball of mass 200 g rolls towards the right-hand cushion of a billiard table at 2.0 m/s and rebounds straight back at 2.0 m/s.
   (a) What is its change in momentum as a result of hitting the cushion?
   (b) What impulse is given to the ball by the cushion?

   $(-0.80$ kg·m/s[R], 0.80 kg·m/s[L])

2. A hockey puck of mass 0.20 kg is sliding along a smooth, flat section of ice at 18 m/s when it encounters some snow. After 2.5 s of sliding through the snow, it returns to smooth ice, continuing at a speed of 10 m/s.
   (a) What is the change in momentum of the puck?
   (b) What impulse does the snow exert on the puck?
   (c) What average frictional force does the snow exert on the puck?

   $(-1.6$ kg·m/s[forward], 1.6 kg·m/s[backward],
   0.64 N[backward])

3. A frictionless disc of mass 0.50 kg is moving in a straight line across an air table at a speed of 2.4 m/s when it bumps into an elastic band stretched between two fixed posts. If the elastic band exerts an average opposing force of 1.4 N on the disc for 1.5 s, what will be the final velocity of the disc?

   $(-1.8$ m/s[forward] or 1.8 m/s[backward])

4. A 2.0 kg skateboard is rolling across a smooth, flat floor when a small girl kicks it, causing it to speed up to 4.5 m/s in 0.50 s without changing direction. If the average force exerted by the girl on the skateboard in its direction of motion was 6.0 N, with what initial velocity was it moving?   (3.0 m/s[forward])

Perhaps the first person to publish a statement regarding impulse and momentum was John Wallis, an English mathematician. His findings concerning conservation of momentum were published in 1670 in a book called *Mechanica* and formed the basis for Newton's later statement in his *Principia*.

8.3 Conservation of Momentum

During the 17th century, Newton and others before him had measured the momentum of colliding objects before and after collision, and had discovered a strange phenomenon: the total momentum of the colliding objects was the same after the collision as it was before. In fact, Newton had used this discovery as the basis of his Third Law. It can be demonstrated as follows.

Consider this "head-on" collision between two objects:

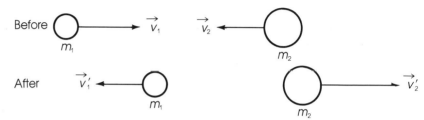

The "primed" designation on the velocities and momenta (below) denotes their values after the collision.

Before the collision,

$$\vec{p}_{total} = m_1\vec{v_1} + m_2\vec{v_2}$$

After the collision,

$$\vec{p}\,'_{total} = m_1\vec{v}\,'_1 + m_2\vec{v}\,'_2$$

But, since $\vec{p}_{total}$ and $\vec{p}\,'_{total}$ were found, experimentally, to be equal,

$$m_1\vec{v_1} + m_2\vec{v_2} = m_1\vec{v}\,'_1 + m_2\vec{v}\,'_2$$

$$m_1\vec{v_1} - m_1\vec{v}\,'_1 = m_2\vec{v}\,'_2 - m_2\vec{v_2}$$

$$-m_1(\vec{v}\,'_1 - \vec{v_1}) = m_2(\vec{v}\,'_2 - \vec{v_2})$$

If both sides of this equation are divided by Δt, the time for which the colliding objects are in contact, we have

$$-m_1\left(\frac{\vec{v}\,'_1 - \vec{v_1}}{\Delta t}\right) = m_2\left(\frac{\vec{v}\,'_2 - \vec{v_2}}{\Delta t}\right)$$

but

$$\frac{\vec{v}\,'_1 - \vec{v_1}}{\Delta t} = \vec{a_1} \quad \text{and} \quad \frac{\vec{v}\,'_2 - \vec{v_2}}{\Delta t} = \vec{a_2}$$

so that

$$-m_1\vec{a_1} = m_2\vec{a_2}$$

or

$$-\vec{F_1} = \vec{F_2}$$

where $\vec{F_1}$ and $\vec{F_2}$ are the forces acting on m_1 and m_2, respectively.

That is, the colliding objects exert forces on each other during the collision that are equal in magnitude but opposite in direction.

The conservation of momentum is not limited to just two objects, but can be extended to include any number of interacting objects that are free from external forces. Newton expressed this relationship in the Law of Conservation of Momentum, as follows:

If the net external force acting on any object, or system of objects, is zero, then the total momentum of the object or system of objects remains constant.

$$\text{If } \vec{F}_{net} = 0, \ \Delta\vec{p}_{total} = 0$$
$$\text{and } \vec{p}_{total} = \vec{p}'_{total}$$

Any group of interacting objects may be thought of as a system whose total momentum remains constant as long as the only interactions that occur are between the objects in the system. When no external force acts on the system, we say the system is "isolated".

A ball falling freely towards the ground is not an isolated system, since it has the external force of the Earth pulling down on it. Its momentum does not remain constant. However, if we were to consider the system as consisting of the falling ball and the Earth, then the total momentum of this system does remain constant. The increase in downward momentum of the ball is equal to the increase in upward momentum of the Earth as it is attracted upward towards the falling ball (remember Newton's Law of Universal Gravitation).

The Law of Conservation of Momentum is very useful in predicting what will happen whenever two or more objects collide or explode.

Collisions are important in many fields of science. Gas molecules colliding with the walls of a container exert a force (or pressure). The mass of a neutron may be determined by allowing it to collide head-on with the nucleus of a hydrogen atom. Positive alpha particles deflected away from the positive nucleus of gold atoms tell us a great deal about atomic structure (Section 19.1). Quantum "packets" of light energy colliding like bullets with electrons transfer momentum to these electrons and give them enough energy to escape (Section 18.3). And even the remote "slow" interactions, such as the gravitational effects of the Earth on the moon, the moon on the Earth (tides), and the galactic centre of our universe on the stars of our galaxy, obey the principles of momentum conservation.

A few sample problems, using more familiar interactions and collisions, will illustrate.

If we were to begin with Newton's Third Law ($\vec{F}_1 = -\vec{F}_2$), we could work backward and derive an expression for the conservation of momentum ($\Delta\vec{p} = 0$).

The principle of conservation of momentum provides a valuable tool for analysing the data from collisions between elementary particles (Chapter 20).

Sample problems

1. A loaded railway car of mass 6000 kg is rolling to the right at 2.0 m/s when it collides and couples with an empty freight car of mass 3000 kg, rolling to the left on the same track at 3.0 m/s. What is the speed and direction of the pair after the collision?

   Since momentum is a vector quantity, directions are significant. We will assume that velocities to the right are positive, and to the left negative. Primed symbols indicate the value of a quantity *after* collision.

   Before the collision,

$$\vec{p}_1 = m_1\vec{v}_1 \quad = (6000 \text{ kg})(2.0 \text{ m/s})$$
$$= 1.2 \times 10^4 \text{ kg·m/s[right]}$$

$$\vec{p}_2 = m_2\vec{v}_2 \quad = (3000 \text{ kg})(-3.0 \text{ m/s})$$
$$= -9.0 \times 10^3 \text{ kg·m/s[right]}$$

   therefore $\vec{p}_{\text{total}} = \vec{p}_1 + \vec{p}_2 = 1.2 \times 10^4 \text{ kg·m/s} - 9.0 \times 10^3 \text{ kg·m}$
$$= 3.0 \times 10^3 \text{ kg·m/s[right]}$$

   After the collision,

$$\vec{p}'_{\text{total}} = (m_1 + m_2)\vec{v}'_{12} = (9000 \text{ kg})\vec{v}'_{12}$$

   But, since the system is isolated, $\Delta\vec{p} = 0$.

$$\text{therefore } \vec{p}'_{\text{total}} = \vec{p}_{\text{total}}$$

$$(9000 \text{ kg})\vec{v}'_{12} = 3.0 \times 10^3 \text{ kg·m/s}$$

$$\vec{v}'_{12} = 0.33 \text{ m/s[right]}$$

   Thus, the pair of coupled cars move off to the right (positive direction) at a speed of 0.33 m/s.

2. Calculate the recoil velocity of an unconstrained rifle of mass 5.0 kg after it shoots a 50 g bullet at a speed of 300 m/s, with respect to the Earth.

   It is very important to keep frames of reference straight in recoil problems. The system consisting of the bullet and the rifle is isolated.

$$\Delta\vec{p} = 0$$
$$\vec{p}_{\text{total}} = \vec{p}'_{\text{total}}$$
$$\vec{p}_b + \vec{p}_r = \vec{p}'_b + \vec{p}'_r \qquad \text{where r and b represent the rifle and bullet respectively}$$

$$m_b\vec{v}_b + m_r\vec{v}_r = m_b\vec{v}'_b + m_r\vec{v}'_r$$

   If the bullet is assumed to be shot in the positive direction,

$$(0.050 \text{ kg})(0) + (5.0 \text{ kg})(0) = (0.050 \text{ kg})(300 \text{ m/s}) + (5.0 \text{ kg})v'_r$$

$$v'_r = \frac{-15 \text{ kg·m/s}}{5.0 \text{ kg}}$$
$$= -3.0 \text{ m/s}$$

Note that, because of its much larger mass, the speed of the rifle is much less than the speed of the bullet. The negative sign indicates that the rifle's velocity (and hence, its momentum) is in the opposite direction to that of the bullet. Notice also that the speed of the bullet with respect to the rifle is 303 m/s. This is the "muzzle velocity".

Exactly the same principle applies in rocket propulsion. Small amounts of gas (the bullets) are ejected at a high velocity from the tail of the rocket (the rifle). The massive rocket increases its velocity in the forward direction to keep the momentum of the system unchanged.

The analysis is complicated by two factors:
(i) the mass of the rocket is not constant — it continually decreases as gas is released for propulsion;
(ii) it is the velocity of the ejected gas with respect to the rocket that normally remains constant. This becomes even more significant as the rocket's speed increases. It is possible for the absolute speed of the rocket to exceed the relative speed of the exhaust.

The result is a forward force on the rocket, called the thrust, that is given by the following equation:

$$F_T = v_g \frac{\Delta m_g}{\Delta t}$$

where v_g is the exhaust speed of the gases, relative to the rocket, and $\frac{\Delta m_g}{\Delta t}$ is the rate at which mass is ejected from the rocket.

3. A 1.0 kg ball moving with a velocity of 2.0 m/s to the right collides straight-on with a stationary 2.0 kg ball. After the collision, the 2.0 kg ball moves off to the right with a velocity of 1.2 m/s. What is the velocity of the 1.0 kg ball after the collision?

Since the two balls are considered to be an isolated system,

$$\Delta \vec{p}_{total} = 0$$
$$\vec{p}_{total} = \vec{p}\,'_{total}$$
$$\vec{p_1} + \vec{p_2} = \vec{p}\,'_1 + \vec{p}\,'_2$$

If we assume that vectors to the right are positive,

$$(1.0 \text{ kg})(2.0 \text{ m/s}) + 0 = (1.0 \text{ kg})(v'_1) + (2.0 \text{ kg})(1.2 \text{ m/s})$$
$$v'_1 = \frac{-0.40 \text{ kg·m/s}}{1.0 \text{ kg}}$$
$$= -0.40 \text{ m/s}$$

"Everyone is ignorant, only on different subjects."

Will Rogers

The negative sign indicates that the 1.0 kg ball, initially moving to the right, rebounds and moves to the left at 0.40 m/s after the collision.

4. A competition is held between two teams of physics students, each team made up of three members, and each member having a mass of 60 kg. The teams will take turns climbing onto a cart and jumping off. They want to see whose cart will be moved fastest by propelling it with a jump. They will start at the west end of a cart of mass 120 kg that is free to roll without friction on a level, east-west track. The plan is to run east along the cart and then jump off with a velocity of 10 m/s, with respect to the cart.

The first team decides that its three members will run and jump off together. The second team decides that one member will depart according to the rules, followed by the second, and then, finally, the third.

Calculate the final velocity of the cart for each team, and discuss the results.

Assume that vectors to the east are positive and omit vector notation.

For the first team: Let the velocity acquired by the cart with respect to the Earth be V. The velocity of the three students relative to the Earth, v, will be $10 + V$.

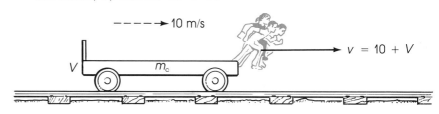

$$\vec{p}\,(\text{total}) = \vec{p}\,'(\text{total}) = 0$$
$$0 = m_c V + 3\,m_s(10 + V)$$
$$= 120\,V + 180(10 + V)$$
$$300\,V = -1800$$
$$V = -6.0 \text{ m/s} \quad \text{and} \quad v = 4.0 \text{ m/s}$$

Note: The negative sign for V indicates a velocity to the west.

For the second team: Let the velocity of the cart after each successive student has jumped be V_1, V_2, and V_3, and let the velocities of the three students relative to the Earth be v_1, v_2, and v_3.

Remember relative velocities from Chapter 3:

$$\vec{v}_{sE} = \vec{v}_{sc} + \vec{v}_{cE}$$
where s = student
       c = cart
       E = Earth
$$\vec{v}_{sc} = 10 \text{ m/s[E]}$$

Then, in this example
$$v = 10 + V$$

In problems such as this, it is logical that the final velocity of the cart will be towards the west; nevertheless, if we let its velocity be V, without regard for direction, and follow the rules of algebra, the negative value that results confirms our thinking.

After the first student has jumped,

$$\vec{p}\,(\text{total}) = \vec{p}\,'(\text{total}) = 0$$

$$0 = m_cV_1 + 2\,m_sV_1 + m_s(10 + V_1)$$
$$= 120\,V_1 + 120\,V_1 + 60(10 + V_1)$$
$$300\,V_1 = -600$$
$$V_1 = -2.0 \text{ m/s, or } 2.0 \text{ m/s[W], and } v_1 = 8.0 \text{ m/s}$$

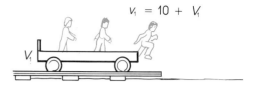

After the second student has jumped,

$$0 = m_cV_2 + m_sV_2 + m_s(10 + V_2) + m_sv_1$$
$$= 120\,V_2 + 60\,V_2 + 60(10 + V_2) + 60(8.0)$$
$$240\,V_2 = -1080$$
$$V_2 = -4.5 \text{ m/s, or } 4.5 \text{ m/s[W], and } v_2 = 5.5 \text{ m/s}$$

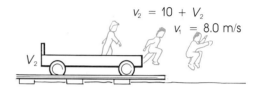

Finally, after the third student has jumped,

$$0 = m_cV_3 + m_s(10 + V_3) + m_sv_2 + m_sv_1$$
$$= 120\,V_3 + 60(10 + V_3) + 60(5.5) + 60(8.0)$$
$$180\,V_3 = -1410$$
$$V_3 = -7.8 \text{ m/s, or } 7.8 \text{ m/s[W], and } v_3 = 2.2 \text{ m/s}$$

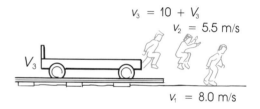

As can be seen from the result, the team that chose to have its members jump separately was able to give the cart a greater velocity in the opposite direction. This is what happens in a rocket as the engines burn and eject mass in continuous small amounts, instead of ejecting it all in one large burst.

Of course, as the rocket engines expel exhaust gases backward to provide forward momentum, the mass of the rocket slowly decreases. For that reason, the last kilogram of gases ejected produces the greatest increase in velocity.

Practice
(All velocities are relative to the Earth unless otherwise specified.)
1. A 5000 kg boxcar moving at 5.2 m/s on a level, frictionless track, runs into a stationary 8000 kg tank car. If they hook together in the collision, how fast will they be moving afterwards?
(2.0 m/s[forward])
2. A 75 kg girl running at 3.0 m/s jumps onto a sled that has a mass of 10 kg and that is already moving in the same direction as the girl, at 2.0 m/s. What will be the final velocity of the girl and the sled, assuming that the sled is on level snow and that there is no friction? (2.9 m/s[forward])
3. A 100 g ball moving at a constant velocity of 200 cm/s strikes a 400 g ball that is at rest. After the collision, the first ball rebounds straight back at 120 cm/s. Calculate the final velocity of the second ball. (80.0 cm/s[forward])

4. A 25 kg object moving with a velocity of 3.0 m/s to the right collides with a 15 kg object moving to the left at 6.0 m/s. Find the velocity of the 25 kg object after the collision, if the 15 kg object **(a)** continues to move to the left but at only 0.30 m/s, **(b)** rebounds to the right at 0.45 m/s, and **(c)** sticks together with the 25 kg object.

           (0.42 m/s[left], 0.87 m/s[left], 0.38 m/s[left])

5. A 1.5 kg wooden trolley on wheels is stationary on a horizontal, frictionless track. What will be the final velocity of the trolley if a bullet of mass 2.0 g is fired into it with a horizontal velocity of 300 m/s along the direction of the track? (The bullet remains embedded in the trolley.)   (0.40 m/s[forward])

6. An experimental rocket sled on a level, frictionless track has a mass of 1.4×10^4 kg. For propulsion, it expels gases from its rocket engines at a rate of 10 kg/s and at an exhaust speed of 2.5×10^4 m/s relative to the rocket. For how many seconds must the engines burn in order that the sled acquire a velocity of 50 m/s starting from rest? You may ignore the small decrease in mass of the sled and the small speed of the rocket compared to the exhaust gas.   (2.8 s)

8.4 The Vector Nature of Momentum

In the straight-line problems we have encountered so far in this chapter, we have taken into account the vector nature of momentum by assigning momenta in one direction as positive and in the other direction as negative. This is all that is necessary in head-on or one-dimensional collisions or interactions.

The vector nature of momentum becomes more evident if we study a two-dimensional interaction, such as an off-centre collision between two billiard balls on a smooth, horizontal surface.

The following illustration depicts a strobe photograph taken at 30 flashes/s. It shows a moving ball entering at the bottom of the picture, striking a stationary ball, and then glancing off to the left. The target ball moves off to the right as a result of the collision. The picture is one-eighth full size, and the mass of each ball is 180 g.

The picture enables us to measure the speed and direction of each ball both before and after the collision and, as a result, calculate each ball's momentum before and after the collision.

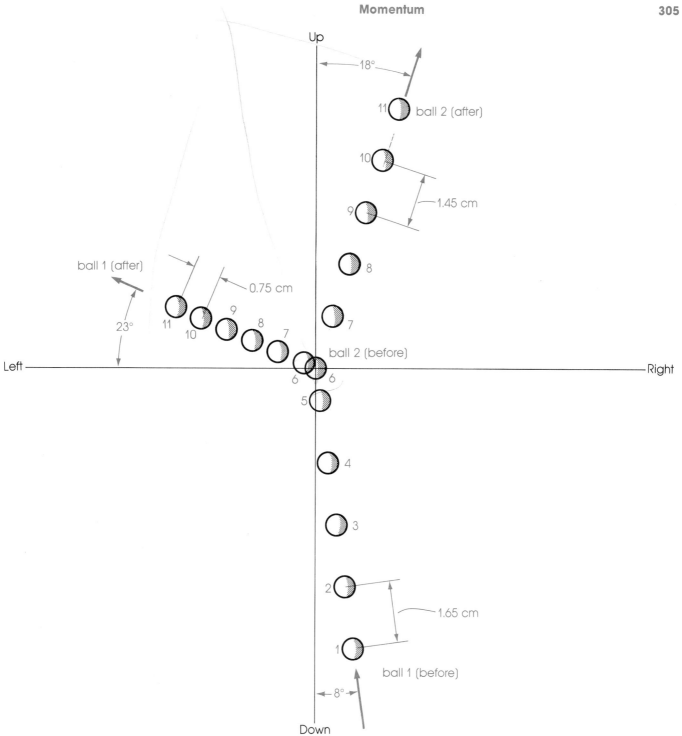

Remember, the picture is 1/8 full size, so that all length measurements must be multiplied by 8.

The velocity of the moving ball, $\vec{v_1}$, before impact is

$$\vec{v_1} = 8\left(\frac{1.65 \text{ cm}}{1/30 \text{ s}}\right)$$
$$= 396 \text{ cm/s, or } 4.0 \text{ m/s[U8°L]}$$

Since its mass is 180 g, or 0.180 kg, its initial momentum is

$$\vec{p_1} = m_1\vec{v_1}$$
$$= (0.180 \text{ kg})(4.0 \text{ m/s})$$
$$= 0.72 \text{ kg·m/s[U8°L]}$$

The initial momentum of the stationary ball, $\vec{p_2}$, is zero, since it is at rest before the collision. Thus the total momentum of the system before the collision is

$$\vec{p}_{\text{total}} = \vec{p_1} + \vec{p_2}$$
$$= 0.72 \text{ kg·m/s[U8°L]} + 0$$
$$= 0.72 \text{ kg·m/s[U8°L]}$$

The velocity of ball 1 after the collision is

$$\vec{v_1'} = 8\left(\frac{0.75 \text{ cm}}{1/30 \text{ s}}\right)$$
$$= 180 \text{ cm/s, or } 1.8 \text{ m/s[L23°U]}$$

And its momentum is

$$\vec{p_1'} = m_1\vec{v_1'} = (0.180 \text{ kg})(1.8 \text{ m/s})$$
$$= 0.32 \text{ kg·m/s[L23°U]}$$

Similarly, for ball 2 after the collision,

$$\vec{v_2'} = 8\left(\frac{1.45 \text{ cm}}{1/30 \text{ s}}\right)$$
$$= 3.48 \text{ m/s[U18°R]}$$

and

$$\vec{p_2'} = m_2\vec{v_2'}$$
$$= (0.180 \text{ kg})(3.48 \text{ m/s})$$
$$= 0.63 \text{ kg·m/s[U18°R]}$$

The total momentum of the system after the collision is given by the vector expression

$$\vec{p'}_{\text{total}} = \vec{p_1'} + \vec{p_2'}$$

and may be found using the vector diagram on the next page.

Note that $\vec{p}_{\text{total}}$, drawn to the right of the vector diagram, and $\vec{p'}_{\text{total}}$ are equal (the vectors have the same length and are in the same direction). Momentum is conserved in a two-dimensional system such as this one, which has no external forces in the horizontal plane.

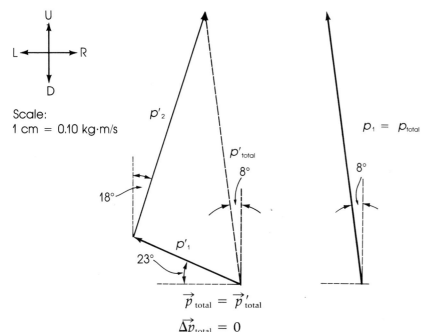

U
L ← → R
D

Scale:
1 cm = 0.10 kg·m/s

p'_2

p'_{total}

8°

$p_1 = p_{total}$

8°

18°

23°

p'_1

$$\vec{p}_{total} = \vec{p}'_{total}$$

$$\Delta\vec{p}_{total} = 0$$

Another way of looking at this type of collision is to calculate the change in momentum of each ball, as a result of the collision.

For ball 1,

$$\Delta\vec{p}_1 = \vec{p}'_1 - \vec{p}_1$$

which may be determined from the vector subtraction diagram below.

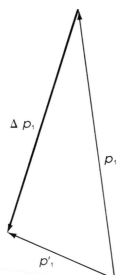

Δp_1

p_1

p'_1

Remember the rules for vector subtraction outlined in Section 3.4 on page 94.

Similarly for ball 2, whose initial momentum is zero, we have

$$\vec{\Delta p_2} = \vec{p}\,'_2 - \vec{p_2}$$

$$= \vec{p}\,'_2 \quad \text{since } \vec{p_2} = 0$$

These vector diagrams show clearly that $\vec{\Delta p_2} = -\vec{\Delta p_1}$

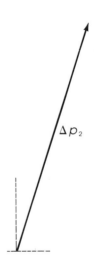

Δp_2

Notice that $\Delta \vec{p_2}$ and $\Delta \vec{p_1}$ are vectors of the same length but opposite direction.

In other words, the gain in momentum for ball 2 ($\vec{\Delta p_2}$) is equal to the loss in momentum for ball 1 ($-\vec{\Delta p_1}$).

$$\vec{\Delta p_2} = -\vec{\Delta p_1}$$

$$\vec{\Delta p_2} + \vec{\Delta p_1} = 0$$

$$\vec{\Delta p}_{\text{total}} = 0$$

Once again, the total momentum of the system remains constant. During the collision, momentum is transferred from ball 1 to ball 2, but none is "lost" in the transfer.

The pictures that follow show the same type of collision between **(a)** two balls of equal mass, and **(b)** two balls of unequal mass, that are both moving prior to colliding. The vector diagrams show the total momentum before and after the collision, in each case.

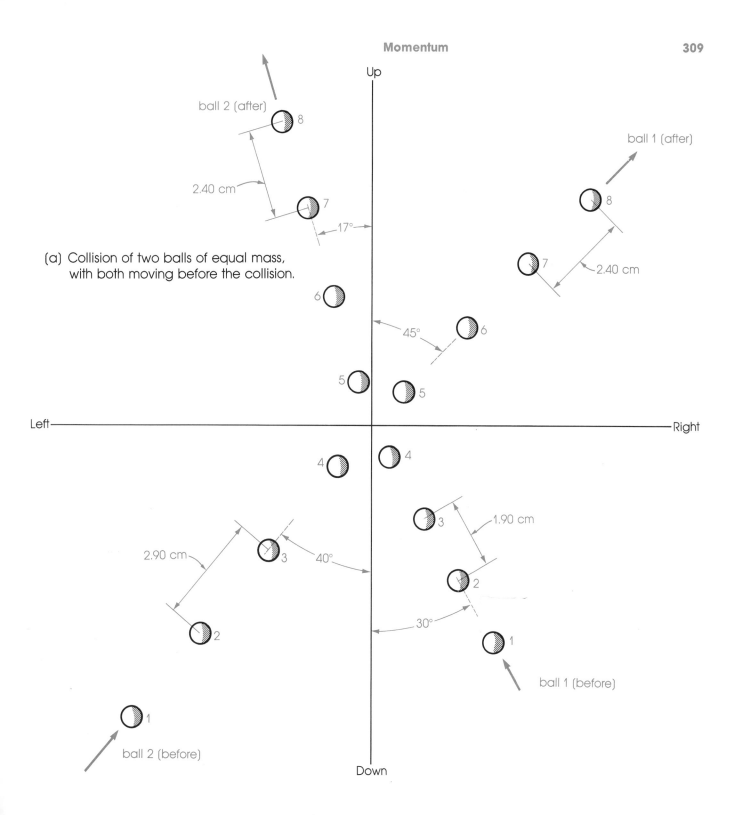

(a) Collision of two balls of equal mass, with both moving before the collision.

(b) Collision of two balls of unequal mass, with both moving before the collision.

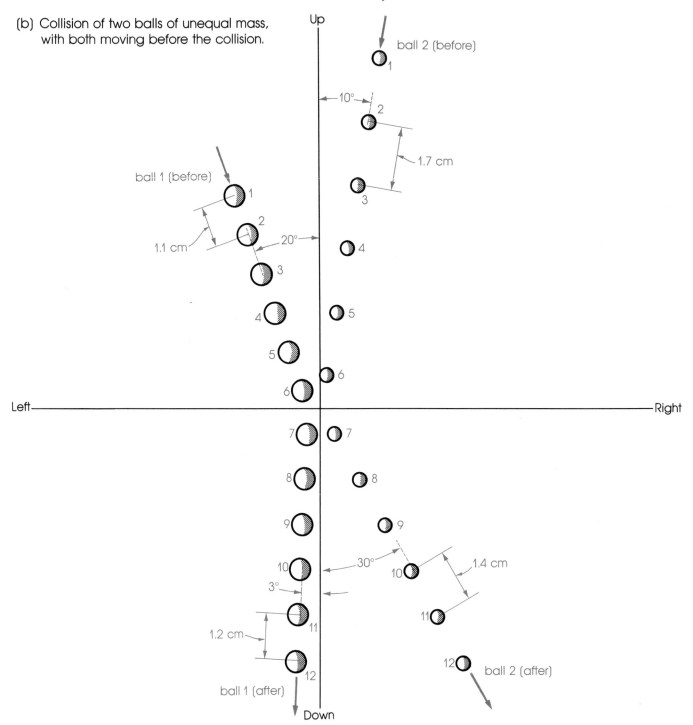

$\vec{p_1} = m_1 \vec{v_1} = 0.82$ kg·m/s [U 30° L]

$\vec{p_2} = m_2 \vec{v_2} = 1.25$ kg·m/s [U 40° R]

$\vec{p'_1} = m_1 \vec{v'_1} = 1.04$ kg·m/s [U 45° R]

$\vec{p'_2} = m_2 \vec{v'_2} = 1.04$ kg·m/s [U 17° L]

Scale: 1 cm = 0.20 kg·m/s

$m_1 = m_2 = 180$ g

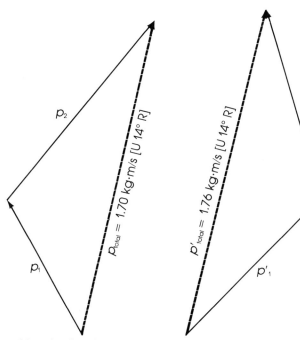

(a) Collision of two balls of equal mass, with both moving before the collision

$\vec{p_1} = m_1 \vec{v_1} = 0.53$ kg·m/s [D 20° R]

$\vec{p_2} = m_2 \vec{v_2} = 0.35$ kg·m/s [D 10° L]

$\vec{p'_1} = m_1 \vec{v'_1} = 0.58$ kg·m/s [D 3° L]

$\vec{p'_2} = m_2 \vec{v'_2} = 0.29$ kg·m/s [D 30° R]

Scale: 1 cm = 0.10 kg·m/s

$m_1 = 200$ g $m_2 = 86$ g

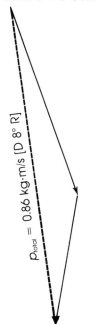
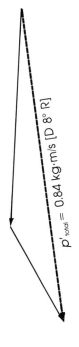

(b) Collision of two balls of unequal mass, with both moving before the collision

The importance of the Law of Conservation of Momentum lies in its generality. It applies to any isolated interaction between two or more objects, whether or not kinetic energy is also conserved. It is just as valid when automobiles involved in a crash are permanently deformed as it is when two steel balls bounce off one another without any physical change. It is true when a thrown grenade explodes in mid-air, with its many fragments moving off in all directions at various speeds. Momentum is conserved regardless of whether the kinetic energy of the fragments is conserved or not. The discussion of the transfer and conservation of kinetic energy in a collision will be dealt with in Section 9.3. The only condition required for the Law of Conservation of Momentum to be applicable to a situation is that the system be isolated, with no net external force acting on it.

Since momentum is a vector quantity, it is also conserved in certain specific directions. For example, in a game of billiards played in a vertically accelerating elevator, momentum would still be conserved in the horizontal plane of the table, since there would be no external horizontal forces acting on the system consisting of the balls and the table. Someone vertically above the table, viewing a collision between several balls, would not be able to determine that the table was accelerating, or even moving, vertically. Momentum in the vertical direction would not be conserved, of course, because external unbalanced forces act in that direction. How else could the elevator accelerate?

Sample problem

A grenade of mass 1.20 kg is at rest on a smooth, frictionless surface when it suddenly explodes into three pieces. A 0.50 kg piece flies off horizontally to the north at 3.0 m/s, and a 0.30 kg piece flies off horizontally to the southwest at 4.0 m/s. What is the horizontal speed and direction of the third piece?

The total momentum of the system before the explosion is zero, since the grenade is at rest.

$$\vec{p}_{\text{total}} = \vec{p}\,'_{\text{total}} = \vec{p}\,'_1 + \vec{p}\,'_2 + \vec{p}\,'_3 = 0$$

but
$$\vec{p}\,'_1 = m_1\vec{v}\,'_1 = (0.50 \text{ kg})(3.0 \text{ m/s})$$
$$= 1.5 \text{ kg·m/s[N]}$$

and
$$\vec{p}\,'_2 = m_2\vec{v}\,'_2 = (0.30 \text{ kg})(4.0 \text{ m/s})$$
$$= 1.2 \text{ kg·m/s[SW]}$$

Thus, the final momentum of piece three, $\vec{p}\,'_3$, is the vector that, together with $\vec{p}\,'_1$ and $\vec{p}\,'_2$ adds to give zero, the total momentum before the explosion. This vector addition may be done using the vector diagram to the right.

$$\vec{p}\,'_3 = 1.1 \text{ kg·m/s[E37°S]}$$

Since the mass of piece three is 0.40 kg, its velocity after the explosion is given by

$$\vec{v}\,'_3 = \frac{\vec{p}\,'_3}{m_3}$$

$$= \frac{1.1 \text{ kg·m/s[E37°S]}}{0.40 \text{ kg}}$$

$$= 2.8 \text{ m/s[E37°S]}$$

This problem may also be solved by considering the components of the momentum vectors, in the north-south-east-west directions.

$$\vec{p}_1 + \vec{p}_2 + \vec{p}_3 = 0$$

In the north, or y, direction,

$$p_{1_y} + p_{2_y} + p_{3_y} = 0$$

$$1.5 \text{ kg·m/s} + (-1.2 \cos 45° \text{ kg·m/s}) + p_{3_y} = 0$$

$$p_{3_y} = 0.85 \text{ kg·m/s} - 1.50 \text{ kg·m/s}$$

$$= -0.65 \text{ kg·m/s}$$

In the east, or x, direction,

$$p_{1_x} + p_{2_x} + p_{3_x} = 0$$

$$0 + (-1.2 \sin 45° \text{ kg·m/s}) + p_{3_x} = 0$$

$$p_{3_x} = 0.85 \text{ kg·m/s}$$

then $\quad |\vec{p}_3| = \sqrt{(p_{3x})^2 + (p_{3y})^2}$

$$= \sqrt{(0.85 \text{ kg·m/s})^2 + (-0.65 \text{ kg·m/s})^2}$$

$$= \sqrt{1.15 (\text{kg·m/s})^2}$$

$$= 1.1 \text{ kg·m/s}$$

and $\quad \theta = \tan^{-1} \dfrac{p_{3_y}}{p_{3_x}}$

$$= \tan^{-1} \frac{0.65 \text{ kg·m/s}}{0.85 \text{ kg·m/s}}$$

$$= \tan^{-1} 0.76$$

$$= 37°$$

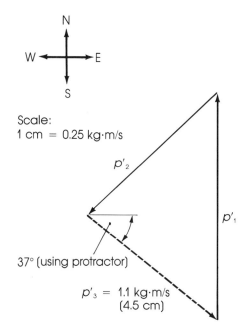

N

W ← → E

S

Scale:
1 cm = 0.25 kg·m/s

p'_2

p'_1

37° (using protractor)

$p'_3 = 1.1$ kg·m/s
(4.5 cm)

Thus, using components, $\vec{p_3} = 1.1$ kg·m/s[E37°S]

and
$$\vec{v_3} = \frac{\vec{p_3}}{m_3}$$

$$= \frac{1.1 \text{ kg·m/s[E37°S]}}{0.40 \text{ kg}}$$

$$= 2.8 \text{ m/s[E37°S]}$$

Practice

1. The diagram below shows two identical billiard balls before and after a glancing collision.

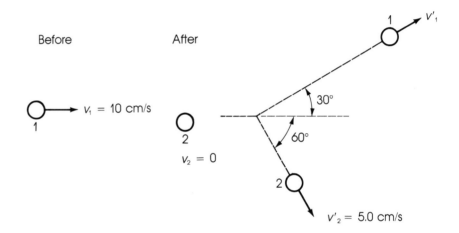

Before   After

$v_1 = 10$ cm/s

1

2

$v_2 = 0$

1   v'_1

30°

60°

2

$v'_2 = 5.0$ cm/s

Draw a vector diagram for the collision, and determine the speed of ball 1 after the collision.   (8.7 cm/s)

2. Repeat the sample problem, but this time assume that the grenade was moving at a constant velocity of 1.5 m/s[E] just before it exploded. (Assume that the final speeds and directions of pieces one and two remain the same.)   (6.8 m/s[E14°S])

3. A bomb initially at rest on a smooth, horizontal surface is exploded into three pieces. Two pieces fly off horizontally at a 60° angle to each other, a 2.0 kg piece at 20 m/s and a 3.0 kg piece at 12 m/s. The third piece flies off horizontally at 30 m/s.
   (a) Determine the direction of motion of the third piece.
   (b) What is its mass?
          (148° counterclockwise from the 3.0 kg piece, 2.2 kg)

4. The drawings on pages 315 and 316 show glancing collisions between a moving ball and a stationary target ball of equal mass. In each drawing, part of the path of one of the balls has been

blacked out. Use the Law of Conservation of Momentum to reconstruct the part that has been deleted, by finding the position of the missing ball at each flash of the strobe.

(a) Find the direction of the path taken by the target ball after the collision, and the distance between its images in the diagram. (47° left, 1.0 cm)

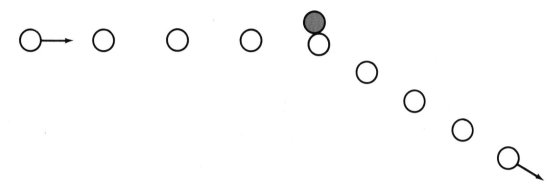

(b) Find the direction of the path taken by the moving ball after the collision, and the distance between its images in the diagram. (24° right, 2.2 cm)

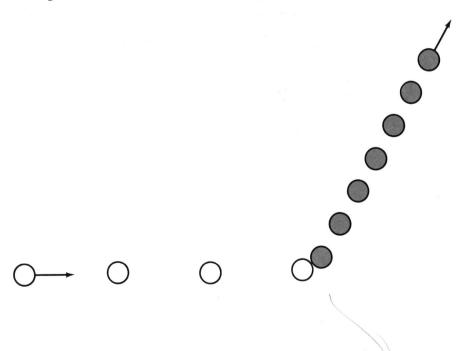

(c) Find the direction of the path taken by the moving ball before the collision, and the distance between its images in the diagram.   (131°, 2.3 cm)

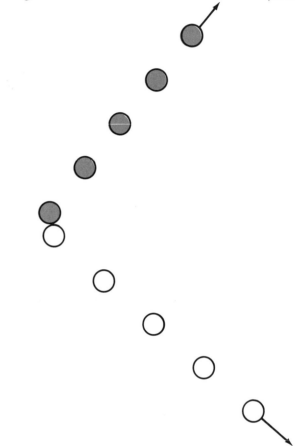

8.5 Centre of Mass

For a full discussion of the centre of mass, see Section 6.4, beginning on page 221.

The behaviour of solid objects under the influence of gravity or other forces indicates that there is a point in any object, called its centre of mass (or centre of gravity), where the entire mass of the object can be considered to act. For regularly shaped objects of uniform composition, the centre of mass is located at the geometric centre of the object. For any object, in general, the centre of mass is the point at which the object will "balance". It may be found experimentally, as shown.

If the object is suspended at any point and allowed to hang freely, it will rotate so that its centre of mass lies directly below the point of suspension.

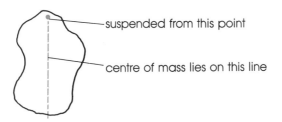

Suspending the object from a second point and finding the intersection of the two dotted lines will locate the centre of mass.

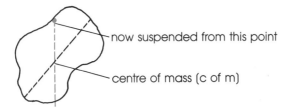

The centre of mass of a system of colliding or exploding objects has a great deal of significance so far as conservation of momentum is concerned. A re-examination of the collision of two moving billiard balls of unequal mass will reveal this significance.

The centre of mass of a system of two balls of unequal mass lies on the straight line joining the two balls, at a point (closer to the more massive ball) that divides the line into two segments in inverse ratio to the masses of the balls. In the drawing on the next page, the masses of the balls are in the ratio 7:3, so that the centre of mass divides the line joining the balls into two segments in the ratio 3:7. The centre of mass has been located as though for each flash of a strobe, and is marked with an X.

On the next page is a picture of the collision analysed on page 310 to show that the total momentum before the collision and the total momentum after the collision were equal (0.85 kg·m/s[D8°R]. Note that the Xs fall in a straight line and are equally spaced. This means that the centre of mass is moving with a constant velocity. If all the mass were concentrated at the centre of mass, then the momentum of the system obviously would remain constant before and after the collision.

To calculate the total momentum using the centre of mass, remember that the total mass may be considered to be concentrated at the centre of mass. In this case,

Note, in the accompanying photograph of a spinning hammer thrown through the air (with its centre of mass marked with an X), that the centre of mass follows the exact parabolic path that a small sphere, whose mass was equal to that of the hammer, would follow.

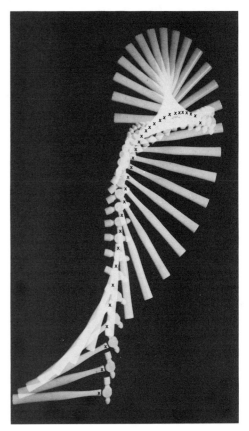

Collision of two balls, of unequal
mass, showing the centre of mass of
the system

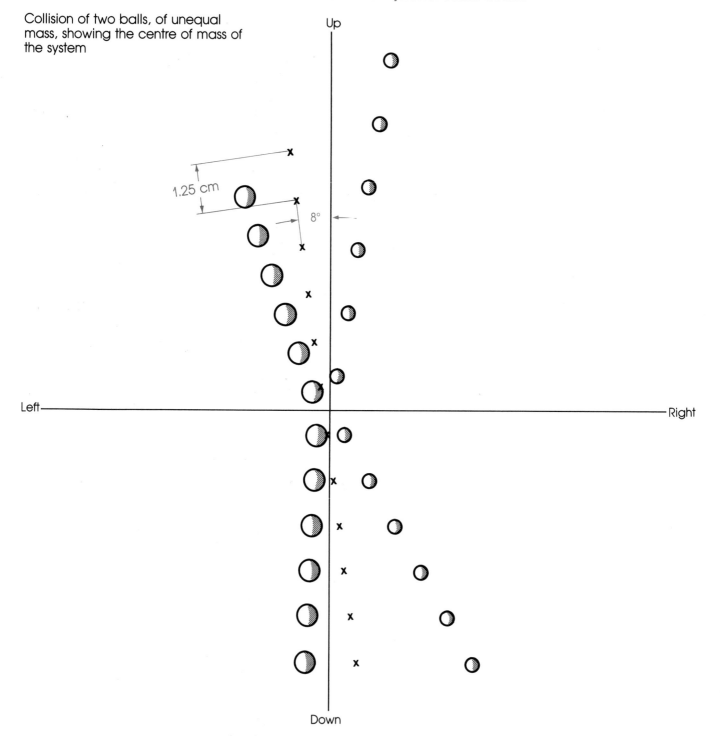

$$m_{total} = m_1 + m_2$$
$$= 200 \text{ g} + 86 \text{ g}$$
$$= 0.286 \text{ kg}$$

From the drawing, $\vec{v}_{c \text{ of m}} = 8\left(\dfrac{1.25 \text{ cm}}{1/30 \text{ s}}\right)$

$$= 3.0 \text{ m/s}[D8°R]$$

Thus, its momentum is

$$\vec{p}_{c \text{ of m}} = m_{c \text{ of m}} \, \vec{v}_{c \text{ of m}}$$
$$= (0.286 \text{ kg})(3.0 \text{ m/s})$$
$$= 0.86 \text{ kg·m/s}[D8°R]$$

Note that this is the same, within the limits of experimental accuracy, as the value for the total momentum of the system both before and after the collision has taken place.

$$\vec{p}_{total} = \vec{p}'_{total} = \vec{p}_{c \text{ of m}}$$

Clearly, the centre of mass of a system is a special point. Whether the two balls collide or not, they form an isolated system. As long as there are no external forces acting on the system, its centre of mass will obey Newton's Law of Inertia, and move in a straight line at a constant speed. As a matter of fact, if we were to move along with the centre of mass, using it as our frame of reference, the total momentum of the system, measured relative to this frame of reference, would be zero. Thus, any collision that resulted in one ball changing its momentum (measured in the centre-of-mass frame of reference) would require that the other ball change its momentum by an equal amount in the opposite direction, so that the total momentum would remain zero, in that frame.

The location of the centre of mass for some typical 2-ball systems:

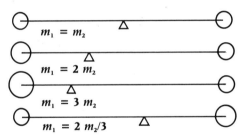

$m_1 = m_2$

$m_1 = 2\,m_2$

$m_1 = 3\,m_2$

$m_1 = 2\,m_2/3$

In general, $m_1 r_1 = m_2 r_2$, where r_1 and r_2 are the distances from m_1 and m_2 to the centre of mass, respectively.

8.6 Angular Momentum

The momentum we have been discussing so far in this chapter is called linear, or translational, momentum. It is not the only type of momentum an object can possess. An object that is rotating possesses a different type of momentum, which we call **angular momentum**. A merry-go-round, the flywheel on a motor, and a skater doing a camel-spin all have angular momentum. If the centre of mass of the spinning object, such as a moving bicycle wheel, has linear momentum, then it will have both linear and angular momentum.

Linear momentum and angular momentum are similar in many ways. Recall that linear momentum is the product of an object's mass and its instantaneous velocity. The angular momentum of a rotating object is given by the product of its angular velocity and its **moment of inertia**. Just as a moving object's inertial mass is a measure of its resistance to linear acceleration, a rotating object's moment of inertia is a measure of its resistance to angular acceleration. The moment of inertia of a rotating object depends on its mass, and also on the distribution of its mass about the axis of rotation. If an object's mass is concentrated very close to its axis of rotation, its moment of inertia will be small, and it will be relatively easy to get it rotating with a certain angular velocity. On the other hand, an object of equal mass, with its mass more spread out from the axis of rotation, will have a greater moment of inertia, and will be more difficult to accelerate to the same angular velocity. The diagram shows two barbells of equal mass but of much different moment of inertia.

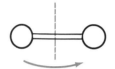
smaller moment of inertia

larger moment of inertia

There is a Law of Conservation of Angular Momentum for rotating systems that have no external torques, or moments, applied to them. Many interesting phenomena can be explained using this law. Everyone is familiar with a spinning skater who, all of a sudden, begins to spin with a much greater angular velocity, with no apparent external force acting on her. She begins by spinning with her arms outstretched, creating a large moment of inertia for herself. When she quickly pulls her arms in close to her axis of rotation, her moment of inertia decreases. But her angular momentum, which is the product of angular velocity and moment of inertia, remains constant, since she is isolated. Therefore, her angular velocity increases by the same factor that her moment of inertia decreased. A similar situation occurs when a diver begins to execute a somersault. He begins by slowly starting to rotate with arms and legs outstretched. Then he quickly tucks them in close to his body and spins very quickly through one or two revolutions, before again extending his limbs and slowing down his angular velocity in preparation for entering the water.

The principles of conservation of angular momentum also apply to the motion of governors on motors and flywheels on large machinery, and to the stability of gyroscopes. Although a full treatment of these phenomena is beyond this text, your school library may have books to help you if you are interested in learning more about them.

8.7 Investigations

Investigation 8.1: Conservation of Momentum in Linear Collisions

Problem:
How does a collision between two dynamics carts affect the momentum of each?

Materials:
2 dynamics carts
2 ticker-tape timers, and ticker tape
1 large hatpin and 1 cork
several 100 g masses

Procedure:
Part A: Collision between a moving cart and a stationary cart if they stick together
1. These trials should be done on a smooth, flat tabletop; however, there is still some friction present between the wheels of the cart and the table. To compensate for this frictional force, insert several thicknesses of cardboard under the legs at one end of the table. Attach a tape to the cart, feed the tape through a timer, start the timer, and give the cart a gentle push down the table. If friction has been adequately overcome, the cart should move down the table with a uniform velocity, as indicated by an equal spacing of dots on the tape. Add or remove cardboard from under the table legs until this is so.
2. Attach the hatpin to the front of one cart, and the cork to the rear of the other, as shown in the diagram.

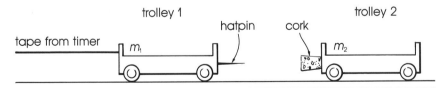

Place the cart with the cork attached near the middle of the table, and the cart with the pin attached at the higher end of the table. Attach a tape to this cart, feed it through the timer, and start the timer. Start this cart gently down the table so that it collides with the other cart, causing the pin to penetrate

the cork so that the two carts move on stuck together. Label and save the tape for analysis later.
3. Measure and record the mass of each loaded cart.

Part B: Collision between a moving cart and a stationary cart if they do not stick together
1. This trial is performed in a manner that is very similar to Part A, except that the pin and cork are replaced by a spring bumper attached to the moving cart, to ensure that the carts do not stick together on impact.
2. As a result, two tapes and timers are required to record the motion of each cart, as shown in the diagram.

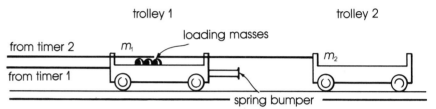

3. Load cart 1 with several 100 g masses, start both timers, then gently start the cart down the table so that it collides with the stationary cart 2, using the spring bumper to cushion the collision. Try to ensure that the two tapes do not tangle during the collision. Again, label and save both tapes for analysis later.
4. Measure and record the mass of each loaded cart.

Part C: Explosion involving two carts at rest
1. Remove the cardboard from under the table legs, so that the table is once again level. Use a cart that has a spring bumper that can be compressed, latched, then "triggered" by tapping lightly on a plunger, vertically above the spring.
2. Add several 100 g masses to one of the carts, then place them in contact, end to end, at the centre of the table, with the spring bumper compressed. Attach a tape to each, and feed the tapes through timers at the opposite end of the table from each cart, as shown in the diagram.

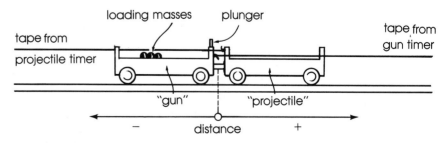

3. Start both timers, then cause the two carts to "explode" by tapping gently on the vertical trigger. Each cart will move away from its original position, pulling its tape through the corresponding timer. Label and save the tapes for analysis later.

4. Measure and record the mass of each cart.

Calculations:

1. By using the period of the timer (either 1/60 s, or some other value known from a previous investigation) and the distance measured between successive dots on the tape, calculate the velocity of each cart in each part of the investigation. Remember that in part A, all three velocities may be determined from the same tape; in part B, the velocity of the moving cart both before and after the collision can be found from its tape.

2. Record all of the data in a chart, similar to the one shown.

Part	Cart 1					Cart 2					Total momentum	
	m_1	v_1	v_1'	p_1	p_1'	m_2	v_2	v_2'	p_2	p_2'	p_{total}	p_{total}'
	kg	m/s		kg·m/s		kg	m/s		kg·m/s		kg·m/s	
A												
B												
C												

3. Calculate the momentum of each cart, both before and after the interaction, in each part of the investigation, and include these values in the chart.

4. Determine the total momentum of the system of two carts, both before and after the interaction in each part, and include these values in the chart.

5. Save all of the labelled tapes for analysis later, as part of an investigation on kinetic energy in Chapter 9.

Questions:

1. In this investigation, the system consists of both of the carts involved in the interaction. In each case, how does the total momentum of the system before the interaction compare with its total momentum after?

2. For each interaction, calculate the percentage difference in the momentum before and after the interaction. Explain why these two values might not have been precisely equal.

Investigation 8.2: Collisions in Two Dimensions

Problem:
Is momentum conserved in a two-dimensional collision?

Materials:
2 steel balls (ball bearings)
1 glass ball (marble)
carbon paper
masking tape, paper
C-clamp
2-D collision apparatus
(set up as in diagram)

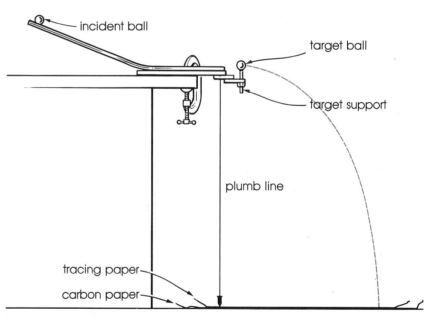

Procedure:
1. Swivel the target support around until it is lined up with the curved ramp. Place a steel ball on the target support and adjust the distance to the end of the ramp so that the support is two radii (2R) from it (see illustration).

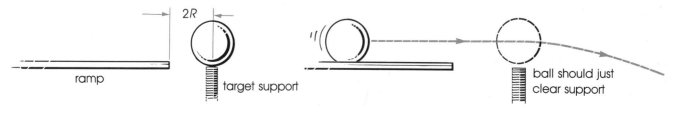

2. Remove the steel ball from the target support and place it on the ramp exactly 25 cm from the end. Release it from this point. It should just clear the support. If a small click is heard, the ball is touching the support as it is launched. Adjust the height of the target support to prevent this.

3. Place carbon paper on the floor, black side up. Cover it completely with a large piece of tracing paper or newsprint. Position the paper so that the plumb line, suspended from the target support, hangs over the middle of one end of the paper, approximately 10 cm from a corner. Tape the paper to the floor. Mark the point directly beneath the plumb bob with an X.

4. Determine the initial horizontal momentum of the incident ball before the collision, by releasing it about 10 times. Circle the distribution of "landings" on the paper. Using a ruler, draw a vector from the point X to the centre of the distribution of points. This vector represents the initial momentum of the incident ball (see marginal note).

5. Place an identical steel ball on the target support. Swivel the support sideways about 45° to produce an off-centre collision between the incident and the target balls. Record the point of collision, X_1, directly below the plumb bob. The incident ball is released from the 25 cm mark on the ramp. The two balls should hit the paper at two different points. Mark both impact points 1.

6. Swivel the target ball to different positions and repeat step 5 for at least four more collisions. Label the pairs of impact points 2, 3, 4, etc., and the corresponding points of collision X_2, X_3, X_4, ...

7. To draw the vectors representing the momenta after collision, join the point X_n to the impact points for both the incident ball and the target ball for the X_n collision.

8. Add the two momentum vectors graphically (on the paper) for each collision, placing the tail of the momentum vector for the target ball at the head of the momentum vector for the incident ball. Compare this vector sum with both the magnitude and the direction of the momentum vector of the incident ball before the collision (step 4). For each collision determine whether momentum is conserved (in a two-dimensional collision).

9. Repeat the investigation, using the same incident steel ball but a lighter target glass ball of the same diameter. Using a new sheet of tracing paper, record the incident velocity of the steel ball (see step 4). Next, place the glass target ball on the target support and record at least four off-centre collisions. Finally,

Step 4

The velocity of the incident steel ball is directly proportional to its horizontal displacement, that is, $v \propto \Delta d$ if Δt is constant. But the momentum of the ball is directly proportional to the velocity (from $\vec{p} = m\vec{v}$). Thus the displacement vector from X to the centre of the distribution of landings can represent both the initial velocity and the initial momentum of the incident ball.

Step 6

From projectile motion (see Section 5.8) we know that when an object is projected horizontally, the time it takes for the object to fall to the ground is independent of its horizontal velocity. This means that if two balls fall simultaneously from the same height, they both hit the ground at the same time, even if the horizontal velocities are different. Since the velocities of the balls in this investigation are relatively low, air resistance can be ignored.

Step 8

Since the masses of both the incident ball and the target ball are identical, the displacement vectors drawn on the paper represent both the velocity and the momentum vectors before and after the collisions. That is,

$$\Delta \vec{d}_i = \Delta \vec{d}_i' + \Delta \vec{d}_T'$$

But the time to fall, Δt, is identical for both incident and target balls,

$$\frac{\Delta \vec{d}_i}{\Delta t} = \frac{\Delta \vec{d}_i'}{\Delta t} + \frac{\Delta \vec{d}_T'}{\Delta t}$$

$$\vec{v}_i = \vec{v}_i' + \vec{v}_T'$$

and the mass, m, is identical for both balls.

$$m\vec{v}_i = m\vec{v}_i' + m\vec{v}_T'$$

$$\therefore \vec{p}_i = \vec{p}_i' + \vec{p}_T'$$

Step 11
Previously, since the masses of both incident and target balls were equal, the velocity vectors could be used as momentum vectors. In the case of unequal masses this is not true. As $\vec{p} = m\vec{v}$, the velocity vector must be multiplied by the mass to produce the momentum vector. The mass alters the length of the velocity vector but not the direction. If the mass of the steel ball is considered to be 1, then its velocity vector also represents the momentum vector, i.e., $\vec{p_s} = m_s\vec{v_s}$. On the other hand, in the case of the glass ball the momentum vector must be reduced, since the mass of the glass ball is less than that of the steel ball. Thus, the length of the momentum vector of the glass ball is calculated from

$$p_{glass} = \left(\frac{m_{glass}}{m_{steel}}\right) v_{glass}$$

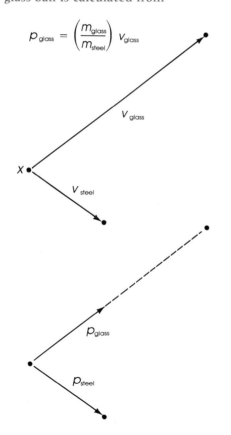

draw in the velocity vectors for each collision.

10. Check to see whether the vector sum of the velocity vectors of both balls after the collision is equal to the velocity vector of the incident steel ball. Discuss.

11. Using a balance, determine the masses of the steel ball and the glass ball. What is the ratio of the mass of the glass ball to that of the steel ball?

12. Convert the velocity vectors in the collision to momentum vectors, using the mass ratio calculated in step 11 (see marginal note). Is momentum conserved when unequal masses collide?

13. Save all of the paper records of these collisions for analysis later in an investigation on kinetic energy in Chapter 9.

8.8 Review

Discussion

1. State Newton's Second Law as it was originally proposed, in terms of momentum and force. Write an equation expressing this relationship.

2. For what types of forces does the concept of impulse prove most helpful, when analysing the changes in motion that occur as a result of the force?

3. A falling rock seems to gain momentum as its speed increases, and yet it might seem to be an "isolated system". Explain this apparent contradiction of the Law of Conservation of Momentum.

4. An astronaut is stranded in space a short distance from his spacecraft. Explain how he might use the Law of Conservation of Momentum to travel safely to his ship. Describe what he does at both the beginning and end of this travel.

5. Describe the beneficial effects of "air bags" used in modern cars to cushion passengers from collisions with the dashboard during an accident. Explain from the point of view of impulse and momentum.

6. A rocket is travelling in outer space, in a straight line towards the sun. Describe how it could alter its direction by 30° to the left without changing its speed. Draw a vector diagram showing its original momentum, final momentum, and its change in momentum, and describe how the change in momentum was accomplished.

7. A grenade is thrown into the air at an angle of 50° to the ground. In mid-air it explodes into many pieces, shooting off in all directions. Describe the path of the centre of mass of the grenade both before and after the explosion.

8. A railway freight car carrying sand is travelling at a uniform velocity on a straight level track. A leak develops in the flat bottom, and the sand begins to pour out of a hole onto the ground. Assuming there are no external forces on the freight car, including friction, does the velocity of the car increase, decrease, or remain the same? Explain your answer.

9. Describe the difference in the propulsion mechanisms of a propeller driven aircraft and a jet aircraft, making specific reference to the way in which the vehicle is made to move forward. Describe the success of each in the vacuum of outer space.

10. The police report of an accident between two cars at an intersection contains the diagram shown, and describes the cars as identical models and the road conditions as icy. Which car was travelling faster at the moment of impact, and how much faster? (Make direct measurements from the diagram if necessary.)

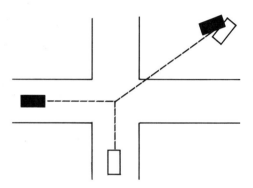

Problems

11. What is the speed of an 1800 kg car with a momentum of 3.0×10^4 kg·m/s?

12. A 1.5×10^3 kg car accelerates from rest at 4.0 m/s² for 6.0 s. (a) What momentum does it acquire in that time? (b) What was the impulse exerted on it?

13. A child hits a ball with a force of 350 N. (a) If the ball and bat are in contact for 0.12 s, what impulse does the ball receive? (b) What is its change in momentum?

14. A golf club exerts an average force of 7.2×10^3 N on a ball for the 5.0×10^{-4} s they are in contact.
    (a) Calculate the impulse of the impact on the ball.
    (b) If the ball has a mass of 45 g, what velocity will it have as it leaves the club face?

15. The average accelerating force exerted on a 5.0 kg shell in a gun barrel is 5.0×10^4 N, and the muzzle velocity is 200 m/s. Calculate (a) the impulse on the shell, and (b) the length of time it takes to move up the heavy gun barrel.

16. A 200 kg shot is discharged horizontally from a cannon, of mass 2.0×10^4 kg, with a speed of 250 m/s relative to the ground.
    (a) Find the steady force which, acting on the cannon, will stop its recoil in 2.0 s. (b) How far will the cannon recoil?

17. A 300 g ball is struck by a bat with an impact that lasts 0.020 s. If the ball moves through the air towards the bat at 50 m/s and leaves at 100 m/s in the opposite direction, calculate the average force exerted by the bat on the ball.

18. When a person parachutes, the impact velocity is equal to that attained in free fall from a height of 4.5 m. After contacting the ground, the jumper's momentum is quickly brought to zero by the Earth. What is
    (a) the impact velocity?
    (b) the impulse of the ground on the jumper, assuming a mass of 80 kg?
    (c) the average force on the jumper's feet if
        (i) he lands stiff-legged and the impulse only lasts 0.019 s?
        (ii) he lands with his knees flexed, so that the impulse is extended over a time interval of 0.050 s?

19. (a) A girl on skis (total mass 60 kg including skis) reaches the bottom of a hill moving at 20 m/s. What is her momentum?
    (b) She encounters deeper snow and stops in 3.0 s. What average force does the deeper snow exert on the girl?
    (c) How far into the deeper snow does she penetrate, assuming that the snow exerts a constant force on her?

20. A bullet of mass 0.050 kg, moving with a velocity of 400 m/s, penetrates a distance of 0.10 m into a wooden block firmly attached to the Earth. If the resisting force is assumed constant, calculate:
    (a) the acceleration of the bullet
    (b) the average force exerted on the bullet
    (c) the time required for it to stop
    (d) the impulse of the collision
    (e) the original momentum of the bullet

21. An 8.0 g bullet, moving at 400 m/s, goes through a stationary block of wood in 4.0×10^{-4} s, emerging at a speed of 100 m/s.
    (a) What average force did the wood exert on the bullet?
    (b) How thick is the wood?

22. A toy rocket develops an average forward thrust of 4.0 N when the velocity of the exhaust gases relative to the engine is 30 m/s. Calculate the mass of gases ejected per second.

23. A 1.2×10^4 kg railroad car is coasting along a level, frictionless track at a constant speed of 25 m/s, when a 3000 kg load is dropped vertically onto the car from above. What will its new speed be, assuming the load stays on the car?

24. A 45 kg boy is running at 4.0 m/s when he jumps onto a 15 kg sled, at rest on a frozen lake. What is the velocity of the boy and sled, if he hangs on?

25. A stationary Volkswagen Rabbit of mass 1.0×10^3 kg is rammed from behind by a Ford Escort of mass 1.2×10^3 kg, travelling at 20 m/s on an icy road. If they lock bumpers in the collision, how fast will the pair move forward?

26. An arrow travelling at 40 m/s strikes and imbeds itself in a 400 g apple at rest. The apple with the arrow in it moves off horizontally at 10 m/s after the impact. What is the mass of the arrow?

27. A shell of mass 8.0 kg leaves the muzzle of a cannon with a horizontal velocity of 600 m/s. Find the recoil velocity of the cannon, if its mass is 500 kg.

28. On a frictionless air track, a 30 g glider moving to the right at 4.0 cm/s collides with an 80 g glider moving to the left at 1.5 cm/s. If the two gliders stick together in the collision, what is their final velocity?

29. A 125 kg astronaut (with all his equipment) pushes off from his 2500 kg space capsule, acquiring a velocity of 2.0 m/s. (Assume that both astronaut and spacecraft are at rest to begin with.)
    (a) What is the velocity of the space capsule, after he pushes off?
    (b) If he is tethered to the space capsule by a 25 m line, what time will elapse before the line becomes taut?
    (c) Where is the centre of mass of the system, when this happens, and what is its momentum?

30. A 24 g bullet is fired horizontally, embedding itself in a 10 kg block initially at rest on a horizontal ice surface. The block slides along the ice, coming to rest in 2.0 s at a distance of 60 cm from its original position. Assuming that the frictional force stopping the block was constant, calculate the velocity of the bullet.

31. An atom of uranium disintegrates into two particles, one of which has a mass 60 times as great as the other. If the larger particle moves to the left with a velocity of 2.3×10^4 m/s, with what velocity does the lighter particle move?

32. An 80 kg man standing at rest on a smooth, level ice surface throws a 200 g ball horizontally with a speed of 25 m/s, relative to the Earth.
    (a) With what speed and in what direction does the man move?
    (b) If the man throws six such balls every 5.0 s, what is the average force acting on him?

33. (a) A polar bear of mass 999.9 kg lies sleeping on a horizontal sheet of ice. A hunter fires a 0.10 kg bullet at the bear with a speed of 1000 m/s. How fast does the bear (with the bullet embedded in a non-vital area) slide, after being hit?

    (b) Another polar bear, of mass 990 kg, is wearing a 10 kg bulletproof vest, and is hit by the same hunter. In this case, the bullet bounces straight back with negligible change in speed. How fast does this bear slide, after being hit?

34. A 2000 kg car travelling east at 24 m/s enters an icy intersection and collides with a 3600 kg truck travelling south at 10 m/s. If they become coupled together in the collision, what is their velocity immediately after impact?

35. A nucleus, initially at rest, decays radioactively. In the process, it emits an electron horizontally to the east, with momentum 9.0×10^{-21} kg·m/s and a neutrino horizontally to the south, with momentum 4.8×10^{-21} kg·m/s.
    (a) In what direction does the residual nucleus move?
    (b) What is the magnitude of its momentum?
    (c) If the mass of the residual nucleus is 3.6×10^{-25} kg, what is its recoil velocity?

36. A steel ball of mass 0.50 kg, moving with a velocity 2.0 m/s, strikes a second ball of mass 0.30 kg, initially at rest. The collision is a glancing one, causing the first ball to be deflected by an angle of 30°, with a speed of 1.50 m/s. Determine the velocity of the second ball after the collision, giving both its speed and direction.

37. A 3000 kg space capsule is travelling in outer space with a velocity of 200 m/s. In an effort to alter its course, it fires a 25.0 kg projectile perpendicular to its original direction of motion at a speed of 2000 m/s. What is the new speed of the space capsule and by what angle has its direction changed?

38. A 70 kg boy sits in a 30 kg canoe at rest on the water. He holds two cannonballs, each of mass 10 kg. He picks them up and throws both together over the stern of his canoe. The two balls leave his hands with a velocity of 5.0 m/s relative to the canoe.

    A 50 kg girl sits in a 50 kg canoe, also at rest on the water. She also holds two 10 kg cannonballs. However, she throws them over the stern of her canoe one at a time, each ball leaving her hands with a velocity of 5.0 m/s relative to the canoe.

    Assuming negligible friction between the water and the canoe (a poor assumption), calculate the final velocity for each canoe. (SIN '76).

39. A hunter shoots a 500 g arrow at a 2.0 kg bird perched on a tall tree growing on flat, level ground. The arrow is launched from ground level with a speed of 40 m/s at an angle of 30° above the horizon. It is travelling horizontally when it strikes and embeds in the bird. How far from the base of the tree do the bird and arrow land? (SIN '75)

40. A dog of mass 10.0 kg is standing on a raft so that he is 20.0 m from shore. He walks 8.00 m along the raft towards shore and then halts. The raft has a mass of 40.0 kg, and we can assume there is no friction between the raft and the water. How far is the dog from shore when he stops? (SIN '70)

41. Two men, of mass 100 kg each, stand on a cart of mass 300 kg. The cart can roll with negligible friction along a north-south track, and everything is initially at rest. One man runs towards the north and jumps off the cart at a speed of 5.0 m/s, relative to the cart. After he has jumped, the second man runs towards the south and jumps off the cart, again with a speed of 5.0 m/s relative to the cart. Calculate the speed and direction of the cart after both men have jumped off. (SIN '72).

42. A 1000 kg plane is trying to make a forced landing on the deck of a 2000 kg barge at rest on the surface of a calm sea. The only frictional force to consider is between the plane's wheels and the deck, and this braking force is constant and equal to one-quarter of the plane's weight. What must the minimum length of the barge be, in order that the plane can stop safely on deck, if the plane touches down just at the rear end of the deck with a velocity of 50 m/s towards the front of the barge? (SIN '76)

"The one who defines the terms wins the argument."

Chinese proverb

9 Kinetic Energy

9.1 Work — Force and Displacement

When used in everyday language, the term "work" has a great many meanings. In physics it has a very specific meaning, and has to do with what is accomplished when a force acts on an object that moves.

To begin with, consider an object at rest on a flat, frictionless surface. When a constant horizontal force, $\vec{F}$, is exerted on it for a time Δt, it undergoes a horizontal acceleration and moves through a displacement $\Delta \vec{d}$, in the direction of the applied force.

In this simplest case, the work done depends on the magnitude of the force applied and on the displacement the object undergoes as a result of the application of the force. The work done may be calculated as follows:

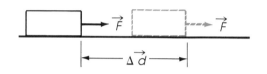

$$W = \vec{F} \cdot \Delta \vec{d}$$

where $\vec{F}$ is the force applied to the object, in newtons

$\Delta \vec{d}$ is the displacement of the object, in metres

The unit of work is the newton metre (N·m). In SI, a special name is given to this unit, the joule (J), after James Prescott Joule (1818–1889), a famous English scientist who did pioneering research into the relationship between work and heat.

1 J is the work done by an applied force of 1 N acting through a displacement of 1 m in the same direction.

1 J = 1 N·m

A few sample problems will illustrate how work done may be calculated in this simple case where force and displacement are in the same direction.

Sample problems

1. An applied force of 20 N accelerates a block across a level, frictionless surface from rest to a velocity of 8.0 m/s in a time of 2.5 s. Calculate the work done by this force.

This is clearly a problem where force and displacement are in the same direction. In this case, it is permissible to omit the vector notation by assigning motion in the initial direction as $+$ and in the opposite direction as $-$, even though in this example there is no motion in the opposite direction.

$$W = F\Delta d$$

where

$$\Delta d = \left(\frac{v_1 + v_2}{2}\right)\Delta t$$

$$= \left(\frac{0 + 8.0 \text{ m/s}}{2}\right)(2.5 \text{ s})$$

$$= 10 \text{ m}$$

Therefore

$$W = (20 \text{ N})(10 \text{ m})$$

$$= 200 \text{ J, or } 2.0 \times 10^2 \text{ J}$$

2. Calculate the work done in lifting a 12 kg crate from the floor to a platform 3.0 m above floor level.

The force necessary to lift any load and keep it moving slowly upward at constant speed is equal in magnitude to the force of gravity, $\vec{F}_g$. Again, in this problem, force and displacement are in the same direction, with [up] as positive.

$$W = F\Delta d$$

and

$$F = F_g = mg$$

$$= (12 \text{ kg})(9.8 \text{ N/kg})$$

$$= 118 \text{ N}$$

Therefore

$$W = (118 \text{ N})(3.0 \text{ m})$$

$$= 354 \text{ J, or } 3.5 \times 10^2 \text{ J}$$

Any extra, positive work done to start the crate moving upward will come back as negative work done in stopping it at the end of the lift.

3. How much work is done on an 8.0 kg wagon rolling along a flat sidewalk, if an applied force of 60 N opposite to its direction of motion brings it to rest in 2.0 s?

In this case, force and displacement are in opposite directions. We can deal with this situation easily, though, by again assigning positive values to vectors in the direction of motion, and negative values to vectors in the opposite direction.

$$a = \frac{F}{m}$$

$$= \frac{-60 \text{ N}}{8.0 \text{ kg}}$$

$$= -7.5 \text{ m/s}^2$$

$$\Delta d = v_2\Delta t - \frac{1}{2}a(\Delta t)^2$$

$$= 0 - \frac{1}{2}(-7.5 \text{ m/s}^2)(2.0 \text{ s})^2$$

$$= 15 \text{ m}$$

$$W = F\Delta d$$

$$= (-60 \text{ N})(15 \text{ m})$$

$$= -900 \text{ J, or } -9.0 \times 10^2 \text{ J}$$

Note that, in this case, the work done is negative. The significance of a negative amount of work done will be clear, later, when we discuss the relationship between work and energy, and the effect of an applied force that opposes an object's motion.

4. A truck pushes a car by exerting a horizontal force of 500 N on it. A frictional force of 300 N opposes the car's motion as it moves 4.0 m. Calculate the work done on the car by the truck.

$$W = F\Delta d$$
$$= (500 \text{ N})(4.0 \text{ m})$$
$$= 2000 \text{ J, or } 2.0 \times 10^3 \text{ J}$$

The work done is 2000 J. 1200 J of work are done by the truck just to overcome the frictional resistance to motion. The other 800 J of work (sometimes called the "useful work done") is used to increase the speed of the car, as you will learn in Section 9.2. Work done to overcome friction ends up as heat.

Practice

1. Calculate the amount of work done by the appropriate agent in each of the following cases:
   (a) A workman exerts a horizontal force of 30 N to push a 12 kg table across a level floor a distance of 4.0 m.
   (b) A horse pulls a sled 12 m along the ground at a constant speed of 2.0 m/s against a frictional force of 1500 N.
   (c) A man exerts a force of 150 N, parallel to a slope, to slide a 50 kg mass 8.0 m up the slope.
   (d) A 1.6 kg block is lifted vertically at a constant speed of 1.2 m/s through a height of 20 m.
   (e) A girl pushes a skateboard forward with a thrust of 120 N against the frictional force of the sidewalk of 40 N, while moving 2.5 m.

   $$(1.2 \times 10^2 \text{ J}, 1.8 \times 10^4 \text{ J}, 1.2 \times 10^3 \text{ J},$$
   $$3.1 \times 10^2 \text{ J}, 3.0 \times 10^2 \text{ J})$$

2. From what height must a 10 kg hammer fall in order to do 240 J of work on a stake being driven into the ground? (Hint: The gravitational force must first do 240 J of work on the hammer.)

   (2.4 m)

Work is a Scalar

Note that the calculation in the defining equation for work involves the multiplication of a vector, $\vec{F}$, and another vector, $\Delta \vec{d}$, and yet the product, W, is not a vector but a scalar. This equation is an example of a special type of multiplication of vectors, described previously in Section 3.5, called the "vector dot product". The defining equation for work, when properly written in vector notation, appears as

$$W = \vec{F} \cdot \Delta\vec{d}$$

The result of this multiplication is a scalar whose magnitude is $|\vec{F}|\,|\Delta\vec{d}|\cos\theta$, where θ is the angle between the directions of $\vec{F}$ and $\Delta\vec{d}$. Problems in which the applied force and the displacement are not in the same direction may be solved by using the component of the applied force in the direction of the displacement, as the sample problems that follow will illustrate.

Work may also be taken as the product of the applied force $|\vec{F}_a|$ and the component of displacement in the direction of this force $|\Delta\vec{d}\cos\theta|$.

Sample problems

1. Calculate the work done by a horse that exerts an applied force of 100 N on a sleigh, if the harness makes an angle of 30° with the ground, and the sleigh moves 30 m across a flat, level ice surface.

   In this problem, the force exerted by the horse makes an angle of 30° with the horizontal direction of the displacement. One solution involves resolving the 100 N force exerted by the horse into horizontal and vertical components, as shown,

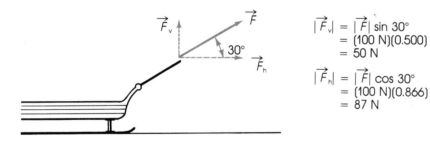

$$|\vec{F}_v| = |\vec{F}|\sin 30°$$
$$= (100\ N)(0.500)$$
$$= 50\ N$$

$$|\vec{F}_h| = |\vec{F}|\cos 30°$$
$$= (100\ N)(0.866)$$
$$= 87\ N$$

Since the horizontal component, $\vec{F}_h$, is in the same direction as the displacement, the work done by it can be calculated as

$$W = \vec{F}_h \cdot \Delta\vec{d}$$
$$= (87\ N)(30\ m)(\cos 0°)$$
$$= 2610\ J,\ or\ 2.6 \times 10^3\ J\ (\text{since } \cos 0° = 1)$$

The vertical component, $\vec{F}_v$, is at a 90° angle with respect to the displacement. To determine the work done by this component, we again use the vector dot product.

$$W = \vec{F}_v \cdot \Delta\vec{d}$$
$$= (50\ N)(30\ m)(\cos 90°)$$
$$= 0\ (\text{since } \cos 90° = 0)$$

Of course we could just write it down directly as

$$W = \vec{F} \cdot \Delta \vec{d} = |\vec{F}| |\Delta d| \cos \theta = (100 \text{ N})(30 \text{ m})(0.8660)$$
$$= 2.6 \times 10^3 \text{J}$$

Thus, the total work done by the horse on the sleigh is the work done by the horizontal component of the applied force, namely 2.6×10^3 J. This solution highlights a very important aspect of work done by a force not in the direction of the displacement: it is only the component of force in the direction of the displacement that does work; no work is done by the component of force perpendicular to the displacement.

2. How much work is done on a stone whirled in a horizontal circle at the end of string that exerts a centripetal force of 72 N while the stone moves 0.40 m along its circular path?

In cases such as this, it may be difficult to visualize the object's displacement vector. At any point in the circular motion, its direction is tangential to the path, and at right angles to the direction of the centripetal force.

$$W = \vec{F}_c \cdot \Delta \vec{d}$$
$$= (72 \text{ N})(0.40 \text{ m})(\cos 90°)$$
$$= 0 \text{ (since } \cos 90° = 0)$$

The force changes the object's direction but does not cause it to undergo a displacement in the direction of the force, and has no effect on its speed.

Practice

1. Calculate the amount of work done in each of the following:
   (a) A gardener pushes down the handle of a lawnmower at an angle of 45° with an applied force of 141 N, while pushing the mower 8.5 m along level ground.
   (b) A 40 kg girl on skates is swung through one revolution in a horizontal circle at the end of a 10 m rope held by a stationary boy at the centre of the circle. The rope has a tension of 50 N in it.

$$(8.5 \times 10^2 \text{ J, 0 J})$$

Work — Area Under the *F-d* Graph

The equation $W = F \Delta d \cos \theta$ may be used to calculate the work done by an applied force, only if the force remains constant during the displacement $\Delta \vec{d}$. In the following, we will assume that $\vec{F}$ lies along $\Delta \vec{d}$ so that $\theta = 0$ and $\cos \theta = 1$. Graphically, the work done is equal to the area of the shaded rectangle on the *F-d* graph, as shown.

When you speed up the stone, your hand moves in a smaller circle, so that the string leads the stone by a bit. The tension is no longer at exactly 90° to the velocity but has a small component in the direction of motion, so that the stone speeds up.

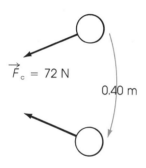

$\vec{F}_c = 72$ N

0.40 m

The net work done by the moon on the Earth in one revolution is zero. Similarly, the net work done by the sun on the Earth is also zero.

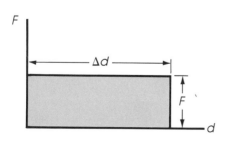

In many real situations, however, the applied force may vary in magnitude and direction during the displacement. You will recall that we encountered the same problem in determining displacement (using $\vec{v}\Delta t$) when the velocity changed during Δt, and in evaluating impulse (using $\vec{F}\Delta t$) when the force changed during Δt. In both cases, we were able to show that the "product" was equivalent to the area under the corresponding graph (*v-t* for $\Delta\vec{d}$, and *F-t* for impulse). The same analysis applies to this situation: the work done by a force that varies in magnitude during the displacement is given by the area under the *F-d* graph for the force, as shown.

(b) When the force changes non-uniformly

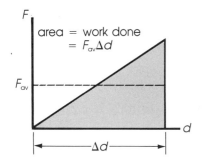 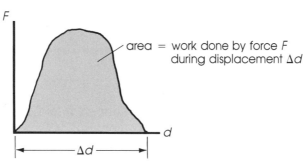

As a previous sample problem demonstrated, it is possible to have a negative value of work done (when the force and displacement are in opposite directions). The graphical significance of negative work is the area *above* the *F-d* graph during the interval when the force is negative.

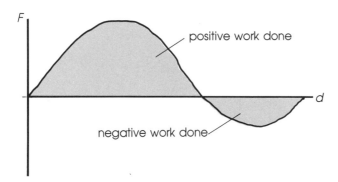

Remember, for graphs that have a regular geometric shape, use the formulae for the areas of rectangles, squares, triangles, or trapezia to find the total area. If the graph's shape is irregular, you may have to count squares and partial squares to estimate the total area.

Even if the force changes direction, we may still make use of a graph of $F \cos \theta$ versus *d* to calculate work done.

To summarize this new concept of work:

- Work is done, in physics, only when an applied force acts on an object, and the object undergoes a displacement that has a component in the direction of the applied force.
- The amount of work done, measured in joules (1 J = 1 N·m) is given by the equation $W = \vec{F} \cdot \Delta\vec{d}$, where $\vec{F}$ is in newtons, and $\Delta\vec{d}$ is in metres.

- To evaluate the vector dot product $\vec{F} \cdot \Delta\vec{d}$, multiply the component of the applied force (in the direction of the displacement) by the displacement. The result will be a scalar quantity whose magnitude is $|\vec{F}|\,|\Delta\vec{d}|\cos\theta$. The result may be positive, negative, or zero.
- If the applied force varies in magnitude or direction during the displacement, then the work done is given by the area under the graph of $F\cos\theta$ versus d during the interval $\Delta\vec{d}$.

Practice

The graph shows the magnitude of the horizontal force applied to a 4.0 kg wagon, initially at rest on a horizontal, frictionless surface. Draw a corresponding graph of work done on the object, as a function of its displacement from the starting point.

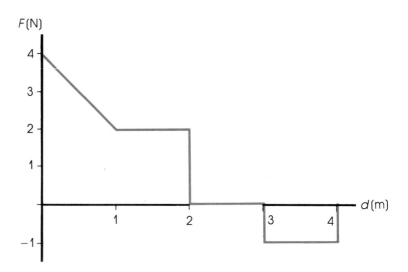

9.2 Kinetic Energy

In the previous section we learned how to calculate the amount of work done on an object when a force acts on it, as it moves through a displacement. But how is the object different as a result of having work done on it? To answer that question, let's look again at a simple case of work being done — a constant force applied to an object initially at rest on a straight, horizontal, frictionless track.

A constant force, $\vec{F}$, acts on the object for a time Δt during which it has a displacement $\Delta \vec{d}$ and acquires a velocity $\vec{v_2}$, both in the direction of the applied force. Again, since the motion occurs in a straight line, vector notation may be omitted, for simplicity. Using our definition of work,

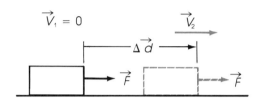

$$W = F\Delta d$$

But, from Newton's Second Law,

$$F = ma = m\left(\frac{v_2 - v_1}{\Delta t}\right) = \frac{mv_2}{\Delta t} \text{ (since } v_1 = 0)$$

and the equations of uniformly accelerated motion,

$$\Delta d = \left(\frac{v_1 + v_2}{2}\right)\Delta t = \frac{v_2\Delta t}{2} \text{ (since } v_1 = 0)$$

we have $\quad W = F\Delta d$

$$= \left(\frac{mv_2}{\Delta t}\right)\left(\frac{v_2\Delta t}{2}\right)$$

$$= \frac{1}{2}mv_2{}^2$$

In simplest terms, the work done on the object is equal to the quantity $\frac{1}{2}mv_2{}^2$, an expression involving only the mass and final velocity of the object that the work is done on. We call this expression the object's "kinetic energy" or energy of motion, E_k, so that, in general terms,

$$E_k = \frac{1}{2}mv^2$$

where E_k is the kinetic energy, in joules
$\quad m$ is the mass, in kilograms
$\quad v$ is the velocity, in metres per second

In the simple case we considered, the initial velocity, and hence kinetic energy, of the object was zero. As a result, the work done

In proper vector notation, the equation for kinetic energy would be written as

$$E_k = \frac{1}{2}m\vec{v} \cdot \vec{v}$$

$$= \frac{1}{2}m\,|\vec{v}\,||\,\vec{v}\,|\cos 0°$$

$$= \frac{1}{2}mv^2 \quad \text{(since } \cos 0° = 1)$$

This result is called the "work-energy" theorem. It can be developed for the general case of motion along an arbitrary path, with force variable in magnitude and direction.

on the object was equal to its change in kinetic energy. This result is generally true, whether the object was at rest initially or was moving.

$$W = \Delta E_k$$

It should be noted that kinetic energy, like work, is a scalar quantity, even though it is the product of $1/2\ m$, a scalar, and $(\vec{v}^2)$, the square of a vector. Again, in proper vector notation, $(\vec{v}^2)$ would be written as $\vec{v} \cdot \vec{v}$, the dot product of a vector and itself, which is the scalar $|\vec{v}|^2$, or simply v^2.

Kinetic energy is measured in joules, since, by substituting units into the defining equation, we see that

$$E_k = \frac{1}{2} mv^2$$
$$= (\text{kg})(\text{m/s})^2$$
$$= (\text{kg·m/s}^2)(\text{m})$$
$$= \text{N·m}$$
$$= \text{J}$$

Sample problems

1. What is the kinetic energy of a rock of mass 12 kg sliding across the ice at 2.0 m/s?

$$E_k = \frac{1}{2} mv^2$$
$$= \frac{1}{2} (12 \text{ kg}) (2.0 \text{ m/s})^2$$
$$= 24 \text{ J}$$

2. What is the speed of an electron in a television tube, if its mass is 9.1×10^{-31} kg, and its kinetic energy is 9.2×10^{-18} J?

$$E_k = \frac{1}{2} mv^2$$
$$v^2 = \frac{2\,E_k}{m}$$
$$= \frac{2(9.2 \times 10^{-18} \text{ J})}{9.1 \times 10^{-31} \text{ kg}}$$
$$= 20.2 \times 10^{12}(\text{m/s})^2$$
$$v = 4.5 \times 10^6 \text{ m/s}$$

3. How much work must be done to accelerate an 800 kg car from 15 m/s to 30 m/s?

$$W = \Delta E_k$$
$$= E_{k_2} - E_{k_1}$$
$$= \frac{1}{2} mv_2{}^2 - \frac{1}{2} mv_1{}^2$$
$$= \frac{1}{2} (800 \text{ kg}) (30 \text{ m/s})^2 - \frac{1}{2} (800 \text{ kg}) (15 \text{ m/s})^2$$
$$= 3.6 \times 10^5 \text{ J} - 9.0 \times 10^4 \text{ J}$$
$$= 2.7 \times 10^5 \text{ J}$$

4. A sledge hammer has a mass of 4.0 kg and is moving down at a speed of 6.0 m/s when it strikes a fence post, driving it 10 cm farther into the ground.

(a) What was the kinetic energy of the sledge hammer?

$$E_k = \frac{1}{2} mv^2$$
$$= \frac{1}{2} (4.0 \text{ kg}) (6.0 \text{ m/s})^2$$
$$= 72 \text{ J}$$

(b) What is the average force exerted on the fence post by the hammer?

The kinetic energy of the hammer changes from 72 J to zero, so that -72 J of work must have been done on it. This work was done by the post, pushing on the hammer with a constant force of F_{av}[up], as the hammer (and post) moved down 10 cm.

$$W = \Delta E_k = E_{k_2} - E_{k_1} = 0 - 72 \text{ J} = -72 \text{ J}$$

but
$$W = \vec{F} \cdot \Delta \vec{d}$$
$$-72 \text{ J} = F_{av} (0.10 \text{ m})(\cos 180°)$$

$$= -F_{av}(0.10 \text{ m}) \quad \text{(since } \vec{F}_{av} \text{ and } \Delta \vec{d} \text{ are in}$$
$$\text{opposite directions)}$$

$$\vec{F}_{av} = 7.2 \times 10^2 \text{ N[up]}$$

Therefore, the force exerted by the hammer on the post must also be 7.2×10^2 N, but in the opposite direction, i.e., down (Newton's Third Law). This ignores the gravitational force on the hammer, which would add another 39 N.

Kinetic Energy and Momentum

As you can see, the variables in the expression for kinetic energy are the same as those in the expression for momentum. Although momentum is a vector, and kinetic energy is a scalar, their *magnitudes* are related in a convenient way by the following:

$$\text{Since } p = mv$$
$$p^2 = m^2v^2$$
$$\text{but } E_k = \frac{mv^2}{2}$$

$$E_k = \frac{p^2}{2\,m}$$
$$p = \sqrt{2\,mE_k}$$

Sample problems

1. What is the kinetic energy of a wagon of mass 15 kg whose momentum is 30 kg·m/s?

$$E_k = \frac{p^2}{2\,m}$$
$$= \frac{(30 \text{ kg·m/s})^2}{2(15 \text{ kg})}$$
$$= 30 \text{ J}$$

2. What is the momentum of an electron whose kinetic energy is 5.0 keV ($m_e = 9.1 \times 10^{-31}$ kg, 1 eV $= 1.6 \times 10^{-19}$ J)?

$$p = \sqrt{2\,mE_k}$$
$$= \sqrt{2(9.1 \times 10^{-31} \text{ kg})(5.0 \times 10^3 \text{ eV})(1.6 \times 10^{-19} \text{ J/eV})}$$
$$= 3.8 \times 10^{-23} \text{ kg·m/s}$$

Practice

1. Calculate the kinetic energy of each of the following:
   (a) an 800 kg automobile moving at 15 m/s
   (b) a 2.0 g rifle bullet moving at 500 m/s
   (c) a 0.50 kg ball accelerated from rest by a force of 8.0 N for 3.0 m
   (d) a stone of mass 0.25 kg being whirled in a circle of radius 2.0 m with a period of $\pi/4$ s
   $(9.0 \times 10^4 \text{ J}, 2.5 \times 10^2 \text{ J}, 24 \text{ J}, 32 \text{ J})$

2. Two small toys, one with a mass of 3.2 kg and the other with a velocity of 2.4 m/s, each have the same kinetic energy of 16 J. Determine the velocity of the first toy, and the mass of the second. (3.2 m/s, 5.6 kg)

3. A baseball of mass 250 g, pitched with a speed of 40 m/s, is caught by the catcher, whose glove moves backward 0.25 m while stopping the ball.
   (a) What was the kinetic energy of the ball?

(b) How much work did the catcher's glove do on the ball?
(c) What average stopping force was exerted on the ball?

$$(2.0 \times 10^2 \text{ J}, -2.0 \times 10^2 \text{ J}, -8.0 \times 10^2 \text{ N})$$

4. A bullet of mass 12 g strikes a stationary fixed block of wood at a speed of 400 m/s, penetrating to a depth of 3.0 cm. Calculate the average net force acting on the bullet while it is in the wood. Calculate the average force exerted on the wood by the bullet.

$$(-3.2 \times 10^4 \text{ N}, 3.2 \times 10^4 \text{ N})$$

5. The graph shows the horizontal force on a 2.0 kg trolley as it moves 5.0 m along a straight, level, frictionless track, starting from rest. Determine its kinetic energy and velocity after each metre that it moves.

(1 J, 1 m/s; 4 J, 2 m/s; 8 J, 2.8 m/s; 8 J, 2.8 m/s; 7 J, 2.6 m/s)

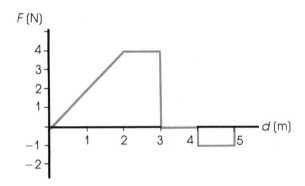

9.3 Work, Kinetic Energy, and Conservation of Energy

The equation $W = \Delta E_k$ is reversible. That is, an object with kinetic energy can expend some of this energy by doing work on another object, thereby transferring energy to it. In that case, $\Delta E_k = W$. In fact, the definition of energy, in general terms, derives from the expression: "Energy is the ability to do work."

Moving objects possess energy because they are capable of doing work on other objects. Many other objects, because of their particular state, also have the ability to do work and transfer energy to other objects with which they interact. As a result, they are also said to possess energy. Some examples of objects that have energy are:

(a) a rock at the top of a hill
(b) a compressed or stretched spring

The need for more energy has stimulated the development of new technologies that utilize the abundant energy of the sun, wind, and tides, and the immense thermal energy in the Earth's core. These activities have also opened up many new career opportunities in the energy field.

(c) two magnets whose similar poles are close together

(d) two similar electric charges close together

(e) two opposite electric charges far apart

(f) a can of gasoline and a room full of air

(g) a quantity of uranium-235

The ability of these objects to do work and transfer energy is not easy to visualize. The type of energy they possess is called "potential energy". It is a type of energy that is stored, capable of being transformed into other types of energy. We will discuss several of these types of potential energy in detail in Chapter 10.

The relationship between work and energy forms the basis of one of the most fundamental laws of nature, the Law of Conservation of Energy, which states:

Energy is not created or destroyed in any interaction, but is merely transformed from one type of energy into another. In any interaction, the total amount of energy, in all forms, remains constant.

This transformation from one type of energy to another is accomplished when one part of an interacting system does work on another part. Some examples of the conversion of potential energy into kinetic energy are:

(a) A rock at the top of a hill transfers gravitational potential energy into kinetic energy as it falls towards the Earth. (Gravitational force does positive work on the rock.)

(b) A stretched slingshot containing a stone transfers elastic potential energy stored in the stretched rubber into the kinetic energy of the stone, when it is released. (The rubber band does positive work on the stone.)

(c) The magnetic latch mounted on a refrigerator attracts its slightly open door, transferring magnetic potential energy into kinetic energy of the door as it closes. (A magnetic force does positive work on the door.)

(d) A mixture of gasoline vapour and air explodes in a cylinder and converts chemical potential energy into thermal energy, some of which may create the kinetic energy of a piston, when the mixture is ignited.

As we continue the study of work and energy, we will encounter many more examples of situations where work is done, causing energy to be converted from one type to another. Yet, in all situations, the total amount of energy, in all forms, remains constant. For the moment, we will concentrate on the ability of moving objects to do work and transfer kinetic energy as a result of collisions with other objects.

We continue to design ingenious machines to convert energy from one form to another. Most of these energy transformations are relatively inefficient in regard to retaining useful energy, and thereby tend to contribute to our energy shortage.

9.4 The Transfer of Energy in Simple Collisions

A billiard ball moving across a flat, smooth surface collides with a second, stationary billiard ball, and both move off in different directions after the collision. The stationary ball is at rest until it is struck by the moving ball. In the very short time that they are touching, the moving ball exerts a force on the stationary ball, doing work on it and transferring kinetic energy to it. At the same time, the moving ball experiences a force exerted back upon it by the stationary ball (doing work on it in turn) and its kinetic energy is decreased. Some of the energy may be stored as potential energy of deformation for a short time during the impact.

Alternatively, we may say the second ball did negative work on the first ball, decreasing its kinetic energy.

The illustration on the next page shows these two billiard balls colliding. It is one-eighth full size, the flash rate is 30 flashes/s, and the mass of each ball is 180 g. By taking measurements from the illustration, we can calculate the kinetic energy of each ball, both before and after the collision.

Before the collision:

moving ball (ball 1)

$$E_{k_1} = \frac{1}{2} m_1 v_1{}^2$$

$$= \frac{1}{2} (0.180 \text{ kg}) (3.96 \text{ m/s})^2$$

$$= 1.41 \text{ J}$$

stationary ball (ball 2) $\quad E_{k_2} = 0$

After the collision:

ball 1:

$$E'_{k_1} = \frac{1}{2} m_1 v_1'^2$$

$$= \frac{1}{2} (0.180 \text{ kg}) (1.80 \text{ m/s})^2$$

$$= 0.29 \text{ J}$$

ball 2:

$$E'_{k_2} = \frac{1}{2} m_2 v_2'^2$$

$$= \frac{1}{2} (0.180 \text{ kg}) (3.48 \text{ m/s})^2$$

$$= 1.09 \text{ J}$$

Therefore, for the moving ball, the energy change due to the collision is

$$\Delta E_{k_1} = E'_{k_1} - E_{k_1}$$

$$= 0.29 \text{ J} - 1.41 \text{ J}$$

$$= -1.12 \text{ J}$$

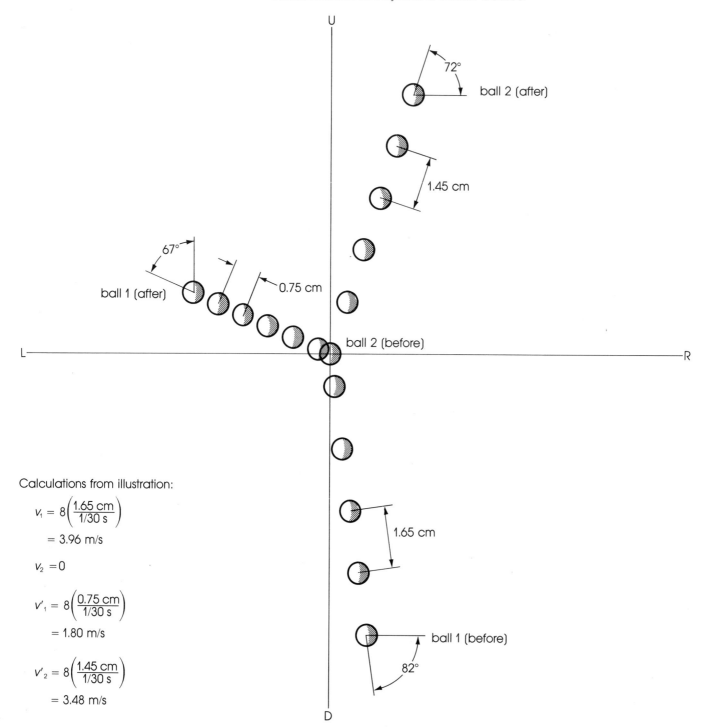

ball 2 (after)

72°

1.45 cm

67°

ball 1 (after)

0.75 cm

ball 2 (before)

L ———————————————————— R

U

D

1.65 cm

ball 1 (before)

82°

Calculations from illustration:

$$v_1 = 8\left(\frac{1.65 \text{ cm}}{1/30 \text{ s}}\right)$$

$$= 3.96 \text{ m/s}$$

$$v_2 = 0$$

$$v'_1 = 8\left(\frac{0.75 \text{ cm}}{1/30 \text{ s}}\right)$$

$$= 1.80 \text{ m/s}$$

$$v'_2 = 8\left(\frac{1.45 \text{ cm}}{1/30 \text{ s}}\right)$$

$$= 3.48 \text{ m/s}$$

This represents a loss in kinetic energy for the moving ball, due to work done by it on the stationary ball.

For the stationary ball, the energy change due to the collision is

$$\Delta E_{k_2} = E'_{k_2} - E_{k_2}$$
$$= 1.09 \text{ J} - 0 \text{ J}$$
$$= 1.09 \text{ J}$$

This represents a gain in kinetic energy for the stationary ball due to work done on it by the moving ball.

Another way of looking at this collision would be to consider the total kinetic energy of the system of two billiard balls, both before the collision begins and after it is over.

Before:
$$E_{k_{total}} = E_{k_1} + E_{k_2}$$
$$= 1.41 \text{ J} + 0 \text{ J}$$
$$= 1.41 \text{ J}$$

After:
$$E'_{k_{total}} = E'_{k_1} + E'_{k_2}$$
$$= 0.29 \text{ J} + 1.09 \text{ J}$$
$$= 1.38 \text{ J}$$

This type of collision, in which the total kinetic energy, both before and after the collision, is equal, within experimental limits, is called an **elastic collision**. No energy is lost or dissipated during the collision. All of the kinetic energy lost by the moving ball is transferred to the other ball in the form of kinetic energy. Most real-life collisions, with the exception of those at the atomic level, are not elastic; some energy is usually dissipated during the time the colliding objects are in contact. This energy may have been used to produce heat, light, sound, or some permanent deformation of the colliding objects. In Section 9.6 we will learn more about what causes a collision to be elastic or inelastic.

9.5 A Closer Look at an Elastic Collision

In the last section, we studied the collision between a moving billiard ball and a stationary billiard ball. We concluded that the collision was elastic (or very nearly so) by comparing the total kinetic energy of the two balls before the collision, and after. The kinetic energy lost by the moving ball was approximately equal to the kinetic energy gained by the stationary ball. This transfer of kinetic energy from the moving to the stationary ball occurs very quickly for colliding billiard balls — during the very short time that they are in contact. If we want to understand more about how this energy transfer occurs, we must study a "slower" collision, one in which the colliding objects are "in contact" for a longer interval of time.

Let's begin by examining a hypothetical collision between two carts on a straight, horizontal, frictionless track. Cart 1 has a mass of m_1 and is moving initially with a velocity $\vec{v_1}$. Cart 2, of mass m_2, is initially at rest. On the front of cart 1 is a special "bumper", to cushion the impact and provide a "slow" mechanism for the transfer of energy to cart 2. The bumper has a normal length x_0 and exerts no forces when it is that length. When compressed, it exerts a constant force F_0 in opposite directions on both objects compressing it, unlike a normal spring whose force depends on the amount by which it is compressed. Again, since the collision is in a straight line, vector considerations can be taken care of by assigning right as positive and left as negative.

A graph of force versus length for this special bumper is shown.

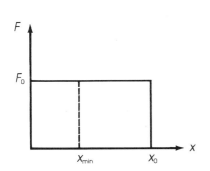

Stages in a simple elastic collision between a moving and a stationary object

(a) Before the collision begins

(b) Just as the collision begins

(c) At mid-collision (minimum separation)

(d) Just as the collision ends

(e) After the collision is over

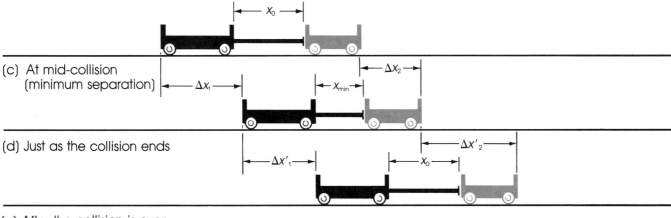

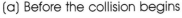

The collision proceeds in five distinct stages, as follows:

(1) Before collision: As m_1 approaches m_2, so long as they are greater than x_o apart, the bumper exerts no force on either cart. Therefore, m_1 continues with velocity v_1 and kinetic energy E_{k_1}, while m_2 remains at rest.

(2) Approaching minimum separation: At a separation distance of x_o, the bumper begins to act, and the actual collision begins. The bumper pushes forward on m_2 with a constant force F_o, causing it to accelerate. It also pushes backward on m_1 with the same force, causing it to decelerate. However, even though m_1 is decelerating and m_2 is accelerating, m_1 still has a greater velocity. Thus, the two carts are getting closer together and the bumper is being compressed more. This continues as long as $v_1 > v_2$.

(3) At minimum separation: When $v_1 = v_2$, the bumper will be compressed to its minimum length, x_{min}, and the two carts will be at their minimum separation distance. If the displacements of the carts, since the collision began, are Δx_1 and Δx_2, respectively, then:

The change in kinetic energy for mass 1 is
$$\Delta E_{k_1} = -F_o \Delta x_1$$
The work done on m_1 is negative, since the force exerted on it by the bumper is in the opposite direction to its motion ($\cos 180° = -1$).

The change in kinetic energy for mass 2 is
$$\Delta E_{k_2} = F_o \Delta x_2$$
For m_2, the force exerted on it by the bumper is in the direction of motion, so the work done on it is positive ($\cos 0° = 1$).

The total change in kinetic energy for the system is
$$\Delta E_{k_{total}} = \Delta E_{k_1} + \Delta E_{k_2}$$
$$= -F_o \Delta x_1 + F_o \Delta x_2$$
$$= -F_o(\Delta x_1 - \Delta x_2)$$

But $\Delta x_1 - \Delta x_2$ is just the amount by which the bumper is compressed at minimum separation, i.e., $x_o - x_{min}$.

therefore $\Delta E_{k_{total}} = -F_o(x_o - x_{min})$
$$= - \text{(area under the bumper's}$$
$$\text{F-x graph, from } x_o \text{ to } x_{min})$$

The value of $\Delta E_{k_{total}}$ is negative at this point, representing a loss in total kinetic energy during this part of the collision. This energy is, in fact, not lost but stored in the bumper, as potential energy. It will remain stored in the bumper as long as it is compressed. We will study this type of energy more closely in the next chapter.

In describing such collisions, the interval during which the separation decreases from x_o to x_{min} is often referred to as "the first half of the collision", or as the interval where the colliding objects are "coming together" or "going into the collision". Conversely, the interval during which the separation increases again, as the objects are "moving apart" or "coming out of the collision", is called the "second half".

(4) Moving apart after minimum separation: As the collision continues, the bumper still pushes forward on m_2, causing it to accelerate, and backward on m_1, causing it to decelerate. As a result, $v_2 > v_1$, and the two carts begin to get farther apart. The potential energy stored in the compressed bumper now begins to reappear as kinetic energy.

(5) After collision: When the separation distance again reaches x_o, the bumper ceases to exert forces on the two carts, and the collision is "over". If the displacements of the two carts, since minimum separation, are $\Delta x_1'$ and $\Delta x_2'$, respectively, then the change in kinetic energy for mass 1 is

$$\Delta E_{k_1} = -F_o \, \Delta x_1'$$

The change in kinetic energy for mass 2 is

$$\Delta E_{k_2} = F_o \, \Delta x_2'$$

The total change in kinetic energy for the system, during the "second half" of the collision is

$$\Delta E_{k_{total}} = \Delta E_{k_1} + \Delta E_{k_2}$$
$$= -F_o \Delta x_1' + F_o \Delta x_2'$$
$$= F_o(\Delta x_2' - \Delta x_1')$$
$$= F_o(x_o - x_{min})$$

Note that this gain in total kinetic energy during the second half of the collision is equal to the loss in total kinetic energy during the first half of the collision. It represents energy taken out of storage and converted from potential energy into kinetic energy.

During the collision (i.e., while the bumper is exerting forces on the two carts), mass 1 has had a displacement of $\Delta x_1 + \Delta x_1'$ while a force of F_o acted on it, in a direction opposite to its motion. The work done on it by this force, and hence its change in kinetic energy, is

$$\Delta E_{k_1} = -F_o(\Delta x_1 + \Delta x_1')$$

Mass 2 has had a displacement of $\Delta x_2 + \Delta x_2'$ while an accelerating force of F_o acted on it. The work done on it by this force, and hence its change in kinetic energy, is given by

$$\Delta E_{k_2} = F_o(\Delta x_2 + \Delta x_2')$$

But $\Delta x_1 + \Delta x_1'$ and $\Delta x_2 + \Delta x_2'$ are equal (since the two carts are a distance x_o apart just as the collision begins and just as it ends). Therefore

$$\Delta E_{k_1} = -\Delta E_{k_2}$$

or

$$\Delta E_{k_{total}} = \Delta E_{k_1} + \Delta E_{k_2} = 0$$

The collision is elastic.

During the collision, the total kinetic energy decreases as the two carts move closer together, compressing the bumper and storing potential energy in it. The maximum amount of stored potential energy occurs when the collision is half over, when the carts are at minimum separation and moving with the same velocity. At that point, and indeed at any other point during the collision, the potential energy stored in the bumper is equal to the loss in kinetic energy of the system.

As we have shown, this maximum amount of stored energy is simply the area under the bumper's force-compression graph, from x_o to x_{min}.

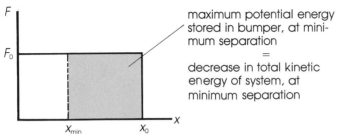

maximum potential energy stored in bumper, at minimum separation

=

decrease in total kinetic energy of system, at minimum separation

Sample problem

The force-separation graph for a linear collision between a 5.0 kg cart moving initially at 2.0 m/s and a 3.0 kg cart at rest, is shown below.

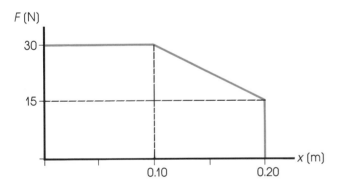

(a) What is the total initial kinetic energy of the two carts?
$$E_k(\text{total}) = E_k(\text{cart 1}) + E_k(\text{cart 2})$$
$$= \frac{1}{2} mv_1^2 + 0$$
$$= \frac{1}{2} (5.0 \text{ kg})(2.0 \text{ m/s})^2$$
$$= 10 \text{ J}$$

(b) What is the total kinetic energy of the two carts at a separation distance of 0.05 m?
$$E_k (\text{at } x = 0.05 \text{ m}) = E_k (\text{initial}) - (\text{area under } F\text{-}x \text{ graph} $$
$$\text{from 0.20 m to 0.05 m})$$

$$= 10\,\text{J} - [\tfrac{1}{2}(15\,\text{N} + 30\,\text{N})(0.10\,\text{m})$$
$$+ (0.05\,\text{m})(30\,\text{N})]$$
$$= 10\,\text{J} - [2.25\,\text{J} + 1.5\,\text{J}]$$
$$= 6.25\,\text{J} \approx 6.3\,\text{J}$$

(c) What happened to the remaining initial kinetic energy?
The 3.7 J of kinetic energy that has disappeared is stored in the collision mechanism as potential energy, to be released later as the collision proceeds.

Practice

1. A 1.5 kg trolley moving to the right collides head-on with a 3.0 kg trolley initially at rest. The *F-x* relationship for the collision is shown.

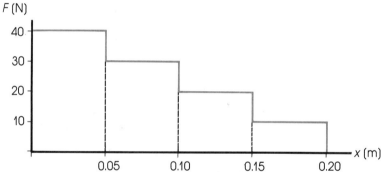

If the total kinetic energy of the two trolleys is 4.5 J when the separation distance between them is 0.05 m, what was the initial kinetic energy and velocity of the moving trolley?

(7.5 J, 3.2 m/s)

2. A 1.0 kg cart moving at 2.5 m/s collides head-on with a 4.0 kg cart moving in the same direction at 0.50 m/s. The *F-x* graph for the collision is shown.
The total kinetic energy at minimum separation is 2.0 J. What is the minimum separation of the two trolleys during the collision?

(0.09 m)

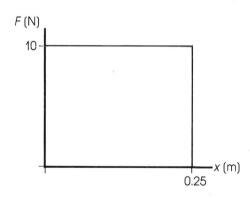

9.6 Elastic and Inelastic Collisions

We have defined an elastic collision as one in which no kinetic energy is lost as a result of the collision. The total kinetic energy after the collision is equal to the total kinetic energy before.

We did find, however, that even in an elastic collision, some kinetic energy appears to have been lost part way through the collision. This energy, however, is not lost; it is stored as potential energy during the collision and reappears as kinetic energy after the collision is over.

For a collision to be elastic, then, it is necessary that all of the energy stored as potential energy during the first part of the collision (as the objects approach minimum separation) be retrieved from storage and converted back into kinetic energy in the second part of the collision. Whether this occurs or not depends only on the force-separation graph of the mechanism acting during the collision. For the simple case studied in Section 9.5, the force-separation graph for the bumper appeared as shown.

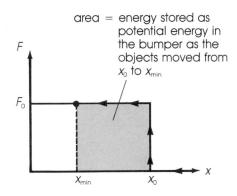

area = energy stored as potential energy in the bumper as the objects moved from x_0 to x_{min}

In the first half of the collision, as the separation of the two objects decreases from x_0 to x_{min}, the potential energy stored in the bumper is given by the shaded area shown on the graph. In the second half of the collision, the potential energy retrieved from storage in the bumper, as the separation increases from x_{min} to x_0, is given by the shaded area on the second graph.

These areas are equal, since the F-x graph for the bumper is the same regardless of whether the separation is decreasing or increasing. It depends only on the separation distance between the two objects. In fact, that is the only significant issue! Regardless of the shape of the force-separation graph for a collision, the collision will be elastic as long as the graph is the same going into the collision as it is coming out. In mathematical terms, the collision will be elastic if, and only if, the force-separation graph for the collision is a function of the separation alone. That is, for any value of separation, x, there is only one value of the force, F, regardless of whether x is decreasing (first half of collision) or increasing (second half of collision).

A typical graph of such a force-separation function is shown on the next page.

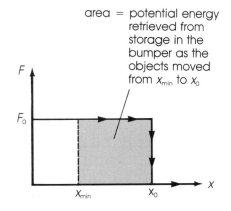

area = potential energy retrieved from storage in the bumper as the objects moved from x_{min} to x_0

F−x graph going into the
collision (as x decreases)

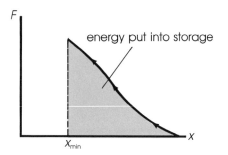

F−x graph coming
out of the collision (as x
increases)

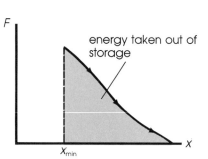

F−x graph for the entire
collision

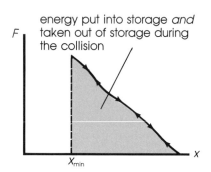

If the force-separation graph differs coming out of the collision from what it was going into the collision, the collision will be inelastic. The example below illustrates such a collision.

F−x graph going into the
collision (as x decreases)

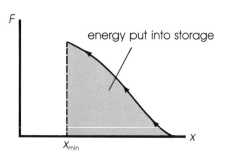

F−x graph coming
out of the collision (as x
increases)

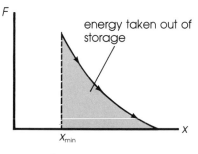

F−x graph for the entire
collision

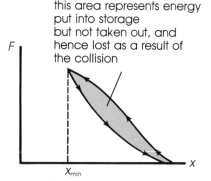

this area represents energy
put into storage
but not taken out, and
hence lost as a result of
the collision

The area under the upper curve represents energy put into storage as the objects come closer together, while the area under the lower curve represents energy taken out of storage as the objects move apart. Therefore, the energy lost during the collision (i.e., energy put into storage but not taken out) is given by the area between the two curves.

The shock absorbers mounted on the bumpers of most new cars have this type of F-x graph. The kinetic energy of colliding cars is absorbed as work done on the shock absorber in the bumper as it is compressed. Much of this energy is dissipated as heat in the shock absorbing mechanism, so that the cars rebound from the collision with considerably less kinetic energy.

The crumpling sheet metal of car bodies is another example of an energy dissipation mechanism; it doesn't usually spring back.

9.7 Solving Elastic Collision Problems

In the previous three sections of this chapter we have learned that, in an elastic collision between two objects, total kinetic energy is conserved. Mathematically, we can write

$$E_{k_1} + E_{k_2} = E'_{k_1} + E'_{k_2}$$

$$\frac{1}{2}m_1v_1^2 + \frac{1}{2}m_2v_2^2 = \frac{1}{2}m_1v_1'^2 + \frac{1}{2}m_2v_2'^2$$

where the primed quantities represent values after the collision is over

Also, from the work of the previous chapter, we have learned that, for any isolated interaction between two objects, total momentum is conserved.

$$\vec{p_1} + \vec{p_2} = \vec{p_1}' + \vec{p_2}'$$

$$m_1\vec{v_1} + m_2\vec{v_2} = m_1\vec{v_1}' + m_2\vec{v_2}'$$

These two equations may be used together to solve problems involving the elastic collision of two objects. They will enable us to predict the velocities of the objects after the collision, if we know what they were before. To begin with, we will limit ourselves to collisions that occur in a straight line, called "head-on" collisions. We will take the vector nature of momentum into account by assuming that all vectors pointing to the right are positive, and all pointing to the left are negative.

The head-on collision between a moving object and a stationary object is so common that it is useful to develop the following equations for the velocities of the two objects after the collision.

The assigned arrows do not rule out the possibility of a rebound, since v_1' could be negative.

Since the collision is elastic, total kinetic energy is conserved.

$$\frac{1}{2}m_1v_1^2 + 0 = \frac{1}{2}m_1v_1'^2 + \frac{1}{2}m_2v_2'^2 \tag{1}$$

And since momentum is conserved in any isolated collision,

$$m_1v_1 + 0 = m_1v_1' + m_2v_2' \tag{2}$$

Multiplying both sides of equation (1) by 2, and rearranging, we have

$$m_1(v_1^2 - v_1'^2) = m_2v_2'^2 \tag{1a}$$

Rearranging the order of equation (2), we have

$$m_1(v_1 - v_1') = m_2v_2' \tag{2a}$$

Then dividing equation (1a) by equation (2a), we have

$$\frac{m_1(v_1^2 - v_1'^2)}{m_1(v_1 - v_1')} = \frac{m_2v_2'^2}{m_2v_2'}$$

$$\text{or} \qquad v_1 + v_1' = v_2' \tag{3}$$

Before

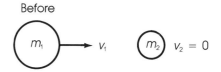

After

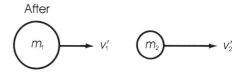

Substituting this value from equation (3) for v_2' in equation (2), we have

$$m_1 v_1 = m_1 v_1' + m_2(v_1 + v_1')$$
$$\text{or} \quad m_1 v_1 = m_1 v_1' + m_2 v_1 + m_2 v_1'$$

so that

$$v_1' = \left(\frac{m_1 - m_2}{m_1 + m_2}\right) v_1$$

Similarly, substituting the value from equation (3) for v_1' in equation (2), we have

$$m_1 v_1 = m_1(v_2' - v_1) + m_2 v_2'$$
$$\text{or} \quad m_1 v_1 = m_1 v_2' - m_1 v_1 + m_2 v_2'$$

so that

$$v_2' = \left(\frac{2 m_1}{m_1 + m_2}\right) v_1$$

It is interesting to examine these equations for the final velocities of the two objects, under three sets of conditions:

(1) When the moving object has the greater mass ($m_1 > m_2$), then v_1' is positive, indicating that the moving ball continues in the same direction at a slower speed after the collision (for $m_1 >>> m_2$, $v_1 \approx v_1'$, and $v_2' \approx 2 v_1$).

(2) When the moving object has the smaller mass ($m_1 < m_2$), then v_1' is negative, indicating that the moving ball rebounds in the opposite direction at a slower speed after the collision (for $m_1 <<< m_2$, $v_1' \approx -v_1$, and $v_2' \approx 0$).

(3) When the moving object has the same mass ($m_1 = m_2$), then $v_1' = 0$, indicating that the moving object stops as a result of the collision.

Note that for all three cases v_2' is positive, and that for case (3) $v_2' = v_1$. It is interesting to verify these three relationships using gliders with spring bumpers, on an air track.

It is absolutely essential to remember that these equations have been developed for one special case only — where the collision is perfectly elastic and head-on, and where m_2 is initially at rest.

To solve problems for any other elastic collision, we must go back to first principles and apply equations 1 and 2, found earlier in this section, expressing the conservation of kinetic energy and the conservation of momentum for the collision. A general result could be derived for $v_2 \neq 0$.

A familiar example occurs when a billiard ball, with little spin, hits another ball head-on.

The following example will demonstrate how these equations may be used. An air track glider of mass 0.200 kg, moving at 1.0 m/s, collides elastically with another glider of mass 0.050 kg, which is initially at rest. What are the velocities of each glider after the collision?

Since the collision is head-on and elastic, and one of the objects is stationary, the specific equations developed would apply.

$$v_1' = \left(\frac{m_1 - m_2}{m_1 + m_2}\right) v_1$$

$$= \left(\frac{0.200 \text{ kg} - 0.050 \text{ kg}}{0.200 \text{ kg} + 0.050 \text{ kg}}\right) 1.0 \text{ m/s}$$

$$= 0.60 \text{ m/s}$$

and

$$v_2' = \left(\frac{2 \, m_1}{m_1 + m_2}\right) v_1$$

$$= \left(\frac{2 \, (0.200 \text{ kg})}{0.200 \text{ kg} + 0.050 \text{ kg}}\right) 1.0 \text{ m/s}$$

$$= 1.6 \text{ m/s}$$

Because of our agreement on the signs of vector quantities, we can conclude that after the collision the 0.200 kg glider continues to the right at 0.60 m/s and the 0.050 kg glider moves to the right at 1.6 m/s.

We may wish to determine how much potential energy is stored in the bumper between the two gliders during the collision.

Remember that, at minimum separation, when the stored potential energy is a maximum, $v_1 = v_2 = v_o$, where v_o is the velocity of each glider at the moment of minimum separation. Even though kinetic energy is not conserved *during* the collision, total momentum is!

Therefore
$$p_{total} = p'_{total} = p_{total} \text{ (at minimum separation)}$$
$$m_1 v_1 + m_2 v_2 = m_1 v_o + m_2 v_o$$
$$(0.200 \text{ kg})(1.0 \text{ m/s}) + 0 = (0.200 \text{ kg})v_o + (0.050 \text{ kg})v_o$$
$$(0.250 \text{ kg}) \, v_o = 0.200 \text{ kg·m/s}$$
$$v_o = 0.80 \text{ m/s}$$

The total kinetic energy before the collision is
$$E_{k_{total}} = E_{k_1} + E_{k_2}$$
$$= \frac{1}{2} m_1 v_1{}^2 + 0$$
$$= \frac{1}{2} (0.200 \text{ kg})(1.0 \text{ m/s})^2$$
$$= 0.10 \text{ J}$$

The total kinetic energy at minimum separation is

$$E_{k_{total}} = E_{k_1} + E_{k_2}$$

$$= \frac{1}{2} m_1 v_o^2 + \frac{1}{2} m_2 v_o^2$$

$$= \frac{1}{2} (0.200 \text{ kg})(0.80 \text{ m/s})^2 + \frac{1}{2} (0.050 \text{ kg})(0.80 \text{ m/s})^2$$

$$= 0.064 \text{ J} + 0.016 \text{ J}$$

$$= 0.08 \text{ J}$$

Therefore, the change in kinetic energy at minimum separation, and hence the potential energy stored in the bumper, is

$$\Delta E_{k_{total}} = E_{k_{total}}(\text{at minimum separation}) - E_{k_{total}}(\text{before})$$

$$= 0.08 \text{ J} - 0.10 \text{ J}$$

$$= -0.02 \text{ J}$$

Remember that the negative sign indicates a loss in total kinetic energy at minimum separation, with a gain in potential energy stored.

The equations developed previously apply only to the very specific case of a head-on, perfectly elastic collision in which one of the objects is stationary prior to the collision. Can we predict the final velocities after a head-on, elastic collision if both objects are moving initially?

One solution would be to make use of the two original equations involving the conservation of kinetic energy and the conservation of momentum, and solve them as a linear-quadratic system of two equations in two unknowns (v_1' and v_2'). Unfortunately, the algebra involved in this process becomes very awkward and often leads to confusion and errors. A simpler technique, demonstrated in the following sample problem, involves viewing the collision from the frame of reference of one of the moving objects. This way, the object seems to be initially at rest, and the specific equations developed earlier apply. Of course, you must remember to revert back to the Earth's frame of reference after the collision is over.

Sample problem

A 4.0 kg ball moving to the right at 5.0 m/s collides head-on with a 2.0 kg ball moving to the left at 4.0 m/s. If the collision is elastic, determine the direction and speed of each ball after the collision.

Since both balls are moving before the collision, the specific equations developed earlier do not apply. However, if the collision is viewed from the frame of reference of the 2.0 kg ball before the collision, they do apply.

In that frame of reference, i.e., a frame moving to the left at 4.0 m/s, .

Fixed frame of reference

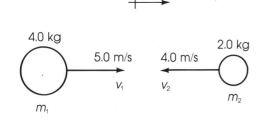

$$v_1 = 9.0 \text{ m/s} \quad \text{and} \quad v_2 = 0$$

(Motion to the right is still taken as positive.)

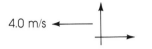

Moving frame of reference

Therefore
$$v_1' = \left(\frac{m_1 - m_2}{m_1 + m_2}\right) v_1$$

$$= \left(\frac{4.0 \text{ kg} - 2.0 \text{ kg}}{4.0 \text{ kg} + 2.0 \text{ kg}}\right) 9.0 \text{ m/s}$$

$$= 3.0 \text{ m/s}$$

and
$$v_2' = \left(\frac{2 \, m_1}{m_1 + m_2}\right) v_1$$

$$= \left(\frac{2 \, (4.0 \text{ kg})}{4.0 \text{ kg} + 2.0 \text{ kg}}\right) 9.0 \text{ m/s}$$

$$= 12 \text{ m/s}$$

However, both of these velocities are measured in a frame of reference moving to the left at 4.0 m/s. Therefore, in the Earth's frame of reference,

$$v_1' = -1.0 \text{ m/s}$$
$$v_2' = 8.0 \text{ m/s}$$

That is, the 4.0 kg ball rebounds to the left at 1.0 m/s, while the 2.0 kg ball rebounds and moves to the right at 8.0 m/s.

Practice

1. A sphere, A, of mass 2.4 kg, moving in a straight line with velocity 10 m/s makes a head-on collision with sphere B, of mass 3.6 kg, which is initially at rest. The collision is cushioned by a perfectly elastic bumper.
   (a) What is the velocity of each sphere after the collision?
   (b) What percent of A's kinetic energy is transferred to B by the collision?   (-2.0 m/s, 8.0 m/s; 96%)
2. A 2.0 kg trolley moving east at 3.0 m/s collides head-on with a 1.0 kg trolley moving west at 2.0 m/s. After the collision, the 2.0 kg trolley has a velocity of 1.0 m/s[E].
   (a) What is the final velocity of the 1.0 kg trolley?
   (b) Is the collision elastic or inelastic?   (2.0 m/s [E])
3. Two air track gliders of mass 300 g and 200 g are moving towards each other in opposite directions with speeds of 50 cm/s and 100 cm/s, respectively. Take the direction of the more massive glider as positive.
   (a) If the collision is elastic, find the velocity of each glider after the collision.

(b) The most "inelastic" collision would occur if the two gliders stuck together on impact. If this were the case, find the velocity of the pair after the collision and the kinetic energy lost as a result of the collision.

(−70 cm/s, 80 cm/s; −10 cm/s, 0.135 J)

4. A 6.0 kg trolley moving at 6.0 m/s[right] overtakes and collides with a 2.0 kg trolley moving at 2.0 m/s in the same direction on the same track. The collision is cushioned by a perfectly elastic bumper attached to one of the trolleys.
   (a) What is the speed and direction of each trolley after the collision?
   (b) What is the maximum amount of potential energy stored in the bumper during the collision?

(4.0 m/s[right], 8.0 m/s[right]; 12 J)

5. A 4.0 kg object is at rest on a horizontal, frictionless surface when it is hit head-on by a 12.0 kg object moving forward at 0.80 m/s. The force separation graph for the collision is given.
   (a) Is the collision elastic or inelastic? Justify your answer.
   (b) Calculate the velocity of each object after the collision.
   (c) Calculate the velocity and kinetic energy of each object at minimum separation.
   (d) What is the minimum separation of the two? [Hint: Your answer to (c) enables you to find the loss in E_k at minimum separation, which is equal to the potential energy stored in the bumper.]

(0.40 m/s, 1.2 m/s; 0.60 m/s, 2.88 J; 0.040 m)

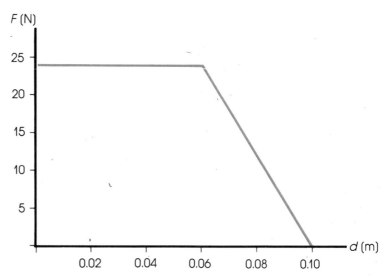

9.8 Investigations

Investigation 9.1: Transfer of Energy in Linear Collisions

Problem:
Is kinetic energy conserved in a linear collision?

Materials:
ticker-tape records of the 3 collisions studied in investigation 8.1

Procedure:
1. For each of the three ticker tapes from Parts A, B, and C of 8.1, measure the average distance between dots just before the collision occurs, and just after.
2. Recall the mass of each cart, and record this data in a chart similar to the one used in 8.1.

Calculations:
1. Determine the velocity of each cart, before and after the collision; then calculate the kinetic energy of each, before and after the collision.
2. For each case, calculate the total kinetic energy of both carts, before and after the collision. Express the total kinetic energy after the collision as a percentage of the total kinetic energy before.

Questions:
1. Describe each of the collisions as inelastic or elastic.
2. Account for the lost energy in those collisions that are not elastic.

Investigation 9.2: Transfer of Energy in Two-Dimensional Collisions

Problem:
Is kinetic energy conserved in a two-dimensional collision?

Materials:
carbon paper records of the landing positions of the moving and target balls, from investigation 8.2

Procedure:
1. Using the subscripts 1 to refer to the moving ball and 2 to refer

to the target ball, the kinetic energy before the collision is given by $\frac{1}{2}m_1v_1^2$ and after the collision by $\frac{1}{2}m_1v_1'^2 + \frac{1}{2}m_2v_2'^2$. If kinetic energy is conserved in the collision, that is, if the collision is elastic, then

$$\frac{1}{2}m_1v_1^2 = \frac{1}{2}m_1v_1'^2 + \frac{1}{2}m_2v_2'^2$$

2. In the first collision in 8.2, the moving and target balls had the same mass; therefore, the expression above becomes

$$v_1^2 = v_1'^2 + v_2'^2$$

Using the paper record of the collision, measure the magnitude of the velocity vectors for each ball. Square these magnitudes, and add as above, to determine whether the collision was elastic. Repeat the procedure for each trial of the equal-mass collision.

3. In the second collision in 8.2, the moving and target balls had different masses. Determine the mass ratio $\frac{m_1}{m_2}$ for the balls. For this collision to be elastic,

$$\frac{m_1}{m_2}v_1^2 = \frac{m_1}{m_2}v_1'^2 + v_2'^2$$

4. Using the paper record of this collision, measure the magnitude of the velocity vectors for each ball, multiply by the mass ratio, where appropriate, and determine whether the collision was elastic.

Investigation 9.3: Linear Collisions on an Air Track

Problem:
What are the momentum and kinetic energy relationships in a linear collision?

Materials:
air track, with a source of air
3 air track gliders, two of equal mass, and one of different mass
2 photogate timers (photoelectric cell with electronic timing device)

Procedure:
1. Set up the air track, attach the air supply, and level the track carefully. The track may be considered level when a glider placed anywhere on the track remains essentially at rest, with the air supply on, over a 30 s period.
2. Set up a photogate timer near each end of the track. Attach a cardboard shield to each glider and adjust the height of the photogate so that, as the glider passes through the gate, the cardboard shield interrupts the light beam and starts or stops

the timer. Practise sending a glider through either photogate at fast and slow speeds, and record the time it takes for the shield to pass through the timing gate.

3. In the first experiment, use gliders that have either band steel bumpers attached to them or magnets of opposite poles attached to them, to give an elastic collision.

4. Place one glider at rest near the centre of the track. Start another glider moving towards the stationary glider from one end of the track, so that it passes through the photogate before the collision. After the collision the stationary glider will always pass through the second photogate. The moving glider may stop, rebound back through the first photogate, or continue on and follow the stationary glider through the second photogate. In either case, when two times are to be recorded by the same gate, you must write down the first time, and then reset the timer quickly before the second glider reaches it. This experiment must be repeated three times, for each of the following cases:
   (a) a moving glider and stationary glider of equal mass
   (b) a moving glider heavier than a stationary glider
   (c) a moving glider lighter than a stationary glider

5. In the second experiment, use gliders that have a pin attached to the front end of the moving glider, and a cork attached to the trailing end of the stationary glider. This way, when the two gliders collide they will stick together and move off as a coupled pair. Repeat the same three trials. This time the timing is easier, since both photogates record only one reading.

6. Record the results of all six trials in a table such as the one shown.

7. Measure the mass of each of the gliders with the bumpers, etc., attached, and record these values in the chart. Also, measure the length of the cardboard shield used on each cart.

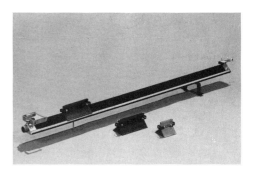

Mass of gliders (kg)		Times recorded on photogates (s)			Velocities of gliders (m/s)		
Moving	Stationary	Moving glider		Stationary glider	Moving glider		Stationary glider
		Before	After	After	Before	After	After

Masses of equal-mass gliders = _____
Mass of different-mass glider = _____
Length of shield on equal-mass gliders = _____
Length of shield on different-mass glider = _____

Calculations:

1. For each of the six trials, determine the velocity of each glider both before and after the collision. Then determine the momentum and kinetic energy of each glider before and after the collision as well. Remember, momentum is a vector quantity; to the right is positive and to the left is negative.
2. For each of the six trials, compare the total momentum before the collision with the total momentum after the collision. In each case, determine the percentage difference between the total momentum before and after the collision.
3. Once more, for each of the six trials, compare the total kinetic energy before and after the collision. Again, determine the percentage difference between the total kinetic energy before and after the collision.

Questions:

1. What is the significant difference, in terms of conservation of kinetic energy, between using spring bumpers to cushion the collision and using a pin and cork to couple the gliders? Describe each of the two types of collision.
2. Is there a comparable difference, in terms of conservation of momentum, between the two types of collision? What seems to be true about the effect of the collision on total momentum that differs from its effect on kinetic energy?

Investigation 9.4: Magnetic Collisions on an Air Table

Problem:

How do colliding, magnetized air pucks transfer energy?

Materials:

air table and air supply
magnetized air pucks of equal and unequal mass
calibrated stroboscopic light
polaroid camera and film
overhead projector

Procedure:

1. Follow the manufacturer's instructions to level the air table. With the air supply on, a puck placed anywhere on the air table should remain at rest.
2. Mount the camera above the table and sight through the viewfinder to ensure that the entire air table is within the field of view.

3. Position the strobe light above and to the side of the table, to illuminate the top surface of the pucks without producing glare from the tabletop itself.
4. Turn on the air supply, place a magnetized puck at the centre of the table, and practise launching an identical puck towards it, creating a glancing collision in which both pucks move off afterwards with about a 90° angular separation.
5. Now record a similar collision on polaroid film. Turn on the strobe light, launch the puck, and then quickly open the camera's shutter. Note: Be certain to close the shutter *just before* either puck hits the edge of the air table.
6. Repeat the procedure, using pucks of different mass. Also, try to photograph a collision in which both pucks are moving prior to impact.

Calculations:
1. For ease of measurement, the strobe photo should be enlarged to a known fraction of full-size (one-half, one-third, etc.). To do so, make a pin-hole in the photo at the centre of each image of each puck, place the perforated photo on an overhead projector, and project its image onto a large piece of paper on a nearby wall. A series of pin-holes at each corner of the air table will enable you to produce an image that is half full-size, by moving the projector closer to the wall or farther away.
2. When the correctly scaled image has been obtained, mark the position of each puck image (a bright spot) on the paper, and label this record with the mass of each puck used.
3. To co-ordinate corresponding images of both pucks, number each image of the moving puck, beginning with 1 and continuing until the last image has been numbered. Now, for the other puck, start numbering with this last number, and work backward towards its initial image. Several images will be superimposed at its original position, indicating the number of times the strobe flashed before it began to move.
4. Calculate the velocity of each puck at the time of each strobe flash by measuring its total distance from the previous image to the next image, and then dividing by the time required for two strobe flashes. Remember the scale factor; e.g., if f = 10 flashes/s, then T = 1/10 s, and the scale is 1/2 full-size.

scale factor

$$v_{11} = \frac{2(3.0\ \text{cm} + 2.6\ \text{cm})}{2/10\ \text{s}}$$

$$= 56\ \text{cm/s}$$

5. Now calculate the kinetic energy of each puck at the time of each strobe flash, e.g., in the example above, if the puck's mass is 100 g,

$$E_{k_{11}} = \frac{1}{2} mv_{11}{}^2$$
$$= \frac{1}{2} (0.100 \text{ kg})(0.56 \text{ m/s})^2$$
$$= 1.57 \times 10^{-2} \text{ J}$$

6. Finally, measure the separation distance of the two pucks at the time of each strobe flash, and include all of the measured and calculated data in a data table, like the one shown.

Image #	v_1	v_2	E_{k_1}	E_{k_2}	Separation distance (x)
	m/s	m/s	J	J	m

7. Draw a graph of E_k versus x for each puck. Plot E_k vertically and x horizontally. Use small circles to plot points approaching minimum separation, and small triangles to plot points after minimum separation. Draw a separate curve for each puck. Also plot $E_{k_{total}}$ on the same set of axes.
8. Repeat for each separate collision.

Questions:

1. Compare $E_{k_{total}}$ before and after the collision. Is each collision elastic?
2. At what image number does the collision "begin" and "end"? How did you decide?
3. At what image number is the separation of the pucks a minimum? What is the total kinetic energy at this separation? How does it compare with the total kinetic energy before and after the collision?
4. What is the maximum potential energy stored in the magnetic field of the two pucks during the collision?
5. Comment on the two curves (the one marked with circles and the other by triangles) drawn in calculation 7.

9.9 Review

Discussion

1. Describe three situations in which a force is exerted on an object and yet no work is done.
2. It is often possible to do work in pushing an object without transferring any energy to the object being pushed. What happens to the energy associated with the work done in this case?
3. A baseball and a shot have the same kinetic energy. Which has the greater momentum? Why?
4. Two rocks of unequal mass have the same kinetic energy and are sliding across a flat, level ice surface in the same direction. If each is subjected to the same retarding force, how will their stopping distances compare?
5. Compare the kinetic energies of two objects that are identical in every respect, except that
   (a) X is moving twice as fast as Y.
   (b) X is moving east, Y is moving west.
   (c) X is moving in a horizontal circle, Y in a straight line.
   (d) X has one-third the mass of Y.
6. Two dynamics carts are moving in a straight line towards each other, and the ensuing collision is cushioned by a spring between them. During the collision there is a point where both carts are momentarily at rest. Where has all the kinetic energy that the carts possessed before the collision gone?
7. A heavy lab cart with a spring mounted on its front end collides elastically with a stationary, lighter cart, head-on on a level, frictionless surface. Sketch a graph of the kinetic energy of each cart as a function of separation distance between the two carts, showing clearly the interval before, during, and after the collision. Sketch a graph of the total energy throughout, as well.
8. Draw a representative sketch of the graph of force versus separation for each of the following collisions:
   (a) A billiard ball bounces off a cushion, leaving at the same speed as it approached.
   (b) A tin can collides with a brick wall and is slightly dented before bouncing off at a slower speed.
   (c) A ball of soft putty is thrown at a wall and sticks to it in the collision.
9. The high cost of fuel has spurred development of more efficient automobiles. In a short essay discuss the physics involved in their design. Include the following topics: mass of car, air re-

sistance, tire design, friction, and the conversion of chemical energy into mechanical energy.

10. The need for more and cheaper energy has led to the development of new technology involving the conversion of energy from the sun and from alternate fuels. In a minimum of 500 words, explain how one of these processes works and predict the future application and success of the technology.

Problems

11. Calculate the work done by the obvious agent in each case below:
    (a) A locomotive exerts a constant forward force of 5.4×10^4 N while pulling a train at a speed of 20 m/s for 1.0 h.
    (b) A horse is towing a canal boat with a rope that makes an angle of 15° with the canal; the tension in the rope is 500 N and the canal is 120 m long.
    (c) A 30 kg child climbs a flight of stairs 5.0 m high.
    (d) A 12 kg suitcase is carried a horizontal distance of 30 m.
    (e) An 8.0 kg sled experiences the horizontal force shown in the graph on a flat, frictionless sheet of ice.

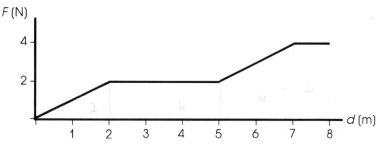

12. A 40 kg wagon is moving with a constant horizontal velocity of 10 m/s.
    (a) How much work must be done to double this velocity?
    (b) How much work must be done to halve the original velocity?

13. From what height must a 1500 kg piledriver fall, to drive a pile 0.50 m into the ground against an average opposing force of 3.5×10^5 N? (Ignore the weight of the piledriver over the 0.50 m path.)

14. A 10 kg block is pushed from rest along a horizontal, frictionless surface with a horizontal force given by the graph to left.
    (a) How much work is done in moving the block the first 2.0 m?

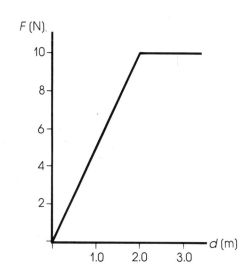

(b) What is the block's kinetic energy after it has moved 3.0 m?

(c) What is its velocity at the 3.0 m mark?

15. A force that increases gradually from 0 to 100 N at a rate of 10 N/s does 12 500 J of work on an object, accelerating it from rest to a velocity of 50 m/s on a flat, frictionless surface.

(a) What is the mass of the object?

(b) What constant force would have given the object the same final velocity if the force had acted over a distance of 5.0 m?

16. A 4.0 kg rock moving at 20 m/s has the same momentum as a 10.0 kg rock.

(a) What is the velocity of the 10.0 kg rock?

(b) What is the kinetic energy of each?

17. What is the momentum of a 5.0 kg briefcase with a kinetic energy of 5.0×10^2 J?

18. What constant force is required to stop a 1000 kg car travelling at a velocity of 20 m/s in a distance of 1.5 m? Compare this force to the force of gravity on the car.

19. What is the kinetic energy of an electron of mass 9.1×10^{-31} kg in a TV picture tube, if it hits the screen with a velocity of 1.0×10^7 m/s?

20. A pellet of mass 5.0 g is fired from a heavy gun whose barrel is 100 cm long. The force on the pellet while it is in the barrel is given by the graph. What is the muzzle velocity of the pellet?

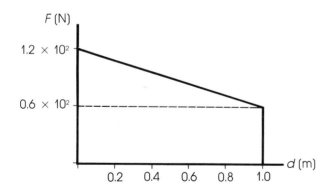

21. A horizontal force of 50 N is applied to a 2.0 kg trolley, initially at rest, and it moves a distance of 4.0 m along a level, frictionless track. The force then changes to 20 N and acts for an additional distance of 2.0 m.

(a) What is the final kinetic energy of the trolley?

(b) What is its final velocity?

22. A 20 kg sled carrying a 40 kg girl is sliding at 12 m/s on smooth, level ice, when it encounters a rough patch of snow.
    (a) What is the initial kinetic energy of the girl and sled?
    (b) If the rough ice exerts an average opposing force of 540 N, in what distance does the sled stop?
    (c) What work is done by the rough ice in stopping the sled?

23. A ball of mass 0.80 kg moving initially at 8.0 m/s has a head-on collision with a 0.40 kg ball that is at rest. If the collision is perfectly elastic, what is the velocity of each ball after the collision?

24. A truck of mass 3000 kg, moving at 5.0 m/s on a level, icy road, bumps into the rear of a car moving at 2.0 m/s in the same direction. After the impact the truck has a velocity of 3.0 m/s and the car a velocity of 6.0 m/s, both forward.
    (a) What is the mass of the car?
    (b) Calculate the total kinetic energy before and after the collision.
    (c) Was the collision elastic?

25. A 1.0 kg magnetized air puck moving across a level table at 0.24 m/s approaches head-on a stationary, similarly magnetized air puck of mass 0.50 kg. If the "magnetic collision" is repulsive and perfectly elastic, determine:
    (a) the velocity of each puck after the collision
    (b) the velocity of both pucks at minimum separation
    (c) the total kinetic energy at minimum separation
    (d) the maximum potential energy stored in the magnetic force field during the collision

26. On a frictionless air track, a 0.30 kg glider moving at 0.40 m/s to the right collides with a 0.80 kg glider moving at 0.15 m/s to the left. The collision is cushioned by a bumper made of perfectly elastic spring steel.
    (a) What is the velocity of each glider after the collision?
    (b) What is the minimum amount of total kinetic energy during the collision?
    (c) Where is the missing energy?

27. Two identical billiard balls are at rest on a level, frictionless surface, just touching each other at one common point, as shown. A third, identical ball, the cue ball, is approaching along the common tangent with a constant speed of 20 m/s, as shown. Assuming a completely elastic collision, with no spin on any of the balls, and making (reasonable) assumptions about symmetry, calculate the velocity of the cue ball after the collision. (SIN '78)

20 m/s

28. A bullet of mass 4.0 g, moving horizontally with a velocity of 500 m/s, strikes a wooden block of mass 2.0 kg, initially at rest on a rough, horizontal surface. The bullet passes through the block in a negligible time interval, emerging with a velocity of 100 m/s and causing the block to slide 40 cm along the surface before coming to rest.

(a) With what velocity does the wood block move just after the bullet exits?

(b) What is the maximum kinetic energy of the block?

(c) What is the average frictional force stopping the block?

(d) What is the decrease in kinetic energy of the bullet?

(e) Explain why the decrease in E_k of the bullet and the maximum E_k of the block are not equal. What happened to this difference in energy?

29. A massless spring is compressed between blocks of mass m and 5 m on a smooth, horizontal table. When the system is released, the energy of the spring is shared between the blocks. What fraction of the total energy does the smaller block acquire? (SIN '69)

30. A 2.5 kg mass, at rest, is approached head-on by a 5.0 kg mass moving at 0.60 m/s. The force-separation graph for the ensuing collision is given.

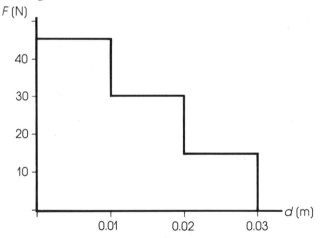

(a) What is the total kinetic energy before the collision? After?

(b) What is the velocity of each mass at minimum separation?

(c) What is the total kinetic energy at minimum separation?

(d) How much energy is stored at minimum separation?

(e) What is the minimum separation distance?

(f) What is the magnitude of the force acting on each mass at minimum separation?

Numerical Answers to Review Problems

11. (a) 3.9×10^9 J (b) 5.8×10^4 J
(c) 1.5×10^3 J (d) 0 (e) 18 J

12. (a) 6.0×10^3 J (b) -1.5×10^3 J

13. 12 m

14. (a) 10 J (b) 20 J (c) 2.0 m/s

15. (a) 10 kg (b) 2.5×10^3 N

16. (a) 8.0 m/s
(b) 8.0×10^2 J, 3.2×10^2 J

17. 71 kg·m/s

18. -1.3×10^5 N, 13.3 F_g

19. 4.6×10^{-17} J

20. 1.9×10^2 m/s

21. (a) 2.4×10^2 J (b) 15 m/s

22. (a) 4.3×10^3 J (b) 8.0 m
(c) -4.3×10^3 J

23. 2.7 m/s, 10.7 m/s

24. (a) 1.5×10^3 kg
(b) 4.1×10^4 J, 4.1×10^4 J
(c) elastic

25. (a) 0.080 m/s, 0.32 m/s (b) 0.16 m/s
(c) 1.9×10^{-2} J (d) 9.6×10^{-3} J

26. (a) -0.40 m/s, 0.15 m/s (b) 0
(c) stored in spring bumper

27. -4.0 m/s

28. (a) 0.80 m/s (b) 0.64 J (c) -1.6N
(d) -4.8×10^2 J
(e) heat, noise, deformation

29. 5/6

30. (a) 0.90 J, 0.90 J (b) 0.40 m/s
(c) 0.60 J (d) 0.30 J
(e) 0.015 m (f) 30 N

10 Potential Energy

In Chapter 9, as a result of our study of elastic collisions, we discovered that some kinetic energy "disappears" during a collision, only to "reappear" after the collision is over. In fact, we concluded that the apparently lost energy was there all the time, but was in a different form than kinetic energy. We called this energy "potential energy" and concluded that it was stored somehow in the collision mechanism, while the collision was in progress.

In this chapter, we will look closely at two specific types of potential energy — elastic potential energy and gravitational potential energy. We will come to understand how kinetic energy can be transformed into each of these types of energy, and vice versa.

10.1 Hooke's Law for a Spring

Elastic potential energy may be stored in any object that, once temporarily deformed by the application of a force, returns to its original shape as the force is removed. The work that was done on the object to create the deformation is returned as work done by the object as it regains its original shape. Some common examples of objects that can store elastic potential energy are:
(a) a diving board
(b) a trampoline
(c) the rubber band in a sling shot
(d) a leaf or coil spring in a car
(e) the spring in a pogo stick
(f) the spring in a wind-up toy

As discussed in Chapter 6 and reviewed here, the British scientist Robert Hooke (1635-1703) was one of the first to study the elasticity of matter. In 1678, he published his now-famous statement of Hooke's Law:

The amount of deformation of an elastic object is proportional to the force applied to deform it.

To begin with, we will study Hooke's Law as it applies to a simple coiled spring that is either stretched or compressed by an applied force. If we call the deformation of the spring x (i.e., x is the amount by which it is stretched or compressed from its normal length), a graph of F versus x has the form shown on page 373.

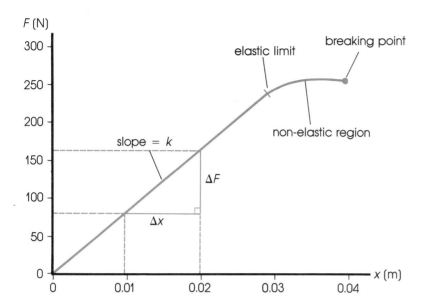

Notice that the *F-x* graph is a straight line up to a point called the elastic limit of the spring. If the spring is deformed beyond this limit, the graph is no longer linear, and the spring may not return to its original shape after the force is removed. In fact, if deformed too far beyond the elastic limit, the spring may fracture.

For the linear portion of the graph (sometimes called the "Hooke's Law region"), its constant slope, *k*, is given by

$$k = \frac{\text{rise}}{\text{run}} = \frac{\Delta F}{\Delta x}$$

and the equation relating force and deformation (extension or compression) is

---

$$F = kx$$

---

where *F* is the force exerted on the deformed spring, in newtons

x is the amount of deformation of the spring, in metres

k is the force constant of the spring, in newtons per metre

We can distinguish between compressions of the spring and extensions of it by adopting a simple sign convention. When the spring is compressed, both *x* and *F* are negative ($-$); when the spring is stretched, both *x* and *F* are positive ($+$). Notice that the force exerted on the spring and the deformation of the spring are always in the same direction, so that *k* is always positive.

For the spring whose *F-x* graph is shown above,

$$k = \frac{\Delta F}{\Delta x}$$

$$= \frac{165 \text{ N} - 80 \text{ N}}{0.02 \text{ m} - 0.01 \text{ m}}$$

$$= \frac{85 \text{ N}}{0.01 \text{ m}}$$

$$= 8.5 \times 10^3 \text{ N/m}$$

Sample problem

A spring whose force constant is 48 N/m has a 0.25 kg mass suspended from it. What is the extension of the spring?

If the spring obeys Hooke's Law,

$$F = kx$$

therefore $$x = \frac{F}{k}$$

but $$F = mg$$
$$= (0.25 \text{ kg})(9.8 \text{ m/s}^2)$$
$$= 2.4 \text{ N}$$

therefore $$x = \frac{2.4 \text{ N}}{48 \text{ N/m}}$$
$$= 0.050 \text{ m, or } 5.0 \text{ cm}$$

Practice

1. What force is necessary to stretch a spring whose force constant is 120 N/m by an amount of 30 cm?   (36 N)
2. A spring with a force constant of 600 N/m is used in a scale for weighing fish. What is the mass of a fish that stretches the spring 7.5 cm from its normal length?   (4.6 kg)
3. A spring in a pogo stick is compressed 12 cm when a 40 kg boy stands on the stick. What is the force constant for the pogo stick's spring?   (3.3×10^3 N/m)
4. The force applied to a dynamics cart is measured with a stretched spring. What is the acceleration of a 2.0 kg cart on a flat, frictionless surface if pulled by a spring, of force constant 40 N/m, stretched by a constant amount of 8.0 cm?   (1.6 m/s²)

10.2 Elastic Potential Energy Stored in a Spring

In Section 10.1 we learned that a force applied to an elastic spring will cause the spring to compress or extend, according to the relation

$$F = kx$$

The graph of the force-deformation relationship for such a spring is shown.

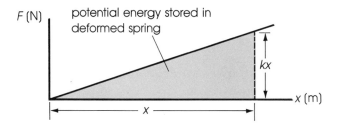

In Section 9.1 we learned that a force exerted over a displacement in the direction of the force does work, and that the amount of work done by a changing force over a displacement is given by the area under the corresponding force-displacement graph. In the case of a stretched spring, the displacement is just the extension, x, and the work done in extending the spring by an amount x is equal to the elastic potential energy stored in the extended spring.

elastic potential energy
   stored in spring   = work done to extend spring
                      = area under F-x graph, from 0 to x

This area is a triangle and is the product $\frac{1}{2}$ (base)(height) which, from the graph, is given by

$$E_e = \frac{1}{2}(x)(kx)$$

so that

$$E_e = \frac{1}{2}kx^2$$

where E_e is the elastic potential energy stored in the deformed spring, in joules
   k is the spring's force constant, in newtons per metre
   x is the deformation (extension or compression) of the spring, in metres
Note that the units of E_e are energy units.

$$E_e = \frac{1}{2}kx^2$$
$$= (N/m)(m)^2$$
$$= N \cdot m$$
$$= J$$

This expression makes it possible to solve a great variety of problems involving the collision between objects cushioned by springs, and the launching of objects propelled by a compressed spring. A few sample problems will illustrate.

Many objects in the world around us behave like springs. Girders in bridges bend, tables in kitchens sag, wings on airplanes flex, and cables in elevators stretch.

Sample problems

1. What is the elastic potential energy stored in a spring whose force constant is 160 N/m when it is compressed 8.0 cm?

$$E_e = \frac{1}{2} kx^2$$

$$= \frac{1}{2} (160 \text{ N/m})(-0.080 \text{ m})^2$$

$$= 0.51 \text{ J}$$

2. A block of mass 2.5 kg is sliding across a smooth, level surface at 3.0 m/s when it hits a stationary spring bumper, fixed at one end as shown, whose force constant is 360 N/m. By what amount does the block compress the spring, before coming to rest?

The negative sign is needed with ΔE_k, since E_k is lost and E_e is gained. To be mathematically equal, ΔE_k and ΔE_e would have to be of the same sign.

The block loses kinetic energy by doing work that compresses the spring, and stores elastic potential energy in it.

$$- \Delta E_k \text{ (block)} = \Delta E_e \text{ (spring)}$$

$$\frac{1}{2} mv^2 = \frac{1}{2} kx^2$$

$$x^2 = \frac{mv^2}{k}$$

$$= \frac{(2.5 \text{ kg})(3.0 \text{ m/s})^2}{360 \text{ N/m}}$$

$$= 0.0625 \text{ m}^2$$

Therefore $x = \pm 0.25 \text{ m}$

Since the spring is compressed, the + solution is inadmissible.

3. A block of mass 0.50 kg is placed on a level, frictionless surface, in contact with a spring bumper, of force constant 100 N/m, that has been compressed by an amount 0.30 m. The spring, whose other end is fixed, is then released. What is the speed of the block at the instant when the spring is still compressed by 0.10 m?

Calculating the elastic potential energy stored in the spring,

at $x = -0.30$ m, $E_e = \frac{1}{2} kx^2$

$$= \frac{1}{2} (100 \text{ N/m})(-0.30 \text{ m})^2$$

$$= 4.5 \text{ J}$$

at $x = -0.10$ m, $E_e = \frac{1}{2} (100 \text{ N/m})(-0.10 \text{ m})^2$

$$= 0.50 \text{ J}$$

Therefore, as the spring expands from a compression of 0.30 m to 0.10 m, the change in stored potential energy is given by

$$\Delta E_e = E_{e_2} - E_{e_1}$$
$$= 0.50 \text{ J} - 4.5 \text{ J}$$
$$= -4.0 \text{ J}$$

This change in elastic potential energy for the spring represents a loss in stored energy, and the amount of energy lost is equal to the kinetic energy gained by the block.

$$\Delta E_k = \frac{1}{2}mv^2$$

$$4.0 \text{ J} = \frac{1}{2}(0.50 \text{ kg})\, v^2$$

$$v^2 = 16 \text{ (m/s)}^2$$
$$v = 4.0 \text{ m/s}$$

Note: In this type of energy transfer, the total energy of the system of the block and spring, at all times, is given by

$$E_{total} = E_k \text{ (block)} + E_e \text{ (spring)} = \text{constant}$$
$$= 4.5 \text{ J in this case}$$

In practice, frictional effects will usually cause some of the total energy to dissipate as heat. These frictional forces usually act in the opposite direction to the motion, so that they do negative work.

Practice

1. What is the force constant of a Hooke's Law spring if the extension of the spring is 0.15 m when 0.72 J of potential energy is stored in it?   (64 N/m)
2. How much work must be done on a spring with a force constant $k = 80$ N/m to stretch the spring 20 cm?   (1.6 J)
3. How much would a spring scale with $k = 120$ N/m stretch, if it had 3.75 J of work done on it?   (0.25 m)
4. A 5.0 g pellet is placed in the barrel of a toy gun and is propelled by a spring of force constant 50 N/m that has been compressed 20 cm and then released. Calculate the maximum velocity of the pellet when shot horizontally.   (20 m/s)
5. The force-deformation graph for a non-Hooke's Law spring is shown.
   (a) How much work must be done to compress the spring 0.16 m?
   (b) How much potential energy is stored in the spring at this compression?
   (c) What speed would a 1.0 kg mass acquire if it were placed next to this compressed spring, on a smooth, horizontal surface, and then released?   (0.72 J, 0.725 J, 1.2 m/s)

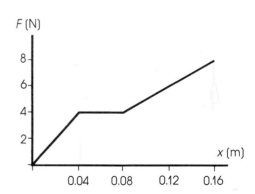

10.3 Springs and Elastic Collisions

In Chapter 9 we analysed elastic collisions between objects by assuming that the collision was cushioned by some sort of "flexible bumper", or by a repulsive magnetic field. We discussed the ability of this bumper to store energy, in the form of potential energy, as the kinetic energy first decreases and then increases again during the collision. A spring that obeys Hooke's Law is an excellent bumper for such a collision. In fact, since we now know expressions for the force necessary to compress such a spring, and for the potential energy stored in it when compressed, we can analyse collisions cushioned by Hooke's Law springs even more closely. A sample problem will illustrate.

Sample problem

A cart of mass 2.0 kg is moving to the right along a smooth, horizontal track at 3.0 m/s. A Hooke's Law spring, of force constant 1200 N/m and normal length 25 cm, is attached to its front. It collides "head-on" with a 4.0 kg cart, initially at rest.

(a) What is the velocity of each cart after the collision?

Since the collision is head-on, with one cart initially at rest, and is perfectly elastic (cushioned by a Hooke's Law spring), the specific equations developed in Section 9.7 apply.

Again, the vector nature of momentum and velocity may be accommodated by assigning vectors to the right as positive and to the left as negative.

$$v_1' = \left(\frac{m_1 - m_2}{m_1 + m_2}\right) v_1 = \left(\frac{2.0 \text{ kg} - 4.0 \text{ kg}}{2.0 \text{ kg} + 4.0 \text{ kg}}\right) 3.0 \text{ m/s} = -1.0 \text{ m/s}$$

$$v_2' = \left(\frac{2 \, m_1}{m_1 + m_2}\right) v_1 = \left(\frac{2 \, (2.0 \text{ kg})}{2.0 \text{ kg} + 4.0 \text{ kg}}\right) 3.0 \text{ m/s} = 2.0 \text{ m/s}$$

The 2.0 kg cart rebounds and moves to the left at 1.0 m/s, while the 4.0 kg cart moves to the right at 2.0 m/s.

(b) What is the velocity of each cart at minimum separation?

At minimum separation, the velocities of the two carts are equal, and total momentum is conserved.

Let v_0 be the velocity at minimum separation.

$$\text{since } \Delta p_{\text{total}} = 0$$

$$p_{\text{total}} \text{ (before)} = p_{\text{total}} \text{ (at minimum separation)}$$

$$m_1 v_1 + m_2 v_2 = m_1 v_0 + m_2 v_0 = (m_1 + m_2) v_0$$

$$(2.0 \text{ kg})(3.0 \text{ m/s}) + 0 = (6.0 \text{ kg}) v_0$$

$$v_0 = 1.0 \text{ m/s}$$

If the velocities are not equal, then the carts are still getting closer together, or they already were closer together.

At minimum separation, both carts are moving to the right at 1.0 m/s.

(c) What is the change in total kinetic energy at minimum separation?

$$\Delta E_k = E_k \text{ (at minimum separation)} - E_k \text{ (before)}$$

$$= \left(\frac{1}{2}(m_1 + m_2)v_0{}^2\right) - \left(\frac{1}{2}m_1 v_1{}^2 + 0\right), \text{ since } m_2 \text{ is initially at rest}$$

$$= \frac{1}{2}(6.0 \text{ kg})(1.0 \text{ m/s})^2 - \frac{1}{2}(2.0 \text{ kg})(3.0 \text{ m/s})^2$$

$$= 3.0 \text{ J} - 9.0 \text{ J}$$

$$= -6.0 \text{ J}$$

Note that the change in kinetic energy is negative, representing a loss in total kinetic energy at minimum separation.

(d) What is the compression of the spring at minimum separation?

At minimum separation, the kinetic energy lost has been transformed into elastic potential energy stored in the compressed spring, so that the total energy of the system remains constant.

$$\Delta E_e = -\Delta E_k = 6.0 \text{ J}$$

$$E_e = \frac{1}{2}kx^2$$

$$6.0 \text{ J} = \frac{1}{2}(1200 \text{ N/m})\, x^2$$

$$x = \pm 0.10 \text{ m}$$

But, since the spring is compressed, $x = -0.10$ m

(e) What is the minimum separation of the two carts?

The minimum separation distance, L_0, is the normal length of the spring, L, plus its deformation at minimum separation, x_0.

$$L_0 = L + x_0$$

$$= 0.25 \text{ m} + (-0.10 \text{ m})$$

$$= 0.15 \text{ m}$$

Practice

1. Calculate the force constant of a spring that, when compressed 10 cm between two stationary 2.5 kg carts and released, causes each cart to move off with a velocity of 3.0 m/s.   (4500 N/m)
2. Two carts, of mass 4.5 kg and 1.0 kg, are moving towards each other along the same straight, level track at 2.0 m/s to the right and 4.0 m/s to the left, respectively. Their collision is cushioned by a linear elastic spring between them.
   (a) What is the total energy of the system before the collision?
   (b) At minimum separation, what is the velocity of each cart?

Automobile springs are designed to store energy imparted to the automobile by collisions between its tires and irregularities on rough roads, thus keeping it from bouncing. In order that the car not just rebound, as other masses colliding with springs in this chapter have done, shock absorbers are used to dampen the release of the energy stored momentarily in the springs.

(c) Calculate the total kinetic energy at minimum separation.

(d) If the force constant of the spring is 900 N/m, what is its maximum compression during the collision?

(17 J, 0.91 m/s[right], 2.3 J, 0.18 m)

3. A glider of mass 50 g is moving to the left along an air track at a speed of 4.0 cm/s when it collides with a second glider of mass 30 g moving to the right with a speed of 20 cm/s. The collision is perfectly elastic, cushioned by a steel-loop spring that obeys Hooke's Law.

(a) Determine the velocity of each glider at that point during the collision when their separation distance is a minimum.

(b) Determine the amount of elastic potential energy stored in the spring at that instant.

(c) If the maximum deformation of the spring during the collision is 1.5 cm, what is its spring constant?

$(5.0 \text{ cm/s[right]}, 5.4 \times 10^{-4} \text{ J}, 4.8 \text{ N/m})$

10.4 Gravitational Potential Energy Near the Earth's Surface

In the last section, we learned that exerting a force on a spring to stretch it or compress it from its normal length resulted in elastic potential energy being stored in the deformed spring. That is,

$$\begin{pmatrix} \text{work done to} \\ \text{deform spring} \end{pmatrix} = \begin{pmatrix} \text{elastic potential energy} \\ \text{stored in spring} \end{pmatrix}$$

A similar situation occurs when a force is exerted on a mass, pulling the mass away from the Earth against the force of gravity. Work must be done on the object to lift it higher, but this will be returned as work done by the object on its way back down. In some ways, an object lifted away from the Earth is like an object attached to a long, stretched spring; when the object is released, in either case, a force does work on it, causing it to move and acquire kinetic energy at the expense of potential energy stored in the system. For the mass lifted away from the Earth, the stored energy is called "gravitational potential energy".

Consider the following situation.

An object of mass m is lifted from position 1 to position 2, a vertical distance Δh farther away from the Earth's centre.

Remember, a small mass, m, dropped towards the Earth, whose mass, M_E, is very large compared to m, will cause the Earth to move also. Both objects gain some kinetic energy as the system loses gravitational potential energy (since the separation of m and M_E is decreasing). However, the Earth's motion is negligible.

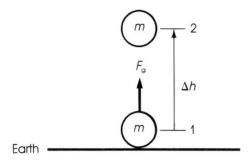

$$\left(\begin{array}{c}\text{work done to}\\ \text{move mass}\end{array}\right) = \left(\begin{array}{c}\text{change in gravitational}\\ \text{potential energy}\end{array}\right)$$

The force necessary to just lift a mass from position 1 to position 2 is given by

$$F_g = mg$$

If Δh is small, compared to the radius of the Earth, the gravitational force constant, g, may be taken as constant over the interval Δh. Hence the force, F_g, required to lift the mass is also constant.

$$\text{work done to lift mass} = F_g \Delta h$$
$$= mg\Delta h$$

And since the work done represents the change in gravitational potential energy of the mass, we have

$$\Delta E_g = mg\Delta h$$

where ΔE_g is the change in gravitational potential energy, in joules
m is the mass, in kilograms
g is the gravitational field constant, in newtons per kilogram
Δh is the vertical displacement, in metres

There are a few important points to remember when using the equation above.

- It is an expression for "change in gravitational potential energy", and NOT for an absolute value of gravitational potential energy. In practical problems involving the use of this equation, the surface of the Earth is often used as a reference level of zero gravitational potential energy, although any other convenient arbitrary level may be chosen.
- The equation may only be used when Δh is small enough that g does not vary appreciably over Δh.

The assumption of zero kinetic energy at the Earth's surface simplifies the discussion but overlooks the fact that the Earth is rotating. In actual fact, only at the poles does an object have no kinetic energy.

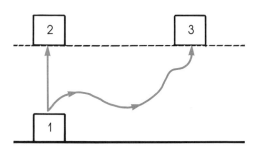

In the diagram, the change in E_g from 1 to 2 and from 1 to 3 is the same, regardless of the path taken.

- The value of Δh to be used in the equation is the vertical displacement of the object away from the centre of the Earth. This means that the path an object follows in changing its vertical height is not significant; only the change in vertical height, Δh, is relevant.
- Values of Δh, and hence ΔE_g, away from the Earth's centre are positive and those towards the Earth's centre are negative.

Many of the physical situations in which this equation is used involve objects thrown or lifted up, away from the Earth, or dropped towards the Earth. In cases such as this, energy is converted from kinetic into gravitational potential as the object moves away from the Earth, and from gravitational potential to kinetic as it falls back towards the Earth, but total energy remains constant. A few sample problems will illustrate.

Sample problems

1. A 50 kg girl climbs a staircase consisting of 15 steps, each with a riser 20 cm high. Calculate her change in gravitational potential energy as a result.

$$\Delta E_g = mg\Delta h$$
$$\text{where } \Delta h = 15(+0.20 \text{ m})$$
$$= 3.0 \text{ m}$$

Therefore
$$\Delta E_g = (50 \text{ kg})(9.8 \text{ N/kg})(3.0 \text{ m})$$
$$= 1470 \text{ J, or } 1.5 \times 10^3 \text{ J}$$

Note that the $+$ value of Δh, representing motion away from the Earth's surface, results in a $+$ value for ΔE_g, representing an increase in gravitational potential energy.

2. A ball of mass 0.25 kg is thrown vertically upward from the roof of a building 18 m high with a speed of 16 m/s, and just misses the building on the way down, as shown.

(a) To what vertical height above the Earth does the ball rise?

The total energy of the system consisting of the ball and the Earth remains constant at all points on the 1 to 2 to 3 path, and is equal to the sum of the initial kinetic energy and the gravitational potential energy. Assuming that the zero level of E_g is the surface of the Earth, $E_{total} = E_k + E_g$ at all points.

Therefore, at point 1
$$E_{total_1} = E_{k_1} + E_{g_1}$$
$$= \frac{1}{2} mv_1{}^2 + mg \, \Delta h_1$$

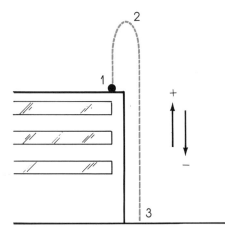

$$= \frac{1}{2}(0.25 \text{ kg})(16 \text{ m/s})^2 + (0.25 \text{ kg})(9.8 \text{ N/kg})(18 \text{ m})$$
$$= 32 \text{ J} + 44 \text{ J}$$
$$= 76 \text{ J}$$

At the instant when the ball reaches its maximum height, $E_{k_2} = 0$, and all of its energy is in the form of gravitational potential.

$$E_{total_2} = E_{k_2} + E_{g_2} = E_{total_1} = 76 \text{ J}$$
$$= 0 + mg\Delta h_2$$
$$\Delta h_2 = \frac{76 \text{ J}}{(0.25 \text{ kg})(9.8 \text{ N/kg})}$$
$$= 31 \text{ m}$$

(b) With what velocity does the ball hit the ground?

When the ball reaches ground level, $E_{g_3} = 0$, and all of its energy is kinetic.

$$E_{total_3} = E_{k_3} + E_{g_3} = 76 \text{ J}$$
$$= \frac{1}{2} mv_3^2 + 0$$
$$v_3^2 = \frac{2(76 \text{ J})}{0.25 \text{ kg}}$$
$$= 608 \text{ (m/s)}^2$$

Therefore $v_3 = -24.7 \text{ m/s}$, or -25 m/s

Identical results are obtained if $E_g = 0$ is chosen at the roof level of the building, but don't forget that E_{g_3} will then be negative at ground level.

Actually, $v_3 = \pm24.7$ m/s, but since the ball is moving down, only the negative solution is admissible.

3. A 1000 kg roller coaster, with its passengers, starts from rest at point A on a frictionless track whose profile is shown in the diagram.

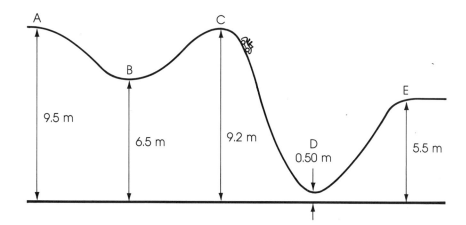

(a) What is its maximum speed?

The total energy of the roller coaster-Earth system remains constant and is equal to the gravitational potential energy at A (take $E_g = 0$ at ground level).

$$E_{total} = E_k + E_g = E_g \text{ (at A)} \quad \text{(since } E_k \text{ (at A)} = 0)$$
$$= mg\Delta h_A$$
$$= (1000 \text{ kg})(9.8 \text{ N/kg})(9.5 \text{ m})$$
$$= 9.3 \times 10^4 \text{ J}$$

The kinetic energy, and hence the velocity, will be a maximum at the point where the gravitational potential energy is a minimum, i.e., at point D.

$$E_g \text{ (at D)} = mg\Delta h_D$$
$$= (1000 \text{ kg})(9.8 \text{ N/kg})(0.50 \text{ m})$$
$$= 4.9 \times 10^3 \text{ J}$$

therefore
$$E_k \text{ (at D)} = E_{total} - E_g \text{ (at D)}$$
$$= 9.3 \times 10^4 \text{ J} - 4.9 \times 10^3 \text{ J}$$
$$= 8.8 \times 10^4 \text{ J}$$

and
$$v = \sqrt{\frac{2E_k}{m}}$$
$$= \sqrt{\frac{2(8.8 \times 10^4 \text{ J})}{1000 \text{ kg}}}$$
$$= 13.3 \text{ m/s, or } 13 \text{ m/s}$$

(b) With what speed does the roller coaster arrive at point E?

$$E_g \text{ (at E)} = mg\Delta h_E$$
$$= (1000 \text{ kg})(9.8 \text{ N/kg})(5.5 \text{ m})$$
$$= 5.4 \times 10^4 \text{ J}$$

therefore
$$E_k \text{ (at E)} = E_{total} - E_g \text{ (at E)}$$
$$= 9.3 \times 10^4 \text{ J} - 5.4 \times 10^4 \text{ J}$$
$$= 3.9 \times 10^4 \text{ J}$$

and
$$v = \sqrt{\frac{2E_k}{m}}$$
$$= \sqrt{\frac{2(3.9 \times 10^4 \text{ J})}{1000 \text{ kg}}}$$
$$= 8.83 \text{ m/s, or } 8.8 \text{ m/s}$$

(c) What constant braking force would have to be applied to the roller coaster at point E, to bring it to rest in a horizontal distance of 5.0 m?

The brakes do work on the roller coaster to reduce its kinetic energy from 3.9×10^4 J to zero.

$$\text{work done} = \text{change in } E_k$$

$$F\Delta d = E_{k_f} - E_{k_i}$$
$$= 0 - 3.9 \times 10^4 \text{ J}$$

therefore
$$F = \frac{-3.9 \times 10^4 \text{ J}}{5.0 \text{ m}}$$
$$= -7.8 \times 10^3 \text{ N}$$

The negative sign indicates a force in the opposite direction to motion, as a frictional braking force would be.

4. A Hooke's Law spring is compressed 10 cm by an applied force of 50 N. This compressed spring is then used to project a 20 g marble straight up into the air. To what maximum height does the marble rise?

After the spring is released, the total energy of the spring-marble-Earth system remains constant. Let the height of the marble, at release, be the zero level of gravitational potential energy. Just before release,

$$E_{total} = E_e + E_g + E_k$$
$$= \frac{1}{2} kx^2 + mg\Delta h + \frac{1}{2} mv^2$$
$$= \frac{1}{2}\left(\frac{F}{x}\right) x^2 + 0 + 0$$
$$= \frac{1}{2}\left(\frac{-50 \text{ N}}{-0.10 \text{ m}}\right)(-0.10 \text{ m})^2$$
$$= 2.5 \text{ J}$$

Then, as the marble reaches its maximum height,

$$E_{total} = E_e + E_k + E_g$$
$$2.5 \text{ J} = 0 + 0 + mg\Delta h$$
$$\Delta h = \frac{2.5 \text{ J}}{(0.020 \text{ kg})(9.8 \text{ m/s})}$$
$$= 12.8 \text{ m}$$

Note that this distance, being positive, is above the starting point. The spring will have expanded 0.10 m to its normal length, so that the marble is 12.7 m above the top of the now-uncompressed spring.

Practice

1. A 70 kg diver jumps from a 12 m tower, with no initial velocity.
   (a) With what velocity does the diver hit the water?
   (b) What would his impact velocity be if, in jumping from the tower, he gave himself an upward initial velocity of 5.0 m/s? (Hint: It is a waste of time to calculate his maximum height reached.) (15 m/s, 16 m/s)

2. What upward velocity must an Olympic high jumper impart to herself in order to clear the 2.0 m height of the bar? (Hint: Assume that she must raise her centre of mass to just above the bar, and that her centre of mass is 0.85 m above ground level when she begins to jump.   (4.7 m/s)

Strictly speaking, she may clear the bar even if her centre of mass is always below it. She can do so by arching her back, as the photograph indicates.

Canadian high jumper Debbie Brill at the 1984 Summer Olympics in Los Angeles.

3. A 2.0 kg mass is placed against a spring of force constant 800 N/m, which has been compressed 0.22 m, as illustrated. The spring is released, and the object moves along the horizontal, frictionless surface and up the slope.

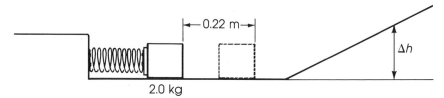

Calculate:
(a) the maximum elastic potential energy of the spring
(b) the maximum velocity of the mass
(c) the maximum vertical height of the mass, up the slope
                    (19 J, 4.4 m/s, 1.0 m)

4. A ball bearing of mass 50 g is sitting on a vertical spring whose force constant is 120 N/m. By how much must the spring be compressed so that, when released, the ball rises to a maximum height of 3.1 m above its release position?   (0.16 m)

5. A bullet's speed may be determined by firing it into a sandbag pendulum, and measuring the vertical height to which the pendulum rises, as shown. (The bullet stays in the sandbag.)

(a) What is the change in gravitational potential energy of the sandbag and bullet during the swing?

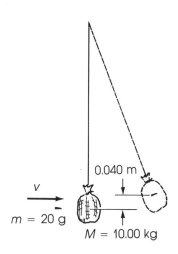

(b) What is the velocity of the sandbag-bullet combination at the start of the swing?

(c) What is the original velocity of the bullet?

(d) Is the collision between the bullet and the sandbag elastic or inelastic?   (3.9 J, 0.89 m/s, 4.5 × 10² m/s)

6. A 30 kg girl goes down a slide at an amusement park, reaching the bottom with a velocity of 2.5 m/s. The slide is 10.0 m long and the top end is 4.0 m above the bottom end, measured vertically.

(a) What is her gravitational potential energy at the top of the slide, relative to the bottom?

(b) What is her kinetic energy when she reaches the bottom?

(c) How much energy is lost due to friction?

(d) Calculate the average frictional force acting on her as she goes down the slide.

(1.2 × 10³ J, 94 J, 1.1 × 10³ J, −1.1 × 10² N)

10.5 Gravitational Potential Energy in General

In the previous section, we developed the equation $\Delta E_g = mg\Delta h$ in order to calculate the change in gravitational potential energy for a mass, m, that undergoes a vertical displacement Δh, near the Earth's surface. As long as the gravitational field strength, g, remains reasonably constant during Δh, the expression is accurate. In practice, this means that we will be fairly accurate for vertical displacements of a few hundred kilometres, but inaccurate beyond that.

The more general problem, however, is to develop an expression for the gravitational potential energy of a system of any two masses a finite distance apart. In the diagram, the two masses, M and m, are moved from a separation of r_1 to a separation of r_2, by a force that just overcomes the gravitational attraction between them at every point along the path. They are at rest at both positions.

As we learned in Chapter 7, the force of gravitational attraction between the two masses, at any separation distance r, is given by

$$F_g = \frac{GMm}{r^2}$$

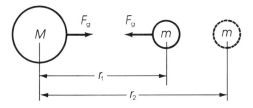

To increase the separation of the two masses from r_1 to r_2 requires work to be done to overcome their force of attraction (just as in stretching a spring). As a result of this work being done, the gravitational potential energy of the system increases, and

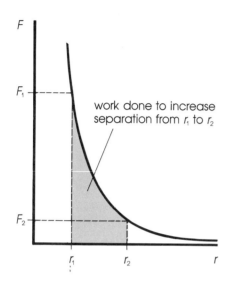

work done to increase separation from r_1 to r_2

Newton, seeing the need to calculate areas such as this more accurately, developed a whole new branch of mathematics to do so. This branch of mathematics is called calculus.

If you can integrate, try evaluating

$$\int_{r_1}^{r_2} F\, dr = \int_{r_1}^{r_2} \frac{GMm}{r^2}\, dr$$

$$\begin{pmatrix} \text{work done to change} \\ \text{separation from} \\ r_1 \text{ to } r_2 \end{pmatrix} = \begin{pmatrix} \text{change in gravitational} \\ \text{potential energy from} \\ r_1 \text{ to } r_2 \end{pmatrix}$$

But we have learned that the work done by a varying force is simply the area under the force-displacement graph for the interval. The force-separation graph, and the area representing the work done to change the separation from r_1 to r_2, is shown.

You may not recognize this area as a well-known geometric shape, and you have no simple formula to determine its area. If the graph were linear, the area would be given by the product $F_{av}(r_2 - r_1)$, where $F_{av} = \dfrac{F_1 + F_2}{2}$. The mathematics for an inverse square relationship involves calculus and is beyond the scope of this book. The result is accurate if, instead of using the arithmetic average of F_1 and F_2, the geometric average is used, i.e., $\sqrt{F_1 F_2}$.

$$\text{area under } F\text{-}r \text{ graph} = \sqrt{F_1 F_2}\,(r_2 - r_1)$$
$$(\text{from } r_1 \text{ to } r_2)$$

$$= \sqrt{\frac{GMm}{r_1^2} \cdot \frac{GMm}{r_2^2}}\,(r_2 - r_1)$$

$$= \frac{GMm}{r_1 r_2}\,(r_2 - r_1)$$

$$= \frac{GMm}{r_1} - \frac{GMm}{r_2}$$

But this area is an expression for the work done in changing the separation of the two masses from r_1 to r_2, as well as an expression for the resulting change in gravitational potential energy.

$$\Delta E_g = E_{g_2} - E_{g_1} = \frac{GMm}{r_1} - \frac{GMm}{r_2}$$

$$= \left(-\frac{GMm}{r_2}\right) - \left(-\frac{GMm}{r_1}\right)$$

Note that, to rewrite the expression in a form that puts the term involving r_2 first, followed by the term involving r_1, each term is changed to negative.

When written this way, the first term in the expression depends only on r_2 and the second term only on r_1. Thus, we may conclude that each term is an expression for the gravitational energy at that separation. Therefore, at any separation distance, r, the gravitational potential energy, E_g, between two masses, M and m, is given by

$$E_g = -\frac{GMm}{r}$$

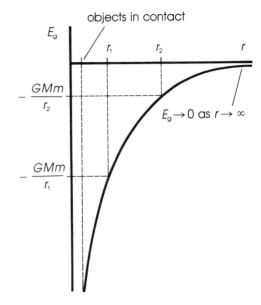

The "r" is the separation between centres; the expression is not valid at points inside either object.

Note that this equation for E_g always produces a negative value. As r increases, that is, as the masses get farther apart, E_g increases by becoming less negative. Also, as $r \to \infty$, $E_g \to 0$. The zero value of gravitational potential energy between two masses occurs when they are infinitely far apart. A graph of E_g versus r for two masses M and m, appears to the right.

This type of potential energy relationship, where two objects have a force of attraction acting between them, resulting in their potential energy being negative, is called a "potential well". The electrostatic force that will be discussed in Sections 15.3 and 15.5 has a similar potential well. We will refer to the gravitational potential well later, in our study of orbiting objects.

One very important property of a general theory is that, under appropriate conditions, it should reduce to the simple theory developed for a particular situation. The expression for gravitational potential energy is no exception. For motion near the Earth's surface,

$$r_1 = r_E \text{ and } r_2 = r_E + \Delta h$$
$$\text{so that } r_1 r_2 \approx r_E^2$$
$$\Delta h = (r_2 - r_1)$$

Therefore
$$\Delta E_g = \left(-\frac{GMm}{r_2}\right) - \left(-\frac{GMm}{r_1}\right)$$
$$= \frac{GMm}{r_1 r_2}(r_2 - r_1) \approx \frac{GMm\Delta h}{r_E^2}$$

but
$$F_g = \frac{GMm}{r_E^2} = mg$$

therefore
$$E_g = mg\Delta h$$

which is the expression developed previously for the special case of a mass near the surface of the Earth.

The choice of reference level for gravitational potential energy is arbitrary. For objects moving near the Earth's surface, the Earth is usually the reference level. For objects moving in outer space, the zero level of E_g is chosen as infinity.

It is a very reasonable assumption that $E_g = 0$ when $r = \infty$, since that is the only point when the two masses have *no* gravitational attraction force between them.

390

Sample problem

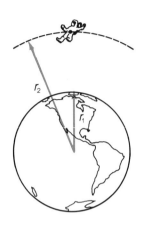

What is the change in gravitational potential energy of a 60 kg astronaut, lifted from the surface of the Earth into a circular orbit of altitude 400 km?

$$m_E = 5.98 \times 10^{24} \text{ kg}$$
$$r_1 = \text{radius of Earth}$$
$$= 6.4 \times 10^6 \text{ m}$$
$$r_2 = r_1 + 400 \text{ km}$$
$$= 6.4 \times 10^6 \text{ m} + 4.0 \times 10^5 \text{ m}$$
$$= 6.8 \times 10^6 \text{ m}$$

On the Earth's surface,

$$E_{g_1} = -\frac{GMm}{r_1}$$

$$= -\frac{(6.67 \times 10^{-11} \text{ N·m}^2/\text{kg}^2)(6.0 \times 10^{24} \text{ kg})(60 \text{ kg})}{6.4 \times 10^6 \text{ m}}$$

$$= -3.75 \times 10^9 \text{ J}$$

In orbit,

$$E_{g_2} = -\frac{GMm}{r_2}$$

$$= -\frac{(6.67 \times 10^{-11} \text{ N·m}^2/\text{kg}^2)(6.0 \times 10^{24} \text{ kg})(60 \text{ kg})}{6.8 \times 10^6 \text{ m}}$$

$$= -3.53 \times 10^9 \text{ J}$$

Therefore

$$\Delta E_g = E_{g_2} - E_{g_1}$$
$$= (-3.53 \times 10^9 \text{ J}) - (-3.75 \times 10^9 \text{ J})$$
$$= 0.22 \times 10^9 \text{ J, or } 2.2 \times 10^8 \text{ J}$$

Note that, even though the values for the astronaut's gravitational potential energy are negative at both positions, the change in E_g when her distance from the Earth increases is positive, indicating an increase in gravitational potential energy. Note also that, even for an altitude of 400 km, the approximation assuming a constant value of g is quite good.

$$\Delta E_g = mg\Delta h$$
$$= (60 \text{ kg})(9.8 \text{ N/kg})(4.0 \times 10^5 \text{ m})$$
$$= 2.4 \times 10^8 \text{ J} \quad \text{(which represents an error of less than 10%)}$$

Practice

1. With what initial velocity must an object be projected vertically upward from the surface of the Earth, in order to rise to a height equal to the Earth's radius? (Neglect air resistance and the rotation of the Earth.) $(7.9 \times 10^3 \text{ m/s})$

2. Calculate the change in gravitational potential energy for a 1.0 kg mass lifted 100 km above the Earth's surface. What percentage error would have been made by using the equation $E_g = mg\Delta h$ and the value of g at the Earth's surface ($m_E = 5.98 \times 10^{24}$ kg, $r_E = 6.37 \times 10^6$ m)? What does this tell you about the need for the more exact treatment in most normal Earth-bound problems? (1.0×10^6 J, 2%)

3. The distance from the sun to the Earth varies from 1.47×10^{11} m, at perihelion (closest approach), to 1.52×10^{11} m at aphelion (farthest distance away). The sun's mass is 1.99×10^{30} kg, the Earth's mass 5.98×10^{24} kg.

   (a) What is the maximum change in the Earth's gravitational potential energy during one orbit of the sun?

   (b) At what point in its orbit is the Earth moving its fastest, and what is its maximum change in kinetic energy?

   (1.8×10^{32} J; perihelion, 1.8×10^{32} J)

10.6 Escape From the Earth's Gravitational Field

In the last section, we learned that any two masses have a gravitational potential energy of $E_g = -\dfrac{GMm}{r}$ at a separation distance r. The negative value of this potential energy is characteristic of a "potential well". When one of the masses is the Earth, the potential well in which any other mass, at or above the Earth's surface, finds itself appears as shown on the next page.

For example, a rocket at rest on the surface of the Earth would have E_g given by point A on the graph. Since its kinetic energy, E_k, at that point in time is zero, then its total energy, E_T, would also be represented by point A, and it would not leave the ground. However, suppose the rocket is given a velocity such that it has kinetic energy represented by the distance AB on the graph. Now its total energy ($E_T = E_g + E_k$) is represented by point B, and the rocket begins to rise. As its altitude increases, E_g increases along the curve AC, and E_T remains constant along the line BC. E_k decreases, and at any point is given by the length of the vertical line from the curve to the horizontal line BC. When the rocket reaches an altitude corresponding to point C, E_k has decreased to zero, so the rocket can go no higher. Instead, it falls back down, with E_k and E_g governed by the same constraints as on the upward trip.

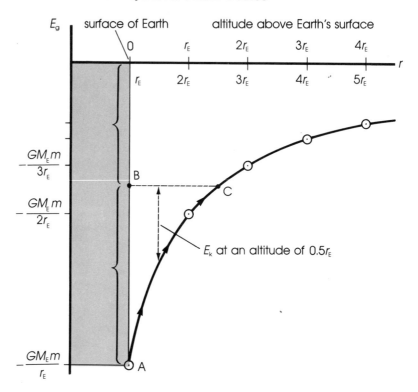

It is an interesting exercise to determine what minimum velocity this rocket would have to be given, at the Earth's surface, to "escape" from the Earth's potential well. To do this, the rocket's initial kinetic energy must just exceed the depth of the potential well at the Earth's surface, thereby making its total energy positive. This also means the rocket must reach an infinite distance, where $E_g = 0$, before coming nearly to rest.

$$E_T = E_k + E_g > 0$$

therefore
$$E_k > |E_g| \quad \text{(since } E_g < 0\text{)}$$

$$\frac{1}{2}mv_e^2 > \left| -\frac{GM_E m}{r_E} \right|$$

$$v_e > \sqrt{\frac{2GM_E}{r_E}}$$

$$> \sqrt{\frac{2(6.67 \times 10^{-11} \text{ N·m}^2/\text{kg}^2)(5.98 \times 10^{24} \text{ kg})}{6.4 \times 10^6 \text{ m}}}$$

$$> 1.12 \times 10^4 \text{ m/s}$$

This is called the **escape velocity**.

Thus, a rocket launched from the Earth with a velocity greater than this will move away from the Earth, losing E_k and gaining E_g as it does so. However, since its E_k is greater than the depth of its E_g well at any point, its total energy will always be positive. Theoretically, then, it will reach an infinite separation distance from the Earth with some E_k left, and escape. For a launch velocity less than the escape velocity, the rocket might come to rest at some finite distance, then fall back to Earth.

A rocket whose total energy is negative will not be able to escape from the Earth's potential well, and is said to be "bound" to the Earth. The **binding energy** of any mass is the amount of additional kinetic energy it needs for escape. For a rocket of mass m, at rest on the Earth's surface, the binding energy is $\dfrac{GM_Em}{r_E}$, since its total energy is

$$E_{total} = E_k + E_g$$
$$= 0 + \left(-\frac{GM_Em}{r_E}\right)$$
$$= -\frac{GM_Em}{r_E}$$

A good example of a bound object is a satellite moving in a circular orbit of radius r_o in the potential well of the Earth. The centripetal force necessary to sustain the circular orbit is provided by the force of gravitational attraction between the satellite and the Earth. If the satellite has a mass m and orbital velocity v_o,

$$F_c = F_g$$
$$\frac{mv_o^2}{r_o} = \frac{GM_Em}{r_o^2} \tag{1}$$

The total energy of the Earth-satellite system is constant, and is given by

$$E_{total} = E_k + E_g$$
$$= \frac{1}{2}mv_o^2 - \frac{GM_Em}{r_o} \tag{2}$$

From equation (1),

$$\frac{1}{2}mv_o^2 = \frac{1}{2}\frac{GM_Em}{r_o}$$

Therefore, equation (2) becomes

$$E_{total} = \frac{1}{2}\frac{GM_Em}{r_o} - \frac{GM_Em}{r_o}$$
$$= -\frac{1}{2}\frac{GM_Em}{r_o}$$
$$= \frac{1}{2}E_g$$

Even though these results have been developed for the special case of a circular orbit, they can be shown to hold true for all orbits, including ellipses.

For objects moving under the influence of gravity alone, the potential energy gained as they move farther apart is equal to the kinetic energy lost as they move more slowly. Satellites in elliptical orbits move more slowly at apogee, faster at perogee.

This is a very significant result. The total energy of a satellite in circular orbit is negative, and is equal to one-half the value of the gravitational potential energy at the separation represented by the radius of its orbit. The graph shows the potential well for the Earth and the position of this orbiting satellite in the well.

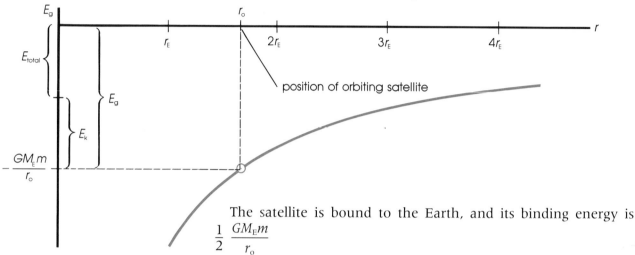

The satellite is bound to the Earth, and its binding energy is

$$\frac{1}{2}\frac{GM_{E}m}{r_{o}}$$

In summary, the total energy of any object in the Earth's gravitational field is composed of kinetic and gravitational potential energy. The graphs below illustrate the three general cases for such an object.

$$E_{T} = E_{k} + E_{g} = \frac{1}{2}mv^{2} - \frac{GM_{E}m}{r}$$

Case 1: $E_{T} = 0$ — object just escapes

Case 2: $E_{T} > 0$ — object escapes with a velocity

Case 3: $E_{T} < 0$ — object is bound to the Earth

Sample problem

A 500 kg communications satellite is to be placed in a synchronous orbit around the Earth.

(a) What is the radius of its circular orbit?

A synchronous satellite remains in the same relative position above the Earth because it has a period of 24 h, the same as that of the Earth's rotation on its axis.

As for any satellite,

$$F_c = F_g$$

$$\frac{4\pi^2 m_s r_o}{T^2} = \frac{GM_E m_s}{r_o^2}$$

$$r_o = \sqrt[3]{\frac{GM_E T^2}{4\pi^2}}$$

$$= \sqrt[3]{\frac{(6.67 \times 10^{-11} \text{ N·m}^2/\text{kg}^2)(5.98 \times 10^{24} \text{ kg})(8.64 \times 10^4 \text{ s})^2}{4\pi^2}}$$

$$= \sqrt[3]{75.4 \times 10^{21} \text{ m}^3}$$

$$= 4.22 \times 10^7 \text{ m}$$

This radius represents an altitude of 3.6×10^4 km above the Earth's surface.

(b) What is the gravitational potential energy of the satellite when it is attached to its launch rocket, at rest on the Earth's surface?

At the surface of the Earth,

$$E_g = -\frac{GM_E m_s}{r_E}$$

$$= -\frac{(6.67 \times 10^{-11} \text{ N·m}^2/\text{kg}^2)(5.98 \times 10^{24} \text{ kg})(5.00 \times 10^2 \text{ kg})}{6.4 \times 10^6 \text{ m}}$$

$$= -3.12 \times 10^{10} \text{ J}$$

(c) What is the total energy of the satellite when synchronous in orbit?

The total energy of a satellite in orbit, bound to the Earth, is given by

$$E_{total} = E_k + E_g = \frac{1}{2} m_s v_o^2 - \frac{GM_E m_s}{r_o}$$

$$= -\frac{1}{2} \frac{GM_E m_s}{r_o}$$

$$= -\frac{1}{2} \frac{(6.67 \times 10^{-11} \text{ N·m}^2/\text{kg}^2)(5.98 \times 10^{24} \text{ kg})(5.00 \times 10^2 \text{ kg})}{4.22 \times 10^7 \text{ m}}$$

$$= -2.36 \times 10^9 \text{ J}$$

$T = (24 \text{ h})(60 \text{ min/h})(60 \text{ s/min})$
$= 8.64 \times 10^4$ s

Actually, it has a period of one sidereal day, about 5 min short of 24 h. This is the rotational period of the Earth in space.

(d) How much work must the launch rocket do on the satellite to place it in orbit?

$$\text{work done} = \Delta E_{\text{total}} = E_{\text{total}} \text{ (in orbit)} - E_{\text{total}} \text{ (on Earth)}$$
$$= -2.36 \times 10^9 \text{ J} - (-3.12 \times 10^{10} \text{ J})$$
$$= 2.88 \times 10^{10} \text{ J}$$

(e) Once in orbit, how much additional energy must the satellite receive, in order to escape from the Earth's potential well?

in orbit, $E_{\text{total}} = -2.36 \times 10^9 \text{ J}$

for escape, $E_{\text{total}} \geqslant 0$

Therefore, in order to escape, the satellite must acquire at least 2.36×10^9 J of additional energy.

Practice

1. The moon is an Earth satellite, of mass 7.35×10^{22} kg, whose average distance from the Earth's centre is 3.85×10^8 m.
   (a) What is the gravitational potential energy of the moon with respect to the Earth?
   (b) What is its kinetic energy and velocity, in Earth orbit?
   (c) What is its binding energy to the Earth?
   $(-7.61 \times 10^{28}\text{J}; 3.81 \times 10^{28}\text{J}, 1.02 \times 10^3 \text{ m/s}; 3.81 \times 10^{28}\text{J})$

2. What is the total amount of energy needed to place a 2000 kg satellite in circular Earth orbit, at an altitude of 500 km?
   $(6.7 \times 10^{10} \text{ J})$

3. How much additional energy would have to be supplied to the satellite in question 2, once it was in orbit, to allow it to escape from the Earth's gravitational field? $(5.8 \times 10^{10} \text{ J})$

4. For the synchronous satellite in the sample problem on the previous page,
   (a) What is the satellite's speed in orbit?
   (b) What speed must it reach during launch, in order to get into the synchronous orbit? (Assume that the fuel is all burned in a short period of time.)
   $(3.1 \times 10^3 \text{ m/s}, 1.0 \times 10^4 \text{ m/s})$

10.7 Investigations

Investigation 10.1: Hooke's Law

Problem:
What is the relationship between the extension in an elastic spring and the applied force?

Materials:
As shown in diagram

Procedure:
1. Set up the apparatus illustrated, without any mass attached. If possible, adjust the height of the spring so that its lower end is at the same height as the zero point on the metre stick. Otherwise, record the vertical height from the floor to the lower end of the spring.
2. Set up an observations chart similar to that illustrated. Record the number of the spring you are using.

Attached mass (kg)	Force (N)	Extension (m)
0	0	0
0.20	1.96	

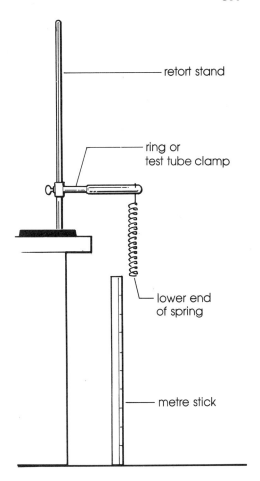

retort stand

ring or test tube clamp

lower end of spring

metre stick

3. Hang a 200 g mass on the spring. Lower the mass gently until the spring supports it. Record the extension of the spring.
4. Attach a 400 g mass and record the extension.
5. Repeat step 4 for 600 g, 800 g, 1.00 kg, 1.10 kg, 1.20 kg, 1.30 kg, and 1.40 kg.
6. Plot a graph of force (F) versus extension (x).
7. From the graph determine the relationship between the force and the extension, expressing it both as a proportion and an equation. This relationship is known as Hooke's Law.
8. Using the graph, determine the extension when the force is (a) 0 N, (b) 8.0 N, and (c) 16 N.
9. Using the equation, determine the extension when the force is (a) 0 N, (b) 8.0 N, and (c) 16 N. Compare your results with those obtained from the graph (step 8).
10. Using the equation, determine the extension when the force is 30 N. Is the answer you have calculated valid? Discuss.
11. Using both the graph and the equation, determine the potential energy stored in the spring when it is held extended by a 10 N force.

If the zero point on the metre stick is not at the zero extension level it will be necessary to subtract one measurement from the other to find the extension (distance from floor to unextended spring − distance from floor to extended spring = extension).

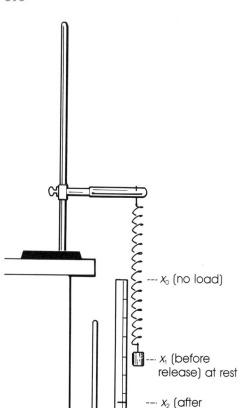

x_0 (no load)

x_1 (before release) at rest

x_2 (after release) maximum extension

Investigation 10.2: Conservation of Energy in an Elastic Spring

Problem:
What are the relationships between the gravitational potential energy of a suspended mass and the elastic potential energy in a stretched spring?

Materials:
As shown in diagram

Procedure:
1. Set up the apparatus illustrated. Use the same numbered spring that was used in the Hooke's Law investigation (page 397).
2. Adjust the metre stick so that its zero point is adjacent to the lower end of the unloaded spring (at x_0).
3. Attach a 1.00 kg mass to the spring and lower it gently so that the spring is stretched to one-half the amount the 1.00 kg mass would normally stretch it (see previous investigation). Designate this position as x_1, and then release the mass so that it falls freely. Note the maximum extension of the spring (x_2) by placing a pencil next to the metre stick.
4. Describe (in words) the types of energy in the spring-mass-Earth system at the points x_0, x_1, and x_2.
5. Determine the loss in gravitational potential energy (ΔE_g) of the mass as it falls from x_1 to x_2.
6. Determine the elastic potential energy (E_e) at positions x_1 and x_2. Calculate the gain in elastic potential energy (ΔE_e) as the spring stretches from x_1 to x_2. Compare this with the loss in gravitational potential energy, ΔE_g.
7. Repeat steps 3 to 6, this time releasing the 1.00 kg mass from a point that represents three-quarters of the normal amount of stretch of the spring (see previous investigation).
8. Repeat steps 3 to 6 once more, this time releasing a 0.500 kg mass from a point that represents one-half of the normal amount of stretch of the same spring by a 0.500 kg mass (see previous investigation).
9. Attach a 0.500 kg mass to the spring. Release the mass from the no-load position (x_0). Record the maximum extension of the spring (x_m). (A number of releases will be necessary to obtain an accurate value.) Determine the midpoint ($x_{\frac{1}{2}m}$) between the extensions x_0 and x_m.
10. Describe (in words) the types of energy in the spring-mass-Earth system at the points x_0, $x_{\frac{1}{2}m}$, and x_m.

11. Calculate the loss in gravitational potential energy as the mass falls from x_0 to $x_{\frac{1}{2}m}$.

12. Calculate the gain in elastic potential energy as the spring stretches from x_0 to $x_{\frac{1}{2}m}$.

13. Compare the loss in gravitational potential energy with the gain in elastic potential energy, from x_0 to the midpoint. Account for any difference.

14. What types of mechanical energy does the system possess when the mass is at the midpoint? Determine the amount of each type. Finally, determine the velocity of the mass at that point.

10.8 Review

Discussion

1. List several other common devices that, like a stretched or compressed spring, can store potential energy when temporarily deformed.

2. Why would car bumpers mounted on springs that obey Hooke's Law not be a good idea?

3. Draw a sketch to show how two springs with different lengths and spring constants might be combined to have the $F-x$ graph shown.

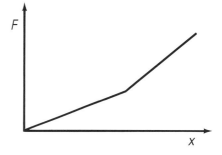

4. Describe what might happen to the internal molecular structure of a spring deformed beyond its elastic limit.

5. How is the work done in pulling a mass away from the Earth different from that done in stretching a spring?

6. When a mass m is dropped towards the Earth, its gain in kinetic energy is *not exactly* equal to the loss in gravitational potential energy of the system. Explain.

7. Discuss the impact that fibreglass poles have had on the world record for the pole vault, because of their ability to store potential energy when deformed elastically.

8. How does the escape velocity of a tennis ball compare with the escape velocity of a rocket? How do their escape energies compare?

9. When a rocket is given a great enough velocity to "escape" from the Earth, will it also escape from the sun and hence the universe? What happens to the artificial Earth satellites that are sent to explore the space around distant planets like Mars and Saturn?

10. The greater the altitude of an Earth satellite, the longer it takes to complete one orbit. Discuss the statement that it is impossible for any vehicle to go around the Earth in less than about 80 min.

Problems

11. A 2.5 kg roast of beef is suspended from a vertical spring in a butcher's scale whose force constant is 200 N/m.
    (a) What is the extension of the spring?
    (b) How much energy is stored in the spring?

12. A linear elastic spring can be compressed 10.0 cm by an applied force of 5.0 N. A 4.5 kg crate of apples, moving at 2.0 m/s, collides with this spring, as shown.
    What will be the maximum compression of the spring?

13. The force-compression graph of a hypothetical spring is shown below.
    (a) How much work is done in compressing the spring 0.60 m?
    (b) What is the potential energy stored in the spring when compressed this amount?
    (c) A 5.0 kg toy car is placed on a level, frictionless surface against the spring when compressed 0.60 m, and the spring is released. The other end of the spring is fixed. Determine the velocity of the car when it has moved a distance of 0.20 m.

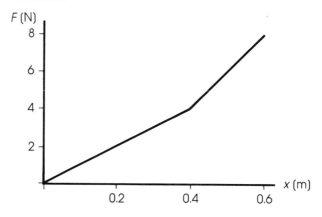

14. A spring bumper, whose force-compression relationship is given by $F = 50\,x$, is compressed 0.20 m.
    (a) What is the potential energy stored in the spring at a compression of 0.20 m?
    (b) The spring is compressed further to 0.60 m. What will be the change in elastic potential energy?

(c) A 0.40 kg cart is placed against the compressed spring on a horizontal, frictionless plane, and the system is released. With what velocity will the cart leave the spring?

15. The spring in a toy gun has a force constant of 500 N/m. It is compressed 5.0 cm, and a ball of mass 10 g is placed next to it in the barrel.
    (a) What is the ball's maximum velocity, when the trigger releases the spring? Assume that there is no friction, and that the gun barrel is level.
    (b) Determine the muzzle velocity if an average retarding force of 0.80 N acts on the ball, and the barrel is 0.25 m long.

16. A rifle bullet of mass 10.0 g strikes and becomes embedded in a wooden block of mass 490 g, which is at rest on a horizontal, frictionless surface and is attached to a spring bumper, as shown. The impact compresses the spring, whose force constant is 100 N/m, by 20 cm.

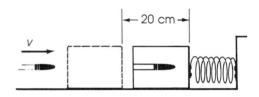

    (a) What is the maximum potential energy of the spring?
    (b) Determine the velocity with which the block and bullet first begin to move.
    (c) What was the initial velocity of the bullet?
    (d) What was the initial kinetic energy of the bullet?
    (e) Explain any difference between (a) and (d).

17. A 2.4 kg dynamics cart is moving to the right at 1.5 m/s, with a linear elastic spring attached to its front end, when it collides head-on with a stationary cart of mass 3.6 kg.
    (a) Calculate the total energy of the system before the collision.
    (b) What is the velocity of each cart at minimum separation?
    (c) Calculate the change in total kinetic energy of the system at minimum separation.
    (d) If the maximum compression of the spring during the collision is 12 cm, what is its force constant?

18. Two trolleys, of mass 1.2 kg and 4.8 kg, are at rest with a compressed spring between them, held that way by a string tied around both. When the string is cut, the trolleys spring apart. If the force constant of the spring is 2400 N/m, by how much must it have been compressed in order that the 4.8 kg cart move off at 2.0 m/s?

19. A 3.0 kg ball is dropped from a height of 0.80 m onto a vertical spring of force constant 1200 N/m. What is the maximum compression of the spring?

20. A 60 kg person jumps from a platform onto a trampoline 10 m below, stretching it 1.0 m from its initial position. Assuming that the trampoline behaves like a simple elastic spring, how much will it stretch if the same person jumps from a height of 20 m?

21. A linear elastic spring is 15.0 cm long. When the upper end is held in the hand and a 500 g mass is suspended from the lower end, its length becomes 22.0 cm. If the hand is now jerked quickly upward, the spring first extends to a length of 28.5 cm, then the mass starts to move up. The hand is then held still.
    (a) Calculate the acceleration with which the mass first begins to move.
    (b) Calculate the speed of the mass when the length of the spring becomes 22.0 cm again.
    (c) Calculate the length of the spring when the mass comes to rest at its highest point.

22. A block of mass 1.0 kg, at rest on a horizontal table as shown, is attached to two rigid supports by springs A and B. A force of 10 N stretches spring A alone by 0.25 m while a force of 2.5 N extends spring B alone by the same amount.

    Initially the block is at rest between unstretched springs; then it is pushed to the side a distance of 0.50 m by a variable horizontal force F, compressing one spring and extending the other.
    (a) What is the total work done by the force F? (The block is held at rest.)
    (b) If the block is then released, with what velocity does it move through its original equilibrium position?
    (c) What would be the spring constant of a single spring that would duplicate A and B?

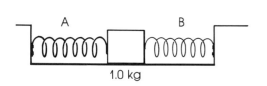

A   B

1.0 kg

23. A 1.0 kg lead sphere is suspended from the ceiling by a wire 5.0 m long. The ball is pulled sideways and up, until the wire is horizontal, and then released. Find:
    (a) the maximum velocity acquired by the ball
    (b) the tension in the wire at the lowest point in the swing

24. A toy cart of mass 5.0 kg is projected up a ramp inclined at 30° to the horizontal, with an initial velocity of 6.0 m/s. If the frictional force opposing its motion is 4.0 N, find the distance it travels before stopping, and its increase in gravitational potential energy at that point.

25. A new amusement park ride is shown in the diagram.

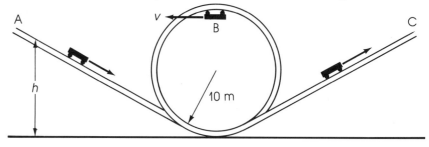

A v B   C

h 10 m

The mass of the small car, including its contents, is 400 kg, and the radius of the loop is 10 m. Assume that the track is frictionless and that no mechanism holds the car in contact with the track.

(a) In order that the car stay on the track at B, what minimum velocity must it have at that point?

(b) From what minimum height, h, must the car start from rest in order to do this?

(c) Is the mass of the car a factor in determining h? Explain.

26. Two boxes are connected by a smooth rope over a light, frictionless, fixed pulley, as shown.

Use the principle of conservation of energy to determine the velocity with which the 15.0 kg box strikes the floor, after the system is released from rest.

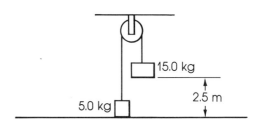

27. A 1.0 kg tetherball is suspended by a string 0.80 m long from a nail at point X, 0.50 m vertically above a horizontal rod at Y. When the ball is released from Z, on the same horizontal level as Y, it swings down, and the string catches on Y.

(a) What is the initial gravitational potential energy of the 1.0 kg tetherball relative to point X?

(b) What is its initial potential energy relative to point Y?

(c) Determine the location of points A, B, and C, where the mass has, respectively:

  (i) maximum kinetic energy

  (ii) maximum velocity

  (iii) maximum potential energy with respect to Y after it is released

  Calculate the value of each of the quantities in (i), (ii), and (iii).

(d) How high above Y must the tetherball be released so that it will swing completely around a circle of radius 0.30 m about point Y?

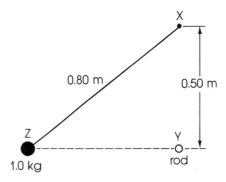

28. Isaac Newton was *not* inspired by an apple falling on his head. Actually, he was lying down and the apple struck his stomach. It then bounced straight back up, having lost 10% of its kinetic energy in the collision. How high did it rise on the first bounce if it had originally dropped from a branch 1.0 m above Isaac's stomach? (SIN '72)

29. The apple, in question 28, continued to bounce, losing the same fraction of its kinetic energy each time. If you ignore the slight deformation of Isaac's stomach during each bounce, what was the total distance travelled by the apple from the time it left the tree until it eventually came to rest on Isaac's stomach? (SIN '72)

30. The space shuttle ejects a 1200 kg booster tank so that the tank is momentarily at rest at an altitude of 2000 km. Neglecting atmospheric effects, determine:
    (a) how much work is done on the booster by the force of gravity in returning it to the Earth's surface
    (b) the velocity with which it strikes the surface of the Earth
31. A space vehicle, launched as a lunar probe, arrives at the upper limit of the Earth's atmosphere. At this point, its kinetic energy is 5.0×10^9 J and its gravitational potential energy is -6.4×10^9 J. What is its binding energy?
32. An artificial Earth satellite, of mass 2.00×10^3 kg, has an elliptical orbit, with a mean altitude of 400 km.
    (a) What is its mean value of gravitational potential energy while in orbit?
    (b) What is its mean value of orbital kinetic energy?
    (c) What is its total energy while in orbit?
    (d) If its perogee is 280 km, what is it orbital velocity at perogee?
33. A 500 kg satellite is in circular orbit 200 km above the Earth's surface. Calculate:
    (a) the gravitational potential energy of the satellite
    (b) the kinetic energy of the satellite
    (c) its binding energy
    (d) the percentage increase in launching energy required to make it escape from Earth?
34. A rocketship, of mass 1.00×10^4 kg is located 1.00×10^{10} m from the centre of the Earth.
    (a) Determine its gravitational potential energy at this point, considering only the Earth.
    (b) How much kinetic energy must it have, at this point, to be capable of escaping from the Earth's gravitational field?
    (c) What is its escape velocity from Earth, at this point?
35. (a) Calculate the escape velocity from our solar system (i.e., from the surface of the sun, whose mass is 1.98×10^{30} kg, and whose radius is 6.96×10^8 m).
    (b) What velocity would an object leaving Earth need, to escape from our solar system?
36. The mass of the moon is approximately 6.7×10^{22} kg, and its radius is 1.6×10^6 m.
    (a) With what velocity must an object be projected from the moon's surface in order to rise to an altitude equal to the moon's radius?
    (b) If a woman can raise her centre of gravity 2.0 m vertically in a high jump at the Earth's surface, how high could she jump with the same muscular effort on the moon's surface?

"Perogee" is that point in a satellite's elliptical orbit where it most closely approaches the Earth. Can you guess what "apogee" is?

Numerical Answers to Review Problems
11. (a) 0.12 m (b) 1.5 J
12. 0.60 m
13. (a) 2.0 J (b) 2.0 J (c) 0.69 m/s
14. (a) 1.0 J (b) 8.0 J (c) 6.7 m/s
15. (a) 11 m/s (b) 9.2 m/s
16. (a) 2.0 J (b) 2.8 m/s (c) 1.4×10^2 m/s
    (d) 1.0×10^2 J
17. (a) 2.7 J (b) 0.60 m/s (c) -1.6 J
    (d) 2.3×10^2 N/m
18. 0.20 m
19. 0.18 m
20. 1.33 m
21. (a) 9.1 m/s² (b) 0.77 m/s (c) 15.5 cm
22. (a) 6.3 J (b) 3.5 m/s (c) 50 N/m
23. (a) 9.9 m/s (b) 29 N
24. 3.2 m, 77 J
25. (a) 9.9 m/s (b) 25 m (c) no
26. 4.9 m/s

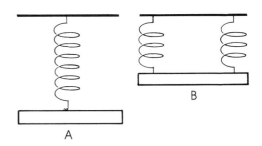

37. A uniform bar of iron is supported by a long, uniform Hooke's Law spring as shown in A.

   The spring is cut exactly in half and the two pieces are used to support the same bar, as shown in B. If the whole spring stretched by 4 cm in A, by how much would each half spring stretch in B? (SIN '69)

38. Realizing that he could not drive up a 30°, ice-covered hill because there was no friction, Sir Isaac Newton had stopped his cart, of total mass 500 kg, at the bottom. He was struck in the rear by a London stage coach, of total mass 1500 kg, travelling at 20 m/s. The two vehicles stuck together, with nothing breaking loose, and slid up the hill in a straight line. How far up the slope did the wreckage get before coming to rest? (SIN '70)

39. Tarzan is hanging on the end of a vine, at point A, over an alligator-infested river. He must reach point B, in a tree, to be safe. Tarzan's monkey, Cheetah, located at C in a nearby tree, jumps, and is moving horizontally when Tarzan catches him.

   Given the following data, calculate the minimum horizontal speed, v, of the monkey, necessary for the two to reach safety. Length of vine = 30 m; mass of Tarzan = 75 kg; mass of monkey = 25 kg.

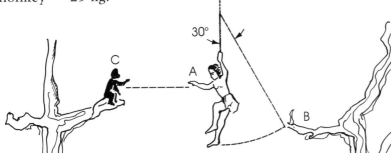

40. A very light basket hangs from the limb of a tree by a long spring. The limb extends out over a pond, and the spring holds the basket 3.0 m above the surface of the pond. Three girls of equal mass carefully lower themselves into the basket, one after the other, causing the spring to stretch 1.0 m for each additional girl, so that with all three aboard, the basket just touches the water. The girls then jump into the water, and the basket returns to its original position. Once back on shore, one of the girls climbs to a higher limb of the tree and steps off, landing in the basket and causing the spring to stretch until the basket just touches the water's surface again, for an instant. From what height above the water's surface did the girl step from the higher limb? (SIN '73)

27. (a) −4.9 J (b) 0 (c)(i) 2.9 J
   (ii) 2.4 m/s (iii) 0 m (d) 0.45 m
28. 0.90 m
29. 19 m
30. (a) −1.8 × 10¹⁰ J (b) 5.4 × 10³ m/s
31. 1.4 × 10⁹ J
32. (a) −1.18 × 10¹¹ J (b) 5.88 × 10¹⁰ J
   (c) −5.88 × 10¹⁰ J (d) 7.74 × 10³ m/s
33. (a) −3.03 × 10¹⁰ J (b) 1.52 × 10¹⁰ J
   (c) −1.52 × 10¹⁰ J (d) 94%
34. (a) −3.99 × 10⁸ J (b) >3.99 × 10⁸ J
   (c) 2.82 × 10² m/s
35. (a) 6.16 × 10⁵ m/s (b) 4.34 × 10⁴ m/s
36. (a) 1.7 × 10³ m/s (b) 11 m
37. 1 cm
38. 23 m
39. 36 m/s
40. 4.5 m

11 Geometric Optics

We are all familiar with light — or think we are. Our eyes respond to the light we receive from the objects all around us. This light enables us to see the sun, the moon, the stars, and the sky. We see blue water, brown earth, green plants, a red rose. But what is light — this mysterious phenomenon that moves at incredible speed from its source to our eye?

The study of light must have begun before the dawn of history, but the earliest surviving records are from the ancient Greeks. Pythagoras (in the 6th century B.C.) theorized that light consisted of a stream of particles emitted from a source of light. Aristotle (in the 4th century B.C.) disagreed. He believed that light moved as a wave, like ripples on water. This debate continued down through the centuries. In the 17th century, Isaac Newton (1642–1727) postulated that light moves as a stream of particles, while Christiaan Huygens (1629–95) and others supported the wave theory of light and provided experimental evidence for their belief.

In the early part of the 20th century, it was shown that both theories have some validity. But, before examining the evidence, we must grasp the fundamental properties of light, including those that have to do with its transmission, reflection, refraction, and dispersion. Then, using our knowledge of waves, we can examine the question of what light is.

11.1 The Transmission of Light

When light from a candle falls on a solid obstacle that is sitting on a table, a sharp shadow is produced on the surface of the table. The sharp edges of the shadow remind us that light travels in straight lines, a property called **rectilinear propagation**. We use this property when we hold a needle up to the light to thread it, or when we line up the sights on a rifle. Later, in Chapter 14, we will see that this rule has exceptions, when light passes through very small openings and past very small obstacles. But for most purposes we may assume that light travels in straight lines.

Sometimes, when there is dust in the air, we see "rays" of sunlight streaming into the room. Or at sunset we may see the sun's rays breaking through the clouds. In everyday language, "ray" means a narrow stream of light energy, but in physics we give it a more precise meaning. A **ray**, in physics, is the path taken by light energy, and it is usually represented by a solid line with an arrow indicating its direction of travel. A **beam** of light is a stream of light rays and is represented, diagrammatically, by a number of rays. The rays may be converging, diverging, or parallel.

Although the ray does not adequately explain the actual nature of light, it is a useful notion, because it can explain the behaviour of many aspects of light, such as reflection, refraction, and the formation of images in mirrors and lenses. Such explanations involve the geometric analysis of rays that move in straight lines. The study of these rays is called **geometric optics**.

11.2 The Speed of Light and the Index of Refraction

When we turn on an electric light bulb, the light moves almost instantaneously from the bulb to our eye. We can see that light travels at a very high speed, but at what speed, exactly?

Galileo (1564–1642) made the first serious attempt to measure the speed of light. He instructed an assistant on a hilltop about a kilometre away to flash his lantern when he saw the flash of Galileo's lantern. By timing the interval between his flash and the assistant's flash he hoped to measure the speed of light. This experiment failed because the reaction time of the experimenters was much longer than the time the light took to make the round trip. Galileo recognized this fact and concluded that light moved too quickly to be measured by this technique.

Speculation about the movement of the moons of Jupiter has added to our knowledge of the speed of light. Jupiter has twelve moons, four of which are easily seen with a simple telescope. All of the moons move relatively quickly around Jupiter. One of them has a period of only 42.5 h. Although the accurate measurement of their periods had been made earlier, it was Olaus Roemer (1644–1710), a Danish astronomer, who attempted to predict the precise moment at which they would be eclipsed by Jupiter (as viewed from the Earth).

To his surprise, the eclipses came progressively earlier at the times of the year when the Earth approached Jupiter and progressively later when it was moving away from Jupiter. Roemer concluded, correctly, that light must travel at a finite speed, and that the eclipses were delayed because the light had to travel a greater distance when the Earth and Jupiter were farther apart. He calculated that when the Earth and Jupiter were farthest apart, it took 22 min, or 1320 s, for light to cross the diameter of the Earth's orbit.

A few years later, Christiaan Huygens, a Dutch mathematician and scientist, calculated the diameter of the Earth's orbit and, using Roemer's data, calculated the speed of light as follows:

$$AB = 3.0 \times 10^{11} \text{ m} \qquad v = \frac{\Delta d}{\Delta t}$$
$$\Delta t = 22 \text{ min}$$
$$= 1320 \text{ s} \qquad\qquad = \frac{3.00 \times 10^{11} \text{ m}}{1320 \text{ s}}$$
$$= 2.3 \times 10^8 \text{ m/s}$$

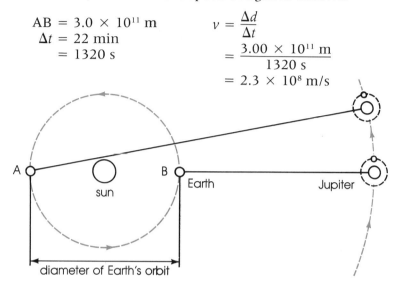

diameter of Earth's orbit

Modern telescopes and accurate timers have enabled scientists to determine that the time difference is 1.00×10^3 s; nevertheless, Huygens' calculation was astonishingly accurate considering the equipment he had. The value Roemer and Huygens gave for the speed of light was so great that their fellow scientists rejected it at first. The work of these two scientists was not accepted until after both were dead.

In 1905, Albert Michelson (1852–1931), an American scientist, made very accurate measurements of the speed of light. His work was recognized, and he was awarded the Nobel Prize for Physics in 1907. Michelson's method involved an ingenious arrangement of mirrors (see diagram on next page). Light from a very bright source was reflected from surface A, on an eight-sided, rotatable mirror, to a mirror located about 35 km away. The distant mirror reflected the light back to surface G where it was observed in a telescope. The octagonal mirror rotated, and there were only certain positions in which it reflected light that could be seen in the telescope. These positions occurred every one-eighth of a rotation. If the mirror moved by this amount in the time interval taken by a light pulse making the round trip, then the telescope would detect the pulse reflected from face A via face F, in its new position.

For this to happen, the octagonal mirror had to rotate very quickly — approximately 32 000 times/min. The period of rotation of the mirror was accurately determined, and the time for the light to make the round trip was measured. The speed of light could then be calculated, using this time and the distance travelled by the light on its round trip.

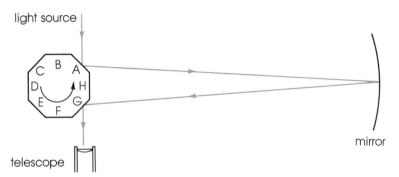

In 1933, Michelson supervised the re-measurement of the speed of light with a long, evacuated tube in which light rays were repeatedly reflected for a total distance of over 16 km. Although he died before the final results were calculated, his experiment produced an even more accurate value for the speed of light.

Today we have very accurate measurements made with lasers. The currently accepted value for the speed of light in a vacuum, c, is $c = 2.997\ 924\ 562\ \pm\ 0.000\ 000\ 011\ \times\ 10^8$ m/s. This value is usually rounded off to 3.00×10^8 m/s, except where greater accuracy is required.

In air, the speed of light is only about $0.000\ 87 \times 10^8$ m/s less than in a vacuum. Thus the value 3.00×10^8 m/s can be used for air or a vacuum. In other transparent media, such as water or glass, the speed is significantly smaller. It was a French scientist, Jean Foucault, who, in 1862, devised a method for measuring the speed of light in both air and water. He found that light travels in water at approximately three-quarters the speed it travels in a vacuum, i.e., at 0.75 c. Other materials produce different values, but the speed is always smaller than the speed of light in a vacuum. The term "optically dense" is used when referring to a medium in which the speed of light decreases.

The ratio of the speed of light in a vacuum (c) to the speed of light in a given material (v) is called the **index of refraction** (n) of that material. That is,

$$n = \frac{c}{v}$$

The indices for various materials are given in the table on the next page. As we will see in Chapter 14, n varies slightly with the

Modern physics states that light travels at a constant speed only through a vacuum; and that when it passes through a material medium it travels more slowly because the light excites the molecules of matter to radiate themselves. The time lag caused by the molecules' becoming excited and emitting a new photon effectively slows down the entire wave packet of light (see Chapter 18).

Measuring the speed of light using a laser, operating in a vacuum, in a mine shaft.

Indices of Refraction

Substance	Index of refraction (n)
vacuum	1.0000
air (0°C, 101 kPa)	1.0003
water	1.33
ethyl alcohol	1.36
quartz (fused)	1.46
glycerine	1.47
Lucite or Plexiglas	1.51
glass (crown)	1.52
sodium chloride	1.53
glass (crystal)	1.54
ruby	1.54
glass (flint)	1.65
zircon	1.92
diamond	2.42

Note: for yellow light, wavelength = 589 nm

wavelength of the light, except in a vacuum. The values in the table are for a specific colour of yellow light.

The higher the index of a given substance, the more the light is slowed down when it travels from a vacuum into the substance. Air, with an index of refraction of 1.0003, slows it down very little. Zircon, with an index of 1.92, slows it down considerably more.

Sometimes the index of refraction for light going from a vacuum into a substance is referred to as the **absolute refractive index**. The value of the index for light travelling from air into the substance is so close to the value of the absolute refractive index that we only distinguish between them in rare instances. In this text, when the term "index of refraction" is used we are using the value of the absolute refractive index. When light travels between two materials with different indices of refraction, the ratio of their absolute indices of refraction is referred to as the **relative index of refraction**. For example, for light travelling from water into glass the relative index of refraction is:

$$_w n_g = \frac{n_g}{n_w} = \frac{1.50}{1.33} = 1.13$$

For light travelling from glass into water the relative index of refraction is:

$$_g n_w = \frac{n_w}{n_g} = \frac{1.33}{1.50} = 0.89$$

Sample problem

Using the table in the margin, calculate the speed of light in Lucite.

$$n = \frac{c}{v}$$

Therefore

$$v = \frac{c}{n}$$

$$= \frac{3.00 \times 10^8 \text{ m/s}}{1.51}$$

$$= 1.99 \times 10^8 \text{ m/s}$$

Practice

1. What is the index of refraction of a liquid in which the speed of light is 2.50×10^8 m/s? (1.20)
2. The index of refraction of diamond is 2.42. What is the speed of light in diamond? (1.24×10^8 m/s)

11.3 The Pinhole Camera

This device was originally called a "camera obscura" when it was invented in the 16th century. It consists of a light-proof box with a pinhole in one end and a screen of frosted glass or tracing paper at the other end. An image is formed on the screen by light travelling in straight lines from an object to the screen. It is easier to see the image on the screen if external light is excluded by shielding the outside of the box with a dark cloth or other covering.

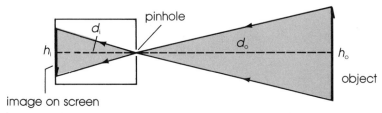

The formation of an image in a pinhole camera

The rays of light from various parts of the object travel in straight lines through the pinhole and together form an inverted image on the screen. That the image is produced in this way justifies our earlier statement that light travels in straight lines. If a line is drawn through the pinhole and perpendicular to both the image and the object, it can be shown by similar triangles that

$$\frac{h_i}{h_o} = \frac{d_i}{d_o}$$

The magnification, M, of any optical device is defined as the ratio of the height of the image to the height of the object, that is, h_i/h_o. The relationship $M = h_i/h_o = d_i/d_o$ is referred to as the **magnification equation.**

An image that can be formed on a screen is called a **real image.** An image that cannot be formed on a screen is called a **virtual image.** The image formed in a pinhole camera is a real one.

In physics, the **characteristics of an image** are stated in terms of its attitude (erect or inverted), its size (larger, smaller, or the same size in comparison with the object), and its type (real or virtual). The characteristics of the image formed in a pinhole camera are that it is inverted, smaller, and real.

If the screen is replaced by a photographic plate, or film, pictures of stationary objects may be taken, provided that a long time exposure is used. Today, most photographs are taken with lens cameras. These admit more light than pinhole cameras, making shorter exposure times possible.

To remember that the magnification is d_i over d_o and not the reverse, note that "i" occurs before "o" in the alphabet.

A negative sign is included in the magnification if the image is inverted.

It would be possible to have the image larger than the object, just by bringing the object close to the pinhole.

Sample problem

Calculate the size of the image of a tree that is 8.0 m high and 80 m from a pinhole camera that is 20 cm long.

$$\frac{h_i}{h_o} = \frac{d_i}{d_o}$$

$$h_i = \left(\frac{d_i}{d_o}\right) h_o$$

$$= \left(\frac{0.20 \text{ m}}{80 \text{ m}}\right) (8.0 \text{ m})$$

$$= 0.020 \text{ m, or } 2.0 \text{ cm}$$

Practice

1. Calculate the distance from the pinhole to an object that is 3.5 m high, and whose image is 10 cm high in a pinhole camera 20 cm long.   (7.0 m)
2. Calculate the height of a building 300 m away from the pinhole that produces an image 3.0 cm high in a pinhole camera 5.0 cm long.   (1.8×10^2 m)
3. A 1.5 cm inverted image is produced on the screen of a camera when a picture is taken of an 80 m tall tree. What is the magnification?   (-1.9×10^{-4})

11.4 Plane Reflectors

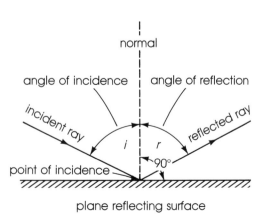

plane reflecting surface

Light travels in a straight line until it strikes an object. Its transmission is interrupted, therefore, when it hits something opaque, like a piece of wood. If light meets a transparent object, it passes through.

Mirrors and brightly polished opaque surfaces reflect light in predictable ways. When light strikes a plane (or flat) surface, angles are formed by the incident and reflected rays, as illustrated. The angle of incidence, i, is defined as the angle between the incident ray and the normal (or perpendicular) line constructed at the point of incidence. The angle of reflection, r, is the angle between the reflected ray and the normal.

The angle of incidence equals the angle of reflection for any ray directed towards a plane mirror. This is true even when a ray strikes a plane mirror straight on, since the value of both angles is zero, and it holds without exception for all reflecting surfaces. Therefore, we can use the term "law" when describing this relationship between the angle of incidence and the angle of reflection. Also, the incident ray, the normal, and the reflected ray all lie in the same plane. This is another law of reflection.

Laws of Reflection

- **The angle of incidence is equal to the angle of reflection.**
- **The incident ray, the reflected ray, and the normal all lie in the same plane.**

Spherical Reflectors

A spherical, curved mirror may be thought of as a section of a hollow sphere. If the inside of the sphere is polished to reflect light, the resulting mirror has a **concave** shape and makes parallel light rays converge on each other. The shiny outside of a similar section has a **convex** surface and makes parallel light rays diverge. Hence the terms **converging mirror** and **diverging mirror**.

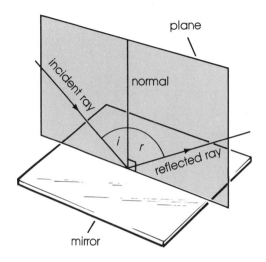

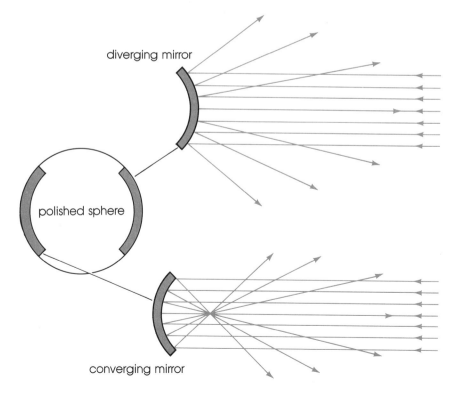

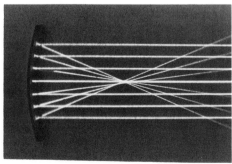

The centre of such a spherical reflecting surface is called the **centre of curvature** (*C*), and the **radius of curvature** (*R*) is any straight line drawn from the centre of curvature to the curved surface. The geometric centre of a curved mirror is called the **vertex** (*V*), and the straight line passing through *V* and *C* is called the **principal axis** (**P.A.**).

If a group of rays parallel to the principal axis strikes a converging mirror, the rays are nearly all reflected to the same point on the principal axis, called the **principal focus** (*F*). The distance along the principal axis between the principal focus and the vertex is called the **focal length** (*f*).

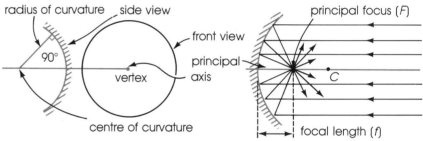

The Laws of Reflection hold for each of these rays (see illustration). Note that the principal focus is located half-way between the vertex and the centre of curvature, that is, $f = R/2$. This can be shown using simple geometry for small converging mirrors.

Some rays, near the edge of a large, spherical converging mirror, are not reflected to the principal focus. This defect is called **spherical aberration**. It may be avoided by using a mirror whose width is smaller than its radius of curvature, or by designing mirrors of parabolic rather than spherical shape. In our subsequent discussions of spherical mirrors, we will limit discussion to small mirrors that do not exhibit spherical aberration.

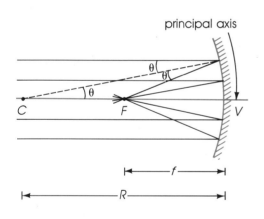

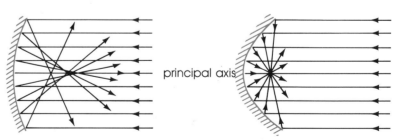

Failure of rays parallel to the principal axis to meet at a common focus is called spherical aberration.

In a parabolic mirror, all rays parallel to the principal axis are reflected to the same focus.

If a group of rays parallel to the principal axis strikes a diverging spherical mirror, the rays reflect as shown. Notice that if the reflected rays are projected backward through the surface, they appear to have passed through a common point *F*. This point is the principal focus of the diverging mirror. It is called a **virtual focus**, since it is located behind the mirror where no rays can actually pass through it. Notice that the ray directed towards *C*, the centre of curvature, is reflected back along the same path.

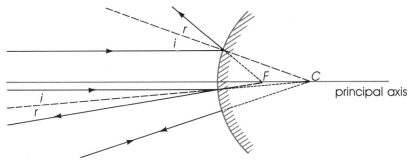

11.5 The Formation of Images in Mirrors

Plane Mirrors

You know what it is like to stand in front of a plane mirror: if you move towards the mirror, your image in the mirror appears to move closer to you. Our experience is that the image is always the same distance from the mirror surface as the object is.

To understand the position of the image, it is necessary to consider how the eye sees light rays coming from an object.

Although a lighted object gives off light in all directions, your eye only sees the particular diverging cone of rays that is coming towards it. If you go to the other side of the object, a different cone of rays will enter your eye.

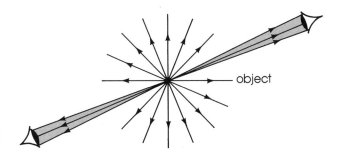

Although an object gives off light in all directions, the eye sees only a diverging cone of rays.

When you see an object in a plane mirror, the cone of rays is reflected by the mirror, as illustrated. Your eye cannot tell that the light has been reflected and assumes that, since light travels in straight lines, the origin of the cone of light rays is behind the mirror.

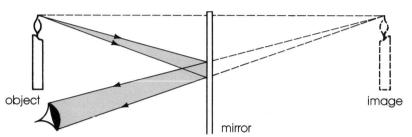

object   image

mirror

Therefore, when you look into a plane mirror, you see an image of your face, without any magnification, apparently located behind the mirror. Unlike the image formed in the pinhole camera, which was formed on a screen and said to be real, the image we see in a plane mirror cannot be formed on a screen and is therefore described as "virtual". The image in a plane mirror is produced at the point where the reflected rays, extended behind the mirror, appear to intersect.

In summary, the characteristics of an image in a plane mirror are:
- It is the same size as the object.
- It is vertically erect.
- It is virtual.

Curved Mirrors

If several groups of parallel rays are reflected by a converging mirror, each group converges at a point. Each such point is a focus. When all the foci, including the principal focus, are joined, they form the **focal plane**, perpendicular to the principal axis. Thus, if a converging mirror is pointed at a distant object, the cones of rays coming from many different points on the object and reaching the mirror at slightly different angles converge at different points on the focal plane, producing a real image there. Closer objects form images located closer to the mirror.

A small object (O) in front of a mirror emits light in all directions. Only some of these rays are reflected from the curved mirror, always, of course, according to the Laws of Reflection. All of the reflected rays would intersect after reflection, forming an image of the small object. To find the location of the image in this way

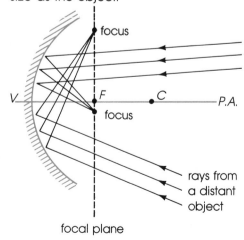

An image in a plane mirror is the same size as the object.

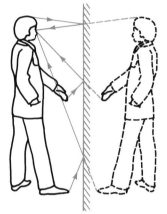

focus

V ———— F   C ———————— P.A.

focus

rays from a distant object

focal plane

would be a laborious process. Also, only a real image can be located in this way.

To determine the position of an image (*I*) in a converging mirror it is necessary to use only two rays that intersect. But which two rays? In a converging mirror, any ray parallel to the principal axis is reflected through the principal focus (*F*). Conversely, any ray through *F* is reflected parallel to the principal axis. So we select two of the rays radiating out from the tip of the object — the one that passes through *F* and the one that is parallel to the principal axis.

Another ray we can use is the one that goes through the centre of curvature (*C*) from the tip of the object. Since it moves along a radius of curvature, it hits the mirror with an angle of incidence of 0°. The reflected ray goes back along the same path as the incident ray, since the angle of reflection is 0°. (Sometimes one or the other of the above rays does not hit the mirror.)

1. Object between *F* and *C*

The image is: beyond *C*, real, inverted, larger than the object.

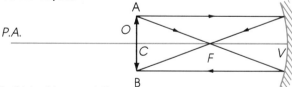

2. Object at *C*

The image is:
at *C*, real, inverted, the same size as the object.

3. Object beyond *C*

The image is:
between *C* and *F*
real, inverted, smaller than
the object.

4. Object at *F*

No image is formed.

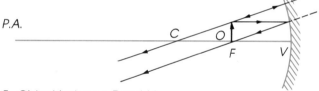

5. Object between *F* and *V*

The image is:
beyond the mirror,
virtual, erect, larger than
the object.

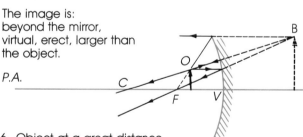

6. Object at a great distance

The image is:
at *F*, real, inverted, smaller than
the object.

rays from the same point
on a distant object

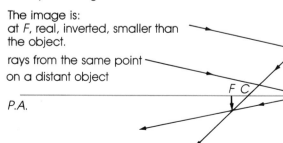

Using these three rays, let us consider how an image is formed for an object located between F and C in front of a converging mirror (diagram 1). Ray 1 passes through F and is reflected parallel to the principal axis. Ray 2 is drawn parallel to the principal axis and is reflected through F. Ray 3 passes through C and is reflected back along the same path. The point at which all three rays intersect is the image (I) location. Actually only two of these rays are required, but the third can act as a check.

Because the light actually passes through the image, it is called a real image. As noted in diagram 1, the characteristics of this particular image are that it is real, inverted, and larger than the object. The image positions for other object locations are illustrated on the previous page. Note that in diagram 4 no clear image is formed, because the rays do not intersect on either side of the mirror. Also, note that in diagram 5 the reflected rays appear to diverge from a point behind the mirror and do not intersect in front of the mirror. The image is located behind the mirror by extending the reflected rays backward as dotted lines. The image formed is virtual, erect, and larger. This type of image is found in cosmetic and shaving mirrors, which magnify the object reflected — your face.

In diverging mirrors, the same three rays are used to locate the image. But F and C are both virtual, since they are located behind the mirror. As illustrated in the bottom diagram, the rays may be extended behind the mirror, using dotted lines. Where these extensions of the reflected rays intersect is the image position.

Unlike the converging mirror, which produces real or virtual images depending on the location of the object, the diverging mirror produces only virtual images. These virtual images are all erect, smaller than the object, and located between the vertex and the principal focus.

The rules for drawing ray diagrams for curved mirrors of both types are summarized below.

Rules for Rays in Curved Mirrors of Both Types

1. A ray that is parallel to the principal axis is reflected through (or as if it had gone through) the principal focus — real or virtual.
2. A ray passing through (or appearing to pass through) the principal focus is reflected parallel to the principal axis.
3. A ray passing through (or appearing to pass through) the centre of curvature is reflected back along the same path.

Image formed by a diverging mirror

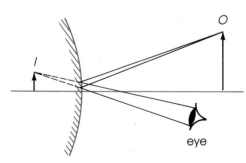

How the eye sees a virtual image in a diverging mirror

11.6 Equations for Curved Mirrors

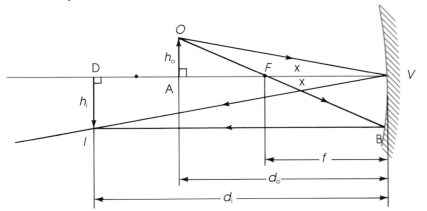

In the diagram, two rays are used to locate the image. The light ray OBI is the same as ray 2 in the previous section. The ray OVI, although it is not one of the convenient rays used in the previous section, also obeys the Laws of Reflection.

As a result, the triangles AOV and DIV are similar. Therefore,

$$\frac{AO}{DI} = \frac{AV}{DV}$$

or $\quad \dfrac{h_o}{h_i} = \dfrac{d_o}{d_i}$

This is, of course, the magnification equation (Section 11.3) that holds for curved mirrors as well as pinhole cameras.

Using the other ray, OFB, the triangles FAO and FVB are similar. Therefore,

$$\frac{AO}{VB} = \frac{AF}{VF}$$

Since $AO = h_o$ and $VB = h_i$,

$$\frac{h_o}{h_i} = \frac{d_o - f}{f}$$

but $\quad \dfrac{h_o}{h_i} = \dfrac{d_o}{d_i}$

Therefore $\quad \dfrac{d_o}{d_i} = \dfrac{d_o - f}{f}$

Dividing both sides by d_o and rearranging, we obtain

$$\mathbf{\frac{1}{d_o} + \frac{1}{d_i} = \frac{1}{f}}$$

In this derivation for small mirrors we will consider insignificant the very slight error introduced by the curvature VB.

Note also that for a plane mirror $1/f$ approaches 0 and that $d_i = -d_o$ (the same distance behind the mirror as the object is in front).

This is called the **mirror equation**. It is very useful, because it relates both image and object distances and the focal length. Note that if the object distance approaches infinity $(d_o \to \infty)$, $\frac{1}{d_o}$ approaches 0, making $d_i = f$. Thus the image is located on the local plane, as discussed on page 416.

As we have seen, an image is sometimes formed in front of a curved spherical mirror and sometimes behind it. This makes it necessary to have a sign convention, so that we can distinguish between real and virtual images and also get the correct answer when using the mirror equation.

Sign Convention

1. All distances are measured from the vertex of a curved mirror.
2. Distances of real objects and images are positive.
3. Distances of virtual objects and images are negative.
4. Object heights and image heights are positive when measured upward and negative when measured downward from the principal axis.

According to this convention, a converging mirror has a real principal focus and thus a positive focal length. A diverging mirror has a virtual principal focus and a negative focal length.

Using this convention for a real image formed by a converging mirror, h_o is positive and h_i is negative, whereas d_o and d_i are both positive. A negative sign must be added to the magnification equation so that it agrees with the sign convention.

$$M = \frac{h_i}{h_o} = -\frac{d_i}{d_o}$$

The orientation of the image can be predicted, using the sign convention. The magnification is positive for an erect image and negative for an inverted image.

Sample problems

The mirror equation can also be written as

$$\frac{1}{d_o} + \frac{1}{d_i} = \frac{2}{R} \left(\text{since } f = \frac{R}{2} \right)$$

where R is the radius of curvature.

1. An object is located 30.0 cm from a converging mirror with a radius of curvature of 10.0 cm.
   (a) At what distance from the mirror will the image be formed?
   (b) If the object is 4.0 cm tall, how tall is its image?

   (a) Since $R = 10.0$ cm, $f = \frac{R}{2} = 5.0$ cm.

$$\frac{1}{d_o} + \frac{1}{d_i} = \frac{1}{f}$$

$$\frac{1}{30.0 \text{ cm}} + \frac{1}{d_i} = \frac{1}{5.0 \text{ cm}}$$

$$d_i = 6.0 \text{ cm}$$

The positive value of d_i indicates that the image is real.

(b)
$$\frac{h_o}{h_i} = -\frac{d_o}{d_i}$$

$$h_i = -\left(\frac{d_i}{d_o}\right) h_o$$

$$= -\left(\frac{6.0 \text{ cm}}{30 \text{ cm}}\right) 4.0 \text{ cm}$$

$$= -0.80 \text{ cm}$$

Since h_i is negative, the image is inverted.

2. A diverging mirror with a focal length of -5.0 cm produces an image of an object located 15.0 cm from the mirror.
   (a) What is the distance of the image from the mirror?
   (b) What is the magnification?
   Since it is a diverging mirror, the focal length is negative.

(a)
$$\frac{1}{d_o} + \frac{1}{d_i} = \frac{1}{f}$$

$$\frac{1}{15.0 \text{ cm}} + \frac{1}{d_i} = \frac{1}{-5.0 \text{ cm}}$$

$$d_i = -3.8 \text{ cm}$$

The image is virtual, since d_i is negative, and it is observed to be 3.8 cm behind the diverging mirror.

(b)
$$M = -\frac{d_i}{d_o}$$

$$= -\frac{-3.8 \text{ cm}}{15.0 \text{ cm}}$$

$$= 0.25$$

The magnification is positive, indicating that the image is erect.

Practice

1. Determine the image distance in each of the following:
   (a) A converging mirror has a focal length of 15 cm. The object is placed at (i) 40 cm, and (ii) 10 cm from the mirror.
   (b) A diverging mirror has a focal length of -20 cm. An object is placed (i) 10 cm, and (ii) 30 cm from the mirror.
   $$(24 \text{ cm}, -30 \text{ cm}; -6.7 \text{ cm}, -12 \text{ cm})$$

2. A candle 3.0 cm high is placed 30 cm from a converging mirror with a focal length of 20 cm.
   (a) By means of a scale diagram, locate the image and determine its height. State the characteristics of the image.
   (b) Using the mirror and magnification equations, determine the image position and its height. Compare your results with those obtained in part (a).   ($d_i = 60$ cm, $h_i = -6.0$ cm)
3. A converging mirror has a focal length of 20 cm. Where should an object be placed so that its virtual image will be twice as tall as the object?   (10 cm)

11.7 Refraction

A straight stick appears bent when partially immersed in water; the sun appears oval rather than round when it is about to set; a stream may appear to be much shallower than you know it to be; the pavement shimmers on a hot summer's day. These are some of the effects caused by the **refraction**, or change in direction, of light as it passes at an angle from one medium into another.

When light passes obliquely from air to glass, it immediately changes direction. Also, at the boundary between the air and the glass, most of the light passes through the glass, but some is reflected according to the Laws of Reflection. This is called **partial reflection and partial refraction**. The diagram illustrates this phenomenon, and shows the angles used when describing refraction. The **angle of incidence** (i in the diagram) is the angle between the incident ray and the normal at the point of incidence. The **angle of refraction** (R) is the angle between the refracted ray and the normal.

In both the photograph and the illustration, note that the ray of light is bent towards the normal when it passes from air into glass. This is always the case when light passes from one medium to another that is optically denser. As we discussed in Section 11.2, the speed of light is reduced when it passes into an optically denser medium, as in the transition from air to glass. Thus, "optically denser" and "the speed of light is reduced" are synonymous when discussing the properties of a transparent medium.

If the light travels from one medium into a less optically dense medium where its speed is greater, the ray bends away from the normal. This is shown in the photograph for a ray of light travelling from glass to air.

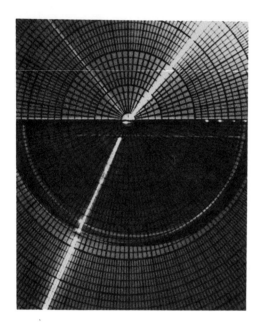

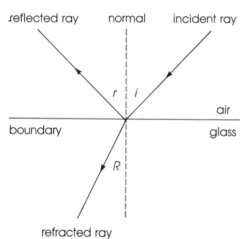

Although the phenomenon of refraction had been known for centuries, it was not until 1621 that Willebrord Snell (1591–1626), a Dutch mathematician, determined the exact relationship between the angle of incidence and the angle of refraction. This enabled scientists to predict the direction a ray of light would take in various media. **Snell's Law** says:

$$\frac{\sin i}{\sin R} = \text{constant}$$

This relationship tells us that for all angles of incidence greater than 0°, the ratio $\sin i / \sin R$ gives the same value for a boundary between two transparent media. In the case of an air-glass interface, the value is approximately 1.5.

It has been found that the Snell's Law constant and the index of refraction (n) are one and the same thing. Consequently, the Snell's Law relationship may be rewritten as:

$$\frac{\sin i}{\sin R} = n$$

where n is the index of refraction of the second medium with respect to the first.

For example, if light travels from air into glass,

$$\frac{\sin i}{\sin R} = {_a}n_g$$

where ${_a}n_g$ is the refractive index for light travelling from air to glass.

Since ${_a}n_g$ represents the ratio $\dfrac{n_g}{n_a}$, the above relationship can be rewritten as:

$$\frac{\sin i}{\sin R} = \frac{n_g}{n_a}$$

In developing a general equation for the refraction of light, we replace the angle of incidence (i) in the first medium with the symbol θ_1, and the angle of refraction in the second medium with the symbol θ_2. The index of refraction of the first medium, air, in our example, is replaced by the symbol n_1; and the index of the second medium, n_g, is replaced by the symbol n_2. Thus the above expression is rewritten as:

$$\frac{\sin \theta_1}{\sin \theta_2} = \frac{n_2}{n_1}$$

$$n_1 \sin \theta_1 = n_2 \sin \theta_2$$

The subscripts denote the different media. It is customary to use subscript 1 for the incident medium and subscript 2 for the re-

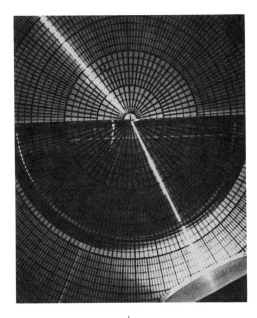

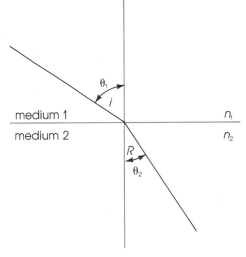

fracting medium. The general expression of Snell's Law may be used in solving any refraction problem.

Sample problems

1. Light travels from crown glass (g) into air (a). The angle of refraction in air is 60°. What is the angle of incidence in glass?

$$n_g \sin \theta_g = n_a \sin \theta_a$$
$$1.52 \sin \theta_g = 1.00 \sin 60$$
$$\sin \theta_g = \frac{1.00\,(0.866)}{1.52}$$
$$= 0.570$$
$$\theta_g = 34.7°$$

2. Light travels from crown glass (g) into water (w). The angle of incidence in crown glass is 40°. What is the angle of refraction in water?

$$n_g \sin \theta_g = n_w \sin \theta_w$$
$$1.52 \sin 40° = 1.33 \sin \theta_w$$
$$(1.52)(0.643) = 1.33 \sin \theta_w$$
$$\sin \theta_w = \frac{(1.52)(0.643)}{1.33}$$
$$= 0.735$$
$$\theta_w = 47.3°$$

Practice

1. Light passes from air into diamond. The angle of incidence is 60°. What will be the angle of refraction?   (21°)
2. A transparent substance has a refractive index of 1.30. What is the angle of incidence in air when the angle of refraction in the substance is 45°?   (67°)
3. What is the index of refraction of a material if the angle of incidence in air is 50° and the angle of refraction in the material is 40°?   (1.19)
4. If the index of refraction for diamond is 2.42, what will be the angle of refraction in diamond for an angle of incidence, in water, of 60°?   (28°)
5. A ray of light passes from water ($n_w = 1.33$) into carbon disulphide ($n_{CS_2} = 1.63$) with an angle of incidence of 30°. What is the angle of refraction in the carbon disulphide?   (24°)

11.8 Total Internal Reflection

When light travels from one medium to another where its speed changes, some of the light is reflected and some is refracted. This property of light is referred to as partial reflection/partial refraction, as stated previously. In cases where the speed of the light increases, for example from glass to air, the light is reflected to a greater extent than in cases where the speed decreases.

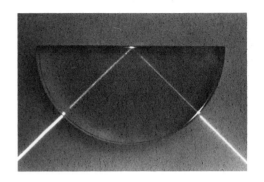

As the angle of incidence increases, the intensity of a reflected ray becomes progressively stronger and the intensity of a refracted ray progressively weaker. Also, as the angle of incidence increases, the angle of refraction increases, eventually reaching a maximum of 90°. Beyond this point, refraction ceases, and all the incident light is reflected, at the boundary, back into the optically denser medium. This phenomenon is called **total internal reflection**. It can only occur when light rays travel into a medium where the speed of the light increases and, hence, the angle of refraction is always greater than the angle of incidence.

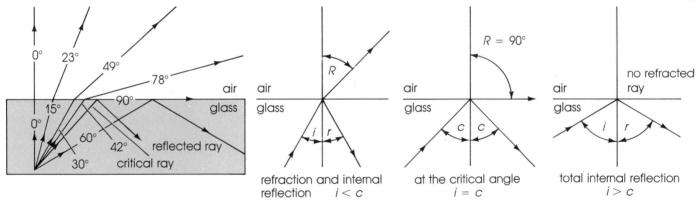

| refraction and internal reflection $i < c$ | at the critical angle $i = c$ | total internal reflection $i > c$ |

What happens when light rays pass from glass into air

When the angle of refraction is 90°, the incident ray forms an angle of incidence that has a unique value for any two materials. This unique angle of incidence is called the "critical angle of incidence", or simply the **critical angle**. For light travelling from crown glass to air, the critical angle can be determined as follows:

$$n_g \sin \theta_g = n_a \sin \theta_a$$
$$1.52 \sin \theta_g = 1.00 \sin 90°$$
$$\sin \theta_g = \frac{(1.00)(1.00)}{1.52} = 0.658$$
$$\theta_g = 41°$$

For water, with an index of refraction of 1.33, the critical angle is approximately 49°. For zircon ($n_z = 1.92$) the critical angle is 31°. Substances with higher indices of refraction refract the light to a greater degree and thus have lower critical angles. The critical angle for diamond ($n_d = 2.42$), for example, is only 24.5°.

Total internal reflection has many applications. For example, if, when you swim underwater, you look up at the smooth surface, you will see the world compressed into a circle. This circle is defined by the critical angle of water, which is 49° (see diagram). Beyond this circle, the surface of the water reflects light from objects beneath it, and appears as a large mirror.

This phenomenon is difficult to see, because most water surfaces are not perfectly flat. Viewed at an angle, from underwater, the water's surface is a shimmering mirror.

Ordinary mirrors reflect less than 100% of the light they receive. Total internal reflection reflects almost 100% of the light, making the images brighter. This is important in such optical devices as binoculars and cameras, where total internal reflecting prisms are used extensively.

Another application of the phenomenon of total internal reflection is the "light rod", a product of the new technology of fibre optics. Light rods are made from very thin glass and plastic fibres, sometimes as small as 15μm in diameter. These are so designed that the light undergoes total internal reflection every time it encounters an internal surface. Even if the fibres are bent or twisted, the critical angle is not usually exceeded, and the light energy is transmitted undiminished to the other end. A bundle of these tiny fibres is called a "light pipe".

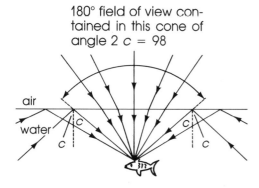

180° field of view contained in this cone of angle 2 c = 98

Even within this circle, the world above is distorted by refraction at the surface. The distortion is least at the centre of the circle.

Individual fibres are now replacing the thousands of wires that connect telephone substations, and may eventually be connected to each home. In this application, the telephone signal modulates (changes the intensity of) a small laser. The laser light is transmitted through a glass fibre, carrying with it many more telephone calls at one time, with much less loss in energy than would be the case with copper wire. It is possible to send information both ways, simultaneously, on the same fibre.

In medicine, fibre optics bundles are used to transmit pictures of internal organs. For example, a patient's stomach can be examined by inserting a flexible light pipe down her throat and into her stomach. Light sent down some of the fibres illuminates the stomach wall. Other fibres carry the reflected light back to a small television camera. The light transmitted through each fibre forms part of the picture of the stomach wall. This picture, which is a mosaic formed by all the fibres, is magnified and displayed on a television screen. The more fibres there are, and the smaller they are, the more detailed the picture. (A typical bundle has 5×10^4 fibres and a diameter of 3 mm.) Such inspections of the esophagus, stomach, bowel, and even the inside of the heart, allow safe examinations that would not normally be possible without surgery.

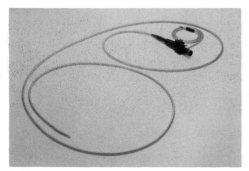

Fibrescope used by doctors to examine interior organs

11.9 Dispersion

It has been known, at least since the days of the ancient Egyptians, that fragments of clear, colourless glass and precious stones emit the colours of the rainbow when placed in the path of a beam of white light. It was not until 1666, however, that this phenomenon, called **dispersion**, was systematically investigated. The refracting telescope had recently been invented by a Dutch eyeglass maker named Lippershey, and Isaac Newton — then 23 years old — was starting to search for a technique that would remove coloration from the images seen through telescopes.

In 1672, Newton described his experiments to the Royal Society in London. His theory, that white light was made up of many colours, was revolutionary, and was greeted with scepticism. Indeed, Newton and another English physicist, Robert Hooke, became involved in a bitter debate, and Newton refused to publish his conclusions until after Hooke's death, 32 years later!

As a source of light, Newton used a small round hole in one of his window shutters at Cambridge. A prism placed in a beam of sunlight coming through the hole produced an elongated patch of multi-coloured light on the opposite wall. Newton called this a **spectrum** and noted the colours — red, orange, yellow, green, blue, indigo, and violet.

The dispersion of light is simply the result of different colours of light being refracted by different amounts. In other words, each colour has a slightly different index of refraction in the same medium. Media that disperse white light into the colours of the spectrum are called **dispersive media**.

The colours of the spectrum may be recombined by means of a lens to form white light. This process, called **recomposition**, may also be achieved with a series of mirrors, as illustrated. Newton also demonstrated recomposition by painting the spectral colours on a disc and rotating the disc at a high speed. The rotating disc appeared white.

If light from the sun is directed through a prism, it can be shown that invisible radiation is produced beyond either end of the visible spectrum. Just beyond the red end of the spectrum is a region occupied by a radiation called **infrared**. This was discovered in 1800 by the English astronomer William Herschel (1738-1822). He used a blackened thermometer bulb on the various regions of the spectrum and found a heating effect beyond the visible red.

It has since been found that more than half of the energy coming from the sun is infrared radiation, and that infrared radiation provides most of the heat energy requirement of the Earth. It can

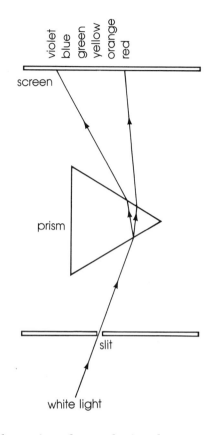

The notion of seven basic colours comes from ancient times; today we refer to only six basic colours, because most people are unable to see indigo as a distinct colour. Actually, there is an infinite number of different colours, for each basic colour of the spectrum merges gradually with the next.

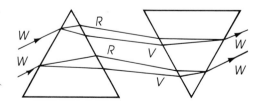

Recomposition using a second prism and a lens

penetrate clouds, smoke, and haze. It is useful for photography from high altitudes, military reconnaissance, photography in the dark, "heat" photography of the human body to assist in the detection of cancer, and the locating of heat losses in a building. Infrared light also has a therapeutic effect when used on damaged muscles. Infrared heat lamps or radiators are used to keep food warm in restaurants, to dry paint in car body shops, and to keep spectators warm in outdoor arenas. Further applications of infrared radiation are discussed in Chapter 16.

The year after Herschel's discovery, Johann Ritter (1776-1810) placed certain salts in the region beyond the visible violet and found that they glowed, or were fluorescent, in the dark. Quinine sulphate, vaseline on paper, most white shirts, and natural white teeth are examples of other substances that are fluorescent under **ultraviolet** light.

Although easily absorbed by clouds, smoke, and haze, ultraviolet radiation has the ability to burn the outer layer of the skin, causing sunburn. It also has the beneficial effect of accelerating the manufacture of vitamin D in the skin. Ultraviolet light from sun lamps must be treated with respect. Excessive exposure may produce a bad sunburn or cause destruction of areas in the retina of the eye, resulting in blind spots. Carbon arc lamps and mercury vapour lamps also emit ultraviolet light, as well as visible light, and thus should be used with care. Most of the ultraviolet light received by the Earth from the sun is absorbed by our atmosphere.

infrared	visible						ultraviolet
	r	o	y	g	b	v	

Freshly washed white shirts usually fluoresce under ultraviolet light, because there is a residue of detergent left in the cloth. To make a shirt "whiter than white", as television commercials claim, most manufacturers of detergents use chemicals (sometimes called "bluing" agents) that fluoresce under blue light as well as under ultraviolet light. The bluing adds white fluorescence to the white light normally reflected by a white surface.

11.10 Lenses

Refraction of Light in Lenses

Lenses are not a recent invention. They were used by the Greeks and later, in medieval times, by the Arabs. They are used in cameras, telescopes, microscopes, and projectors, and in eyeglasses they enable millions of people to read comfortably and to see clearly.

A lens is usually a circular piece of glass with uniformly curved surfaces that change the direction of light passing through it. When a set of rays passes through a lens, each ray is refracted by a different amount, at each surface. Rays striking the lens near the edge are bent the most, because the effect of the curvature is greatest there. The least bending occurs at the centre of the lens, because the two surfaces are nearly parallel there. Parallel rays striking a **converging lens** are refracted inward. A **diverging lens** spreads parallel rays outward uniformly, as illustrated.

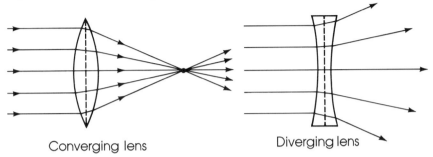

Converging lens   Diverging lens

In such lenses, the geometric centre is called the **optical centre** (O). A line drawn through the optical centre perpendicular to the surfaces of the lens is the **principal axis**. If a lens is thin, a group of rays parallel to the principal axis is refracted through a point on the principal axis called the **principal focus** (F). The **focal length** (f) is the distance between the principal focus and the optical centre, measured along the principal axis.

Other groups of parallel rays, not aligned with the principal axis, also converge at focal points, but not on the principal axis. All focal points, including the principal focus, lie on the **focal plane**, perpendicular to the principal axis. When a converging lens refracts light from a distant object, the rays arriving at the lens are nearly parallel; thus, a real image is formed on a screen at a distance of one focal length from the lens.

A lens may be turned around so that the light can pass through it from the opposite side. It is found that the focal length is the same on both sides, even if the curvature is different. To distinguish between them, the secondary principal focus is usually expressed as F'.

Converging lenses are also called convex lenses because of their convex surfaces. Diverging lenses are also called concave lenses because of their concave surfaces. Many lenses are constructed of both convex and concave surfaces. Eyeglasses are a good example. It is more instructive to name a lens by what it does to light than by its shape.

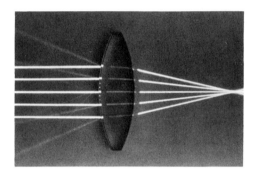

Just as light reflected from the edges of large mirrors missed the focal point and gave spherical aberration, similar effects can happen in large lenses. Dispersion in the optical glass can also give colour aberration. Corrections for both defects are made in high quality optical systems.

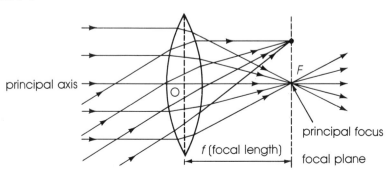

principal axis →

O

F

principal focus

f (focal length)

focal plane

In a diverging lens, parallel rays are refracted so that they appear to radiate out from a virtual focus, as illustrated.

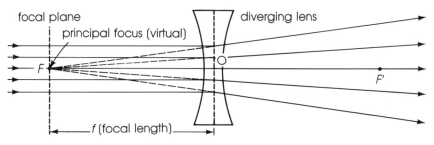

Images in Lenses

An object gives off light rays in all directions, but, for the purpose of locating its image, we are interested only in those rays that pass through the lens. Of these, as in the case of curved mirrors (Section 11.5), three are particularly convenient for locating the tip of the image. The following are the three rays that may be used, although two are enough.

The non-refraction of the ray passing through the optical centre may seem strange, since most rays passing through the optical centre are laterally displaced. The explanation is that, in the thin lenses we are using, the lateral displacement of the ray is so small that we may assume that the ray is not refracted.

Rules for Rays in Thin Curved Lenses of Both Types

1. A ray that is parallel to the principal axis is refracted so that it passes through (or appears to pass through) the principal focus (F).
2. A ray that passes through (or appears to pass through) the secondary principal focus (F') is refracted parallel to the principal axis.
3. A ray that passes through the optical centre goes straight through, without bending.

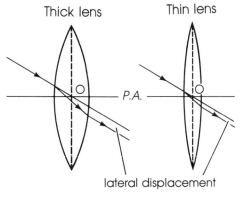

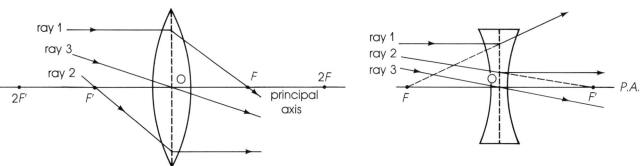

If an object is located more than $2f$ from the optical centre (diagram 1 below), a ray parallel to the principal axis refracts through F; a ray through F' refracts parallel to the principal axis; and a ray through O passes straight through. The image is located where the three rays intersect.

As with converging mirrors, only two rays are required. The third ray acts as a check. Often one of these three rays fails to pass through the lens and cannot be used. As noted in diagram 1, the characteristics of the particular image are real, inverted, and smaller than the object. The image positions for other object locations are illustrated. Note that in diagram 4 no clear image is produced, because the rays do not intersect on either side of the lens. In diagram 5, the image is located on the same side of the lens as the object. It is virtual, erect, and larger.

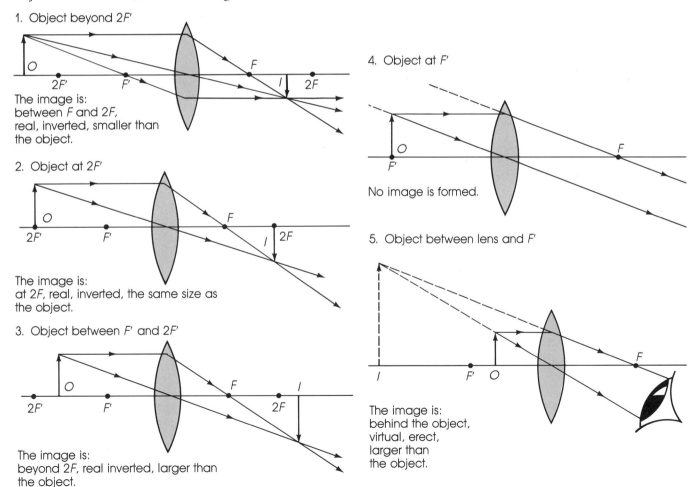

1. Object beyond 2F'

The image is:
between F and 2F,
real, inverted, smaller than
the object.

2. Object at 2F'

The image is:
at 2F, real, inverted, the same size as
the object.

3. Object between F' and 2F'

The image is:
beyond 2F, real inverted, larger than
the object.

4. Object at F'

No image is formed.

5. Object between lens and F'

The image is:
behind the object,
virtual, erect,
larger than
the object.

The rays we use to locate the position of the image in a diverging lens are similar to those we used with converging lenses. As a result, one set of rules is used for all lenses. The important difference is that the principal focus in the converging lens is real, whereas in the diverging lens it is virtual.

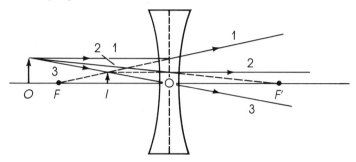

The Thin Lens Equation

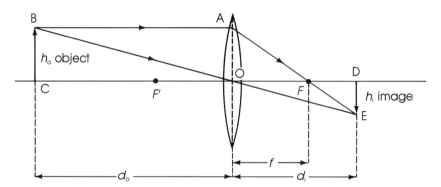

Just as we did for the curved mirrors, we can derive an equation for thin lenses, relating the image distance, the object distance, and the focal length.

In the diagram, the triangles AOF and EDF are similar.

Therefore, $$\frac{AO}{OF} = \frac{ED}{DF}$$

or $$\frac{h_o}{f} = \frac{h_i}{d_i - f}$$

and $$\frac{h_i}{h_o} = \frac{d_i - f}{f}$$

But $$\frac{h_i}{h_o} = \frac{d_i}{d_o} \qquad \text{(because triangle BCO is}$$
$$\text{similar to triangle EDO)}$$

Therefore $$\frac{d_i}{d_o} = \frac{d_i - f}{f}$$

We now divide both sides by d_i and rearrange to obtain

$$\frac{1}{d_o} + \frac{1}{d_i} = \frac{1}{f}$$

This is called the **lens equation**. It is exactly the same as the mirror equation. As was the case with the mirror equation, a sign convention must be used with the lens equation.

Sign Convention

1. All distances are measured from the optical centre of the lens.
2. Distances of real objects and images are positive.
3. Distances of virtual objects and images are negative.
4. Object heights and image heights are positive when measured upward and negative when measured downward from the principal axis.

In this convention, a converging lens has a real principal focus and a positive focal length. A diverging lens has a virtual principal focus and a negative focal length.

As was the case for curved mirrors, the magnification is positive for an erect image and negative for an inverted image. The form of the magnification equation to be used is:

$$M = \frac{h_i}{h_o} = -\frac{d_i}{d_o}$$

Since the focal length is positive for a converging lens, the lens is sometimes called a positive lens. Similarly, a diverging lens can be called a negative lens.

Sample problems

1. An object 8.0 cm high is 18 cm from a converging lens having a focal length of 10 cm.
   (a) How far is the image from the lens?
   (b) How tall is the image?

   (a) $\quad \frac{1}{d_o} + \frac{1}{d_i} = \frac{1}{f}$

   $\quad \frac{1}{18 \text{ cm}} + \frac{1}{d_i} = \frac{1}{10 \text{ cm}}$

   $\quad\quad d_i = 22.5 \text{ cm}$

   (b) $\quad \frac{h_i}{h_o} = -\frac{d_i}{d_o}$

   $\quad h_i = -\left(\frac{d_i}{d_o}\right) h_o$

   $\quad\quad = -\left(\frac{22.5 \text{ cm}}{18 \text{ cm}}\right)(8.0 \text{ cm})$

   $\quad\quad = -10 \text{ cm}$

   The image is real, since d_i is positive. The image is inverted, since h_i is negative.

For the lenses of their patients' eyeglasses, ophthalmologists and optometrists use a unit of measurement called a dioptre (D). The power (P) of a lens is the reciprocal of the focal length, expressed in metres.

$$P = \frac{1}{f}$$

Thus $1\ D = 1\text{ m}^{-1}$. For example, a 25 cm focal length lens has a power of

$$P = \frac{1}{0.25 \text{ m}} = 4.0\ D$$

It follows from the sign convention that the power of a converging lens (in dioptres) is positive, whereas the power of a diverging lens is negative.

2. A diverging lens has a focal length of -4.0 cm. If an object is placed 8.0 cm from the lens, how far from the lens is the image?

$$f = -4.0 \text{ cm} \qquad \text{(since it is a diverging lens)}$$

$$\frac{1}{d_o} + \frac{1}{d_i} = \frac{1}{f}$$

$$\frac{1}{8.0 \text{ cm}} + \frac{1}{d_i} = \frac{1}{-4.0 \text{ cm}}$$

$$d_i = -2.7 \text{ cm}$$

Since the image distance is negative, the image is virtual. It is located on the same side of the lens as the object.

3. Where must a postage stamp be placed in front of a magnifying glass (converging lens; $f = 10$ cm), if a virtual image is to be formed 25 cm in front of the lens? What is its magnification?

$$d_i = -25 \text{ cm} \qquad \text{(since it is a virtual image, on the same side of the lens as the object)}$$

$$\frac{1}{d_o} + \frac{1}{d_i} = \frac{1}{f}$$

$$\frac{1}{d_o} + \frac{1}{-25 \text{ cm}} = \frac{1}{10 \text{ cm}}$$

$$d_o = 7.1 \text{ cm}$$

The diagram for this problem would be similar to diagram 5 on page 431.

$$M = -\frac{d_i}{d_o}$$

$$= -\frac{-25 \text{ cm}}{7.1 \text{ cm}}$$

$$= 3.5$$

The image is erect, as indicated by a positive value for the magnification.

Practice

1. An object 8.0 cm high is placed 80 cm in front of a converging lens of focal length 25 cm.
   (a) By means of a scale ray diagram, locate the image and determine its height.
   (b) Using the lens and magnification equations, determine the image position and its height.   (36 cm, -3.6 cm)
2. A lamp 10 cm high is placed 60 cm in front of a diverging lens of focal length -20 cm.
   (a) By means of a scale ray diagram, locate the image and determine its height.
   (b) Using the appropriate equations, calculate the image position and the height of the image.   (-15 cm, 2.5 cm)

3. A typical single lens reflex (SLR) camera has a converging lens with a focal length of 50.0 mm. What is the position and size of the image of a 25 cm candle located 1.0 m from the lens?

$$(5.3 \text{ cm}, -1.3 \text{ cm})$$

4. A converging lens with a focal length of 20 cm is used to create an image of the sun on a paper screen. How far from the lens must the paper be placed to produce a clear image?   (20 cm)
5. The focal length of a slide projector's converging lens is 10.0 cm.
   (a) If a 35 mm slide is positioned 10.2 cm from the lens, how far away must the screen be placed to create a clear image?
   (b) If the height of a dog on the slide film is 12.5 mm, how tall will the dog's image on the screen be?
   (c) If the screen is then removed to a point 15 m from the lens, by how much will the separation between film and lens have to change from part (a)?

$$(5.10 \text{ m}, 62.5 \text{ cm}, 0.13 \text{ cm})$$

11.11 Investigations

Investigation 11.1: Images Formed by a Converging Mirror

Problems:
1. What is the focal length of a converging mirror?
2. What are the characteristics and locations of the images formed by an object located at various positions in front of a converging mirror?
3. Is the mirror equation valid for this mirror?

Materials:
light source (candle, small electric bulb)
optical bench
converging mirror
white paper screen

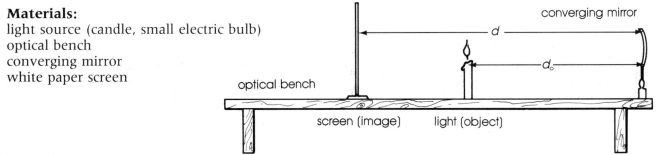

Procedure:
1. Hold the mirror in the darkest part of the room and point it at an object some distance away, such as a window frame or a house near the school.

2. Move the cardboard screen back and forth until the object is clearly focused on the screen. Measure the distance between the mirror and the screen. This is the focal length of the mirror.

3. Using your measured value for the focal length, calculate the distances from the mirror of objects at the following object distances: 2.5 f, 2 f, 1.5 f, f, 0.5 f. Record your observations and calculations in your notebook, making a suitable chart.

Observa-tion	Object distance (d_o)	Image distance (d_i)	Characteristics			$\frac{1}{d_o}$	$\frac{1}{d_i}$	$\frac{1}{d_o} + \frac{1}{d_i}$
			size	attitude	type			
1	2.5 f =							
2	2 f =							
3	1.5 f =							
4	f =							
5	0.5 f =							

4. Place the mirror at one end of the optical bench. It is more convenient to measure the distance of objects and images if the mirror is placed at the zero end of the scale.

5. Using chalk or masking tape, mark on the bench the object positions calculated in step 3.

6. Place the object at 2.5 f. Move the screen back and forth until the image is clearly in focus on the screen. Some tilting of the mirror may be necessary so that the light from the candle is not blocked by the screen. Record the image distance and the characteristics of the image.

7. Repeat step 6 for the other object distances. If an image is virtual, you should not record its distance.

8. As the object is moved closer to the mirror, what changes occur in the size of the image, the distance of the image, and the attitude of the image?

9. At what image distance was it difficult, if not impossible, to locate a clearly focused image?

10. Where would you place an object, relative to the principal focus, in order to form a real image? A virtual image?

11. Complete the columns $\frac{1}{d_o}$, $\frac{1}{d_i}$, and $\left(\frac{1}{d_o} + \frac{1}{d_i}\right)$ for the first three observations only.

12. Determine the value of the reciprocal of the focal length (f). How does it relate to the value of $\left(\frac{1}{d_o} + \frac{1}{d_i}\right)$ in each case?

Investigation 11.2: Refraction of Light

Problems:

1. How is light refracted when it passes from air into an optically denser medium, like glass?
2. How is light refracted when it passes from glass into a medium that is less optically dense, such as air?

Materials:

ray box (single-slit)
semi-circular glass block
polar co-ordinate paper

Plastic blocks are often used, instead of glass blocks, because they do not break easily. Plastic and glass have similar optical properties.

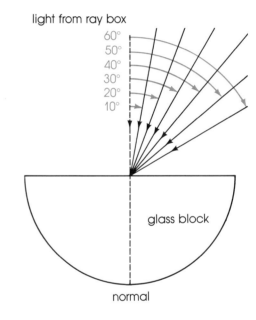

light from ray box

glass block

normal

Procedure:

1. Place the glass block on the polar co-ordinate paper, as illustrated. Note that the 0°-180° line acts as a normal and passes through the centre of the flat surface.
2. Direct a single ray of light at the flat surface of the glass, along the normal. Make absolutely sure that the ray passes through the centre of the flat surface. Measure the angle of refraction, and record it in your notebook in a chart, as illustrated.

Observation	Angle of incidence (i)	Angle of refraction (R)	sin i	sin R	$\frac{\sin i}{\sin R}$
1	0°				
2	10°				
3	20°				
4	30°				

3. Repeat the procedure for angles of incidence of 10°, 20°, 30°, 40°, 50° and 60°.
4. When the light travels obliquely from an optically less dense medium to an optically denser medium, how is the light bent in relation to the normal? At what angle of incidence is there no bending?
5. Determine the value of the sin i/sin R ratio for each pair of angles. What conclusion can you make concerning the sin i/sin R ratio?
6. Draw another chart in your notebook and repeat the same procedure, this time for light travelling from glass to air.
7. When light travels from an optically denser medium to a less optically dense medium, e.g., glass to air, at an angle greater than 0°, how is it bent in relation to the normal?

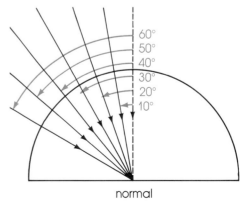

normal

8. What is the value of the $\sin i/\sin R$ ratio for glass-air interface? What is the relationship between this value and the value determined in step 5?
9. Why is there no refraction at the curved surface in all cases?
10. What other phenomenon occurs increasingly as the angle of incidence increases?
11. Above 42°, what happens to all the light once it reaches the boundary between the glass and the air?
12. At what angle of incidence is the angle of refraction 90°? Determine the answer experimentally and check your answer mathematically.

Investigation 11.3: Images Formed by a Converging Lens

Problems:

1. What are the characteristics and locations of the images formed by an object located at various positions in front of a converging lens?
2. Is the lens equation valid for this lens?

Materials:
optical bench
converging lens
light source
white paper screen

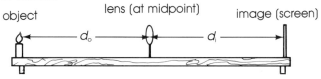

Procedure:

1. Hold the lens in a dark part of the room so that light from a distant object passes through it and onto the screen. Move the screen back and forth until the image is clearly focused. Measure the distance between the lens and the screen. This distance is the focal length (f) of the lens.
2. Repeat step 1, this time turning the lens around so that the other side of it faces the screen. Compare the numerical values of the focal length, measured on both sides of the lens. How do the two focal lengths compare?
3. Using the value of the focal length obtained in step 1, calculate the following object distances: 2.5 f, 2.0 f, 1.5 f, f, and 0.5 f. Record the information in a chart in your notebook.

Observation	Object distance (d_o)	Image distance (d_i)	Characteristics			$\frac{1}{d_o}$	$\frac{1}{d_i}$	$\frac{1}{d_o} + \frac{1}{d_i}$
			size	attitude	type			
1	$2.5\,f =$							
2	$2\,f =$							
3	$1.5\,f =$							
4	$f =$							

4. Place the lens in the exact centre of the optical bench.

5. Using chalk or masking tape, mark the object distances calculated in step 3 on the optical bench.

6. Place the object at 2.5 f. Move the screen back and forth until the image is focused clearly on the screen. Record the image distance and the characteristics of the image.

7. Repeat step 6 for the other object distances. Image distances for virtual images are not required.

8. As the object moves closer to the lens, what regular changes occur in the size of the image? The distance of the image? The attitude of the image?

9. At what distance was it difficult, if not impossible, to locate a clearly focused image?

10. Where would you place an object, in relation to the principal focus, to form a real image? To form a virtual image?

11. Using ray diagrams, locate the image for each object position in the investigation. To fit the diagram on your page, use a focal length of 3.0 cm. An object 1.0 cm high is recommended.

12. Complete columns $\frac{1}{d_o}$, $\frac{1}{d_i}$ and $\left(\frac{1}{d_o} + \frac{1}{d_i} \right)$ for the first three observations only.

13. Determine the value of the reciprocal of the focal length (f). How does it relate to the value of $\left(\frac{1}{d_o} + \frac{1}{d_i} \right)$ in each case?

14. Each of the diagrams drawn in step 11 represents the ray diagram for an application of the converging lens. Beside each diagram, place an appropriate label chosen from the following: "copy camera" (image is the same size and real), "hand magnifier" (image is larger and virtual), "slide projector" (image is larger and real), "35 mm camera" (image is smaller and real), "spot light" (parallel light — there is no image).

11.12 Review

Discussion

1. The index of refraction for blue light in glass is slightly higher than that for red light in glass. What does this indicate about (a) the relative speeds of red light and blue light in glass, and (b) the angles of refraction for each colour, for the same angle of incidence?

2. Light travels from medium A to medium B. The angle of refraction is greater than the angle of incidence.
   (a) Which medium has the higher index of refraction?
   (b) In which medium does the light travel at a lower speed?

3. A playful physics student uses a grease pencil to print the word "PHYSICS" on the outside surface of the rear window of the physics teacher's car. Some time later, the teacher glances into the inside rear vision mirror while driving the car. What pattern is seen? (SIN '73)

4. A boy with one "black eye" stands and looks at himself in the corner area of two vertical plane mirrors joined at right angles along a vertical line. A view of the situation as seen from above is shown. Which of the following does he see?
   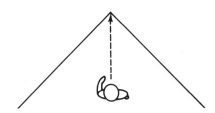
   (a) himself as others see him
   (b) a normal mirror image of himself
   (c) two black eyes
   (d) two normal eyes
   (e) two black eyes and two normal eyes (SIN '74)

5. How does refraction lengthen a day at both sunrise and sunset?

6. Hot air rises over a heated stove element. The wall behind the stove appears to shimmer. Explain.

7. To successfully spear a fish, you must aim below the apparent position of the fish. Explain.

8. In which medium does light travel faster — one with a critical angle of 27° or one with a critical angle of 32°? Explain. (For both cases, air is the second medium.)

9. Is the critical angle for glass with an index of refraction of 1.53 greater or less than that for glass with an index of refraction of 1.60? Would your answer be different if the second medium were water instead of air?

10. Total internal reflection is easily seen in an aquarium. Where does it occur — at the boundary between the water and the glass, or at the boundary between the glass and the air? Explain your answer.

11. Diamond has a critical angle of 24°. Crown glass has a critical angle of 42°. Why does a diamond sparkle more in bright light than a piece of crown glass does, even with the equivalent shape?

12. Sunlight is made up of most of the colours of the spectrum. Although it is refracted by the atmosphere, it is not dispersed as it travels through the air. What does this tell you about the relative speeds of the various colours of the spectrum in air?

13. What observation shows that diamond has a slightly different index of refraction for each of the various colours of the spectrum?

14. A converging lens of diamond and a lens of crown glass have the same shape. Which lens will have the larger focal length? Explain your answer.

15. A copy machine has a converging lens with a focal length of 40 cm. How far from the lens must documents be placed if the copies are to be exactly the same size as the original?

16. The focal length of a lens is determined, using red light from a helium-neon laser. How will the focal length compare with that measured using the green light from an argon laser?

Problems

17. The speed of light in a certain plastic is 2.0×10^8 m/s. What is the refractive index of the plastic?

18. The index of refraction of crown glass for violet light is 1.53, and for red light 1.52. Assuming that the velocity of light in a vacuum is 3.00×10^8 m/s, what are the speeds of violet light and red light in crown glass?

19. A woman looks at herself in a magnifying converging cosmetic mirror whose focal length is 20 cm. If her face is 10 cm from the mirror,
    (a) at what distance from the mirror is her image?
    (b) what is the magnification of her face?

20. A converging mirror has a focal length of 15 cm. Where would you place an object in order to produce an erect virtual image twice as tall as the object?

21. A trucker sees the image of a car passing her truck in her diverging rear-view mirror, whose focal length is −60 cm. If the car is 1.5 m high and 6.0 m away, what is the size and location of the image?

22. A spherical, polished metallic ball is used as a diverging mirror ($f = -20$ cm) over a bird bath. A bird, 25 cm tall, standing 50 cm away, looks directly at the mirror. What are the size and position of the bird's image?

23. A ray of light passes from air into water ($n_w = 1.33$) at an angle of incidence of 50°. What is the angle of refraction?

24. Light travels from air into water. If the angle of refraction is 30°, what is the angle of incidence?

25. A ray of light in air strikes a block of quartz at an angle of incidence of 30°. The angle of refraction is 20°. What is the index of refraction of the quartz?

26. Prove, geometrically, that a ray of light entering a plate of glass always emerges in a direction parallel to the incident ray.

27. From inside an aquarium, a ray of light is directed at the glass so that the angle of incidence, in water, is 30°.
    (a) Determine the angle of refraction when the ray emerges from the glass into the air.
    (b) If the angle of incidence in the water is 52°, at what angle will the rays emerge from the glass?

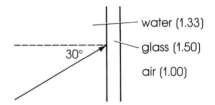

28. Several transparent liquids are carefully poured, one after another, into a glass container, as illustrated. Each liquid is immiscible (will not mix) with its neighbour. A ray of light, with an angle of incidence in the glass of 10°, is projected up through the liquids. What will be the angle of refraction in air?

air ($n = 1.00$)

oleic acid ($n = 1.43$)

water ($n = 1.33$)

carbon disulphide ($n = 1.46$)

glass ($n = 1.50$)

10°

29. An underwater swimmer looks up towards the surface of the water on a line of sight that makes an angle of 25° with a normal to the surface of the water. What is the angle of incidence in air for the light rays that enter the swimmer's eye?

30. Light strikes an equilateral glass prism at an angle of incidence of 30°. If the index of refraction is 1.51, what angle with respect to the normal does the ray make at the point of emergence? What is the total angular deviation?

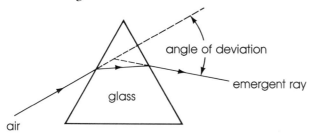

31. Archimedes left a gold crown lying on the bottom of his partly-filled rectangular bath tub, at the point C. Although he did not know Snell's Law, or that the index of refraction for bath water was 1.33, he did observe that a light ray from the crown bent farther away from the normal when it left the water. It then travelled at an angle of 30° measured from the water's surface, just missing the tub at A. If AB = BC = 1.00 m, how deep was the water? (SIN '80)

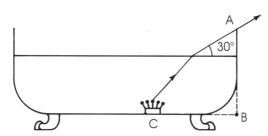

32. Swimming near the shore of a calm lake, a small child develops a leg cramp at point G. A lifeguard at L hears him scream. She can run 8.0 m/s and swim 3.0 m/s. Which route of those shown in the diagram should she take to reach the child most quickly? (SIN '72)

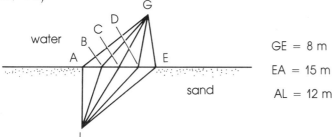

GE = 8 m

EA = 15 m

AL = 12 m

Fermat's Principle
When a light ray proceeds from one point to another, it follows the optical path that requires the least possible time. This is obvious for line-of-sight paths, and nearly obvious for reflection. (Students wishing to exercise their calculus skills might wish to verify it for reflection.) Refraction is much more difficult. Hero of Alexander used "the least possible time" as an explanation for reflection, but it was Fermat who showed that it could be much more generally applied. Thus, it is called *Fermat's Principle.*

Numerical Answers to Review Problems

17. **1.5**
18. **1.96×10^8 m/s, 1.97×10^8 m/s**
19. **(a) -20 cm (b) 2**
20. **7.5 cm**
21. **0.14 m, -0.55 m**
22. **7.2 cm, -14 cm**
23. **35°**
24. **42°**
25. **1.46**
27. **(a) 42° (b) no ray emerges**
28. **15°**
29. **34°**
30. **80°, 50°**
31. **83.4 cm**
32. **D**
33. **2.3 km**
34. **(a) 41° (b) 61°**
35. **(a) 37° (b) 1.56**
36. **75 cm**
37. **9.1 cm**
38. **60 cm, -10 cm**
39. **42 cm**
40. **7.2 cm, 3.6**
41. **-15.3 cm from the eyepiece, -31 cm**

33. An eager student is hurrying from his home (H) to his high school (S) to write a physics test. He sets out running at 4.0 m/s along the paved road, HZ, but at point Y he takes a short cut. On his path, YS, the school yard is being plowed for planting grass seed, so he can run at only 2.0 m/s along the path. How far should he run (HY) along the road, so that he arrives at school in the shortest possible time? (SIN '79)

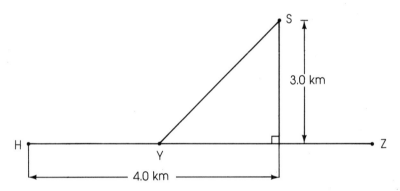

34. What is the critical angle for light rays passing from (a) crown glass ($n_g = 1.52$) into air, and (b) crown glass into water ($n_w = 1.33$)?

35. In each of the following questions, the second medium is air.
    (a) What is the critical angle for the first medium if its index of refraction is 1.68?
    (b) What is the index of refraction of the first medium if the critical angle is 40°?

36. A lens has a focal length of $+20$ cm and a magnification of 4. How far apart are the object and the image?

37. A projector is required to make a real image, 0.5 m tall, of a 5.0 cm object placed on a slide. Within the projector, the object is to be placed 10.0 cm from the lens. What must be the focal length of the lens?

38. An object 5.0 cm high is placed at the 20 cm mark on a metre stick optical bench. A converging lens with a focal length of 20 cm is mounted at the 50 cm mark. What are the position and size of the image?

39. A camera lens has a focal length of 6.0 cm and is located 7.0 cm from the film. How far from the lens is the object positioned if a clear image has been produced on the film?

40. A philatelist (stamp collector) uses a magnifying glass with a focal length of 10 cm. In order to examine a rare postage stamp, he holds the lens 4.0 cm from his eyes. If the distance for the most comfortable viewing of the image is 30 cm from his eyes, how far from the lens must the postage stamp be placed in order that the image be in focus at this position? What will the magnification be?

Good quality microscopes, binoculars, and cameras may contain 6 to 10 thin lenses. A single lens camera is not made up of one lens but a series of lenses (see photograph).

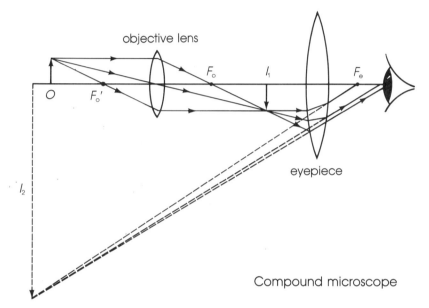

objective lens

F_o I_1 F_e

O F_o'

eyepiece

I_2

Compound microscope

41. In a compound microscope, the image is formed by two converging lenses. The real image, formed by the first lens (called the objective), is then used as the object by the second lens, called the eyepiece, to create a larger, virtual image. Use the following information to determine the position and size of the final image created by the two lenses: the object is 1.0 cm in height and is placed 2.5 cm from the objective lens ($f = 2.0$ cm); the eyepiece is 12 cm from the objective lens and has a focal length of 2.3 cm.

More than one lens or mirror may be combined in an optical system. The analysis is straightforward. The image from the first element becomes the object for the second, and so on, in a logical progression. Indeed, this is the only way in which we can ever have a virtual object.

12 Waves Travelling in One Dimension

Energy can be transferred from one place to another by a moving object, such as a baseball thrown from a pitcher to a catcher. The kinetic energy given to the ball by the pitcher is transferred to the catcher. But this is not the only way to effect a transfer of energy. Energy can also be transferred without the movement of matter from a source to a receiver — it can be transferred by means of a wave.

When you shake a rope, you send waves down its length. When you shake a spiral "slinky" spring, the energy you impart is transferred from coil to coil down the spring. When you throw a rock into a pool of water, circular waves radiate out from the point of contact. Energy is transferred as a wave from one water molecule to the next by the forces that hold the molecules together: the water only moves up and down as the wave passes.

A **wave**, then, is a transfer of energy in the form of a disturbance, usually, but not always, through a material medium.

Waves, whether water waves, sound waves, waves in a rope, or earthquake waves, have as their source a vibration. Sound waves originate from a vibrating tuning fork or a vibrating guitar or piano string. A water wave can result from the vibration caused by a rock thrown into water. In every case, the vibrating source supplies the energy that is transferred through the medium as a wave.

Because waves and vibrations are so intimately related, we will discuss both in this chapter. After discussing the basic properties of vibrating objects, we will deal with simple waves such as those found in vibrating springs and ropes. In later chapters we will discuss other forms of the wave, including electromagnetic waves, light waves, and even matter waves.

12.1 Vibrations

Most waves originate from objects that are vibrating so rapidly that they are difficult to observe with our unaided senses. For the purpose of observing the properties of vibrating objects, therefore, a slowly moving device such as a mass bouncing on a spring or, alternatively, a pendulum, is ideal. These are what we will use as our examples.

When an object repeats a pattern of motion — as a bouncing spring does — we say the object exhibits **periodic motion**. The vibration, or oscillation, of the object is repeated over and over with the same time interval each time.

When we describe the motion of a vibrating object, we call one complete oscillation a **cycle**. The number of cycles per second is called the **frequency** (*f*). The unit used to measure frequency is the **hertz** (Hz), named after a German scientist, Heinrich Hertz (1857-94), the discoverer of electromagnetic waves. (See Section 16.8). Another term used in describing vibrations is the **period** (*T*). Period is the time required for one cycle. Usually the second (s) is used for measuring the period, but for a longer period, like that of the rotation of the moon, the day (d) is used, or even the year (a).

Frequency and period are reciprocals. If the frequency is 60 Hz, the period is 1/60 (or 0.017) s. If the period is 0.010 s, the frequency is 100 Hz.

$$\text{frequency} = \frac{\text{cycles}}{\text{time}} \qquad \text{period} = \frac{\text{time}}{\text{cycles}}$$

$$f = \frac{1}{T} \qquad\qquad T = \frac{1}{f}$$

The distance in either direction from equilibrium to maximum displacement is called the **amplitude** (*A*) (see diagram).

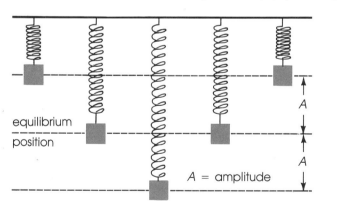

The rest position is where the object will remain at rest. The object can move through its rest position.

Sample problem

A pendulum completes 30 cycles in 15 s. Calculate its frequency and its period.

Hz = cycles per second

$$f = \frac{\text{cycles}}{\text{time}} = \frac{30 \text{ cycles}}{15 \text{ s}} = 2.0 \text{ Hz}$$

$$T = \frac{1}{f} = \frac{1}{2.0 \text{ Hz}} = 0.50 \text{ s}$$

Practice

1. Determine the frequency for each of the following:
   (a) A bouncing spring completes 10 vibrations in 7.6 s.
   (b) An atom vibrates 2.5×10^{10} times in 5.0 s.
   (c) A sound wave from a guitar string has a period of
       3.3×10^{-3} s.   (1.3 Hz, 5.0×10^9 Hz, 3.0×10^2 Hz)
2. Find the period for each of the following:
   (a) A pendulum swings back and forth 20 times in 15 s.
   (b) A light wave has a frequency of 5.0×10^{14} Hz.
   (c) The moon travels around the Earth six times in 163.8 d.
                                    (0.75 s, 2.0×10^{-15} s, 27.3 d)

12.2 Simple Harmonic Motion

As a mass hanging from an ordinary spring bounces up and down, we see that its speed is greatest when it is at the midpoint, whether it is going up or down. We see also that it slows down at both ends of its path, momentarily stopping before it reverses direction. This is because, except at the equilibrium position where the net force is zero, there is always an unbalanced force that acts to restore the mass to the equilibrium position.

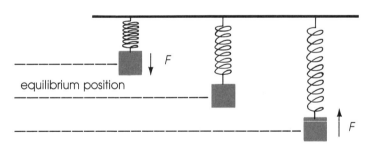

As the mass vibrates up and down, $F \propto x$ and $a \propto x$. These are the conditions that define simple harmonic motion.

Assuming the ideal condition of a massless spring, the mass moves the same distance above the equilibrium position as it moves below, completing each half-cycle in the same amount of time. At every point, including the equilibrium position, the net force exerted on the mass, and therefore the resulting acceleration, is proportional to the displacement of the mass from the equilibrium position. Both the force and the acceleration act towards the equilibrium position. This type of oscillation, where the restoring force is proportional to the displacement, is known as a **simple harmonic motion (S.H.M.)**. In other words, for simple harmonic motion, $F \propto x$.

You will note that this takes the form of Hooke's Law, that is, $F = kx$ (Section 6.7). Thus a loaded spring or flexible beam, a stretched wire, a twisted steel rod, a vibrating guitar string — any elastic system obeying Hooke's Law — may oscillate with simple harmonic motion. There are many other phenomena with characteristics resembling simple harmonic motion. This is why the analysis of simple harmonic motion is widely used in physics.

Period of Simple Harmonic Motion — The Reference Circle

As illustrated, alongside a ball bouncing on a spring is a turntable rotating at a uniform speed. The plane of the turntable is vertical and perpendicular to this page. When lighted from in front, shadows of both the ball and a knob on the turntable are projected on a screen side by side. The speed of the turntable can be adjusted to make the two shadows move in unison.

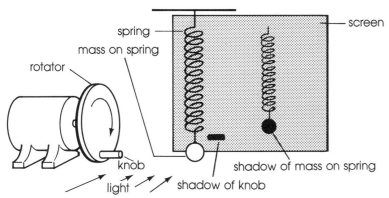

A side view of a ball bouncing on a spring and a rotating turntable, each with the same frequency. The shadow of the knob will be projected on the screen alongside the shadow of the ball.

While the knob on the turntable continues to move with uniform circular motion, its shadow, or projection, moves up and down along a line parallel to a diameter of the circular turntable. However, although the speed of the knob on the turntable is constant, the velocity of the shadow is constantly changing. At any instant, the velocity of the shadow, v, is equal to the vertical component of the velocity of the knob, v_o (see illustration on next page).

At the midpoints, B and B', the vertical component of the knob velocity is the same as the velocity of the knob itself, with the shadow moving at maximum velocity. This parallels the case for the spring as it moves through the equilibrium position. At the end points, A and C, the vertical component of the knob velocity is

The net force, F_{net}, acting upward on the mass contains one upward component, F_s, due to the spring, and one downward component, F_g, due to gravity.
At equilibrium, $F_{net} = F_s - F_g = 0$ and $F_s = F_g$, or $mg = kx$ where x is the stretch of the spring at the equilibrium position.

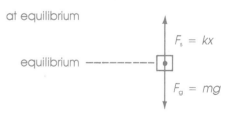

at equilibrium

$$F_s = kx$$
equilibrium $----------$
$$F_g = mg$$

At a displacement Δx above the equilibrium position, the spring is shorter and

$$F_s = k (x - \Delta x)$$
$$= kx - k\Delta x$$
However, F_g is unchanged, so
$$kx = mg$$
Therefore $F_s = mg - k\Delta x$
Since $F_{net} = F_s - F_g$
then $F_{net} = mg - k\Delta x - mg$
$$= -k\Delta x$$

above equilibrium

$$F_s$$
$----------$
$$\Delta x$$
equilibrium $----------$ F_g

Above the equilibrium position, F_{net} acts downward to return the mass to the equilibrium position.
Similarly, for Δx below the equilibrium position,
$$F_{net} = +k\Delta x$$
Below the equilibrium position, F_{net} acts upward to return the mass to the equilibrium position.
So the spring and gravity combine to give a restoring force proportional to the displacement, and the constant is simply the spring constant.

zero, and the shadow is momentarily at rest. When the knob revolves in a circle, its shadow moves up and down with a velocity that varies from zero at the end points to a maximum at the midpoint. The shadow projected on the screen exhibits the same simple harmonic motion as the bouncing ball on the spring.

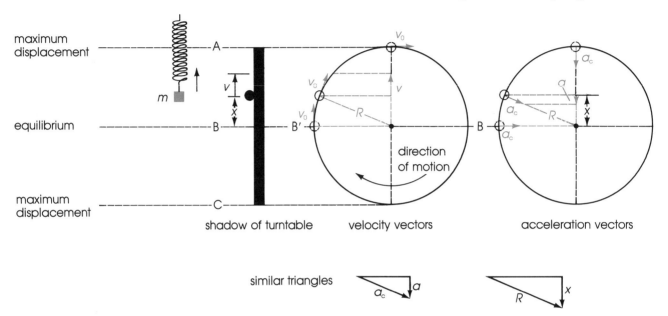

maximum displacement

equilibrium

maximum displacement

shadow of turntable   velocity vectors   acceleration vectors

similar triangles

To further demonstrate that the motion of the shadow is S.H.M., a reference circle has been drawn to the right of the velocity circle to show the acceleration of the knob. Since there is uniform circular motion, the knob will have a constant centripetal acceleration, a_c of constant magnitude. At any instant, the acceleration of the shadow, a is equal to the vertical component of the centripetal acceleration of the knob. Thus, at the midpoint the acceleration of the shadow is zero, while at the end points it is at a maximum — downward when at the top and upward when at the bottom. In all cases the acceleration of the shadow acts towards the midpoint, which is a characteristic property of S.H.M.

Examining the acceleration reference circle, we can see from the similar triangles that $\frac{a}{x} = \frac{a_c}{R}$ where x is the vertical displacement from the equilibrium position. But, a_c and R are constant throughout the motion, that is, $\frac{a_c}{R}$ = constant; therefore $\frac{a}{x}$ = constant, or $a \propto x$. The acceleration is directly proportional to the displacement.

This is a general property of all S.H.M.

The centripetal acceleration for an object moving with a uniform speed in a circle is given by $a_c = \dfrac{4\pi^2 R}{T^2}$ (Section 3.9). Therefore the ratio a_c/R reduces to:

$$\frac{a_c}{R} = \frac{4\pi^2 R/T^2}{R} = \frac{4\pi^2}{T^2}$$

But since $\quad \dfrac{a}{x} = \dfrac{a_c}{R}$

then $\quad \dfrac{a}{x} = \dfrac{4\pi^2}{T^2}$ where T is the period of oscillation.

This relationship is true for all forms of simple harmonic motion; the ratio $\dfrac{a}{x}$ is always $\dfrac{4\pi^2}{T^2}$. When solved for T, this will give an expression for the period of any simple harmonic motion.

$$T = 2\pi \sqrt{\frac{x}{a}}$$

where T is the period, in seconds

$\quad x$ is the displacement from equilibrium, in metres

$\quad a$ is the acceleration, in metres/second squared

The accelerations of the shadow, a, and the knob, a_c, are equal in magnitude when x is at its maximum value. Thus, in this equation x can be replaced by the amplitude, A, provided a represents the maximum acceleration of the object undergoing simple harmonic motion.

Now we shall apply this relationship to two examples of simple harmonic motion, the period of a mass hung from a spring and the period of a simple pendulum.

Period of a Mass Hung from a Spring

A mass is supported by an ideal spring that obeys Hooke's Law, i.e., $F = kx$. If the mass undergoes an acceleration, Newton's Second Law applies, i.e., $F = ma$. At the end points of the oscillation, where x equals the amplitude, the acceleration is a maximum and can be determined as follows:

$$ma = kx$$

$$a = \left(\frac{k}{m}\right) x$$

Substituting in

$$T = 2\pi \sqrt{\dfrac{x}{a}}$$

$$T = 2\pi \sqrt{\dfrac{x}{\left(\dfrac{k}{m}\right)x}}$$

$$T = 2\pi \sqrt{\dfrac{m}{k}}$$

This derivation for the period of the mass of the spring does not include the analysis described in the marginal note on page 449. However, gravity "cancels out", as shown there.

This equation tells us that where k is large (as for a stiff spring) the period of vibration is small. It also shows that a larger mass vibrates more slowly: when m is larger, T is larger. Note that the period of the vibration does not depend on its amplitude. It makes no difference whether the body vibrates over a large distance or a small one. The period remains the same, provided the amplitude does not exceed the elastic limit of the spring.

Period of a Simple Pendulum

A simple pendulum consists of a mass, usually called a pendulum bob, suspended from the end of a light string. We assume that the mass of the string is negligible, and ignore it in our analysis.

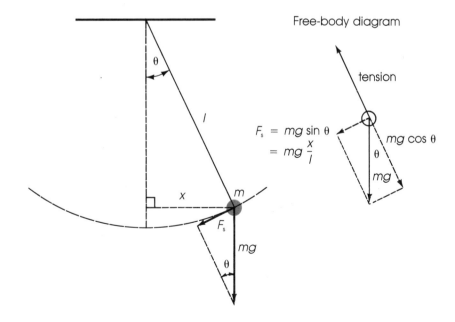

As the pendulum swings back and forth, the net force on the pendulum bob along the arc is F_s, the restoring force. F_s is the component of F_g that is tangent to the arc of motion, as illustrated. At any instant, the component of the weight (mg) in the direction of the tangent provides the restoring force.

The tension in the string has no component in the direction of the motion.

From the similar triangles we can write

$$\frac{F_s}{mg} = \frac{x}{l}$$

where l is the length of the pendulum and x is the horizontal displacement from the equilibrium position

Rewriting this equation, we have

$$F_s = \frac{mg}{l}x$$

Since mg and l are constants for a given pendulum, $F_s \, \alpha \, x$. But to be S.H.M., the restoring force would have to be proportional to the displacement of the bob *along the arc*, not to the horizontal displacement. For small angles of swing, that is, where θ is small, the distance x and the distance along the arc are very nearly equal in length. Thus we can conclude that the pendulum does exhibit S.H.M., but only for small angles of swing.

Since $F_s \, \alpha \, x$, the relationship has the same form as $F \, \alpha \, x$, or $F = kx$ (Hooke's Law).

$$F_s = \frac{mg}{l}x$$

$$kx = \frac{mg}{l}x$$

and

$$k = \frac{mg}{l}$$

Substituting in $T = 2\pi \sqrt{\dfrac{m}{k}}$ (from the spring example)

$$T = 2\pi \sqrt{\dfrac{m}{\dfrac{mg}{l}}}$$

$$\boldsymbol{T = 2\pi \sqrt{\dfrac{l}{g}}}$$

It is important to note that this equation is only an approximation, but it is a valid one for small angles of swing. It is also important to note that neither the mass nor the amplitude appears in the final equation. Thus, the period of a pendulum is independent of both the mass and the amplitude of swing. On the other hand, since g appears in the equation, this equation can be used to determine the value for the acceleration of gravity.

Simple pendulums were used in the past to measure the strength of the Earth's gravitational field (g) at various points on the Earth's surface. Variations in gravity readings indicated the possible presence of iron and other heavy ores under the ground. Today, sensitive electronic gravitometers, pulled behind airplanes, have replaced the pendulum in this application.

The sinusoidal nature can be illustrated by going back to the reference circle (see page 450). Since the circle is travelled once in time T, it follows that

$$\frac{\theta}{2\pi} = \frac{t}{T}$$

$$\text{or } \theta = \frac{2\pi t}{T}$$

$$x = R \sin \theta$$

$$= R \sin \frac{2\pi t}{T}$$

2π radians = 360°

(one rotation)

When $\sin \theta$ is a maximum ($\theta = 90°$), R is called the amplitude A.

Therefore, $x_{max} = A \sin \frac{2\pi t}{T}$ (as indicated in the text).

Another reason for studying sinusoidal waves is that any periodic wave of arbitrary form can be broken down into a set of sinusoidal components. This mathematical process is called Fourier analysis.

The phase angle is simply $2\pi \frac{t}{T}$ radians.

S.H.M. is Sinusoidal

If a pen were attached to a vibrating mass on a spring, and a sheet of paper were moved at a constant rate behind it and in contact with the pen, a curve would be drawn as illustrated.

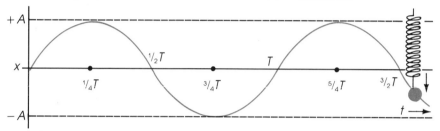

This curve has precisely the same shape as a sine curve, so called because it is like the graph of the sine function in trigonometry. Thus, the sinusoidal nature of S.H.M. can be expressed as

$$x = A \sin \frac{2\pi t}{T}$$

where x is the displacement from equilibrium
t is the time
T is the period
A is the amplitude

The sinusoidal function can be used to describe simple harmonic motion, using an angle instead of time as the variable. For example, in the case where a pendulum is at the centre, the angle is 0°. When it swings to maximum amplitude in one direction, the angle is 90°. When it returns to the equilibrium position, the angle is 180°. When it swings to maximum amplitude in the opposite direction, the angle is 270°, and when it returns to centre, the angle is 360°. These angles are called **phase angles**, and must not be confused with the angular position of the pendulum.

phase angles

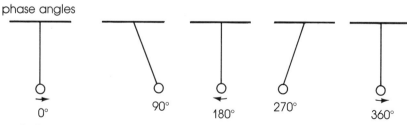

If identical objects are vibrating **in phase**, with the same amplitude and frequency, at any given moment they have the same displacement from the rest position and are moving in the same direction and with the same speed. When this condition is not met, we say that the vibrating objects are vibrating **out of phase**. It is customary to describe the phase of two oscillating objects using phase angles. For example, if two identical objects are vibrating in phase, the difference in phase angle between them is zero. If they are vibrating out of phase, in such a way that they are equal distances from the rest position but travelling in opposite directions, we would say that the phase angle between them, or the phase difference, is 180° (see illustration). A phase difference of 360° means they are both in phase again.

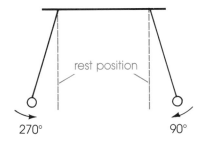

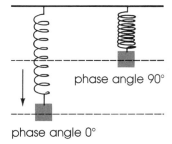

The pendulums are vibrating 180° out of phase.

The springs are vibrating 90° out of phase.

The amplitude of most vibrating objects slowly decreases with time until the oscillations stop completely. This is generally produced by air resistance and internal friction within the vibrating system. The lost energy, usually dissipated as heat, results in a decreased amplitude of oscillation. Such a phenomenon is known as a **damped harmonic motion**. A typical graph of displacement versus time for a damped harmonic motion is illustrated below.

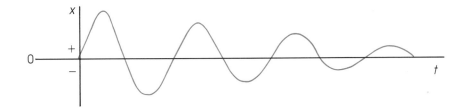

These damped oscillating systems are the rule in everyday life, but we study (undamped) simple harmonic motion because it is much easier to analyse mathematically. Except where damping is large, there is little effect on the period of vibration, and the equations for simple harmonic motion can be used.

Sample problems

1. A 1.0 kg mass is hung from a spring whose constant, k, is 100 N/m. What is the period of oscillation of this mass when it is allowed to vibrate?

$$T = 2\pi \sqrt{\frac{m}{k}}$$

$$= 2\pi \sqrt{\frac{1.0 \text{ kg}}{100 \text{ N/m}}}$$

$$= 0.63 \text{ s}$$

2. What is the period of a pendulum 0.40 m long?

$$T = 2\pi \sqrt{\frac{l}{g}}$$

$$= 2\pi \sqrt{\frac{0.40 \text{ m}}{9.8 \text{ m/s}^2}}$$

$$= 1.3 \text{ s}$$

3. A 50 kg gymnast carefully steps onto a trampoline and finds that it is depressed vertically 30 cm when it supports her mass in equilibrium. Assuming the trampoline has negligible mass and that it vibrates with S.H.M., find the natural period of oscillation of the gymnast if her feet never leave the trampoline.

$$F = mg$$
$$= (50 \text{ kg}) (9.8 \text{ N/kg})$$
$$= 490 \text{ N}$$

This is the force exerted down upon the trampoline when she is standing on it.

The force constant for the trampoline is given by $F = kx$,

$$\text{so } k = \frac{F}{x}$$

$$= \frac{490 \text{ N}}{0.30 \text{ m}}$$

$$= 1.6 \times 10^3 \text{ N/m}$$

For S.H.M.,

$$T = 2\pi \sqrt{\frac{m}{k}}$$

$$= 2\pi \sqrt{\frac{50 \text{ kg}}{1.6 \times 10^3 \text{ N/m}}}$$

$$= 1.1 \text{ s}$$

4. A pendulum vibrates with a period of 2.0 s and an amplitude of 50 cm. What will be its displacement from the equilibrium position 0.75 s after passing through it? 1.5 s after passing through it?

$$x_1 = A \sin \frac{2\pi t}{T}$$

$$= (0.50 \text{ m}) \sin \frac{360° \ (0.75 \text{ s})}{2.0 \text{ s}}$$

$$= (0.50 \text{ m}) \sin 135°$$

$$= 0.35 \text{ m}$$

Note: The positive value of x_1 indicates that the pendulum is on the same side of the equilibrium position that it entered as the problem began.

$$x_2 = (0.50 \text{ m}) \sin \frac{360°(1.5 \text{ s})}{2.0 \text{ s}}$$

$$= 0.50 \sin 270°$$

$$= -0.50 \text{ m}$$

The negative value of x_2 indicates that the pendulum has moved to the opposite side of the equilibrium position.

Practice

1. Calculate the period for a spring whose force constant is 15 N/m, if the mass on the spring is 1.0 kg. (1.6 s)
2. What is the period of a pendulum suspended from the CN tower in Toronto by a light string 4.96×10^2 m long? (44.7 s)
3. You are designing a pendulum clock. How far must the centre of mass of the simple pendulum be located from the pivot point of rotation to give the pendulum a period of 1.0 s? (25 cm)
4. A 2.5 kg object, vibrating with simple harmonic motion, has a frequency of 1.0 Hz and an amplitude of 0.50 m. What is the restoring force on the object at the ends of the swing? (49 N)
5. A 0.020 kg cart is held between two identical, stretched springs on the air track illustrated. A force of 2.0 N is employed to hold the cart in a position 0.10 m from equilibrium. The cart is then released and allowed to vibrate from the 0.10 m position.
   (a) What is the force constant for the springs/cart system?
   (b) What is the frequency of vibration?
   (c) What is the maximum kinetic energy of the cart?
   (d) Where does (c) occur?
   (e) What is the cart speed in (c)?
   (20 N/m, 5.0 Hz, 0.10 J, 3.2 m/s)

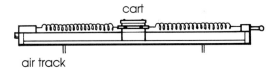

12.3 Wave Motion

A high wire artist kicks one end of the wire before starting to cross. She sees a small transverse movement dart along the wire and reflect back from the far end. The time taken for this round trip will tell her if the tension is correct. A football coach blows his whistle, creating fluctuations in the positions of air molecules and air pressure within it that make a shrill sound. A group of children drop pebbles into a pond; the surface of the water oscillates up and down, and concentric ripples spread out in ever-expanding circles. Electrons shift energy levels at the surface of the sun, sending fluctuating electric and magnetic fields through the vacuum of space; eight minutes later they deepen a sun-bather's golden tan. These are all examples of wave transmission.

We should be quite clear about what is being transmitted. It is a disturbance from some normal value of the medium that is transmitted, not the medium itself. For the wire, it was a small sideways displacement from the normal equilibrium position. For the sound, it was a slight forward and backward motion of air molecules about their normal average position. (Alternatively, the sound disturbance could be described as a slight increase and decrease of local pressure as the bouncing molecules crowded closer together or spread farther apart.) In the water, the disturbance was a raising and lowering of the water level from equilibrium. The activity within the sunshine is a little harder to imagine, but here the disturbance is a fluctuating electromagnetic field where none normally exists.

The disturbance travels with a speed fixed by the properties of the medium. These properties are fairly easy to identify for the first three cases. There is some force driving the medium back to equilibrium: the tension in the wire, the "springiness" of air, the gravitational and buoyant forces on the humps and hollows of water. There is some mass resisting a change in velocity: the wire, the air molecules, the water. In each case these two effects combine to fix the speed of the wave.

We live surrounded by waves. Some are visible, others are not. We can see water waves and waves in a wire, but sound waves, light waves, and radio waves we cannot see. By studying the properties of visible waves in ropes, springs, and water we can discover the properties that all waves have in common.

Wave Terminology

The waves described above are examples of **periodic waves**, where the motions are repeated at regular time intervals. But a wave can also consist of a single disturbance called a **pulse**, or **shock wave**. Sometimes it is easier to observe a single pulse in a spring than to try to study a wave consisting of a series of pulses.

When a water wave moves across an ocean or a lake, it moves at a uniform velocity. But the water itself remains in essentially the same position, merely moving up and down as the wave goes by. Similarly, when a rope is being vibrated at one end, the rope itself does not move in the direction of the wave motion: sections of the rope move back and forth or up and down as the wave travels along it.

Pulses in a rope usually move too quickly to be properly observed, so we use a device such as a wave in a spiral spring, in which the speed of the pulse is relatively low.

Transverse wave in a coiled spring

Water waves and waves in a rope are examples of transverse waves. In a **transverse wave** the particles in the medium vibrate at right angles to the direction in which the wave travels. The high section of the wave is called a **crest** and the low section a **trough**. Since the crest lies above and the trough below the equilibrium position (zero displacement), a crest is sometimes referred to as a **positive pulse** and a trough as a **negative pulse**.

In periodic waves, the lengths of successive crests and troughs are equal. The distance from the midpoint of one crest to the

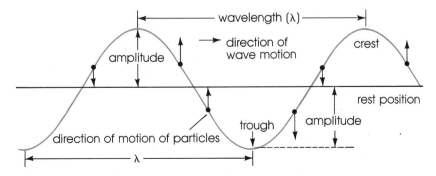

midpoint of the next, or from the midpoint of one trough to the midpoint of the next, is called the **wavelength** and is represented by the Greek letter λ (lambda). Note that in the previous illustration some of the pairs of particles on the wave are in phase; that is, they are moving in the same direction and are the same distance from the rest position. You can see that the distance between successive pairs of particles in phase is also one wavelength.

We have said that the amplitude of a wave is the distance from the equilibrium position to maximum displacement. For a simple periodic wave, the amplitude is the same on either side of the rest position. As a wave travels through a medium, its amplitude usually decreases because some of its energy is being lost to friction. If no energy were required to overcome friction, there would be no decrease in amplitude and the wave would be what is called an ideal wave. As a rule, to make analysis easier, we will assume that the waves we are examining are ideal waves.

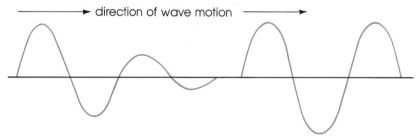

direction of wave motion

Most waves lose energy in the medium, resulting in a decrease in amplitude.

Ideal wave — no decrease in amplitude

In some types of waves the particles vibrate parallel to the direction of motion of the wave, and not at right angles to it. Such waves are called **longitudinal waves**. Longitudinal waves can be produced in "slinky" springs by moving one end of the spring back and forth in the direction of its length (see illustration).

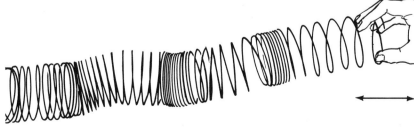

Longitudinal wave in a coiled spring

The most common longitudinal waves are sound waves, where the molecules, usually air, are displaced back and forth in the direction of the wave motion. In a longitudinal wave, the regions where the particles are closer together than normal are called **compressions**, and the regions where they are farther apart are called **rarefactions**.

Polarization

If the displacement of the particles of a medium by a transverse wave is all in the same plane, we say that the wave is **plane-polarized**. A transverse wave vibrating in a variety of planes can be generated in a rope by moving it up and down and then sideways in rapid succession. If the rope passes through a vertical slit, the waves will be confined to vibrating up and down in the vertical plane. If these vertically polarized waves encounter a second slit that is horizontal, the energy will be absorbed and the wave stopped completely, as illustrated.

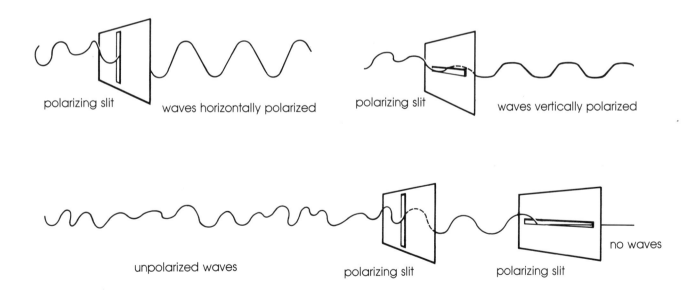

polarizing slit   waves horizontally polarized

polarizing slit   waves vertically polarized

unpolarized waves   polarizing slit   polarizing slit   no waves

Only transverse waves can be polarized. Longitudinal waves cannot. Sound waves, for example, are not appreciably affected when they pass through a slit. They are longitudinal anyway, so their particles vibrate parallel to the direction of the wave motion.

12.4 Transmission of Waves

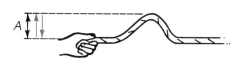

If you hold a piece of rope with your hand, and move your hand up and down, a wave will travel along the rope, away from you. Your hand, then, is the vibrating source of energy, and the rope is the material medium through which the energy is transferred. By moving your hand through one-half of a cycle, as illustrated, you can create a crest, or positive pulse, along the rope. When you move your hand in the opposite direction, a trough is produced that also travels along the rope, right behind the crest. If the hand motion is continued, a series of crests and troughs move along the rope at a uniform velocity. One cycle of the source produces one crest and one trough. The **frequency of the wave** is defined as the number of crests and troughs, or complete cycles, that pass a given point in the medium per unit of time (usually 1 s). The frequency of the wave is exactly the same as that of the source. It is the source alone that determines the frequency of the wave. Once the wave is produced, its frequency never changes, even if its speed and wavelength do. This behaviour is characteristic of all waves.

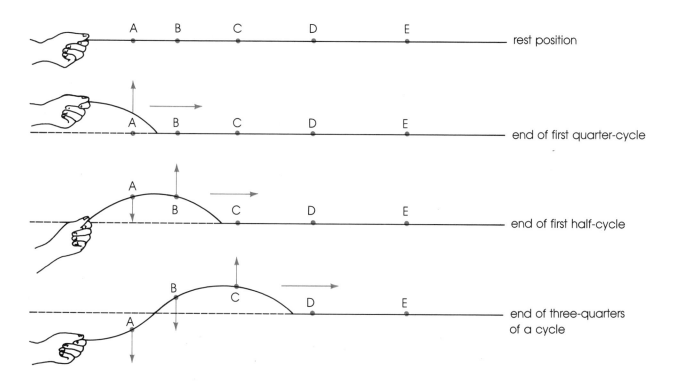

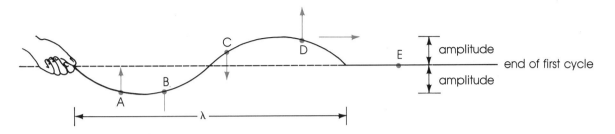

distance travelled by wave during
one cycle or period of the source.

When a wave is generated in a spring or a rope, the wave travels
a distance of one wavelength (λ) along the rope in the time required
for one complete vibration of the source. Recall that this time is
defined as the period (T) of the source.

$$\text{Since } v = \frac{\Delta d}{\Delta t}$$
$$\text{and } \Delta d = \lambda \text{ and } \Delta t = T$$
$$\text{therefore } v = \frac{\lambda}{T}$$
$$\text{But } f = \frac{1}{T}$$

Therefore

$$v = f\lambda$$

This equation is known as the **Wave Equation** because it applies
to all waves, visible and invisible.

Sample problems

1. The wavelength of a water wave in a ripple tank is 0.080 m. If
    the frequency of the wave is 2.5 Hz, what is its speed?
    $$v = f\lambda$$
    $$= (2.5 \text{ Hz})(0.080 \text{ m})$$
    $$= 0.20 \text{ m/s}$$
2. The distance between successive crests in a series of water waves
    is 4.0 m, and the crests travel 9.0 m in 4.5 s. What is the fre-
    quency of the waves?

$$v = \frac{\Delta d}{\Delta t}$$
$$= \frac{9.0 \text{ m}}{4.5 \text{ s}}$$
$$= 2.0 \text{ m/s}$$
$$f = \frac{v}{\lambda}$$
$$= \frac{2.0 \text{ m/s}}{4.0 \text{ m}}$$
$$= 0.50 \text{ Hz}$$

3. The period of a sound wave from a piano is 1.18×10^{-3} s. If the speed of the wave in air is 3.4×10^{2} m/s, what is its wavelength?

$$v = f\lambda$$
$$\text{or } v = \frac{\lambda}{T}$$
$$\text{Therefore } \lambda = vT$$
$$= (3.4 \times 10^{2} \text{ m/s})(1.18 \times 10^{-3} \text{ s})$$
$$= 0.40 \text{ m}$$

Practice

1. A source with a frequency of 20 Hz produces water waves that have a wavelength of 3.0 cm. What is the speed of the waves?
   (0.60 m/s)
2. A wave in a rope travels at a speed of 2.5 m/s. If the wavelength is 1.3 m, what is the period of the wave?   (0.52 s)
3. A given crest of a water wave requires 5.2 s to travel between two points on a fishing pier located 19 m apart. It is noted in a series of waves that 20 crests pass the first point in 17 s. What is the wavelength of the waves?   (3.1 m)
4. An FM station broadcasts radio signals with a frequency of 92.6 MHz. If these radio waves travel at a speed of 3.00×10^{8} m/s, what is their wavelength?   (3.2 m)

12.5 Transmission and Reflection

Water waves and waves in long springs travel at a uniform speed as long as the medium they are in does not change. But if, for example, two long springs having different force constants are joined together, we find that the speed of a wave changes abruptly at the junction between the two springs. With a speed change there is a corresponding wavelength change. This wavelength change is predicted by the Wave Equation, $v = f\lambda$. Since the frequency of a wave remains constant once the wave is generated, the wavelength is directly proportional to the speed, that is, $\lambda \propto v$.

When a wave travels from a light rope into a heavy rope having the same tension (a transition from a less dense medium to a denser medium), the wave slows down and the wavelength decreases. On the other hand, if the wave travels from a heavy rope to a light rope (or less dense medium), both the speed and the wavelength increase. These properties are true of all waves. A change in medium results in changes both in the speed of the wave and in its wavelength. In a medium where the speed is constant, the relationship $v = f\lambda$ predicts that $\lambda \propto 1/f$. In other words, if the frequency of a wave increases, its wavelength decreases, a fact easily demonstrated when waves of different frequencies are generated in a rope or spring (see investigation on page 476).

One-dimensional waves such as those in a spring or rope behave in a special way when they are reflected. In the case of reflection from a rigid obstacle, usually referred to as **fixed-end reflection**, the pulse is inverted. A crest is reflected as a trough and a trough is reflected as a crest. On the other hand, if the reflection occurs from a **free end**, where the medium is free to move, there is no inversion — crests are reflected as crests and troughs as troughs. In both fixed-end and free-end reflection there is no change in the frequency or wavelength. Nor is there any change in the speed of the pulse, since the medium is the same.

The terms *more dense* and *less dense* do *not* refer to physical density, that is, to the m/v ratio. They are a carry-over from geometric optics, where the media in which the light's speed decreased were referred to as "more dense", and media where the light's speed increased were referred to as "less dense".

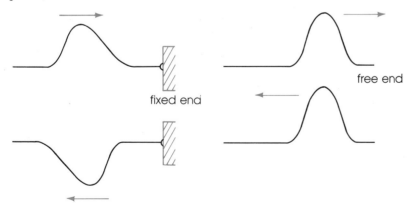

fixed end

free end

On the other hand, when a wave travels into a different medium, its speed and wavelength change, as noted earlier. Also, at the boundary between the two media, some reflection occurs. This is called **partial reflection**, because some of the energy is transmitted into the new medium and some is reflected back into the

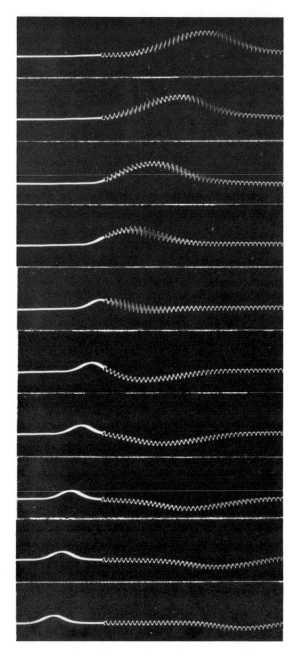

A pulse passing from a light spring to a heavy spring

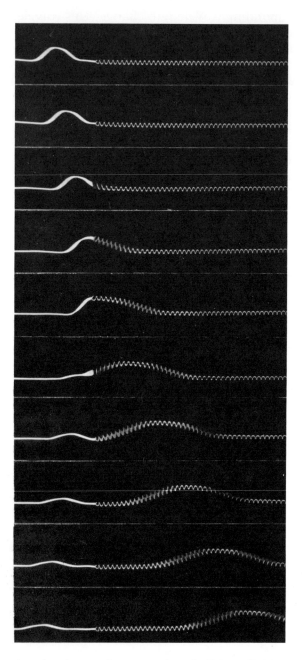

A pulse from a heavy spring (left) to a light spring (right)

original medium. This phenomenon is illustrated for a wave passing from a fast medium to a slow medium. Since the particles of the slower medium have greater inertia, this medium acts like a rigid obstacle, and the reflected wave is inverted. The transmitted wave is not inverted, however.

A reflected wave has a smaller amplitude than the original wave, because only some of the energy is reflected. For the same reason, the transmitted wave also has less amplitude. The wavelength of the transmitted wave is likewise smaller, because the speed in the new medium is slower. The wavelength and speed of the reflected wave remain unchanged because it stays in the same medium. The transmitted pulse does not travel as far from the boundary as does the reflected pulse in the same amount of time, because its speed is less.

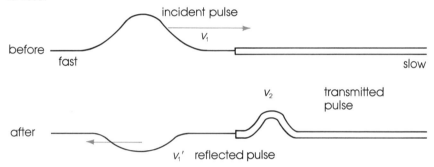

When a wave travels from a slow medium to a fast medium, the fast medium acts like a "free-end" reflection. No inversion occurs in either the reflected or transmitted wave, but there are changes in the wavelength and in the distance travelled by the transmitted wave, as illustrated below.

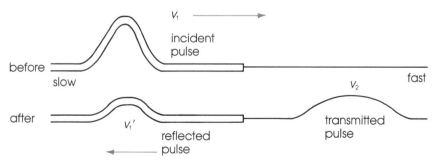

To summarize, then: when waves strike the boundary between two different media, partial reflection occurs. The phase of transmitted waves is unaffected in all partial reflections, but inversion of the reflected wave occurs when the wave passes from a fast medium to a slow medium.

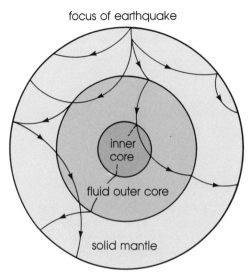

Seismic waves passing through the Earth

Whether the composition of the Earth's interior was fluid or solid was a matter of debate in the 19th century. Then, in 1926, the English astronomer and geophysicist, Harold Jeffreys, used a combination of geophysical and seismological data to show that the Earth must be fluid below a depth of 2600 km, since no transverse waves pass through its core. (It was generally believed that transverse waves can only pass through a solid.)

However, in 1936, the Danish seismologist Inge Lehmann reached the conclusion that the Earth had a smaller, solid, inner core, with a radius of approximately 1400 km. She had analysed the records of several earthquake waves that had reached the centre of the Earth, and determined that the solid core had reflected these waves. This was a very important discovery in the field of geophysics.

Recent theories of the Earth's magnetic field assign a role to the inner core. Its gradual growth by solidification of the liquid outer core may provide the energy needed to drive the geomagnetic generator that creates the Earth's magnetic field.

12.6 Interference of Waves

Up to this point, we have been dealing with one wave at a time. What happens when two waves meet? Do they bounce off each other? Do they cancel each other out? When pulses travel in *opposite* directions in a spiral spring or rope, they pass through one another unaffected. This behaviour is common to all types of waves. But continuous waves travelling out from a source may encounter other waves that either come from another source or are reflected waves from the same source. What happens, then, to certain particles in the medium when both waves continue to act on them at the same time?

When two or more waves act simultaneously on the same particles of a medium, whether in a simple rope or spring, or in water or air, we speak of **wave interference**. The resultant displacement of a given particle is equal to the sum of the displacements that would have been produced by each wave acting independently. This is called the **Principle of Superposition**. Note that the individual displacements may be positive (+) or negative (−). A plus or a minus sign must be included in each calculation of the resultant displacement.

In the example illustrated, pulses A and B are interfering, each making its own contribution to the resultant displacement of the particles in a medium. For example, point P in No. 3 is moved upward 8 mm by pulse A and up another 4 mm by pulse B for a total displacement of + 12 mm. Other particles are moved varying distances from the rest position, each displacement being determined by the sum of the contributions of the two pulses. The solid lines represent the resultant displacement of all the particles at a given instant. The dotted lines represent the individual displacements of pulses A and B and are not seen when interference occurs. Only the resultant displacement is seen (solid line).

When pulses A and C interfere (next page), pulse A displaces the particles upward, whereas pulse C displaces them downward. Particle P is moved up 11 mm by pulse A and down 5 mm by pulse C, giving it a resultant displacement at one instant of + 6 mm. The solid line indicates where other particles would be displaced by the interference of the two waves. Note that, in the areas of the medium where interference does not occur, the position of the particles in the medium (represented by the solid line) is that created by each individual wave.

Another statement of the Principle of Superposition is: "The resultant displacement of an individual particle is the algebraic sum of its separate displacements."

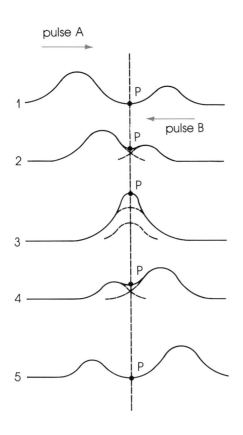

When two or more waves interfere to produce a resultant displacement *greater* than the displacement that would be caused by either wave, by itself, we call it **constructive interference**. When the resultant displacement is *smaller* than the displacement that would be caused by one wave, by itself, we call it **destructive interference**.

The Principle of Superposition may be used to find the resultant displacement of any medium when two or more waves of different wavelengths interfere. In every case, the resultant is determined by an algebraic summing of all the individual wave displacements. These displacements may be added together electronically and the resultant displacement displayed on an oscilloscope, as illustrated. Once again, the resultant wave is the only one seen, not the individual interfering waves.

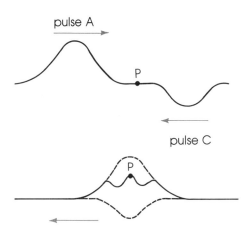

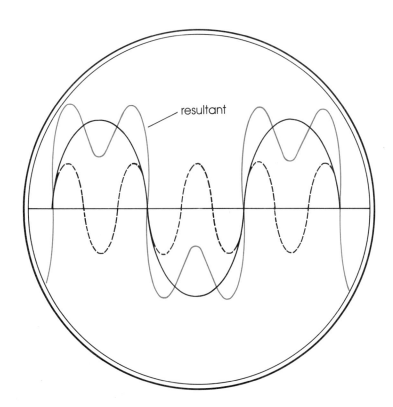

Resultant displacement as displayed on an oscilloscope. Note that only the solid line would be observed.

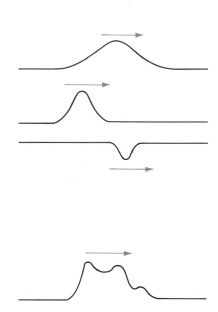

Three pulses and the resultant displacement that is produced by superposing them

12.7 Standing Waves — a Special Case of Interference in a One-Dimensional Medium

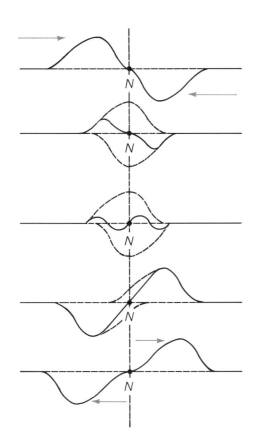

N = nodal point

The amplitude and the wavelength of interfering waves are often different. But if conditions are controlled so that the waves have the same amplitude and wavelength, yet travel in opposite directions, the resultant interference pattern is particularly interesting. It is referred to as a **standing wave interference pattern** or simply a standing wave. Whereas in most cases of interference the resultant displacement remains for only an instant, making it difficult to analyse the interference, standing wave interference remains relatively stationary. This makes it much easier to analyse and, therefore, a useful tool in the study of waves. Later, in Chapter 19, we will see its importance in the study of the quantum model of the atom.

When positive and negative pulses of equal amplitude and length, travelling in opposite directions, interfere, there is a point that remains at rest throughout the interference of the pulses. This point is called a **node**, or **nodal point** (*N*). In the larger diagram given here, two identical waves, A and B, are interfering. The resultant displacement caused by their interference produces areas of constructive and destructive interference. Note that the nodes are equidistant and that their spacing is equal to one-half of the wavelength of the interfering waves. Midway between the nodes are areas where double crests and double troughs occur. These areas are called **loops** or **antinodes**.

Standing waves may be produced by means of a single source. Reflected waves, for instance, will interfere with incident waves, producing standing waves. Since the incident waves and the reflected waves have the same source, and cross the same medium without loss, they have the same frequency, wavelength, and amplitude. The distance between nodal points may be altered by changing the frequency of the source. However, for a given length of rope or of any other medium, only certain wavelengths are capable of maintaining the standing wave interference pattern, because the reflecting ends must be nodal points.

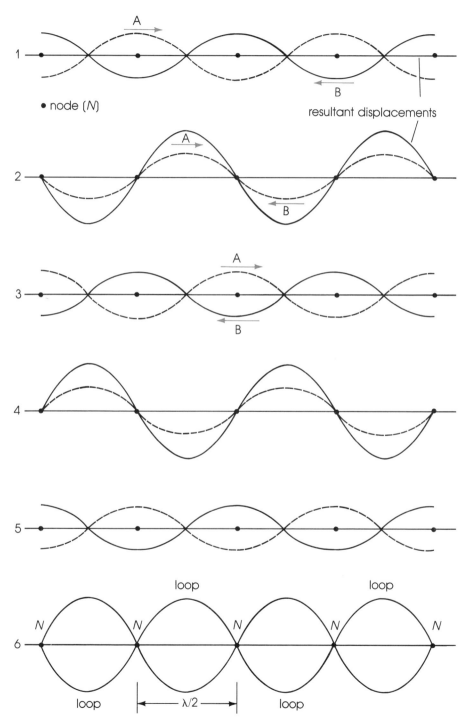

1

A →

• node (N)

resultant displacements

2

A →

← B

3

A →

← B

4

5

6

loop

loop

N   N   N   N   N

loop   ← λ/2 →   loop

Diagrams 1, 3, and 5 show the two identical waves interfering so that destructive interference occurs at every point in the medium. Thus, the resultant displacement line is horizontal. Diagrams 2 and 4 show the two waves interfering in such a way that there is constructive interference. Diagram 6 shows the resulting "standing wave interference pattern" created as the waves continually pass through one another.

Sample problem

The distance between two successive nodes in a vibrating string is 10 cm. The frequency of the source is 30 Hz. What is the wavelength of the waves? What is their velocity?

The distance between successive nodes is $\frac{1}{2}\lambda$. Therefore the wavelength is 2(10 cm) = 20 cm.

$$v = f\lambda$$
$$= (30 \text{ Hz}) (20 \text{ cm})$$
$$= 6.0 \times 10^2 \text{ cm/s}$$

This is the velocity of waves travelling along the string, not to be confused with the velocity of sound that we may hear through the air.

Practice

1. A standing wave interference pattern is produced in a rope by a vibrator with a frequency of 28 Hz. If the wavelength of the waves is 20 cm, what is the distance between successive nodes? (10 cm)

2. The distance between the second and fifth nodes in a standing wave is 60 cm. What is the wavelength of the waves? What is the speed of the waves, if the source has a frequency of 25 Hz? (40 cm, 10 m/s)

12.8 Modes of Vibration in a Stretched String

The frequencies at which standing waves can exist in a rope of a given length whose ends are fixed are the natural frequencies, or **resonant frequencies**, of the rope. Some vibrating objects such as a tuning fork, a pendulum, or a mass bouncing on a spring usually have only a single resonant frequency. A rope, a stretched spring, and even the air in an air column, such as that used in some musical instruments, have a large number of resonant frequencies, each of which is a whole-number multiple of the lowest resonant frequency, called the **fundamental**.

If a string is stretched between two fixed supports and then plucked, waves of a variety of wavelengths will travel along the string in both directions, will be reflected at the ends, and will travel back in the opposite directions. Most of these waves quickly die away, because they interfere in a random way. However, those waves that have a frequency equal to one of the resonant frequencies of the string will persist.

What determines the resonant frequencies of a particular string? In a vibrating string stretched between two fixed points, nodes must occur at both ends. In its simplest mode of vibration, the **fundamental mode**, the string vibrates in one segment, producing its lowest frequency, the **fundamental frequency**, f_o. If the string vibrates in more than one segment, the resulting modes of vibration are called **overtones**. Since the string can only vibrate in certain patterns, always with nodes at each end, the frequencies of the overtones are simple (whole numbered) multiples of the fundamental frequency, such as $2 f_o$, $3 f_o$, $4 f_o$, and so on.

This is easily seen. The string must have a length, L, equal to an integral number, say n, of half-wavelengths.

$$L = n \left(\frac{\lambda}{2} \right) = \left(\frac{n}{2} \right) \left(\frac{v}{f} \right)$$

$$f = n \left(\frac{v}{2L} \right)$$

$$= n f_o$$

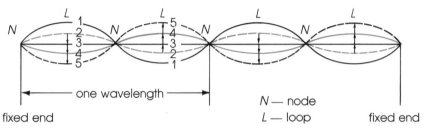

N — node
L — loop

one wavelength

fixed end   fixed end

Motion of string in which there is a stationary wave

The various resonant frequencies of standing waves are often called **harmonics**, because in music they harmonize. The fundamental frequency is called the first harmonic, and the overtones are called the second harmonic, third harmonic, fourth harmonic, and so on (see diagram of overtones and harmonics on next page).

Overtone vibration can be demonstrated with a sonometer. In this device, the string is touched at its exact centre with a feather, or lightly with a finger, and simultaneously stroked with a bow at the point midway between the centre and the bridge. The string is able to vibrate in only two segments, producing the first overtone, which has twice the frequency of the fundamental. By adjusting the position of the feather, or bow, the string can be made to vibrate in three or more segments, producing frequencies that are simple multiples of the fundamental frequency.

The strings of violins and other stringed instruments vibrate in a complex mixture of overtones superimposed on the fundamental. Very few vibrating sources can produce a note free of overtones. An exception is the tuning fork, whose overtones disappear quickly, making it a valuable instrument in the study of sound.

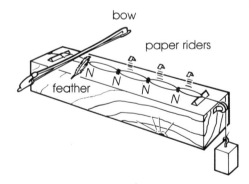

Demonstrating loops and nodes with a sonometer

fundamental (*f*)

1st harmonic

first overtone (2*f*)

2nd harmonic

second overtone (3*f*)

3rd harmonic

third overtone (4*f*)

4th harmonic

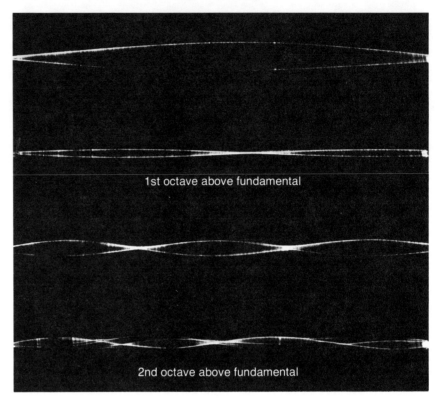

12.9 Investigations

Investigation 12.1: Simple Harmonic Motion

Problem:
How does the mass suspended from a spring affect its period of
vibration?

Materials:
spring
set of masses, 200 g to 1.00 kg
metre stick
spring support
stopwatch

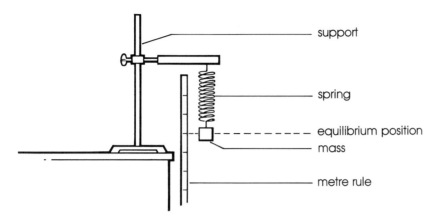

Procedure:
1. Set up the apparatus as illustrated.
2. Using the series of masses, determine the spring constant k for the spring you are using (or use the same spring used in the investigation on Hooke's Law, page 397).
3. Place a 500 g mass on the spring. Note the equilibrium position and determine the extension produced. Pull the mass 10 cm below the equilibrium position, making the amplitude 10 cm. Carefully release the mass and time 10 complete vibrations. Calculate the period. Try it again, releasing it from 10 cm *above* equilibrium.
4. Repeat for an amplitude of 15 cm. What is the effect of amplitude of vibration on the period?
5. Determine the periods for five more masses in the range 200 g to 1.00 kg. Plot a graph of period versus mass.
6. Using graphing and proportioning techniques, determine the relationship between the period and the mass, writing it as a proportionality statement and an equation.
7. Attach an unknown mass, for example a C-clamp, to the spring. Determine its period and, using this value, determine its mass. Have you determined the inertial mass or the gravitational mass in this step?
8. Check the mass of the clamp, using a balance. What was your experimental error?
9. What assumptions have you made about the mass of the spring throughout the investigation?
10. Why does the bouncing mass on the spring exhibit simple harmonic motion?
11. Describe the steps in an experiment to determine the value of a spring constant, using the period and the mass.

The amplitudes chosen will vary from spring to spring. The coils of the spring should not close completely at the highest position of the mass. If they do, use a smaller initial amplitude. In other words, the amplitude should be such that the spring is under tension throughout the entire cycle.

A vibration is a complete oscillation, up and down.

Investigation 12.2: Transmission and Reflection of One-Dimensional Waves

Problem:
How is a transverse wave in a coiled spring transmitted and reflected?

Materials:
long spiral spring

Procedure:
1. With the help of your partner, stretch the spring to a length of approximately 5 m on a smooth, clean floor. Your partner should hold one end of the spring rigid throughout this investigation.
2. Create a pulse at your end of the spring by moving your hand quickly from the rest position to one side and back to the rest position, at right angles to the length of the spring.
3. Describe the motion you observe of a point near the middle of the spring as the pulse passes.
4. Move your hand in such a way as to generate single pulses with different amplitudes. Does the amplitude of a pulse change as the pulse moves from one end of the spring to the other? Why?
5. Generate two pulses, one right after the other. Note how the distance between them changes as they move along the spring. What does this tell you about the speed of the pulses? Generate two more pulses, close together and one distinctly larger than the other. How does the amplitude of each pulse affect its speed?
6. Stretch the spring 2 m farther. How is the speed of each pulse affected by the change in the tension of the spring?
7. During the investigation, the pulses you generated at the free end of the spring were "reflected" from the fixed end. Compare the reflected pulses with the original pulses.
8. Suspend the spring vertically from a high point in the room so that it stretches close to, but does not touch, the floor. Avoid obstructions, since the spring must move freely along its whole length. (It may be necessary to bunch together some of the coils at the top.) Generate a transverse pulse at the top of the spring. Note whether the pulse is inverted when it is reflected from the "free" end of the spring. Compare the properties of fixed-end and free-end reflections.

Investigation 12.3: Interference of Waves in a One-Dimensional Medium

Problem:
How do waves, moving in opposite directions, interfere in a one-dimensional medium?

Materials:
a spiral spring with tabs or a length of rubber tubing (or a Bell Wave Machine)

Procedure:
1. Stretch the spiral spring or the rubber tubing between yourself and your partner. Or use the Bell Wave Machine.
2. Simultaneously, generate positive pulses from both ends of the medium. Are the two pulses reflected off each other or do they pass through each other unaffected? Check your answer by simultaneously generating a positive pulse from one end and a negative pulse from the other.
3. Noting a specific point near the middle of the medium, simultaneously generate positive pulses from both ends. How is the point affected when the two pulses act on it at the same time? What do you predict would happen if two negative pulses were used? Check your prediction.
4. Simultaneously generate a positive pulse from one end and a negative pulse from the other. How are certain points, located near the middle of the medium, affected when these two pulses act on them at the same time?
5. Simultaneously generate waves of equal frequency and amplitude from each end of the medium (spring or tubing). This is not an easy task, so practice will be required. Adjust the frequency until the medium maintains a fixed pattern. Compare the displacement of certain particles in the medium with that of other particles. Draw a sketch illustrating the resultant displacement of the medium. On your sketch of the standing wave interference pattern indicate nodes and loops (antinodes).
6. Change the frequency of the waves. How is the pattern affected when the frequency is increased? When it is decreased? For "complete destructive interference" at the nodal points, what must be true of the wavelengths and amplitudes of the two waves?
7. Fix one end of the medium rigidly. Generate a series of waves towards the fixed end. What is the effect on the medium when the incident waves interfere with the reflected waves? What is

the resultant displacement, at all times, of the end of the medium where the wave is reflected?

8. In the standing wave interference pattern, what distance constitutes a wavelength? Why is it easier to measure the wavelength of a wave using the standing wave interference pattern than it is to measure it directly?

12.10 Review

Discussion

1. A spring-mass system vibrates with simple harmonic motion. If the mass is doubled, by what factor will its frequency change?
2. How will the period of a simple pendulum change if:
   (a) the length is quadrupled?
   (b) the length is halved?
   (c) the amplitude is halved?
   (d) the mass is doubled?
3. How could a pendulum be used to measure variations in the value of g at various points on the Earth's surface?
4. You send a pulse down a string that is attached to a second string with unknown properties. The pulse returns to you inverted and with a smaller amplitude. Is the speed of the waves faster or slower in the second string? Explain your reasoning.
5. When standing waves are produced in a string, total destructive interference occurs at the nodes. What has happened to the wave energy?
6. Why are standing waves not produced in a swimming pool? How could you produce standing waves in a long narrow cake pan?

Problems

7. A tuning fork completes 2048 cycles in 8.0 s. What is its frequency?
8. The tine of a tuning fork vibrates with an amplitude of 0.13 cm. If the frequency of the fork is 200 Hz, what total distance will the tine travel in 1.00 min?

9. Thirty waves strike a concrete breakwater in 1.00 min. What is the period of the waves, in seconds?
10. Calculate the period when a spring, whose force constant is 20 N/m, is suspended vertically and loaded with a mass of 1.0 kg.
11. What is the period of an 80 cm pendulum on the moon, where the acceleration due to gravity is 1.6 m/s²?
12. On a particular planet, the period of a 0.50 m pendulum is 1.8 s. What is the acceleration due to gravity on this planet?
13. A grandfather clock had a pendulum exactly 1.00 m long and kept perfect time. A naughty grandson broke the pendulum. When repaired, it was exactly 2.0 cm shorter than before.
    (a) Did the repaired clock lose or gain time?
    (b) What would the accumulated error be after one day of operation?
    (c) If the repaired clock were set correctly at midnight on New Year's Eve, when would it next indicate the correct time?
14. A spring vibrates with a frequency of 2.2 Hz when a mass of 0.50 kg is hung from it. What will its frequency be if a 1.00 kg mass is hung from it?
15. A series of strobe photos shows that a mass on a spring is located 10 cm from its equilibrium position 0.20 s after passing it, without having changed its direction of motion. What is the period of the vibrating mass if its amplitude is 20 cm?
16. This full-scale diagram shows a series of wave crests, all of which will pass a point in 0.50 s.
    (a) What is the wavelength in centimetres?
    (b) What is the frequency?
    (c) What is the velocity of the waves?

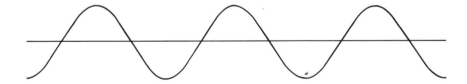

17. What are the wavelengths in air of the lowest and the highest audible frequencies if the range of human hearing is 20 Hz to 20 kHz and the speed of sound is 342 m/s?
18. Two men are fishing from small boats located 30 m apart. Waves pass through the water, and each man's boat bobs up and down 15 times in 1.0 min. At a time when one boat is on a crest, the other one is in a trough, and there is one crest between the two boats. What is the speed of the waves?

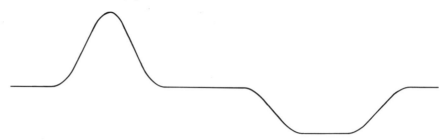

19. Two pulses move towards each other as illustrated. Sketch the resultant shape of the medium when the two pulses overlap.

20. A triangular pulse is created in medium A. The speeds of pulses in mediums A, B, and C are 1.0 cm/s, 2.0 cm/s, and 1.5 cm/s, respectively. Draw a diagram to show the nature and position of the reflected and transmitted pulses when the original pulse reaches the middle of medium C.

A   B   C

Numerical Answers to Review Problems

7. 2.6×10^2 Hz
8. 62 m
9. 2.0 s
10. 1.4 s
11. 4.4 s
12. 6.1 m/s²
13. (b) 14.5 min (c) 99.3 d later
14. 1.6 Hz
15. 2.4 s
16. (a) 3.8 cm (b) 6.0 Hz (c) 23 cm/s
17. 1.7×10^{-2} m
18. 5.0 m/s
22. (a) 21 cm (b) 21 m/s
23. 800 Hz, 1200 Hz, 1600 Hz
24. 450 Hz

21. A light string is fastened to a heavy cord which in turn is fastened to a wall. The light string is 3.0 m long, and a pulse travels in it at a velocity of 2.0 m/s. The heavy cord is 0.50 m long, and the velocity of the pulse in it is 1.0 m/s. Discuss all the reflections and transmissions that occur up to 2.6 s after a short pulse is introduced at the end of the light string. Indicate the time at which each change occurs, noting any phase changes.

22. Standing waves are set up in a string by a source vibrating at 100 Hz. Seven nodes are counted in a distance of 63 cm (including one node at each end).
    (a) What is the wavelength of the waves travelling in the string?
    (b) What is the speed of these waves?

23. If the fundamental frequency produced by a guitar string is 400 Hz, what are the frequencies of the second, third and fourth harmonics?

24. If two successive overtones of a vibrating string differ by 450 Hz, what is the frequency of the fundamental?

Physics – a Career

Why Study Physics?

Physics is so fundamental a subject that there is scarcely an area of modern life unaffected by it. If we want to consider ourselves educated and part of a civilized society, each of us must study the main ideas of physics.

The impact of physics on our society can be seen in most of our products, processes, and services. For example, the communications industry evolved almost entirely because of research by physicists. The telephone, satellite television, transistors, integrated circuits, fibre optics, cable television, and laser discs all depend on the laws of physics. In the medical field, the applications of physics are familiar to us all: X-rays, CAT scans, ultrasonic diagnosis, radiation therapy, hearing aids, heart pacers, and laser scalpels. All have a basis in physical principles. Communications, medicine and many other fields such as geology, energy, transportation, and astronomy are extremely important in our modern technological society.

Many students find that they enjoy the challenge and application of physics, and so may consider it as a career. Others may choose to pursue a career in a field related to physics, such as engineering, geology, oceanography, computer electronics, archaeology, or patent law. In both cases, the study of physics at secondary school, college, or university will be a prerequisite.

The Canadarm, used on the U.S. space shuttle, is a prime example of the work done by physicists and engineers.

What Do Physicists Do?

Men and women physicists are engaged in a variety of activities in industry, in research at university, government, and private laboratories, and in education. In research, physicists design and perform experiments to test and modify available theories and, as well, deduce ways of putting the principles involved to practical use. Other researchers, more interested in the mathematical aspects of physical theories, derive equations and develop mathematical models used to better understand the physical world. Many physicists are concerned with the application of physics to the needs of society. Some of them are teachers at secondary, college, and university levels. Finally, some physicists are administrators in government, universities and high-technology industries, where research and development are of paramount importance.

Careers in Physics

Physics Specialities
Astronomy
Astrophysics
Meteorology
Geophysics
Acoustics
Electronics
Solid-State Physics
Spectroscopy
Particle Physics
Nuclear Physics
Computer Technology
Plasma Physics
Optics and Laser Physics
Biophysics
Low Temperature Physics
Teaching Physics
Medical Physics

Engineering Specialities
Civil
Mechanical
Electrical
Geological
Industrial
Metallurgical
Aeronautical
Maritime
Chemical
Systems Design

13 Waves Travelling in Two Dimensions

13.1 Water Waves

Water waves are approximately transverse, but the water molecules move slightly back and forth as well as up and down. In fact, an individual particle actually moves in a small oval path, as we see a cork move in water, and as is illustrated here. This characteristic helps cause ocean waves to "break" if they become too large or when they approach a beach. Because small water ripples are very nearly transverse, we can use the water in lakes and the water in ripple tanks in our study of waves. The ripples move slowly enough that we are able to study them directly.

Waves in a stretched spring or rope illustrate some of the basic concepts of wave motion in a one-dimensional medium. We may study the behaviour of waves in two dimensions by observing water waves in a ripple tank.

The ripple tank is a shallow, glass-bottomed tank on legs. Water is put in the tank to a depth of approximately 2 cm. Light from a source above the tank passes through the water and illuminates a screen on the table below. The light is made to converge by wave crests and to diverge by wave troughs, as illustrated, creating bright and dark areas on the screen. The distance between successive bright areas, caused by crests, will be one wavelength (λ). Circular waves may be generated on the surface of the water by a point source like a finger or a drop of water from an eye-dropper. Straight waves may be produced by rolling a dowel in the water.

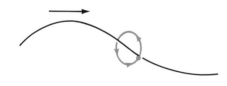

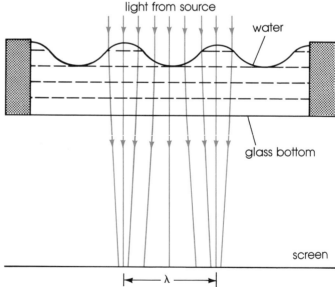

Bright lines occur on the screen where light rays converge.

Straight waves are equivalent to circular waves a very long way from the source.

A wave coming from a point source is circular, whereas a wave originating from a linear source is straight. As a wave moves away from its constant frequency source, we observe that the spacing between successive crests or successive troughs remains the same as long as the speed of the wave does not change. This behaviour is true for all waves, circular or straight — the wavelength remains constant if the speed does not change. When the speed decreases, as it does in shallow water, the wavelength also decreases. That is, wavelength is directly proportional to the speed ($\lambda \propto v$). When the frequency of a source is increased, the distance between successive crests becomes smaller. In other words, waves with a higher frequency have a shorter wavelength. The wavelength of a wave is inversely proportional to its frequency ($\lambda \propto 1/f$).

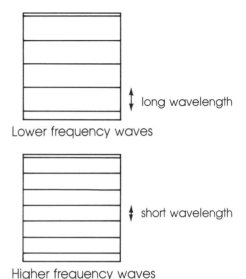

Lower frequency waves

Higher frequency waves

Periodic circular waves

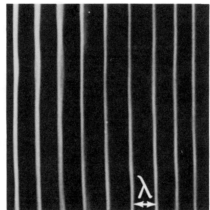

Periodic straight waves

If these two relationships are combined, as was done in Section 12.4, the result is the Wave Equation, $v = f\lambda$. This equation holds for all types of waves — one-dimensional, two-dimensional, and three-dimensional as well.

A continuous crest or trough is referred to as a **wavefront**. To show the direction of travel, or transmission, of a wavefront, an arrow is drawn at right angles to the wavefront, as illustrated. This line is called a **wave ray**. Sometimes we refer to wave rays instead of wavefronts when describing the behaviour of a wave.

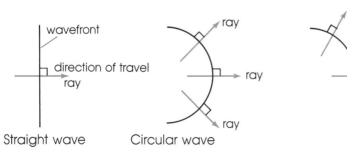

Straight wave   Circular wave   Irregular wave

13.2 Reflection of Water Waves

Reflection from a Straight Barrier

When a straight wave runs into a straight barrier, head on, it is reflected back along its original path, as illustrated.

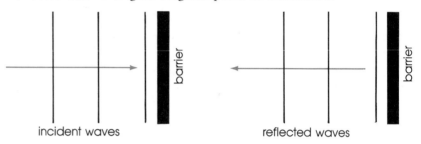

If a wave encounters a straight barrier at an angle (obliquely), the wavefront is also reflected at an angle to the barrier. The angle formed by the incident wavefront and the barrier is equal to the angle formed by the reflected wavefront and the barrier. These angles are called the **angle of incidence** (*i*) and the **angle of reflection** (*r*), respectively.

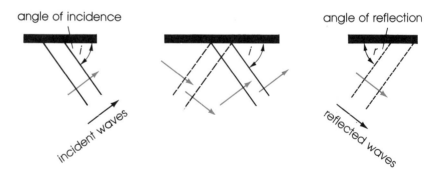

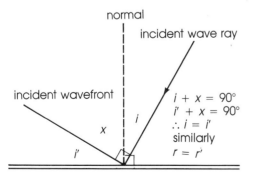

$$i + x = 90°$$
$$i' + x = 90°$$
$$\therefore i = i'$$
similarly
$$r = r'$$

When describing the reflection of waves, using wave rays instead of wavefronts, the angles of incidence and reflection are measured relative to a straight line perpendicular to the barrier, called the **normal**. This line is constructed at the point where the incident wave ray strikes the reflecting surface. As may be seen from the geometrical analysis illustrated, the angle of incidence has the same value whether wavefronts or wave rays are used to measure it. In both cases the angle of incidence equals the angle of reflection. (In other words, water waves obey the same Law of Reflection discussed in Section 11.4 for light.)

When a circular wave is reflected by a plane obstacle, the angle of incidence also equals the angle of reflection, although this is a little more difficult to see. The circular reflected wavefront appears to originate from an imaginary point behind the reflector, much as reflecting light rays appear to originate from a virtual image on the other side of a plane mirror.

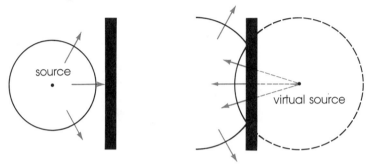

Circular wavefront

When straight waves strike a parabolic reflector, the straight waves obey the Law of Reflection and are reflected to the focal point (see diagram). This behaviour is exactly the same as when light rays are reflected by a converging mirror. When a circular wave is generated at the principal focus of the parabola, it is reflected as a straight wave.

In summary, the reflection of both straight and circular waves is predicted by the Law of Reflection. This is even more evident when wave rays are used to show the direction of the wave travel before and after the reflection. Also, in all wave reflection there is no change in the wavelength or the speed of the wave.

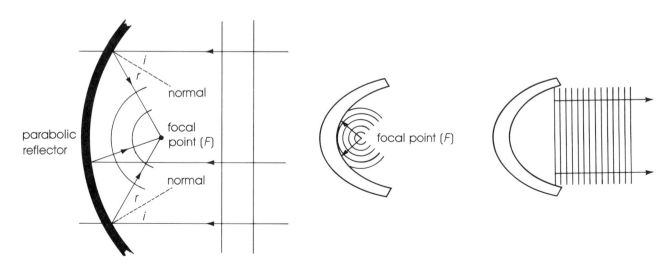

13.3 Refraction of Water Waves

When a wave enters a medium in which it moves more slowly, its wavelength decreases. For example, when a water wave travels from deep water to shallow water, its speed decreases. At the same time, its wavelength decreases, as illustrated.

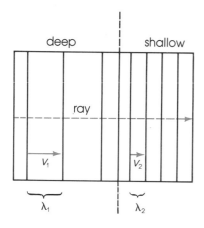

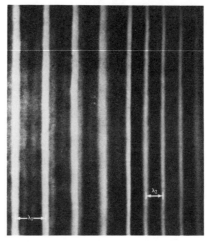

Periodic straight waves travelling from deep water to shallow water, left to right

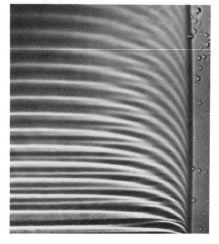

Waves encountering shallow water on the right; note the decrease in wavelength.

The wave travelling in deep water has a speed that is expressed by the equation $v_1 = f_1\lambda_1$ (the Wave Equation). Similarly, $v_2 = f_2\lambda_2$, for the wave in shallow water. But the frequency of a water wave is determined by the wave generator, and does not change when the speed changes. Thus $f_1 = f_2$.

If we divide the first equation by the second equation, we get

$$\frac{v_1}{v_2} = \frac{f_1\lambda_1}{f_2\lambda_2}$$

But
$$f_1 = f_2$$

Therefore,

$$\frac{v_1}{v_2} = \frac{\lambda_1}{\lambda_2}$$

Sample problem

A water wave has a wavelength of 2.0 cm in the deep section of a tank and 1.5 cm in the shallow section. If the speed of the wave in the shallow water is 12 cm/s, what is its speed in the deep water?

$$\frac{v_1}{v_2} = \frac{\lambda_1}{\lambda_2}$$

$$v_1 = \left(\frac{\lambda_1}{\lambda_2}\right)(v_2)$$

$$= \left(\frac{2.0 \text{ cm}}{1.5 \text{ cm}}\right)(12 \text{ cm/s})$$

$$= 16 \text{ cm/s}$$

Practice

1. The speed and the wavelength of a water wave in deep water are 18.0 cm/s and 2.0 cm, respectively. If the speed in shallow water is 10.0 cm/s, what is the corresponding wavelength?
(1.1 cm)

2. A wave travels 0.75 times as fast in shallow water as it does in deep water. What will the wavelength of the wave in deep water be, if its wavelength is 2.7 cm in shallow water? (2.0 cm)

3.6 cm

When a wave travels from deep water to shallow water, in such a way that it meets the boundary between the two depths straight on, no change in direction occurs. On the other hand, if a wave meets the boundary at an angle, the direction of travel does change. This phenomenon is called **refraction**.

We usually use wave rays to describe refraction. In Section 11.7, it was explained that the normal is a line drawn at right angles to a boundary at the point where an incident light ray strikes the boundary. The angle formed by an incident wave ray and the normal is called the angle of incidence (i). The angle formed by a refracted wave ray and the normal is called the angle of refraction (R).

When a wave travels at an angle into a medium in which its speed decreases, the refracted wave ray is bent (refracted) towards the normal. If the wave travels at an angle into a medium in which its speed increases, the refracted wave ray is bent away from the normal.

You will note that geometrically we can show (see margin) that the angle of incidence (i) is equal to the angle between the incident wavefront and the boundary (i') and that the angle of refraction (R) is equal to the angle between the refracted wavefront and the

When water waves travel obliquely into a slower medium, the wave ray bends towards the normal, whereas if the medium is a faster one the wave ray bends away from the normal.

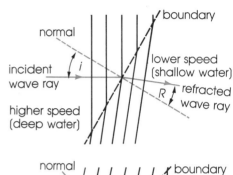

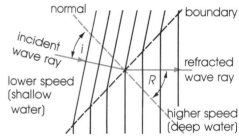

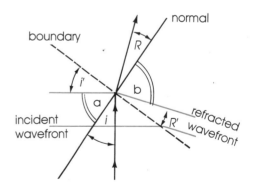

$i + a = 90°$
$i' + a = 90°$
$\therefore i = i'$

$R + b = 90°$
$R' + b = 90°$
$\therefore R = R'$

boundary (R'). In the ripple tank it is usually easier to measure the angles between the wavefronts and the boundary, that is, i' and R'.

If we use trigonometry when we analyse two wavefronts refracted at a boundary, we can express the angles of incidence and refraction as $\sin i = \lambda_1/xy$ and $\sin R = \lambda_2/xy$.

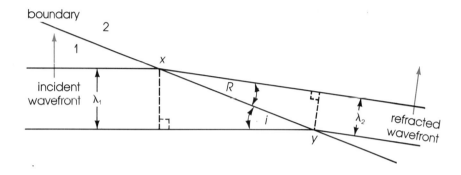

The ratio of the sines gives
$$\frac{\sin i}{\sin R} = \frac{\lambda_1/xy}{\lambda_2/xy}, \text{ which reduces to}$$

$$\frac{\sin i}{\sin R} = \frac{\lambda_1}{\lambda_2}$$

For a specific change in medium, the ratio λ_1/λ_2 has a constant value. Thus the ratio $\sin i/\sin R$ = constant. This is Snell's Law (Section 11.7) developed for water waves.

But
Thus
$$\frac{v_1}{v_2} = \frac{\lambda_1}{\lambda_2}$$

$$\frac{\sin i}{\sin R} = \frac{v_1}{v_2}$$

Recall that in optics the ratio of the speeds was defined to be equal to the index of refraction. That is,

$$_1n_2 = \frac{v_1}{v_2}$$

Therefore
$$\frac{\sin i}{\sin R} = {_1n_2}$$

Sample problems

1. A 5.0 Hz water wave, travelling at 30 cm/s in deep water, enters shallow water so that the angle between the incident wave in the deep water and the boundary is 50°. If the speed of the wave in the shallow water is 27 cm/s, what is:
   (a) the angle of refraction in the shallow water?
   (b) the index of refraction for the media?
   (c) the wavelength of the wave in the shallow water?

(a)
$$\frac{\sin i}{\sin R} = \frac{v_1}{v_2} \quad \text{or} \quad \sin R = \left(\frac{v_2}{v_1}\right) \sin i$$
$$= \left(\frac{27 \text{ cm/s}}{30 \text{ cm/s}}\right) \sin 50°$$
$$= 0.689$$
$$R = 43.6°, \text{ or } 44°$$

(b)
$$_1n_2 = \frac{v_1}{v_2}$$
$$= \frac{30 \text{ cm/s}}{27 \text{ cm/s}}$$
$$= 1.1$$

(c) The wavelength in the shallow water is
$$\lambda_2 = \frac{v_2}{f_2} \quad \text{but } f_2 = f_1 = 5.0 \text{ Hz}$$
$$= \frac{27 \text{ cm/s}}{5.0 \text{ Hz}}$$
$$= 5.4 \text{ cm}$$

Practice

1. A 10 Hz water wave travels from deep water, where its speed is 40 cm/s, to shallow water where its speed is 30 cm/s. The angle of incidence is 30°. Find (a) the index of refraction, (b) the wavelengths in the two media, and (c) the angle of refraction in the shallow water. (1.33, 4.0 cm and 3.0 cm, 22°)
2. Water waves travelling at a speed of 28 cm/s enter deeper water at an angle of incidence of 40°. What is the speed in the deeper water if the angle of refraction is 46°? (31 cm/s)
3. The velocity of a sound wave in cold air is 320 m/s, and in warm air, 384 m/s. If the wavefront in cold air is nearly linear, what will be the angle of refraction in the warm air if the angle of incidence is 30°? (37°)
4. What would be the angle of refraction in question 3 if the angle of incidence were 60°? Explain your answer.

As has been previously noted, the frequency of a wave does not change when its velocity changes (see Section 12.4). Therefore, since $v_1/v_2 = \lambda_1/\lambda_2$, we might expect that the index of refraction and the amount of bending would not change for waves of different frequencies, provided the medium remained the same — for example, water of the same depth in both cases.

However, as seen in the photographs, this is not always the case. In the first photograph, the low-frequency (long-wavelength) waves are refracted, as indicated by a rod placed on the screen of the ripple tank. The rod is exactly parallel to the refracted wavefronts. In the second photograph, the frequency has been increased (wavelength decreased), with the rod left in the same position. Note that the rod is no longer parallel to the refracted wavefronts. The higher-frequency waves are refracted in a slightly different direction than were the low-frequency waves, although the angle of incidence has remained unchanged. It appears that the amount of bending, and hence the index of refraction, is affected slightly by the frequency of a wave. We can conclude that, since the index of refraction represents a ratio of speeds in two media, the speed of the waves in at least one of those media must depend on their frequency. Such a medium, in which the speed of the waves depends on the frequency, is called a **dispersive medium**.

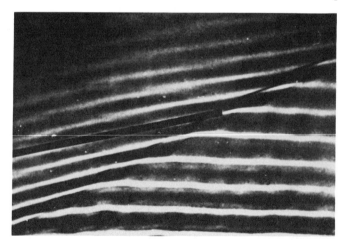

The refraction of straight waves, with a black marker placed parallel to the refracted wavefronts in the first photograph. In the second photograph, the refracted wavefronts of the higher frequency waves are no longer parallel to the marker.

Previously, we made the statement that the speed of waves depends only on the medium. This statement is obviously an idealization, considering the above evidence. Nevertheless, this idealization is a good approximation of the actual behaviour of waves, since the dispersion of a wave is the result of minute changes in its speed. These go unnoticed in most observations, and it is acceptable to make the assumption that frequency does not affect the speed of waves in most applications.

When refraction occurs, some of the energy is usually reflected as well as refracted. This phenomenon was referred to in Chapter 11 as partial reflection, partial refraction, a description that can be used when we refer to this behaviour in waves. In the ripple tank, where the waves are travelling from deep to shallow water, this behaviour is only apparent at large angles of incidence (see photograph).

The amount of reflection is more noticeable when a wave travels from shallow to deep water, where the speed increases, and it becomes more pronounced as the angle of incidence increases. In fact, as seen in the series of diagrams, an incident angle is reached where the wave is refracted at an angle approaching 90°. After that, there is no refraction and all the wave energy is reflected. This total internal reflection of the waves at high angles of incidence, for waves travelling into a faster medium, is analogous to the total internal reflection of light (Section 11.8), and will be discussed further in Chapter 14.

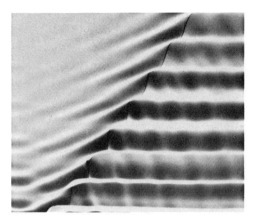

At higher angles of incidence, there is reflection as well as refraction. This can be seen on the right.

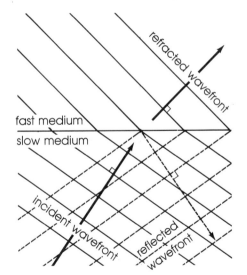

Partial refraction, partial reflection

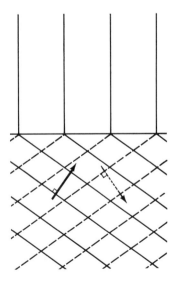

At the critical angle

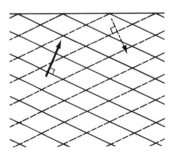

Total internal reflection

13.4 Diffraction of Water Waves

The ripple tank is probably the best device with which to observe the diffraction of waves. When periodic straight waves are produced in a ripple tank, they travel in a straight line as long as the depth of the water remains uniform. This direction of motion is indicated by a wave ray drawn at right angles to the wavefront. If an obstacle is put in the path of these waves, the waves are blocked. But, if they are allowed to pass by a sharp edge of the obstacle, or through a small opening or aperture in the obstacle, the waves change direction as illustrated in the photograph. This bending is called **diffraction**. How much the waves are diffracted depends on both their wavelength and the size of the opening in the barrier. As seen in the illustrations, short wavelengths are diffracted slightly. Longer wavelengths are diffracted to a greater extent by the same edge or aperture.

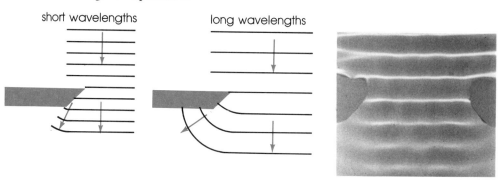

In the case of diffraction through an aperture, the amount of diffraction is increased when the relative size of the opening is decreased. This is apparent in the three photographs that follow. In each case the size of the opening is the same. In the first photograph, the wavelength (λ) is approximately 3/10 of the size of the opening (w). Only part of the straight wavefronts pass through, to be converted to small sectors of a series of circular wavefronts. In the second photograph, the wavelength is approximately 5/10 of w and there is considerably more diffraction. But there are still shadow areas to the left and right, where none of the wave is diffracted. In the third photograph, the wavelength is approximately 7/10 of w. Here the small sections of the straight wave that get through the opening are almost entirely converted into circular wavefronts. The wave has bent around the corner of the opening, filling almost the complete region on the other side of the aperture.

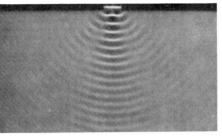

As the wavelength increases, the amount of diffraction increases.

In a similar demonstration (see investigation, page 505), we can keep λ fixed and change *w*, to find that the amount of diffraction increases as the aperture decreases. In both demonstrations, if waves are to be strongly diffracted they must pass through an opening that has a width comparable to their wavelength. This means that, if the wavelength is very small, a very narrow aperture is required to produce any significant diffraction.

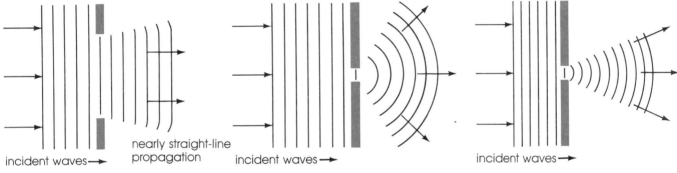

incident waves→   nearly straight-line propagation

Large opening

incident waves→

Small opening

incident waves→

Shorter wavelength, no change in opening

The amount of diffraction does not depend on either λ or *w* separately, but on the relationship between the two. Stated mathematically, the ratio λ/*w* must have a value of about 1, or greater, for any significant diffraction to be apparent.

Perhaps the most common example of the diffraction of waves occurs with sound. The sounds of a classroom can be heard through an open door, even though the students are out of sight and behind a wall. Sound waves are diffracted around the corner of the doorway primarily because they have relatively long wavelengths. If a high fidelity sound system is operating in the room, its low frequencies (long wavelengths) will be diffracted around the corner more easily than will its higher frequencies (shorter wavelengths).

13.5 Interference of Waves in Two Dimensions

As discussed in the previous chapter with waves in a one-dimensional medium, constructive and destructive interference may occur in two dimensions, sometimes producing fixed patterns of interference. To produce such a fixed pattern, it is necessary that the interfering waves have the same frequency (wavelength) and amplitude as one another. Let us see what patterns of interference occur between two identical waves when they interfere in a two-dimensional medium like the ripple tank.

Note that a standing wave interference pattern is produced on the line joining the two point sources. Note also that the nodes in the standing wave are located on the nodal lines of the larger interference pattern.

The photograph shows two vibrating point sources that were attached to the same generator and thus had identical frequencies and amplitudes. Also, they were in phase. Just as was the case with the one-dimensional medium, the waves passed through one another unchanged. As successive crests and troughs travelled out from each source, however, they interfered with each other, sometimes crest on crest, sometimes trough on trough, and sometimes crest on trough. Thus, areas of constructive and destructive interference were produced.

These areas moved out from the source in symmetrical patterns, producing nodal lines and areas of constructive interference, as illustrated. When illuminated from above, the nodal lines appeared in the ripple tank as stationary, grey areas. Between the nodal lines were areas of constructive interference that appeared as alternating bright (double-crest) and dark (double-trough) lines of constructive interference. In the illustration below, you can see how these alternating areas of constructive and destructive interference are produced. Note that, although the nodal lines appear to be straight, their paths from the sources are actually curved lines. Mathematicians call these hyperbolae. The pattern of constructive and destructive interference does not stay at rest, as in the case of standing waves in a linear medium such as a long rope. The pattern moves out from the source.

The interfering waves require equal amplitudes for total destructive interference. The resulting pattern is still observable if the amplitudes vary slightly, but the nodal lines will not be as distinct.

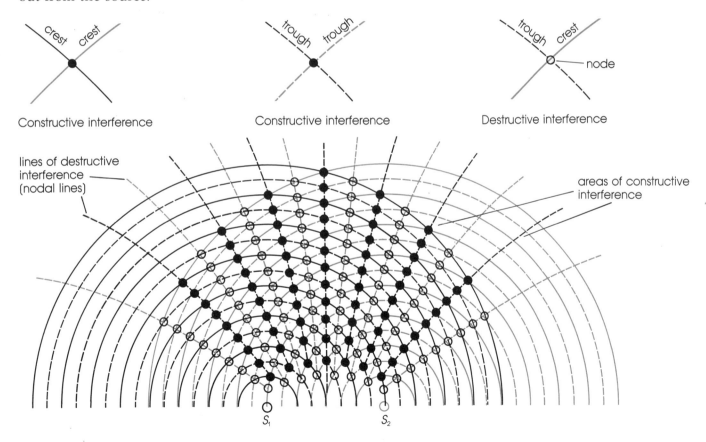

crest   crest

Constructive interference

trough   trough

Constructive interference

trough   crest

node

Destructive interference

lines of destructive interference (nodal lines)

areas of constructive interference

S_1 S_2

The interference pattern between two identical sources (S_1 and S_2), vibrating in phase, is a symmetrical pattern of nodal lines and areas of constructive interference in the shape of hyperbolae.

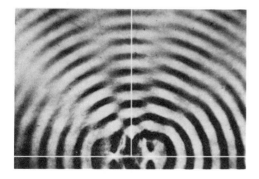

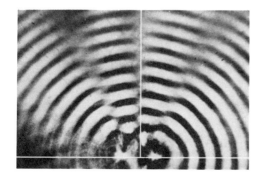

The interference patterns for two point sources with different phase delays. In the top photograph, the sources are in phase. In the bottom photograph, the phase delay is 180°.

This symmetrical pattern will remain stationary, provided three factors do not change. These factors are: the frequency of the two sources, the distance between the sources, and the phase of the sources. When the frequency of the sources is increased, the wavelength decreases, bringing the nodal lines closer together and increasing their number. If the distance between the two sources is increased, the number of nodal lines will also increase. Neither of these factors changes the symmetry of the pattern — there is an equal number of nodal lines on either side of the right bisector if the two sources are in phase, and an area of constructive interference runs along the right bisector. On the other hand, if other factors are kept constant and the relative phase of the two sources changes, the pattern shifts (as illustrated in the photographs), but the number of nodal lines remains the same.

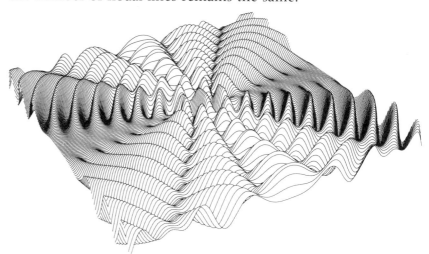

Two-point-source interference pattern generated by a computer graphics program

13.6 The Mathematical Analysis of the Two-Point-Source Interference Pattern

Like the standing wave interference pattern, the two-point-source interference pattern is useful because it allows direct measurement of the wavelength while the interference pattern remains relatively stationary. By taking a closer look at the two-point interference pattern we can develop some mathematical relationships that will be useful in the next chapter in analysing the interference of other kinds of waves.

We will analyse the interference pattern of two identical point sources, S_1 and S_2, in phase and separated by three wavelengths. In this pattern there are an equal number of nodal lines on either side of the right bisector. These lines are numbered 1, 2, 3, etc., on both sides of the right bisector. This means that there are two nodal lines labelled $n = 1$: the first line on either side of the right bisector. If we take a point P_1 on one of the first nodal lines and connect it to the two sources by drawing the lines P_1S_1 and P_1S_2 as shown, we might find that $P_1S_1 = 4\lambda$ and $P_1S_2 = 7/2\lambda$. The difference between these two distances, called the **difference in path length**, is

$$|P_1S_1 - P_1S_2| = \frac{1}{2}\lambda$$

This relationship holds for any point on the first nodal line on either side of the right bisector.

The difference in path length for any point, P_2, on a nodal line second from the centre can be measured in the same way and the relationship found to be

$$|P_2S_1 - P_2S_2| = \frac{3}{2}\lambda$$

Continuing this procedure, we can arrive at a general relationship for any point P on an nth nodal line as follows:

$$|P_nS_1 - P_nS_2| = (n - \frac{1}{2})\lambda \qquad \text{Equation 1}$$

This relationship can be used in the ripple tank to find the wavelengths of interfering waves. A wavelength can be calculated simply by locating a point on a specific nodal line, measuring the path lengths, and substituting in the above equation.

If the wavelengths are too small and/or the point P is too far away from the two sources, the difference in path length will be too small to be measured accurately. Thus, another technique is necessary.

For any point P_n, the difference in path length is the distance AS_1, seen in the diagram. That is, $P_nS_1 - P_nS_2 = AS_1$.

When P_n is very far away compared to the separation, d, of the two sources, the lines P_nS_1 and P_nS_2 are very nearly parallel. In this case, the line AS_2 forms a right angle with both of these lines, as illustrated, making the triangle S_1S_2A a right-angled triangle. Therefore the difference in path length can be expressed in terms of the sine of the angle θ_n as follows:

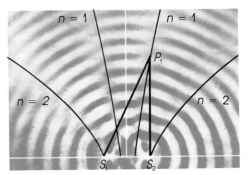

For any point P_1 on the first nodal line, the difference in path length from P_1 to S_1 and from P_1 to S_2 is half a wavelength. For any point P_2 on the second nodal line, the difference in path length is $3/2\lambda$.

The absolute signs are used when expressing the difference in path length, because only the positive value has any validity in this application.

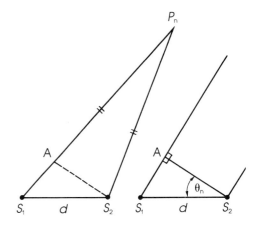

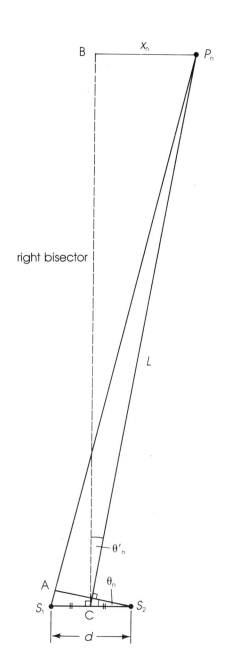

$$\sin \theta_n = \frac{AS_1}{d}$$

$$\text{or } AS_1 = d \sin \theta_n \qquad\qquad \text{Equation 2}$$

But $AS_1 = P_nS_1 - P_nS_2$. Therefore, by combining equations 1 and 2 we get

$$d \sin \theta_n = (n - \tfrac{1}{2})\lambda$$

$$\mathbf{\sin \theta_n = (n - \tfrac{1}{2})\frac{\lambda}{d}}$$

where θ_n is the angle for the nth nodal line, λ is the wavelength, and d is the distance between the sources.

This equation allows us to make a quick approximation of the wavelength for a specific interference pattern. Since $\sin \theta_n$ cannot be greater than 1, $(n - 1/2)\,\lambda/d$ cannot be greater than 1. The largest value of n that satisfies this condition is the number of nodal lines on either side of the right bisector. By measuring d and counting the number of nodal lines, the wavelength can be approximated. For example, if d is 2.0 cm and the number of nodal lines is 4, the wavelength would be determined as follows:

$$\sin \theta_n = (n - \tfrac{1}{2})\frac{\lambda}{d}$$

But the maximum value of $\sin \theta_n$ is 1,

$$\text{thus } (n - \tfrac{1}{2})\frac{\lambda}{d} \approx 1$$

$$\text{or } (4 - \tfrac{1}{2})\frac{\lambda}{2} \approx 1$$

$$\text{and } \lambda \approx 0.6 \text{ cm}$$

In the ripple tank, it is relatively easy to measure the angle θ_n, but this will not be the case for other kinds of waves where both the wavelength and the distance between the sources are very small and the nodal lines are close together. Therefore, we must derive another way to measure the value of $\sin \theta_n$ without measuring θ_n itself.

As noted earlier in this section, a nodal line has the shape of a hyperbola. But at positions on nodal lines relatively far away from the two sources, these lines are nearly straight, appearing to originate from the midpoint of a line joining the two sources.

For a point P_n located on a nodal line, far away from the two sources, the line from P_n to the midpoint between the two sources, P_nC, is essentially parallel to P_nS_1. This line is also perpendicular to AS_2. Since the right bisector (CB) is perpendicular to S_1S_2, you can easily show that $\theta_n' = \theta_n$.

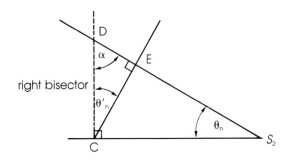

$$\theta'_n + \alpha = 90° \quad \Delta DEC$$

$$\theta_n + \alpha = 90° \quad \Delta DS_2C$$

$$\therefore \theta'_n + \alpha = \theta_n + \alpha$$

$$\text{or } \theta'_n = \theta_n$$

In the figure, $\sin \theta'_n$ can be determined from the triangle PBC as follows:

$$\sin \theta'_n = \frac{x_n}{L}$$

Since $\sin \theta_n = (n - \frac{1}{2}) \frac{\lambda}{d}$

and $\sin \theta'_n = \sin \theta_n$

then $\dfrac{x_n}{L} = (n - \frac{1}{2}) \dfrac{\lambda}{d}$

and

$$\lambda = \left(\frac{x_n}{L}\right)\left(\frac{d}{n - 1/2}\right)$$

where d is the distance between the sources, x_n is the perpendicular distance from the right bisector to the point on the nodal line, L is the distance from the point P to the midpoint between the two sources, and n is the nodal line number. It should be noted that the above relationship is only valid for two point sources in phase.

Sample problems

1. Two point sources generate identical waves that interfere in a ripple tank. The sources are located 5.0 cm apart, and the frequency of the waves is 8.0 Hz. A point on the first nodal line is located 10 cm from one source and 11 cm from the other.
   (a) What is the wavelength of the waves?
   (b) What is the speed of the waves?

(a)
$$|PS_1 - PS_2| = (n - \frac{1}{2}) \lambda$$

$$|11 \text{ cm} - 10 \text{ cm}| = (1 - \frac{1}{2}) \lambda$$

$$\lambda = 2.0 \text{ cm}$$

(b)

$$v = f\lambda$$
$$= (8.0 \text{ Hz})(2.0 \text{ cm})$$
$$= 16 \text{ cm/s}$$

2. A page in a student's notebook lists the following information, obtained from a ripple tank experiment with two point sources operating in phase: $n = 3$, $x_3 = 35$ cm, $L = 77$ cm, $d = 6.0$ cm, $\theta_3 = 25°$, and 5 crests $= 4.2$ cm. Determine the wavelength of the waves, using various methods.

Method 1

$$5 \text{ crests} = 4\lambda = 4.2 \text{ cm}$$
$$\lambda = \frac{4.2 \text{ cm}}{4}$$
$$= 1.1 \text{ cm}$$

Method 2

$$\lambda = \frac{d \sin \theta}{(n - \frac{1}{2})}$$
$$= \frac{(6.0 \text{ cm})(\sin 25°)}{(3 - \frac{1}{2})}$$
$$= 1.0 \text{ cm}$$

Method 3

$$\lambda = \left(\frac{x_n}{L}\right)\left(\frac{d}{n - \frac{1}{2}}\right)$$
$$= \left(\frac{35 \text{ cm}}{77 \text{ cm}}\right)\left(\frac{6.0 \text{ cm}}{3 - \frac{1}{2}}\right)$$
$$= 1.1 \text{ cm}$$

Note that the three answers are slightly different because of experimental error and rounding off, which is to be expected.

Practice

1. In a ripple tank, a point on the third nodal line from the centre is 35 cm from one source and 42 cm from the other source. The sources are separated by 11.2 cm and vibrate in phase at 10.5 Hz. Calculate (a) the wavelength of the waves, and (b) the velocity of the waves.   (2.8 cm, 29 cm/s)
2. Two sources 6.0 cm apart, operating in phase, produce water waves. A student selects a point on the first nodal line and measures from it 30.0 cm to a point midway between the sources

and 5.0 cm (on the perpendicular) to the right bisector.
(a) What is the wavelength of the waves?
(b) When the student selects a point on the second nodal line, he finds that it is 38.0 cm from the midpoint and 21.0 cm from the bisector. Determine the wavelength.
(c) What would be the value of the angle θ for distant points on the first and second nodal lines described above?

(2.0 cm, 2.2 cm, 9.6° and 34°)

13.7 Investigations

Investigation 13.1: Transmission and Reflection of Water Waves

Problem:
How are water waves transmitted and reflected in a ripple tank?

Materials:
ripple tank
wooden dowel
wax blocks
50 cm of rubber tubing

Procedure:
1. Put water in the ripple tank to a depth of approximately 1 cm. Level the tank to ensure that the depth of the water is uniform. (If necessary, place screen dampers at the perimeter of the tank to reduce reflection.)
2. Touch the surface of the water lightly at the centre of the tank with your finger. What is the shape of the wave produced by such a point source? Make a sketch showing the wave and the source of the wave. How can you tell by the shape of the wave whether its speed is the same in all directions?
3. On your sketch, at four equally spaced points on the crest of the wave, draw arrows indicating the direction of wave travel. What is the direction of the wave's travel relative to the crest of the wave?
4. Generate a straight wave with the dowel by rocking it back and forth across the surface. Does the wave remain straight as it travels across the tank? Does its speed change? In what direction does the wave move, relative to its crest? Draw a straight wave, showing the direction of its motion.

5. Generate continuous straight waves by rocking the dowel back and forth steadily. What happens to the wavelength if you reduce the frequency? How is the wavelength affected if the frequency increases? How is the speed of a wave affected by a change in frequency?

6. Prop up the tank so that the water at one end is only 1 mm deep. Send straight waves from the deep end to the shallow end. In what ways do the speed and the wavelength change as the waves move to the shallow end? Make a sketch illustrating the changes in wavelength.

7. Reduce the depth of the water to approximately 0.5 cm and level the tank.

8. Form a straight barrier at one end of the tank, using the wax blocks sitting on edge on the bottom. Send straight waves towards the barrier so that their wavefronts are parallel to the barrier. How does the direction of travel of the incoming, or incident, wavefronts compare with that of the reflected wavefronts? Does the speed or the wavelength of a wave change after it has been reflected? Make a diagram illustrating your observations.

9. Now arrange the barrier so that the waves strike it at an angle. How does the angle between incident wavefronts and the barrier compare with the angle between reflected wavefronts and the barrier? To help you judge the angles, align rulers or other straight objects on the screen with the wavefront images. Make a diagram showing incident wavefronts and reflected wavefronts and their directions of travel.

10. Place the rubber tubing in the tank, allowing it to fill with water. Bend the tubing into the approximate shape of a parabola. With the dowel, generate straight waves towards the open side of the parabola. Observe how the wavefronts move before and after they strike the curved barrier. Find the focus of the parabolic reflector by observing the reflection of the straight pulses. Record your observations in a sketch. Using your finger, generate circular pulses at the focal point. What is the shape of the reflected pulses?

Investigation 13.2: Production and Measurement of Straight Periodic Waves in a Ripple Tank

Problem:
What are the frequency, wavelength, and velocity of a straight periodic wave in a ripple tank?

Materials:
ripple tank
motor-driven wave generator
hand stroboscope
stopwatch
light source
metre stick
screen

Procedure:
1. Put water in a level ripple tank to a depth of approximately 0.5 cm.
2. Clip the straight wave attachment to the wave generator and place it at one end of the tank. Submerge the straight wave generator to approximately three-quarters of its height. It should not be touching the glass bottom of the tank.
3. Adjust the frequency of the generator to produce periodic waves with a low frequency. Do not change the frequency of the generator until after step 5. Using a four-slit hand stroboscope, stop the motion of the waves. (It may be necessary to change the number of slits, depending on the frequency chosen.) Make sure that the strobe is rotating at the highest "stopping" frequency and that multiple images are not being observed.
4. Have your partner determine the frequency of the stroboscope by measuring the time for, say, 20 r (revolutions). Using the "look" frequency, calculate the frequency of the waves.
5. To find the wavelength on the screen, stop the wave pattern at the correct stroboscope frequency and have your partner place two pencils parallel to the wave images and several wavelengths apart. Determine the value of the wavelength in centimetres.
6. To find the actual wavelength, you must scale the wavelength measured on the screen. Place an object, for example, a wax block, in the ripple tank. Measure its true length and the length of its image. Determine the factor by which any image length must be multiplied to give the true length. Calculate the true wavelength of the waves.

At low frequencies the bar should be submerged to three-quarters of its height. It should be raised correspondingly at successively higher frequencies up to approximately 18 Hz. At the higher frequencies, the straight wave generator should be only slightly submerged. It is important that the wave generator be kept level with the water surface so that clearly defined, undistorted straight wave patterns are produced.

7. Using the Wave Equation, determine the velocity of the water waves in the ripple tank.
8. Repeat steps 4 to 7 with waves of a higher frequency. Compare your answers for the velocities of the waves. What effect do changes in either the frequency or the wavelength of a wave have on its velocity?
9. Increase the depth of the water in the ripple tank to 1.0 cm. Repeat steps 4 to 7. What effect does a change in depth have on a wave's speed in water?
10. Repeat for another depth of water.

Investigation 13.3: Refraction of Water Waves

Problem:
How do the wavelength and the direction of transmission of a wave change when its velocity changes?

Materials:
ripple tank
wooden dowel
straight wave generator
glass plate
glass plate supports (if necessary)

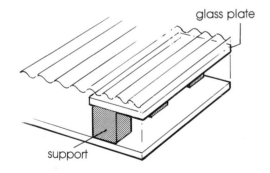

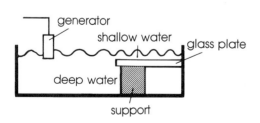

Procedure:
1. Support a glass plate on the spacers so that it is approximately 1.5 cm above the bottom of the tank and about 15 cm from the wave generator. Its longest edge should be parallel to the generator.
2. Put enough water in the tank to cover the glass plate to a depth of about 1 mm. Adjust the height of the wave generator so that the bottom of the vibrator is just below the surface of the water.
3. Adjust the generator so that it produces waves with a long wavelength in the deep water. As the waves pass from the deep water to the shallow water, what changes occur in their speed, their direction of motion, and their wavelength? Sketch the pattern produced.
4. Look at the waves through a hand stroboscope, adjusting the stroboscope frequency so that waves in the deep water are "stopped". Are the waves in the shallow water "stopped" as well? Explain your answer.
5. Determine the shadow wavelength of the waves in both deep and shallow water by measuring the wavelengths of their proj-

ected images. What is the value of the ratio $\lambda_{deep}/\lambda_{shallow}$? What is the corresponding value of the ratio $v_{deep}/v_{shallow}$? Explain how you determined this velocity ratio.

6. Set the edge of the glass plate at an angle of approximately 45° to the incoming waves. Note any changes that occur in the direction of travel of the waves. Does the refracted wavelength change from its value in step 5? Is any part of the wave reflected? Draw a diagram showing a series of wavefronts and their directions of travel in both deep and shallow water.

7. Lay a ruler on the screen so that it is perpendicular (normal) to the boundary between the two depths of water. Lay a pencil along the line of incidence, which is the direction in which the incident wave is moving. Similarly, lay another pencil along the line of refraction. How does the angle of refraction compare with the angle of incidence? Has the wave bent towards or away from the normal? Measure the angle of incidence and the angle of refraction.

8. Repeat step 7 for a different angle of incidence.

9. Given that the relative index of refraction is equal to v_1/v_2, show that Snell's Law holds for water waves by using data collected in steps 5, 7, and 8.

10. What changes in the wavelength, speed, and direction do you predict for waves passing obliquely from shallow water to deep water? Draw a sketch illustrating your prediction. Test your prediction in the ripple tank, using the wooden dowel as a wave generator in the shallow end.

Investigation 13.4: Diffraction of Water Waves

Problem:
What factors affect the diffraction of a wave?

Materials:
ripple tank
wave generator
wax blocks of various sizes

Procedure:

Diffraction around an Obstacle
1. Put water in the tank to a depth of 1 cm.
2. Place a full wax block in the tank, end up, parallel to and about 10 cm from the straight wave generator. Position the light source directly above the block. Using the wave generator,

generate a straight periodic wave with a long wavelength. Make a sketch showing a series of wavefronts on both sides of the wax block.

3. Gradually reduce the wavelength of the wave by increasing the frequency. How is the pattern behind the block affected when the wavelength is reduced?

Diffraction around an Edge

4. Place a wax block, with one side bevelled, at the centre of the wave tank, about 10 cm away from the wave generator. Line up the other wax blocks so that they prevent wavefronts from passing by the other side of the first wax block.

5. Generate a straight periodic wave with a long wavelength, and observe how the wavefronts pass by the bevelled edge of the block. Record your observations in a sketch showing a series of wavefronts on both sides of the block.

6. Slowly decrease the wavelength of the wave. Does this make the amount of diffraction greater or smaller than before? Draw a sketch to illustrate your answer.

Diffraction through an Opening

7. Using two bevelled pieces of wax, create a barrier about 10 cm from the wave generator, with an opening of approximately 4 cm. Generate a wave with a long wavelength, observing the amount of bending that occurs. Increase the frequency gradually. Does the amount of diffraction increase or decrease? Record your observations in the form of sketches.

8. While generating a wave with a constant frequency, slowly decrease the size of the opening by moving one of the blocks. How does the size of the opening affect the diffraction? How must a wavelength compare with the size of opening so that a wave passes through the opening with minimal diffraction?

9. To summarize, answer the following questions:
   (a) Which wavelengths are diffracted more — long ones or short ones?
   (b) What is the approximate relationship between the size of an opening and the amount of diffraction?
   (c) Describe two conditions for maximum diffraction through an opening in a barrier.

Investigation 13.5: Interference of Waves in Two Dimensions

Problem:
What patterns of interference are produced by two identical water waves in a ripple tank?

Materials:
ripple tank
wax blocks
wave generator
2 point sources

Procedure:
1. Set up the ripple tank and put water in it to a depth of 1 cm. Make sure that the tank is level.
2. Make a wave with one finger and then start a second wave some distance away. Observe the two waves. Repeat the procedure for various points in the tank. Do the two waves affect each other? Are they changed as a result of interference?
3. Connect the two point sources to the generator so that they are about 6.0 cm apart. Make sure that the two sources are in phase. (If your generator has a phase adjustment, set it at 0.)
4. Place the generator so that the two point sources are dipping equally into the water at one end of the tank. Generate waves with a moderate frequency of approximately 10 Hz. Examine the pattern on the screen. Identify the nodal lines and the lines of constructive interference. Draw a sketch of the nodal line pattern.
5. Stop the generator. On the screen, mark the positions of S_1 and S_2. Draw a line joining the sources. Next, draw the right bisector of this line, extending it across the screen.
6. Adjust the frequency of the generator so that three nodal lines are produced on either side of the right bisector. Choosing one nodal line, mark three nodal points (P_1, P_2, and P_3) on the screen. Make sure that one of these points is fairly close to S_1 and S_2, and that one is quite far away.
7. By making the appropriate measurements, determine the wavelength of the waves on the screen. This is to be accomplished two ways, using the relationships

$$|PS_1 - PS_2| = (n - \frac{1}{2})\lambda \text{ and } \frac{X}{L} = \frac{(n - 1/2)\lambda}{d} \text{ for each point.}$$

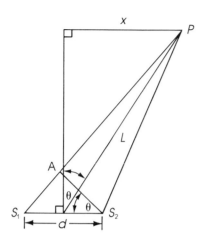

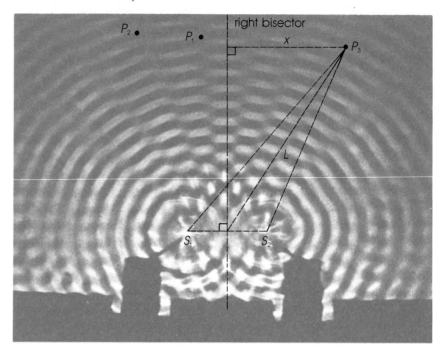

8. Repeat step 7 for three points on a different nodal line, on the other side of the right bisector.
9. Increase and decrease the frequency of the generator. What effect does a change in frequency have on the interference pattern?
10. Keeping the frequency constant, change the separation of the sources. How does the separation of the sources affect the interference pattern?
11. Set up the apparatus illustrated, using a single point source and a paraffin block. Describe the resulting interference pattern. Explain the results.

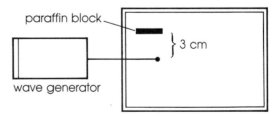

12. The phase of two sources also affects the interference pattern. Adjust the frequency of the generator so that a clearly visible pattern is produced on the screen. Place a pencil or other straight object on the screen so that it lies on a nodal line. Turn

the phase control of the generator from 0 to 1/2 (or 180°) and then back to 0. Describe the changes in the interference pattern.

13. If the phase between the two sources is constantly changing, the interference will constantly change as well. This can be illustrated by using two separate wave generators, each with one source in the same tank. (This may require co-operation with another group of students.) Set up the generators so that the point sources are approximately 6 cm apart. Adjust the generators so that they appear to have the same frequency. Adjust one generator so that its frequency is slightly greater than that of the other generator. Describe the results. Adjust the generators to slightly different frequencies so that their relative phase constantly varies. What happens to the pattern?

14. Generate an interference pattern by using a single straight source and diffraction as illustrated. Place the wax blocks so that two small openings are created, approximately 6 cm apart and 10 cm from the generator. With the generator operating, sketch the resulting interference pattern.

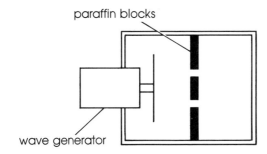

13.8 Review

Discussion

1. A circular series of waves is produced in the water when a rock is dropped into a lake. State two reasons why the amplitude decreases as the waves travel away from the source.
2. Why does the height of a water wave increase as the wave enters shallow water at the beach?
3. What relationship between λ and d would produce no nodal lines?

4. Why is the interference pattern between two point sources difficult to see if (a) the distance between the sources is too large or (b) the phase of the sources is constantly changing?

5. AM radio transmission towers are often arranged fairly close together in a straight line. Radio waves are relatively long (200-600 m). If two such radio towers, transmitting in phase, are in a north-south line, in what direction will the areas of greatest intensity be located? of least intensity? By changing the phase of the signals transmitted by each tower, the direction of the strongest signal can be changed. Explain why.

Problems

6. A straight wave is generated in a ripple tank, and the images on the screen below the ripple tank are "stopped" by using a six-slit stroboscope that turns 20 times in 25 s. The distance between the first and fifth bright lines is 12 cm.
   (a) Assuming the strobe is at the highest "stopping" frequency, what is the frequency of the wave?
   (b) What is the wavelength of the "shadow" wave?

7. In a ripple tank, one complete wave is sent out every 1/10 s. The wave is stopped with a stroboscope, and it is found that the separation between the first and sixth crests is 12 cm.
   (a) What is the wavelength?
   (b) What is the speed of the wave?

8. The frequency of the vibrator in a ripple tank is 8.0 Hz.
   (a) What would be the frequency of the resulting wave?
   (b) If you were looking at the wave through a stroboscope with four slits open, what would you see if the rotational frequency of the strobe were 1, 2, and 4 r/s?
   (c) In order to measure the wavelength, you place an object of known length in the tank and find that the magnification factor is 2.5/1 for this screen. The distance on the screen between the first and sixth crests is 24 cm.
      (i) What is the wavelength of the water wave?
      (ii) What is the velocity of the wave in the ripple tank?

9. A circular wave having a speed of 30 cm/s is set up in a ripple tank. The radius of each wavefront differs from the preceding one by 3.0 cm. Calculate the frequency of the source.

10. A ripple tank wave passes from a deep to a shallow region with an angle of incidence of 60° and an angle of refraction of 45°. What are the ratios in the two media of (a) the wavelengths, (b) the velocities, and (c) the frequencies?

11. A straight wave in the deep region of water in a ripple tank has a speed of 24 cm/s and a frequency of 4.0 Hz. It strikes the boundary between deep and shallow water, the angle between the wavefront and the boundary being 40°. If the speed in the shallow region is 15 cm/s, (a) what angle does the refracted wavefront make with the boundary? (b) What is the wavelength in shallow water?

12. The wavelength of a straight wave in the deep end of a ripple tank is 2.0 cm, and the frequency is 11 Hz. Wavefronts strike the boundary of the shallow section of the tank at an angle of 60° and are refracted at an angle of 30°. Calculate the speed of the wave in deep water and in shallow water.

13. When a straight periodic wave crosses a boundary between deep and shallow water, the following observations are made: ten wavefronts cross the boundary every 5.0 s, and the distance across three wavefronts is 24.0 cm in deep water and 18.0 cm in shallow water.
    (a) Calculate the velocity of the wave in deep water and in shallow water.
    (b) Calculate the relative refractive index.

14. A plane wave generator with a frequency of 6.0 Hz creates a water wave with a wavelength of 2.0 cm in region A of a ripple tank. The angle between the wave crests and the straight boundary between regions A and B of the tank is 30°. In region B the angle is 20°, as illustrated in the diagram.

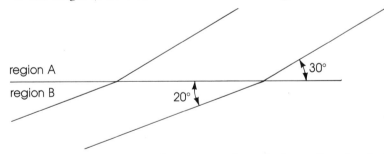

    (a) Use Snell's Law to determine the relative refractive index of the two regions.
    (b) Find the velocity in each region.

15. Longitudinal earthquake waves travelling through rock at 7.75 km/s enter a different body of rock at an angle of incidence of 20°. If the speed in the second body of rock is 7.72 km/s, what is the angle of refraction?

16. An interference pattern is set up by two point sources of the same frequency, which are in phase. A point on the second nodal line is 25 cm from one source and 29.5 cm from the

other source. The speed of the waves is 7.5 cm/s. Calculate (a) the wavelength and (b) the frequency of the sources.

17. Two sources are vibrating in phase, and set up waves in a ripple tank. A point *P* on the second nodal line is 12.0 cm from source A and 20.0 cm from source B. When the sources are started, it takes 2.0 s for the first wave to reach the edge of the tank, 30 cm from the source. Find the velocity, wavelength, and frequency of the wave.

18. In a ripple tank experiment to demonstrate interference, two point sources having a common frequency of 6.0 Hz are used. The sources are 5.0 cm apart and are in phase. A metre stick is placed above the water, parallel to the line joining the two sources. The first nodal lines (one on each side of the central axis) cross the metre stick at the 35 cm and 55 cm marks. Each of the crossing points is 50 cm from the midpoint of the line joining the two sources. Calculate the wavelength and speed of the waves.

19. Two very small, identical loudspeakers, each of which is radiating sound uniformly in all directions, are placed at points S_1 and S_2 as shown in the diagram. They are connected to a source so that they radiate, in phase, a sound with a wavelength of 2.00 m. The speed of sound may be taken as 340 m/s. (a) What is the frequency of the radiated sound?

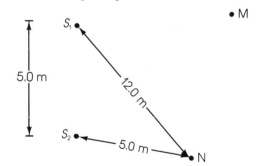

(b) Point *M*, a nodal point, is 7.0 m from S_1 and more than 7.0 m from S_2. What are three possible distances *M* could be from S_2?

(c) Point *N*, also a nodal point, is located 12.0 cm from S_1 and 5.0 cm from S_2. On what nodal line is it located?

20. The antenna of a radio station consists of two towers (to be considered as point sources) 400 m apart along an east-west line, broadcasting in phase. The broadcast frequency is 1.0×10^6 Hz. (Radio waves travel at 3.00×10^8 m/s.)

(a) In what directions is the intensity of the radio signal at a maximum for listeners 20 km north of the transmitter (but not necessarily directly north of it)?

(b) If the two towers were to transmit in opposite phase, state the directions in which the intensity would be at a minimum north of the transmitter.

21. A police cruiser has an unusual radar speed trap set up. It has two transmitting antennae at the edge of a main road that runs north and south. One antenna is 2.0 m[west] of the other, and they are both fed from a common transmitter with a frequency of 3.0×10^9 Hz. These antennae can be considered as point sources of continuous radio waves. The trap is set for cars travelling south. A student drives his car along an east-west road that crosses the main road at a level intersection 100 m[north] of the radar trap. The student's car has a "radar detector", so he hears a series of beeps as he drives west through the intersection. If the time interval between successive quiet spots is 1/5 s, as he crosses the main road, what is his speed?
(SIN '71)

22. A student is carrying a small radio receiver that receives a signal from a transmitter located a few kilometres north of her position. It also receives from the same transmitter a signal reflected from the aluminum siding on a house a few hundred metres south of her position. As she carries the receiver 9.0 m north she notices that the sound level changes from a maximum to a minimum. Assuming that radio waves travel at the speed of light, what is the frequency of the radio transmitters?
(SIN '69)

14 Waves and Light

14.1 The Nature of Light

Light carries energy with it. It is a form of energy. This is obvious to anyone standing out in the sun on a hot summer's day. But how does light travel, and how is the energy of light carried from a source of energy, such as the sun?

Two ways in which energy can be carried from one place to another are as the energy of moving objects or particles, and as the energy of waves. In Chapter 9 we discussed the kinetic energy possessed by moving particles, whether they are as small as sub-atomic particles, such as electrons, or as large as baseballs or rock-etships. In every case, we found that the object had to have both mass and velocity if it was to transfer energy. In Chapters 12 and 13 we found that energy is conveyed over long distances in waves, even though individual particles do not travel these distances.

The earliest recorded views on the nature of light come to us from the Greeks. Plato thought that light consisted of "streamers", or filaments, emitted by the eye and that when these streamers came in contact with an object, sight was achieved. Euclid agreed with him, arguing, "How else can we explain that we do not see a needle on the floor until our eyes fall on it?" Not all Greeks held the same view. The Pythagoreans believed that light travelled as a stream of fast-moving particles, while Empedocles taught that light travelled as a wave-like disturbance.

By the 17th century, these apparently contradictory views of the nature of light placed scientists in two camps. Newton was the principal advocate of the particle, or corpuscular, theory. He was supported by the French mathematician, physicist, and astronomer La Place. On the other hand, the wave theory was upheld principally by Christiaan Huygens of Holland, also a mathematician, physicist, and astronomer. He, in turn, was supported by Robert Hooke of England, president of the Royal Society and a vigorous personal opponent of Newton. Because of the plausibility of both theories, a scientific debate developed between the followers of Newton and the followers of Huygens that continued for more than a century. By the late 19th century, however, there appeared to be overwhelming evidence that the nature of light could be explained much better using the wave model. In this chapter we will see how appropriate these two theories are for explaining the observed properties of light.

Robert Hooke (1635–1703), an English physicist, invented (or perfected) the air pump, the balance spring for watches, the first efficient compound microscope, the wheel barometer, the hygrometer, a wind gauge, a spiral gear, the iris diaphragm, the refractometer, and the universal joint. He also made the first microscopic study of insect anatomy, was the first to use the word "cell" in biology, proposed zero as the freezing point of water, was the first to study crystal structure, gave the first explanation for fossils, explained the nature of colour in thin films, formulated the law of elasticity, surveyed London after the Great Fire, was the architect of Bedlam Hospital, and discovered (but was unable to prove) the inverse square law for gravitation. He is remembered today primarily because he quarrelled with Newton.

Before beginning this discussion, it is important to recall the two chief functions of a scientific model or theory (the two terms are used interchangeably). These are: to explain the known properties of a phenomenon, and to predict new behaviour for it, or new properties. In evaluating a theory, the first step is to attempt to use the theory to explain the known properties of the phenomenon. We will begin by showing how Newton used the corpuscular theory to explain the nature of light, as light was known in his time. His arguments are significant, historically, but, more important, his analysis is useful in illustrating how a theory should be tested against experimental evidence.

14.2 The Corpuscular Theory

Building on an earlier theory by Descartes, Isaac Newton imagined that light consisted of streams of tiny particles, that he called "corpuscles", shooting out like bullets from a light source. Let us examine the arguments used by supporters of the particle theory to explain the various phenomena known to them.

Rectilinear Propagation

Sharp shadows, and "rays" from the sun streaming through the clouds, show that light travels in straight lines. This is sometimes referred to as the "rectilinear propagation of light". On the other hand, a ball thrown through space follows a curved path, because of the influence of gravity, while the path of a bullet shot from a gun curves less because the speed of the bullet is greater.

As with the ball, particles travelling at normal speeds are observed to follow a curved path, due to the effect of gravity. However, faster particles curve less over the same distance. Since the path of light has no noticeable curve, this tells us that the speed of light must be extremely high. Newton had argued this. He had also argued that, since light does not exert any noticeable pressure, the mass of the particles must be extremely small.

In 1905, as part of his General Theory of Relativity, Einstein proposed that light does bend slightly when it passes through the strong gravitational field near a star or our sun. Experimental observation during a total solar eclipse verified this in 1919. This bending is so slight that one can say, for most applications of light, that it travels in straight lines.

Diffraction

Newton further argued that light does not travel "around a corner", as do waves. In this case Newton discounted the work of Francesco Grimaldi, an Italian Jesuit mathematician who had shown that a

Francesco Grimaldi (1618–1663). Grimaldi was a Jesuit professor at the University of Bologna; his most important discovery, the diffraction of light, was published two years after his death.

beam of light passing through two successive, narrow slits produced on a screen a band of light slightly larger than the width of the slits. Grimaldi believed that the beam had been bent slightly outward at the edges of the second aperture, a phenomenon he called diffraction. It was Newton's position that this effect resulted from interactions and collisions between the light particles at the edges of the slit.

Reflection

When light falls on the smooth surface of a mirror, we know that it is reflected according to the Laws of Reflection. How do particles behave under similar conditions? The first photograph shows light rays "bouncing off" a mirror, and the second shows a series of images of a steel ball bouncing off a steel plate.

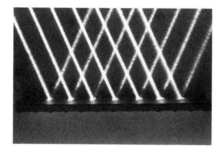
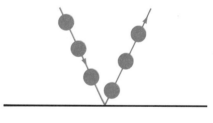

Newton demonstrated that, in a perfectly elastic collision, the Laws of Reflection can be derived from the Laws of Motion. An incident, hard, spherical particle approaches a frictionless, horizontal surface with a velocity whose components are v_x and v_y, respectively. When the particle is reflected, there is no change in the horizontal velocity component v_x. The vertical velocity component, v_y, is reversed in direction, because of the reactive force of the surface on the ball, and its magnitude is unchanged. (Elastic collision: $\Delta E_k = 0$.) Thus the incident velocity is equal in magnitude to the reflected velocity, and the angle of incidence equals the angle of reflection.

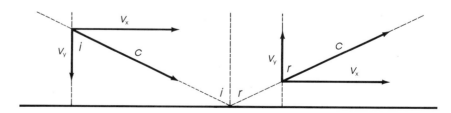

Refraction

Newton was also able to demonstrate the nature of refraction with the particle model, as follows. When light passes from air to water it bends towards the normal. Particles, too, will bend towards the normal if their speed increases. For example, if a ball is rolled at a transverse angle down a ramp from a raised horizontal surface to a lower horizontal surface, it will bend or refract, as illustrated, towards the normal.

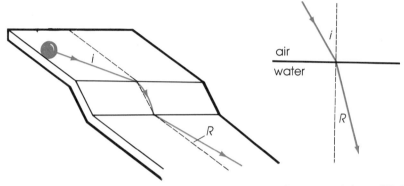

Newton believed that water attracts approaching particles of light in much the same way that gravity attracts a rolling ball on an incline. The rolling ball demonstration implies that the light particles accelerate as they pass from air into a medium with a higher index of refraction, such as glass or water. Newton predicted that the speed of light in water would be greater than the speed of light in air. At the time, the speed of light in water was not known. It was not until 123 years after Newton's death, in 1850, that the French physicist, Jean Foucault, demonstrated experimentally that the speed of light in water is, in fact, less than the speed of light in air — the reverse of that predicted by the particle theory.

Partial Reflection — Partial Refraction

When light refracts, some of the light is reflected. Newton had difficulty explaining this phenomenon with the corpuscular theory. Newton's explanation was the so-called "theory of fits": particles of light arrived at a surface sometimes in a "fit" of easy reflection and sometimes in a "fit" of easy refraction. This was obviously a weak explanation, as Newton himself recognized.

Jean Foucault (1819–1868). Although trained as a physician, Foucault at an early stage took up the study of physics and made it his life's work. He and another French physicist, Armand Fizeau (1819–1896), together developed a system of rotating mirrors and a spinning, toothed wheel with which to measure the velocity of light. They obtained a value slightly less than the value ultimately obtained by Michelson (see page 408). Using the same apparatus, Foucault measured the speed of light through water and other transparent media. In 1853 he showed that the velocity of light was less in water than in air, providing strong support for the Wave Theory of Light. It was only one step farther to show that the ratio of the velocity of light for air and for the media was the same as the Snell's Law ratio (sin *i*/sin *R*). Foucault's name is remembered today more for his work with pendulums. These are used to illustrate the rotation of the Earth in space (see page 188).

Dispersion

When white light passes through a glass prism, the light is refracted by different amounts, and the spectral colours result. This is called dispersion. This phenomenon has been known since at least the time of the ancient Egyptians. It was not until 1666, however, that it was systematically investigated by Newton, as described in Chapter 11.

To explain dispersion, using the corpuscular theory, Newton hypothesized that each particle in the spectrum had a different mass. Since the violet particles are refracted more than the blue, Newton argued that the violet particles must have smaller mass than the blue (smaller masses would be diverted more easily). The blue particles, then, would be diverted more than the green, because the green are more massive than the blue, and so on, to red light, which would have the particles with the largest mass in the visible spectrum.

Newton's corpuscular theory provided a satisfactory explanation for four properties of light: straight-line transmission, reflection, refraction, and dispersion. It was weak in its explanation of diffraction and of partial reflection and partial refraction. Considering the evidence available to Newton, his hypothesis was valid. It was, in its day, superior to the competing wave theory of light because it used the laws of mechanics that had been proven to be valid in other areas of physics. When new evidence became available that could not be explained using Newton's corpuscular theory, this was bound to give stronger support to the wave theory. However, Newton's stature and authority were so compelling that the Corpuscular Theory of Light dominated for over a century. In fact, his successors adhered to the corpuscular view of light more strongly than Newton ever did himself.

Newton recognized that the experimental evidence was not strong enough for either particles or waves. Although he preferred the particle theory, he was not dogmatic about it. He considered both theories to be hypotheses — theories that required further testing.

The lesson to be learned from Newton's example is that the theories — in fact, any pronouncements — of esteemed, famous people should be evaluated on the basis of supporting evidence. A theory should not be accepted simply because it is put forward by an eminent person.

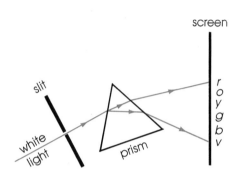

Clarke's First Law: "When a distinguished but elderly scientist states that something is possible, he is almost certainly right. When he states that something is impossible, he is very probably wrong."

Arthur C. Clarke

14.3 The Wave Theory of Light

The Wave Theory of Light was proposed by Robert Hooke in 1665. Twenty years later it was improved upon by the Dutch scientist, Christiaan Huygens. He developed a technique for predicting the future position of a wavefront based on an earlier position of the same wave. It is still useful today, and is known as **Huygens' Principle**:

> Every point on a wavefront can be considered as a point source of tiny secondary wavelets that spread out in front of the wave at the same speed as the wave itself. The surface envelope, tangent to all the wavelets, constitutes the new wavefront.

As a simple example of the use of Huygens' Principle, consider the wavefront AB that is travelling away from the source *S*, at some instant in time. The points on the wavefront represent the centres of the new wavelets, seen as a series of small circles. The common tangent to all these wavelets, the line A'B', is the new position of the wavefront a short time later.

Christiaan Huygens

Christiaan Huygens (1629-1695). Although Huygens' early training was in mathematics, he did most of his work in astronomy and physics. He discovered a new and better method for grinding lenses, and, using his improved telescope, discovered Titan (the largest satellite of Saturn), the rings of Saturn, and the "markings" on the planet Mars. As mentioned on page 408, he used Roemer's measurements to determine the speed of light.

One of his most important inventions was the pendulum clock. Although it was first proposed by Galileo, it was Huygens who improved it so that it kept accurate time. This was an important contribution to the development of science.

In 1660, Huygens was elected to the Royal Society in London. Louis XIV of France honoured him, also. Today he is primarily remembered because of the Wave Theory of Light.

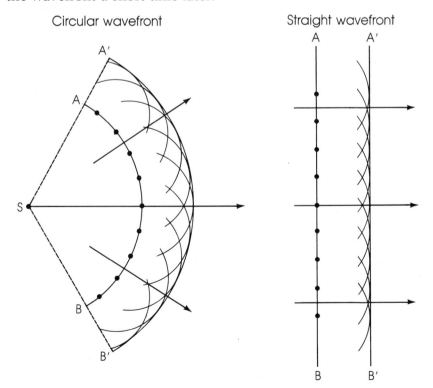

Circular wavefront   Straight wavefront

Huygens also established the Principle
of Conservation of Kinetic Energy for
elastic collisions, in 1678.

Huygens and his supporters were able to use the wave theory
to explain some of the properties of light, including reflection,
refraction, partial reflection and partial refraction, and diffraction.
However, they encountered difficulty when trying to explain rectilinear propagation. (This was the primary reason for Newton's
rejection of the wave theory.) The following will show how the
wave theory explains the various properties of light.

Reflection

In Chapters 11 and 13 it was explained how both waves and light
obey the Laws of Reflection. In each case, the angle of incidence
equals the angle of reflection both for plane and curved surfaces.
This is illustrated below.

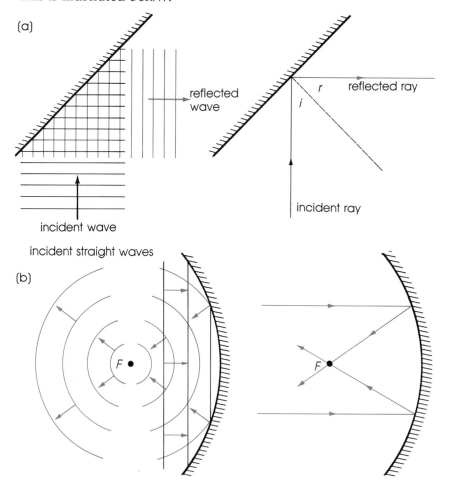

Refraction

Huygens, using his wavelet concept, predicted that light is bent towards the normal as it passes into an optically denser medium such as glass, because its velocity is slower in the second medium ($v_2 < v_1$). As illustrated in the diagram to the right, the wavelet beginning at point A travels a shorter distance ($v_2\Delta t$) than does the wavelet whose source is B ($v_1\Delta t$). The new wavefront is tangent to these wavelets and forms the line CD. Newton's corpuscular theory predicts the reverse, that is, $v_2 > v_1$ for light bending towards the normal. The issue could not be decided at the time, since the speed of light in a medium other than a vacuum had not yet been measured. It was not to be measured until 1850 (by Foucault). By that time the wave theory was fully accepted, as we shall soon see.

Snell's Law holds for light as it does for waves. The direction of the refracted wave can be determined by using the ratio of the velocities in the two media: $\dfrac{\sin i}{\sin R} = n = \dfrac{v_1}{v_2} = \dfrac{\lambda_1}{\lambda_2}$.

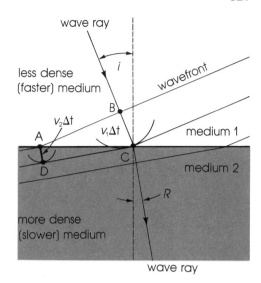

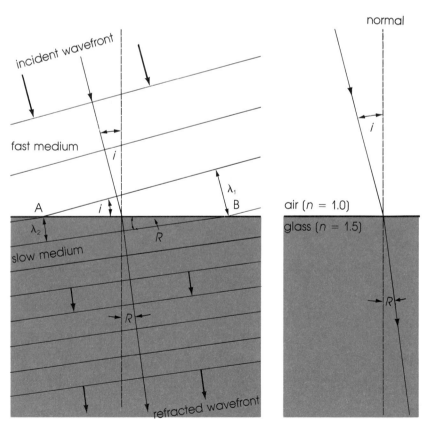

Partial Reflection — Partial Refraction

Waves partially reflect and partially refract whenever there is a change in velocity. The amount of partial reflection varies with the angle of incidence and is much more apparent when there is an increase in the velocity than when there is a decrease. This is just like the behaviour of light. In fact, it can be shown, using a ripple tank, that there is a critical angle for waves, just as there is for light. For angles of incidence greater than the critical angle, all the waves are reflected and none are refracted, a behaviour of light referred to as total internal reflection (see Section 11.8). It should be noted that total internal reflection only occurs for waves travelling from a slow to a fast medium, as is the case for light.

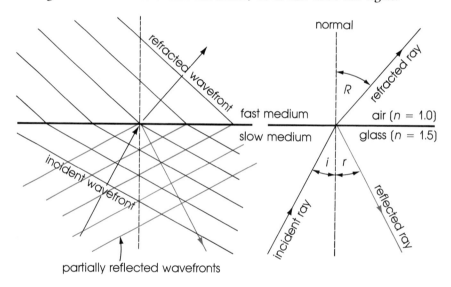

partially reflected wavefronts

Diffraction

Waves diffract; does light diffract? As mentioned on page 515, Grimaldi had observed the diffraction of light when a ray was directed through two successive narrow slits. Newton had said that if light was a wave, then light waves should bend much more than what was observed by Grimaldi. As we saw in Chapter 13, there is considerable diffraction only when the size of the aperture is of approximately the same order of magnitude as the wavelength of the waves. Thus, if the wavelength is very small, the amount of diffraction will be minimal, unless the opening is extremely small, too.

"The universe is full of magical things, patiently waiting for our wits to grow sharper."

Eden Phillpots

Huygens' Principle is consistent with diffraction around the edge of an obstacle, through a large aperture and through an aperture whose size is on the same order of magnitude as the wavelength of the wave, as illustrated. Neither Newton nor Huygens had been able to determine what is now known — that the wavelengths of visible light are so incredibly small that diffraction effects must be very small as well. In their day, diffraction was adequately explained by both theories, but once the minuteness of the wavelength of light was known, the wave theory was acknowledged to be superior.

(a)

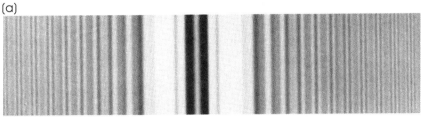

(b)

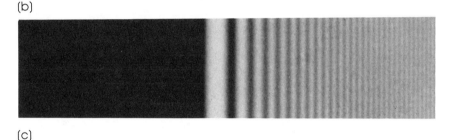

(c)

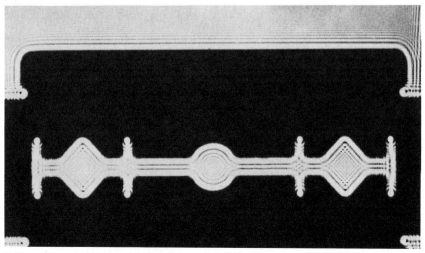

Diffraction patterns of (a) a fine wire, (b) a sharp edge, and (c) a razor blade

Rectilinear Propagation

The term "rectilinear propagation" is commonly used to describe the appearance light gives, of travelling in a straight line. Actually, this expression implies much more. The term "rectilinear" refers to the fact that light travels not only in a straight line but also as a transverse wave.

The wave theory treats light as a series of wavefronts perpendicular to the paths of the light rays. Huygens thought of the rays as simply representing the direction of motion of a wavefront. Newton felt that this did not adequately explain rectilinear propagation of light, since waves emitted from a point source spread out in all directions rather than travelling in a straight line. For this property of light, Newton's corpuscular theory was better than the wave theory.

To summarize, then. Huygens' wave theory explained many of the properties of light, including reflection, refraction, partial reflection-partial refraction, diffraction, and rectilinear propagation. The wave theory was more valid at that time than Newton's corpuscular theory. But, because of Newton's reputation in other areas of physics, the corpuscular theory was to dominate for 100 years, until new and definitive evidence was provided by Thomas Young in 1807.

14.4 Interference — Young's Double-Slit Experiment

Thomas Young

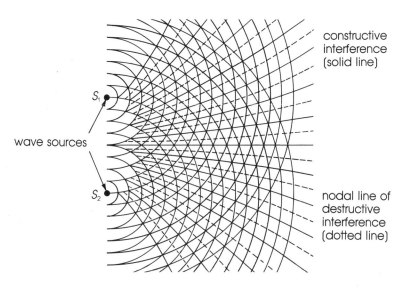

constructive interference (solid line)

S_1

wave sources

S_2

nodal line of destructive interference (dotted line)

Interference of circular waves produced by two point sources in phase

If light has wave properties, two sources of light emitting light waves should produce a result similar to that for waves in a ripple tank. (Waves generated by two point sources in a ripple tank interfere with each other to produce areas of constructive and destructive interference, as illustrated on the previous page.) Light should be brighter in areas of constructive interference, and there should be darkness in areas of destructive interference.

Many scientists attempted to observe the interference of light. In most cases they placed two sources of light side by side. The light from the two sources, falling on a nearby screen, was carefully examined, but no interference was ever observed. The scientists conducting these experiments did not know that the wavelength of light is extremely small. In a ripple tank, where the frequency of the sources is large and the wavelength small, the distance between adjacent nodal lines is very small. In these experiments with light, the distance between the nodal lines was so small that no nodal lines could be observed.

Also there was a second, and more basic, problem. In the ripple tank, if the phase of the vibrating sources is altered, then the interference pattern will shift. When two incandescent light sources are used side by side, the light is emitted randomly by the atoms in each source, in bursts, not necessarily in phase. When the light strikes the screen, a constantly varying interference pattern is produced, and no single pattern is observed.

In the years 1802 to 1804, Thomas Young performed a number of experiments. Instead of using two separate sources, he used only one source, directing it through two pinholes placed very close together. The light was diffracted through each pinhole so that each acted as a point source of light. Since the sources were close together, the spacing between the nodal lines was great enough that the pattern could be seen. Because the light from the two pinholes actually came from the same source, the two interfering beams of light were always in phase and a single, fixed interference pattern could be created on the screen.

The two major problems in observing the interference of light were resolved. In Young's experiment, the two sources were in phase, and the distance between sources was small enough that a series of light and dark bands, called **interference fringes**, were created on a screen placed in the path of the light. This experiment, now commonly called **Young's Experiment**, provided very strong evidence for the wave theory of light.

Thomas Young (1773–1829). Young, an English physicist and physician, was a child prodigy who could read at the age of two and was called the "Phenomenon Young" at Cambridge University.

Although his training was in medicine he spent most of his time in research. His early studies included basic studies of the eye and the functions of the heart and arteries. While studying the human voice, he became interested in the physics of waves, and was able to demonstrate that the wave theory explained the behaviour of light. His work met with initial hostility in England, because the particle theory was considered to be "English" and the wave theory "European". It thus fell to two Frenchmen, Fresnel and Arago, to establish Young's findings.

Young's interest in light led to the analysis of colour perception. It was he who proposed that any colour in the spectrum could be produced by using the additive primary colours, red, green, and blue. Colour television and colour photography use this three-colour theory today.

Young was interested in forms of energy other than light. In 1810 he first used the term "energy" in the sense in which we use it today, that is, the property of a system that gives it the ability to do work.

He contributed to the understanding of surface tension in liquids and of the elastic properties of other substances. The constant used in equations describing the behaviour of elastic substances is today called "Young's Modulus" (see Chapter 6).

Besides his contributions to science, he made progress in deciphering the ancient hieroglyphic language of the Egyptians.

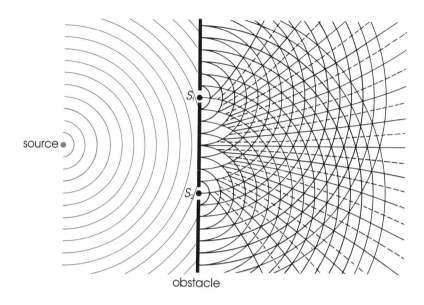

Interference in a wave tank, produced by waves from a single source passing through adjacent openings

Here we repeat, for light waves, the discussion of Section 13.5 that referred to waves in a ripple tank. In the photograph, light waves falling upon a barrier with two slits are diffracted and produce an interference pattern similar to that produced by two point sources vibrating in phase in a ripple tank.

In the diagrams on the next page, light waves in phase are shown encountering slits S_1 and S_2, which are a distance d apart. The waves spread out in all directions after passing through the slits but (as with the water waves) we will analyse them for only three different angles (θ). In diagram (a) ($\theta = 0$), both of the waves reach the centre of the screen in phase, because they travel the same distance, and constructive interference occurs (the bright spot on the screen). When the waves from slit S_2 travel an extra distance of $1/2\lambda$ to reach the screen, in diagram (b), the waves from the two sources arrive at the screen 180° out of phase. Destructive interference occurs, and the screen is dark at this point ($n = 1$). Moving farther away from the centre of the screen, a point is reached where the path difference is λ, diagram (c), and the two waves are now back in phase. This is because the waves from S_2 are one whole wavelength behind those from S_1, and constructive interference occurs (the bright spot).

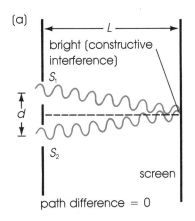

(a)

bright (constructive interference)

S_1

d

S_2

screen

L

path difference = 0

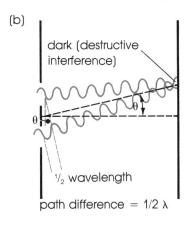

(b)

dark (destructive interference)

θ

θ

½ wavelength

path difference = 1/2 λ

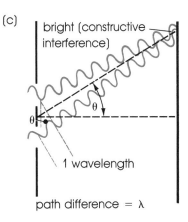

(c)

bright (constructive interference)

θ

θ

1 wavelength

path difference = λ

Recalling the analysis in the ripple tank, constructive interference occurs when the path difference, $d \sin \theta$, is expressed as follows:

$$d \sin \theta_n = n\lambda, \text{ where } n = 0,1,2,3 \ldots$$

Destructive interference occurs when

$$d \sin \theta_n = (n - 1/2)\lambda, \text{ where } n = 1,2,3 \ldots$$

Since the dark fringes created on the screen by destructive interference are very narrow, measurements are made using the nodal lines and not the bright areas. Also, $\sin \theta$ is determined more easily by using the ratio x/L, where x is the distance of the nodal line from the centre line on the screen, and L is the distance from the midpoint between the two slits, S_1 and S_2, to the screen.

The wavelength of the water waves was calculated from the equation $\lambda = \dfrac{d(x/L)}{(n - 1/2)}$ (see page 498).

Rearranging this equation, we obtain

$$x_n = (n - 1/2) L(\lambda/d) \quad \text{where } x_n \text{ is the distance to the } n^{\text{th}} \text{ nodal line, measured from the right bisector}$$

Actually, $\frac{x}{L} = \tan \theta$. But, for $L \gg x$, $\tan \theta$ is very nearly equal to $\sin \theta$. Thus, $\frac{x}{L} = \sin \theta$.

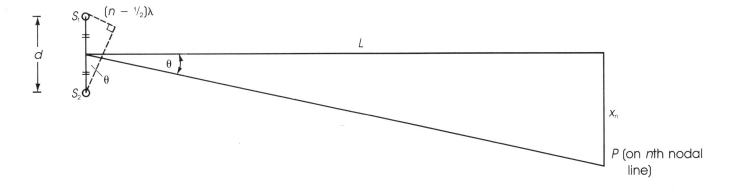

S_1

$(n - \frac{1}{2})\lambda$

d

θ

θ

S_2

L

x_n

P (on nth nodal line)

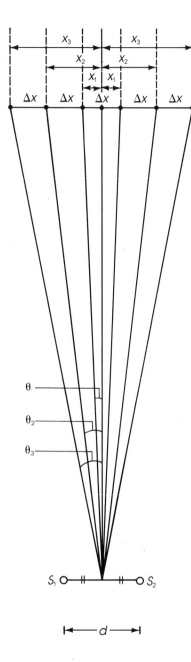

For each nodal line, a separate value for x can be derived from this equation, as follows:

$$x_1 = \left(1 - \frac{1}{2}\right) L\left(\frac{\lambda}{d}\right) = \frac{L\lambda}{2d}$$

$$x_2 = \left(2 - \frac{1}{2}\right) L\left(\frac{\lambda}{d}\right) = \frac{3L\lambda}{2d}$$

$$x_3 = \left(3 - \frac{1}{2}\right) L\left(\frac{\lambda}{d}\right) = \frac{5L\lambda}{2d}$$

etc.

Although L was different in the earlier equation, in this case L is so large compared to d, and the values of L to each nodal line are so similar to one another, that we assume that L is essentially constant and equal to the perpendicular distance from the slits to the screen.

As seen in the diagram below, the displacement between adjacent nodal lines (Δx) is given by: $(x_2 - x_1)$, $(x_3 - x_2)$, and $(x_1 + x_1)$. In each case the value is: $\Delta x = L(\lambda/d)$.

Rearranging the equation, we obtain

$$\lambda = \Delta x \ (d/L)$$

---

where Δx is the distance between adjacent nodal lines on the screen

            d is the separation of the slits

            L is the perpendicular distance from the slits to the screen

Sample problem

A student measuring the wavelength produced by a sodium vapour lamp directed the sodium light through two slits with a separation of 0.15 mm. An interference pattern was created on the screen, 3.0 m away. The student found that the distance between the first and the eighth consecutive dark lines was 8.0 cm. What was the wavelength of the light emitted by the sodium vapour lamp?

8 nodal lines = $7\Delta x$

$$\Delta x = \frac{8.0 \text{ cm}}{7} = 1.14 \text{ cm} = 1.14 \times 10^{-2} \text{ m}$$

$$d = 0.15 \text{ mm} = 1.5 \times 10^{-4} \text{ m}$$

$$\lambda = \frac{\Delta x d}{L}$$

$$= \frac{(1.14 \times 10^{-2}\,\text{m})(1.5 \times 10^{-4}\,\text{m})}{3.0\,\text{m}}$$
$$= 5.7 \times 10^{-7}\,\text{m, or } 5.7 \times 10^{2}\,\text{nm}$$

Practice

1. A student doing Young's Experiment finds that the distance between the first and the seventh nodal lines is 6.0 cm. If the screen is located 3.0 m from two slits, whose separation is 220 μm, what is the wavelength of the light? $(7.3 \times 10^{-7}\,\text{m})$

2. An interference pattern is formed on a screen when helium-neon laser light ($\lambda = 6.328 \times 10^{-7}\,\text{m}$) is directed towards it through two slits. If the slits are 43 μm apart and the screen is 2.5 m away, what will be the separation of adjacent nodal lines?   (3.7 cm)

3. In an interference experiment, red light (600 nm) passes through a double slit. On a screen 1.5 m away, the distance between the 1st and 11th dark bands is 13.2 cm. What is the separation of the slits? What would the spacing be, between adjacent nodal lines, if blue light (450 nm) were used?   (68 μm, 1.0 cm)

Young did a calculation similar to the one in our sample problem and determined the wavelength of various colours of light, including red and blue. When he announced his results in 1807, he took great pains to remind his audience that Newton had made several statements favouring a theory that had some aspects of the behaviour of waves, even though Newton was considered to be a supporter of the particle theory. Nevertheless, Newton's influence was still too strong, and Young and his work were not taken seriously by the scientific establishment.

It was not until 1818, when the French physicist Augustin Fresnel proposed his own mathematical wave theory, that Young's research was accepted. Fresnel's work was presented to a group of physicists and mathematicians, most of them strong supporters of the particle theory. One mathematician, Simon Poisson, took Fresnel's wave equations and showed that if these equations really did describe the behaviour of light, they would predict a unique diffraction pattern when light is directed past a small solid disc. He claimed that if light really did behave like a wave, the light diffracting around the edges of the disc should interfere constructively and produce a small bright spot at the exact centre of the diffraction pattern on the screen. (According to the particle theory, constructive interference at this position was impossible.) Poisson did not observe a bright spot, and felt he had refuted the wave theory of light.

Augustin Fresnel

Augustin Fresnel (1788–1827). Fresnel, a French physicist, spent most of his life working for the government as a civil engineer. It was Fresnel's mathematical analysis that provided the theoretical basis for the transverse wave model of light. The greatest victory for this view was the explanation of the phenomenon of double refraction in Iceland spar (polarization — see page 557). Using his analysis of light, Fresnel designed a "flat" lens, which was used in the lighthouses of his day. These lenses were much more efficient than the mirrors they replaced. Today the Fresnel lens is used in overhead projectors, beacon lights, and solar collectors, among many applications.

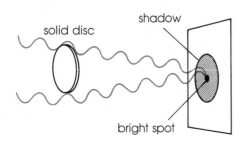

If light is a wave, a bright spot will appear at the centre of the shadow of a solid disc illuminated by a point source of monochromatic light.

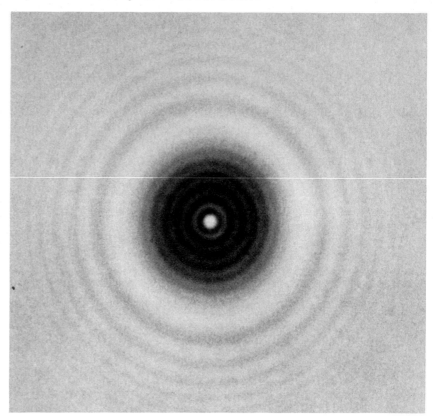

Poisson's Bright Spot is also known as Arago's Bright Spot.

Dominique Arago (1786–1853). Arago, a French physicist, made a contribution to many fields of science, including astronomy and mathematics. After studying the physics of light, he at first supported the particle theory; later, however, he was converted to the wave theory. It was he who introduced Fresnel, who was working on the mathematics of the wave theory, to the work of Young. Fresnel and Arago worked together for a time, but parted following Fresnel's adoption of Young's hypothesis of transverse light waves.

Arago did some of the pioneer work in electromagnetism, based on the discoveries of Oersted (see page 623). He was also a fiery political figure, involved in the French revolutions of 1830 and 1852.

However, in 1818, Poisson's prediction was tested experimentally by Dominique Arago, and the bright spot was seen at the centre of the shadow. Because he had predicted that there would be a bright spot at the centre of the shadow if the wave theory worked, even though he refuted the wave theory, this phenomenon is known as "Poisson's Bright Spot". (Note that there is interference near the edge of the disc as well.)

By 1850 the validity of the wave theory of light had been generally accepted. For some time afterward, the mathematical consequences of the wave theory were applied to numerous aspects of the properties of light, some of which we will discuss in the following sections.

But the wave theory was not adequate to explain the movement of light through the vacuum of space, since waves required a material medium for their transmission. The power of the wave theory was now so great, however, that scientists theorized a "fluid" filling all space, from the space between atoms to the space between planets. They called it "ether". Many experiments were attempted to detect this ether, but none was successful (see Section 17.3).

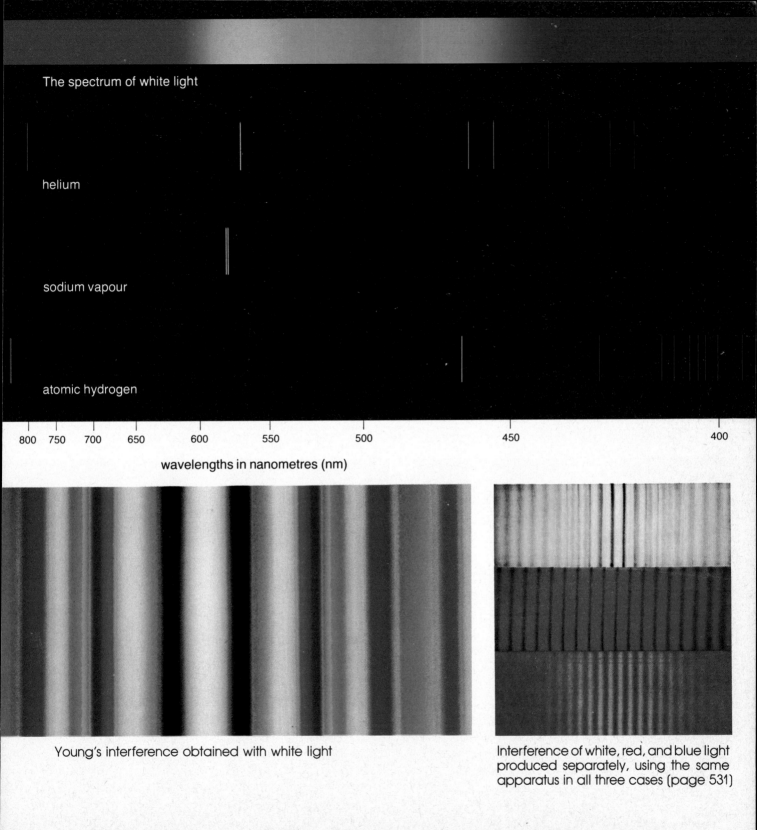

The spectrum of white light

helium

sodium vapour

atomic hydrogen

800   750   700   650   600   550   500   450   400

wavelengths in nanometres (nm)

Young's interference obtained with white light

Interference of white, red, and blue light produced separately, using the same apparatus in all three cases (page 531)

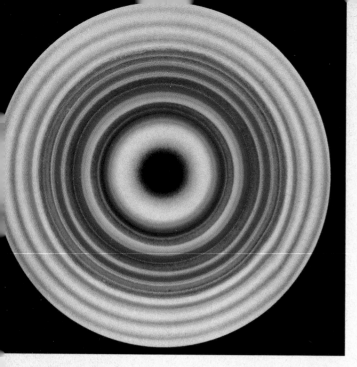

Newton's rings interference pattern (page 547)

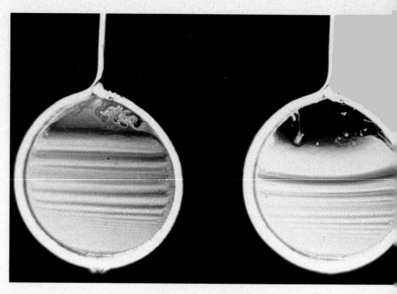

Interference in a thin soap film as seen by reflected light, right, and transmitted light, left (page 546)

Single-slit diffraction of white, blue, and red light (page 536)

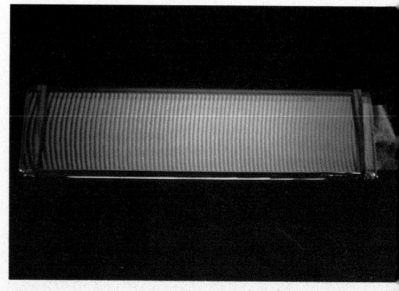

Interference in an air wedge illuminated by sodium light (page 546)

In 1887, Albert Michelson and another American scientist, Edward W. Morley, attempted to measure the presumed motion of the Earth through the "ether". Essentially they were trying to measure the effect of the "ether wind" on the velocity of light as measured from a moving platform, the Earth. Using a device called an interferometer (see page 550), they produced the result that no change in the velocity of light was detectable; that is, the velocity of light was constant, independent of the motion of the observer. Also, no ether was detected, and it did not, in fact, exist. It was not until the turn of the 20th century that this problem was resolved, but we leave that discussion until Chapter 17.

14.5 Colour and the Wavelength of Light

The photograph on the colour plate shows two interference patterns, one for red light and one for blue light. Note that separation of the nodal lines is greater for red light than it is for blue. This is to be expected, since red light has a larger wavelength than blue. Using the relationship $\lambda = \Delta x(d/L)$, it can be shown that the wavelength for red light is approximately 6.5×10^{-7} m, and the wavelength for blue light is approximately 4.5×10^{-7} m. Similar determinations produce values for all the colours in the visual spectrum. Some of these are given in the chart in the margin.

When white light passes through two narrow slits, the central bright areas in the interference patterns are white, but at the edges the spectral colours appear (see colour plate). If each spectral colour has its own band of wavelengths, each will interfere constructively at specific locations in the interference pattern. Thus, the colours of the spectrum are observed in the interference pattern because each band of wavelengths is associated with its own colour.

On passing through a prism, white light is broken up into its components to form the spectrum. Each of the colours bends by a different amount and emerges from the prism at a slightly different angle. Newton called this dispersion.

To explain dispersion, the wave theory must show that waves of different wavelengths are bent by slightly different amounts when they are refracted. Careful measurements in a ripple tank demonstrate this, as the photographs on page 490, Section 13.3, show. Thus, if the wavelength (frequency) of a wave varies, the amount of refraction varies slightly as well, thereby explaining dispersion.

Colour	Wavelength (nm)
violet	400-450
blue	450-500
green	500-570
yellow	570-590
orange	590-610
red	610-750

Note: 1 nm = 10^{-9} m

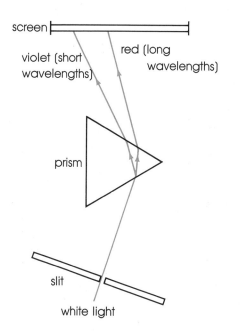

Although the wavelength of the light does affect the amount of refraction, the behaviour is the reverse of that of water waves in a ripple tank. Shorter wavelengths, such as those at the violet end of the spectrum, are refracted more than the larger wavelengths in the red region. Each spectral colour, having a wavelength different from the others, is refracted a different amount. This explains the prism's separation of white light into the spectrum.

Since each of the wavelengths of visible light undergoes a slightly different amount of refraction by the prism, the glass must have a slightly different index of refraction for each colour. For example, the index of refraction of crown glass for violet light is 1.53 and for red light 1.51. The velocity of violet light in glass is slightly less than that for red.

From the time the wave theory of light was shown to be valid, many of the mathematical relationships governing waves in ropes and in water have been applied to light waves,

namely: $\quad v = f\lambda, \quad _1n_2 = \dfrac{v_1}{v_2}, \quad \dfrac{v_1}{v_2} = \dfrac{\lambda_1}{\lambda_2}, \quad$ and $\sin i / \sin R = n$.

Using the equation $v = f\lambda$, we find that the frequency of red light, with a wavelength of 6.5×10^{-7} m, is:

$$f = \frac{v}{\lambda} = \frac{c}{\lambda} \quad \text{where } c = 3.00 \times 10^8 \text{ m/s (the velocity of light)}$$

$$= \frac{3.00 \times 10^8 \text{ m/s}}{6.5 \times 10^{-7} \text{ m}}$$

$$= 4.6 \times 10^{14} \text{ Hz}$$

It may be obvious to us now, but it was not obvious to the experimenters in the 18th century, that to produce an interference pattern, it would be necessary to have two point sources of light in phase. Although the frequency of light sources is very high, what makes interference impossible is the way light is emitted from an incandescent source. The light from each source comes from a large number of individual atoms. An atom in a source sends out a burst of light waves in a time interval of about 10^{-9} s. The probability that the atoms or groups of atoms in each source would emit their light waves in phase is nearly zero. Therefore, the interference pattern produced by two point sources changes in an irregular fashion every 10^{-9} s or so, and is impossible for an observer to see. In recent years it has been possible to produce interference with two lasers. Laser light is **monochromatic**, meaning that it is composed of only one colour and has one wavelength. In the case of helium-neon laser light, the wavelength is 6.328×10^{-7} m. When two lasers have been made to operate in phase (they are said to be "phase locked"), the interference fringes are seen, but some drifting of the pattern occurs. Even today, with modern technology available, the easiest way to show the interference of light is to use the same technique that Young used.

Sample problem

Red light with a wavelength of 650 nm travels from air into glass ($n = 1.51$).
(a) What will its velocity be in the glass?
(b) What will its wavelength be in the glass?

(a)
$$n = \frac{v_a}{v_g} \text{ or } v_g = \frac{v_a}{n}$$
$$= \frac{3.00 \times 10^8 \text{ m/s}}{1.51}$$
$$= 1.99 \times 10^8 \text{ m/s}$$

(b)
$$\frac{v_a}{v_g} = \frac{\lambda_a}{\lambda_g} \text{ or } \lambda_g = \frac{v_g}{v_a} \lambda_a$$
$$= \left(\frac{1.99 \times 10^8 \text{ m/s}}{3.00 \times 10^8 \text{ m/s}}\right) 650 \text{ nm}$$
$$= 430 \text{ nm}$$

Practice

1. If the wavelength of orange light is 6.0×10^{-7} m in air, what is its frequency? $(5.0 \times 10^{14} \text{ Hz})$
2. The frequency of a light is 3.80×10^{14} Hz. What is its wavelength in air, in nanometres? (789 nm)
3. A certain shade of violet light has a wavelength in air of 4.4×10^{-7} m. If the index of refraction of alcohol relative to air for violet light is 1.40, what is the wavelength of the violet light in alcohol? $(3.1 \times 10^{-7} \text{ m})$
4. The index of refraction of turpentine relative to air for red light is 1.47. A ray of red light ($\lambda_r = 6.5 \times 10^{-7}$ m) strikes an air-turpentine boundary with an angle of incidence of 40°.
   (a) What is the wavelength of red light in turpentine?
   (b) What is the angle of refraction in turpentine?
   $(4.4 \times 10^{-7} \text{ m}, 26°)$

Laser Radiation

Conventional light sources are essentially "hot bodies." For example, the electrons in the tungsten filament of a common light bulb are agitated and excited to higher energy levels (see Section 19.5) by high temperatures. Once excited, they emit light as they return to a lower energy state. Similarly, in a gas lamp such as a fluorescent tube, it is the electron current passing through the gas that excites the atoms to high energy levels. They give up this excitation energy by radiating it as light waves. Spontaneous emission from each single electron or atom takes place independently of the emission from the others. The overall energy produced by either of these conventional light sources, the incandescent lamp or the fluorescent lamp, is a jumble of waves from numerous individual atoms. Each wave emitted has its own phase that changes randomly from moment to moment and point to point. Therefore, the light from conventional sources is said to be **incoherent**.

In contrast to this, laser light is **coherent**. This means that the emitted light waves are in phase, that is, almost all the crests and troughs are in step. This coherence arises because the atoms are stimulated to emit waves of light that are in phase (see page 754 for a more detailed explanation). By constructive interference, the light waves combine their energies to produce powerful and intense laser light. Since the emitted light has consistent wavelength or colour, laser light is said to be **monochromatic**. Finally, the light waves are emitted primarily in one direction.

Lasers are valuable sources of light for exciting and practical demonstrations in the classroom. Usually a low-powered helium-neon laser is used to emit a beam of orange-red light (see page 754). Even though the power is low and the radiation is not harmful, the beam should be treated with caution and common sense. It is concentrated and intense and could cause damage to the eye if viewed directly for longer than a few seconds. Just as no one should stare directly at the sun, at arc lamps, or at a welder at work, no one should look directly into a laser beam or at its bright reflections.

These properties of directionality, intensity, and coherence, make laser beams suitable for a wide range of scientific, commercial, medical, and military applications. Because a laser beam is one-directional, it spreads out very little; it can travel long distances with little divergence. This property makes it useful for surveying; as a directional reference for drilling tunnels; for measuring the very small movement in the continents of the Earth; in the determination of the distance to the moon (accurate to a few metres); as a guide for agricultural tile layers; and as a guide for missiles.

The intensity of laser beams makes them useful in cutting and welding metals and other materials. An industrial laser can easily concentrate ten thousand million watts for short intervals. With no blades to break or bits to wear, lasers can precisely cut fabric for suits, weld dishwasher doors, plate easily-corroded metals, etch the patterns of microcircuits, and drill eyes in surgical needles.

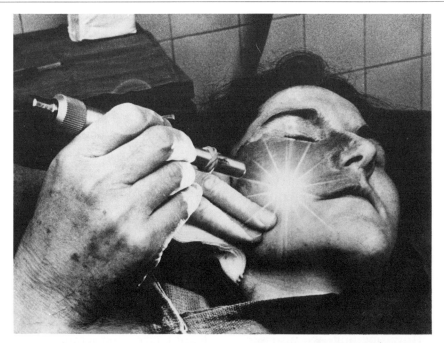

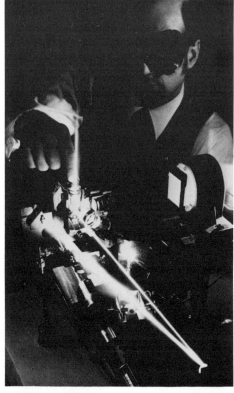

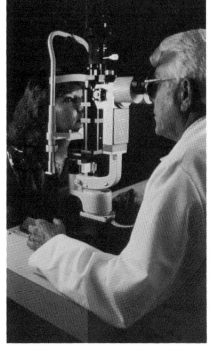

14.6 Diffraction of Light from a Single Slit

As predicted by the wave theory of light, when light passes through a single narrow slit it is diffracted. The narrower the slit width, the greater the amount of diffraction. But the light is not just spread out by diffraction, interference also occurs. As seen in the photograph below and in the investigation (page 563), a pattern of bright and dark lines is produced on the screen. The pattern consists of a bright central region (**central maximum**) with dark regions of destructive interference alternating with progressively less intense areas of light (**secondary maxima**) on either side. Although the pattern has some similarities to Young's pattern, the spacing of the bright and dark areas is quite different.

If we look carefully at the diffraction of water waves through a narrow opening, we also see nodal lines (see photographs), an indication that wave theory does predict the single-slit diffraction pattern for light. To see how such a diffraction pattern arises, let us analyse the wave behaviour of monochromatic light passing through a single slit.

Diffraction of water waves through (left) a single opening, and (right) a narrower opening

The slit may be considered as a row of n point sources, close together and vibrating in phase, each source producing secondary circular wavelets. At any point on the screen, the resultant interference will be the sum of the contributions from each of the n point sources, taking into account the phase of each contribution as it reaches the screen.

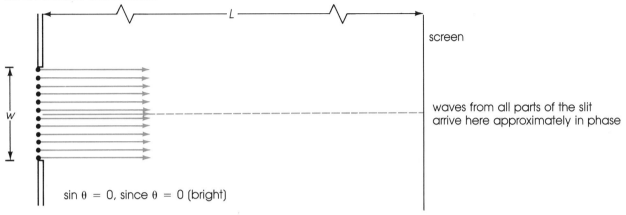

sin θ = 0, since θ = 0 (bright)

To simplify the diagram, we will use the wave rays to represent the direction of motion of the individual Huygens wavelets produced in the slit opening. First, let us consider the case for light waves that pass straight through the slit. Since the wavelets all start in phase, and travel approximately the same distance to the screen, they arrive in phase. Constructive interference produces a bright spot on the screen. This is the central maximum.

For light diffracted downward through an angle, the waves from the top of the slit travel farther than the waves from the bottom. If the path difference is one wavelength, the light waves from the centre of the slit will travel one half-wavelength farther than those from the bottom of the slit; they will be out of phase, and destructive interference will occur. Similarly, waves slightly above the bottom and slightly above the central point will cancel. In fact, the wavelet coming from each point in the lower half of the slit will cancel the wavelet originating from a corresponding point in the upper half of the slit. As a result, all of the waves will interfere destructively in pairs, and a dark fringe will appear on the screen. In the same manner, destructive interference occurs at an equal distance above the central maximum. As can be seen from the diagram on page 538, for the first minimum, the path difference of one wavelength is given by $w \sin \theta_1 = \lambda$. Rearranging this equation, the angle θ at which the first minimum appears is given by:

$$\sin \theta_1 = \frac{\lambda}{w} \text{ (1st minimum)}$$

We assume L is large enough that the parallel bundles of rays converge on a spot. Alternately, a lens can focus them if it is placed a distance f from the screen.

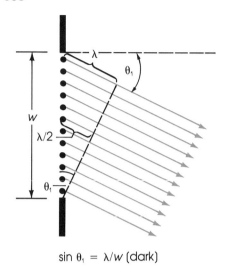

$\sin \theta_1 = \lambda/w$ (dark)

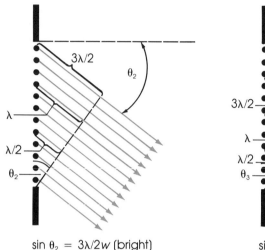

$\sin \theta_2 = 3\lambda/2w$ (bright)

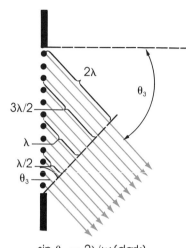

$\sin \theta_3 = 2\lambda/w$ (dark)

If we now consider a larger value of θ, so that the path difference between the top and the bottom of the slit is $3\lambda/2$, we find that for each point source in the bottom third of the slit there exists a corresponding point source in the middle third that is $\lambda/2$ farther from the screen, so that each of these pairs of point sources interferes destructively. However, the waves from the top third of the slit still reach the screen roughly in phase, and a bright spot is produced. The bright spot is not as intense as the central maximum, since most of the light passing through the slit at this angle will interfere destructively. This angle, θ_2, is given by $\sin \theta_2 = 3\lambda/2w$.

For an even larger angle θ_3, the top waves travel a distance of 2λ farther than those from the bottom of the slit. Waves from the bottom quarter cancel, in pairs, with those in the quarter just above, because their path lengths differ by $\lambda/2$, and those in the quarter above the centre cancel, in pairs, with those in the top quarter. At this angle, θ_3, given by $\sin \theta_3 = 2\lambda/w$, a second line of zero intensity occurs in the diffraction pattern.

In summary, areas of minimum intensity occur at $\sin \theta = \dfrac{\lambda}{w}, \dfrac{2\lambda}{w}, \dfrac{3\lambda}{w}$, etc., while bright areas occur at $\sin \theta = 0, \dfrac{3\lambda}{2w}, \dfrac{5\lambda}{2w}$, etc.

Since, for each successive bright area, more of the "n" light sources interfere destructively, in pairs, the intensity of the light decreases. This can be seen in the graph of intensity versus $\sin \theta$ for a single-slit diffraction pattern.

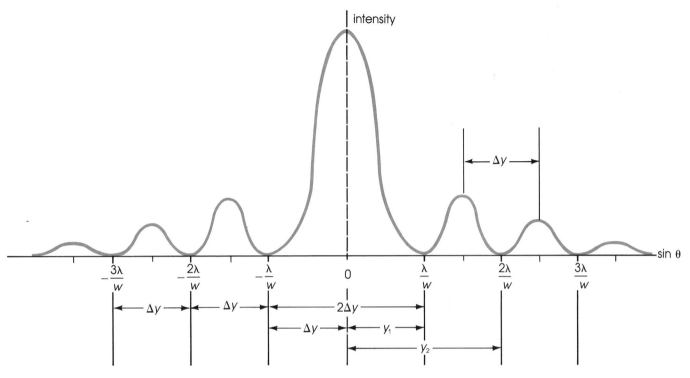

As in the analysis of the double-slit interference pattern, the value of $\sin \theta_1$ can be determined from the ratio y_1/L, where y_1 is the distance from the centre point in the diffraction pattern and L is the perpendicular distance from the slit to the screen.

$$\sin \theta \approx \tan \theta = \frac{y}{L} \text{ for } L >> y.$$

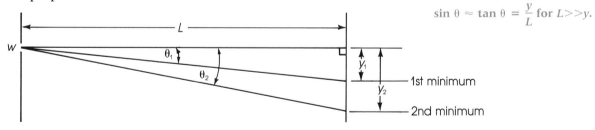

For the position of the first minimum on the screen, this equation becomes

$$\sin \theta_1 = \frac{\lambda}{w}$$

$$\frac{y_1}{L} = \frac{\lambda}{w}$$

$$\lambda = \frac{wy_1}{L}$$

The general equation would be:

dark lines — $\sin \theta = \dfrac{n\lambda}{w}$

bright lines — $\sin \theta = \dfrac{(n - \frac{1}{2})\lambda}{w}$

where $n = 1, 2, 3 \ldots$
Note that for $\theta = 0$ there is a bright central maximum that is twice as wide as all others.

The relation $\lambda = \dfrac{w\Delta y}{L}$ can be derived if we use the same analysis as that used on page 528 for double slits. This equation can be used either to analyse the single-slit diffraction pattern so as to find the wavelength of light, or to predict the dimensions of the pattern and the positions of the nodal lines. (Care must be taken, since the central maximum is twice as wide as all others.) A sample problem will illustrate.

Sample problem

Light with a wavelength of 670 nm passes through a slit with a width of 12 μm. Viewed on the screen, 30 cm away: **(a)** How wide is the central maximum in **(i)** degrees and **(ii)** centimetres? **(b)** What is the separation of adjacent minima (excluding the pair on either side of the central maximum)?

(a)(i) $\qquad \sin \theta_1 = \dfrac{\lambda}{w}$

$$= \dfrac{670 \text{ nm}}{12 \text{ μm}} = \dfrac{6.7 \times 10^{-7} \text{ m}}{1.2 \times 10^{-5} \text{ m}}$$
$$= 0.0558$$

Thus, $\theta_1 = 3.2°$, and the width is $2 \times 3.2° = 6.4°$.

(ii) $\qquad \sin \theta_1 = \dfrac{y_1}{L}$ or $y_1 = L \sin \theta_1$

$$= 0.30 \text{ m } (5.58 \times 10^{-2})$$
$$= 1.67 \times 10^{-2} \text{ m}$$
$$= 1.7 \text{ cm}$$

The width of the central maximum is $2y_1$, or $2 \times 1.7 \text{ cm} = 3.4 \text{ cm}$.

(b) Rearranging $\quad \lambda = \dfrac{w\Delta y}{L}$, we obtain

$$\Delta y = \dfrac{L\lambda}{w}$$

$$= \dfrac{(0.30 \text{ m})(6.7 \times 10^{-7} \text{ m})}{1.2 \times 10^{-5} \text{ m}}$$
$$= 1.7 \text{ cm}$$

Note that the central maximum is exactly twice the width of the separation of other adjacent nodal lines.

Practice

1. At what angle will 750 nm light produce a second minimum if the single-slit width is 2.0 μm?   (49°)

2. If the first nodal line in a single-slit diffraction pattern occurs at an angle of 15° for light with a wavelength of 580 nm, what is the width of the slit? *(2.2 μm)*

3. Helium-neon laser light ($\lambda = 6.328 \times 10^{-7}$ m) passes through a single slit with a width of 43 μm onto a screen 3.0 m away. What is the separation of adjacent minima, other than the central maximum? *(4.4 cm)*

As seen in the sample problem, the wave theory predicts that the width of the central maximum is twice the separation of adjacent minima. An examination of the photograph on page 536 shows that this is true. Our wave interpretation of both Young's Experiment and single-slit diffraction seems to be correct, offering further support for the wave theory of light.

In Young's Experiment, each individual slit produces its own single-slit diffraction pattern, the pattern centres being a distance *d* apart. The central maximum produced by each narrow slit covers a large lateral distance when it reaches the screen, relatively far away. As a result, the two central bright areas overlap and interfere. The double-slit interference pattern is, in reality, the resultant interference of two single-slit diffraction patterns. The other maxima of the single-slit diffraction pattern occur far out to the sides and are usually too weak to be seen. If wider slits are used, these maxima become more visible, as shown in the photographs.

The top photograph illustrates the interference pattern produced by two single slits with wider slits. The bottom photograph is an enlargement of the central section of the top photograph. It is only the central region that is observed in most double-slit interference patterns, where narrow slits are used.

14.7 Other Interference Effects

Resolution

As we have seen, light waves passing around an obstacle or through a small opening are diffracted. The smaller the opening or obstacle, the greater the diffraction. The diffraction of light is important in the design of microscopes and telescopes.

When light from two sources passes through the same small hole, the light from each source will be diffracted and the diffraction patterns will overlap. This makes the images fuzzy, as illustrated. If the hole is very small and the sources are very close, they may overlap so that the individual images cannot be distinguished. The separation of the two images is called **resolution**. Resolution in an optical instrument is the ability to separate two closely spaced images.

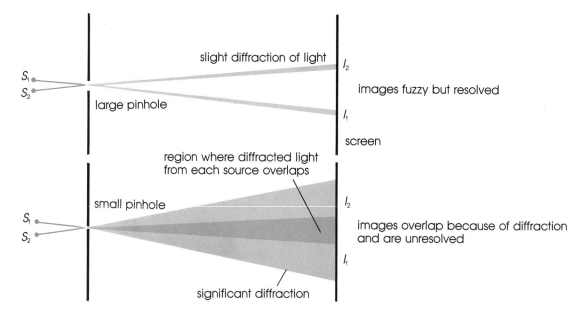

If, instead of a small hole, a lens is substituted, resolution becomes the ability of the lens to produce two sharp and separate images. As with the hole, the smaller the lens, the more difficult it is to separate two closely spaced objects, because they have overlapping diffraction patterns. This is seen in the photographs, which illustrate this behaviour for three different diameters of lens. As the lens becomes larger, the resolution increases.

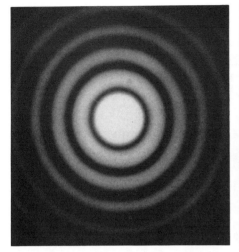

In a microscope, the objective lens has a small diameter. This limits the use of even the best optical microscope to a maximum magnification of approximately 600, since even the best objective lens can only resolve detail to a certain point.

In telescopes, this problem is reduced by using large lenses or mirrors to increase the resolution. The largest telescopes are used to view the farthest distances in space, not only because they receive more light, but also because they are able to resolve individual stars that appear very close together in the sky.

Diffraction Gratings

A device for wave analysis having a large number of equally spaced parallel slits is called a **diffraction grating**. The slits in the grating act as individual line sources. The wave analysis of the pattern produced by these openings is similar to that for the double slit. The waves passing through the several slits interfere constructively on the screen when $\sin \theta_n = n\lambda/d$, where $n = 0,1,2,3 \ldots$ (n is called the "order" of the bright line). This is easily seen by noting the path difference $\Delta l = d \sin \theta$ between successive pairs of slits in the grating.

There are important differences between the double-slit and the multi-slit interference patterns, however. First, since there are more slits, the multi-slit source delivers more light energy, and the resulting interference pattern is brighter. Secondly, the bright maxima are much sharper and narrower when produced by a diffraction grating. And thirdly, since the slits are usually closer together, the

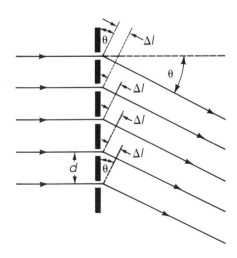

Diffraction grating

separation between successive maxima is greater. For these reasons, the diffraction grating proves to be a very precise device for measuring the wavelength of light.

Gratings are of two types, transmission and reflection. A single piece of glass can be used for both, when fine lines are ruled on it with a diamond tip. The spaces between the lines transmit the

A master grating being ruled by a diamond tip scribe

A microscopic view of a ruled grating

light; the lines are opaque. Gratings containing 10 000 lines/cm are possible with this technique. When the lined glass is used as a reflection grating, light falling on it is reflected only in the untouched segments. This reflected light effectively comes from a series of equally spaced sources, that provide the diffraction grating interference pattern reflected onto the screen. Lined gratings on shiny metal can also be used as a reflection diffraction grating.

If the light striking the grating is not monochromatic, but consists of a large number of wavelengths, each wavelength will produce a pattern of bright maxima at different locations on the screen. This is what occurs when white light is directed through a diffraction grating. The central maximum will be a sharp white peak, but, for other specific colours, the maxima will occur at different positions on the screen, giving the effect of a spectrum. The result is the same as the result for the prism, except that the spectral pattern is much more spread out and easier to observe.

In a spectroscope, the light from a source is first directed through a collimator (see diagram next page). The system of lenses or mirrors in a collimator makes the light rays from the source essentially parallel. This parallel light is directed through a diffraction grating, and the resulting interference pattern is viewed through a tele-

This effect can be easily seen by reflecting light from the surface of a clear vinyl phonograph record, a video disc, or a compact disc.

scope. The angle θ can be measured accurately and the wavelength of the light determined with a high degree of accuracy.

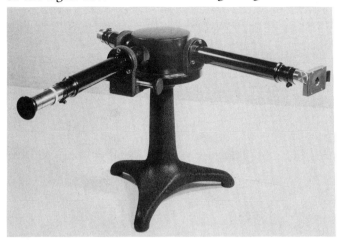

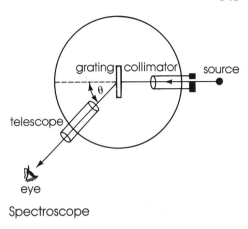

Spectroscope

The spectroscope is used in the investigation in Chapter 19.

Interference in Thin Films

You have probably noticed the swirling colours of the spectrum that result when gasoline or oil is spilled on water. Or you have seen the colours of the spectrum shining on a soap bubble. These effects are produced because interference occurs when light is reflected by or transmitted through a thin film.

Let us assume that we have a horizontal film like a soap bubble that is extremely thin, compared to the wavelength of monochromatic light being directed at it from above, in air. When the light rays strike the upper surface of the film, some of the light is reflected and some is refracted. Similar behaviour occurs at the lower surface. As a result, two rays are reflected to the eye of an observer; the first, ray 1, from the top surface and the second, ray 2, from the bottom. These two light rays travel different paths in arriving at the eye. Whether they interfere constructively or destructively depends on their phase difference when they reach the eye.

We show an angle for clarity, but all rays are nearly vertical.

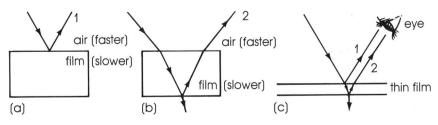

Light waves undergo a 180° phase change when reflected as at (a), but there is no phase change when reflected as at (b).

destructive interference (dark)

air
soap $t << \lambda$
air

path difference approaches zero

constructive interference (bright)

$t = \lambda/4$

path difference is $\lambda/2$

destructive interference (dark)

$t = \lambda/2$

path difference is λ

Note: The diagrams are schematic and not drawn to scale.

You will recall that, when waves pass into a slower medium, the partially reflected waves are inverted (a positive pulse is reflected as a negative — see Section 12.5). Transmitted waves are never inverted; nor are reflected waves, when the transition is from a slow medium to a fast medium. Both rays originate from the same source, so they are initially in phase, but ray 1 will be inverted when it is reflected, whereas ray 2 will not. Because the film is very thin, the extra distance travelled by ray 2 is negligible and the two rays, being 180° out of phase, interfere destructively. For this reason, a dark area occurs at the top of a vertical soap film, since it is very thin in this region (see colour plate).

Let us now consider what happens if the soap film is a little thicker. In this case, ray 2 will have an appreciable path difference when compared with ray 1. If the thickness of the film is $\lambda/4$, the path difference is $2 \times \lambda/4$, or $\lambda/2$ for nearly normal paths. This path difference delays ray 2 by $\lambda/2$ (180° phase delay) and the two rays that were out of phase because of reflection are now back in phase again. Constructive interference occurs, and a bright area is observed.

When the thickness of the film is $\lambda/2$ and the path difference is λ, the two rays are again out of phase, and there is destructive interference. There will be dark areas when the thickness of the film is 0, $\lambda/2$, λ, $3\lambda/2$, etc; bright areas will occur when the thickness is $\lambda/4$, $3\lambda/4$, $5\lambda/4$, etc. It must be emphasized that λ here is the wavelength of light *in the film*, less than in air by a factor of *n*, the index of refraction.

In a vertical soap film, because of the effects of gravity, the film is wedge-shaped, thin at the top and thick at the bottom. The thickness changes uniformly, producing successive horizontal segments of dark and bright reflections (see colour plate).

When viewed under white light, the soap film produces a different effect. Since the spectral colours have different wavelengths, the thickness of the film required to produce constructive interference will be different for each colour. For example, a thickness of $\lambda/4$ for red light will be greater than that for $\lambda/4$ for blue light, because the wavelength of red light is larger than that for blue. Blue light will therefore reflect constructively from a different thickness of the film than red light will. Each colour of the spectrum, then, is reflected constructively from different areas of the film, and the spectral colours are observed (see colour plate).

Thin films, such as oil on water or air wedges trapped between two glass plates, also produce similar interference patterns. As with the soap film, the interference patterns consist of parallel light and dark areas that are usually equally spaced, because the path difference varies uniformly with the distance along the film. In an air wedge, for example, at the point of contact, the path difference is zero. In this case, ray 1 is not inverted, while ray 2 is, making the two rays 180° out of phase. Destructive interference occurs at this point. As the thickness of the air wedge increases, $\lambda/4$, $3\lambda/4$, etc., successive bright bands occur.

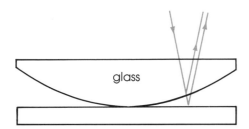

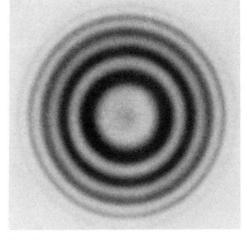

Newton's rings

When a curved glass surface is placed in contact with a flat glass surface, and it is illuminated by monochromatic light, a series of concentric rings is seen. Called **Newton's Rings**, they result from the interference between the rays reflected by the top and bottom of the variable air gap created between the two pieces of glass.

These interference effects are quite useful. For example, the surface of an optical part that is being ground to some desired curvature may be compared with that of another surface, known to be correct, by observing the interference "fringes". Or, if a very flat piece of glass called an "optical flat" is used, the "flatness" of, for example, a ground piece of metal may be checked by placing the "optical flat" on the metal. In the areas where the metal is not flat, air gaps will form, creating interference patterns, and revealing the points on the metal that are not "true". Then corrections can be made, and the work checked again. Precision to the order of a wavelength of light can thus be achieved.

When light is reflected from a thin layer of oil floating on water, the brilliant colours produced come from interference between the rays reflected from the surface of the oil and those reflected from the surface of the water. Usually the oil film does not have a uniform thickness. In fact, the thickness of the film changes constantly on the surface of the water. As with the soap bubble, different thicknesses will produce constructive interference for different colours.

The colours of the spectrum reflected from oil on water constantly change position as the thickness of the oil film changes,

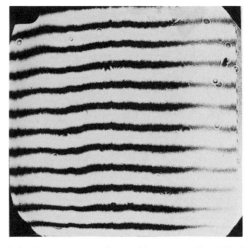

Interference produced by an optical flat

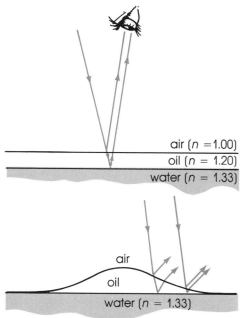

and a swirling of the spectral colours results. Note that, in this case, both reflected rays are phase-inverted, A at the air-oil interface and B at the oil-water interface (but only if the index of the oil is between the indices for air and water).

Interference also occurs when light is transmitted through a thin film. We will use the soap film as an example. When the film is extremely thin ($t << \lambda$), the transmitted light is made up of two rays: ray 1 is transmitted without any phase change; ray 2, although reflected twice internally, is also transmitted without a phase change. (When there is reflection from a slow medium to a fast medium there is no phase change.) Since the path difference is negligible, the two rays emerge in phase, and constructive interference (a bright area) is produced. This is the opposite of the result for light reflected from the same thin film. Bright transmission areas appear when the thickness is 0, $\lambda/2$, λ, $3\lambda/2$, etc. (Remember that the path difference is twice the film thickness.) Dark areas of destructive interference for transmission occur when the thickness is $\lambda/4$, $3\lambda/4$, $5\lambda/4$, etc. In all cases, λ is the wavelength of the light in the film material, which will be less than that in air by a factor of n, the index of refraction.

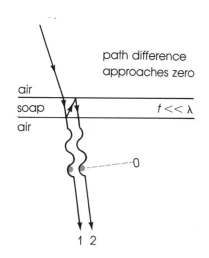

Light reflected from upper and lower surfaces of a thin film of oil lying on water

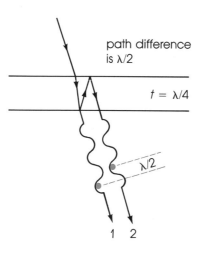

constructive interference (bright)

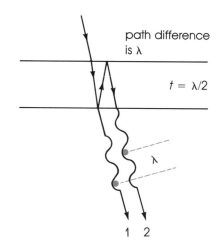

destructive interference (dark)

constructive interference (bright)

Note: The diagrams are schematic and not drawn to scale.

An important application of thin films is in the coating of the lenses found in optical instruments. A glass surface reflects about four per cent of the light passing through it. At each surface, internal reflections can create multiple or blurred images. Since a camera, for example, can contain up to ten separate lenses, this is a problem that cannot be ignored. These effects are reduced by applying a very thin coating on the surface of each lens, of such a thickness that light reflected from both surfaces of the coating interferes destructively. A coating material is chosen whose refractive index is midway between that for air and that for glass. In this way, the amount of reflection at each surface is about equal, and destructive reflected interference can occur for a chosen wavelength, depending on the thickness of the film. The usual choice is close to the midpoint of the visual spectrum (550 nm). Reflected light near the extremes of the spectrum — violet and red — will not be reduced very much, so the surface of the coated lens will appear purple — a mixture of red and violet reflected light. If multiple coatings are used, a wider range of wavelengths can be reduced. Reflected light cannot be entirely eliminated. Typically, a single coating reduces reflection to one per cent of the incident light.

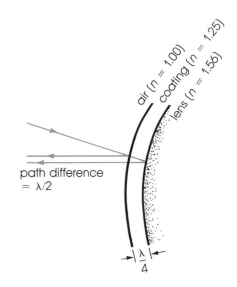

Mathematical Analysis of Interference in an Air Wedge

The spacing of successive dark fringes in the reflection interference pattern may be found as follows:

Using similar triangles,

$$\frac{x_n}{L} = \frac{n(\lambda/2)}{t} \qquad \text{or } x_n = \frac{Ln\lambda}{2t}$$

$$\frac{x_{n+1}}{L} = \frac{(n+1)(\lambda/2)}{t} \qquad \text{or } x_{n+1} = \frac{L(n+1)\lambda}{2t}$$

$$\Delta x = x_{n+1} - x_n = \frac{L(n+1)\lambda}{2t} - \frac{Ln\lambda}{2t}$$

$$\Delta x = L\left(\frac{\lambda}{2t}\right)$$

where L is the length of the air wedge
$\quad t$ is the thickness of the base of the wedge
$\quad \lambda$ is the wavelength of the light in the wedge

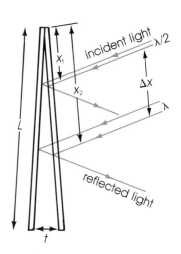

Interference in an air wedge

Sample problem

(a) What is the spacing of the dark fringes in an interference pattern reflected from an air wedge between two microscope slides 10 cm long, separated at one end by a paper of thickness 0.10 mm, illuminated with red light of wavelength 660 nm?

(b) How would the spacing change if the wedge were filled with water (refractive index 1.33)?

(a)
$$\Delta x = L\left(\frac{\lambda}{2t}\right) = (10 \text{ cm}) \left(\frac{6.60 \times 10^{-5} \text{ cm}}{2(1.0 \times 10^{-2} \text{ cm})}\right)$$

$$= 3.3 \times 10^{-2} \text{ cm, or } 0.33 \text{ mm}$$

(b) If air is replaced by water, $\lambda_{water} = \dfrac{\lambda_{air}}{n}$

$$= \frac{6.60 \times 10^{-5} \text{ cm}}{1.33}$$

$$= 4.96 \times 10^{-5} \text{ cm}$$

$$\Delta x = \frac{(10 \text{ cm})(4.96 \times 10^{-5} \text{ cm})}{2(1.0 \times 10^{-2} \text{ cm})}$$

$$= 2.5 \times 10^{-2} \text{ cm, or } 0.25 \text{ mm}$$

Practice

1. An air wedge 9.8 cm long is separated at one end by a piece of paper 1.9×10^{-3} cm thick. The distance between centres of the first and eighth successive dark bands is 1.23 cm. What is the wavelength of the light being used? $(6.8 \times 10^{-7} \text{ m})$

2. Light with a wavelength of 640 nm illuminates an air wedge 7.7 cm long. If the spacing between fringes is 0.19 cm, what is the thickness of the paper at the end of the air wedge?
$(1.3 \times 10^{-3} \text{ cm})$

Michelson's Interferometer

Albert Michelson (page 408) constructed an interferometer as illustrated on the next page. Monochromatic light strikes a half-silvered mirror M. (Such a mirror is called a **beam splitter**.) Half the light is reflected up to the movable mirror M_1, where it is reflected back and enters the eye of the observer. The other half is reflected back by the fixed mirror M_2, and is finally reflected by mirror M into the eye of the observer. If the two path lengths are identical, the two beams enter the eye in phase, and constructive interference occurs. If the movable mirror (M_1) is moved a distance equal to $\lambda/4$, one beam travels an extra distance of $\lambda/2$, and destructive interference occurs. If M_1 is moved farther, constructive or destructive interference occurs, depending on the path difference. If either M_1 or M_2 is tipped slightly, both constructive and destructive fringes will appear, because the path lengths are different for different points on the surface of the tilted mirror.

As the movable mirror M_1 is moved through a distance of $\lambda/2$, a given fringe will change from dark to light and back to dark again. However, the overall effect will be that the fringe pattern has shifted one position. (One dark fringe is replaced by the next dark fringe relative to a fixed reference point.) By counting the number of fringes that move laterally in this way, the total motion of the movable mirror can be calculated in terms of the wavelength of light. For example, if monochromatic light with a wavelength of 6.4×10^{-7} m is used in an interferometer, and 100 fringes move past the reference point, the path difference is 100 λ, or 6.4×10^{-5} m. The mirror has moved half this distance, or 3.2×10^{-5} m (0.032 mm).

Michelson used his interferometer to determine the length of the standard metre in terms of the wavelength of a red line in the cadmium spectrum. He was searching for a length standard that would be more precise, and also reproducible anywhere in the world. As we discussed in Chapter 1, this technique was accepted and the metre redefined in 1961, in terms of the wavelength of the orange-red line in the spectrum of krypton-86.

Another important historic use of the interferometer was to measure the velocity of light in various media by placing the transparent medium in one beam of the interferometer. These measurements further illustrate the relationship between the refractive index of a material and the velocity of light in it, another verification of the wave theory of light.

Probably the most famous use of this instrument was in Michelson's verification that the speed of light was constant, and independent of the motion of the observer. These important findings were used by Einstein in his Special Theory of Relativity, discussed in Chapter 17.

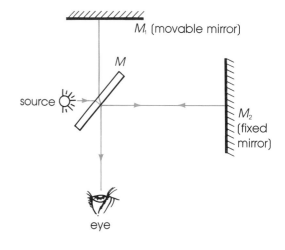

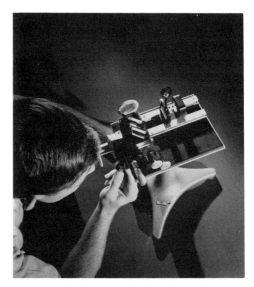

Using the Michelson interferometer

Wave Optics in a Videodisc

Recording on a Videodisc

When the video and audio components of a movie or television program are to be recorded, they are combined electronically. There are two waves involved. One radio wave contains the video information, and the other the audio information. When these waves are superimposed upon one another, interference occurs. The resultant radio wave is put through an electronic device called a limitter that shapes the resultant waveform into a "square wave". The square wave turns an infrared laser off and on, burning pits in the photoresist surface of the master disc. The pits formed are etched in a continuous spiral from the outside of the master disc to the inside. The spacing and the length of the pits record the original video and audio information in digital form.

The master disc is used to make copies for videodisc machines. These duplicate discs are made of transparent plastic on which a thin coating of aluminum has been placed. This acts as a reflector. When laser light is directed at this surface, it is reflected back. The intensity of the reflected light is determined by both the number and size of the pits.

The pit depth is designed to be one-quarter the wavelength of laser light in plastic. In thin films (see page 546), where the thickness is one-quarter of the wavelength of the reflected light.

the light reflected from the bottom surface is 180° out of phase compared to light from the top surface. The resulting interference produces a decrease in the intensity of the reflected light from the pits, compared to the non-pitted areas of the disc.

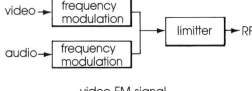

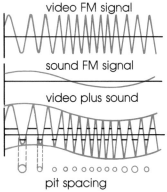

Encoding information onto a master disc

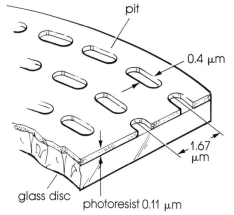

The thickness of the photoresist (0.11 μm) is exactly equal to $\lambda/4$ for helium-neon laser light.

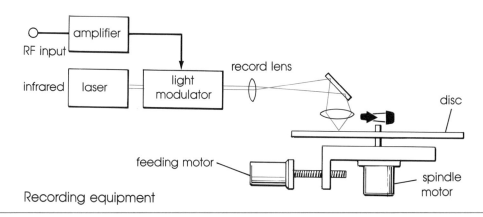

Recording equipment

Optical playback system

As illustrated in the diagram, the laser light is reflected by a series of mirrors and lenses, to make the system more compact.

The original laser beam is vertically plane polarized, so it is transmitted through the polarized beam splitter (P.B.S.) with no reflection. The light passes through a device called a quarter-wave plate on its way to the videodisc, and back through it after reflection. The quarter-wave plate affects the polarization of the wave in such a way that in the two transitions the beam emerges horizontally plane polarized. Because of this property, the beam splitter reflects

nearly all of the beam into the photodiode detector.

The variation in the intensity of light striking the photodiode produces an electric signal having the same characteristics as the original square wave etched on the master disc. Using electronic circuits, this electric signal is analysed, amplified, and transmitted by cable to a television receiver or monitor.

A similar technology is used in digital audiodisc systems, commonly called compact discs, or CDs. Since only the sound information is recorded digitally on the disc, the audiodisc has a smaller diameter than the

videodisc. The laser playback system is smaller and more compact than that in the videodisc machine since there are fewer tracking problems, but the operational principles are the same. The results represent a quantum leap over the quality of the stylus-and-groove players that have been used for years. There is little background distortion or background noise, each note has unvaried pitch, the dynamic range is superior, and discs last indefinitely, because there is no physical contact with the disc.

Compact disc

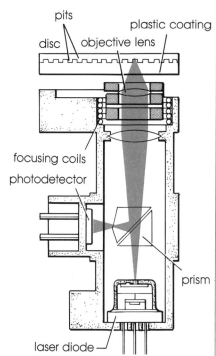

Videodisc

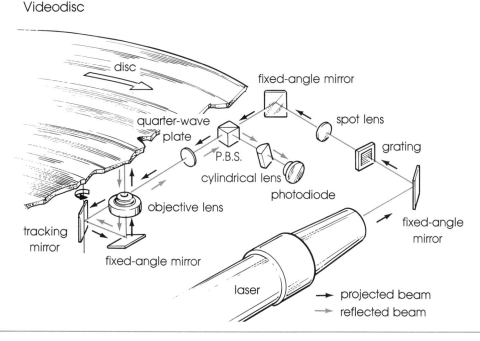

Holography

When a photograph is taken of your face, the image is recorded on the photographic film. With the appropriate lens located at the correct distance from the film, a sharp image is obtained. (If there were no lens in the camera, the pattern of scattered light on the film would be uniform and without detail.) But the lens only focuses the detail in one direction. To obtain a three-dimensional picture of your face, the camera would have to be moved to countless different positions.

A technique to produce a three-dimensional image on a single film was discovered in 1947 by a Hungarian-born physicist working in London at the Imperial College, Dr. Dennis Gabor. Dr. Gabor was in the midst of trying to improve the images created by the electron microscope (see page 717). Only small areas of the tiny object being viewed were in focus. He reasoned that the answer might lie in taking a bad electron picture, but one which had all the information radiated from the illuminated object. The area of interest could then be sharpened by optical means. In other words, he envisioned a method by which the picture would be taken, not of the scene itself, but of the light from the scene.

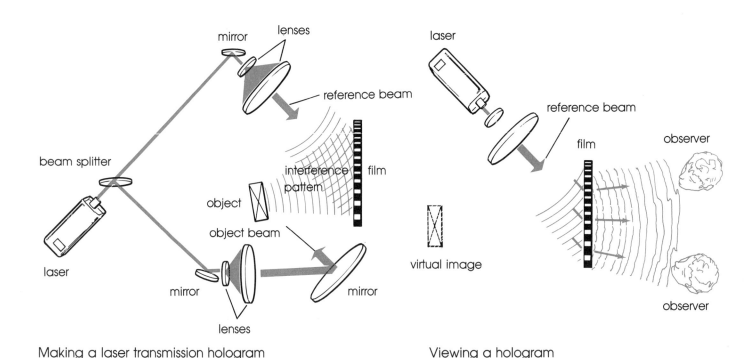

Making a laser transmission hologram   Viewing a hologram

Gabor's theories assumed that the light waves radiating from the various points on an illuminated object would interfere with each other and that therefore the images recorded on the photographic film would be the resulting interference patterns. After the film had been developed and light passed through it, the original image should be produced. Gabor called this film a **hologram**, from the Greek words "holos" and "gramma", meaning the "whole message."

Gabor was able to demonstrate that his ideas worked, using white light. However, the images, while three-dimensional, were anything but sharp. The problem was that white light is incoherent. It has a large range of frequencies that produce a jumble of interference patterns. The construction of the first lasers in 1960 provided a high intensity, coherent light source.

E.N. Leith and Juris Upatnieks, two American physicists working at the University of Michigan, produced the first laser holograph in 1963. They illuminated a subject with a laser beam that scattered the laser light onto a photographic film. From the first beam they split off a second reference beam, and used mirrors to direct it at the film. When light from the two beams interfered on its surface, the film recorded the interference pattern. To the naked eye it appeared as nothing but gray smudges. But when these patterns

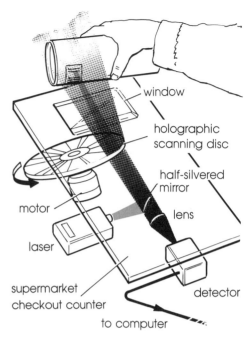

A low-powered laser bounces from a mirror to a rotating disc with 21 pie-shaped facets. Each facet is a separate hologram that directs the light in a unique direction, with a different angle, elevation, and focal length than the other facets. One of the sweeps will reach and be reflected by the Universal Product Code (UPC) on the grocery item, and will be reflected back to a photodetector that converts the optical signals to electric pulses. A computer then interprets the information and records the purchase.

Producing a three-dimensional image using a helium neon laser

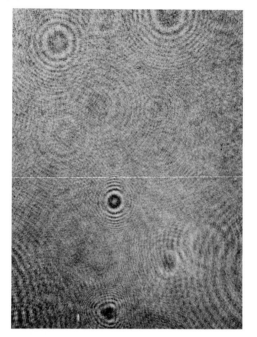

A hologram film

were illuminated with the same laser light, a three-dimensional holographic image was created. Nearly all scientific and commercial holographic images are now created this way. The tremendous implications of Dennis Gabor's work having been recognized, in 1971 he was awarded the Nobel Prize for Physics.

The technique of holography holds many potential applications. Today it is used to create holographic pictures of many different subjects. Using coherent ultrasonic sound waves to form a hologram, three-dimensional images of the internal structures and organs of the human body can be produced.

Holographic pictures appear on credit cards to discourage counterfeiters, and the principles of holography are used to record the bars and stripes of the Universal Product Code (UPC) that identifies the groceries scanned by a laser at a check-out counter (see diagram on previous page). Using laser light and an apparatus similar to Michelson's interferometer (see page 550), holography is used to find invisible defects in such products as tires, pipes, aircraft parts, computer disc drives, and even tennis rackets. In the future, holograms taken with X-ray lasers (yet to be developed) could provide detailed images of microscopic objects. Eventually, also, true three-dimensional films, television, and computer graphics will be produced by holography.

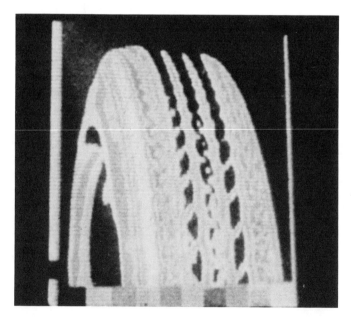

This hologram of a tire indicates any areas of tire separation.

Close-up of the tire hologram

14.8 Polarization

The phenomenon of interference is a crucial test for the wave theory of light, but it gives no clue as to whether light waves are transverse or longitudinal. (It is possible to produce a two-source interference pattern with longitudinal sound waves in air and with transverse water waves in a ripple tank.)

In 1669, Erasmus Bartholinus, a Danish scientist, noted that when he directed a single ray of light into a crystal of Iceland spar, or calcite, the ray was split into two rays. This effect can be observed if a calcite crystal is placed over a written word. As seen in the photograph, a double image is created by the two rays. What causes the light to split into two rays travelling along different paths?

The double image is created because light is polarized. Let us hypothesize that the vibrations in a light wave are transverse, and that the vibrations go in all directions, perpendicular to the direction in which the light is travelling. If such a transverse wave passes through a filter that allows the wave to vibrate only in one plane, then the wave has been **polarized**, as illustrated. This can be demonstrated using a mechanical model. Transverse waves generated in a rope that is moved up and down and then sideways in rapid succession are unpolarized transverse waves. If the rope passes through a vertical slit, the transmitted waves will vibrate only up and down, in the vertical plane. If these vertically polarized waves encounter a second slit, this time horizontal, the energy will be absorbed or reflected, and the wave transmission will be almost completely stopped.

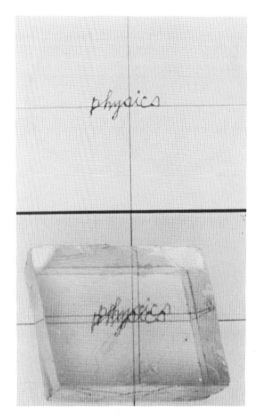

Polarization in a calcite crystal

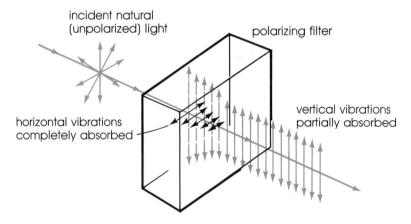

linearly polarized transmitted light

Vertically polarized waves in a rope are stopped almost completely by a horizontal polarizing slit.

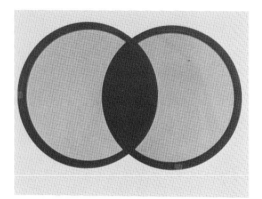

Polarizing lenses with axes
perpendicular

Polarizing lenses with axes parallel

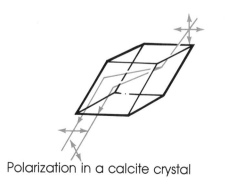

Polarization in a calcite crystal

When light is passed through a polarizing filter, the light waves are polarized in one plane. If the vertically polarized light next falls on a second filter that polarizes light in the horizontal plane, the light energy is almost completely absorbed. This occurs whenever the axes of the polarizing filters are at right angles to each other. When the axes of the two filters are parallel, the light polarized by the first filter passes through the second filter without further absorption (see photographs and illustrations).

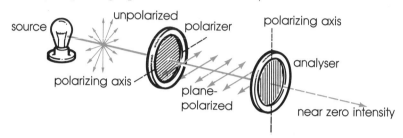

Could these results be explained by longitudinal waves? If light travelled as a longitudinal wave, the vibrations would vibrate in only one direction, namely, the direction in which the wave was travelling. Such a wave would pass through a pair of polarizing filters unaffected. In other words, a longitudinal wave cannot be polarized. Based on the polarization evidence, we may conclude that light, if it is wavelike, behaves like a transverse wave, not a longitudinal wave.

Longitudinal waves (in a spring above) pass through polarizing filters unaffected.

To go back to the calcite crystal used by Bartholinus, why did it produce two light rays from one? When the unpolarized light wave strikes the calcite crystal, it is separated by the crystal structure into two beams polarized at right angles, as illustrated. Experimentally, it is found that one of the beams does not obey Snell's Law in its simple form. For example, if monochromatic light with a wavelength of 590 nm strikes a calcite crystal, it is found that the refractive index of one beam has a constant value of 1.66, whereas the other beam shows an index of refraction varying from 1.49 to 1.66, depending on the angle of incidence. This difference suggests that the light beams travel through the crystal at different speeds, determined by the orientation of the planes within the crystal structure. The analysis of this phenomenon is extremely complex.

Calcite, tourmaline, and other naturally occurring polarizing crystals proved to be scarce and fragile, and polarization was a laboratory curiosity until 1928. Then Edwin H. Land, still a student at a university, invented a synthetic, polarizing plastic sheet he called **Polaroid**. The original polarizer was made of microscopic, needle-like crystals of herapathite. He later improved on this by using long crystals of iodine. With the second polarizer, many applications for everyday use became possible.

Light is polarized naturally in many ways. One of the most common is by reflection. Light reflected from a flat surface, such as a body of water or a road, is partially polarized in the horizontal plane. The polarizing filters in Polaroid sunglasses are arranged in the vertical plane, and therefore absorb the horizontally polarized light reflected from the flat surface. This reduces the glare coming from the reflecting surface.

Materials such as glass and Lucite, which become doubly refractive when subjected to mechanical stress, are said to be **photoelastic**. When a photoelastic material is placed between polarizing and analysing discs, the strain patterns (and thus the stress distributions) are revealed, as shown in the photographs. Engineers find this a useful technique. Models of an object to be tested are made of Lucite plastic. When the models are placed under mechanical stress, areas of stress concentration are easily observable, and design changes can be made before the object is constructed.

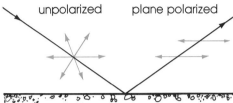

Light reflected by a non-metallic surface is partially polarized in the horizontal plane.

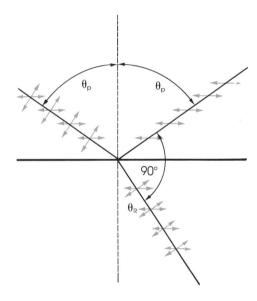

The amount of polarization by reflection depends on the angle of incidence. It varies from zero polarization, when $\angle i = 0°$, to 100% polarization at a specific angle of incidence known as the *polarizing angle* (θ_p), or the *Brewster angle*. At the Brewster angle, the reflected and refracted rays are at an angle of 90° to one another, that is, $\theta_p + \theta_R = 90°$.

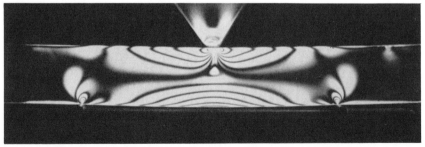

The sun's light becomes polarized when it is scattered in the atmosphere. You can test this by rotating a Polaroid sheet while looking through it at the sky. The amount of polarization will depend on the direction in which you look, and will be greatest at 90° to the direction of the sun. Photographers use Polaroid filters to enhance photographs of sky and clouds. If the filters are aligned properly, the blue polarized light is absorbed while the white light

The bottom photograph was taken by the same camera, with a Polaroid filter in front of the lens.

Although we talk about transverse vibrations associated with light, it is, in fact, transverse magnetic and electric fields that are rapidly fluctuating as the light wave travels through space or a material (see Chapter 16).

from the clouds passes through. In the photograph, the sky appears darker compared to the white clouds.

Our eyes require an external polarizing filter if we are to detect polarized light. The eyes of certain creatures, such as ants, horseshoe crabs, and honey bees, are sensitive to polarized light, and they can use the polarized light from the sky as a navigational aid.

14.9 Waves and Light — A Status Report

By the end of the 19th century, the wave theory of light was the accepted theory. It had been used to explain reflection, refraction, diffraction, dispersion, interference, and polarization. The discoveries made by Foucault and others between 1850 and 1870, that the speed of light in glass and water was considerably less than in air, provided the last pieces of evidence. Two questions remained to be answered. First, what was the medium that transmitted the energy of light in the form of a transverse wave? Second, what was the nature of the wave's vibrations?

In Chapters 12 and 13 we described a wave as a disturbance that travels in some substance, or medium, such as a rope, a spring, or water in a ripple tank. But light travels through the vacuum of space with no difficulty. As we saw, scientists tried to explain this phenomenon by promoting the idea of the "ether". But Michelson and Morley showed experimentally that the "ether" does not exist. Light simply does not require a medium for its transmission.

The failure of the wave theory to explain this property of light may be disappointing, but our observations have shown us that it is still an extremely useful theory. It will simply have to be modified to explain the transmission of light in a vacuum. This modification will utilize some of the concepts originally expressed in Newton's corpuscular theory, supplemented by the work of Planck, Einstein, and others. We will leave this discussion to Chapter 18.

The answer to the second question asked above, concerning the nature of the vibrations transmitted by light, was given by James Maxwell (1831-79), a Scottish physicist. He predicted that, when electric charges vibrate, they should generate transverse waves that travel through a vacuum at the speed of light. He called them **electromagnetic waves**. To understand what is meant by electromagnetic waves, we must have some basic knowledge of electricity and magnetism. These topics will be discussed in the next two chapters.

14.10 Investigations

Investigation 14.1: Double-Slit Interference — Young's Experiment

Problem:
(a) What interference pattern is produced when light passes through two closely spaced, narrow slits?
(b) What are the wavelengths of light as it is transmitted in various colours?

Materials:

clear, showcase lamp   helium-neon laser
metre rule   white screen
retort stand and clamp   red and green transparent filters
double-slit plate
commercial diffraction gratings
single-slit plate

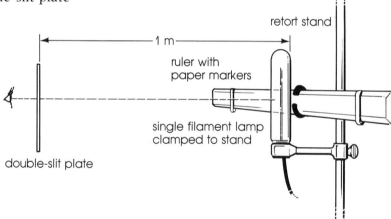

Procedure:

Part A
1. Set up the apparatus as illustrated, making certain that the slits are parallel to the filament of the lamp. View the clear lamp through the double slit. Describe the pattern seen on either side of the lamp filament.
2. Cover the upper half of the bulb with the green filter and the lower half with the red filter, holding each in place with rubber bands. Compare the interference pattern observed for green light with that observed for red light.

3. Cover the lamp completely with the red filter. Using the ruler mounted behind the light, count the number of nodal lines visible in a fixed distance. The distance can be fixed by paper sliders on the ruler.

4. Leaving the paper sliders in place, replace the red filter with the green filter. View the interference pattern from the same position as in step 3, and count the number of nodal lines visible between the paper sliders.

5. Using the number of nodal lines counted for the same viewing distance in steps 3 and 4 above, determine the ratio, number of red lines/number of green lines, and from this ratio $\lambda_{red}/\lambda_{green}$.

6. Cover the lamp completely with the red filter. View the red light through the double slit from a distance of exactly 1.0 m from the ruler. Adjust the paper sliders so that they are located on two nodal lines at opposite ends of the pattern. Count the number of bright lines between the markers. Measure the distance between the paper sliders, and calculate the average separation of adjacent nodal lines (Δx).

7. Using the relationship $\lambda = \Delta x(d/L)$ (see Section 14.4), determine the wavelength of the red light. The value of d, the distance between the slits, is either recorded on the slit plate or can be obtained from your instructor. L is the perpendicular distance from the slits to the ruler (1.0 m).

8. Repeat the procedure in steps 6 and 7, this time for green light.

Part B
CAUTION: Low-power helium-neon laser light can cause temporary retinal damage. DO NOT look into the laser beam or into the reflection of the beam from a shiny surface.

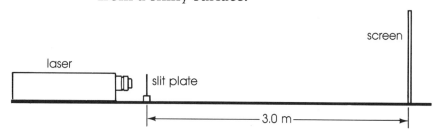

9. Direct the laser light through a double slit onto the screen, located at least 3 m away. Measure the distance over at least seven bright points, and determine Δx. Determine the wavelength of the helium-neon laser light, using the relationship from step 7.

10. Repeat step 9 for one other pair of slits that has a different slit separation (d).
11. The value for the wavelength of helium-neon laser light is 6.328×10^{-7} m. Determine the experimental error for the average of your two calculations above.
12. As noted in the investigation concerning the interference of water waves between two point sources (page 507), both the separation of the sources (d) and the wavelength (λ) affected the number of nodal lines produced. Using your results from steps 5, 9, and 10, determine the effects of both source separation and wavelength on the nodal line structure for light. Compare these results with those observed for water wave interference.
13. When laser light is transmitted through a series of narrow parallel slits that are closely spaced, each slit produces a diffraction pattern that overlaps the patterns produced by the others. If the slits are evenly spaced, a pattern results that is very similar to that produced by a double slit, except that the pattern is much brighter. Because it is much brighter, it can be spread out more by moving the screen farther away. The same relationship, $\lambda = \Delta x(d/L)$, holds, except that d represents the separation of the individual slits in the diffraction grating. Place the diffraction grating in front of the laser beam. Calculate the wavelength as you did for the double slit, determining the separation (Δx) by measuring the distance over seven bright spots on the screen. Determine the experimental error.
14. Repeat step 13 with a diffraction grating having a different slit separation (d).
15. Why is this investigation so important in validating the Wave Theory of Light?

Investigation 14.2: Diffraction of Light in a Single Slit

Problem:
(a) What are the conditions for the diffraction of light?
(b) What is the relationship between the wavelength of light and the amount of diffraction?
(c) What are the characteristics of the diffraction pattern produced by a single slit?

Materials:

long-filament, showcase lamp   helium-neon laser
red and green transparent filters   diverging lens
single-slit plate   white screen
2 new razor blades   metric measuring tape
2 diffraction gratings

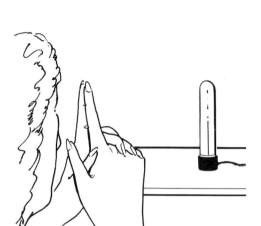

Procedure:

1. Set up the lamp so that the filament is vertical.

2. Press the pads of your two forefingers against each other, creating a small slit. The slit width can be changed by changing the pressure of your finger tips.

3. Position your finger slit so that it is parallel to the filament of the lamp. Vary the width of the slit, observing any changes in the light passing through the slit. What size of slit is required to produce diffraction of light? What does this indicate about the size of the wavelength of light?

4. View the long filament again, this time using a prepared slit. Record your observations in a simple sketch.

5. Attach both the red and the green filters to the lamp with an elastic band so that very little white light is emitted in the direction of the single slit. Do not let the filters overlap. Simultaneously, view the red light and green light through the single slit. When you compare the diffraction of red and of green light, which do you conclude has the longer wavelength? Why?

6. Remove the filters from the lamp so that only white light is emitted. View the white light through the single slit. What colours do you observe, in addition to the white light? Are the colours in any special order? What does this indicate to you about the various wavelengths of the spectral colours?

7. Cover the lamp completely with the red filter. View the red light through a series of single slits with different widths. Describe the changes in the pattern as the slit width (w) is increased. (The distance from the slit to the light and the wavelength are kept constant.) How is the width of the central maximum affected by changes in the slit width? How does the size of the slit width affect the distance to the first nodal line (y)? Write your answer as a proportion involving w and y.

8. Viewing the light through a narrow, single slit, slowly move the slit away from the light source and then back towards it. What is the relationship between the distance from the central line to the first minimum (y), and the distance from the light source to the first minimum (L)? Write your answer as a proportion.

9. Cover the light source with the red and green filters so that the upper half emits red light and the lower half green. Keeping the distance from the light fixed, compare the displacement of the first minimum from the central line (y) for red and for green light. Which has the larger value? What is the relationship between y and the wavelength of light (λ)? Express your answer as a proportion.

10. Combine the proportionality statements in the last three steps into one proportionality statement involving y, L, w, and λ. Make λ the dependent variable.

> **CAUTION: Low-power helium-laser light can cause temporary retinal damage. DO NOT look into the laser beam or into the reflection of the beam from a shiny surface.**

11. Using the helium-neon laser, aim the beam at the white screen located approximately 1 m from the laser. Slowly slide the edge of one razor blade into one side of the beam. Describe the results produced on the screen.

12. Using magnets, position two razor blades on the laser, one on each side. Direct the laser beam at the screen. Slowly decrease the slit width created by the two razor blades, recording any changes in the pattern on the screen.

13. Pass the laser beam through a commercially prepared, narrow, single slit, then enlarge the beam with a diverging lens. Describe the pattern that falls on the screen.

14. (Optional) Using a sensitive photometer in a darkened room, record the light intensity variations that occur at 0.5 cm intervals as the photometer is moved across the screen from one end of the pattern to the other. Plot a graph of light intensity versus distance, fixing zero distance at the centre of the pattern.

15. With the screen still located 1 m in front of the laser aperture, remove the single slit, and mark on the screen the exact middle of the laser beam. Measure the distance from the laser aperture to this point on the screen (L).

16. Place a single slit in the beam of the laser so that a diffraction pattern is produced on the screen. Some adjustment of the slit may be necessary to ensure that the exact middle of the central maximum strikes the point marked on the screen in step 15.

17. Measure the distances, on the screen, from the centre of the central maximum to the first nodal line on each side of the pattern. Average the two measurements (y_1).

18. Record the width (w) of the single slit. Using the relationship $\lambda = \dfrac{wy}{L}$, determine the wavelength of the light.

19. The wavelength of helium-neon laser light is 6.328×10^{-7} m. Compare your value with this figure by calculating your percentage error.

20. Repeat steps 16 to 19, using a different slit. This time, since the wavelength of light is known, determine the width of the slit. Ask your instructor for the correct value, and determine your experimental error.

Investigation 14.3: Interference in Thin Films and Air Wedges

Problem:
(a) What is the pattern of interference in a thin soap film?
(b) How can air wedges be used to measure either the wavelength of light or the thickness of material?

Materials:

soap-glycerine solution	helium-neon laser
clear, showcase lamp	white screen
wire loop	air wedge
diverging lens (-8 mm)	tissue paper
converging lens ($+167$ mm)	aluminum foil
microscope slide	red and green transparent filters

Procedure:
1. Cover the clear, showcase lamp with the red filter.
2. Dip the wire loop into the soap solution. Holding the loop in a vertical position, view the soap film by reflected red light. Describe the interference pattern observed on the film over a period of at least 1 min, recording any changes. (Note the brightness at the top of the pattern where the film is thinnest.)
3. Remove the red filter on the light and replace it with the green filter. Repeat step 2, observing similarities and differences between the red and the green interference patterns.
4. Remove the filter from the light so that white light strikes the soap film, and repeat the procedure. Compare the interference pattern seen with the white light with those observed for red and green light. Using the wave theory of light described in the text (Section 14.7), explain (a) the general appearance of the pattern, (b) the variation in the spacing of the horizontal interference bands, and (c) the appearance of the film in the area near the top.
5. Arrange the white light and the soap film so that the light passes through the film. How does the interference pattern for

transmitted light differ from that for reflected light? Explain, using the wave theory of light.

6. Place the diverging lens (−8 mm) and the converging lens (+167 mm) in the laser beam. Adjust their separation so that a spot about 15 cm in diameter is produced on the screen, 1 m away.

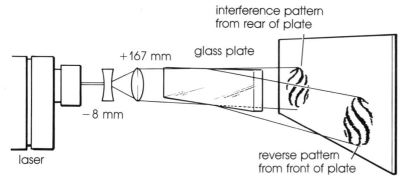

7. Place a microscope slide in the beam so that its surface makes a 90° angle with the beam. Move the slide slightly, and note the interference pattern on the screen.

8. Adjust the position of the microscope slide so that it is almost parallel to the beam. Both transmitted and reflected light should now produce interference patterns on the screen. Record the similarities and the differences between the two interference patterns. Use your knowledge of the wave theory of light and the phase changes that occur when light waves are reflected at the interfaces between air and glass to explain your observations.

9. Mount the air wedge in front of the laser beam, as illustrated. Enlarge the laser beam by placing the diverging lens in the beam, after it has passed through the air wedge. Place the

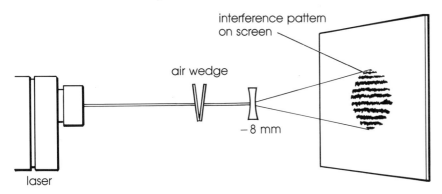

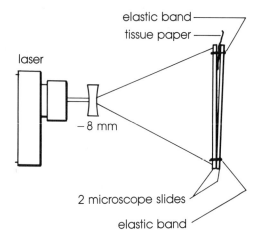

laser

elastic band
tissue paper
−8 mm
2 microscope slides
elastic band

screen 1-2 m away. Rotate the air wedge so that it is at an angle of approximately 20° with the laser beam, producing pronounced dark fringes on the screen.

10. Vary the thickness of the air film wedge by squeezing the glass plates together. Record any changes in the interference pattern.

11. Construct an air wedge, using two microscope slides attached together with elastic bands, as illustrated. Separate the ends of the glass plates at one end and insert a single thickness of tissue paper between them.

12. Place the diverging lens in front of the laser beam so that a diverging laser light illuminates the air wedge.

13. Measure the distance covered by four or more bright fringes. (Consider one bright fringe to be from the middle of one dark fringe to the middle of the next dark fringe.) Find the average separation between adjacent dark fringes.

14. Measure the total length of the air wedge. Using the relationship $\Delta x = L(\lambda/2t)$, determine the thickness of the tissue paper ($\lambda = 6.328 \times 10^{-7}$ m).

15. With a micrometer, measure the thickness of ten pieces of tissue paper placed together, and then calculate the thickness of one piece of paper. Compare the paper thickness values measured by each method. Calculate the percentage difference.

16. Repeat the procedure in steps 12 to 15, this time placing one thickness of aluminum foil in one end of the air wedge.

17. Explain how interference can be used to determine whether a piece of metal has been ground flat.

14.11 Review

Discussion

1. Newton hypothesized in his Corpuscular Theory that light particles must have extremely small masses. How would you show that this was true, experimentally?

2. When a ''particle'' such as a steel ball strikes a hard surface, its speed is usually reduced. How do you know that the speed of light does not change when it is reflected?

3. Why can light be described both as waves and as rays?

4. When a screen is illuminated by two closely spaced, parallel, single-filament light sources, no interference is observed. What major condition for interference has not been satisfied?
5. Using a laser of known wavelength, how might you determine the separation of two slits? The width of a single slit?
6. If Young's Experiment were done completely in glass, how would the interference pattern change from that observed in air, using the same equipment and experimental set-up?
7. Sound diffracts easily, light does not. Explain.
8. What is the maximum width of a single slit that will produce no nodal lines? Express your answer in terms of the incident wavelength.
9. Why is a diffraction grating superior to a prism when used in a spectroscope?
10. Interference fringes can be seen in a thin film, like a soap bubble, but not in a thick piece of glass. Explain.
11. When seen by reflected light, a soap bubble appears dark at its top edge, where it is thinnest; yet the film from an oil drop on water appears bright at its edges, where it is thinnest. Account for the difference.
12. Coated camera lenses appear purple when seen by reflected white light. Explain.
13. How could Michelson's interferometer be used to determine the index of refraction of air or water?
14. Light can be polarized when it passes through certain substances in solution, such as sugar, insulin, and collagen. The resulting polarization has enabled scientists to obtain much information on the shape and other properties of molecules in such solutions. Do some research, then write a short report describing one example of this phenomenon.
15. Write a short report on Huygens' work related to wave theory.
16. Laser beams have many applications in medicine and manufacturing. Describe in 300 words or less one application in each area.
17. Holography is opening up new frontiers in science that may affect our lives. In 200 words or less, describe an application of holography.

Problems

18. The index of refraction of one type of glass is 1.50. According to the particle theory of light, what should be the speed of light in that glass?

"The aims of scientific thought are to see the general in the particular and the eternal in the transitory."
Alfred North Whitehead

19. Light travels in water at three-quarters the speed it travels in air. If the angle of incidence in air is 30°, what would the angle of refraction be in water, according to a particle theorist? According to a wave theorist?

20. The wavelengths of the visible spectrum range from 400 nm to 750 nm. What is the range of the frequencies of visible light?

21. A radiation has a frequency of 3.75×10^{14} Hz. What is its wavelength? In what part of the spectrum is this radiation found? Assume that the radiation travels at the speed of light.

22. A certain shade of red light has a wavelength in air of 7.5×10^{-7} m. If the index of refraction of alcohol relative to air is 1.40, what is the wavelength of this red light in alcohol?

23. A student doing Young's Experiment measures a distance of 6.0 cm between the first and seventh nodal points on a screen located 3.0 m from the slit plate.
    (a) If the slit separation is 220 μm, what is the wavelength of the light being used?
    (b) What is the colour of the light?

24. With two slits 0.12 mm apart, and a screen at a distance of 80 cm, the third bright line to one side of centre in an interference pattern is found to be displaced 9.0 mm from the central line. What was the wavelength of the light used? What colour was it?

25. Red light, of wavelength 600 nm, passes through two parallel slits. Nodal lines are produced on a screen 3.0 m away. The distance between the 1st and the 10th nodal lines is 5.0 cm. What is the separation of the two slits?

26. A student measuring the wavelength of a narrow, monochromatic source uses a double slit with a separation of 0.15 mm. A second student places markers on a screen 2.0 m in front of the slits at the positions of successive dark bands in the pattern. She finds that the dark bands are 0.56 cm apart.
    (a) Calculate the wavelength of the source in nanometres.
    (b) Calculate what the spacing of the dark bands would be if a source of wavelength 600 nm were used.

27. In an interference experiment, red light with a wavelength of 6.0×10^{-7} m passes through a double slit. On a screen 1.5 m away, the distance between the 1st and 11th dark bands is 2.0 cm.
    (a) What was the separation of the slits?
    (b) What would the spacing be, between adjacent nodal lines, if blue light were used? ($\lambda_{blue} = 4.5 \times 10^{-7}$ m)

28. Monochromatic light from a point source illuminates two parallel, narrow slits. The centres of the slit openings are 0.80 mm apart. An interference pattern forms on a screen placed parallel to the plane of the slits and 50 cm away. The distance between two adjacent dark interference fringes is 0.30 mm.
    (a) Determine the wavelength of the light.
    (b) What would be the separation of the nodal lines if the slit centres were narrowed to 0.60 mm?

29. Monochromatic sodium light (589 nm) passes through a single slit 1.10×10^{-3} cm wide. If a screen is placed 2.00 m from the slit, calculate the positions of the first and second minimums, measured from the centre of the pattern.

30. If 600 nm light falls on a single slit 1.5×10^{-2} mm wide, what is the angular width of the central maximum?

31. When 640 nm light passes through a single slit, the central maximum produced on a screen 2.0 m away is 8.0 cm wide. What is the width of the slit?

32. Monochromatic light is directed through a slit 1.0×10^{-2} mm wide. If the angle contained between the first minimum on either side of the central maximum is 8°, what is the wavelength of the light?

33. A diffraction grating has 1000 slits/cm. When blue light ($\lambda = 480$ nm) is directed through the grating, what will be the separation of the bright points on a screen 4.00 m away?

34. A soap film with a thickness of 93 nm has a refractive index of 1.35. When viewed perpendicularly in white light, what colour is strongly reflected?

35. A camera lens ($n = 1.52$) is coated with a film of magnesium fluoride ($n = 1.25$). What should the least thickness of the film be to minimize reflected light with a wavelength of 550 nm?

36. Two plane glass surfaces are separated by an air film with a uniform thickness of 870 nm. If the film is illuminated perpendicularly by light having a wavelength of 580 nm, predict whether a bright or dark area will be seen by reflected light.

37. Light with a wavelength of 550 nm is used in a Michelson interferometer.
    (a) If 100 fringes move by the reference point, how far has the movable mirror shifted?
    (b) If the mirror moves 0.30 mm, how many fringes will move past the reference point?

Numerical Answers to Review Problems

18. 4.50×10^8 m/s
19. 42°, 22°
20. 7.50×10^{14} Hz to 4.00×10^{14} Hz
21. 8.00×10^{-7} m, infrared
22. 5.4×10^{-7} m
23. (a) 7.3×10^{-7} m (b) red
24. 4.5×10^{-7} m, blue
25. 3.2×10^{-4} m
26. (a) 4.2×10^2 nm (b) 8.0×10^{-3} m
27. (a) 4.5×10^{-4} m (b) 1.5×10^{-3} m
28. (a) 4.8×10^{-7} m (b) 4.0×10^{-4} m
29. 10.7 cm, 21.4 cm
30. 4.6°
31. 3.2×10^{-5} m
32. 7.0×10^{-7} m
33. 19.2 cm
34. green (5.0×10^{-7} m)
35. 1.1×10^{-7} m
36. dark
37. (a) 2.8×10^{-5} m (b) 1090 fringes

For incident light not perpendicular to the film, the path difference created by the thin film depends on the angle of refraction as well as the thickness of the film. The larger the angle of incidence, the greater the path difference.

15 Electric Charges and Electric Fields

15.1 Electric Charge and the Electrical Structure of Matter

Chapters 1 to 10, on mechanics, discussed some of the properties of forces in general, and of the force of gravity in particular. However, gravitational forces are not the only forces that can act between objects. For example, a small magnet will lift a nail off the ground, overcoming the gravitational attraction of the entire Earth; a comb rubbed on your sweater will then lift small pieces of paper. In the first case, the force that is acting is a magnetic one; in the second case, the force is electric. The utilization of these forces has played a major role in the development of the way we live in the 20th century. They are also fundamental to our understanding of the structure of all matter, and form the basis for our study in this part of the book.

The existence of electrical forces has been known since the days of the early Greeks, when scientists observed that amber, rubbed, could attract small bits of dried straw. They called this phenomenon "the amber effect". The Greek word for amber is "elektron" and the effect soon became known as "electriks", or electricity.

Any material that behaved like rubbed amber was said to be electrified, or electrically charged. Materials that showed no amber effect were said to be neutral.

Systematic study of electricity began only during the Renaissance, when it was found that many other substances, not only amber, became electrified when rubbed. It was also observed that these substances fell into two distinct categories. In the first case, when two pieces of the same material were electrified by being rubbed with a third material, they always repelled each other. But when each was rubbed with a different material, they either attracted or repelled each other, depending on the other materials.

There seemed to be two "electric states". Benjamin Franklin first identified these two states, and he gave them the names that we still use today — positive charges and negative charges. He concluded that all objects possess electricity and that a neutral object possesses what he called a "normal" amount. To charge an object positively, he thought, meant adding to the normal amount of electricity, whereas to charge an object negatively meant taking away from the normal amount.

For purposes of identification, he described as "negative" the charge that an ebonite rod acquires when rubbed with fur. Accordingly, any other charged object that is repelled by such a charged ebonite rod must likewise be charged negatively. Conversely, any charged object that is attracted to a charged ebonite rod, such as a glass rod rubbed with silk, must be charged positively.

Now we can state the fundamental Law of Electric Charges:

Opposite electric charges attract each other.
Similar electric charges repel each other.
Charged objects attract some neutral objects.

To understand fully how a charged object, whether positive or negative, can attract a neutral object, we need to understand something of the structure of matter. Fortunately, scientists have met this need by providing a simple model of the structure of matter that we can use to explain electrification. (A more detailed model of the present concept of the structure of matter will be discussed in Chapter 19.)

A Simple Model of the Structure of Matter

Scientists have developed highly sophisticated and extremely accurate models of the structure of solids, liquids, and gases. But, for a basic understanding of the electrical effects under consideration here, a rather simpler model, often used just before the turn of the century, will serve us well enough.

The principal concepts embodied in this model may be summarized as follows:

1. All matter is composed of sub-microscopic particles, called **atoms**.
2. Electric charges are carried by particles within each atom that are called **electrons** and **protons**.
3. Protons are found in a small central region of the atom, called the **nucleus**. They are small, heavy particles, and each one carries a positive electric charge of a specific magnitude, called the **elementary charge**.
4. Electrons move about in the vast space around this central nucleus. They are small, very light particles (each with only slightly more than 1/2000th the mass of a proton), yet each of them carries a negative electric charge equal in magnitude to that of the proton.
5. Atoms are normally electrically neutral, because the number of positive protons in the nucleus is equal to the number of negative electrons moving around the nucleus.

6. **Neutrons** are small, heavy particles (each slightly heavier than a proton) found in the nucleus, and they carry no electric charge.

7. An atom may gain electrons. Then it is no longer neutral, but instead has an excess of electrons and, therefore, a net negative charge. Such an atom is called a **negative ion**.

8. An atom may also lose electrons. As a result, it will have a deficit of electrons and, therefore, a net positive charge. Such an atom is called a **positive ion**.

Consider, first, the electrical effects in solids. The atoms of a solid are held tightly in place; their nuclei are not free to move about within the solid. Since these fixed nuclei contain all of the protons, the amount of positive charge in a solid remains constant and fixed in position. However, it is possible for some of the negative charges within some solids to move, for electrons have the ability to move from atom to atom, especially those farthest from the nucleus.

Objects that are negatively charged have an excess of electrons. Objects positively charged have a deficit of electrons. Both types always have their normal number of protons.

All electric charges in solids result from either an excess or a deficit of electrons.

Most solids fall into one of two broad categories, so far as their electrical properties are concerned — conductors and insulators.

A conductor is a solid in which electrons are able to move easily from one atom to another. Most metals are excellent conductors, some common ones being silver, copper, and aluminum. Some of the electrons in these conductors have been called "free electrons", for the way they can move about within the atomic framework of the solid.

An insulator is a solid in which the electrons are not free to move about easily from atom to atom. Plastic, cork, glass, wood, and rubber are all excellent insulators.

Certain liquids are also conductors of electricity, while others are not. The molecules of a liquid are free to move about. In an insulator these molecules are neutral, so there is no net movement of electric charge through the liquid. If, however, the molecules of the liquid are charged particles (positive and negative ions) the liquid will become a conductor. For example, pure water is an insulator; its molecules are neutral. However, when a chemical such as table salt (or copper sulphate, potassium nitrate, hydrochloric acid, etc.) is added to the water, the solution becomes a conductor. Many chemicals dissociate (break apart) into positive and negative ions when dissolved in water, and it is the presence of these charged particles that makes the solution capable of conducting electric current.

Recently, a new category of electrical materials has been developed, called semiconductors. A semiconductor is a material that is intermediate between a conductor and an insulator, in that it has very few free electrons for conduction in its pure, or "intrinsic", state. Semiconductors become very useful in the conduction of electricity, however, when a small amount of a particular impurity is added to them, in a process called "doping". Semiconductors are solids at normal temperatures, so that the field of semiconductor physics is referred to as "solid state". The most commonly used semiconductors are silicon and germanium. Transistors and integrated circuits made from semiconductors have revolutionized electronics.

Gases, also, can be either conductors or insulators, depending on the electrical nature of their molecules. A charged object exposed to dry air will remain charged for a long time, which shows us that air cannot discharge the object by conduction. On the other hand, if the air were exposed to X-rays or nuclear radiation, the object would begin to discharge immediately. Again, the molecules of a gas are normally neutral, but the presence of X-rays or other radiation can cause these neutral gas molecules to ionize (break apart into positive and negative ions), and the ionized gas that results becomes a good conductor. Humid air, containing a large number of water molecules in the form of water vapour, is also a good conductor, because water molecules are able to partially separate into positive and negative charges. More importantly, there are usually dissolved materials that ionize.

It is currently believed that a fourth state of matter exists, often at very high temperatures, called a "plasma", that has very different properties from the three traditional states of matter. Essentially, a plasma is a very hot collection of positive and negative ions, and electrons. Examples of plasmas range from neon lights to nuclear fusion reactions.

15.2 Transfer of Electric Charge

Electric charges on solid objects result from an excess or deficit of electrons. The charging of an object, then, simply requires a transfer of electrons to or away from the object. If electrons are removed from the object, it will be charged positively; if electrons are added, it will be charged negatively.

Neutral and charged objects can be represented by sketches, with positive and negative signs marked on the objects, as shown.

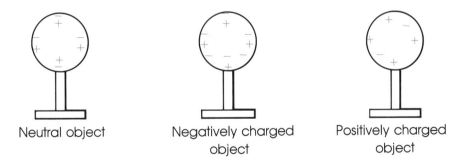

Neutral object   Negatively charged object   Positively charged object

The number of + and − signs is not intended to represent the actual number of positive and negative charges on an object, but is merely a way of representing an excess, a deficit, or a balance between the number of negative and positive charges on the object. Notice that in the above example the number of + signs is the same in each case, and they are fixed in position, in a regular pattern.

Charging By Friction

In Section 15.1 you read that some substances acquire an electric charge when rubbed with another substance. For example, an ebonite rod became negatively charged when rubbed with fur. We can explain this phenomenon with the help of the model of the electrical structure of matter described in Section 15.1.

An atom holds on to its electrons by the force of electrical attraction to its oppositely-charged nucleus. Some atoms exert stronger forces of attraction on their electrons than others. When ebonite and fur are rubbed together, some of the electrons from the fur are "captured" by the atoms of the ebonite, which exert stronger forces of attraction on them than do the atoms making up the fur. Thus, after rubbing, the ebonite has an excess of electrons and the fur has a deficit.

The same explanation holds for many other pairs of substances, such as glass and silk. The electrostatic series table lists many of the substances that can be charged by friction. If two substances in the table are rubbed together, the substance that is higher in the table becomes negatively charged, while the other substance becomes positively charged.

An electroscope is a simple device that can be used to detect and compare electric charges. Most electroscopes are variations of the metal-leaf electroscope shown.

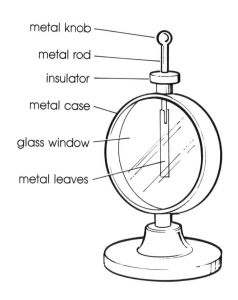

metal knob

metal rod

insulator

metal case

glass window

metal leaves

Metal-leaf electroscope

A charge transferred to the knob of the electroscope spreads out over the entire conducting system, including the leaves, causing them to diverge and so to indicate the presence of a charge. A greater divergence of the leaves indicates an increase in the charge. The instrument detects positive and negative charges equally well.

Electrostatic Series

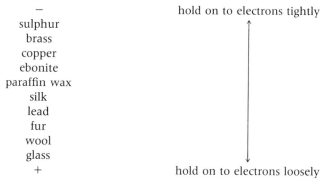

—
sulphur
brass
copper
ebonite
paraffin wax
silk
lead
fur
wool
glass
+

hold on to electrons tightly

hold on to electrons loosely

Induced Charge Separation

The positive charges on a solid conductor are fixed and cannot move. Some of the negative electrons are quite free to move about from atom to atom. When a negatively charged ebonite rod is brought near a neutral, metallic-coated pith ball or metal-leaf electroscope, some of the many free electrons are repelled by the ebonite rod and move to the far side of the pith ball or metal-leaf electroscope (conductor).

The separation of charge on each of these objects is caused by the presence of the negative distribution of charge on the ebonite rod. This separation is called an **induced charge separation**.

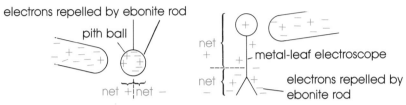

Induced charge separation caused by the presence of a charged ebonite rod

A charge separation will also result from the presence of a positively charged rod.

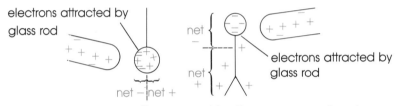

Induced charge separation caused by the presence of a charged glass rod

In both examples involving the neutral pith ball, the charge induced on the near side of the pith ball is of opposite type to the charge on the rod. As a result, the pith ball is attracted to the rod, whether the rod is charged postively or negatively. This is how a charged object can attract some neutral objects, as was mentioned in Section 15.1.

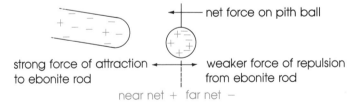

Attraction of a neutral pith ball by a charged ebonite rod

It is true that there is a repulsion between the rod and the similar charge on the far side of the ball. However, the strength of the electric forces between similar and opposite charges depends on the distance between the charges. As the distance increases, the magnitude of the force of attraction or repulsion decreases, as you will learn in more detail in Section 15.3. Hence, there is a net attraction of the neutral ball.

Charging by Contact

When a charged ebonite rod is touched to a neutral pith ball, some of the excess electrons on the ebonite rod, repelled by the close proximity of their neighbouring excess electrons, move over to the pith ball. The pith ball and the ebonite rod share the excess of electrons that the charged rod previously had. Both have some of the excess and hence both are negatively charged. A similar sharing occurs when a charged ebonite rod is touched to the knob of a metal-leaf electroscope.

When a positively charged glass rod is used, some of the free electrons on the pith ball or metal-leaf electroscope are attracted over to the glass rod to reduce its deficit of electrons. The electroscope and the rod share the deficit of electrons that the rod previously had, and both have a positive charge.

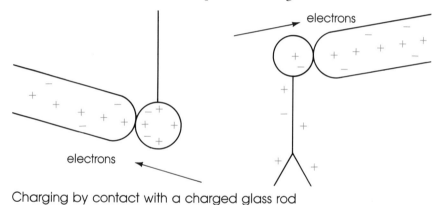

Charging by contact with a charged glass rod

An object charged by contact has the same sign as the charging rod.

Charging By Induction

We learned that a charged rod can induce a charge separation on a neutral conductor. When a charged ebonite rod is brought near the knob of a neutral metal-leaf electroscope, free electrons on the electroscope move as far away as possible from the negative rod. If you touch the electroscope with your finger, keeping the ebonite rod in place, electrons are induced to vacate the electroscope and flow through your finger. When your finger is removed, the electroscope is left with a deficit of electrons and, therefore, a positive charge. The leaves will remain apart even when the ebonite rod is removed.

A positively charged rod held near the knob of an electroscope induces electrons to move through your finger onto the electroscope. Now, when the finger is removed, the electroscope is left with an excess of electrons and, therefore, a negative charge.

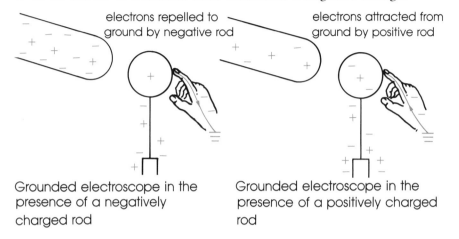

electrons repelled to ground by negative rod

electrons attracted from ground by positive rod

Grounded electroscope in the presence of a negatively charged rod

Grounded electroscope in the presence of a positively charged rod

---

An object that is charged by induction has a charge opposite to that of the charging rod.

15.3 Electric Forces — Coulomb's Law

Early work in electrostatics revealed the fundamental law of electric charges — opposite charges exert forces of attraction on each other, and similar charges exert repelling forces. It was left to the French physicist Charles Augustin de Coulomb (1736-1806) to establish, experimentally, in about 1785, the quantitative nature of the electric force between charged particles.

Coulomb used a torsion balance similar to that used by Cavendish in his study of gravitational forces. Rather than using small masses, Coulomb used the electric force between small charged spheres to cause the torsion balance to rotate.

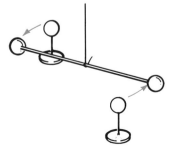

Charles Augustin de Coulomb

Through knowing the torsional properties of the suspension wire, and by changing the distance between the charged spheres, Coulomb was able to determine the relationship between the electric force acting between two charged spheres and their separation distance. He found that the magnitude of the electric force is inversely proportional to the square of the distance between the centres of the charged spheres.

$$F \propto \frac{1}{d^2}$$

where d is the distance between the centres of the charged spheres.

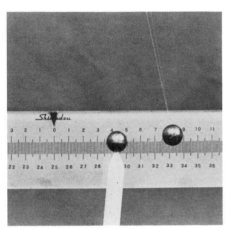 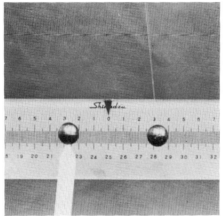 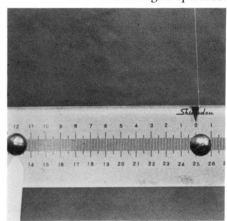

The electrostatic force of repulsion on the suspended charged sphere caused by the presence of an identical fixed charged sphere, at different separation distances

Coulomb also investigated the effect on the electric force of changing the amount of electric charge on either sphere. By touching either charged sphere with an identical neutral sphere, he was able to divide its charge in half and note the resulting effect on the electric force. He found that the magnitude of the electric force is directly proportional to the product of the magnitudes of the charges on each sphere.

$$F \propto q_1 q_2$$

where q_1 and q_2 are the magnitudes of the charges on sphere 1 and sphere 2, respectively

Combining these two results, we have what has become known as Coulomb's Law of Electric Forces.

$$F \propto \frac{q_1 q_2}{d^2}$$

$$F = k \frac{q_1 q_2}{d^2}$$

Notice the similarity between Coulomb's Law and Newton's Law of Universal Gravitation.

$$F_g = \frac{Gm_1 m_2}{d^2}$$

where k is a proportionality constant, known as Coulomb's constant.

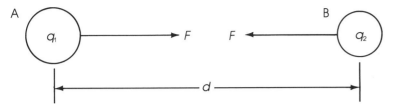

It is very important to realize that Coulomb's Law applies only when A and B are "point charges". To be considered point charges, A and B must be so far apart, compared to their own actual dimensions, that the detailed positions of the charged particles making up q_1 and q_2 are not significant.

In order to calculate the magnitude of an electric force quantitatively, in newtons, using Coulomb's Law, it is necessary to measure the magnitude of each electric charge, q_1 and q_2, as well as to establish a numerical value for the Coulomb proportionality constant, k.

Electric charge is measured in units called coulombs (abbreviated, C). The exact definition of a coulomb of charge depends on the force acting between conductors through which charged particles are moving. This will be explained fully, when we learn about these forces in Chapter 16. For now, to give you an idea of the magnitude of a coulomb, 1 C is approximately the amount of electric charge that passes through a standard 60 W light bulb in 2 s. An electrostatic shock that you might receive from walking across a wool rug and then touching a metallic doorknob would involve the transfer of a few microcoulombs.

The value of the proportionality constant, k, may be determined using a torsional balance similar to that used by Cavendish (Chapter 7). By placing charges of known magnitude a given distance apart, and measuring the resulting "twist" of the suspending wire, a value can be found for the electric force causing the twist. Then, using Coulomb's Law in the form

$$k = \frac{F\,d^2}{q_1\,q_2}$$

a value for k may be determined. Over the years, a great deal of effort has gone into the design of intricate equipment for measuring k accurately.

The accepted value for this constant, used in Coulomb's Law to calculate the electric force between point charges, is

$$k = 9.0 \times 10^9\ \frac{\text{N·m}^2}{\text{C}^2}$$

The following sample problems will illustrate how we can use Coulomb's Law to calculate the magnitude of the electric force between two point charges.

Actually, the law holds for larger objects as well, provided that the charges on each object are distributed with spherical symmetry.

Strictly speaking, this would only be true if the current in the bulb flowed steadily in one direction, not back and forth as it does in our AC systems.

In some applications of Coulomb's Law, especially involving subatomic particles whose electric charge is only a small number of elementary charges, it is convenient to measure q_1 and q_2 in elementary charges, rather than coulombs. Although these are not strictly SI units, they are acceptable, but require a different value of k, the constant in Coulomb's Law. In these units, $k = 2.306 \times 10^{-28}$ N·m²/elem chg². For example, the force of electrostatic repulsion between two electrons a distance of 1.0 m apart is

$$F = k\frac{q_1\,q_2}{d^2} = \frac{(2.306 \times 10^{-28})(1)(1)}{(1.0)^2}$$

$$= 2.3 \times 10^{-28}\,\text{N}$$

Sample problems

1. The electrostatic force between two small charged objects is 5.0×10^{-5} N. What effect would each of the following changes have on the magnitude of this force, considered separately?

   (a) The distance between the charges is doubled.

   Since $\qquad F \alpha \dfrac{1}{d^2}, \qquad \dfrac{F_1}{F_2} = \left(\dfrac{d_2}{d_1}\right)^2$

   Then $\qquad\qquad\qquad\qquad F_2 = F_1 \left(\dfrac{d_1}{d_2}\right)^2$

   $$= (5.0 \times 10^{-5} \text{ N}) \left(\dfrac{1}{2}\right)^2$$

   $$= 1.3 \times 10^{-5} \text{ N}$$

   (b) The charge on one object is tripled, while the charge on the other is halved.

   Since $\quad F \alpha \, q_A \, q_B, \qquad \dfrac{F_1}{F_2} = \dfrac{q_{A1} \, q_{B1}}{q_{A2} \, q_{B2}}$

   Then $\qquad\qquad\qquad F_2 = F_1 \left(\dfrac{q_{A2}}{q_{A1}}\right) \left(\dfrac{q_{B2}}{q_{B1}}\right)$

   $$= (5.0 \times 10^{-5} \text{ N}) \left(\dfrac{1}{2}\right) \left(\dfrac{3}{1}\right)$$

   $$= 7.5 \times 10^{-5} \text{ N}$$

   (c) Both of the above changes occur simultaneously.

   Since $\quad F \alpha \dfrac{q_A \, q_B}{d^2}, \qquad \dfrac{F_1}{F_2} = \left(\dfrac{q_{A1} \, q_{B1}}{q_{A2} \, q_{B2}}\right) \left(\dfrac{d_2}{d_1}\right)^2$

   Then $\qquad\qquad\quad F_2 = F_1 \left(\dfrac{q_{A2}}{q_{A1}}\right) \left(\dfrac{q_{B2}}{q_{B1}}\right) \left(\dfrac{d_1}{d_2}\right)^2$

   $$= (5.0 \times 10^{-5} \text{ N}) \left(\dfrac{3}{1}\right) \left(\dfrac{1}{2}\right) \left(\dfrac{1}{2}\right)^2$$

   $$= 1.9 \times 10^{-5} \text{ N}$$

2. What is the force of repulsion between two small spheres 1.0 m apart, if each has a charge of 1.0×10^{-12} C?

   $$F = k\dfrac{q_1 q_2}{d^2}$$

   $$= (9.0 \times 10^9 \, \dfrac{\text{N·m}^2}{\text{C}^2}) \dfrac{(1.0 \times 10^{-12} \text{ C})(1.0 \times 10^{-12} \text{ C})}{(1.0 \text{ m})^2}$$

   $$= 9.0 \times 10^{-15} \text{ N} \quad \text{which is, as you can see, a very small force.}$$

Practice

1. Two charged spheres 10 cm apart attract each other with a force of 3.0×10^{-6} N. What force results from each of the following changes, considered separately?
   (a) Both charges are doubled and the distance remains the same.
   (b) An uncharged, identical sphere is touched to one of the spheres, and then taken far away.
   (c) The separation is increased to 30 cm.
   $(1.2 \times 10^{-5}\text{ N}, 1.5 \times 10^{-6}\text{ N}, 3.3 \times 10^{-7}\text{ N})$

2. The force of electrostatic repulsion between two small positively charged objects, A and B, is 3.6×10^{-5} N when AB $= 0.12$ m. What is the force of repulsion if AB is increased to (a) 0.24 m, (b) 0.30 m, and (c) 0.36 m?
   $(9.0 \times 10^{-6}\text{ N}, 5.8 \times 10^{-6}\text{ N}, 4.0 \times 10^{-6}\text{ N})$

3. Calculate the force between charges of 5.0×10^{-8} C and 1.0×10^{-7} C if they are 5.0 cm apart. $\qquad (1.8 \times 10^{-2}\text{ N})$

4. What is the magnitude of the force a 1.5×10^{-6} C charge exerts on a 3.2×10^{-4} C charge located 1.5 m away? $\qquad (1.9\text{ N})$

5. Two charged spheres; 4.0 cm apart, attract each other with a force of 1.2×10^{-9} N. Determine the magnitude of the charge on each, if one has twice the charge (of the opposite sign) as the other. $\qquad (1.0 \times 10^{-11}\text{ C}, 2.0 \times 10^{-11}\text{ C})$

6. Two equal charges of magnitude 1.1×10^{-7} C experience an electrostatic force of 4.2×10^{-4} N. How far apart are the centres of the two charges? $\qquad (0.51\text{ m})$

7. Two identical, small spheres of mass 2.0 g are fastened to the ends of a 0.60 m long light, flexible, insulating fishline. The fishline is suspended by a hook in the ceiling at its exact centre. The spheres are each given an identical electric charge. They are in static equilibrium, with an angle of 30° between the string halves, as shown. Calculate the magnitude of the charge on each sphere. $\qquad (1.2 \times 10^{-7}\text{ C})$

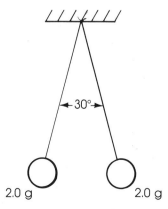

30°

2.0 g   2.0 g

Coulomb's Law also has a vector nature. A charged particle may be subject to more than one electric force at a time, and the net result must be determined by adding, vectorially, all of the electric forces acting on it. Two sample problems will illustrate.

Sample problems

1. Charged spheres A and B are fixed in position, as shown, and have charges of $+4.0 \times 10^{-6}$ C and -2.5×10^{-7} C, respectively. Calculate the net force on sphere C, whose charge is $+6.4 \times 10^{-6}$ C.

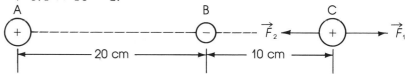

Since all three charges are in a straight line, we can take the vector nature of force into account by assigning forces to the right as positive. Sphere C has forces acting on it from spheres A and B.

For the force from sphere A:

$$F_1 = k \frac{q_A q_C}{d_{AC}^2}$$

$$= \frac{(9.0 \times 10^9 \text{ N·m}^2/\text{C}^2)(4.0 \times 10^{-6} \text{ C})(6.4 \times 10^{-6} \text{ C})}{(0.30 \text{ m})^2}$$

$\therefore \vec{F_1} = 2.6$ N, to the right

And for the force from sphere B:

$$F_2 = k \frac{q_B q_C}{d_{BC}^2}$$

$$= \frac{(9.0 \times 10^9 \text{ N·m}^2/\text{C}^2)(2.5 \times 10^{-1} \text{ C})(6.4 \times 10^{-6} \text{ C})}{(0.10 \text{ m})^2}$$

$\therefore \vec{F_2} = 1.4$ N, to the left

The net force acting on sphere C is the sum of $\vec{F_1}$ and $\vec{F_2}$

$$\vec{F}_{net} = \vec{F_1} + \vec{F_2}$$
$$= 2.6 \text{ N[right]} + 1.4 \text{ N[left]}$$
$$= 1.2 \text{ N[right]}$$

2. Four identical, charged spheres, A, B, C, and D, each with a charge of magnitude 5.0×10^{-6} C, are situated at the corners of a square whose sides are 25 cm long. If two diagonally opposite charges are positive and the other two negative, as shown, calculate the net force acting on each.

Each sphere will experience three electric forces, one from each of the two adjacent charges (acting along the sides of the square) and one from the other charge (acting along the diagonal). While some of the 12 forces acting will be attractions and some will be repulsions, in terms of magnitude only there will be just two values — one for equal charges 25 cm apart, and one for equal charges 35.4 cm apart (the length of the diagonal). Let us first calculate the magnitude of each of these forces.

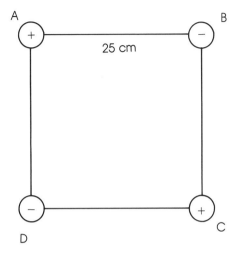

$$F_{side} = k \frac{q_1 q_2}{s^2}$$
$$= \frac{(9.0 \times 10^9 \text{ N·m}^2/\text{C}^2)(5.0 \times 10^{-6} \text{ C})^2}{(0.25 \text{ m})^2}$$
$$= 3.6 \text{ N}$$

and
$$F_{diag} = k \frac{q_1 q_2}{d^2}$$
$$= \frac{(9.0 \times 10^9 \text{ N·m}^2/\text{C}^2)(5.0 \times 10^{-6} \text{ C})^2}{(0.35 \text{ m})^2}$$
$$= 1.8 \text{ N}$$

Then, drawing a vector diagram showing each of these forces with its vector in the appropriate direction, whether an attraction or repulsion, we have:

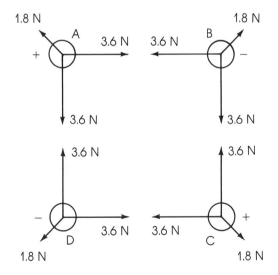

Note that the forces acting on each sphere are similar: an attraction of 3.6 N along each side, and a repulsion of 1.8 N along the diagonal. The net force on each sphere is the vector

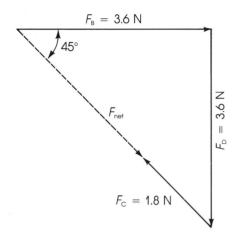

sum of these three forces. As an example, let us draw the vector diagram to find the sum for sphere A.

Using the rules for vector addition (Chapter 3), and drawing the vectors tip-to-tail, we have:

The vector sum (dotted vector) is the hypotenuse of the vector triangle minus the 1.8 N vector. The magnitude of the hypotenuse is

$$\sqrt{(3.6 \text{ N})^2 + (3.6 \text{ N})^2} = 5.1 \text{ N}$$

Therefore
$$\vec{F}_{net} = 5.1 \text{ N} - 1.8 \text{ N}$$
$$= 3.3 \text{ N [right 45° down]}$$

The same calculation at each of the other three corners would produce the same result: a net force of 3.3 N directed inward along the corresponding diagonal.

The same problem may be readily solved using components of the forces, in the X and Y directions, acting on each sphere.

For the force on sphere A,

$$\vec{F} = \vec{F}_B + \vec{F}_C + \vec{F}_D$$
$$F_{Ax} = F_{Bx} + F_{Cx} + F_{Dx} = 3.6 \text{ N} + (-1.8 \text{ N} \cos 45°) + 0$$
$$= 2.3 \text{ N}$$
$$F_{Ay} = F_{By} + F_{Cy} + F_{Dy} = 0 + (+1.8 \text{ N} \cos 45°) + (-3.6 \text{ N})$$
$$= -2.3 \text{ N}$$
$$\therefore F_A = \sqrt{(F_{Ax})^2 + (F_{Ay})^2} = \sqrt{(2.3 \text{ N})^2 + (-2.3 \text{ N})^2}$$
$$= 3.3 \text{ N}$$

$$\theta = \tan^{-1} \frac{|F_{Ay}|}{|F_{Ax}|} = tan^{-1}1 = 45°$$

$$\therefore \vec{F}_A = 3.3 \text{ N [right 45° down]}$$

Practice

1. Three negatively charged spheres, each with a charge of 4.0×10^{-6} C, are fixed at the vertices of an equilateral triangle whose sides are 20 cm long. Calculate the magnitude and direction of the net electric force on each sphere.

(6.2 N [outward, 150° away from each side])

2. Three objects, carrying charges of -4.0×10^{-6} C, -6.0×10^{-6} C, and $+9.0 \times 10^{-6}$ C, respectively, are placed in a line, equally spaced from left to right by a distance of 0.5 m. Calculate the magnitude and direction of the net force acting on each that results from the presence of the other two.

(0.54 N [left], 2.8 N [right], 2.3 N [left])

3. Two small spheres, with charges 1.6×10^{-5} C and 6.4×10^{-5} C, are situated 2.0 m apart. They have the same sign. Where, relative to these two objects, should a third object be situated, of the

opposite sign and whose charge is 3.0×10^{-6} C, so that it experiences no net electrical force? Do we really need to know the charge or sign of the third object?
(on the line joining them, 0.67 m from the 1.6×10^{-5} C charge)

15.4 Electric Fields

Electric charges exert forces of attraction or repulsion on each other, even when they are not in contact with each other. As we have learned, the magnitude of the force between any two point charges is given by:

$$F_e = k \frac{q_1 q_2}{d^2}$$

This kind of "action-at-a-distance" force is already familiar to us: the gravitational force existed between two masses, even though they were not touching. The gravitational force that one mass exerts upon another was explained in terms of a gravitational field of force. When a mass was placed in the gravitational field of another mass, the first mass experienced a force of attraction towards the second mass.

The same kind of reasoning may be used to explain electric forces. Every charged object creates an electric field of force in the space around it. Any other charged object in that space will experience a force of attraction or repulsion from the presence of the electric field.

The electric field may be represented by drawing a series of force vectors around the charged object. Force vectors show the direction and magnitude of the electric force on a small, positive test charge placed at each and every point in the field. For the sake of simplicity, continuous field lines are usually drawn to show the direction of this force at all points in the field, as shown.

The presence of electric fields can often be "felt", particularly on cold, dry days, when reaching for a metal door handle after walking across a carpeted room. Small hairs on the hand and forearm may stand on end, even before the hand touches the knob. These electrical effects can be useful in many ways, even though they are often a nuisance.

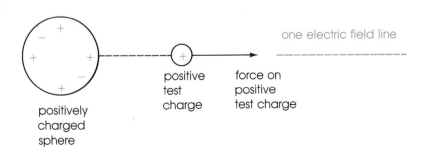

Electric field intensity, $\vec{\mathcal{E}}$, is a vector quantity, with a magnitude and direction. As before, in problems where only its magnitude is of significance, the vector notation will often be omitted. Remember that, at any point, its direction is that of the electric force on a positive test charge.

The field lines are there regardless of whether or not a test charge is present.

The "electric field intensity", $\vec{\mathcal{E}}$, at any point is defined as the electric force per unit positive charge, and is a vector quantity.

$$\vec{\mathcal{E}} = \frac{\vec{F_e}}{q}$$

where the units are newtons per coulomb.

In an electric field diagram, the electric field intensity at any point is indicated by the relative distance between adjacent field lines. In a region where the electric field is strong, adjacent field lines are close together. More widely spaced field lines indicate a weaker electric field.

Consider, for example, what the electric field around a small, positively charged sphere might be like. If we place a positive test charge just to the right of the positively charged sphere, the force on the test charge will be a repulsion, and it will move to the right. If the positive test charge is then placed at other, similar, points around the sphere, and in each case a field line is drawn, the entire electric field will appear as shown.

If the positively charged sphere is small enough to be considered a point charge, then the electric field intensity, at any point a distance r from the centre of the sphere, would point radially outward and have a magnitude of

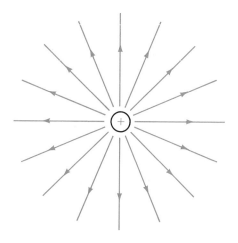

Positively charged sphere

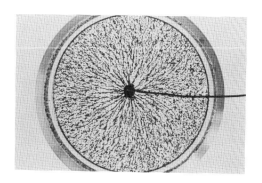

$$\mathcal{E} = \frac{F_e}{q}$$
$$= k\frac{q_1 q}{r^2 q}$$
$$= k\frac{q_1}{r^2} \qquad \text{where } q_1 \text{ is the charge on the sphere}$$

The electric field of a negatively charged sphere would be identical, except that the field lines would point in the opposite direction, inward.

More complex electric fields result when more than one point charge is present, or when the object is too large to be considered a point charge. In such cases, the electric field at any point is the vector sum of the electric fields of all of the point charges contributing to the electric force at that point. The electric fields of some typical charge distributions are shown.

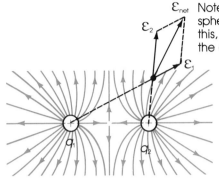

$\mathcal{E}_{net}$ Note: The electric field of two negative spheres close together is identical to this, except that the field lines point in the opposite direction.

Two small positive spheres close together

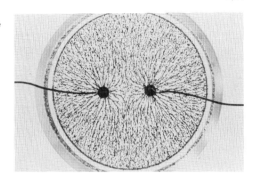

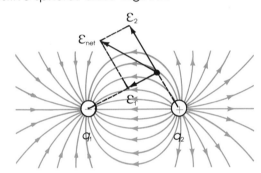

Two small, oppositely charged spheres close together

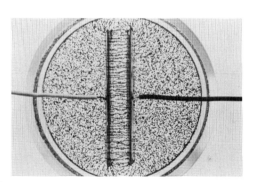

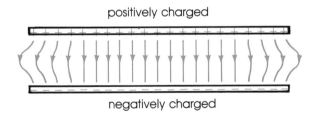

positively charged

negatively charged

Two large, equally but oppositely charged parallel plates close together

The electric field of two large, oppositely charged parallel plates close together is a special case. The plates are too large, compared to their separation distance, to be considered point charges. Instead, each plate would have to be considered as n point charges, distributed uniformly side by side on a plane. Thus, in determining the net electric force at any point in the vicinity of the plates, the contribution from each of the $2n$ point sources (n on each plate), each a different distance and direction away, would have to be

Note that, in these examples, the electric field at the point shown is the vector sum of the electric fields of the two point charges, q_1 and q_2.

n evenly distributed + point charges

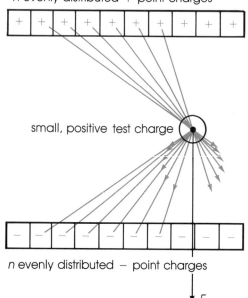

small, positive test charge

n evenly distributed – point charges

F_{net}

(the sum of the 2 n individual forces acting on the small, positive test charge)

In many cases, the plates are charged by connecting each plate to one of the terminals of a battery. To double the charge on each plate would require using two identical batteries, connected together as shown, to charge the plates.

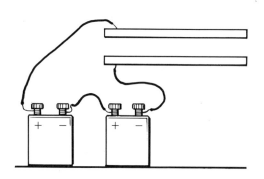

considered. The net electric force on a small, positive test charge at any point would be the vector sum of the electric forces acting on it from each of the 2 *n* point charges. In the diagram, a few of these 2 *n* force vectors are shown. For each, the magnitude of its contribution to the total force would be determined by Coulomb's Law. The direction of each force is along the straight line joining the point charge to the positive test charge.

To determine the sum of these 2 *n* force vectors at each point is a problem that requires calculus, or other techniques beyond the scope of this book; however, the results of such an analysis are significant, and somewhat surprising:

- The electric field intensity in the region outside the parallel plates is zero (except for a slight bulging of the field near the edges of the plates).
- The electric field intensity is constant everywhere in the space between the parallel plates. The electric field lines are straight, equally spaced, and perpendicular to the parallel plates.
- The magnitude of the electric field intensity at any point between the plates (except near the edges) depends only on the magnitude of the charge on each plate.

$$\mathcal{E} \propto q, \text{ where } q \text{ is the charge per unit area on each plate}$$

A field such as this is called a uniform electric field, because it is constant in both magnitude and direction. It is very useful in the study of the motion of charged particles.

Sample problems

1. What is the electric field intensity 0.50 m away from a small sphere with a positive charge of 1.6×10^{-8} C?

$$\vec{\mathcal{E}} = \frac{\vec{F_e}}{q} = \frac{k\,q}{d^2}$$

$$= \frac{(9.0 \times 10^9 \text{ N·m}^2/\text{C}^2)(1.6 \times 10^{-8} \text{ C})}{(0.50 \text{ m})^2}$$

$$= 5.8 \times 10^2 \text{ N/C [radially outward]}$$

2. Calculate the electric field intensity midway between two negative charges of 3.2×10^{-9} C and 6.4×10^{-9} C that are 30 cm apart.

There will be an electric field at the midpoint due to each of the two charges. The net field will be the vector sum of the two separate fields. Calling these fields $\vec{\mathcal{E}}_1$ and $\vec{\mathcal{E}}_2$, respectively, we have

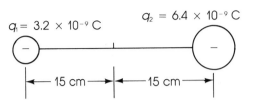

$$\vec{\mathcal{E}}_1 = \frac{k\,q_1}{d_1{}^2}$$

$$= \frac{(9.0 \times 10^9 \text{ N·m}^2/\text{C}^2)(3.2 \times 10^{-9} \text{ C})}{(0.15 \text{ m})^2}$$

$$= 1.3 \times 10^3 \text{ N/C [left]}$$

also $\qquad \vec{\mathcal{E}}_2 = \dfrac{k\,q_2}{d_2{}^2}$

$$= \frac{(9.0 \times 10^9 \text{ N·m}^2/\text{C}^2)(6.4 \times 10^{-9} \text{ C})}{(0.15 \text{ m})^2}$$

$$= 2.6 \times 10^3 \text{ N/C [right]}$$

Thus, the net electric field intensity, at the mid point, is the vector sum of these two fields, which is

$$\vec{\mathcal{E}}_{net} = 1.3 \times 10^3 \text{ N/C [right]}$$

3. The electric field intensity between the plates of a parallel plate apparatus is 1.5×10^2 N/C. What is the effect on the electric field intensity of each of the following changes, considered separately?
   (a) The charge on each plate is doubled.

   Since $\mathcal{E} \propto q$, then $\qquad \dfrac{\mathcal{E}_2}{\mathcal{E}_1} = \dfrac{q_2}{q_1}$

   and $\qquad \mathcal{E}_2 = \mathcal{E}_1 \left[\dfrac{q_2}{q_1}\right]$

   $$= (1.5 \times 10^2 \text{ N/C})(2)$$
   $$= 3.0 \times 10^2 \text{ N/C}$$

   (b) The plates are moved 3 times as far apart.

   Since $\mathcal{E} \propto q$ only, changing d has no effect.
   $$\therefore \quad \mathcal{E}_2 = \mathcal{E}_1 = 1.5 \times 10^2 \text{ N/C}$$

Practice

1. A negative charge of 2.4×10^{-6} C experiences an electric force of magnitude 3.2 N, acting to the left. What is the magnitude and direction of the electric field at that point?

   $(1.3 \times 10^6 \text{ N/C [right]})$

Enormous electric fields are evident in such natural phenomena as lightning, the aurora borealis, and the eruption of sunspots. They can provide much beauty and pleasure, and yet be frightening and destructive.

2. At a certain point in an electric field, the magnitude of the electric field intensity is 12 N/C. Calculate the magnitude of the electric force exerted on a point charge of 2.5×10^{-7} C, located at this point in the field.   (3.0×10^{-6} N)

3. What is the magnitude and direction of the electric field intensity at a point 3.0 m to the right of a positive point charge of 5.4×10^{-4} C?   (5.4×10^{5} N/C [right])

4. What is the magnitude and direction of the electric field at point Z in the diagram below, due to the charged spheres at points X and Y?   (2.0×10^{5} N/C[left])

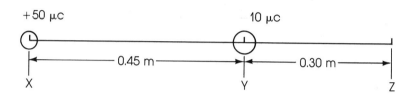

5. Determine the magnitude and direction of the electric field at point Z in the diagram below, due to the charges at points X and Y.   (1.2×10^{5} N/C [up])

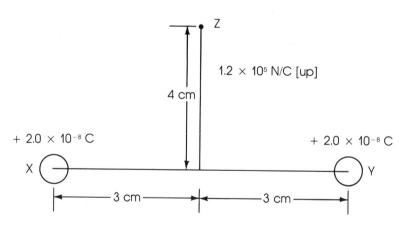

6. The electric field strength midway between a pair of oppositely charged parallel plates is 3.0×10^{3} N/C. What is the electric field intensity halfway between this point and the positively charged plate?   (3.0×10^{3} N/C)

7. In the parallel plate apparatus in 6, what would the electric field intensity become, if half of the charge were removed from each plate and the separation of the plates was changed from 12 mm to 8 mm?   (1.5×10^{3} N/C)

15.5 Electric Potential

We have learned that an electric charge creates an electric field of force in the space surrounding it, much like the gravitational field in the space around a mass. In the case of an electric field, the force can be either attractive or repulsive, whereas gravitational fields can only exert forces of attraction between masses.

We found, in Chapter 10, that two masses exerting forces of attraction on each other given by

$$F_g = \frac{G \, m_1 \, m_2}{d^2}$$

have a corresponding gravitational potential energy that is given by

$$E_g = - \frac{G \, m_1 \, m_2}{d}$$

where the zero value of gravitational potential energy is chosen as the value when the two masses are an infinite distance apart. The negative sign associated with this expression for gravitational potential energy is an indication that the force between the two masses is a force of attraction. Energy is stored by moving them farther apart.

For the electrical analogy, consider a small test charge q_2, a distance r from a spherical point charge q_1, as shown.

From Coulomb's Law, the magnitude of the force of attraction or repulsion between these two charges is:

$$F_e = \frac{k \, q_1 \, q_2}{r^2}$$

Therefore, it seems reasonable that an approach similar to that used in Chapter 10 for the gravitational potential energy in a system of two masses would yield a corresponding result for electric potential energy stored in the system of two charges q_1 and q_2.

$$E_e = \frac{k \, q_1 \, q_2}{r}$$

Notice that the sign for electric potential energy, E_e, is positive in this equation. If q_1 and q_2 are opposite charges, they attract, and the electric potential should have a negative value that is identical to the gravitational case. However, if q_1 and q_2 are similar charges, they repel, and the electric potential energy should be positive. That is to say, energy is stored by moving them closer together. In either case, substituting the sign of the charge ($+$ or $-$) for q_1 and q_2 will yield the appropriate results, so far as the sign of E_e is concerned. Also, in both cases, the zero level of electric potential energy occurs when the charges q_1 and q_2 are an infinite distance apart.

Also, as in the gravitational analogy, the zero level of electric potential energy in a system of two charged spheres is chosen to be when they are at an infinite separation distance. A graph of E_e vs r has two curves, as shown, one for forces of attraction between opposite charges (negative curve) and one for forces of repulsion between similar charges (positive curve).

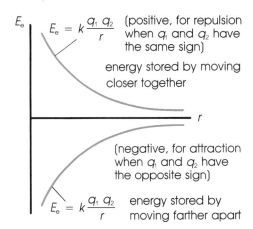

To look at the concept of electric potential energy in a systematic way, we consider the electric potential energy not just of any charge q_2, but of a unit positive test charge when in the field of any other charge q_1. We call this value of potential energy per unit positive charge the **electric potential**, and give it the symbol V. It is a property of the electric field of the charge q_1, and represents the amount of work necessary to move a unit positive test charge from rest at infinity to rest at any specific point in the field of q_1.

Thus, at a distance r from a spherical point charge q_1, the electric potential is given by

> We must always be very careful to distinguish between E_e, the electric potential energy of a charge at a point, and V, the electric potential at the point. They are related by the equation $E_e = qV$.

$$V = \frac{E_e}{q}$$

$$= \frac{\dfrac{k\,q_1\,q}{r}}{q}$$

$$= \frac{k\,q_1}{r}$$

The units of electric potential are joules per coulomb, or volts, and:

---

1 V is the electric potential at a point in an electric field if 1 J of work is required to move 1 C of charge from infinity to that point.

$$1\ V = 1\ J/C$$

This concept of electric potential can be extended to include the electric fields that result from any distribution of electric charge, rather than just a single point charge. The definition of electric potential in these cases is the same: it is the work done per unit positive test charge to move the charge from infinity to any given point. It is more common, however, not to think of the work necessary to move a unit test charge from infinity to a particular point in a field, but rather from one point to another in the field. In this case we are concerned with the difference in electric potential between these two points, commonly called the **potential difference** or **voltage difference**.

> It is quite common to use the term "voltage" when referring to a potential difference between two points. For example, household "line voltage" of 120 V AC means that there is an average potential difference of 120 V between the two wires in the various circuits, and its polarity fluctuates at a frequency of 60 Hz.

If A and B are two points in an electric field, and q is a positive charge moving from A to B,

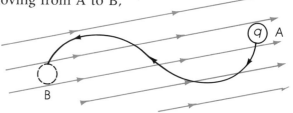

then, regardless of the actual path taken by the charge q, in moving from A to B,

$$\left\{\begin{array}{l}\text{the change in electric}\\\text{potential energy of } q, \text{in}\\\text{moving from A to B}\end{array}\right\} = \left\{\begin{array}{l}\text{the work required to}\\\text{move } q \text{ from A to B,}\\\text{against the electric field}\end{array}\right\}$$

$$\Delta E_e = q\,V_B - q\,V_A$$
$$= q\,(V_B - V_A)$$
$$= q\,\Delta V$$

ΔV is the potential difference between points B and A in the field, and is often shortened to V_{BA}. The potential always decreases in the direction of the electric field, and increases in the opposite direction.

As an example of this type of calculation, consider the electric field between two large, oppositely charged parallel plates that are close together.

Recall that the electric field between the plates is uniform; that is, it is constant in magnitude and direction at all points, and is defined as the force per unit positive charge.

$$\vec{\mathcal{E}} = \frac{\vec{F}_e}{q}$$

The increase in electric potential energy of the charge q, in moving from plate B to plate A, is equal to the work done in moving it from B to A. To do so, a force $\vec{F}$, equal in magnitude but opposite in direction to $\vec{F}_e$, must be applied over a distance d. The magnitude of the work done is given by:

$$W = Fd \qquad \text{since } F \text{ and } d \text{ are in the same direction}$$
$$= q\,\mathcal{E}d \qquad \text{since } F = F_e = q\mathcal{E}$$

Therefore, since $\Delta E_e = W$

$$q\,V_{AB} = q\,\mathcal{E}\,d$$
$$or \quad \mathcal{E} = \frac{V_{AB}}{d}$$

This is an expression for the magnitude of the electric field at any point in the space between two large parallel plates, a distance d apart, with a potential difference V_{AB}. Remember, the electric field direction is from the + plate to the − plate, in the direction of decreasing potential.

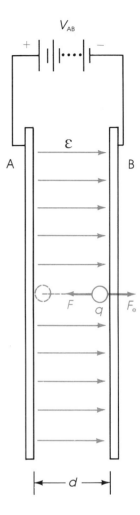

Sample problems

Very high potential differences exist between electrical transmission lines and ground, even though they often run very close to populated areas. Young children should be cautioned about the danger of playing near these lines and their towers.

1. Calculate the electric potential a distance of 0.40 m from a spherical point charge of $+6.4 \times 10^{-6}$ C. (Take $V = 0$, at infinity.)

$$V = \frac{kq}{r}$$
$$= \frac{(9.0 \times 10^9 \text{ N·m}^2/\text{C}^2)(6.4 \times 10^{-6} \text{ C})}{0.40 \text{ m}}$$
$$= 1.4 \times 10^5 \text{ J/C}, \quad \text{or } 1.4 \times 10^5 \text{ V}$$

Note that the value for the potential created by a positive charge has a positive value, characteristic of a system where the force acting on the test charge is a repulsion. If the spherical point charge in the above example had been a negative charge, then substituting a negative value for q would have yielded a negative value for V, which is consistent with a system in which the force acting is an attraction.

2. How much work must be done to increase the potential of a charge of 3.0×10^{-7} C by 120 V?

$$W = \Delta E_e = q\Delta V$$
$$= (3.0 \times 10^{-7} \text{ C})(1.20 \times 10^2 \text{ V})$$
$$= 3.6 \times 10^{-5} \text{ J}$$

3. In a uniform electric field, the potential difference between two points 10 cm apart is 80 V. Calculate the magnitude of the electric field intensity.

$$\mathcal{E} = \frac{V}{d}$$
$$= \frac{80 \text{ V}}{0.10 \text{ m}}$$
$$= 8.0 \times 10^2 \text{ N/C}$$

Electric field strength is often expressed in V/m.
Note: V/m = J/C/m
             = N·m/C·m
             = N/C

4. The electric field intensity in the region between two parallel plates is 400 N/C. If the plates are connected to a battery with a potential difference of 90 V, what is the separation of the plates?

For parallel plates, $\quad \mathcal{E} = \dfrac{V}{d}$

Thus $\qquad\qquad\qquad d = \dfrac{V}{\mathcal{E}}$
$$= \frac{90 \text{ V}}{400 \text{ N/C}}$$
$$= 0.23 \text{ m}$$

Practice

1. The potential at a distance of 25 cm from a point charge is
   -6.4×10^4 V. What is the sign and magnitude of the point
   charge? $(-1.8 \times 10^{-6}$ C$)$
2. It takes 4.2×10^{-3} J of work to move 1.2×10^{-6} C of charge
   from point X to point Y in an electric field. What is the potential
   difference between X and Y? $(3.5 \times 10^3$ V$)$
3. Calculate the magnitude of the electric field in a parallel plate
   apparatus whose plates are 5.0 mm apart and have a potential
   difference of 300 V between them. $(6.0 \times 10^4$ N/C$)$
4. What potential difference would have to be maintained across
   the plates of a parallel plate apparatus, if they are 1.2 cm apart,
   to create an electric field of intensity 1.5×10^4 N/C?
                                                              $(1.8 \times 10^2$ V$)$

15.6 The Millikan Experiment — Determination of the Elementary Charge

At the turn of the century, when our understanding of electric
forces was beginning to increase, two fundamental questions arose,
regarding the nature of electric charge:

1. Does there exist, in nature, a smallest unit of electric charge of
   which all other units are simple multiples?
2. If so, what is this elementary charge, and what is its magnitude,
   in coulombs?

To answer these questions, an American physicist, Robert Andrews
Millikan (1868-1953), devised and performed a series of very creative experiments. He reasoned that the elementary charge would
be the charge on an individual electron. He assumed, further, that
when tiny oil drops are sprayed in a fine mist from an atomizer,
they become electrically charged by friction — some acquiring an
excess of a few electrons, others acquiring a deficit. Although there
was no way of knowing how many extra electrons there were on
any oil drop, or how many were missing, Millikan hypothesized
that if he were able to measure the total charge on any oil drop,
it would have to be some small integral multiple of the elementary
charge.

To measure this charge, Millikan made use of the uniform electric
field in the region between two oppositely charged parallel plates.
He charged the plates by connecting each to opposite terminals of
a large bank of storage batteries whose potential difference could

Robert Millikan

be varied. He was able to use this apparatus, called an electrical microbalance, to isolate and suspend charged oil drops, and ultimately to measure the total charge on each.

Once a mist of oil drops is sprayed through a small hole in the upper plate, it is possible, by carefully adjusting the potential difference between the plates, to "balance" a particular drop that has the same sign as the charge on the lower plate. When the drop is balanced, the gravitational force exerted downward upon it is equal to the electrical force acting upward.

For a positively charged drop of mass m and charge q, the electric force acts upward.

$$F_e = q\,\mathcal{E}$$ where $\mathcal{E}$ is the electric field intensity between the plates

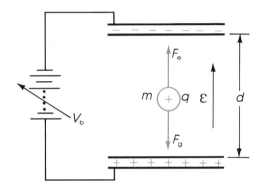

When the drop is in balance,

$$F_e = F_g$$
$$q\,\mathcal{E} = mg$$

But, in Section 15.5, we learned that the electric field intensity in the region between two parallel plates is constant, and is given by

$$\mathcal{E} = \frac{V}{d}$$ where V is the potential difference between the plates
d is the separation distance between the plates

So, for an oil drop of mass m and charge q, balanced by a potential difference V_b,

$$q = \frac{mg}{\mathcal{E}}$$ V_b is the balancing value of potential difference between the plates
$$= \frac{mgd}{V_b}$$

Thus, it is possible to determine the total charge on an oil drop if its mass is known. The mass of any individual drop may be determined by measuring the terminal velocity with which it falls when the electric balancing force is removed (when the batteries are disconnected) and when gravity, alone, is acting on it.

According to Stoke's Law, a small sphere of radius r and density ρ will fall with a terminal velocity v_0 through a fluid of density ρ_0 and viscosity η, where

$$v_0 = \frac{2}{9}\frac{r^2 g}{\eta}(\rho - \rho_0)$$

The Greek letters ρ (rho) and η (eta) are commonly used as symbols for density and viscosity, respectively. You are already familiar with density, but viscosity is probably a new term. Viscosity is a measure of the "internal friction" in a fluid. It is a result of cohesive forces between the molecules of a liquid and of collisions between the molecules of gas. It is somewhat related to the "thickness" of a liquid: syrup is more viscous than water, grease is more viscous than oil. The viscosity of air at room temperature is about 1.8×10^{-5} N·s/m², while the viscosity of corn syrup is about 1.2 N·s/m².

Rearranging this expression, for r we have

$$r = \sqrt{\frac{9}{2}\frac{\eta v_0}{g\,(\rho - \rho_0)}}$$

Then, assuming that the oil drop is a sphere, whose volume is given by the expression $4/3\pi r^3$, its mass will be the product of its volume and density, namely:

$$m = \frac{4}{3}\pi r^3 \rho$$

$$= \frac{4}{3}\pi\rho\left(\frac{9\eta v_0}{2g\,(\rho - \rho_0)}\right)^{\frac{3}{2}}$$

This value for m is then used in the equation for q, on page 598.

Thus, by actually measuring the terminal velocity of an oil drop as it falls under the force of gravity alone, Millikan was able to calculate its mass, using the relationship above. Then, by also measuring the value of potential difference between the plates necessary to balance the drop, he was able to calculate the total electric charge on the drop.

Millikan repeated the experiment laboriously, many times, meticulously balancing a charged oil drop, measuring its balancing voltage, and then allowing the drop to fall under gravity and measuring its terminal velocity. The list of values he determined for the total electric charge on each of the drops he studied was long, but it had a very significant pattern. All of the values were simple multiples of some smallest value. Some of the drops had this smallest value of charge on them, but none had less. Millikan assumed that this smallest value represented the smallest quantity of electric charge possible, the charge on an electron, or the elementary charge. Accurate measurements of the elementary charge have yielded values very close to that determined by Millikan, and the currently accepted value for the elementary charge, commonly called e, is

$$e = 1.602 \times 10^{-19}\ \text{C}$$

Knowing the value of the elementary charge enables us to understand the nature of electric charge on a much more fundamental level. In Section 15.1 we suggested that all electric charges in solids occurred from an excess or deficit of electrons. If we now know a value for the charge on an individual electron, we can calculate the number of excess or deficit electrons that constitute any electric charge.

Millikan's work on the determination of the elementary charge took place over the seven-year period from 1906 to 1913. He often used the same drop for hours, first balancing it, and then changing its charge by passing ionizing X-ray radiation through the air in the space between the plates. When a balanced oil drop picked up one of these ionized air particles, its change in charge was immediately evident. It would begin to move towards one plate or the other, and a new value of potential difference would be required to balance it.

Robert Andrews Millikan obtained his doctorate in physics from Columbia University in 1895. After post-doctoral work in Germany, he was appointed Professor of Physics at the University of Chicago, in 1910. He initially used charged water droplets in his famous experiment but switched to oil to overcome the problems of evaporation. His determination of the elementary charge earned the Nobel Prize for Physics for him, in 1923. He also performed the very delicate experiments necessary to verify Einstein's interpretation of the photoelectric effect (Section 18.2), and named and identified the origin and nature of "cosmic radiation" (Section 16.8). As the son of a minister, he was one of the small number of scientists of his time who actively sought to reconcile religion and science.

An object with an excess (or deficit) of N electrons has a charge q that is given by

$$q = Ne$$

Of course, whether the charge is positive or negative will depend on whether N is a deficit or excess of electrons.

Sample problems

1. Calculate the charge on a small sphere with an excess of 5.0×10^{14} electrons.

$$q = Ne$$
$$= (5.0 \times 10^{14})(1.6 \times 10^{-19} \text{ C})$$
$$= 8.0 \times 10^{-5} \text{ C}$$

The charge is negative as a result of the excess of electrons.

2. In a Millikan type experiment, two horizontal plates are 2.5 cm apart. A latex sphere of mass 1.5×10^{-15} kg remains stationary when the potential difference between the plates is 460 V, with the upper plate positive.

   (a) Is the sphere charged negatively or positively?

   The electric force must be up, to balance the downward force of gravity. Since the upper plate is positive, the latex sphere must be charged negatively, to be attracted to the upper plate and repelled by the lower plate. The electric field is downward, giving an upward force on a negative charge.

   (b) What is the magnitude of the electric field intensity between the plates?

   For a parallel plate apparatus,

   $$\mathcal{E} = \frac{V}{d}$$
   $$= \frac{460 \text{ V}}{2.5 \times 10^{-2} \text{ m}}$$
   $$= 1.84 \times 10^4 \text{ N/C} \qquad \text{This field is directed downward.}$$

   (c) Calculate the magnitude of the charge on the latex sphere.

   When the sphere is balanced,

   $$F_e = F_g$$
   $$q\mathcal{E} = mg$$
   $$q = \frac{mg}{\mathcal{E}}$$
   $$= \frac{(1.5 \times 10^{-15} \text{ kg})(9.8 \text{ m/s}^2)}{1.84 \times 10^4 \text{ N/C}}$$
   $$= 8.0 \times 10^{-19} \text{ C}$$

(d) How many excess or deficit electrons does the sphere have?

$$N = \frac{q}{e}$$

$$= \frac{8.0 \times 10^{-19} \text{ C}}{1.6 \times 10^{-19} \text{ C}}$$

$$= 5 \text{ excess, since the charge was negative}$$

Practice

1. How many electrons must be removed from a neutral, isolated conducting sphere to give it a positive charge of 8.0×10^{-8} C?
   (5.0×10^{11} electrons)

2. What will be the force of electric repulsion between two small spheres placed 1.0 m apart, if each has a deficit of 10^{8} electrons?
   (2.3×10^{-12} N)

3. A small object has an excess of 5.00×10^{9} electrons. Calculate the magnitude of the electric field intensity and the electric potential at a distance of 0.500 m from the object.
   (-28.8 N/C, -14.4 V)

4. Two large, horizontal metal plates are separated by 0.050 m. A small plastic sphere is suspended halfway between them, and experiences an electric force of 4.5×10^{-15} N that just balances the force of gravity on it.
   (a) What is the potential difference between the plates, if the charge on the plastic sphere is 6.4×10^{-19} C?
   (b) Calculate the mass of the plastic sphere.
   (3.5×10^{2} V, 4.6×10^{-16} kg)

5. An oil drop, whose mass is found to be 4.95×10^{-15} kg, is balanced between two large, horizontal parallel plates 1.0 cm apart, by a potential difference of 510 V, with the upper plate positive. What is the charge on the drop, both in coulombs and in elementary charges, and is it an excess or deficit of electrons?
   (9.5×10^{-19} C, 6 e, excess)

6. Delicate measurements indicate that the Earth has an electric field surrounding it, similar to that around a positively charged sphere. Its magnitude at the surface of the Earth is about 100 N/C. What charge would an oil drop of mass 2.0×10^{-15} kg have to have, in order to remain suspended by the Earth's electric field? Give your answer in both coulombs and elementary charges.
   (1.96×10^{-16} C, 1.2×10^{3} e)

15.7 The Motion of Charged Particles in Electric Fields

In the Millikan experiment, when charged particles (oil drops) were sprayed between two charged parallel plates, the electric field they experienced caused some of them to move slowly in one direction while others moved more slowly or more quickly in the other direction. By adjusting the magnitude of the electric field between the plates, it was even possible to get some drops to remain stationary, balanced by the downward force of gravity and the upward force of the electric field.

The Millikan apparatus does not, however, give a true picture of the motion of charged particles in an electric field, because of the presence of air and its resistant effect on the motion of such tiny particles. Consider a small positive charge q_1, with a very small mass m, in a vacuum a distance r from a fixed positive charge q_2. We will assume that the mass m is so small that gravitational effects may be neglected.

Indeed, it is this resistant force, provided by the air and changing with the particle's velocity, that establishes the terminal velocity of fall that is so essential to the Millikan technique.

The charge q_1 experiences a Coulomb force, to the right in this case, whose magnitude is given by

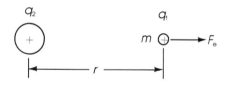

$$F_e = k\frac{q_1 q_2}{r^2}$$

If it is free to move from its original position, it will accelerate in the direction of this electric force (Newton's Second Law) with an acceleration whose magnitude is given by

$$a = \frac{F_e}{m}$$

Describing its subsequent motion becomes difficult, from the point of view of dynamics, because, as it begins to move, r increases, causing F_e to decrease, so that a decreases as well. Motion with a decreasing acceleration poses a difficult analytical problem.

If we use considerations of energy to analyse its motion, it becomes much simpler. As the separation distance between q_1 and q_2 increases, the electric potential energy decreases and the charge q_1 begins to acquire kinetic energy. The Law of Conservation of Energy requires, however, that the total energy remain constant as q_1 moves away from q_2.

At r_1, the system has electric potential energy only, since q_1 is initially at rest.

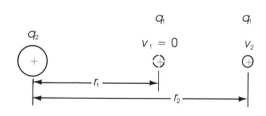

$$E_1 \text{ (total)} = E_{e_1} = +k\frac{q_1 q_2}{r_1} \quad \text{since } F_e \text{ is a force of repulsion}$$

At r_2, the system still has electric potential energy, but also has kinetic energy in the form of the moving mass m.

$$E_2 \text{ (total)} = E_{e_2} + E_{k_2}$$

$$= +k\frac{q_1 q_2}{r_2} + \frac{1}{2}mv_2^2$$

Since total energy is conserved as q moves from r_1 to r_2,

$$E_1 \text{ (total)} = E_2 \text{ (total)}$$

$$k\frac{q_1 q_2}{r_1} = k\frac{q_1 q_2}{r_2} + \frac{1}{2}mv_2^2$$

$$-\left[k\frac{q_1 q_2}{r_2} - k\frac{q_1 q_2}{r_1}\right] = \frac{1}{2}mv_2^2$$

$$-\Delta E_e = \Delta E_k$$

That is, the charged particle q_1 moves in the electric field of q_2 in such a way that the electric potential energy it loses ($-\Delta E_e$) is equal to the kinetic energy it gains (ΔE_k). A sample problem will illustrate.

Sample problems

A small pith ball of mass 1.0×10^{-5} kg and charge $+2.0 \times 10^{-9}$ C is at rest 25 cm from a fixed positive charge of 5.0×10^{-6} C. Neglecting gravitational effects and air resistance, with what speed will the pith ball be moving when it is 50 cm from the other charge?
At a distance $r_1 = 0.25$ m,

$$E_{e_1} = k\frac{q_1 q_2}{r_1}$$

$$= \frac{(9.0 \times 10^9 \text{ N·m}^2/\text{C}^2)(5.0 \times 10^{-6} \text{ C})(2.0 \times 10^{-9} \text{ C})}{(0.25 \text{ m})}$$

$$= 3.6 \times 10^{-4} \text{ J}$$

At a distance $r_2 = 0.50$ m,

$$E_{e_2} = k\frac{q_1 q_2}{r_2}$$

$$= 1.8 \times 10^{-4} \text{ J}$$

Therefore, in moving from r_1 to r_2,

$$\Delta E_e = E_{e_2} - E_{e_1}$$

$$= 1.8 \times 10^{-4} \text{ J} - 3.6 \times 10^{-4} \text{ J}$$

$$= -1.8 \times 10^{-4} \text{ J}$$

But, this loss in electric potential energy is gained by the pith ball as kinetic energy.

$$\Delta E_k = 1.8 \times 10^{-4} \text{ J} = \frac{1}{2}mv^2$$

$$v = \sqrt{\frac{2\Delta E_k}{m}}$$

$$= \sqrt{\frac{2(1.8 \times 10^{-4} \text{ J})}{1.0 \times 10^{-5} \text{ kg}}}$$

$$= 6.0 \text{ m/s}$$

When the electric field in which the charged particle is moving is a uniform electric field, its motion is much simpler. In a uniform electric field

$$\vec{F_e} = q\vec{\mathcal{E}} = \text{constant}$$

Therefore $$\vec{a} = \frac{\vec{F_e}}{m} = \text{constant, also}$$

Thus, the charged particle moves with uniform acceleration. This will be the case for small charged particles (such as ions, electrons, and protons) where gravitational effects are negligible and they are moving between two parallel plates in a vacuum.

Besides, the work done by a constant force is just the product of the force and the displacement. In a parallel plate apparatus, whose separation is d, the work done in moving a charge q from one plate to the other is

$$W = \vec{F_e} \cdot \vec{d}$$

$$= \mathcal{E}qd \quad \text{since } \vec{\mathcal{E}} \text{ and } \vec{d} \text{ are in the same direction}$$
$$= \frac{V}{d}qd = Vq$$

This amount of work is equal in magnitude to the change in electric potential energy and also the change in kinetic energy of the particle as it moves from one plate to the other. A sample problem will illustrate many of these relationships.

Sample problems

The potential difference between two parallel plates is 8000 V. If a "free" electron, of mass 9.1×10^{-31} kg and charge 1.6×10^{-19} C, is released at the negative plate, with what speed does it hit the positive plate?

For the free electron,

$$-\Delta E_e = \Delta E_k \qquad \text{(electric potential energy lost}$$
$$qV = \frac{1}{2}mv^2 \qquad \text{equals kinetic energy gained)}$$

$$v = \sqrt{\frac{2\,qV}{m}}$$

$$= \sqrt{\frac{2(1.6 \times 10^{-19}\ \text{C})(8.0 \times 10^3\ \text{V})}{9.1 \times 10^{-31}\ \text{kg}}}$$

$$= 5.3 \times 10^7\ \text{m/s}$$

Note that this speed is not negligible, compared to the speed of light (about 18%). This analysis becomes unsatisfactory for electrons accelerated by potentials of more than a few thousand volts, as they begin to show relativistic effects (see Chapter 17).

Practice

1. The potential difference between two parallel plates is 1.5×10^2 V. If 0.24 J of work is required to move a small charge from one plate to the other, what is the magnitude of the charge? (1.6×10^{-3} C)

2. An alpha particle has a positive charge of 2 e and a mass of 6.6×10^{-27} kg. With what velocity would an alpha particle reach the negative plate of a parallel plate apparatus with a potential difference of 2.0×10^3 V, if it started, at rest,
   (a) next to the positive plate?
   (b) at the midpoint between the plates?
   (4.4×10^5 m/s, 3.1×10^5 m/s)

3. A pith ball of mass 1.0×10^{-5} kg with a positive charge of 4.0×10^{-7} C is slowly pulled by a string a distance of 50 cm through a potential difference of 8.0×10^2 V. It is then released from rest and "falls" back to its original position. Calculate:
   (a) the work done by the string in moving the pith ball
   (b) the average force required to do this work
   (c) the kinetic energy with which the pith ball reaches its original position
   (d) its speed just as it reaches its original position
   (3.2×10^{-4} J, 6.4×10^{-4} N, 3.2×10^{-4} J, 8.0 m/s)

4. Two electrons are held, at rest, 10^{-12} m apart, and then released. With what kinetic energy and speed is each moving when they are a "large" distance apart? (1.2×10^{-16} J, 1.6×10^7 m/s)

5. What potential difference is required to accelerate a deuteron, of mass 3.3×10^{-27} kg and charge 1.6×10^{-19} C, from rest to a speed of 5.0×10^6 m/s? (2.6×10^5 V)

15.8 Investigations

Investigation 15.1:
The Millikan Experiment (Method 1)

Problem:
How can you demonstrate that a smallest unit of electric charge exists, and compare the charges on small charged spheres?

Materials:
Millikan apparatus, designed for use with latex spheres, such as the Macalaster apparatus
stopwatch
a supply of latex spheres

Procedure:
1. Connect the light to a 6.3 V AC source of power. The light must be adjusted so that the image of the bulb's filament is located right at the centre of the plates. To make this adjustment, hold a piece of paper vertically above the centre of the plates and tilt the light slightly so that it shines on the paper. Now, slide the tube containing the filament back and forth until a sharp image is formed on the paper. The filament should be vertical.
2. Plug the two wires from the plates into the proper terminals on the switch, and then connect the two wires from the switch to a source of 200 V DC. The voltage in the power supply is high, so do not turn it on until you have finished making all the necessary connections.
3. The switch controls the charges on the plates. In the centre position, there is no charge on either plate. With the switch up, one plate is positive and the other negative; with the switch down, these polarities are reversed. By moving the switch, the direction of motion of a charged latex sphere is controlled.
4. With the switch centred, squeeze the bulb once, quickly, to bring a cloud of latex spheres between the plates. If no spheres appear, squeeze the bulb again. If you still cannot see any spheres, probably the light needs repositioning, the telescope is not in focus, or the atomizer nozzle is plugged. The nozzle can be cleaned by removing it and blowing water through it until the spray is clear.
5. Once the latex spheres appear clearly, note their motion. Remember that, through a telescope, everything appears inverted.

Select a small sphere and measure its time of travel over 10 spaces on the grid in the telescope. DO NOT LOSE THIS SPHERE!

6. Place the switch in the up position, and again time the sphere over 10 spaces. Now, place the switch in the down position, and measure the time it takes to travel 10 spaces a third time. Note the relationship between the velocity of the same sphere under the force of gravity alone, under the force of gravity plus the electric field, and under the force of gravity minus the electric field.

7. Bring in a new batch of spheres, by squeezing the bulb. Moving the switch quickly from the centre position to the up and then the down position will cause any fast-moving, highly charged spheres to accelerate towards one plate or the other, and so leave the field of view. Those that remain should be slower moving, with a smaller charge, and should be easier to manipulate.

8. For each of at least 15 different spheres, measure the time taken to move 10 grid spaces, both with the switch up and with it down. Why should you not have to measure the time each takes with the switch in the centre position?

Analysis and conclusions:

1. Using 10 spaces as your unit of length, convert all of the times you measured to velocities; for example, if a sphere moved 10 spaces in 4.2 s, its velocity, for our purposes, is

$$v = \frac{d}{t} = \frac{10 \text{ spaces}}{4.2 \text{ s}}$$
$$= 2.4 \text{ spaces/s}$$

2. Using v^+ to denote a velocity when the gravitational and electrical force are in the same direction ($F_g + F_e$), and v^- to denote a velocity when they are in opposite directions ($F_g - F_e$), tabulate all of your data in the form shown.

Sphere	v^+	v^-	$v^+ + v^-$	$v^+ - v^-$

For spheres with relatively small charges on them, v^+ will be the greater of the two velocities measured (i.e., the smaller time). Two oppositely charged spheres will move with v^+ when the switch is in opposite positions.

The principle responsible for this technique has to do with the terminal velocity with which a sphere will move through a resistant fluid, such as the air between the plates. In such a case terminal velocity $\propto$ driving force and, due to their very small mass, latex spheres will accelerate to their terminal velocity almost instantaneously.

3. For each sphere, calculate the sum and difference of v^+ and v^- and include these values in the appropriate columns of your table.

4. Fragments and clumps of spheres are quite common in this experiment, and the results obtained from trials where these occur should be eliminated from the analysis. To do this, we make use of the following relationship:

$$\text{Since } v^+\alpha \ (F_g + F_e) \quad \text{and} \quad v^-\alpha \ (F_g - F_e)$$
$$\text{Then } (v^+ + v^-) \ \alpha \ (F_g + F_e) + (F_g - F_e)$$
$$\alpha \ 2 \ F_g$$

But $2 \ F_g$ should be a constant, if all of the spheres have the same mass (and are not fragments or clumps). Therefore, the sum $v^+ + v^-$ should be quite constant, for spheres of the same mass, and any spheres whose value of $v^+ + v^-$ differs significantly from the rest should be rejected.

5. Using the same analysis for the remaining spheres (not rejected due to mass variation),

$$v^+ - v^- \ \alpha \ (F_g + F_e) - (F_g - F_e)$$
$$\alpha \ 2F_e$$

Thus, since F_e depends only on the charge on the sphere, $v^+ - v^-$ can be used as a measure of the charge on each sphere.

6. Plot a bar graph using an arbitrary horizontal scale and a vertical scale that includes the largest values of $v^+ - v^-$ obtained. What evidence do you see from this graph for the existence of a small unit of charge? What is the smallest number of charges you measured? What is the smallest change in number of charges you measured? Can you, then, assign a number of elementary charges to each sphere in your table?

Investigation 15.2:
The Millikan Experiment (Method 2)

Problem:
How can you determine a value for the elementary charge?

Materials:
Millikan apparatus, designed for use with oil drops, such as the Griffin-George apparatus
DC power supply, including voltmeter
atomizer and a supply of fine silicon oil
small ruler, calibrated in millimetres

Procedure:

1. Set up the Millikan apparatus, using a small spirit level to ensure that the top plate is perfectly horizontal.
2. Connect the electrical circuitry as shown.

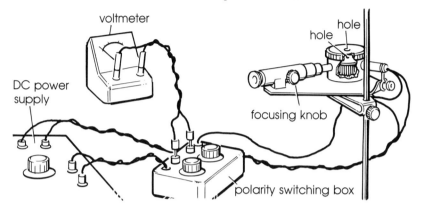

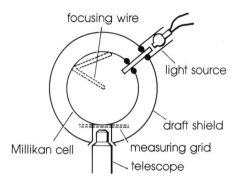

3. Insert a fine wire through the small hole in the upper plate. Using the adjusting knob on the telescope, focus until a sharp image of the wire is visible. Also, adjust the telescope eyepiece until a sharp image of the measuring grid is visible in front of the wire.
4. Spray a fine mist of oil drops from the atomizer just above the hole in the upper plate, letting them drift down towards the plate. Observe these oil drops through the telescope. Why do they appear to rise in the field of view? After a few seconds, the stream of oil drops will become weaker, and a suitable drop must be selected for the experiment. To be useful, the drop must be charged and be as large as possible. To select a suitable drop, apply a large potential difference to the plates, using the variable DC power supply. This potential difference will have no effect on an uncharged drop, but those that are charged will either move faster in the same direction, or in the reverse direction, depending on their charge. It is one of the drops that reverses direction that we want.
5. To balance one of these drops, quickly reduce the potential, thereby causing the drop to lose speed, until it eventually stops and remains balanced between the plates. Other drops in the field of view will soon collide with the top or bottom plate, or drift out of focus because of Brownian motion. At this stage, the field of view should contain one large stationary drop. Re-

A large drop, in addition to being easier to see, is less likely to drift out of the field of view of the telescope as a result of Brownian motion. Brownian motion is the random and chaotic buffeting that small objects experience in collisions with smaller, invisible, but fast-moving molecules. Einstein's explanation of this microscopic observation clinched the atomic theory.

cord the potential difference necessary to balance this drop.

6. Now the terminal velocity of fall under gravity must be measured. To do this, momentarily increase the potential difference so that the drop moves up to a point near the top plate. To stop the drop there, simply return the potential difference to its balancing value. If the potential difference is now reduced to zero (the source is disconnected and the plates are connected together), the drop will fall under the force of gravity and air friction, with a constant terminal velocity, v_o. To determine this velocity, measure the time taken for the drop to fall a given number of scale divisions on the grid. Later, when this grid has been calibrated, this velocity may be calculated in metres per second.

7. Repeat this procedure as many times as possible, each time selecting a new oil drop and measuring both its balancing potential difference and its terminal velocity of fall under gravity.

8. To calibrate the grid, remove the upper plate and hold the small ruler vertically below the place where the hole in the upper plate would have been. By sighting through the telescope, determine the number of grid divisions making up 1 mm.

Calculations:

1. For each drop, carry out the following calculations:
   (a) Determine the terminal velocity: knowing the number of scale divisions making up 1 mm, and the time required to fall a given number of scale divisions, calculate v_o in metres per second.
   (b) Determine the volume of the drop: using the relation from Stokes' Law given on **page 598**, determine, first, the radius of the drop. Your teacher will tell you the density and viscosity of air, as well as the density of the oil you are using. Then, assuming the drop is a sphere, calculate its volume.
   (c) Determine the mass of the drop: since mass is the product of volume and density, the mass of each drop can be calculated.
   (d) Determine the charge on each drop: using the relation developed on page 598, calculate the total charge on each drop, in coulombs.

Analysis and conclusions:

1. Examine the list of values for the total charge on each drop. To create a longer list, share your values with those of your classmates. What is the smallest value you determined for the total charge on an oil drop?
2. Divide this smallest value into each of the other values you calculated. Express the result as a small whole number, if possible. Then divide the total charge on each drop by the small whole number determined for that drop, to obtain a value for the elementary charge from that drop.
3. To arrive at an average value for your experiment, average all of the values for the elementary charge obtained in question 2. Express the accuracy as a percent difference from the accepted value.
4. If, by chance, the smallest value for the total charge on any drop had been the result of an excess or deficit of two, or even three, elementary charges, how might this have been apparent when you divided its value into each of the other values of total charge? What correction would you have to make, before proceeding?

15.9 Review

Discussion

1. Why do certain types of clothing tend to stick together when they are removed from a clothes dryer? How do the new "cling-free" products work to overcome this attraction?
2. Draw a diagram to show the separation of charge that occurs when a negatively charged rod is brought near the ball of a neutral, metal-leaf electroscope.
3. Describe two ways to give a neutral electroscope a positive charge, using only a piece of silk and a glass rod. Could the same materials be used to give it a negative charge? If so, how?
4. Compare Newton's Law of Universal Gravitation with Coulomb's Law, pointing out similarities and differences.
5. Coulomb's Law may only be used to calculate the force between charges under certain conditions. What are those conditions, and why are they imposed?

Even some chemical reactions and biological processes are believed to be caused by electric and/or thermal interactions between particles; e.g., the making and breaking of covalent bonds in molecules and the electrostatic attraction between two DNA molecules to form a chromosome.

An intriguing example of electric fields and charging by contact can be demonstrated by suspending an aluminum-coated pith ball between two oppositely charged, insulated metal plates, as shown. Touch the ball to one plate and observe. Can you explain what happens?

6. Suggest a simple reason why two electric field lines can never cross. (Hint: Consider the field at the point where they would cross, and imagine that you are a small test charge.)

7. Why do we use a "small" test charge to detect and measure an electric field?

8. If a charged particle is free to move in an electric field, in what direction will it always travel?

9. Three small, negatively charged spheres are located at the vertices of an equilateral triangle. If the magnitudes of the charges are equal, sketch the electric field in the region around this charge distribution, including the space inside the triangle.

10. If two points have the same electric potential, is it true that no work is required to move a test charge from one point to the other? Does this mean that no force is required, as well?

11. How much work is required to move a charged particle through an electric field, if it moves along a path that is always perpendicular to an electric field line? How would the potential change along such a path?

12. Most experiments in atomic physics are performed in a vacuum. Describe the effect on the Millikan Oil Drop Experiment, of performing it in a vacuum.

Problems

13. Two small, oppositely charged spheres have a force of electric attraction between them of 1.6×10^{-2} N. What does this force become if each sphere is touched with its identical, neutral mate, and then replaced twice as far apart as before? The mates are taken far away.

14. What is the distance between two protons ($e = +1.6 \times 10^{-19}$ C) when they exert forces on each other of magnitude 4.0×10^{-11} N ?

15. One model of the structure of the hydrogen atom consists of a stationary proton with an electron moving in a circular path around it, of radius 5.3×10^{-11} m. The masses of a proton and an electron are 1.67×10^{-27} kg and 9.1×10^{-31} kg, respectively.
    (a) What is the electrostatic force between the electron and the proton?
    (b) What is the gravitational force between them?
    (c) Which force is mainly responsible for the electron's centripetal motion?
    (d) Calculate the velocity and period of the electron's orbit around the proton.

16. Two small, identical, charged spheres attract each other with a force of 8.0×10^{-5} N, when they are 30 cm apart. They are touched together, and are again placed 30 cm apart, but they now exert a force of repulsion of 1.0×10^{-5} N on each other.
    (a) What is the charge on each sphere after they are touched?
    (b) What was the charge on each before they were touched?

17. Assume that a single, isolated electron is fixed at ground level. How far above it, vertically, would another electron have to be, so that its mass would be supported by the force of electrostatic repulsion between them? (mass of electron = 9.1×10^{-31} kg)

18. Two small charges, $+4.0 \times 10^{-5}$ C and -1.8×10^{-5} C, are placed 24 cm apart. What is the force on a third small charge, of magnitude -2.5×10^{-6} C, if it is placed on the line joining the other two, and
    (a) 12 cm to the outside of them, on the side of the negative one?
    (b) 12 cm to the outside of them, on the side of the positive one?
    (c) midway between them?

19. A charge of 1.2×10^{-3} C is fixed at each corner of a rectangle that is 30 cm wide and 40 cm long. What is the magnitude and direction of the electric force on each charge? What is the electric field and the electric potential at the centre?

20. A small test charge of $+1.0$ μC experiences an electric force of 6.0×10^{-6} N to the right.
    (a) What is the electric field intensity at that point?
    (b) What force would be exerted on a charge of -7.2×10^{-4} C located at the same point, in place of the test charge?

21. What is the magnitude and direction of the electric field 1.5 m to the right of a positive point charge of magnitude 8.0×10^{-3} C?

22. What is the magnitude and direction of the electric field at point Z in the diagram to the right?

23. The electric field intensity at a point between two large parallel plates is 4.8×10^2 N/C. What does the electric field become, as a result of each of the following changes, considered separately (the plates are isolated):
    (a) when the distance between the plates is halved?
    (b) when the amount of charge on each plate is tripled?
    (c) when the plates are connected together by a conducting wire?

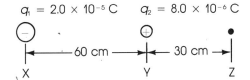

24. Calculate the electric potential 0.50 m from a 4.5×10^{-4} C point charge.

25. A 1.0×10^{-6} C test charge is 40 cm from a 3.2×10^{-3} C charged sphere. How much work was required to move it there from a point 100 cm away from the sphere?

26. How much energy is acquired by an electron, whose charge is 1.6×10^{-19} C, in moving through a potential difference of 2.5×10^4 V?

27. How much work must be done to bring two protons from an infinite distance apart to within 1.0×10^{-15} m of each other? (This shows why particle accelerators are needed!)

28. What is the electric field intensity between two large parallel plates 2.0 cm apart, if a potential difference of 450 V is maintained between them?

29. What potential difference applied between two parallel plates will produce an electric field strength of 2.5×10^3 N/C, if the plates are 8.0 cm apart?

30. How far apart are two parallel plates if a potential difference of 600 V produces an electric field intensity of 1.2×10^4 N/C between them?

31. An oil drop, of mass 2.6×10^{-15} kg, is suspended between two parallel plates 0.50 cm apart, and remains stationary when the potential difference between the plates is 270 V. What is the charge on the oil drop, and how many excess or deficit electrons does it have?

32. A metallic ping-pong ball, of mass 0.10 g, has a charge of 5.0×10^{-6} C. What potential difference, across a large parallel plate apparatus of separation 25 cm, would be required to keep the ball stationary?

33. To neutralize an electroscope with a charge of $+8.0 \times 10^{-12}$ C, how many electrons must be added to it?

34. Determine the electric potential and electric field intensity at a point 0.40 m from a small sphere with an excess of 10^{12} electrons.

35. A ping-pong ball of mass 3.0×10^{-4} kg is hanging from a light thread 1.0 m long, between two vertical parallel plates 10 cm apart, as shown. When the potential difference across the plates is 420 V, the ball comes to equilibrium 1.0 cm to one side of its original position.
    (a) What is the electric field intensity between the plates?
    (b) What is the tension in the thread?
    (c) What is the magnitude of the electric force deflecting the ball?
    (d) What is the charge on the ball?

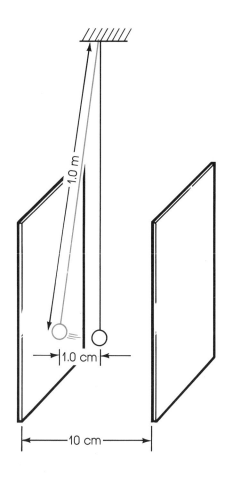

36. An electron is released from rest adjacent to the negative plate in a parallel plate apparatus. A potential difference of 500 V is maintained between the plates, and they are in a vacuum. With what speed does the electron collide with the positive plate?

37. What potential difference would accelerate a helium nucleus from rest to a kinetic energy of 1.9×10^{-15} J ? ($q = +2\,e$, for a helium nucleus)

38. An electron with a velocity of 5.0×10^6 m/s is injected into a parallel plate apparatus through a hole in the positive plate. It moves across the vacuum between the plates, colliding with the negative plate at 1.0×10^6 m/s. What is the potential difference between the plates? (mass of electron $= 9.1 \times 10^{-31}$ kg)

39. Four parallel plates are connected, in a vacuum, as shown:

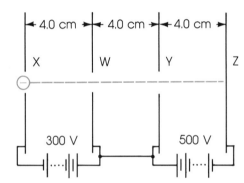

An electron, essentially at rest, drifts into the hole in plate X and is accelerated to the right. Assuming that its vertical motion is negligible, it passes through hole W, goes on through hole Y, and then continues moving towards plate Z. Using the dimensions and potential differences given in the diagram, calculate:
   (a) the velocity with which the electron passes through hole W
   (b) the velocity with which it passes through hole Y
   (c) the distance from plate Z of the point where the electron momentarily comes to rest
   (d) the velocity with which it arrives back at plate X

40. Two alpha particles (mass $= 6.6 \times 10^{-27}$ kg, charge $= 3.2 \times 10^{-19}$ C), separated by an enormous distance, approach each other along a "head-on collision" path. Each has a speed of 3.0×10^6 m/s to begin with. Calculate their minimum separation, assuming no deflection from their original path.

Numerical Answers to Review Problems

13. 1.0×10^{-3} N
14. 2.4×10^{-9} m
15. (a) 8.2×10^{-8} N (b) 3.6×10^{-47} N
    (c) the electrostatic force
    (d) 2.2×10^6 m/s, 1.5×10^{-16} s
16. (a) 1.0×10^{-8} C, same signs
    (b) 4.0×10^{-8} C and 2.0×10^{-8} C, opposite signs
17. 5.1 m
18. (a) 21 N [away from the negative charge]
    (b) 59 N [towards the positive charge]
    (c) 91 N [towards the positive charge]
19. 2.1×10^5 N [at a 145° angle away from each end of each 30 cm side]; 0; 1.7×10^8 V
20. (a) 6.0 N/C [right]
    (b) 4.3×10^{-3} N [left]
21. 3.2×10^7 N/C [right]
22. 5.8×10^5 N/C [right]
23. (a) 4.8×10^2 N/C
    (b) 1.4×10^3 N/C
    (c) 0
24. 8.1×10^6 V
25. 43 J
26. 4.0×10^{-15} J
27. 2.3×10^{-13} J
28. 2.3×10^4 N/C
29. 2.0×10^2 V
30. 5.0×10^{-2} m
31. 4.7×10^{-19} C, ± 3 electrons
32. 49 V
33. 5.0×10^7
34. -3.6×10^3 V, 9.0×10^3 N/C [towards sphere]
35. (a) 4.2×10^3 N/C
    (b) 2.9×10^{-3} N
    (c) 2.9×10^{-5} N
    (d) 7.0×10^{-9} C
36. 1.3×10^7 m/s
37. 5.9×10^3 V
38. 68 V
39. (a) 1.0×10^7 m/s
    (b) 1.0×10^7 m/s
    (c) 1.6 cm, to the left
    (d) 0 m/s
40. 1.6×10^{-14} m
41. (a) 0.41 cm
    (b) 8.0×10^7 m/s [right 5° down]

41. An electron enters a parallel plate apparatus 10 cm long and 2.0 cm wide, moving horizontally at 8.0×10^7 m/s, as shown. If the potential difference across the plates is 600 V, determine:
    (a) the vertical deflection of the electron from its original path.
    (b) the velocity with which it leaves the parallel plate apparatus, in both magnitude and direction.

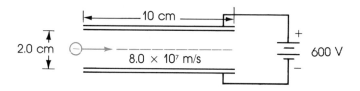

Hint: This problem may be treated the same as if you had a gravitational projectile whose motion is the resultant of uniform motion in the horizontal plane and uniform acceleration in the vertical plane.

The Photocopier

The office photocopier has become an important element in the communication of graphic information. The process used in most photocopiers is called **xerography**, and utilizes the simple laws of electrostatics from this chapter.

The heart of the copying process is an aluminum drum covered by a very thin (< 50 μm thick) coating of a photosensitive substance called selenium. As you will learn in Chapter 18, a photosensitive material is one that gives off an electric charge when exposed to light. The process is started by **charging** the drum to a potential difference of about 700 V. It will retain this charge, distributed uniformly over its surface, as long as it remains in the dark.

When a document to be copied is placed face down on a glass plate, and the cover closed, bright light from a source within the copier is directed onto the original, then reflected from it through a lens and onto the charged selenium drum. In places where the original document is white, light is strongly reflected onto the selenium drum, causing it to discharge in these areas. Conversely, where the original is black, no light is reflected onto the drum, so that it remains charged in these areas. Thus, as a result of the **exposure** of the original to light, an electrical image of it is created on the drum; neutral where the original is white, charged where the original is black. As long as the drum is kept dark, this image will remain.

The electrical image on the drum is **developed** into a dry copy, using a substance called "toner". Except for its black colour, toner looks very much like baking flour. It consists of very tiny (about 0.005 mm diameter) plastic particles, coloured by adding lamp black. In the development process, toner particles are given an opposite charge to that on the selenium drum, and are then "cascaded", or dumped, over the rotating drum. As a result of their opposite charge, they are attracted to the charged areas of the drum. They do not adhere to the neutral areas, falling into a collecting bin for re-use. Thus, a toner-image of the original is created on the drum.

To create a permanent copy of this image, the toner must be **transferred** to paper. To do this, a sheet of paper is given a charge that is opposite to that of the toner particles. As the drum rolls across this paper, toner particles that adhere to the drum will be attracted, instead, to the paper, forming a black-and-white image.

If you rubbed a finger across the paper, at this stage, the toner would smudge terribly. To "fix" the image, heat in the form of radiant energy is allowed to fall on the paper, melting the plastic toner particles and bonding or **fusing** them to the paper to produce a fixed dry copy.

As a final step, the selenium drum must be **cleaned** of any excess toner. It is first charged with the same charge as the toner particles (thereby loosening any that adhere), and then brushed clean with a cotton or rayon material.

As can be seen, the photocopying process involves six distinct steps:

1. charging
2. exposure
3. development
4. transfer
5. fusing
6. cleaning

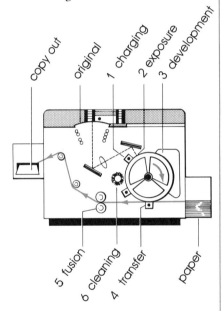

From an understanding of these processes, you can answer the following simple questions about how photocopiers work.

1. Why does the first copy take longer to make than subsequent multiple copies?
2. How are enlarged and reduced photocopies made?
3. Why are copies hot, and why do they often stick together after they are made?
4. Which substances in the process have to be replenished from time to time?

16 Magnetic Fields and Electromagnetism

16.1 Natural Magnetism

Even before 600 B.C., the Greeks had discovered that lodestone, a type of ore containing iron oxide, was able to exert forces of attraction on small iron objects. Also, when pivoted in a horizontal plane and allowed to rotate freely, a needle-shaped piece of lodestone would always come to rest in a north-south position, a fact that led to its widespread use in navigation. Since this type of iron ore was first found near a region in Asia Minor called Magnesia, its effects became known as magnetism.

Magnets

An airport radar antenna

Nowadays, lodestone is rarely used for its magnetic properties, having been replaced by artificial magnets made from various alloys of iron, nickel, cobalt, and gadolinium. When a bar magnet is dipped in iron filings, the filings are attracted to it and accumulate most noticeably around regions at each end of the magnet, called **poles**. When the bar magnet is allowed to rotate freely, the pole that tends to seek the northerly direction is called the "north-seeking pole", or, more simply, the N-pole. The other is called the south-seeking pole, or the S-pole.

By placing two bar magnets first with similar poles together and then with opposite poles together, and noting the interaction, the **Law of Magnetic Poles** is evident:

Opposite magnetic poles attract. Similar magnetic poles repel.

Magnetic Fields

The magnetic force is similar to the gravitational force (Chapter 5) and the electrostatic force (Chapter 15) in that it acts at a distance, creating a magnetic field of force in the region of space around a magnet. A magnetic field can be detected by its effect on a small test compass (magnetized needle); it is depicted visually by drawing magnetic field lines that show the direction in which the north pole of the test compass points, at all locations in the field. Experimentally, the lines in a magnetic field can be easily traced by sprinkling iron filings on a sheet of paper placed in the field. The filings behave like many tiny compasses, and line up in the direction of the field at all points. They produce a "picture" of the magnetic field, as shown.

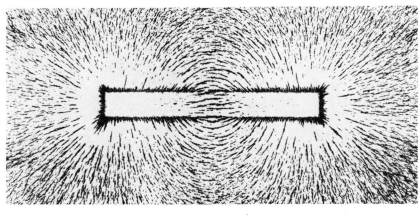

The magnetic field of a bar magnet

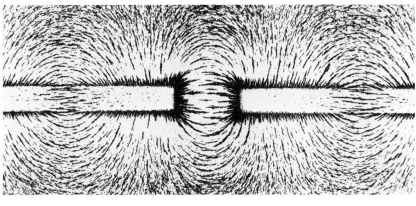

The magnetic field of a pair of opposite poles, close together

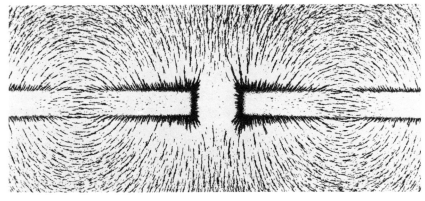

The magnetic field of a pair of similar poles, close together

$\vec{B}$ is in the direction in which an N-pole would move, even though it is impossible to have an isolated single pole.

Since iron filings have no marked N or S poles, they reveal only the pattern of the magnetic field lines, not their direction. The relative strength of the magnetic field is indicated by the spacing of adjacent field lines: where lines are close together, the magnetic field is strong.

The magnetic field strength at any point is a vector quantity, represented by the symbol $\vec{B}$, whose magnitude is related to the torque on a small test compass that is not aligned with the direction of the field. It will be possible to make a more precise definition of $\vec{B}$ later in this chapter, when we are dealing with electromagnetism.

Magnetic Field of the Earth

It may seem confusing that the pole near the north end of the Earth's axis is a south pole, but it must be so if it attracts the north pole of other compasses and magnets.

A pivoted magnet will rotate and point north-south because of its interaction with the Earth's magnetic field. As early as the 16th century, Sir William Gilbert, a distinguished English physicist, had devised a model to explain the Earth's magnetism. He determined that the Earth's magnetic field was similar to that of a large bar magnet, inclined at a slight angle to the Earth's axis and with its south pole in the northern hemisphere. The diagrams show this field and the bar magnet that was thought, in Gilbert's time, to be responsible for it.

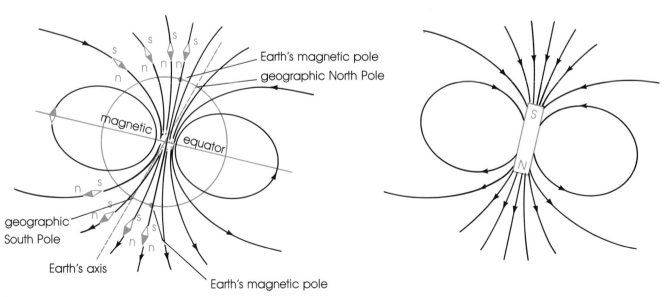

The magnetic field of the Earth

The magnetic field of an inclined bar magnet

A compass points towards the Earth's magnetic north pole, rather than towards its geographic north pole (the north end of its axis of rotation). The angle between magnetic north and geographic north varies from position to position on the Earth's surface, and is called the "magnetic declination". In order to navigate by compass, the angle of declination for a particular location must be known to permit calculation of true north.

As well, the Earth's magnetic field is three-dimensional, with both a horizontal and a vertical component. A magnetic compass on a horizontal surface reveals only the horizontal component. The angle between the Earth's magnetic field, at any point, and the horizontal, is called the "magnetic inclination", or "dip", and is measured with the magnetic dipping needle shown.

A dipping needle is a compass, pivoted at its centre of gravity and free to rotate in a vertical plane. When aligned with a horizontal compass pointing north, it will point in the direction of the Earth's magnetic field, and the angle of inclination can be read directly from the attached protractor.

Inclination and declination charts must be revised from time to time, because the Earth's magnetic field seems to be slowing changing. It is believed that these changes result from the Earth's magnetic field rotating about the Earth's axis, taking about 1000 years to make a complete rotation.

Magnetic dipping needle

Since airport runways are always marked to the nearest 10° on navigational maps, this shifting field direction makes it necessary to relabel these maps occasionally.

Induced Magnetism: Temporary and Permanent Magnets

Some materials, such as iron, nickel, cobalt, and gadolinium, even though not normally magnetized, may, under certain circumstances, become magnetized. They are called "ferromagnetic" materials. How they are able to acquire magnetic properties may be explained satisfactorily using the **Domain Theory of Magnetism**.

Ferromagnetic substances are composed of a large number of tiny regions (less than 1 μm long or wide) called "magnetic domains". Each domain behaves like a tiny bar magnet, with its own north and south poles. When the material is in an unmagnetized state, these millions of domains are oriented at random, so that their magnetic effects cancel each other out, as the diagram indicates.

However, if a piece of iron is placed in a strong enough magnetic field, a strange phenomenon occurs. Some domains actually rotate slightly to align with the external field, while others that are already aligned tend to "grow" at the expense of other non-aligned domains. The net result is that there is a preferred orientation of the domains (in the same direction as the external field), causing the material to behave like a magnet. When the external field is removed, this orientation may remain for a long time, or may disappear almost immediately, depending on the type of material.

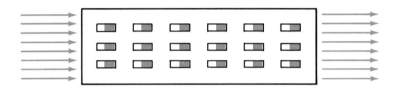

This domain model provides a simple explanation for many common properties of induced magnets:
1. A needle can be magnetized by stroking it in one direction with a strong permanent magnet, thereby aligning its domains.
2. When a bar magnet is broken in two, rather than producing separate north and south poles, two smaller magnets are produced, each with its own north and south poles.
3. Some induced magnets made of soft iron demagnetize instantaneously (temporary magnets such as lifting electromagnets), while others made of hard steel or alloys remain magnetized indefinitely (permanent magnets such as magnetic door catches). Impurities in the alloys seem to "lock" the aligned domains in place and prevent them from relaxing to their random orientation.
4. Heating or dropping a magnet can cause it to lose its magnetization, jostling the domains sufficiently to allow them to move and resume their random orientation.
5. A strong magnetic field can reverse the magnetism in bar magnets so that the pole marked S points north. This occurs when the domains reverse their direction of orientation by 180° due to the influence of the strong external field in the opposite direction.
6. Ships' hulls, columns and beams in buildings, and many other steel structures are often found to be magnetized by the combined effects of the Earth's magnetic field and the vibrations created during construction. The effect is similar to stroking a needle with a strong magnet, in that the domains within the metals are caused to line up with the Earth's magnetic field.

16.2 Electromagnetism

Prior to the 19th century, electricity and magnetism, although similar in many respects, were generally thought to be separate and distinct phenomena. It was left to an accidental discovery by the Danish physicist, Hans Christian Oersted (1777–1851), while teaching at the University of Copenhagen, to reveal the basic relationship between the two. Observing that a magnetic compass needle was deflected by an electric current flowing through a nearby wire, he formulated the basic principle of electromagnetism:

Moving electric charges produce a magnetic field.

Magnetic Field of a Straight Conductor

When an electric current flows through a long, straight wire, the magnetic field created consists of field lines that are concentric circles, with the wire at their centres, as illustrated.

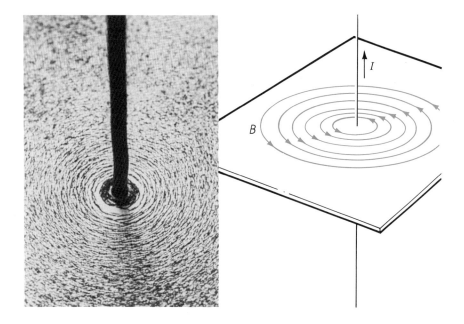

You can remember the direction of these field lines (as indicated by the north pole of a small test compass) if you use the "right-hand rule for a straight conductor":

If a conductor is grasped in the right hand, with the thumb pointing in the direction of the current, the curled fingers will point in the direction of the magnetic field lines.

Magnetic Field of a Loop

When a straight wire is formed into a circular loop, its magnetic field will appear as shown. Note that the field lines inside the loop are closer together, indicating a stronger magnetic field than on the outside of the loop.

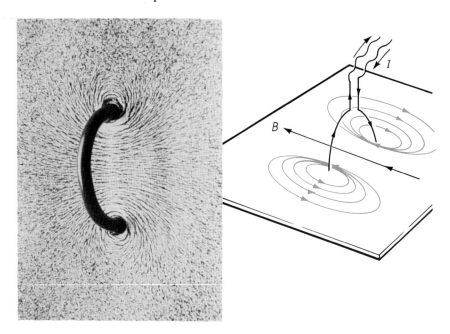

Magnetic Field of a Coil or Solenoid

If a long conductor is wound into a coil with many loops, the coil is called a **solenoid**. The magnetic field of a solenoid is the sum of the magnetic fields of all of its loops. As a result, the field inside the coil can be very strong, consisting of field lines that are straight and very close together, as shown.

A solenoid has a magnetic field very similar to that of a bar magnet. In fact, a solenoid acts in many ways like a bar magnet,

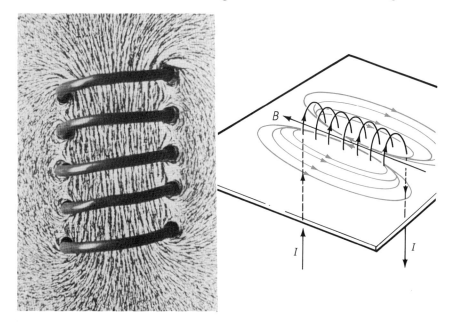

with the exception that its magnetic field can be turned off and on. To remember the direction of the magnetic field of a solenoid and, hence, the polarity of the bar magnet it is similar to, we can make use of a "right-hand rule for a solenoid":

If a solenoid is grasped in the right hand, with the fingers curled in the direction of the electric current, the thumb will point in the direction of the magnetic field lines in its core, and, hence, towards its north pole.

The field lines outside the coil have an enormous volume of space to fill, and therefore they spread out so much that the field strength is negligible.

This rule agrees with the previous one, if we point the right thumb along, or tangent to, the curved wire.

Using Electromagnets and Solenoids

If a piece of a ferromagnetic material, such as iron, is placed in the core of a solenoid, the magnetic field becomes much stronger. The domains in the iron are aligned by the magnetic field of the coil, and the total magnetic field is the sum of the field due to the coil and that due to the magnetized core material. The total field can be thousands of times as strong as that of the coil alone. The ratio of magnetic field strength with a particular core material to magnetic field strength without it is called the permeability of the core material. A table of magnetic permeabilities can be found in the margin.

Table of Magnetic Permeabilities

copper	0.999 99
water	0.999 999
vacuum	1.000 000
oxygen	1.000 002
aluminum	1.000 02
cobalt	170
nickel	1000
steel	2000
iron	6100
permalloy	100 000

Substances in which the ferromagnetic domains quickly return to their random orientation once the external field is removed are called "soft" ferromagnetic materials. Usually, they also have very high permeabilities.

The iron used as a solenoid core must be soft (magnetically, that is), so that when the current in the solenoid is shut off, the core demagnetizes quickly and the magnetic field drops to zero. An iron-core solenoid has many applications related to its ability to be a strong magnet that can be turned on and off. In addition to its use in the well-known lifting electromagnets found in scrap-metal yards, the solenoid has a wide variety of uses in bells, switches, relays, and magnetic speakers, as the diagrams that follow demonstrate.

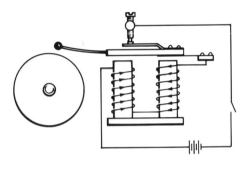
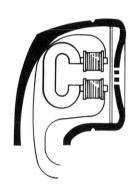
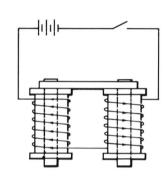

16.3 Magnetic Forces on Conductors and Moving Charges

The basic law of magnetism states that two magnetic fields will interact to produce forces of attraction (with opposite poles) and repulsion (with similar poles). When Oersted discovered that moving electric charges produce a magnetic field, it was only natural for him to investigate the interaction between a magnet and the magnetic field of a conductor carrying a current.

Conductor in a Magnetic Field

One of the simplest examples of a conductor carrying current in a magnetic field occurs when a straight wire carries a current $\vec{I}$ through a magnetic field $\vec{B}$ between the poles of a horseshoe magnet. Since the direction of the current in relation to the direction of the magnetic field is significant, we shall emphasize the vector nature of the electric current by using vector notation on $\vec{I}$.

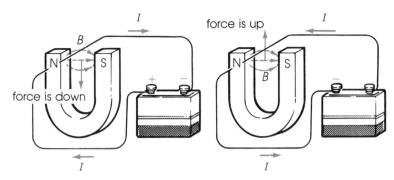

There are several important observations to be made from the use of such an apparatus:
- The force on the conductor $\vec{F}$ is in a direction perpendicular to both the magnetic field $\vec{B}$ and the direction of the current $\vec{I}$.
- Reversing either the current direction or the magnetic field reverses the direction of the force.

Another simple right-hand rule can be used for remembering the relationship between the relative directions of $\vec{F}$, $\vec{I}$, and $\vec{B}$:

If the right thumb points in the direction of the current, and the extended fingers point in the direction of the magnetic field, the force will be in the direction in which the right palm would push.

Experiments can be done with an apparatus similar to that on page 662 to study the factors affecting the magnitude of the force on a current-carrying conductor in a magnetic field. It has been found that
- $F \propto B$, the strength of the magnetic field
- $F \propto l$, the length of the conductor in the magnetic field
- $F \propto I$, the current flowing through the conductor

Also, if the conductor cuts across the magnetic field lines at an angle of θ (in the case of the straight conductor and horseshoe magnet $\theta = 90°$),
- $F \propto \sin\theta$, the angle between $\vec{B}$ and $\vec{I}$

Combining all these factors that have an effect on the magnitude of $\vec{F}$, we can write

$$F \propto B\,I\,l \sin\theta$$
$$\text{or} \qquad F = k\,B\,I\,l \sin\theta$$

as an expression for the force acting on the conductor. In SI, units have already been chosen for length, current, and force, but if we use this equation as the defining equation for the units of magnetic field strength B, we can write

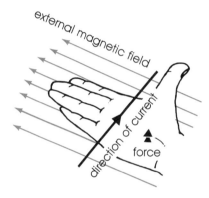

There are useful techniques in vector multiplication that automatically keep track of the direction and the $\sin\theta$ term for us, but we will leave them for a more advanced course.

Many of the quantities discussed in this chapter are vectors whose directions are related to each other by the various right-hand rules. Since these directions are not evident directly from the mathematics, the equations relating them yield expressions for their magnitudes only. When dealing with the magnitudes of vector quantities such as $\vec{F}, \vec{B}, \vec{I}$, and $\vec{v}$, we shall simply write the symbol without the vector sign; i.e., B refers to the magnitude of the vector $\vec{B}$, without regard to its direction.

$$B = \frac{F}{k\,I\,l\,\sin\theta}$$

The SI unit of magnetic field strength is the tesla (T), defined so that:

---

1 T is the magnetic field strength when a conductor with a current of 1 A, and a length 1 m at an angle of 90° to the magnetic field, experiences a force of 1 N.

$$1\text{ T} = 1\text{ N/A·m}$$

A magnetic field of magnitude 1 T is fairly strong—about four or five times the strength of the field of a typical permanent magnet found in a classroom laboratory.

Then, in the expression for B, we have

$$B = \frac{1\text{ N}}{k(1\text{ A})(1\text{ m})(1)}$$

$$1\text{ T} = \frac{1\text{ N/A·m}}{k}$$

As a result, the value of k will always be 1 (when appropriate units are used for $\vec{B}$, $\vec{I}$, $\vec{F}$, and l), so that the expression for the magnitude of the force on a current-carrying conductor in a magnetic field becomes:

$$F = B\,I\,l\,\sin\theta$$

---

where $\vec{F}$ is the force on the conductor, in newtons

$\vec{B}$ is the magnetic field strength, in teslas

$\vec{I}$ is the current in the conductor, in amperes

l is the length of conductor in the magnetic field, in metres

θ is the angle between $\vec{I}$ and $\vec{B}$

Note that the force is a maximum when $\vec{I}$ crosses $\vec{B}$ at 90° and is zero when $\vec{I}$ and $\vec{B}$ are parallel. There is no force on a conductor that carries current parallel to magnetic field lines.

Sample problem

A straight conductor carries a current of 15 A through a magnetic field a distance of 10 cm, when the magnetic field intensity is 0.60 T. Calculate the magnitude of the force on the conductor, when the angle between it and the magnetic field is
(a) 90°
(b) 45°
(c) 0°

In the general case, the magnitude of the force is given by
$$F = BIl \sin \theta$$
$$= (0.60 \text{ T})(15 \text{ A})(0.10 \text{ m}) \sin \theta$$
$$= 0.90 \sin \theta \text{ N}$$
(a) when $\theta = 90°$, $\sin \theta = 1$, and $F = 0.90$ N
(b) when $\theta = 45°$, $\sin \theta = 0.707$, and $F = 0.90\text{N}(0.707) = 0.64$ N
(c) when $\theta = 0°$, $\sin \theta = 0$, and $F = 0$

In each case above, the direction of the force is that given by the right-hand rule on page 627.

Practice

1. A wire in the armature of an electric motor is 25 cm long and remains in, and perpendicular to, a uniform magnetic field of 0.20 T. What force is exerted on the wire when it carries a current of 15 A? (0.75 N)
2. What length of conductor, running at right angles to a 0.033 T magnetic field and carrying a current of 20 A, experiences a force of 0.10 N? (0.15 m)
3. A wire connecting a taillight to a motorcycle battery is 1.0 m long, and is lying perpendicular to the Earth's magnetic field. If it experiences a force of 6.0×10^{-5} N when carrying a current of 1.5 A, what is the magnitude of the Earth's magnetic field at that location? (4.0×10^{-5} T)
4. Two electrical line poles are situated 50 m apart, one directly north of the other, and the horizontal wire running between them carries a DC current of 200 A. If the Earth's magnetic field, in the vicinity, has a magnitude of 5.0×10^{-5} T and the magnetic inclination is 45°, what is the magnetic force on the wire? (0.35 N)

Force on a Moving Charge

The force that a conductor experiences in a magnetic field is due to the motion of charged particles moving through it; if the charged particles within the conductor were stationary, it would carry no current and experience no force. It would seem, then, that a freely moving charged particle, not confined within a conductor, would experience a similar force as it moves through a magnetic field.

Consider a particle of charge q, moving with velocity $\vec{v}$, at an angle θ to a magnetic field $\vec{B}$.

If n such particles pass a given point in a time Δt, they constitute an electric current given by

$$I = \frac{nq}{\Delta t}$$

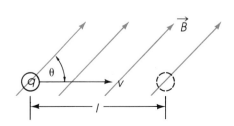

630

Fundamentals of Physics: A Senior Course

Also, if l is the distance travelled through the magnetic field by each of the charges in the time Δt,

$$l = v\,\Delta t$$

Thus, using our previous equation, the magnitude of the total force on the current comprised of these n moving charges is given by

$$F = B\,I\,l\sin\theta$$
$$= B\left(\frac{n\,q}{\Delta t}\right)(v\,\Delta t)\sin\theta$$
$$= n(Bqv\sin\theta)$$

Therefore, the magnitude of the force on each of these n charges is:

$$F = Bqv\,\sin\theta$$

As mentioned before, this is an equation for the magnitude of the force only, involving the magnitudes of the field strength $\vec{B}$, and the velocity of the moving charge $\vec{v}$; the direction of the force can be determined using the right-hand rule.

where $\vec{F}$ is the force on the moving charge, in newtons

$\vec{B}$ is the magnetic field strength, in teslas

q is the value of the moving charge, in coulombs

$\vec{v}$ is the velocity of the moving charge, in metres per second

θ is the angle between $\vec{v}$ and $\vec{B}$

This force is a maximum when the charged particle is moving perpendicular to the magnetic field ($\theta = 90°$), and is zero when the charged particle is moving parallel to the magnetic field ($\theta = 0°$).

Also, the direction of the force will again be given by the same right-hand rule that was used with the equation $F = BIl\sin\theta$. Remember, though, that this right-hand rule involves pointing the thumb in the direction of the electric current; if the moving charged particle is positive, the rule applies as it is. However, if the moving particle is negative, the right thumb must point in a direction opposite to the particle's velocity, since a negative particle moving in one direction constitutes an electric current flowing in the opposite direction.

Several sample problems will illustrate how this equation can be applied to charged particles moving in a magnetic field.

$\vec{B}$ (into page)

Sample problems

1. A uniform magnetic field, of magnitude 0.25 T, consists of field lines pointing into the page, as indicated by the x's (representing the tails of straight arrows moving away from the observer) in the sketch.

A proton with a positive charge of 1.6×10^{-19} C enters this magnetic field at point A, moving with a horizontal velocity of 4.0×10^6 m/s [right], as shown. What is the magnitude and direction of the instantaneous force exerted on it at point A?

The magnitude of the force is

$$F = Bqv \sin \theta$$
$$= (0.25 \text{ T})(1.6 \times 10^{-19} \text{ C})(4.0 \times 10^6 \text{ m/s}) \sin 90°$$
$$= 1.6 \times 10^{-13} \text{ N}$$

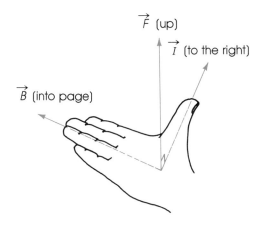

Using the right-hand rule, the direction of the force is up, towards the top of the page, in the plane of the page.

Since a proton is a positive particle, the current it represents as it moves is in the same direction as its velocity. If, however, the particle were an electron, moving to the right, it would constitute a current to the left, so that the force on it would be down, towards the bottom of the page, and opposite to that for a proton.

The situation illustrated in sample problem 1 is very interesting, and is frequently used in high-energy, particle physics research. A charged particle is injected into a uniform magnetic field at right angles to the field lines, and its subsequent motion is observed and analysed.

But what is the motion of such a particle? As it enters the field, it experiences a force of magnitude Bqv (since $\sin \theta = 1$) at right angles to its velocity. Since this force is at right angles to $\vec{v}$, it has no component in the direction of $\vec{v}$, so the magnitude of $\vec{v}$ remains constant. And since q and $\vec{B}$ are given as constant, the magnitude of the magnetic force Bqv is also constant. A constant force acting at right angles to an object's velocity is already familiar to you—it is the centripetal force studied in Chapters 4 and 5. In this case, the magnetic force acting on the particle provides the centripetal force necessary to keep it moving in a circle, of radius r and speed v, in a plane perpendicular to the magnetic field $\vec{B}$. Although the direction of $\vec{v}$ changes, it always remains perpendicular to $\vec{B}$, so the magnitude of $\vec{F}$ stays constant. If the mass of the charged particle is m,

$$F_{\text{magnetic}} = F_{\text{centripetal}}$$
$$Bqv = \frac{mv^2}{r}$$
or $$r = \frac{mv}{Bq}$$

It is interesting to note that the time taken for one complete circular trip through the magnetic field depends on m/q only, and not on v.

$$T = \frac{2\pi r}{v} = \frac{2\pi \dfrac{mv}{Bq}}{v} = \frac{2\pi}{B}\left(\frac{m}{q}\right)$$

Particle accelerators such as cyclotrons make use of this characteristic. (See Chapter 20.)

Often, charged particles acquire their "injection velocities" by being accelerated through a large potential difference in a vacuum, before entering the magnetic field. For a particle of mass m and charge q, accelerated by a potential difference V,

$$-\Delta E_{\text{electric}} = \Delta E_{\text{kinetic}}$$

$$qV = \frac{1}{2}mv^2$$

This simple approach will break down if it predicts speeds approaching that of light (see Chapter 17).

so that $$v = \sqrt{\frac{2qV}{m}}$$

2. An electron, with mass of 9.1×10^{-31} kg and charge of 1.6×10^{-19} C, is accelerated to a velocity of 4.0×10^6 m/s, then enters a uniform magnetic field of 5.0×10^{-3} T at an angle of 90° to the field.

(a) What is the radius of the circular path it follows?

$$r = \frac{mv}{Bq}$$

$$= \frac{(9.1 \times 10^{-31} \text{ kg})(4.0 \times 10^6 \text{ m/s})}{(5.0 \times 10^{-3} \text{ T})(1.6 \times 10^{-19} \text{ C})}$$

$$= 4.6 \times 10^{-3} \text{ m, or 4.6 mm}$$

(b) Through what potential difference was the electron accelerated?

$$qV = \frac{1}{2}mv^2$$

$$V = \frac{mv^2}{2q}$$

$$= \frac{(9.1 \times 10^{-31} \text{ kg})(4.0 \times 10^6 \text{ m/s})^2}{2(1.6 \times 10^{-19} \text{ C})}$$

$$= 46 \text{ V}$$

Note: For a magnetic field pointing into the page, the electron would move in a clockwise circle in the plane of the page. Of course, a positive particle would move in a counterclockwise circle in the same field.

Practice

1. Determine the magnitude and direction of the magnetic force on a proton moving horizontally to the north at 8.6×10^4 m/s, as it enters a magnetic field of 1.2 T, pointing vertically upward.
$$(1.7 \times 10^{-14} \text{ N[E]})$$

2. What is the magnitude and direction of a magnetic field if an electron moving through it at 2.0×10^6 m/s experiences a maximum magnetic force of 5.1×10^{-14} N[to the left] when moving vertically straight up?
$$(0.16 \text{ T[horizontal, towards observer]})$$

3. Calculate the radius of the path taken by an alpha particle (He^{++} ion, of charge 3.2×10^{-19} C and mass 6.7×10^{-27} kg) injected at a speed of 1.5×10^7 m/s into a uniform magnetic field of 2.4 T, at right angles to the field.   (0.13 m)

4. Calculate the velocity of a proton, moving in a circular path of radius 8.0 cm, in a plane perpendicular to a 1.5 T magnetic field. What voltage would be required to accelerate the proton from rest, in a vacuum?   (1.1×10^7 m/s, 6.9×10^5 V)

5. An airplane flying through the Earth's magnetic field at a speed of 200 m/s acquires a charge of 100 C. What is the maximum magnetic force on it in a region where the magnitude of the Earth's magnetic field is 5.0×10^{-5} T?   (1.0 N)

16.4 Ampère's Law

The magnetic fields that we have been considering, when discussing the force on a current-carrying conductor or a moving charged particle, have been uniform magnetic fields. That is, magnetic fields in which $\vec{B}$ is constant, both in direction and magnitude. The magnetic field between the poles of a horseshoe magnet and the magnetic field in the core of a solenoid are both very nearly uniform. Other magnetic fields can vary in magnitude and direction as you move from position to position in the field. It is of interest to us to be able to determine the magnetic field strength at any point in a field, using a mathematical relationship between the physical quantities creating the field.

A simple magnetic field to consider first is that of a long, straight, current-carrying wire, discovered originally by Oersted, and studied in Section 16.2. Recall that its field lines are concentric circles with the wire at their centres, the circles becoming more widely spaced as the distance from the wire increases. Careful measurements of the magnetic field strength a distance r from the wire show that

$$B \propto I, \text{ the current flowing through the wire}$$

$$\text{and } B \propto \frac{1}{r}, \text{ the distance from the wire's centre}$$

Therefore, the magnetic field strength can be written in the form of an equation, as

$$B = k\frac{I}{r}, \text{ where } k \text{ is a proportionality constant}$$

The direction of $\vec{B}$ is given by the right-hand rule discussed earlier.
This mathematical relationship became apparent to Oersted soon after he discovered electromagnetism. It inspired the noted French

Ampère's Law needs to be modified if there is ferromagnetic material nearby. Again, we will leave this to a more advanced course.

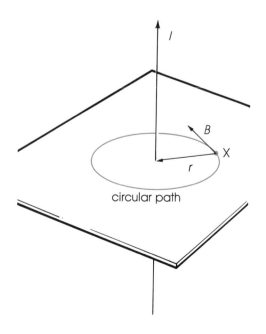

circular path

scientist André Marie Ampère (1775–1836) to begin working on a general relationship between the current flowing through any conductor (not just a straight one) and the strength of the magnetic field it produces. Ampère soon found that there was such a relationship, and proposed the following statement to express it:

Along any closed path through a magnetic field, the sum of the products of the component of $\vec{B}$ parallel to the path segment with the length of the segment is directly proportional to the net electric current passing through the area enclosed by the path.

This relationship, called Ampère's Law, is much easier to visualize when written in mathematical terms.

Along any closed path in a magnetic field,

$$\Sigma\, B_{_\shortparallel}\, \Delta l = \mu_0 I$$

where $B_{_\shortparallel}$ is the component of $\vec{B}$ that is parallel to the path along any small segment of the path Δl

Δl is one of the small segments into which the path can be subdivided

Σ represents the process of summing up all of the products $B_{_\shortparallel}\Delta l$ for every segment along the path

I is the net current flowing through the area enclosed by the path

μ_0 is a proportionality constant, called the permeability of free space, whose value is $4\pi \times 10^{-7}$ T·m/A

To fully appreciate this law, let us apply it to the simple magnetic field whose characteristics Ampère already knew—that of a long, straight wire carrying a current I.

To find the magnitude of the magnetic field strength at a point X, a distance r from the wire, we apply Ampère's Law in the following way. Since it applies along *any* path, let us choose a circle for a path, passing through X in a plane perpendicular to the wire, with the wire as its centre and with radius r. This is a good choice of path, because, from previous work, we observed that the magnetic field at all points along this path is constant in magnitude, and points in a direction tangent to the circular path.

Now, to find the sum of the products $B_{_\shortparallel}\Delta l$ along this path, we will assume that the circle is composed of a very large number n of small, straight-line segments, called Δl_1, Δl_2, Δl_3, up to Δl_n. Thus, it is possible to state Ampère's Law, for the circular path composed of n straight-line segments, as

$$B_{1_{_\shortparallel}}\Delta l_1 + B_{2_{_\shortparallel}}\Delta l_2 + \ldots + B_{n_{_\shortparallel}}\Delta l_n = \mu_0\, I$$

since the net current flowing through the circular area enclosed is I.

For each of these n line segments, the magnetic field $\vec{B}$ is constant in magnitude and already parallel to Δl, since it is tangent to the circle at all points. Therefore,

$$B_{1_{\shortparallel}} = B_{2_{\shortparallel}} = \ldots = B_{n_{\shortparallel}} = B$$

The expression above may be written

$$B\Delta l_1 + B\Delta l_2 + \ldots + B\Delta l_n = \mu_0 I$$
$$B (\Delta l_1 + \Delta l_2 + \ldots + \Delta l_n) = \mu_0 I$$

But, $\Delta l_1 + \Delta l_2 + \ldots + \Delta l_n$ is just the total length of the circular path, which is $2\pi r$.

Therefore, $B(2\pi r) = \mu_0 I$, so that

$$B = \mu_0 \left(\frac{I}{2\pi r} \right)$$

which is the expression for the magnetic field strength a distance r from a long straight conductor carrying a current I.

Note that this is just the relationship that Oersted found experimentally (only with the proportionality constant expressed differently).

Sample problem

What is the strength of the magnetic field 15 cm from a long, straight conductor carrying a current of 100 A?

$$B = \mu_0 \left(\frac{I}{2\pi r} \right)$$
$$= \frac{(4\pi \times 10^{-7} \text{ T·m/A})(100 \text{ A})}{2\pi (0.15 \text{ m})}$$
$$= 1.3 \times 10^{-4} \text{ T}$$

Practice

1. What is the magnetic field strength 20 cm from a long, straight conductor with a current of 60 A flowing through it?
   (6.0×10^{-5} T)
2. What current is flowing through a straight wire if the magnetic field strength 10 cm from the wire is 2.4×10^{-5} T?   (12 A)
3. At what distance from a straight conductor, with a current of 200 A flowing through it, is the magnetic field intensity 8.0×10^{-4} T?   (5.0×10^{-2} m)
4. What is the magnetic field strength at a point midway between two long, parallel wires, 1.0 m apart, carrying currents of 10 A

and 20 A respectively, if the currents are
(a) in opposite directions?
(b) in the same direction? $(1.2 \times 10^{-5}$ T, 4.0×10^{-6} T$)$

5. A long, solid, copper rod has a circular cross-section of diameter 10 cm. It carries a current of 1000 A, uniformly distributed across its area. Calculate the magnetic field strength at these four positions:
(a) at the centre of the rod
(b) 2.5 cm from the centre
(c) 5.0 cm from the centre
(d) 7.5 cm from the centre
        $(0$ T, 2.0×10^{-3} T, 4.0×10^{-3} T, 2.7×10^{-3} T$)$
Hint: Remember, the current in Ampère's Law is the current flowing through the area enclosed by the chosen path.

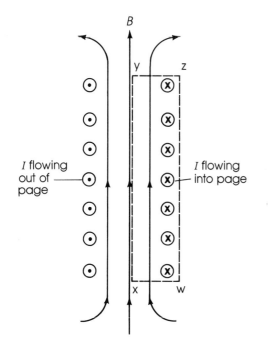

I flowing out of page

I flowing into page

Ampère's Law also allows us to find the magnetic field strength in the core of a solenoid, using the same elegant technique. Recall that the magnetic field of a solenoid consists of straight, equally spaced field lines in the core, bulging out slightly at the ends. There is virtually no magnetic field in the region outside the coil. A cross-section of a long solenoid, of length L, with N loops, carrying a current I appears as shown.

This time, as a closed path around which to apply Ampère's Law, we choose the rectangle wxyz, shown in the diagram. We can consider this path as four distinct line segments, wx, xy, yz, and zw. Then, applying Ampère's Law, we have

$$B_{wx_{//}}(xy) + B_{yz_{//}}(yz) + B_{zw_{//}}(zw) + B_{wx_{//}}(wx) = \mu_0 NI$$

Note that the total current flowing through the area bounded by the path wxyz is NI, since the current I flows down through each of the N conductors within the area.

Along wx and yz, the magnetic field $\vec{B}$ is perpendicular to the path, having no component parallel to it.

$$B_{wx_{//}} = B_{yz_{//}} = 0$$

Along zw, the magnetic field strength $\vec{B}$ is zero, since there is virtually no field outside the coil.

$$B_{zw_{//}} = 0$$

However, along xy the magnetic field $\vec{B}$ is straight, constant, and parallel to xy, so that

$$B_{yz_{//}} = B,\ \text{at all points along xy}$$

And since xy $= L$, the length of the solenoid, we can write

$$BL = \mu_0 NI\ \text{as the expression for Ampère's Law,}$$

so that

$$B = \mu_0 \left(\frac{NI}{L} \right)$$

where B is the magnetic field strength in the core of the solenoid,
in teslas
I is the current flowing through the coil, in amperes
L is the length of the solenoid, in metres
N is the number of turns on the coil
Again, the direction of the magnetic field is given by the right-hand rule.

Sample problem

What is the magnetic field strength in the core of a solenoid 5.0 cm long, with 300 turns and a current of 10 A?

$$B = \mu_0 \left(\frac{NI}{L} \right)$$
$$= \frac{(4\pi \times 10^{-7} \text{ T·m/A})(300)(10 \text{ A})}{5.0 \times 10^{-2} \text{ m}}$$
$$= 7.5 \times 10^{-2} \text{ T}$$

Practice

1. 14-gauge copper wire can safely carry a current of 12 A. How many turns must be wound on a coil 15 cm long in order to produce a magnetic field of strength 5.0×10^{-2} T?

$$(5.0 \times 10^2)$$

2. What is the magnetic field strength in the core of a coil 10 cm long, with 420 turns and a current of 6.0 A? $(3.2 \times 10^{-2}$ T)

3. A coil 8.0 cm long is composed of 400 turns of wire, and produces a magnetic field of strength 1.4×10^{-2} T in its core. What is the current flowing through the coil?   (2.2 A)

The Ampere As a Unit of Electric Current

In Section 15.1, the ampere was introduced as the unit of electric current equivalent to 1 C of charge passing a given point in a conductor in 1 s. This was just a temporary and non-operational description of the ampere, since it is difficult to actually measure how many coulombs of charge pass by a given point. The accepted SI definition of the ampere is a magnetic one, and depends on an understanding of the force between two parallel current-carrying conductors.

Consider two long, straight, parallel conductors, a distance d apart in a vacuum, carrying currents I_1 and I_2, respectively, as shown.

Each wire creates a magnetic field, and the other wire carries its current through, and perpendicular to, that field. The magnetic field created by wire 1 and experienced by wire 2, a distance d away, is given by

$$B_1 = \mu_0 \left(\frac{I_1}{2\pi d} \right)$$

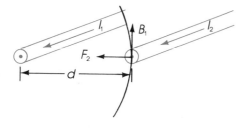

Then, the force acting on wire 2, perpendicular to this field, is given by

$$F_2 = B \, l \, I \sin \theta$$
$$= B_1 \, l \, I_2 \quad \text{since } \sin \theta = 1$$

If we express this as the force per unit length, and substitute the value for B_1 obtained previously, we can write

$$\frac{F_2}{l} = \frac{\mu_0 I_1 I_2}{2\pi d}$$

as the expression for the force acting on wire 2 due to the current in wire 1. However, according to Newton's Third Law, it will also be the force that acts on wire 1 due to the current in wire 2, but in the opposite direction. By applying the right-hand rule, we can see that these mutual forces will cause an attraction if I_1 and I_2 flow in the same direction, or a repulsion if they flow in opposite directions.

Then, using this equation to define the ampere, we simply choose $d = 1$ m and define $I_1 = I_2 = 1$ A, so that

$$\frac{F}{l} = \frac{(4\pi \times 10^{-7}\,\text{T·m/A})(1\,\text{A})(1\,\text{A})}{2\pi\,(1\,\text{m})}$$
$$= 2 \times 10^{-7}\,\text{N/m}$$

That is,

---

1 A is the current flowing through each of two long, straight, parallel conductors 1 m apart in a vacuum, when the magnetic force between them is 2×10^{-7} N per metre of length.

Then the coulomb is defined, using this relationship for the ampere, as

---

1 C is the charge transported by a current of 1 A in a time of 1 s.

$$1\,\text{C} = 1\,\text{A·s}$$

Sample problem

What is the force between two parallel conductors 2.0 m long, carrying currents of 4.0 A and 10.0 A, that are 25 cm apart in a vacuum?

$$\frac{F}{l} = \frac{\mu_0 I_1 I_2}{2\pi d}$$

$$\text{or } F = \frac{\mu_0 I_1 I_2 l}{2\pi d}$$

$$= \frac{(4\pi \times 10^{-7}\,\text{T·m/A})(4.0\,\text{A})(10.0\,\text{A})(2.0\,\text{m})}{2\pi\,(0.25\,\text{m})}$$

$$= 6.4 \times 10^{-5}\,\text{N}$$

Practice

1. Calculate the force per unit length between two parallel conductors, each carrying a current of 8.0 A, if they are 1.0 cm apart. $(1.3 \times 10^{-3}\,\text{N/m})$
2. What is the maximum equal current in each of two parallel conductors 5.0 m long and 12 cm apart, if the force between them must not exceed 2.0×10^{-2} N? (49 A)
3. How far from a wire carrying a current of 5.0 A is a second, parallel wire with a current of 10 A, if the force between them is 3.6×10^{-4} N/m? $(2.8 \times 10^{-2}\,\text{m})$
4. Calculate the force per metre pushing the two wires in an extension cord apart when 1.0 A of DC current flows, to light a 100 W study lamp. The separation of the wires is 2.0 mm and the insulation behaves like a vacuum. $(1.0 \times 10^{-4}\,\text{N/m})$

16.5 The Mass of the Electron and the Proton

Today, elementary school children learn of the electron and proton as a matter of fact, taking their existence for granted. Yet, it was not until the end of the 19th century that the existence of either of these basic, subatomic particles was even proposed, and their fundamental properties described.

The work leading to the "discovery" of the electron began in the late 1800s, with the study of the discharge of electricity between two electrodes in a nearly evacuated glass tube. In this experiment, when a large potential difference is applied to the electrodes, a bright glowing area is observed near the anode, together with a much darker area adjacent to the cathode. Placing a metal target in front of the cathode causes a sharp shadow of it to be cast on the end of the tube next to the anode. Since it seemed that something was being emitted by the cathode, and was travelling down the tube in straight lines towards the anode, these became known as "cathode rays".

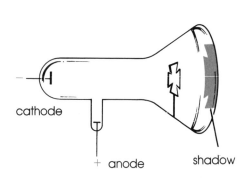

cathode

+ anode   shadow

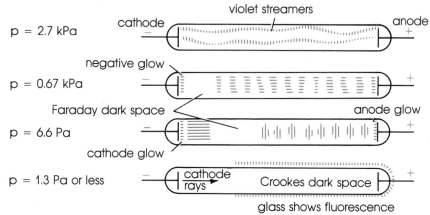

p = 2.7 kPa

cathode   violet streamers   anode
                                            +

p = 0.67 kPa

negative glow

                                            +

Faraday dark space   anode glow

p = 6.6 Pa

                                            +

cathode glow

p = 1.3 Pa or less   cathode rays   Crookes dark space   +

glass shows fluorescence

Electric discharge through air at low pressures

The British scientist J.J. Thomson (1856–1940) studied cathode rays in depth, particularly their deflection by electric and magnetic fields. He drilled a hole in the anode to allow a fine beam of cathode rays to pass through. Applying either an electric field or a magnetic field across the tube caused this fine beam to be deflected up, down, left, or right of its original path, depending on the direction of the electric or magnetic field. In all cases, however, the direction of deflection was that of a negatively charged particle moving from cathode to anode. As a result, Thomson concluded that cathode rays consisted of negatively charged particles moving at high speed from the cathode to the anode. He called these particles "electrons".

To determine some of the properties of electrons, Thomson used a tube containing parallel plates, and coils arranged as shown.

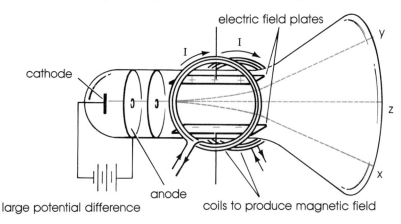

electric field plates

cathode

I   I   y

                                                z

large potential difference

anode   coils to produce magnetic field

x

When a current flows through the coils, it creates a magnetic field $\vec{B}$ that deflects the electrons along a circular arc of radius r, so that they hit the end of the tube at point x. From our previous work on magnetic deflection, we know that

$$F_{\text{magnetic}} = F_{\text{centripetal}}$$

$$evB = \frac{mv^2}{r}$$

where e and v are the electron's charge and velocity, respectively

or

$$\frac{e}{m} = \frac{v}{Br}$$

You can calculate B by knowing the physical dimensions of the coils and the amount of current flowing through them. You can measure r directly.

To determine the electron's speed, v, Thomson made use of the parallel plates. When a potential difference is applied to the plates (with the lower plate negative) and no current is flowing through the coils, an electron would be deflected upwards, reaching the end of the tube at point y. But, with current flowing through the coils and the previous magnetic field again acting on the electrons, the potential difference across the plates could be adjusted until the two deflections (electric and magnetic) cancelled each other out, and the electron beam reached the end of the tube at point z.

When this had been done,

$$F_{\text{magnetic}} = F_{\text{electric}}$$

$$evB = e\,\mathcal{E}$$

where $\mathcal{E}$ is the electric field between the parallel plates, and may be calculated using the equation $\mathcal{E} = V/d$

or

$$v = \frac{\mathcal{E}}{B}$$

Then, Thomson was able to express the ratio of charge-to-mass for electrons as

$$\frac{e}{m} = \frac{v}{Br}$$

$$= \frac{\mathcal{E}}{B^2 r}$$

The value that Thomson was able to calculate, using his apparatus, was very close to the currently accepted value of

$$\frac{e}{m} = 1.76 \times 10^{11} \text{ C/kg}$$

Notice, the path of the electron is only curved while in the magnetic field of the coils or the electric field of the plates. After leaving these fields, the electrons move, in a straight line, to points x or y.

A few years later, the American physicist Robert Millikan was able to determine a value for the charge on an electron (see Section 15.6), 1.6×10^{-19} C, so that combining these two values resulted in a value for the electron's mass of 9.1×10^{-31} kg.

The apparatus used to determine the e/m ratio

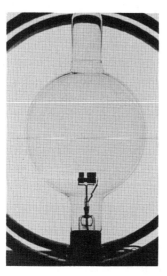

The electron beam moves in a straight line to the left.

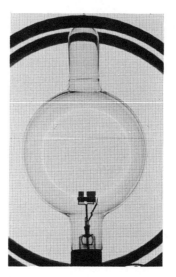

The electron beam moves in a circular path in the magnetic field of the coils.

Increasing the magnetic field strength decreases the radius of the path.

The same relationship that Thomson used may be used to determine the charge-to-mass ratio for any charged particle, moving through known electric and magnetic fields. By measuring the radius of curvature of the charged particle in the magnetic field only, and then adjusting the electric field to produce no net deflection, its charge-to-mass ratio is given by

$$\frac{q}{m} = \frac{\mathcal{E}}{B^2 r}$$

16.6 The Oscilloscope

A device commonly used in the laboratory to analyse and measure electrical signals is the oscilloscope, whose major component is the cathode ray tube (CRT).

A cathode ray tube consists of an electron "gun", vertical and horizontal deflection plates (or coils), and a fluorescent screen, arranged as shown in the diagram.

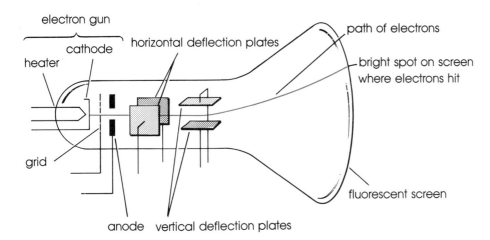

electron gun

cathode

horizontal deflection plates

heater

path of electrons

bright spot on screen
where electrons hit

grid

fluorescent screen

anode   vertical deflection plates

The cathode of the electron gun is heated by a nearby filament until it becomes so hot that thermally agitated electrons "boil off" in a process called **thermionic emission**. The anode is maintained at a potential difference of 200 V to 500 V with respect to the cathode, so that these electrons are attracted across the vacuum towards it. They reach the anode with a maximum velocity v, given by the relation

$$-\Delta E_{electric} = \Delta E_{kinetic}$$

$$eV = \frac{1}{2} mv^2$$

or

$$v = \sqrt{\frac{2\,eV}{m}}$$

A large number of these high-speed electrons line up with a hole in the anode, and as a result pass through it in a fine beam. These electrons move in essentially a straight line, with a constant velocity and energy until they hit the screen. The inside surface of the screen is coated with a fluorescent material, so that a bright spot is produced at the point where the beam hits it.

The beam can be deflected both vertically and horizontally from its path between anode and screen, in two different ways. One method uses horizontal and vertical pairs of parallel plates that have a variable potential difference applied to them. As the beam passes through their respective electric fields, it is deflected towards the positive plate. The amount of deflection will depend on the potential difference between the plates.

The beam can also be deflected by pairs of coils, situated above, below, and to the sides of the beam. A current supplied to these

A small voltage applied to the grid can control the speed of electrons accelerated towards the anode.

The speed of the electrons is kept relatively slow in the "gun" section of the cathode ray tube, since it is easier to deflect them at a slower speed. Most of the acceleration occurs in the larger part of the tube, after they have been deflected.

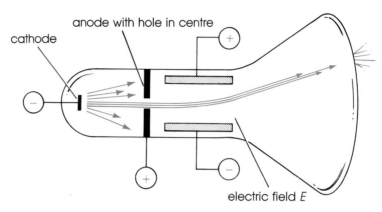

cathode

anode with hole in centre

electric field *E*

coils creates a magnetic field that will deflect the beam up, down, right, or left, according to the relation $F = Bqv \sin \theta$, and in a direction given by the right-hand rule.

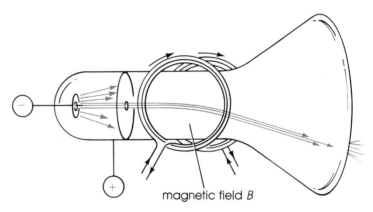

magnetic field *B*

This basic cathode ray tube configuration is the same as that used in most television sets, radar screens, video display terminals, and oscilloscopes. It is the way the CRT and the supporting electronic circuits are used that makes these devices different from each other.

An oscilloscope is a device that permits an electrical signal to be amplified, observed in a stationary pattern, and measured. Other electrical measuring devices (galvanometers, for example) cannot respond quickly enough to measure rapidly changing values of voltage and current in a complex electrical signal.

Within the supporting electronics of the oscilloscope is a "horizontal sweep circuit" designed to supply a signal that deflects the beam horizontally, usually from left to right, at a constant rate. It then returns quickly to the starting position, usually with the beam turned off to avoid confusion, and then repeats the sweep cycle.

The sweep period can be varied from a few seconds to a few micro-seconds, and triggering circuits can synchronize the start of each sweep with the same point in the repetitive wave form being ex-amined. The signal being analysed is then applied to the vertical deflection plates (or coils) so that, as the beam is being swept horizontally, it is also deflected up and down in response to this signal. Thus, the moving electron beam makes a trace on the screen that is a visual plot of the variation of the potential difference in the signal with time. Both the vertical scale (potential difference) and the horizontal scale (time) may be adjusted to make the trace stationary, and a convenient size for taking measurements. To fa-cilitate this, grid lines are usually drawn on the face of the screen, so that direct measurements of voltage and time (or frequency) can be made, according to both scales selected.

16.7 Mass Spectrograph

The technique for measuring the e/m ratio for electrons, used by Thomson, led to the development of a method for measuring the mass of any charged particle. This device, called a mass spectro-graph, or mass spectrometer, is shown in the diagram in simplified form.

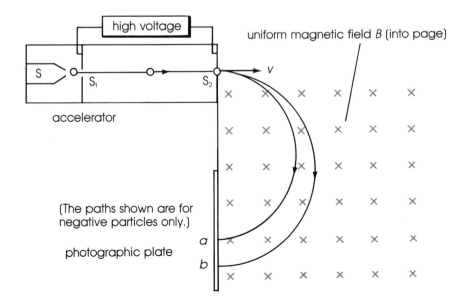

Ions of the substance to be measured are produced by heating or electrical discharge in the source S. Some of these ions drift through slit S_1 in the first parallel plate, and encounter a strong electric field between the parallel plates. The high potential difference between these plates accelerates the ions, and some pass through slit S_2 with a velocity v, given by

$$\frac{1}{2} mv^2 = qV$$

or

$$v = \sqrt{\frac{2\,qV}{m}}$$

These ions, all with velocity v, then enter the uniform magnetic field B (at right angles to the page and their velocity), and are deflected in a circular arc of radius r, striking and exposing the photographic film at point a, as shown. The centripetal force on the ion is magnetic, and is given by

Thermal motion may give the selected ions slightly different initial velocities.

$$qvB = \frac{mv^2}{r}$$

so that

$$v = \frac{qBr}{m}$$

Then, equating these two expressions for v and solving for m, we have

$$\frac{qBr}{m} = \sqrt{\frac{2\,qV}{m}}$$

$$\frac{q^2B^2r^2}{m^2} = \frac{2\,qV}{m}$$

so that

$$m = \frac{qB^2r^2}{2\,V}$$

Note that the path radius for any ion is proportional to the square root of its mass, so that heavier ions would move in a path of larger radius, arriving at point b, while the lighter ions will arrive at point a.

The mass spectrograph depicted is quite crude. More precise instruments use a "velocity selector" similar to that in the Thomson apparatus, where electric and magnetic fields are balanced, allowing only those particles with a particular velocity to pass through along a particular path. In this way, only particles whose velocity is limited to a very small range of values enter the deflecting magnetic field. With this type of spectrograph, masses of charged particles can be determined to a very high degree of precision.

The techniques of mass spectroscopy led to many significant discoveries about the nature of ions and molecules. Even when a "pure" substance was used as a source of ions, particles were often deflected along more than one path, indicating the presence of particles of the "same" substance, but with different masses. These different-mass particles were called **isotopes**, and it was soon found that most pure elements are mixtures of two or more isotopes. Different isotopes of the same element have the same number of protons and electrons, but different numbers of neutrons. A sample calculation based on the results from a typical mass spectrometer will illustrate.

Calculate the radius of curvature in a mass spectroscope, for chlorine-35 and chlorine-37 ions, whose charge is 1.6×10^{-19} C, and whose masses are 5.8×10^{-26} kg and 6.1×10^{-26} kg, respectively. They are accelerated by a potential difference of 250 V and deflected by a magnetic field of 1.0 T.

In such a spectrometer,

$$r = \sqrt{\frac{2\,Vm}{qB^2}}$$

Therefore

$$r_{35} = \sqrt{\frac{2(2.5 \times 10^2 \text{ V})(5.8 \times 10^{-26} \text{ kg})}{(1.6 \times 10^{-19} \text{ C})(1.0 \text{ T})^2}}$$

$$= 1.3 \times 10^{-2} \text{ m, or } 1.3 \text{ cm}$$

and, similarly $r_{37} = 1.4$ cm

Then, if they are allowed to travel in semicircular arcs before they strike the photographic plate, their separation on the plate will be $2(r_{37} - r_{35})$, or 0.2 cm, or 2 mm.

16.8 Electromagnetic Waves

One of the great scientific achievements of the 19th century was the discovery that waves of electromagnetic energy could travel through space. Once the basic relationships between electricity and magnetism had been established, primarily by Oersted and Faraday, it was not long before others began to extend electromagnetic theory in order to understand closely related phenomena.

In 1864, a Scottish physicist and mathematician, James Clerk Maxwell (1831–1879) summarized his theories about electromagnetic fields as four basic relationships, appropriately known as Maxwell's Equations of Electromagnetism. Although these equations were originally expressed in a mathematical notation that is beyond the scope of this book, we can summarize his main ideas in words, as follows.

James Clerk Maxwell

A changing electric field can cause a changing magnetic field, and vice versa, even in a vacuum where no charge can move or accumulate.

1. The distribution of an electric charge, in space, is related to the electric field it produces.
2. Magnetic field lines are continuous, and do not have a beginning or an end, whereas electric field lines begin and end on electric charges.
3. An electric field can produce a magnetic field (due to the presence of moving electric charges), so a changing electric field should produce a changing magnetic field.
4. A changing magnetic field can produce a changing electric field, and hence an induced current and potential difference in a conductor in the changing field.

These statements should already be familiar to you, with the possible exception of 4. It is closely related to Michael Faraday's Law of Electromagnetic Induction, which states that a changing magnetic field in the region of a conductor can induce a potential difference in the conductor, causing a current to flow. Of course, for such an induced current to flow through a conductor, there must be an electric field present in the conductor, causing its charged particles to move.

These two converse phenomena—a changing magnetic field producing an electric field, and a changing electric field producing a magnetic field—led Maxwell to an inevitable conclusion. He predicted that as they continuously changed, these interchanging magnetic and electric fields would actually propagate through space, in the form of an electromagnetic wave.

Such an electromagnetic wave was first produced and detected in the laboratory by the German physicist Heinrich Hertz (1857–1894) in 1887, shortly after Maxwell's death. Using a spark gap, across which electric charges moved rapidly back and forth, Hertz was able to generate electromagnetic waves whose frequency was about 10^9 Hz. (The SI unit for frequency, equivalent to one cycle per second, is named for Hertz, and abbreviated Hz.) He detected these waves from some distance away, using as an antenna a loop of wire in which a potential difference and current were induced by the changing magnetic field of the wave.

Hertz was also able to show that these waves travelled at the speed of light, 3.0×10^8 m/s in a vacuum, and that they exhibited the characteristic wave phenomena: reflection, refraction, interference, and even polarization.

Hertz called these waves radio waves. His discovery was the forerunner of the work done by Marconi and other radio pioneers,

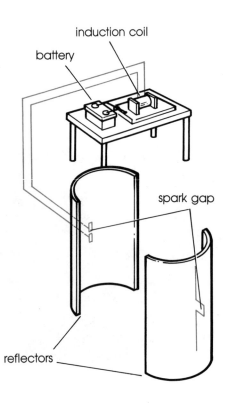

induction coil

battery

spark gap

reflectors

who first transmitted radio waves across the English Channel in 1889, and across the Atlantic Ocean in 1901.

Maxwell not only predicted the existence of electromagnetic waves, but further predicted many of the properties and characteristics of such waves:

1. Electromagnetic waves are produced whenever electric charges are accelerated. The accelerated charge loses energy that is carried away in the electromagnetic wave.
2. If the electric charge is accelerated in periodic motion (in simple harmonic motion, for example), the frequency of the electromagnetic waves produced is exactly equal to the frequency of oscillation of the charge.
3. All electromagnetic waves travel through a vacuum at a common speed c, calculated as 3.0×10^8 m/s, and obey the wave equation $c = f\lambda$.
4. Electromagnetic waves consist of oscillating electric and magnetic fields in a constant phase relation, perpendicular to each other, and both at 90° to the direction of propagation of the wave, as depicted in the sketch.

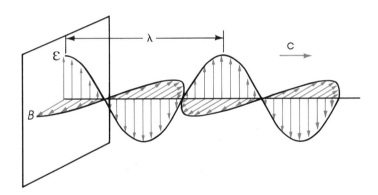

5. Electromagnetic waves exhibit the properties of interference, diffraction, polarization, and refraction, and can carry linear and angular momentum. Their intensity is proportional to the square of the magnitude of the electric (or magnetic) field amplitude, and to the square of the frequency.

Radiation in which the electric field vector always lies in the same plane is said to be "plane polarized". The plane of polarization is the plane containing all of the changing electric field vectors.

Despite predictions that the Earth's curvature would make communication by electric waves impossible over distances of more than 300 km, Marconi succeeded, in 1901, in receiving signals at Telegraph Hill in St. John's, Newfoundland, that were transmitted from Cornwall, England.

This velocity was even predicted by Maxwell, given by $c = \sqrt{\dfrac{1}{\epsilon_0 \mu_0}}$ where ϵ_0 and μ_0 are the permittivity and permeability of free space, respectively.

"The only laws of matter are those which our minds must fabricate, and the only laws of mind are fabricated for it by matter."

James Clerk Maxwell,

The Electromagnetic Spectrum

The prediction by Maxwell, and its verification by Hertz, that electromagnetic waves travel at the speed of 3.0×10^8 m/s — the speed of light — was of paramount significance. For over half a century it had been accepted that light behaves as a wave — but a wave of what? Maxwell, on the basis of his calculated speed for electromagnetic waves, argued that light must be an electromagnetic wave. After Hertz's discovery of radio waves, Maxwell's claim was soon widely accepted.

But visible light and radio waves occupy only two small ranges of all the frequencies possible for oscillating electric and magnetic fields. Today, we know that there is a broad range of frequencies of electromagnetic waves, called the "electromagnetic spectrum", all having the same basic characteristics that Maxwell had predicted. The table shows the names that have been given to the various regions of this spectrum, the approximate frequency range for each region, and a brief description of the type of accelerated charge that leads to the formation of each.

The Electromagnetic Spectrum

Type of Radiation	Frequency Range	Origin of Radiation	Applications or Effects of Radiation
low frequency AC	60 Hz	weak radiation emitted from conductors of AC power	causes interference in radio reception when passing near high voltage transmission lines
radio, radar, TV	$10^4 - 10^{10}$ Hz	oscillations in electric circuits containing inductive and capacitive components	transmission of radio and TV communication signals; ship and aircraft navigation by radar; reception of radiowaves from outer space by radiotelescopes; control of satellites; space probes; and guided missiles
microwaves	$10^9 - 10^{12}$ Hz	oscillating currents in special tubes and solid state devices	long range transmission of TV and other telecommunication information; cooking in microwave ovens

The Electromagnetic Spectrum

Type of Radiation	Frequency Range	Origin of Radiation	Applications or Effects of Radiation
infrared radiation	$10^{11} - 4 \times 10^{14}$ Hz	transitions of outer electrons in atoms and molecules	causes the direct heating effect of the sun and other radiant heat sources; is used for remote sensing and thermography
visible light	$4 \times 10^{14} - 8 \times 10^{14}$ Hz	higher energy transitions of outer electrons in atoms	radiation that can be detected by the human eye, giving the sensation of "seeing"
ultraviolet radiation	$8 \times 10^{14} - 10^{17}$ Hz	even higher energy transitions of outer electrons in atoms	causes fluorescence in some materials; causes "tanning" of human skin; kills bacteria; and aids in the synthesis of vitamin D by the human body
X-rays	$10^{15} - 10^{20}$ Hz	transitions of inner electrons of atoms or the rapid deceleration of high energy free electrons	penetrate soft tissue easily but are absorbed by denser tissue, like bones and teeth, to produce X-ray images of internal body structures; also used for radiation therapy and non-destructive testing in industry
gamma rays	$10^{19} - 10^{24}$ Hz	nuclei of atoms, both spontaneously, and from the sudden deceleration of very high energy particles from accelerators	treatment for localized cancerous tumours
cosmic rays	$> 10^{24}$ Hz	bombardment of Earth's atmosphere by very high energy particles from outer space	

Notice what a small range of frequencies is detected by our eyes.

A sample problem will illustrate how traditional wave analysis can be used to solve problems in various regions of the spectrum.

Sample problem

Microwaves with a wavelength of 1.5 cm are used to transmit television signals coast to coast, using a network of relay towers. (a) What is the frequency of these microwaves?

$$f = \frac{c}{\lambda}$$

$$= \frac{3.0 \times 10^8 \text{ m/s}}{1.5 \times 10^{-2} \text{ m}}$$

$$= 2.0 \times 10^{10} \text{ Hz}$$

(b) How long would it take a TV signal to cross the continent from St. John's, Newfoundland, to Victoria, British Columbia— a distance of 8000 km?

$$\Delta d = v\Delta t$$

But, since $v = c$ $\quad \Delta t = \dfrac{\Delta d}{c}$

$$= \frac{8.0 \times 10^6 \text{ m}}{3.0 \times 10^8 \text{ m/s}}$$

$$= 2.7 \times 10^{-2} \text{ s}$$

Practice

1. What is the frequency range for visible light whose wavelengths are between 400 nm and 750 nm?

    $(4.00 \times 10^{14} \text{ Hz to } 7.50 \times 10^{14} \text{ Hz})$

2. Cosmic rays come from outer space and have a frequency of about 1×10^{26} Hz. What is their approximate wavelength?

    $(3 \times 10^{-18} \text{ m})$

3. How many wavelengths of the radiation emitted by a 60 Hz transmission line would it take to span the North American continent, a distance of about 8.0×10^3 km?

    (1.6 wavelengths)

16.9 Applications of Electromagnetic Waves

In 1975, four members of the National Research Council's Herzberg Institute of Astrophysics in Ottawa used a radio telescope to receive radio waves from a molecule in space that had never been previously detected. The discovery of a molecule, a protein called cyanodiacetylene, suggests the possibility that there may be forms of life in space. Its radio wave emission came from a cluster of stars over 30 000 light-years away.

There are many applications of electromagnetic waves in our 20th century society that improve our standard of living and make our lives more enjoyable. A few of the most significant are described in more detail on the following page.

A. Radio and Television Communications

Marconi first recognized the potential for transmitting information over long distances using electromagnetic waves without any direct connection by wires. From his early dot-dash morse code pulses came the basis for our contemporary, sophisticated network of radio and television transmission and reception systems.

Transmission

The components of a modern communications transmitter are shown. Actual circuits will vary in detail, but this one is typical.

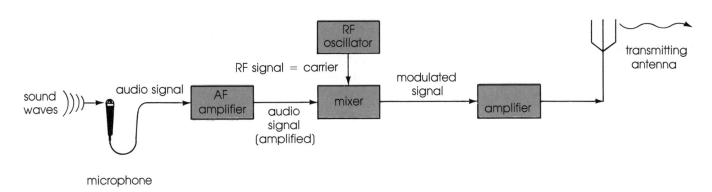

Sound waves are detected by a microphone and converted into a weak audio signal, containing frequencies in the range 20 Hz to 20 000 Hz. This electrical signal is strengthened by an AF (audio frequency) amplifier before passing into a modulator, where it interferes with an RF (radio frequency) carrier signal from the RF oscillator in the mixer. This RF signal, whose frequency is determined by the relative values of inductance and capacitance in the oscillator circuit, is different for each radio station, ranging from 500 kHz to 1600 kHz for AM stations and from 88 MHz to 108 MHz for FM stations. TV carrier frequencies range from 54 MHz to 216 MHz for VHF channels 2 to 13, and from 470 MHz to 890 MHz for UHF channels. The carrier frequency is the frequency you "tune" on your radio or TV dial to receive the station.

The mixing of the audio and carrier signals can be accomplished in two distinct ways. In amplitude modulation (AM), the audio signal is superimposed on the much higher carrier frequency signal to produce a modulated signal of constant frequency, which varies in amplitude according to the audio signal being transmitted. The change in amplitude is greater for "loud" audio and happens more often for "high pitch" audio.

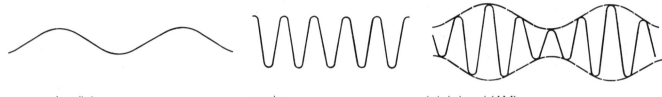

programs (audio)   carrier   total signal (AM)

In frequency modulation (FM), the audio signal is combined with the carrier to produce a modulated signal of constant amplitude that varies in frequency according to the audio being transmitted. The frequency shift is greater for "loud" audio and happens more often for "high pitch" audio.

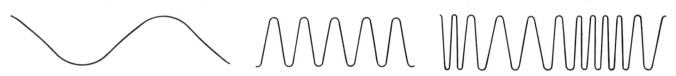

programs (audio)   carrier   total signal (FM)

This modulated signal, of either type, is then further amplified by an RF amplifier, and supplied to an antenna, where the complex mixture of frequencies and amplitudes is sent out in the form of an electromagnetic wave. A television signal is produced in much the same way, but the carrier frequency is mixed with two other signals, an audio and a video signal.

Reception

In the typical receiver shown in the diagram, the receiving antenna detects the incoming electromagnetic wave. In a straight rod antenna, the electric field of the incoming wave exerts forces on free electrons in the conducting rods, causing them to move in response to this electric field signal. A second type of antenna found in most

AM radios consists of a small coil of wire. The rapidly changing magnetic field of the incoming wave induces a corresponding electric current in this coil. In either case, an electrical copy of the signal in the wave is created in the antenna.

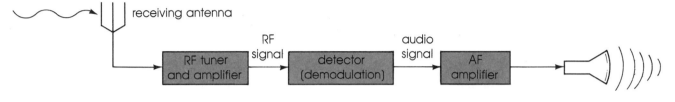

loudspeaker

This small electrical signal produced in the antenna normally contains frequencies from many different transmitting stations mixed together. The first task for the receiver is to select a certain carrier frequency, or small range of frequencies, corresponding to a particular station. This may be accomplished by means of a resonant tuning circuit that contains an inductance (L) and a capacitance (C). A particular station is "tuned" by adjusting the value of C or L so that the resonant frequency in the circuit, given by $f = 1/(2\pi\sqrt{LC})$, equals that of the station's carrier. You adjust the value of C or L when you turn the dial or tuner on your radio or TV set. Modern circuits accomplish the same effect in quite different ways.

This "selected" RF signal is then amplified and sent into a demodulator. At this stage, the audio signal, whether AM or FM, must be separated from the carrier signal. This is accomplished by electronic circuits whose function is beyond the scope of this book. When this AF signal has been successfully separated, it is amplified again, and then sent to the speaker for conversion into sound waves. In TV transmission, two distinct signals are demodulated; the audio signal goes to the speaker, and the video signal goes eventually to the picture tube.

The Canadian and American governments, through the Canadian Radio-television and Telecommunications Commission (CRTC) and the United States Federal Communication Commission (FCC), have the task of assigning carrier frequency ranges for various purposes, so that signals do not overlap and make detection and demodulation impossible. Even within the normal AM and FM broadcast band, stations must receive government approval to transmit, and can only do so within a restricted power range, so as not to interfere with stations transmitting on the same frequency in other parts of the country. The range of some signals changes dramatically at sundown, forcing stations to change their broadcast power levels at that time.

A microwave communications tower has both sending and receiving parabolic antenna.

In addition to radio and TV bands, frequency bands have been assigned for citizen's band (CB) radio, ship-to-shore radio, aircraft, police, military, and amateur radio, cellular telephone, space and satellite communications, radar, etc.

B. X-rays

Wilhelm Roentgen

In December 1895, Wilhelm Roentgen, Professor of Physics at Wurzburg University in Germany, made a remarkable discovery. He noticed that a fluorescent screen placed several metres away from an operating cathode ray tube glowed in the dark, even when the tube was covered with heavy black paper. He also noticed that some covered photographic plates nearby became exposed. He concluded that some mysterious, invisible radiation was being emitted from the cathode ray tube, and that this radiation could penetrate substances opaque to visible light. He called them X-rays since X is commonly used in mathematics as a symbol for the unknown.

Roentgen found that X-rays were not deflected by electric or magnetic fields, and concluded that they were electromagnetic waves of very short wavelength, with properties similar to those of visible light. Later experiments verified that X-rays are produced whenever high speed electrons are decelerated very quickly in striking an obstacle.

A simple X-ray tube is depicted below.

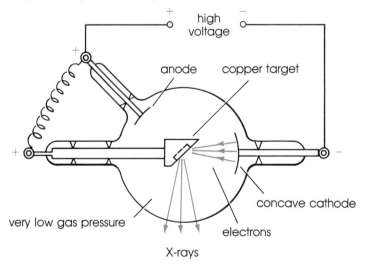

By varying the current in the filament, the number of electrons hitting the target is controlled, and hence the intensity of the resulting X-ray. By varying the potential difference between the cathode and the anode, the kinetic energy of electrons striking the target is controlled. Recall that, for an electron of charge e, accelerated by a potential difference V, its kinetic energy is

$$E_k = \frac{1}{2}mv^2 = eV$$

In Chapter 18, you will learn that the energy in an electromagnetic wave, and hence its penetrating power, comes in small packets given by the equation

$$E = hf$$

where f is the frequency of the electromagnetic wave
and h is a constant of proportionality

Thus, for X-rays from a tube where the accelerating voltage is V, their maximum frequency is given by

$$hf = eV$$

or
$$f = \frac{eV}{h}$$

Thus, the greater the potential difference used, the higher the maximum frequency of X-rays produced, and the greater their penetrating power.

X-rays have the capacity to ionize substances they pass through, by "knocking" electrons loose from their atoms. For example, if a charged electroscope is exposed to X-rays, it will discharge. As X-rays pass through the air surrounding the electroscope, they ionize the gas molecules of the air. Ions or electrons of the same charge as the electroscope are repelled, and move away. Oppositely charged ions or electrons are attracted towards the electroscope, and neutralize it, by contact.

Very powerful X-rays, used in radiation therapy, kill cells by ionization. X-ray-produced ions can interfere with the normal operation of the cell, breaking chemical bonds that hold it together. If a cell does survive, the genetic material in the cell nucleus may become defective, reproducing itself in a defective form, such as cancer. X-ray radiation, even at very low levels, is potentially dangerous, and care should be taken to avoid any unnecessary exposure.

Early X-ray equipment

C. Blackbody Radiation

We are all familiar with the fact that very hot objects emit electromagnetic radiation. At relatively low temperatures we can feel the heat—infrared radiation—from an electric stove burner element. At higher temperatures, the element begins to glow red, indicative of the emission of radiation in the visible region of the spectrum. At even higher temperatures, such as that of an incandescent light bulb filament, a white glow is observed. We can see that, as the temperature of a solid increases, the radiation it emits is of higher and higher frequency. But the lower frequencies are still there; a light bulb still gives off warmth, even at a distance.

The actual spectrum of wavelengths emitted by a hot object at various temperatures is shown in the graph.

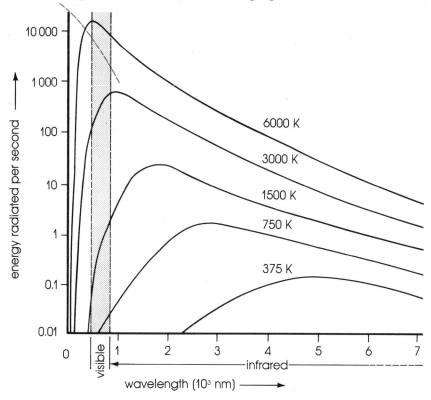

This curve represents the radiation from an object that approximates an ideal emitter or absorber of radiation. Such an object would absorb *all* wavelengths of light striking it, reflecting none. It would, therefore, appear black under reflected radiation, and hence is called a "black body". The radiation coming from it at a particular temperature, as shown in the previous graph, is called "blackbody radiation". The curves illustrate several key points about blackbody radiation:

● At a given temperature, a spectrum of different wavelengths is emitted, of varying intensity, but there is a definite intensity maximum at one particular wavelength.

- As the temperature increases, the intensity maximum shifts to a lower wavelength (higher frequency).

This observed blackbody radiation curve was unexplained prior to 1900. Maxwell's theory suggested that the intensity of radiation from any hot object should continue to increase with increasing frequency, until the object emitted a blue-violet glow. This theoretical prediction is indicated, for the T = 3000 K curve, by the dotted line. The difference between this classically predicted curve and the actual curve became known as "the ultraviolet catastrophe", in recognition that the observed absence of the violet light, and even higher frequency radiation, was not accounted for. It was not until 1900 that the German physicist Max Planck (1858–1947) proposed a new theory, the Quantum Theory, that reconciled these differences and provided a reasonable explanation for blackbody radiation. You will learn more about Planck's Quantum Theory in Chapter 18.

An interesting and important application of blackbody radiation is "the greenhouse effect". White light from the sun contains a mixture of all visible wavelengths, as well as ultraviolet and infrared radiation. The glass roof and walls of a greenhouse are transparent to most of the sun's radiation, so even on the coldest of days, this radiation is absorbed by the earth and vegetation inside. As they warm up, they in turn re-emit radiation, but of a much longer infrared wavelength, due to their comparatively low temperature. This radiation cannot easily penetrate the glass walls of the greenhouse. It is reflected back by the glass, creating the effect of a heat trap and thereby causing the temperature inside to increase. Even in the dead of winter, the temperature inside a greenhouse is warm enough to support the growth of tropical vegetation, at least during daylight hours.

As pollution levels in the Earth's atmosphere increase, the Earth may become like a gigantic greenhouse. Our contaminated atmosphere can allow entry of solar ultraviolet radiation, but would trap more of the infrared radiation re-emitted by the Earth's surface. If this were to occur, the average temperature of the Earth and its atmosphere could gradually increase. Can you imagine the resulting effects on the glacial ice caps at the poles, and on cities near the ocean shores?

Infrared radiation may be detected using a simple device called a "Crooke's radiometer". A pinwheel of four vanes, each silvered on one side and darkened on the other, is pivoted freely in a glass bulb containing air, as shown on the next page. When infrared radiation falls on a vane, the dark side absorbs the radiation, causing its molecules to vibrate faster. The silvered side reflects the radiation, and its molecules continue to vibrate at the same speed. Air

Indeed, if this classical prediction were correct, it would be a great catastrophe! At any temperature, the radiation intensity would increase, without limit at shorter wavelengths. Not only would our skin and eyes be sun-burned by the ultraviolet light, but our bodies would be destroyed by the X-rays and γ rays. The classical prediction was indeed a catastrophe for the theorists. Our very existence proved them wrong.

The glass panels on the southern side of this house act as a passive source of heat, on sunny days, due to the greenhouse effect.

molecules adjacent to the dark side collide with the faster-vibrating molecules, and begin to move faster themselves. Air molecules adjacent to the shiny side continue to move at the same speed. As a result, there is a small increase in pressure on the dark side of the vane, creating a net torque on the pinwheel and thereby causing it to rotate, with the dark side of each vane trailing. The speed of rotation is a measure of the amount of infrared radiation falling on the radiometer.

The most common detector of infrared radiation today is photographic film or a television camera that is sensitive to radiation in the infrared range. Full-colour pictures can show minute variations in the temperature of the object pictured, indicated by a different colour. For example, infrared photographs of the exterior of a house will clearly show "hot" spots around the doors and windows—areas where heat energy is being lost from the house.

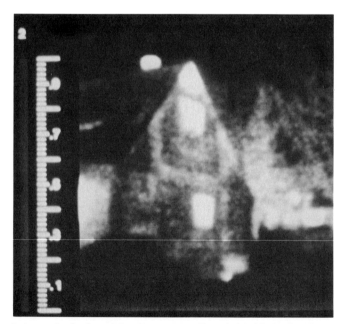

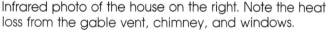
Infrared photo of the house on the right. Note the heat loss from the gable vent, chimney, and windows.

"Heat" images of the human body indicate areas of infection, or possible locations of tumours. Infrared satellite photographs can show, in detail, the type of crops being grown, the population density of urban areas, or the distribution of acid rain, through careful analysis of colour variations in the photographs. Similarly, reconnaissance photographs of military installations can reveal the location of airport runways, hidden factories, or rocket launch sites.

D. Gamma Radiation

In 1896, Antoine Henri Bequerel (1852–1908) found that the mineral pitchblende, containing radium and polonium, would expose a photographic film, even when both were wrapped tightly to exclude any light. Apparently, pitchblende emitted some form of radiation, spontaneously; this new phenomenon was called radioactivity.

Antoine Henri Bequerel

Analysis of the emissions from other radioactive materials revealed that there were three distinct types:

(i) a type of particle similar to high-speed helium nuclei, with poor penetrating power, called alpha particles (α).

(ii) a type of particle similar to high-speed electrons, with the ability to penetrate up to several millimetres of aluminum, called beta particles (β).

(iii) a form of radiation, similar to very high energy X-rays, with the ability to penetrate even several centimetres of lead, called gamma rays (γ).

The three types of radioactive emissions could easily be distinguished in a magnetic field, as shown.

Alpha particles, being positive, were bent one way; beta particles, being negative, were bent the other way; gamma rays, unaffected by the magnetic field, were assumed to be neutral. This and other observations led to the conclusion that gamma rays were very-high-frequency, electromagnetic waves emitted from the nucleus of certain radioactive substances.

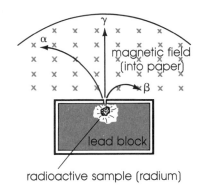

radioactive sample (radium)

One important use of gamma rays is in the treatment of localized cancerous tumours. Rapidly growing malignant cancer cells are more susceptible to damage caused by gamma ray irradiation than are normal cells. To avoid irradiating normal tissue more than necessary, a fine, highly directed beam of gamma rays is focused on the tumour. In addition, the patient's body is slowly rotated during the exposure so that the gamma ray beam, in reaching the tumour, passes through different areas of healthy tissue, keeping the dose low enough to avoid serious damage. Nevertheless, there is usually some destruction of normal cells, so cancer radiation patients often exhibit side effects similar to radiation sickness (nausea, fatigue, loss of hair, etc.).

If the cells damaged by radiation therapy are in the reproductive organs, genetic mutations can occur that may be transmitted to future offspring. Because radiation, even that from the diagnostic use of X-rays, is so widespread, and its effect on the genes quite unknown, there is great concern about the genetic future of the human race.

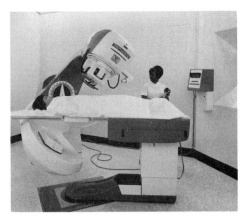

A patient receiving cobalt-bomb radiation treatment.

16.10 Investigations

Investigation 16.1: Force On a Conductor in a Magnetic Field

Problem:
What factors affect the magnitude of the force on a conductor in a magnetic field?

Materials:
current balance and solenoid apparatus
2 DC ammeters
2 DC variable voltage power supplies (0-12 V)
string and scissors
electronic balance

Procedure:
1. Set up the apparatus as shown in the diagram.

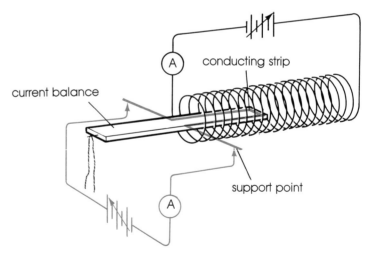

2. By rotating the support points slightly, balance the conducting strip so that, when the power supplies are both off, it remains horizontal and motionless.
3. Turn on the current in the coil and in the conducting strip. Arrange the polarity of both currents so that the end of the strip inside the coil is forced downward. The current in the coil should be adjusted to be approximately at the midpoint of its range of values.

4. Now, increase the current in the conducting strip to its maximum value (thereby forcing the end inside the coil down). Loop a length of string over the other end of the conducting strip, long enough to overbalance the strip and force the end inside the coil up above the balance point. Then, very carefully, cut off small segments of the string with a pair of scissors, until the conducting strip just balances horizontally. Turn off both currents, and weigh the piece of string that was looped over the conducting strip. Record its mass, and the current in the conducting strip, in a table.

5. Repeat this procedure at least four more times, each time using a successively smaller current through the strip. Again, record in your table the value of this current and the mass of string required to balance the strip.

6. Set the current through the conducting strip at a constant value near the middle of its range of values, and repeat the experiment five more times, this time varying the current through the coil from its minimum to its maximum value. For each case, record the current through the coil and the mass of string required to achieve balance.

7. Finally, make very careful measurements of the following quantities:
   (a) the distance from the pivot point of the conducting strip to each of its ends
   (b) the diameter of the coil
   (c) the length of the coil
   (d) the number of turns on the coil

Calculations and Analysis:

1. Using the physical dimensions of the coil and the equation on page 637, calculate the magnitude of the magnetic field intensity (B) in the core of the coil for each value of current through it, and include these values in your table.

2. Using the mass of each piece of string and the lever principle, or torques, determine the magnitude of the magnetic force acting down upon the conducting strip in each case, and include these values in your table.

3. Draw a graph of force on the conducting strip (F) versus current in the conducting strip (I), for a constant value of magnetic field intensity (B). What is the relationship between I and F as revealed by your graph?

4. Draw a separate graph of force on the conducting strip (F) versus magnetic field intensity (B), for a constant value of current in the conducting strip (I). What relationship between F and B is apparent from this graph?

5. Using the results from these two graphs, create an expression that shows how F varies jointly with B and I. What other factor(s) might F depend on, that were not investigated in this experiment?

Investigation 16.2: Properties of Microwaves

Problem:
What can we learn about the properties of electromagnetic radiation from microwaves?

Materials:
microwave generator
microwave detector (diode antenna)
DC microammeter
audio generator and amplifier
audio speaker
double slit baffle, for microwave generator
light meter
2 Polaroid filters
light source
protractor
aluminum barrier

Procedure:
1. Set up the microwave generation and detection apparatus as indicated in the diagram.

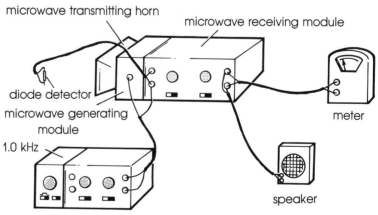

The microwave generator is turned off and on at an audio frequency. This is a form of amplitude modulation. The pulses of microwaves are transmitted by the horn and detected by the diode antenna. The modulated signal from this antenna is amplified and sent to the speaker and the meter. The volume of sound from the speaker gives a qualitative measure of the magnitude of the microwaves received by the antenna. A quantitative measurement can be made from the current reading on the meter.

Part A: Polarization of Microwaves

2. Place the diode antenna about 25 cm in front of the microwave horn. Rotate the antenna slowly in a vertical plane perpendicular to a line from the antenna to the horn. In what position is the signal a maximum? A minimum? What does this reveal about these microwaves? In all future steps in this investigation, always hold the antenna in the position that resulted in the maximum reading in this test.

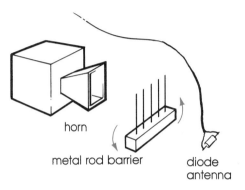

horn

metal rod barrier   diode antenna

3. Using the metal-rod barrier shown, test to see if any microwaves can pass through it and be detected by the antenna. Rotate the barrier in a vertical plane and note the effect on received microwave intensity. For several positions between horizontal and vertical, record the received microwave intensity (from the meter) and the angle between the rods of the barrier and the antenna (using a protractor). Draw a graph of microwave intensity versus angle, from 0° to 90°. Do not change the orientation of the diode antenna.

4. Using two Polaroid filters, a light source, and a light meter, record the intensity of light transmitted through both filters, at various angles between their axes of polarization between 0° and 90°. Draw a graph of light intensity versus angle, on the same graph as in procedure 3, and using a vertical scale that makes the maximum values of light intensity and microwave intensity equal. How do these two graphs compare?

Do not use a laser. It may be polarized already.

Part B: Wavelength of Microwaves

5. Place a flat aluminum reflector plate about 50 cm in front of the horn, as shown.

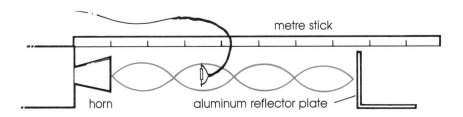

metre stick

horn   aluminum reflector plate

If you have forgotten the properties of standing waves, look back to Chapter 12.

Move the detector back and forth along the line from the horn to the plate, noting the change in microwave intensity. Describe this variation in intensity, and explain why it occurs.

6. Make several determinations of the distance between successive positions of maximum intensity, and determine an average value for this quantity. What does this distance represent? Try again, but use the distance between successive minimum intensity positions. Find the wavelength and frequency of the microwaves used in this investigation. (You know their speed!)

7. Assuming that the square wave audio signal keeps the microwave signal "on" for half the time, how many complete microwave cycles are there in each audio burst?

Part C: Interference of Microwaves

8. Set up the apparatus, as shown, using the double-slit baffle that fits over the microwave horn. This makes two slit sources, transmitting in-phase.

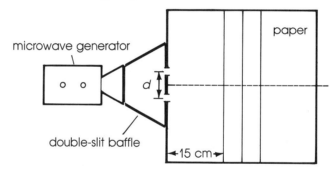

Arrange the paper carefully on the table so that its front edge is parallel to the front of the baffle. Draw a centreline, perpendicular to the horn and midway between the slits. Also draw lines, parallel to the horn, 15 cm, 20 cm, and 25 cm in front of it.

9. With the equipment operating, move the detector very slowly along the 15 cm line, starting from the centreline and working out in each direction. Mark and label clearly all positions of maximum and minimum intensity. Repeat for the other two lines.

10. Using these marked positions, sketch several nodal lines in the interference pattern produced. Make use of the equation developed earlier (Section 14.4) to calculate the wavelength of the microwaves. Measure the distance between the slits directly from the baffle, and use data from each of the three parallel lines to determine an average value. Compare this value of wavelength with that obtained in Part B of your investigation.

16.11 Review

Discussion

1. If you have two identical iron rods, only one of which is a bar magnet, explain how you could determine which is which without using any other materials or objects.
2. Describe the action of a magnetic compass and a magnetic dipping needle at:
   (a) the north pole
   (b) the south pole
   (c) the equator
3. Describe the effect of the Earth's magnetic field on the motion of charged particles approaching from outer space. Is there any direction along which they can reach the Earth without deflection?
4. Iron pipes, steel beams, and other steel structures that remain stationary are often found to be magnetized with a distinct polarity. Explain.
5. Describe the motion of an electron that is initially moving parallel to, and in the same direction as, a magnetic field line. Do the same for the opposite direction.
6. Explain why the magnetic field created by the electric currents flowing through the wires in your home is unlikely to have any effect on a compass placed nearby.
7. How would all of the right-hand rules developed as memory aids in electromagnetism be affected if we thought in terms of electron flow rather than conventional current?
8. A horizontal east-west wire carries a current flowing west. A beam of positive alpha particles is shot directly down at the wire from above. In what direction will they be deflected?
9. A charged particle is moving in a circular path under the influence of a uniform magnetic field. Describe how the path will change in response to each of the following factors, considered separately:
   (a) The intensity of the magnetic field is increased.
   (b) An electric field is added, in the same direction as the magnetic field.
   (c) Both fields are simultaneously turned off.
10. Some oscilloscopes have a "dual trace" feature, affording them the ability to compare two signals simultaneously. Suggest how two separate electron beams can be created and controlled in one cathode ray tube.

11. Two ions of the same substance, one singly ionized and the other doubly ionized, are each accelerated from rest by the same potential difference, and enter the same uniform magnetic field, moving perpendicular to the field. Compare:
    (a) their velocities upon entering the field,
    (b) their radii of curvature, once in the field.

12. Why is a car's radio reception often distorted when the car is driving near high-voltage transmission lines or under steel-reinforced concrete?

13. An electromagnetic wave is travelling straight up, perpendicular to the Earth's surface. If its electric field is oscillating in an east-west plane, what is the direction of oscillation of its magnetic field?

14. Some people claim that care should be taken when connecting speakers to a stereo amplifier, to ensure that the lead wires are of equal length. Do you feel this is necessary? Explain.

15. Why do AM radio waves not cast shadows (regions of no reception) behind obstacles such as buildings and trees?

16. Explain why advances in communications technology that provide television viewers with a wider choice of programming pose a threat to our Canadian identity.

17. Discuss several ecological consequences that could occur, unless atmospheric pollution levels are controlled.

18. Give several examples, both positive and negative, of ways in which electromagnetic radiation directly influences our health and general well-being.

19. Knowledge of the physics of electromagnetic radiation is an important part of the undergraduate education of physicists, engineers, and other scientists. List 10 occupations where a person might work, daily, with devices that require some knowledge of the properties of electromagnetic radiation.

In 1951, Dr. Harold Johns, a professor of physics at the University of Saskatchewan, used cobalt-60 produced at AEC's heavy water reactor at Chalk River, Ontario, to build a cancer treatment unit at the University of Saskatchewan Hospital. Called a cobalt bomb, the unit bombards cancerous tumours with high-energy X-rays and γ-rays given off by radioactive cobalt-60. Johns' work has made Canada a world leader in this field. In 1973, more than 1000 AEC cobalt-60 units had been sold to over 50 foreign countries, prolonging the lives of well over two million cancer victims.

Problems

20. A 15 cm length of wire carrying a current of 20 A is situated at right angles to a uniform magnetic field. If it experiences a magnetic force of 0.40 N, what is the magnetic field intensity?

21. What is the magnetic force on a wire 0.25 m long, carrying a current of 4.0 A, when placed in a uniform magnetic field of 0.50 T, at an angle of 45° to the wire?

22. A conductor 40 cm long has a mass of 15 g and lies in a horizontal position, at a 90° angle to the field lines of a uniform horizontal magnetic field of 0.20 T. What must the current in

the conductor be, so that the magnetic force on it will support its own weight?

23. What is the magnitude and direction of the force on an electron moving horizontally to the west at 3.2×10^6 m/s through a uniform magnetic field of 1.2 T pointing horizontally to the south?

24. An electron, shot at right angles into a uniform magnetic field of 2.0×10^{-3} T, experiences a deflecting force of 2.6×10^{-16} N. With what velocity is it moving?

25. An alpha particle ($q = +3.2 \times 10^{-19}$ C, $m = 6.7 \times 10^{-27}$ kg) is accelerated by a potential difference of 1200 V, and then enters a uniform magnetic field of magnitude 0.25 T, moving at 90° to the field. What is the magnetic force acting on it?

26. What is the magnitude and direction of the magnetic field 20 cm to the east of a straight vertical wire carrying a current of 12 A downward through air?

27. What current in a straight wire produces a magnetic field no greater than 1.0×10^{-4} T, at a distance of 10 cm in air?

28. A straight wire carries a current of 20 A vertically upward, in a vacuum. An electron moves at a speed of 5.0×10^6 m/s, parallel to this wire but vertically downward, a distance of 10 cm from it. Calculate the magnitude and direction of the force on the electron. Will this force remain constant?

29. What is the magnetic field strength in the air-core of a solenoid 10 cm long, consisting of 1200 loops of wire carrying a current of 1.0 A?

30. A coil 15 cm long with 100 turns lies in a horizontal plane, with a light frame supporting conducting wire WXYZ balanced horizontally at its midpoint in the core of the coil, as shown:

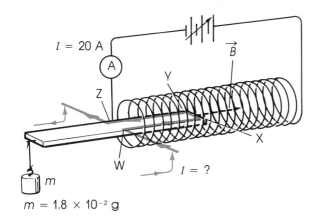

$I = 20$ A

$I = ?$

$m = 1.8 \times 10^{-2}$ g

Sides WX and YZ of the conductor are 5.0 cm long, and are parallel to the axis of the coil, whereas side XY is 1.5 cm long and perpendicular to the axis of the coil. The current flowing through the coil is 20 A. What current must flow through the conductor WXYZ in order to keep it in horizontal balance, when a mass of 1.8×10^{-2} g hangs from the far end of the light frame that holds the conductor?

31. What is the magnetic force between two parallel wires 50 m long and 10 cm apart, each carrying a current of 100 A in the same direction?

32. A wire, whose linear mass density is 150 g/m, carries a current of 40 A (supplied by a flexible connection of negligible weight). This wire lies parallel to, and on top of, another horizontal wire on a table. What current must flow through the bottom wire in order to repel and support the top wire at a height of 4.0 cm above it? (There are frictionless guide plates to keep it on line.)

33. What is the charge-to-mass ratio for a particle accelerated to a velocity of 6.0×10^6 m/s, that moves in a circular path of radius 1.8 cm perpendicular to a uniform magnetic field of 3.2×10^{-2} T?

34. A proton, of mass 1.67×10^{-27} kg, moves in a circle in the plane perpendicular to a uniform 1.8 T magnetic field. If its radius of curvature is 3.0 cm, what is its velocity?

35. A singly ionized particle ($q = +e$) is moving at 1.9×10^4 m/s at right angles to a uniform magnetic field of 1.0×10^{-3} T. If the radius of curvature of its path is 0.40 m, what is its mass?

36. A singly ionized $^{235}_{92}$U ion, of mass 3.9×10^{-25} kg, is accelerated through a potential difference of 1.0×10^5 V.
    (a) What is its maximum velocity?
    (b) What is the radius of the path it would take if injected at 90° into a 0.10 T uniform magnetic field at this velocity?

37. Calculate the quantity indicated for each of the following electromagnetic waves:
    (a) the frequency of a 1.8 cm wavelength microwave
    (b) the wavelength of a 3.2×10^{10} Hz radar signal
    (c) the distance between adjacent maxima of magnetic field strength in the electromagnetic wave coming from a 60 Hz transmission line
    (d) the frequency of red visible light, of wavelength 650 nm

38. Two football fans are listening to the Grey Cup game on radio, one in Montreal where it is being played, and the other in the Northwest Territories, 6000 km away. The distant signal is transmitted by microwaves, using a communications satellite at an altitude of 36 000 km. Making whatever assumptions seem reasonable, determine how much sooner the fan in Montreal hears the results of any play.

39. Ultrasonic waves are used to observe babies as they develop from conception to birth. Typical frequencies are 30 000 Hz to 45 000 Hz.
    (a) What would be the typical wavelengths if these were radio waves?
    (b) What are the actual wavelengths, in air, given that they are high-frequency sound waves with a velocity of 340 m/s?

17 Special Theory of Relativity

By the end of the 19th century, physicists were well satisfied with their understanding of the physical world around them. Newtonian mechanics had been successful in explaining the motion of objects on Earth and in the heavens. Maxwell's Theory of Electromagnetism had consolidated knowledge about the special relationship between electric and magnetic forces, and had predicted the existence of electromagnetic waves with properties similar to those of light—so similar, in fact, that light itself was assumed to be an electromagnetic wave. Physics as it was known up to this time is referred to as **classical physics**.

The puzzles that still remained—the structure of the atom and its nucleus—were expected to be solved by further applications of the currently accepted theories. Such was not to be the case, however. The solution to these puzzles required the proposal of two very revolutionary and clever concepts: the Theory of Relativity and the Quantum Theory. These theories changed our understanding of the universe drastically; their development and application to the search for the atomic structure is referred to as **modern physics**.

This chapter and the remaining three chapters deal with the development of these theories and how they are applied to the problem of understanding atomic and nuclear structure.

17.1 Inertial Frames of Reference

In Chapters 1 to 5, we learned that, to describe and account for the motion of any object, we must adopt a frame of reference from which to view the motion—an arbitrary origin and set of axes from which to measure the changing position of a moving object. Most often we choose the Earth as our frame of reference, assuming it to be stationary, and measure all positions of a moving object relative to some origin and set of axes fixed on the Earth. It was, of course, in the Earth's frame of reference that Newton's First

Law, the Law of Inertia, was discovered. Any frame of reference in which the Law of Inertia holds is called an **inertial frame of reference**. That is, if no net force acts on an object at rest, it remains at rest, or, if in motion, it continues to move in a straight line at a constant speed.

What other frames of reference are inertial frames? Let us consider a moving train. People on the moving train can walk, play cards, eat, and carry out any other normal activity as if the train were stationary, without making any special adjustments as long as the train's velocity remains constant. The well-known laws of physics seem to hold. (We would also find adherence to Newton's Laws if we were moving very slowly on a barge, or very quickly in a spaceship—as long as the frame of reference had a constant velocity.) However, if the train speeds up, slows down, or turns sharply, odd things appear to happen. Objects do not fall straight down; it is more difficult to walk in one direction than in the other; and things may move sideways for no apparent reason. The simple laws of mechanics no longer seem to govern the motion that is occurring.

This leads us to three important statements about relative motion and frames of reference:
- An inertial frame of reference is one that is at rest or moving in a straight line with a constant speed.
- The laws of Newtonian mechanics are only valid in an inertial frame of reference.
- The laws of Newtonian mechanics apply equally in *all* inertial frames of reference; in other words, all inertial frames of reference are equivalent so far as adherence to the laws of physics is concerned.

An interesting phenomenon follows from the equivalence of all inertial frames of reference. If there are two frames of reference, one at rest and one moving with a constant velocity, there is *no* physics experiment that can be done to identify which frame is at rest and which is moving.

The three assumptions above form the basis for the "special theory of relativity", so-called because it deals only with the special case of motion in a frame of reference moving at constant velocity relative to an observer. Athough the motion of the frame of reference has no effect on the validity of the laws of physics, the Special Theory of Relativity does, as you will see, make some very strange predictions about the relationship between space and time that change our way of looking at motion at very high speeds.

17.2 Accelerating Frames of Reference

An accelerating frame of reference is a non-inertial frame; that is, the laws of Newtonian mechanics do not apply to motion viewed in an accelerating frame. For example, consider a ball at rest on a flat, smooth, level table in a car moving in a straight line at a constant speed. Since the car is an inertial frame at the moment, Newton's First Law applies and the ball remains at rest.

However, if the car suddenly accelerates by speeding up, a strange thing happens. The ball, for no reason apparent to the occupants of the car, begins to accelerate towards the rear of the table. Newton's Law of Inertia is violated. Similarly, if the car slows down, the ball begins to move forward; and if the car turned sharply to the right, the ball would begin to move to the left. To observers in the frame of reference of the car, there is no real force acting on the ball causing it to move forward, backward, or sideways.

In each case, however, when the motion is observed from the inertial frame of the Earth, the ball is seen to simply obey the Law of Inertia—to continue moving in a straight line with a constant speed.

$\vec{v} = $ constant $\vec{a} = 0$

$\vec{v}$ increasing $\vec{a} > 0$ (for car)

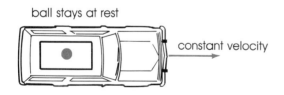

ball stays at rest

constant velocity

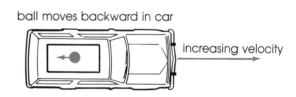

ball moves backward in car

increasing velocity

$\vec{v}$ decreasing $\vec{a} < 0$ (for car)

ball moves forward in car

decreasing velocity

$\vec{v}$ changes direction (car turns right)

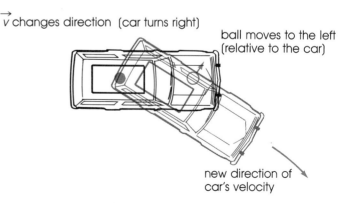

ball moves to the left (relative to the car)

new direction of car's velocity

So firm is our belief in Newton's Laws, that we would rather invent a "fictitious force" to explain these strange motions in non-inertial frames than abandon our belief in Newton's Laws. In the previous example, we would have to assume a fictitious inertial force in a direction opposite to that of the car's acceleration in order to explain the motion of the ball in each case. In the case where the car is turning, this fictitious force is called the "centrifugal force". It is familiar to everyone who has taken a ride at an amusement park.

It is clear that the analysis of motion in non-inertial frames is unnecessarily complicated, and should be avoided. Of course, because of the equivalence of all inertial frames of reference, looking at the same motion from *any* non-accelerating frame provides a much simpler analysis, consistent with Newton's Laws.

17.3 The Special Theory of Relativity

In Chapter 3, we learned how to calculate relative velocities in moving frames of reference, using vector addition. The laws of motion may apply equally in all inertial frames of reference, but the motion has a different appearance, depending on the frame from which it is viewed. For example, if a ball is rolled forward at 10 m/s on a train moving at 30 m/s, from the Earth's frame of reference its velocity would be 40 m/s. Conversely, if it were rolled backward at the same speed on the same train, its velocity relative to the Earth would be 20 m/s. Clearly, the velocity with which the ball is observed to move depends on the frame of reference of the observer.

At the turn of the 20th century, many physicists were intrigued by the application of the same rules to a less tangible motion—that of light. Would light emitted in the forward direction from a source moving relative to the Earth at 1/10 the speed of light have a velocity of 11/10 the speed of light, measured by an observer in the Earth's frame of reference? Also, would light emitted backward from the same source have a measured speed of 9/10 the speed of light? In other words, would the speed of light also depend on the frame of reference from which it is observed?

The first hint that light was somehow different from other phenomena came in the latter half of the 19th century, when James Clerk Maxwell, as part of his famous Theory of Electromagnetism, described light as an electromagnetic wave, and predicted its velocity as 3.0×10^8 m/s. In what reference frame would the speed of light have this value? Was there some special, absolute frame of reference where c would have the value of 3.0×10^8 m/s?

If the ball actually moves in the turning car, another less familiar fictitious "Coriolis force" must also be introduced in the accelerating frame. Just try to play catch on a merry-go-round!

"I can accept the theory of relativity as little as I can accept the existence of atoms and other such dogmas."
Ernst Mach (1838–1916), professor of physics at the University of Vienna

Up to this time, scientists had always associated waves with a medium through which they travelled. It was natural, then, for them to assume that light must also travel through some kind of medium. Perhaps this medium was the absolute frame of reference in the universe, and the speed Maxwell calculated for electromagnetic waves was relative to it. This transparent, zero-density, undetectable medium came to be called **ether**, and it was assumed to be at absolute rest and to permeate all of space.

According to classical mechanics, then, the speed of light measured relative to any frame of reference moving through this ether, such as the Earth, should differ from 3.0×10^8 m/s by the velocity with which the frame was moving, according to the rules for vector addition.

A number of very clever and complicated experiments were designed to measure the speed of the Earth through the ether. The most successful of these was performed in 1887 by two American physicists, A. A. Michelson (1852–1931) and E. W. Morley (1838–1923). The actual details of the Michelson-Morley experiment can be left to a further course in physics, but a brief description of their method and results is necessary to our understanding of special relativity.

Essentially, what they did was to compare the speeds of light travelling in two perpendicular directions relative to the Earth's motion through the ether. From the Earth's frame of reference, the ether could be thought of as moving past the Earth with an equal speed in the opposite direction, the so-called "ether wind". They expected to find a difference in the measured speed of light depending upon how their apparatus was oriented with respect to the ether wind. Just as a boat's velocity is different, as measured from the shore, when it is moving upstream, downstream, or crossstream, so too should the velocity of light differ when it is moving back and forth in the direction of the ether wind, or sideways, at right angles to it. To detect such a small difference in velocity, Michelson and Morley used an interferometer that produced an interference pattern between two parts of a split beam of light, moving parallel to and perpendicular to the ether wind. The diagram on page 677 shows how the two beams were created and the interference pattern was observed. The entire apparatus could be rotated to interchange the positions of the mirrors.

Any small difference in the velocity of light along the two paths would be indicated by a change in the interference pattern as the apparatus rotated. If the apparatus is rotated by 90°, the distance l_1 is now parallel to the ether wind and the distance l_2 is perpendicular to it. Thus, the time taken to travel these distances should

Michelson's Interferometer is described in more detail in Section 14.7.

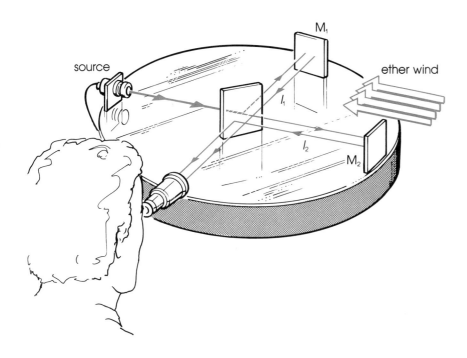

change as the apparatus is rotated. This should produce phase changes in the light that travels each of these paths, resulting in a changing interference pattern.

The great importance of the Michelson-Morley experiment lies in its failure to show what was expected. There was absolutely no change in the interference pattern. The speed of light was the same whether it travelled back and forth in the direction of the ether wind, or at right angles to it. The relative velocity of the ether with respect to the Earth had no effect on the speed of light. This "null" result was one of the great puzzles of physics, at the turn of the century.

Many theories attempting to explain it were proposed by the leading scientists of the day, but the first person to account for it satisfactorily was Albert Einstein (1879–1955) a German working in Switzerland as a patent clerk, who proposed a revolutionary new theory in 1905. Called the **Special Theory of Relativity**, it reconciled the problem in a rather simple way.

In non-inertial frames of reference, the reconciliation of this null result becomes even more complicated by the introduction of gravitational forces. Space and time are fused together into a space-time continuum, and form the basis of Einstein's General Theory of Relativity.

Einstein concluded that the ether, and hence an absolute frame of reference, did not exist. His special theory of relativity was based on two postulates, as follows:

All the laws of physics are valid in all inertial frames of reference.

Light travels through empty space with a definite speed of $c = 3.000 \times 10^8$ m/s, regardless of the speed of the light source or of the observer.

The first statement is just an extension of the idea of Newtonian relativity, already mentioned in this chapter, to include *all* of the laws of physics, particularly those governing electricity and magnetism. The second is more difficult to reconcile in our minds because it contradicts our common-sense notions of relative motion. We would expect two observers, one moving towards a light source and the other moving away from it, to make two different determinations of the relative speed of light. This would be true for sound waves, and produces the well-known Doppler Effect. According to Einstein, however, each would determine the same result, $c = 3.0 \times 10^8$ m/s. Clearly, our everyday experiences and common sense are of no help in dealing with motion at the speed of light. By doing away with the notion of an absolute frame of reference, Einstein's theory solves the dilemma in Maxwell's equations — the speed of light predicted by Maxwell is its speed in *any* inertial frame.

Einstein predicted a number of interesting, but strange, results, based on these two postulates. In the next few sections, we will examine some consequences of these predictions. It is a credit to Albert Einstein's ingenuity that these strange mathematical proposals, made in 1905, have been tested repeatedly over the years and found to be valid. The Special Theory of Relativity and its many implications are now considered as much a part of physics as Newton's Laws. The difference is that to comprehend the many ramifications of the Special Theory of Relativity requires a great deal more mental flexibility and dexterity than did Newtonian mechanics.

17.4 Simultaneity

One of the concepts of classical physics that is the most difficult to abandon is that time is absolute. Surely, an event appearing to a stationary observer to last 2.0 s would also appear to last 2.0 s to an observer moving with respect to the stationary observer. But it is not so!

The Special Theory of Relativity has enabled physicists to account for discrepancies in astronomical measurements that could not be explained using Newtonian mechanics.

In reality, simultaneity, the occurrence of two or more events at exactly the same time, is a relative concept. If an observer sees two events occurring at exactly the same time, it does not necessarily mean they happened simultaneously. Because light travels at a finite speed, c, the event that was farther away from the observer actually occurred first. For example, a sunburst that was observed on Earth to occur just as the clock struck noon actually occurred at about 11:52 a.m. by that same clock. It took about 8 min for light from the sunburst to reach the observer on Earth.

A more intriguing question concerning simultaneity is this: if two events are simultaneous to one observer, are they also simultaneous to another observer, moving relative to the first? A sample analysis will provide an answer.

A stationary observer O_s is standing on a railway platform at the midway point between two lampposts, L_1 and L_2, as shown. A train is moving along a straight track next to the platform with speed v. Observer O_m is on the train.

Einstein devised many of his predictions about the Special Theory of Relativity using "gedanken" or "thought" experiments. Actual verifications of these predictions came many years later.

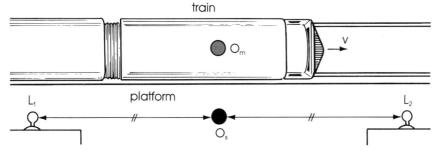

At the instant that O_m is opposite O_s, the lights on both lampposts go on. O_s sees them go on simultaneously, and, knowing that he is an equal distance from L_1 and L_2, correctly concludes that the two events are simultaneous. On the other hand, by the time the light from L_1 and L_2 reaches O_s, O_m will have moved a short distance to the right, as shown.

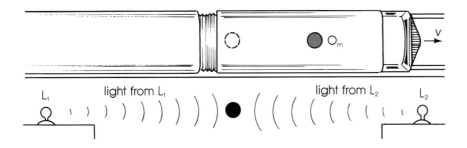

As can easily be seen, at this time O_m will have already received the light from L_2 but will not yet have received any from L_1. To him, L_2 and L_1 are not simultaneous; L_2 occurred first, in his frame of reference.

In general,

Two events that are simultaneous to one observer are not necessarily simultaneous to a second observer, moving relative to the first.

In the previous example, it is tempting to ask which observer, O_s or O_m, is correct. Strangely enough, they both are! Neither frame is better than the other for judging simultaneity. Simultaneity is a relative concept, rather than an absolute one. In everyday life, we are usually unaware of this effect; it becomes much more significant as the relative speed between the two observers increases to a reasonable fraction of c.

17.5 Time Dilation, Length Contraction, and Mass Increase

In Section 17.3, we suggested that Einstein's Special Theory of Relativity had some strange and interesting implications so far as our notions of space and time are concerned. We shall look at a few of these now.

Time Dilation

Suppose, to have an accurate clock, we use a light source giving off a very short pulse of light that travels a distance L, strikes a mirror, is reflected directly back, and is received by a detector that gives off a "tick" sound. Our time unit, then, is t_0, the time taken for light to travel the distance $2L$ at speed c.

Now, suppose this clock is placed in a spaceship moving past the Earth at velocity v, and is observed by an observer on Earth at three different times: when the light is emitted (a), when it is reflected (b), and when it is detected and a tick is registered (c), as shown on the next page.

The spaceship moves to the right with velocity v. The time and distance intervals between positions (a), (b), and (c) are equal, as shown. The dotted diagonal lines represent the path actually taken by the light, as seen by the observer on Earth.

The source and detector are located at the same place, but are offset in this diagram for clarity.

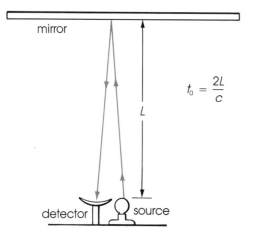

$$t_0 = \frac{2L}{c}$$

mirror

L

detector   source

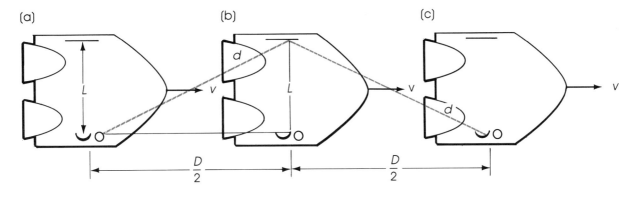

(a)   (b)   (c)

Earth observer

The time unit, t, as seen by the observer on Earth, may be calculated as follows:

In time t, the spaceship travels a distance D given by

$$D = vt$$

According to Einstein's Special Theory of Relativity, the Earth observer sees the light travel along the diagonal path from (a) to (b), at speed c, in time $t/2$, a distance, d, given by

$$d = c\frac{t}{2}$$

Then, applying the Pythagorean theorem to the triangle of which the diagonal path (a) to (b) is the hypotenuse:

$$d^2 = L^2 + \left(\frac{D}{2}\right)^2$$

And, substituting into this equation, we can write

$$\left(c\frac{t}{2}\right)^2 = L^2 + \left(\frac{vt}{2}\right)^2$$

And, simplifying, we have

$$c^2t^2 = 4L^2 + v^2t^2$$

Now, solving for t, we can write

$$t^2(c^2 - v^2) = 4L^2$$

$$t^2 = \frac{4L^2}{c^2 - v^2}$$

or, finally, $t = \dfrac{2L}{c\sqrt{1 - v^2/c^2}}$

Comparing this with $t_0 = \dfrac{2L}{c}$, the unit of time as measured by an observer on the moving spaceship, we have

$$t = \frac{t_0}{\sqrt{1 - v^2/c^2}}$$

Note that t_0, the time measured by an observer at rest relative to the event, is called the "proper time", whereas t, the time measured by an observer moving at speed v relative to the event, is called the "relativistic time".

This result implies that the time between the sending and receiving of the light pulse is greater when measured from Earth than when measured on the moving spaceship. This result of special relativity is called **time dilation**. Stated more simply, it means that to a stationary observer, moving clocks appear to run slow (a longer period means a slower clock).

Notice that, in the equation above, t can be a real number only if the expression $1 - v^2/c^2$ is positive. That is,

$$1 - \frac{v^2}{c^2} > 0$$

$$\frac{v^2}{c^2} < 1$$

$$v^2 < c^2$$

and, finally, $v < c$

This is the famous "speed limit" proposed by Einstein. *No material object, in this case the spaceship carrying the clock, can have a velocity that is equal to, or greater than, that of light.*

Of course, "stationary observer" could be misleading. To *any* observer, a clock in motion relative to one's self runs slow.

Sample problem

There was a young lady named White,
With a speed that was greater than light,
She went out one day,
In a relative way,
And came back the previous night.

An astronaut whose pulse remains constant at 72 beats/min is sent on a voyage in a spaceship, and his pulse is measured by a stationary observer on Earth. What would his pulse beat be when the ship is moving, relative to the Earth, at (a) 0.10 c and (b) 0.90 c?

The time between pulse beats, measured on the spaceship, is

$$t_0 = \frac{1}{72} \text{ min}$$
$$= 0.014 \text{ min}$$

Then, at $v = 0.10 \, c$, $t = \dfrac{t_0}{\sqrt{1 - v^2/c^2}}$

$$= \frac{0.014 \text{ min}}{\sqrt{1 - \dfrac{(0.10 \, c)^2}{c^2}}}$$

$$= \frac{0.014 \text{ min}}{0.995}$$
$$= 0.014 \text{ min, to 2 significant figures}$$

Thus, as measured from the Earth, his pulse rate, at $v = 0.10 \, c$, remains at 72 beats/min.

At $v = 0.90 \, c$,
$$t = \frac{0.014 \text{ min}}{\sqrt{1 - \dfrac{(0.90 \, c)^2}{c^2}}}$$
$$= \frac{0.014 \text{ min}}{0.436}$$
$$= 0.032 \text{ min}$$

Therefore, as measured from the Earth, at $v = 0.90 \, c$, his pulse rate is 31 beats/min, much slower than the 72 beats/min that the astronaut would measure for himself on the speeding spaceship.

Note that time dilation effects only become noticeable at speeds closely approaching the speed of light, and do not, therefore, form any part of our everyday experience.

An interesting "thought experiment" that illustrates time dilation is the "twin paradox". Suppose that one of a pair of identical twins takes off from Earth and travels to a distant star and back, at a speed approaching c. The other twin remains on Earth. Due to time dilation, the moving twin's time clock runs more slowly, so that when he returns to Earth he will have aged less than his Earthbound twin and, for all intents and purposes, be younger.

But wouldn't the twin in the spaceship think the reverse, seeing his twin on Earth first receding at a high speed and then returning? Wouldn't he expect the Earth twin to be younger for the same reason? Is this a paradox?

No! The consequences of the special theory of relativity only apply in an inertial frame of reference, in this case the Earth, and do not hold in the accelerating frame of the spaceship, which must start, reverse, and then stop. It is indeed the twin in the spaceship who returns younger than his twin on Earth.

"When a man sits with a pretty girl for an hour, it seems like a minute. But let him sit on a hot stove for a minute — and it's longer than any hour. That's relativity."

Albert Einstein

Length Contraction

Since time, once assumed to be absolute, slows down at very high speeds, it seems natural to ask if length, another supposedly absolute concept, also changes.

Consider the spaceship from the previous example, making a trip from planet A to planet B, at rest with respect to each other and a distance L_0 apart, at a speed v as measured by an observer on either planet. (Just as t_0 was defined as the "proper time", L_0 is called the "proper distance".)

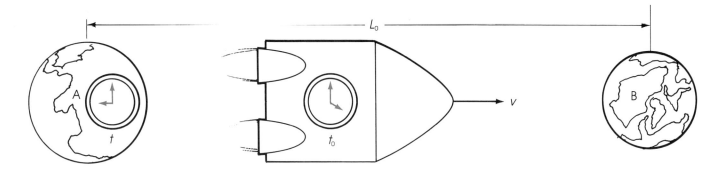

Science fiction authors often refer to relativistic effects such as time and space warps in describing space travel at high speeds.

Time is often thought of as a fourth dimension. An object or event may be specified by four quantities; three to describe where it is in space, and a fourth to describe when it is there, in time. Strangely, when objects move at speeds near c, space and time become interchangeable. A loss in space (length contraction) is accompanied by a gain in time (time dilation). Events look smaller but last longer. Time cannot be thought of as independent of space, or vice versa.

The time required for the trip, as measured by the stationary observer on either planet, is t, where

$$t = \frac{L_0}{v}$$

For the captain of the spaceship, the time for the trip, t_0, is less than this due to time dilation, according to the equation

$$t_0 = t\sqrt{1 - v^2/c^2}$$

Also, he sees himself at rest, with planet A receding and planet B approaching, both at speed v; so that the distance between planets A and B, as he sees it, is the product of their velocity and his time, namely

$$L = vt_0$$
$$= vt\sqrt{1 - v^2/c^2}$$

But, since $L_0 = vt$,

$$L = L_0\sqrt{1 - v^2/c^2}$$

where L_0 is the proper distance between A and B, as measured in the frame of reference at rest, and L is the relativistic distance as measured in the moving spaceship.

Again, since $\sqrt{1 - v^2/c^2} < 1$, $L < L_0$. That is, lengths and distances are measured as shorter when moving than when at rest. This effect is known as **length contraction**, and occurs only in the direction of motion. For example, a cylindrical spaceship moving past the Earth at a very high speed would appear shorter from tip to tail (but of the same diameter) due to length contraction.

Mass Increase

The fundamental quantities of mechanics are time, length, and mass. Both time and length have been shown to be relativistic; that is, their measured value depends on the frame of reference from which they are viewed.

Using a derivation beyond the scope of this book, but based on the Newtonian concept of conservation of momentum, Einstein was able to show that the mass of an object also changes with its speed, according to the equation

$$m = \frac{m_0}{\sqrt{1 - v^2/c^2}}$$

where m_0 is the "rest mass" and m is the relativistic, or moving, mass.

This equation predicts, even further, that no object can be accelerated to the speed of light. For, as $v \rightarrow c$, the expression $\sqrt{1 - v^2/c^2} \rightarrow 0$, and, consequently, $m \rightarrow \infty$. Thus, at the speed of light, m would be infinite, and would have required an infinite amount of energy to accelerate it to the speed c, clearly impossible. Conversely, the fact that light *does* travel at speed c implies that the photon rest mass, even if such a thing exists, must be zero (see Chapter 18).

Practice

1. In SI, the standard units for mass, length, and time are the kilogram, metre, and second. In fact, these standards are defined "at rest". Using the equations developed in this section, complete the following table to show how each of these quantities changes as $v \rightarrow c$.

There was a young fencer named Fisk,
Whose thrust was amazingly brisk,
So, often in action
The Lorentz contraction
Changed his foil from a rod to a disc.

Atomic particles may be made to approach the speed of light, and relativistic effects must be taken into account (see Chapter 20). In the Stanford linear accelerator, which is 3.2 km long, electrons reach 0.9 c in the first few hundred metres, but require the remainder of the 3.2 km of accelerating force to achieve their final speed of more than 0.99 c.

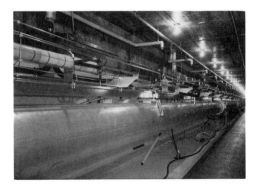

v/c	v^2/c^2	$1-v^2/c^2$	$\sqrt{1-v^2/c^2}$	$1/\sqrt{1-v^2/c^2}$
0.100	0.010	0.990	0.995	1.01
0.200	0.040	0.960	0.980	1.02
0.300	0.090	0.910	0.954	1.05
0.400	0.160	0.840	0.917	1.09
0.500	0.250	0.750	0.866	1.15
0.600	0.360	0.640	0.800	1.25
0.700	0.490	0.510	0.714	1.40
0.800	0.640	0.360	0.600	1.67
0.900	0.810	0.190	0.436	2.29
0.950	0.902	0.098	0.31	3.2
0.960	0.923	0.077	0.28	3.6
0.970	0.941	0.059	0.24	4.2
0.980	0.960	0.040	0.20	5.0
0.990	0.980	0.020	0.14	7.1
0.995	0.990	0.010	0.10	10

v	0	0.10 c	0.50 c	0.80 c	0.90 c	0.95 c	0.98 c	0.99 c	1.00 c
L	1 m								
m	1 kg								
t	1 s								

On the same set of axes, labelled separately for each unit, draw graphs of L, m, and t versus v, from $v = 0$ to $v = c$.

2. A cube of aluminum 1.00 m $\times$ 1.00 m $\times$ 1.00 m is moving at 0.90 c, in an orientation as shown. The rest density of aluminum is 2.70 $\times$ 10^3 kg/m^3.

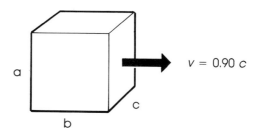

(a) Which of its three dimensions, a, b, or c, is affected by its motion?
(b) Calculate its relativistic volume.
(c) Calculate its relativistic mass.
(d) What is its density at $v = 0.90$ c?
        (b, 0.436 m^3, 6.18 $\times$ 10^3 kg, 1.42 $\times$ 10^4 kg/m^3)

17.6 Interconvertibility of Mass and Energy

When a force is applied to an object on a smooth horizontal plane, work is done on the object as a result, and its kinetic energy increases. In Chapter 9, we learned that

$$\text{work done} = \Delta E_k = E_{k_2} - E_{k_1}$$
$$= 1/2mv_2^2 - 1/2mv_1^2$$
$$= 1/2m\,(v_2^2 - v_1^2)$$

We assumed that the object's mass remained constant, and that any energy transferred to increase its kinetic energy resulted in an increase in speed only. Classically, we would expect this relation to continue to be valid as long as the force continues to act—the speed simply keeps increasing.

We now believe that, at very high speeds, the object's mass would begin to increase as well. It seems that doing work to increase its kinetic energy causes an increase in mass as well as speed. The Newtonian equation for kinetic energy, $E_k = 1/2mv^2$, is not valid at relativistic speeds. Not even using $m = m_0/\sqrt{1 - v^2/c^2}$ to give $E_k = 1/2m_0v^2/\sqrt{1 - v^2/c^2}$ yields the correct expression for relativistic kinetic energies.

Again, using an approach that is beyond the scope of this book, Einstein showed that the kinetic energy of any moving object is given by the expression

$$E_k = mc^2 - m_0c^2 = (m - m_0)c^2$$

where m_0 is its "rest mass" and m is its mass when moving at speed v.

This may be rewritten

$$mc^2 = m_0c^2 + E_k$$

When Einstein examined each term separately, he called m_0c^2 the "rest energy" of the object and mc^2 its total energy. He assumed that an object at rest had an amount of energy $E_0 = m_0c^2$, just due to its mass and not to the fact that it was moving. Hence, we have Einstein's famous mass-energy equivalence equation

---

$$E = mc^2$$

But what does this equation relating mass and energy really mean? In many ways, it means that mass is just one form of energy, and that it ought to be convertible into other more common and useable forms. There are many examples where this conversion of mass into energy can be verified:

- The energy released by the fission of uranium in a nuclear reactor, ΔE, is accompanied by a decrease in mass of the reactants, Δm; and very precise measurements of both have shown that $\Delta m = \Delta E/c^2$.
- When the π^0 meson (an elementary nuclear particle) decays, it completely disappears, losing all of its rest mass, m_0, and producing electromagnetic radiation (photons, see Chapter 20) whose energy E is given by $E = m_0c^2$.
- When hydrogen atoms react in the interior of the sun, in a process called fusion, the tremendous energy released, ΔE, is accompanied by a corresponding loss of mass, Δm, given by $\Delta m = \Delta E/c^2$. In fact, the sun is losing mass by this process at a rate of 1.98×10^7 kg/s.

It is believed that the equation $E = mc^2$ applies to *all* processes, although the changes are usually far too small to be measured. For example, the heat of combustion of coal is approximately 3.2×10^7 J/kg. If 1.0 kg of coal is burned, what change would the

An object's kinetic energy may be rewritten

$$E_k = (m - m_0)c^2$$
$$= m_0c^2 [(1 - v^2/c^2)^{-\frac{1}{2}} - 1]$$

However, when $v<<<c$, the expression $(1 - \frac{v^2}{c^2})^{-\frac{1}{2}}$ may be expanded,

using a binomial series,

$$(1 - \frac{v^2}{c^2})^{-\frac{1}{2}} = 1 + \frac{1}{2}\frac{v^2}{c^2} + \dots \text{ negligible terms}$$

Therefore,

$$E_k = m_0c^2 (1 + \frac{1}{2}\frac{v^2}{c^2} + \dots - 1)$$
$$= \frac{1}{2}m_0v^2$$

which is the familiar expression for kinetic energy at non-relativistic speeds ($v<<<c$).

release of this amount of energy make in the mass of the coal compared to the mass of the products of combustion?

Using $\Delta E = \Delta mc^2$ for an original rest mass of 1.0 kg of coal,

$$\Delta m = \frac{\Delta E}{c^2}$$

$$= \frac{3.2 \times 10^7 \text{ J}}{(3.0 \times 10^8 \text{ m/s})^2}$$

$$= 3.6 \times 10^{-10} \text{ kg}$$

which, as a percentage of the coal's original mass, is

$$\frac{3.6 \times 10^{-10} \text{ kg}}{1.0 \text{ kg}} \times 100\% = 0.000000036\%$$

As you can imagine, such an insignificant loss in mass would not be detectable using even the best electronic balances available. Even if we include the mass of oxygen consumed in the process (as we ought to), the picture doesn't change much.

The equation is, however, a powerful theoretical tool that makes it possible to predict the amount of energy available from any process that results in a decrease in mass. For example, let us calculate the amount of energy available from the *complete conversion* of that same 1.0 kg of coal into energy.

Again using $\Delta E = \Delta mc^2$, and $\Delta m = 1.0$ kg

$$\Delta E = (1.0 \text{ kg})(3.0 \times 10^8 \text{ m/s})^2$$
$$= 9.0 \times 10^{16} \text{ J}$$

and even more energy would be produced if we included the mass of oxygen consumed.

This is about the same amount of energy that results from the combustion of about three thousand million kilograms of coal, so it is no wonder that scientists are searching diligently for more effective methods of converting mass into energy than simple combustion. In our example, we assumed that *all* of the coal's mass was converted into energy. Even in our best nuclear reactors, only a fraction of one percent of the reacting mass is converted to energy, yet the energy yielded is enormous. The solution to the world's energy problems lies in discovering methods of converting even the smallest fraction of normal mass into energy without leaving toxic wastes behind.

17.7 The Life of Albert Einstein

Albert Einstein (1879–1955) was born in the small town of Ulm, Germany, and received his early education there. He showed very little intellectual promise as a child, except in the area of mathematics. He attended university in Switzerland, but was not considered qualified to go on to graduate school. Besides, he was Jewish,

The ability to convert from nuclear mass to energy has placed a tremendous responsibility on governments to ensure that this enormous amount of nuclear energy is utilized for the betterment of society, rather than for its ultimate destruction.

and also not a Swiss citizen, and therefore was denied a university post.

In 1901, he accepted a job as a clerk in the Patent Office in Berne, where he worked until 1909. In 1905, Einstein published papers that described three important new concepts in physics. The first, in the field of quantum theory, was his explanation of the photo-electric effect (to be dealt with in detail in Chapter 18). The second, published two months later, was his mathematical interpretation of the random motion of particles in a fluid, a phenomenon known as "Brownian movement". The third, and possibly his greatest accomplishment, gave us a new outlook on the physical universe, replacing the Newtonian concepts of motion that had been accepted for over 225 years. The Special Theory of Relativity, and the mass-energy relationship $E = mc^2$, described in this chapter, represent a monumental achievement for the power of the human mind; they forced scientists of the day to reconsider all they had always presumed about motion within the physical universe.

By 1909, Einstein's work had been widely recognized, and he was offered university posts, first at the University of Zurich and, in 1913, at the prestigious Kaiser Wilhelm Physical Institute in Berlin (later renamed the Max Planck Institute). In 1915 he published his General Theory of Relativity. This broader theory predicted further effects not forecast by Newtonian mechanics. In it, he proposed a theory a gravitation that treated Newton's theory of gravitation as only a special case of the more general situation. One of the consequences of Einstein's General Theory was that light would be deflected by a gravitational field. This prediction was tested and proved to be correct during the solar eclipse of 1919.

Einstein was then world famous. In fact, no other scientist had been so revered in his own time since Newton. Most scientists considered Newton and Einstein to be the "giants" of science, and this is still the case today. Although most laypeople did not understand his theories and their applications, he was respected and looked upon as the foremost scientist of this century. To many he was a folk hero. His comments and views on many subjects were quoted in the media, and there were even Einstein jokes. He once good-humouredly listed his occupation as "photographer's model". He was newsworthy wherever he went.

In 1930 he went to California as a visiting professor, and subsequently stayed permanently in the United States as an immigrant, because of the rise of Hitler and the Nazis in Germany. Germany was not safe for a Jew, even of Einstein's stature. In 1933 he accepted a post at the Institute for Advanced Studies at Princeton, where he stayed until his death in 1955. For the last twenty-two

Albert Einstein

years of his life, he searched in vain for a theory that would unite all gravitational and electromagnetic phenomena. Such a theory is called a "unified field theory".

Einstein did not accept all of the new ideas in physics, many of which originated with his theories of 1905. In particular, he was sceptical of the theories of Werner Heisenberg, which indicated that many of the properties of the subatomic universe were based on the laws of probability. He made statements such as "God may be subtle, but he is not malicious" and "God does not play at dice".

In 1939, Einstein was to see his famous prediction that mass could be changed into energy realized experimentally when fission was achieved by Otto Hahn and Lise Meitner in Germany. As the most influential scientist in America, Einstein was persuaded by Leo Szilard and others to write to President Franklin D. Roosevelt, urging him to begin a program to develop a nuclear bomb before this was accomplished by the Nazis in Germany. The enormous Manhattan Project was begun, and the bombs were produced and dropped on Japan in 1945, ushering the world into a new nuclear era.

Ironically, Einstein was a confirmed pacifist, who had been opposed to Germany's invasion of Belgium at the start of World War II. During his residence in the United States, he frequently expressed his views on social reform, was a fervent Zionist, and was a lifelong exponent of total disarmament. He died at his home in Princeton, New Jersey, on April 18, 1955. Shortly thereafter, a newly discovered artificial element, with the atomic number 99, was named Einsteinium in his honour.

Financing scientific research in such controversial and theoretical areas requires knowledgeable understanding and trust between scientists, technologists, politicians, and the general public.

17.8 Review

Discussion

1. A woman sitting in a train car that is slowing down throws a heavy ball straight up into the air (as it appears to her). Describe where the ball will fall, relative to her, and explain.
2. Describe several ways in which the authors of science fiction and space travel take the effects of special relativity into consideration.
3. If the speed of light were infinite, what would the effect be on length, mass, and time?
4. How would our lives be affected if the speed of light, the ultimate speed possible, were 100 km/h, or about 28 m/s?

5. "Matter has broken the sound barrier but will not, in all probability, be able to exceed the speed of light." Explain.
6. Describe the significance of the Michelson-Morley experiment. Why was its failure a success?
7. Distinguish between an inertial and a non-inertial frame of reference, and give examples of each. How do we account for some unexpected motions that occur in non-inertial frames?
8. Will two events occurring at the same time for one observer ever appear to be simultaneous to an observer moving with respect to the first observer? Explain.
9. If you were on a spaceship moving away from the Earth at 0.8 c, would you observe any change in your shoe size, your mass, or your pulse? Would an observer watching from Earth with a telescope note any change in these quantities?
10. Do mass increase, length contraction, and time dilation occur at normal travelling speeds of, say, 100 km/h? Explain.
11. Explain how the equation $E = mc^2$ is consistent with the Law of Conservation of Energy.
12. A photon may be thought of as a particle, of specific energy, that moves at the speed of light. What does the equation for relativistic mass suggest must be the rest mass of a photon?

Problems

13. A spaceship passes you at a speed of 0.90 c, and you measure its length to be 50 m. What is its measured length when at rest?
14. It is anticipated that one day intercontinental jet aircraft may be able to cruise at speeds of 4000 km/h (1.1×10^3 m/s). By how much would such a jet appear shortened, when viewed from the ground, if its proper length is 100 m?
15. A beam of unknown elementary particles travels at a speed of 2.0×10^8 m/s. When the particles are moving at this speed, their average lifetime is found by measurement to be 1.6×10^{-8} s. What is their average lifetime when at rest?
16. A distant star has been measured as moving at a speed of 0.8 c away from the Earth. If a planet of this star sends radio signals to Earth once every second (according to their time scale), how often would we receive them (according to our time scale)?
17. The rest mass of a proton is 1.67×10^{-27} kg. What would we measure as the mass of a proton moving at 0.90 c?

When doing some of the problems in this section, it may be helpful to use the data in the chart on page 686.

18. An astronaut who was 20 years old left to explore the galaxy in 1980, on a spaceship travelling at 2.5×10^8 m/s. He returns in 2020. About how old will he appear to be?

19. A K^+ meson has an average rest lifetime of 1.0×10^{-8} s. How fast must it be moving to double its average lifetime?

20. A spaceship must be launched from Earth at a speed of 1.1×10^4 m/s in order to escape from the Earth's gravitational field. By how much would the mass of a 3.0×10^5 kg spaceship increase when launched at this speed? (Ignore the mass of fuel burned.)

21. (a) With what speed must an electron be moving in order that its relativistic mass be 10^2 times its rest mass?
(b) To achieve this speed, electrons may be accelerated through a tube that is 3.0 km long. How long does this tube seem to be to the electron moving at its final speed?

22. A star is 40.0 light-years from Earth (1 light-year is the distance that light travels in 1 year).
(a) How far would you measure this distance to be if you travelled it in a spaceship moving at 1.00×10^8 m/s?
(b) How long would the trip last (for you)?

23. Tiny subatomic particles called mu-mesons (or muons) are created in collisions between cosmic rays and atoms at the upper limit of our atmosphere. At rest, muons have a mean lifetime of only 2.2×10^{-6} s, before disintegrating into other particles.
(a) What is their mean lifetime, if they travel at 0.99 c?
(b) Not taking relativity into account, what is the average distance you would expect muons to move, at this speed, before disintegrating?
(c) What actual distance, on the average, do they move before breaking apart?

24. A spaceship goes past a planet at a speed of 0.80 c. An observer on the planet measures the length of the moving spaceship as 40 m. He also says that his planet has a diameter of 2.0×10^6 m.
(a) How long does the woman on the spaceship measure the ship to be?
(b) What does the woman on the spaceship measure the diameter of the planet to be?
(c) According to the man on the planet, the spaceship takes 8.0 s to reach the next planet in his solar system. How long would the woman on the spaceship say it took?

25. How much energy can be produced by the complete annihilation of 1.0 kg of mass?

26. The Earth, of mass 5.98×10^{24} kg, moves along its solar orbit at an average speed of 2.96×10^4 m/s. How much mass, if converted into energy, could accelerate the Earth from rest to that speed?

27. A nuclear generating plant produces electric power at an average rate of 5.0 GW, by converting the mass of nuclear fuel. How much fuel is converted to energy in one year, if the process is assumed to be 100% efficient?

28. Scientist Ludwig von Drake, while in his laboratory, measures the half-life of some radioactive material which is in a bomb, approaching with speed v. Donald Duck, who is riding on the bomb, also measures the half-life. His answer is a factor of two smaller than Ludwig's. What is the value of v, expressed as a fraction of c? (SIN '79)

29. How much would the energy in problem 25 cost, at 5¢/kW·h, a typical utility price?

"DOES THIS APPLY ALWAYS, SOMETIMES, OR NEVER?"

18 The Quantum Nature of Light

Two major discoveries shook the world of physics in the early part of the 20th century. One was the Special Theory of Relativity. The other was the Quantum Theory. Both theories led to significant changes in how we look at the physical world. The Special Theory of Relativity was the sole creation of one man, Albert Einstein, in a single year, 1905. The Quantum Theory developed more slowly, over a period of 30 years, and was based on work contributed by many scientists. It began in the 1890s with studies of "blackbody" radiation, and reached its climax in the theory of quantum mechanics, used by Heisenberg and Schroedinger in the 1920s to explain the behaviour of electrons in atoms.

The next two chapters of this book are devoted to highlights of the development and application of the Quantum Theory as it relates to light and the energy of electrons in atoms.

18.1 Planck's Hypothesis

At the end of the 19th century, one of the major areas of scientific research was the observation of the spectrum of light emitted by hot solids and gases. Many theories were put forward to explain and predict the details of the observed spectra, but none was adequate.

If a piece of steel is placed in the flame of a welding torch it will begin to glow: first dull red, then a brighter orange-red, then yellow, and finally white. At low temperatures, the electromagnetic radiations from the heated steel cannot be seen by the human eye, although heat, transmitted as infrared radiation, can be felt if the heated steel is placed close to the body. At high temperatures (above 2000 K), the hot steel emits most of the visible colours of the spectrum, as well as infrared radiation. This is indicated by the whitish colour of the radiation. If heated sufficiently, the steel can produce ultraviolet emissions as well. It has been found that this behaviour is similar for all incandescent solids, regardless of the material from which they are made. It has also been determined that the relative brightness of the different colours radiated by an incandescent solid depends mainly on the temperature of the material. Thus, as the temperature increases, the spectrum of the emitted electromagnetic radiation shifts to higher frequencies.

"The great tragedy of science — the slaying of a beautiful hypothesis by an ugly fact."

Thomas Huxley

Many experiments were done to determine the brightness of various frequencies at various temperatures, and the results were graphed. Typical results are shown in the radiation curves illustrated. But finding a theory and an equation to describe the radiation curves proved to be difficult.

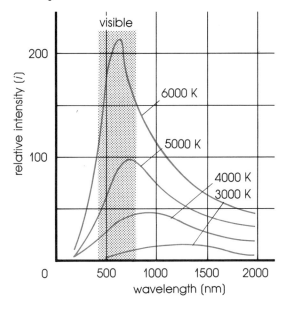

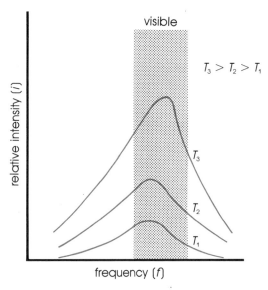

The experimental curves are for non-reflecting objects that appear black at normal temperatures. Thus they are called blackbody radiators. The problem that faced the scientists in the 1890s was how to explain this radiation. According to Maxwell's electromagnetic theory, the radiation originates from the oscillation of electric charges in the molecules of the material (see Section 16.8). As the temperature increases, the frequency of these oscillations also increases. The corresponding frequency of the radiated light should increase as well. According to Maxwell, the intensity versus frequency graph should follow the dotted line on the graph in the margin. But this is not the case. The actual radiations follow the solid line. The region of the graph where theory and experimental data disagree is in the ultraviolet portion of the spectrum. Scientists in the 1890s referred to this problem as the "ultraviolet catastrophe".

In the early 1900s, a German physicist, Max Planck (1858–1947), proposed a new, radical theory that explained the experimental data. He hypothesized that the vibrating molecules in a heated material can only vibrate with specific quantities of energy. When this energy radiates out from the vibrating molecule it is not emitted

Even objects that do not appear black at normal temperatures radiate similar curves.

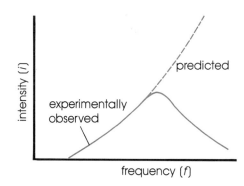

A graph illustrating the "ultraviolet catastrophe". Classical theory predicts the intensity of a black body to be proportional to the square of the frequency.

Planck is pronounced "plonk".

The word quantum, plural quanta, comes from the Latin word quantus, which means "how much".

Max Planck

Planck worked from theory to experiment in developing the Quantum Theory. He first derived the equation that predicted the correct graph of relative intensity versus wavelength. He then found that, by assuming that the individual molecules could only vibrate with discrete energies, he had a physical model that agreed with his empirical equation.

in a continuous, wavelike form, but is, instead, emitted in bundles, or packets, of energy, which Planck called **quanta**. He further proposed that the energy of a single quantum was directly proportional to its frequency.

$$E = hf$$

where E is the energy in joules

f is the frequency in hertz

h is a constant in joule seconds

Planck estimated the value of the constant h by fitting his equation to experimental data. Today the constant h is called **Planck's Constant**. Its accepted value is shown below.

$$h = 6.63 \times 10^{-34} \text{ J·s}$$

Planck further hypothesized that the energy of the emitting molecule must be an integral multiple of the minimum energy occurring where the electromagnetic energy is first radiated. That is, the energy can only be hf, $2hf$, $3hf$, and so on.

$$E = nhf, \text{ where } n = 1, 2, 3 \ldots$$

If light energy is quantized, and the energy of each bundle is determined by the relationship $E = hf$, then the bundles of light in the red region will have low energy and the bundles in the ultraviolet region will have high energy. Using this quantum model and statistical methods beyond the level of this text, Planck explained the shape of the intensity versus frequency graph for all areas of the spectrum, including the ultraviolet.

The concept of quantized values was not exactly new. Dalton, in his theory of the atom 90 years before, had proposed that the structure of matter is based on the smallest indivisible particle, the atom, and this was well accepted in 1900. Also, it had been shown by J.J. Thomson that the electric charge is quantized — the smallest charge found in nature is the charge on the electron. Nevertheless, the idea that energy is quantized was not easy to accept.

Planck's quantum idea was revolutionary for two reasons. First, it challenged the classical wave theory of light by proposing that electromagnetic waves do not transmit energy in a continuous manner but, instead, transmit energy in small packages or bundles. Secondly, it challenged the classical physics of Newton, since it proposed that a physical object is not free to vibrate with any random energy — the energy is restricted to certain discrete values. Planck, himself, was sceptical about his theory. He was not ready to reject the classical theories that were so well accepted by the scientific community. He even stated that, although his hypothesis worked in explaining blackbody radiation, he hoped a better explanation would come forth.

More experimental evidence for the quantum theory was required, and the concept remained generally unaccepted until 1905. In that year Albert Einstein showed that it was not such a bad hypothesis after all. Planck's quantum hypothesis was to become the foundation of a new era in physics. For his initial work, Planck was awarded a Nobel Prize for Physics in 1918.

The Quantum Theory produced such a drastic change in how we look at the physical world that physics prior to 1900 is now known as classical physics and physics after 1900 is known as modern physics. Since Max Planck's work was so important historically, Planck's honour and respect in the scientific community was second only to Einstein's in the first half of this century.

18.2 Einstein and the Photoelectric Effect

In 1887, when the German physicist Heinrich Hertz was testing Maxwell's Theory of Electromagnetic Waves, he noticed that certain metallic surfaces lose their negative charges when exposed to ultraviolet light. This can easily be demonstrated by wiring an insulated, polished zinc plate to a gold-leaf electroscope. When ultraviolet light is directed at the negatively charged zinc plate, the charge is gradually lost. This is indicated by the falling leaves on the electroscope, as illustrated. The incident light has somehow caused the zinc plate to liberate electrons. Because both light and electricity are involved, the term **photoelectric effect** was given to this phenomenon, and the emitted electrons were called **photoelectrons**.

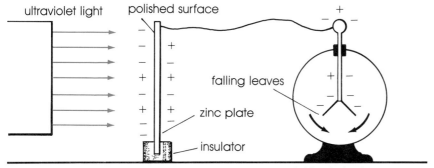

metal-leaf electroscope,
initially charged negatively

The photoelectric effect was studied over a number of years by many physicists, using apparatus similar to that on page 698.

There is a common misconception that for a photocurrent to exist, the collector must be made positive. Note that there is a photocurrent when the retarding potential is zero. When photoelectrons are emitted by cesium atoms, these atoms are neutralized by electrons from the collector plate, moving through the connecting wire. Thus the collector plate remains neutral and does not repel the emitted photoelectrons.

A photosensitive cathode is illuminated by light, of frequency f and intensity i, causing photoelectrons to be emitted from the cathode. These photoelectrons travel across the vacuum tube towards the anode and constitute a photocurrent, I, that is measured by the microammeter. The circuit also contains a variable source of electrical potential, as shown, that can be used to make the anode negative. This has the effect of retarding the photocurrent, by causing photoelectrons to be "turned-back" and not be part of the measured photocurrent.

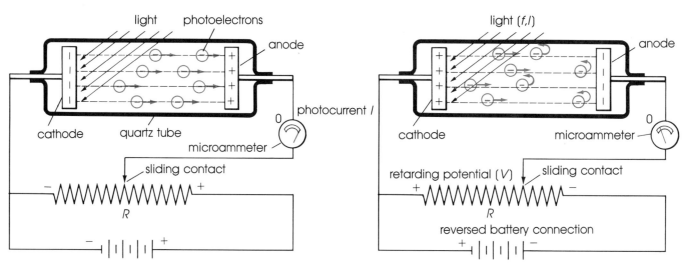

When the anode is positive, a current flows through the tube; but only when light shines on the photo-electric surface (the cathode).

If the anode is made increasingly negative, a potential difference is reached (the cut-off potential) where no current flows. This potential difference indicates the maximum energy of the photoelectrons.

A great many experiments were performed using this apparatus. Their results gave some support to Planck's theories and provided the basis for Einstein's work in this field. Some of the more significant findings are summarized below.

1. Electrons are emitted from the photoelectric surface when the incident light is above a certain frequency f_o, called the **threshold frequency**. Above the threshold frequency, the more intense the light, the greater the current of photoelectrons.

2. The intensity (brightness) of the light has no effect on the threshold frequency. No matter how intense the incident light, if it is below the threshold frequency not a single photoelectron will be emitted. (See the following diagrams.)

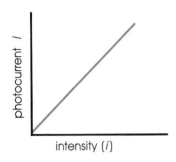

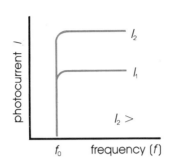

3. The threshold frequency, at which photoelectric emission first occurs, is different for different surfaces. For example, light that causes photoelectric emission from a cesium cathode has no effect on a copper cathode.

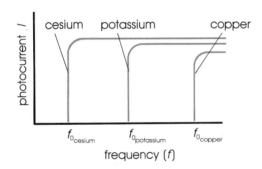

4. As the retarding potential that is applied to the anode is increased, the photocurrent (I) decreases, regardless of the intensity of the light. This indicates that the photoelectrons are emitted with different amounts of energy. A value of the retarding potential V_o, called the **cut-off potential**, is reached, where the photocurrent is zero. Even the most energetic photoelectrons are now prevented from reaching the anode, by its retarding potential.

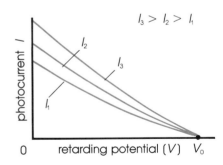

5. If different frequencies of light, all above the threshold frequency, are directed at the same photoelectric surface, the cut-off potential is different for each. It is found that the higher the frequency of the light, the higher the cut-off potential. The cut-off potential is related to the maximum kinetic energy with which photoelectrons are emitted. In fact, for a photoelectron of charge e, with a kinetic energy E_k, that is cut off by a retarding potential V_o, $E_k = eV_o$. (This follows from the definition of potential difference in Chapter 15.)

By illuminating several photoelectric surfaces with light of various frequencies, and measuring the cut-off potential for each surface, values are obtained for the graph shown. Note that each surface has a different threshold frequency, but each has the same slope on the graph.

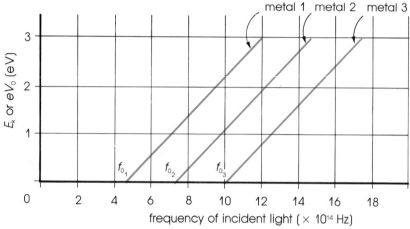

The photoelectric effects for three different metals. The graphs are parallel straight lines with the same slope, but with different threshold frequencies, f_{0_1}, f_{0_2}, and f_{0_3}.

6. When photoemission is occurring, the release of the electron is immediate. That is, there is no appreciable delay between illumination and emission, even for extremely weak light.

It seems that light energy is absorbed by an electron instantaneously, and does not need to "accumulate" to a point where there is sufficient energy to liberate the electron. Classical wave calculations predict time delays of many years for very weak light.

Another way of looking at the photoelectric effect, using the classical wave theory, is to consider that the light wave "shakes" the atom until it loses an electron. According to wave theory, the amplitude and time duration of the wave would determine whether sufficient energy had been transferred to the atom that ejects an electron. The amplitude of the wave is related to the brightness, or intensity, of the light. Thus, more intense beams of light, even of lower frequency, should eject more electrons. But this is not the case. Higher-frequency beams are necessary in most cases (see text).

The word photon is similar to the names given to other small particles, for example, electrons, protons, and neutrons.

Of the experimental findings described above, only the first could be explained on the basis of the classical electromagnetic theory of light. In particular, according to classical wave theory, there is no reason why an intense beam of low-frequency light should not be able to produce a photoelectric current, or why the intensity of the beam should not affect the maximum kinetic energy of the ejected photoelectrons. The classical wave theory of light could not properly explain the photoelectric effect.

Albert Einstein knew about some of these experiments and also about Planck's theory. He made the then radical proposal that the energy of light is not transmitted in a continuous wave but rather is concentrated in bundles of energy he called **photons**. Further, he proposed that the amount of energy in each of these bundles was a discrete, fixed amount, determined by Planck's equation, $E = hf$. Einstein used his Photon Theory of Light to explain some of the experimental results of the photoelectric effect. As well, he predicted new effects, undiscovered at that time.

He reasoned that if an electron, near the surface of a metal, absorbs a photon, the energy gained by the electron might be great enough for the electron to escape from the metal. Some of the absorbed energy would be used to break away from the metal surface and the remainder would show up as the kinetic energy of the electron. Since the energy of one photon is given by hf, the higher the frequency, the greater the kinetic energy of the ejected photoelectron. This behaviour also explained why there is a threshold frequency. The electron has to receive a minimum amount of energy to escape the attractive forces holding it to the metal. When the frequency of the incident light is too low, the photon does not give the absorbing electron sufficient energy and it remains bound to the surface. The intensity (brightness) of the light is only a measure of the rate at which the photons strike the surface, not the energy per photon. This helps explain why the kinetic energy of the emitted photoelectrons and the threshold frequency are independent of the intensity of the incident light.

To summarize, then, when a photon hits a photoelectric surface, its energy is absorbed by a surface electron. Some of the energy is utilized to release the electron, and the remainder becomes the kinetic energy of the ejected photoelectron. Einstein described this mathematically as follows:

$$E_{photon} = W + E_k$$

where E_{photon} is the energy of the incident photon
W is the energy with which the electron is bound to the photoelectric surface
E_k is the kinetic energy of the ejected photoelectron
Rearranging the equation, we obtain

$$E_k = E_{photon} - W$$

This can also be stated as follows:

$$E_k = hf - W$$

which is known as **Einstein's Photoelectric Equation**.

W, as defined above, is called the **work function** of the metal. The work function is different for different metals and is usually less than 1.6×10^{-18} J, or 10 eV.

When the photons are absorbed by surface electrons, many interactions are possible. The absorbing electron may move into the surface and not become a photoelectron at all. Some that become photoelectrons may come off at an angle, or undergo non-elastic collisions before leaving the surface. Others will move directly towards the anode. Yet only a small number of the more energetic photoelectrons will come close to reaching it. These are further inhibited as the retarding voltage approaches the cut-off potential. Therefore, only the most energetic electrons reach the anode. As a result, the cut-off potential V_o measures the maximum possible kinetic energy of the photoelectrons, and in the equation $E_k = hf - W$, E_k represents the maximum kinetic energy of the photoelectrons.

Work Functions for Various Metals

Metal	Work function (eV)
aluminum	4.25
barium	2.48
cadmium	4.07
calcium	3.33
cesium	1.90
copper	4.46
mercury	4.50
nickel	5.01
potassium	1.60
sodium	2.26
tungsten	4.52
zinc	3.31

Note: The values in this table are only useful for purposes of comparison. Actual values vary because of the purity of the metal, the cleanliness of the surface, the orientation of the crystal, and the way in which the value is measured.

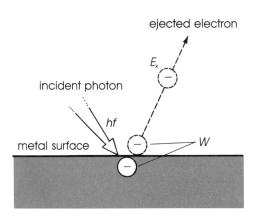

The same mathematical relationship may be derived from the graph in observation 5 (page 699), as follows:

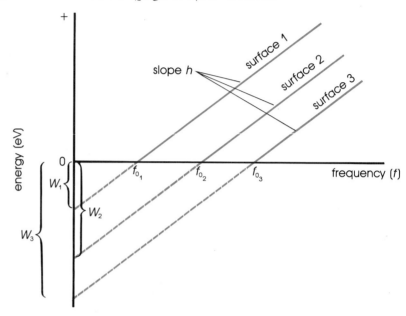

For each photoelectric surface, the graph is a straight line of the form $y = m(x - a)$, where m is the slope and a is the horizontal intercept.

In this case,

$$eV_o = mf - mf_o \quad \text{(since the intercept on the } f \text{ axis is } f_o)$$

But we have already stated that eV_o is equal to the kinetic energy of the emitted photoelectron.

Thus, the equation becomes

$$E_k = mf - mf_o$$

which matches Einstein's equation if m, the slope of the graph, is equal to Planck's constant h, and $W = hf_o$.

Also, if the straight line is extended (dotted) until it crosses the vertical axis, the equation

$$E_k = hf - W$$

is of the form

$$y = mx + b$$

so that the vertical intercept b gives the work function W for that surface.

Note that, on a graph of E_k (or eV_o) versus f, each photosurface has the same slope (h, or Planck's Constant), but each has its own horizontal intercept (f_o, or threshold frequency) and vertical intercept ($-W$, or work function).

"The most beautiful experience we can have is the mysterious. It is the fundamental emotion that stands at the cradle of true art and true science."
Albert Einstein

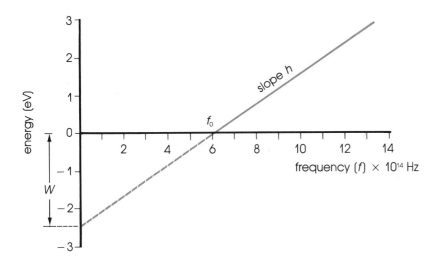

For a sodium, photoelectric surface, the threshold frequency (f_0) is 6.0×10^{14} Hz and the work function is 2.5 eV. These values represent the intercepts on the frequency and energy axes, respectively.

One of the experimental difficulties was that the work function (W) for a metal was affected by impurities on the surface (an oxide forms quickly in air). Millikan designed an apparatus in which the metallic surface was cut clean in a vacuum before each set of readings was taken.

Einstein's photoelectric equation agreed qualitatively with the experimental results available in 1905, but quantitative results were required to find out if the maximum kinetic energy increased linearly with the frequency and if the slope of the graph, h, was the same for all substances.

It was not until 1916 that Robert Millikan showed that, indeed, Einstein's explanation and prediction were correct. Millikan also found that the numerical value of Planck's Constant was the same as that which Planck had earlier calculated, using a completely different method. It was for his explanation of the photoelectric effect, based on the photon theory of light, that Albert Einstein received the Nobel Prize for Physics in 1921. He did not receive it for his work on relativity, as is commonly thought.

Sample problems

1. Calculate the energy of:
   (a) a photon of blue light with a frequency of 6.67×10^{14} Hz.
   (b) a photon of red light with a wavelength of 630 nm.
   (a) $E = hf$
   $ = (6.63 \times 10^{-34} \text{ J·s}) (6.67 \times 10^{14} \text{ Hz})$
   $ = 4.42 \times 10^{-19} \text{ J}$
   $ = \dfrac{4.42 \times 10^{-19} \text{ J}}{1.60 \times 10^{-19} \text{ J/eV}}$
   $ = 2.76 \text{ eV}$

In modern physics, the frequency is usually represented by the Greek letter v (nu), rather than the symbol f. We will retain the symbol f in this text, but when you read more advanced modern physics texts, the symbol v will be used. Equations such as $c = f\lambda$ and $E = hf$ will appear as $c = v \lambda$ and $E = hv$.

Some integrated circuit memories that are reprogrammable are called *eproms* (erasable programmable read-only memory). Electrons can be trapped in particular regions, thus storing the program. This type of chip is erased for reprogramming by exposing it to ultraviolet light (300 to 400 nm) for 15 to 20 min. A window in the top of the device allows the light to enter (see photograph). The ultraviolet photons striking the circuit cause the trapped electrons to move from their fixed positions on the circuit, and the programs on the chip are erased. Eproms should be protected from direct sunlight, since sunlight contains ultraviolet light.

(b) $E = hf$

but $v = f\lambda$

or $c = f\lambda$, and $f = \dfrac{c}{\lambda}$ (where c is the speed of light,

3.00×10^8 m/s)

Thus $E = \dfrac{hc}{\lambda}$ $(\lambda = 630\ \text{nm} = 6.30 \times 10^{-7}\ \text{m})$

$= \dfrac{(6.63 \times 10^{-34}\ \text{J·s})(3.00 \times 10^8\ \text{m/s})}{6.30 \times 10^{-7}\ \text{m}}$

$= 3.16 \times 10^{-19}$ J, or 1.97 eV

2. Light with a wavelength of 600 nm is directed at a metallic surface with a work function of 1.60 eV. Calculate:
   (a) the maximum kinetic energy, in joules, of the emitted electrons.
   (b) their maximum speed.
   (c) the cut-off potential necessary to stop these electrons.

(a) $\lambda = 600\ \text{nm} = 6.00 \times 10^{-7}$ m

$W = 1.60$ eV

$= (1.60\ \text{eV})(1.6 \times 10^{-19}\ \text{J/eV})$

$= 2.56 \times 10^{-19}$ J

$E_k = \dfrac{hc}{\lambda} - W$

$= \dfrac{(6.63 \times 10^{-34}\ \text{J·s})(3.00 \times 10^8\ \text{m/s})}{6.00 \times 10^{-7}\ \text{m}} - 2.56 \times 10^{-19}\ \text{J}$

$= 3.32 \times 10^{-19}\ \text{J} - 2.56 \times 10^{-19}\ \text{J}$

$= 7.6 \times 10^{-20}$ J

(b) $v = \sqrt{\dfrac{2E_k}{m}}$

$= \sqrt{\dfrac{2(7.6 \times 10^{-20}\ \text{J})}{9.11 \times 10^{-31}\ \text{kg}}}$

$= 4.1 \times 10^5$ m/s

(c) $E_k = eV_o$

$V_o = \dfrac{E_k}{e}$

$= \dfrac{7.6 \times 10^{-20}\ \text{J}}{1.60 \times 10^{-19}\ \text{C}}$

$= 0.48$ V

Note that the answer to (c) could have been determined from (a), as follows: $7.6 \times 10^{-20}\ \text{J} = 0.48$ eV. Thus the cut-off potential for electrons would be 0.48 V.

Practice

1. Determine the energy, in eV, for photons with the following characteristics:
   (a) 1.2×10^{18} Hz (X-rays)
   (b) 400 nm (violet)
   (c) 4.4×10^{14} Hz (red)
   (d) 900 nm (infrared)
   $$(5.0 \times 10^3 \text{ eV}, 3.1 \text{ eV}, 1.8 \text{ eV}, 1.4 \text{ eV})$$
2. Calculate the wavelength, in nanometres, of a photon with 3.20×10^{-19} J of energy.   (622 nm)
3. What is the minimum frequency of the photon required to eject electrons from a metal whose work function is 2.4 eV?
   $$(5.8 \times 10^{14} \text{ Hz})$$
4. Barium has a work function of 2.48 eV. What is the maximum kinetic energy of the ejected electrons if the metal is illuminated by light with a wavelength of 450 nm?   (0.28 eV)
5. When 350 nm light falls on a metal, the maximum kinetic energy of the ejected electrons is 1.20 eV. What is the work function of the metal?   (2.35 eV)
6. Light of frequency 8.0×10^{14} Hz illuminates a surface whose work function is 1.2 eV. If the retarding potential is 1.0 V, what is the maximum velocity with which an electron reaches the plate? $(6.3 \times 10^5 \text{ m/s})$

Effects similar to the photoelectric effect are used in the following devices:
- security alarms
- automatic door openers
- smoke detectors
- light meters
- infrared remote controls for television receivers
- radiation dosimeters
- fibre optics communication
- photomultipliers
- control devices on furnaces
- television cameras

18.3 The Compton Effect — Momentum of a Photon

In 1923 the American physicist, A.H. Compton (1892-1962), performed an experiment in which a beam of high-energy X-rays with a known frequency was directed at a thin metal foil. The experiment was similar to the photoelectric experiments except that high-energy X-rays were used instead of light. As well as observing ejected electrons, as with the photoelectric effect, Compton also noted that lower energy X-ray photons were being emitted. Since these photons had a lower energy, they also had a lower frequency. This scattering of lower frequency X-ray photons from a film is known as the **Compton Effect**.

The results from a whole series of experiments, using different metal foils and different beams of X-rays, could not be explained using electromagnetic wave theory. After careful analysis of his

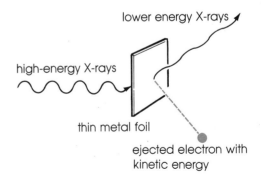

results, Compton proposed that the incident X-ray photon was acting like a particle that collides with an electron in the metal. In such a collision, the photon bounces off an electron, emerging with lower energy, and the electron flies off with the kinetic energy it gained in the collision. If he was correct, the collision would be elastic, that is, both energy and momentum would be conserved. If energy was indeed conserved in the collision, the following would be true:

$$E_{\text{X-ray}_{\text{photon}}} = E'_{\text{X-ray}_{\text{photon}}} + E_{\text{electron}}$$

$$hf = hf' + \frac{1}{2}mv^2$$

Momentum is also conserved in any collision, as we learned in Chapter 8. But what is the momentum of a photon — a bundle of energy with no mass, travelling at the speed of light? Compton solved this problem by using some of Einstein's ideas.

One of the most famous equations of physics is $E = mc^2$. This is the equation Einstein published in his Special Theory of Relativity of 1905, the same year he published his analysis of the photoelectric effect. In this important document, he suggested that mass is another form of energy — that a decrease in the mass of a system should show up as an increase in energy, according to the relationship $E = mc^2$. The equation also indicated that a body with energy E has a **mass equivalence** of E/c^2. Compton's solution was the following.

The magnitude of the momentum (p) of any body is defined as the product of mass (m) and velocity (v), that is, $p = mv$. If m in the equation is replaced by its mass equivalent, E/c^2, we can write

$$p = \left(\frac{E}{c^2}\right)v$$

But a photon travels at the speed of light, making $v = c$.

Therefore,
$$p = \left(\frac{E}{c^2}\right)c$$

$$= \frac{E}{c}$$

The energy of a photon is given by $E = hf$, or $E = hc/\lambda$.

Thus, $$p = \frac{hc/\lambda}{c}$$

and

$$p = \frac{h}{\lambda}$$

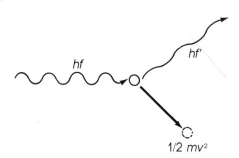

In the Compton Effect, the energy of the incident X-ray photons is so high ($> 5.0 \times 10^4$ eV) in comparison with the work function (< 10 eV) that the work function is not considered in the energy calculations involved in the collision. In fact, most of the energy of the incident photon is found in the "deflected" photon. The recoil electron has very little energy and may not even escape from its parent atom, let alone the "surface".

This relation gives the **momentum of a photon,**
where p is the momentum, in kilogram metres per second
       h is Planck's Constant, 6.63×10^{-34} J·s
       λ is the wavelength, in metres
Remember, of course, that momentum is a vector quantity, so
the expression for conservation of momentum is a vector equation.

$$\vec{p}_{photon} = \vec{p}\,'_{photon} + \vec{p}\,'_{electron}$$

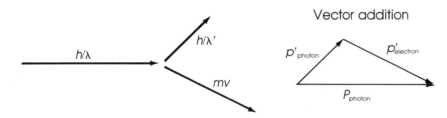

Compton's experiments clearly demonstrated the particle-like
aspects of light, for not only can a discrete energy, hf, be assigned
to a photon, but also a value of momentum, h/λ. His work provided
conclusive evidence for the photon theory. As a result, Compton
was awarded a Nobel Prize in 1927.

Compton pursued this analysis and
found he could explain exactly the
energy of the outgoing X-ray photon as
a function of the scattering angle.

Sample problem

What is the momentum of a photon that has a wavelength of
1.2×10^{-12} m?

$$p = \frac{h}{\lambda}$$
$$= \frac{6.63 \times 10^{-34} \text{ J·s}}{1.2 \times 10^{-12} \text{ m}}$$
$$= 5.5 \times 10^{-22} \text{ kg·m/s}$$

$$\frac{\text{J·s}}{\text{m}} = \frac{\text{kg·m/s}^2\text{·s}}{\text{m}}$$
$$= \text{kg·m/s}$$

Practice
1. Calculate the momentum of a photon whose wavelength is
   500 nm.   (1.33×10^{-27} kg·m/s)
2. What is the momentum of a photon with a frequency of
   4.5×10^{15} Hz?   (9.9×10^{-27} kg·m/s)
3. What is the momentum of a 150 eV photon?
                                    (8.00×10^{-26} kg·m/s)
4. Calculate the wavelength of a photon having the same momentum
   as an electron moving at 1.0×10^6 m/s.   (0.73 nm)

If an intense light beam is directed at the surface of an absorbing material, the energy of the photons is mostly absorbed by that surface, and, as a result, the surface heats up. But, as we have seen in the Compton Effect, photons transfer momentum as well. The sum of the impacts on the surface of all of the photons per unit of time results in pressure on the surface. This pressure is very small, or we would feel the pressure of light when we walk out into strong sunlight or stand under a strong lamp. Today, using very sensitive equipment, we are able to actually measure the pressure of light on a surface. The results confirm that the relationship $p = h/\lambda$ is a valid expression for the momentum of an individual photon.

We have seen, with both the photoelectric effect and the Compton Effect, that when a photon comes in contact with matter, there is an interaction. Five main interactions are possible.

If the surface is highly reflective, each photon undergoes twice as great a change in momentum, and the resulting radiation pressure is twice as great. This is exactly the same as a bouncing ball compared with a chunk of sticky putty.

1. The most common interaction is simple reflection, for example, the reflection of light photons by a mirror.
2. In the case of the photoelectric effect, a photon may liberate an electron and, in the process, disappear.
3. In the Compton Effect, the photon is scattered by an electron, emerging with less energy and momentum. After the interaction, it still travels at the speed of light, but its frequency is lower, and its wavelength is longer.
4. A photon may also interact with an individual atom, and, in the process, elevate an electron to a higher energy level within the atom. In this case, the photon completely disappears. All of its energy has been given to the atom, causing the atom to be in an energized or "excited" state. This will be discussed in more detail in the next chapter.
5. A photon can also disappear and create matter. This occurs in a process called **pair production**. For this process to occur, the photon must have very high energy (>1.02 MeV) and, correspondingly, a very short wavelength (as do X-ray or gamma ray photons). When such a photon collides with a heavy nucleus, it disappears and creates an electron (e^-) and a positron (e^+). (A positron has the same mass as an electron, but the opposite charge.) This creation of mass from energy is in accordance with Einstein's equation, $E = mc^2$. Further discussion of this topic is left until Chapter 20.

gamma ray photon

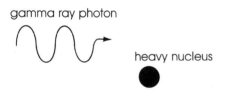

heavy nucleus

Before pair production

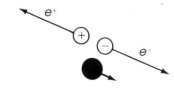

e^+

e^-

After pair production

18.4 Photons and Electromagnetic Waves

The photoelectric effect and the Compton Effect revealed that light and X-rays have a particle nature. That is, photons can act essentially like particles with energy and momentum. However, for the properties of reflection, refraction, diffraction, interference, and polarization, light acts like a wave, and its wave behaviour is more successfully explained by the electromagnetic radiation theory. Clearly, light and many other electromagnetic radiations have two aspects of behaviour: one is wavelike and one is particle-like. In this section we will see how quantum theory reconciles these two apparently contradictory behaviours.

In 1910, Geoffrey Taylor, a young student at Cambridge University in England, set up an experiment to find out whether interference resulted from the interactions of many photons or whether the behaviour of single photons could be predicted by their wave properties. The basic parts used in his experiment are illustrated.

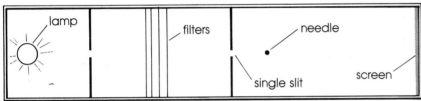

lightproof box

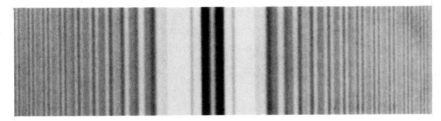

Diffraction pattern created by a needle

Light originating from a small lamp passed through a series of dark filters, which reduced the intensity of the light. After passing through a single slit, the light was diffracted by a vertical needle, and the resulting image was recorded on a photographic plate.

Taylor adjusted the dimensions of the box and its contents so that diffraction bands around the shadow of the needle were plainly visible in bright light. Then he reduced the intensity of light by adding filters. He found that longer and longer exposures were needed to get a well-exposed photographic plate, since fewer and fewer photons passed through the slit each second. Finally he made a very weak exposure that lasted for three months. Even on this plate the diffraction interference fringes were perfectly clear. By calculation, Taylor was able to show that two or more photons would rarely, if ever, be in the box at the same time. In other words, the behaviour of a single photon was predicted by the wave theory.

One way of visualizing the relationship between a photon and its electromagnetic wave is to consider that the electromagnetic wave acts as a "guide" that predicts the probable behaviour of the photon. The electromagnetic wave determines the chance, or probability, that a photon will be at a certain position in space at a given instant in time. Of course, for "pure" particles, not photons, their probability of being in certain places is either 100% (if they are there) or 0% (if they are not). We do not have this exactness for photons. We only know the probabilities determined by the electromagnetic wave. The Quantum Theory assumes that, at any instant, the photon has a probability of being in any position. The probability is greater in those regions where the amplitude of the electromagnetic wave is greater, and smaller in those regions where the amplitude of the wave is smaller.

If an intense beam of light is directed through two adjacent slits, as it is in Young's Experiment (page 524), a series of alternating bands of constructive and destructive interference is created on the screen. The photons pass through the two slits, and their arrival on the screen is predicted by their electromagnetic waves. If two

Double-slit interference

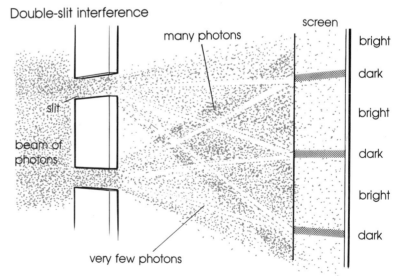

Photons, guided by their electromagnetic waves, pass through two narrow slits and distribute themselves so as to produce a double-slit diffraction pattern.

electromagnetic waves interfere destructively, the amplitude of the resultant displacement is smaller than either of the original waves, and thus the probability of a photon arriving is smaller. When the conditions are such that the resultant amplitude is zero, as it is on a nodal line, the probability of finding a photon at the node is nearly zero. On the other hand, if the two electromagnetic waves interfere constructively, the resultant amplitude is larger and the probability is high that a photon will be in that position, a bright area.

If the screen is replaced by a photographic film, the particle nature of photons becomes evident. A photographic film may be constructed of plastic film on which has been deposited a thin layer of very small silver bromide crystals. Each photon that is absorbed by a silver bromide crystal gives up a fixed amount of energy, freeing the silver and producing a bright area on the resulting picture. The photon's electromagnetic wave gives the probability of its falling on any part of the film. However, its chance of falling in areas of constructive interference is high. As a result, many silver bromide crystals will be changed in these areas by the interaction with photons, and a bright area will be recorded on the picture. In areas of destructive interference, fewer crystals will be changed, and a dark area will be recorded on the picture. In some areas, for example, the nodal lines, almost no crystals will change.

Photons of light forming a complete picture. The number of photons applied to form each reproduction of the same image was as follows:
(a) 3×10^3 photons,
(b) 1.2×10^4 photons,
(c) 9.3×10^4 photons,
(d) 7.6×10^5 photons,
(e) 3.6×10^6 photons,
(f) 2.8×10^7 photons.

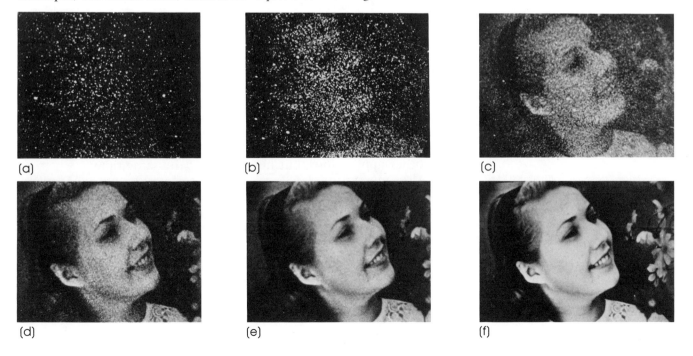

(a) (b) (c)

(d) (e) (f)

A photomultiplier is a device that takes a small amount of light energy, and, using a series of electron-emitting surfaces, amplifies the signal many thousands of times. By placing the device at various locations in an interference pattern, the number of individual photons arriving at the photocathode can be measured.

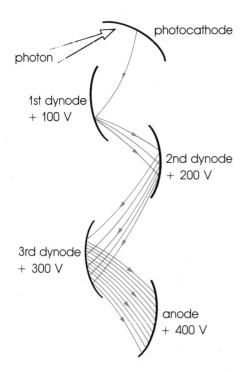

A three-stage photomultiplier tube

Today, using a photomultiplier, photon experiments can be done with much greater speed and sensitivity. All the results point to the same conclusion — the photons arrive one at a time, but their distribution on a screen is predicted by their wave properties.

It has become obvious that light is not just a wave and not just a particle. It is both. It has a dual nature, a property referred to by physicists as **wave-particle duality**. We reach this conclusion because both theories of light have been shown to have validity, based on very strong experimental evidence. It is clear that light is a much more complex phenomenon than just a beam of particles or just a simple wave.

Niels Bohr (1885-1962), the great Danish physicist, clarified the situation partially by proposing his **Principle of Complementarity**. In it, he states: "To understand a specific experiment, one must use either the wave or the photon theory but not both." Understanding both the wave and the particle properties of light is essential if one is to have a full understanding of light. In other words, the two aspects of light complement one another.

If we return to Young's Experiment, we can illustrate how this principle is applied. To understand how light interferes after it passes through two parallel slits, we must use the wave theory, not the particle theory. To understand why the photographic plate is exposed as it is, we must use the photon, or particle, nature of light, not the wave theory.

As a general rule, when light passes through space or through a medium, its behaviour is best explained using its wave properties. But, when light interacts with matter, its behaviour is more like that of a particle.

One of the reasons we have trouble understanding the dual nature of light is human frailty. It is very difficult if not impossible for us to visualize this duality. We cannot draw pictures and create images of a wave-particle combination. We are restricted to creating wave pictures, or images, in some applications and particle pictures in other applications, but never both at the same time.

Also, most of the laws and principles of physics we are familiar with are based on experiments that involve direct observations. In the study of light, particularly as it transfers energy from place to place, we must base our knowledge on indirect experiments. We cannot see directly how light energy is transmitted as a wave or particle. All we can observe are the results of the interaction of light and matter. Our knowledge is limited to indirect information and, therefore, to describe light's dual nature, we cannot use visual means. Further study of quantum mechanics utilizes mathematical models, not visual models, but this method constitutes a part of quantum mechanics that is beyond the scope of this book.

The wave-particle model of light that we use today is much more subtle than Newton's corpuscular theory or Maxwell's electromagnetic theory. Both of these theories were important in their time and contributed much to our understanding of the behaviour of light. But these models were inadequate in themselves for explaining all of the properties of light. Like all models or theories, they can be replaced by better models when new information becomes available. This is the case with the two classical theories of light. They have been superseded by the wave-particle model of light, the only theory that we find acceptable today for a full understanding of the nature of light.

In this text we do not pretend to explain more than a tiny fraction of the Quantum Theory; just enough to gain some insight into the nature of light and to whet the appetite of the student.

18.5 The Wave Nature of Matter

The fact that light energy, transmitted like a wave, can also behave like a particle, suggests that an ordinary particle might also have a wavelike nature. This idea was proposed in 1923 by Louis de Broglie, a young graduate student at the University of Paris. De Broglie hypothesized that since the momentum of a photon was given by the relationship $p = h/\lambda$, any particle with a momentum might also be expected to have an associated wavelength. He further suggested that this wavelength could be determined from the Compton relationship, as follows: If $p = h/\lambda$ for photons, then, for particles

$$\lambda = \frac{h}{p} = \frac{h}{mv}$$

This wavelength is known as the **de Broglie Wavelength**. Since this wavelength has nothing to do with electromagnetic waves, de Broglie waves have since become known as **matter waves**. The concept was so radical at the time, that de Broglie's graduation was held up for one year. (Einstein supported the hypothesis and de Broglie graduated in 1924.) Subsequently, de Broglie was awarded the 1929 Nobel Prize for Physics. Before discussing the implications of his hypothesis, it is important to determine the magnitude of the associated wavelengths of some common particles.

De Broglie's original hypothesis was based on the electron only. In fact, he used the concept immediately to analyse the energy levels in the hydrogen atom. This will be discussed in the next chapter.

"ACTUALLY I STARTED OUT IN QUANTUM
MECHANICS, BUT SOMEWHERE ALONG
THE WAY I TOOK A WRONG TURN."

Sample problems

1. What is the de Broglie wavelength of a 0.10 kg ball moving at 20 m/s?

$$\lambda = \frac{h}{mv}$$

$$= \frac{6.63 \times 10^{-34} \text{ J·s}}{(0.10 \text{ kg})(20 \text{ m/s})}$$

$$= 3.3 \times 10^{-34} \text{ m}$$

Note that for everyday objects the wavelength is extremely small.

2. What is the de Broglie wavelength of an electron that has been accelerated from rest through a potential difference of 50 V?

The energy of the electron is

$$E_k = eV$$

$$= (1.6 \times 10^{-19} \text{ J/eV})(50 \text{ V})$$

$$= 8.0 \times 10^{-18} \text{ J/e}$$

but $$E_k = \frac{1}{2}mv^2$$

Therefore, $$v = \sqrt{\frac{2E_k}{m}}$$

$$= \sqrt{\frac{2(8.0 \times 10^{-18} \text{ J})}{9.11 \times 10^{-31} \text{ kg}}}$$

$$= 4.2 \times 10^6 \text{ m/s}$$

Then $$\lambda = \frac{h}{mv}$$

$$= \frac{6.63 \times 10^{-34} \text{ J·s}}{(9.11 \times 10^{-31} \text{ kg})(4.2 \times 10^6 \text{ m/s})}$$

$$= 1.7 \times 10^{-10} \text{ m}$$

Note that this wavelength is appreciable on the scale of atoms.

Practice

1. Calculate the de Broglie wavelength of each of the following:
   (a) a 2.0 kg ball thrown at 15 m/s
   (b) a proton accelerated to 1.3×10^5 m/s ($m_p = 1.7 \times 10^{-27}$ kg)
   (c) an electron moving at 5.0×10^4 m/s

   (2.2×10^{-35} m, 3.0×10^{-12} m, 1.5×10^{-8} m)

2. What are the wavelengths, in metres, of a 3.0 eV photon and a 5.0 eV electron?   (4.1×10^{-7} m, 5.5×10^{-10} m)

As seen in the sample problems and practice problems above, the matter wavelengths of most ordinary objects, such as baseballs, and even small objects, such as protons, are very small. You will recall (page 525) that the wave nature of light was elusive until the time of Young because light has such a short wavelength. For the same reasons, the matter wavelengths of most particles are so small that it is almost impossible to detect the wave properties of matter. For very small objects, such as electrons, the matter wavelength can be approximately the same as the wavelength of some X-rays.

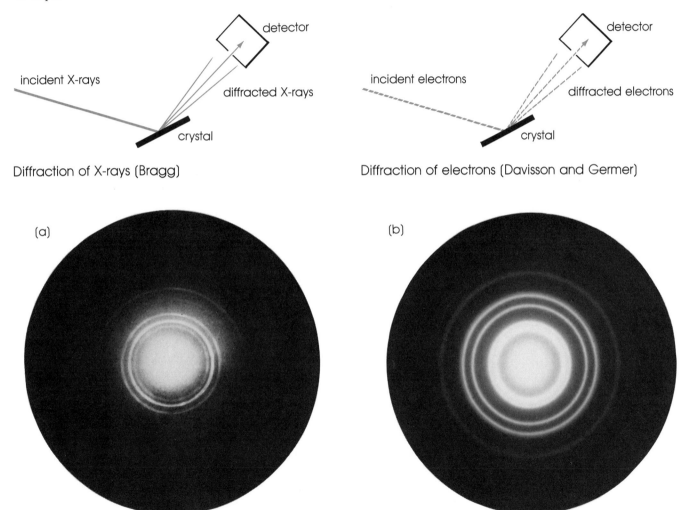

Wave nature of photons and electrons. (a) X-ray diffraction rings due to a crystal of nickel. (b) Diffraction of electrons due to a gold film.

In 1927, two physicists in the United States, C.J. Davisson and L.H. Germer, performed an experiment which showed that de Broglie was correct: matter waves do exist. Earlier, in England, W.H. Bragg (1862–1942) and his son, W.L. Bragg (1890–1971), had developed equations that predicted the diffraction of X-rays by thin crystals. The X-rays were scattered by the crystals, and their magnitude was a maximum at a series of regularly spaced angles, as shown in the diagram on page 715. Davisson and Germer used the Bragg analysis to show that a beam of electrons could be diffracted in much the same way, thereby demonstrating the wavelike properties of particles. A beam of electrons was directed at a single crystal of nickel, and the observed diffraction pattern was in perfect agreement, within the limits of experimental error, with calculations made using the de Broglie wavelength of the electrons. As can be seen in the photographs, the Davisson-Germer experiment gave convincing proof of the validity of de Broglie's hypothesis.

In the same year, G.P. Thomson, in England, passed a beam of electrons through a thin metal foil, and the diffraction pattern was the same as that for X-rays, making suitable allowance for wavelength. The Davisson-Germer and Thomson experiments left little doubt that particles do exhibit wavelike properties. Later experiments using protons, neutrons, helium nuclei, and other small particles, produced similar results.

The particle-wave dualism for small particles matched the wave-particle dualism for the photon, as worked out by Compton. The Principle of Complementarity applies to matter as well as to light. This implies that in order to understand matter we must be aware of both the particle and wave characteristics of matter at one and the same time.

We may now ask, as we did for light, under what conditions matter reveals its wavelike properties. In the case of light, we should recall that for the wave property of diffraction to be evident, the opening or obstacle had to have a size that was similar to the wavelength of the light. Otherwise, the light behaved like a beam of particles moving in a straight line through an opening or past an obstacle, showing little diffraction or interference. This is also the case for matter waves.

Ordinary objects, such as baseballs, have associated matter waves whose wavelength is extremely short compared with the dimensions of other objects or openings that they encounter. Therefore, they act like particles and do not reveal their wave nature. Sub-atomic particles such as electrons have associated matter waves whose wavelength is of the same order of magnitude as the objects they interact with. As a result, they diffract, and interference can occur. The matter waves associated with particles of matter are

It was the discoveries a woman physicist made in X-ray crystallography that had the greatest impact on the advancement of that science. Kathleen Lonsdale (1903–1971) began her work in X-ray crystallography with W.H. Bragg in London, in 1922. Trained as a physicist and mathematician, she helped establish the fundamental methods and procedures of this branch of physics. In 1929 she announced her discovery that the benzene ring is planar, with the carbon atoms arranged in a regular hexagon. This model is the basis for all theoretical explanations of the structure and properties of aromatic compounds in organic chemistry.

It should be noted that another woman, Dorothy Mary Hodgkin, won the Nobel Prize for Chemistry in 1964 for determining the molecular structure of penicillin and vitamin B by X-ray crystallography.

similar to those that predict the behaviour of individual photons. The matter waves predict the probability that a particle will follow a particular path through space.

The fact that particle-wave dualism exists for both matter and light reinforced Einstein's contention that matter was a form of energy ($E = mc^2$) and that the two were interconvertible. By 1927, the concept that matter and energy were interrelated did not seem as astonishing as it had in 1905 when Einstein proposed it. Furthermore, the wave characteristics of the electrons orbiting the nucleus of an atom could now be examined using quantum mechanics. But this we will leave to the next chapter.

It is important to note that matter waves do not carry energy. They only predict behaviour. The particle carries the energy.

18.6 Electron Microscopes

The resolution of an ordinary microscope is limited by the wavelength of the light used. The best magnification obtainable, using an oil-immersion objective, is 1500 ×, and the best resolution is approximately 2.0×10^{-7} m (about one-half the wavelength of light). On the other hand, a beam of electrons having a de Broglie wavelength of less than 1.0 nm could have a resolution of approximately 0.5 nm. This means that if one could get electrons to behave as light does in a microscope, the magnification could be increased to as high as 300 000 ×.

Technological developments in the 1920s, involving the focusing of electron beams by means of magnetic coils, permitted the development of a crude electron microscope in Germany, in 1931. The first North American electron microscope, and the first of immediate practical application anywhere, was designed and built in the winter of 1937–8 by Albert Prebus and James Hillier, two young graduate students at the University of Toronto. By the summer of 1938, they were producing microphotographs with a magnification of 20 000 × and a resolution of 6.0 nm (30 atomic diameters). It was their design that was used by the RCA Corporation to manufacture the first commercial electron microscope.

A **transmission electron microscope** is similar in operation to an ordinary light microscope, except that the glass lenses are replaced by "magnetic lenses". The magnetic "lenses" are constructed of circular electromagnetic coils that create strong magnetic fields. These fields exert forces on the moving electrons, focusing them in much the same way that a glass lens focuses light. As shown in the diagram on the next page, electrons emitted from the hot filament are accelerated by an anode with an electrical potential of 50 000 V to 100 000 V, or more. The electrons are focused into a parallel beam by the condensing "lens" before they

James Hillier with the first commercial electron microscope

In a surface physics laboratory, the energy of the electron beam is increased to the point where some X-rays are produced in addition to the electrons. The detection of these X-rays can reveal what chemical elements are present in the specimen, for example, in an integrated circuit.

pass through the specimen (object). For this to take place, the specimen must be very thin (approximately 20 to 50 nm); otherwise, the electrons would be slowed down too much, or scattered, and the resulting image would be blurred.

Next, the beam of electrons passes through the objective "lens" and then through the projection "lens", which corresponds to the eyepiece in an optical microscope. The beam is projected onto a fluorescent screen or photographic plate, creating a two-dimensional image of the specimen. Since the powerful beam of electrons can very quickly destroy the specimen, short exposure times must be used. Also, the whole system of "lenses", beams, and specimen operates in a high vacuum to avoid scattering of the electron beam by collision with air molecules.

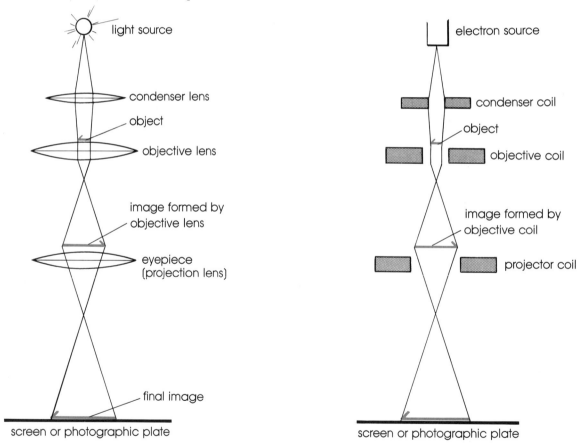

Diagrams showing a comparison between an electron microscope and a compound light microscope. The light microscope is drawn upside down to show the similarities.

In a **scanning electron microscope**, three-dimensional images are possible. In this type of microscope, a carefully directed beam of electrons is moved across the specimen, as illustrated. At each position on the original specimen, the secondary electrons emitted from the surface are collected, and they control a picture element on a television-type tube called a cathode ray tube (CRT). The number of secondary electrons emitted controls the intensity, or brightness, on the CRT. As a result, as the beam "sweeps" the specimen, a corresponding magnified, three-dimensional image is created on the CRT. Since the beam of electrons will damage a biological specimen, the time of exposure must be limited. Usually, the specimen is coated with a thin metallic layer of gold so that it does not accumulate negative charges from the electron beam. This charge would repel the beam and distort the image.

Electron microscopes of both types have extended the frontiers of research in the microscopic world. Although biological specimens produce some of the most dramatic images, the electron microscope has also been used to view atomic and molecular structure. Fuzzy images of larger atoms, such as uranium, have been obtained.

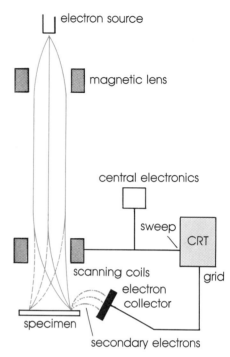

A scanning electron microscope. Scanning coils move an electron beam back and forth across the specimen. Secondary electrons, produced when the beam strikes the specimen, are collected, and modulate the intensity of the beam in the CRT, to produce a picture.

An ant grasping a microchip

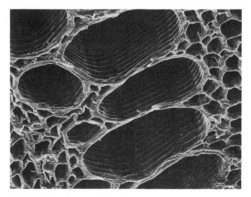

Cell structure of a stem

18.7 Investigations

Investigation 18.1: The Photoelectric Effect

Problem:
What are the conditions necessary for the emission of photo-electrons?

Materials:

zinc plate (minimum 400 cm²)   ebonite and fur
emery paper   electrical wire and clips
metal-leaf electroscope   carbon arc lamp
insulated stand   glass plate (filter)

CAUTION: When operating the carbon arc lamp, do not look directly at the point of discharge. The ultraviolet light can cause eye damage.

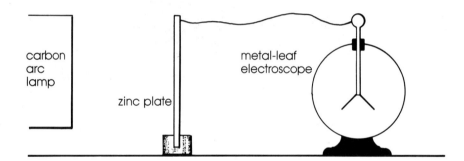

Procedure:
1. Polish one side of the zinc plate with emery paper until it is shiny. Place it on an insulated stand, as illustrated, and connect it to the knob of the electroscope.
2. Charge the zinc plate negatively, using a charged ebonite rod. Allow the apparatus to stand for at least 2.0 min, observing any change in the leaves of the electroscope. If they fall, record the time required for the system to discharge.
3. Place the zinc plate so that the polished side is facing the carbon arc lamp. Place the glass plate between the polished zinc surface and the lamp. Turn on the lamp. Observe any changes in the leaves of the electroscope over a period of 2.0 min. If the leaves fall, record the time for the system to discharge.
4. Repeat step 3, this time removing the glass plate.

5. Repeat steps 3 and 4, this time with the dull side of the zinc plate facing the carbon arc lamp.
6. In each case, compare the rate of discharge for the system with **(a)** no carbon arc light, **(b)** filtered carbon arc light, and **(c)** unfiltered carbon arc light. What type of light radiation does not pass through glass easily? What type of light causes the zinc plate to lose electrons?
7. Compare your observations for dull and polished zinc surfaces.
8. What are the two conditions necessary for the emission of photoelectrons from a zinc plate?
9. Can you think of any other models that would explain these observations (even ones you suspect are not true)?

Investigation 18.2: Analysing the Photoelectric Effect

Problems:
(a) What is the relationship between the energy of incident photons and the frequency of incident light?
(b) What is the relationship between the energy of the incident photons, the energy of the ejected photoelectrons, and the work function of a photoelectric surface?

Materials:

phototube	rheostat
microammeter	6 V battery
voltmeter	connecting wire
monochromatic sources of light	

Description of Apparatus:
The phototube is constructed with a curved, photosensitive cathode, in this case cesium, and a collector electrode (anode). Both of these electrodes are mounted in an evacuated glass tube, with electrical connections outside the tube connected to a variable DC voltage supply. The potential difference is measured by the voltmeter, connected between the photoelectric electrode and the collecting electrode. A sensitive microammeter measures the current (called the photocurrent) through the circuit, and thus the rate at which photoelectrons ejected from the cesium surface reach the collecting electrode, when light is directed on it.

When the phototube is used commercially, the collector is positive, and a photoelectric current flows at any time that light of sufficiently high frequency shines on the photoelectric surface. In this investigation, the collector will usually be negative, impeding

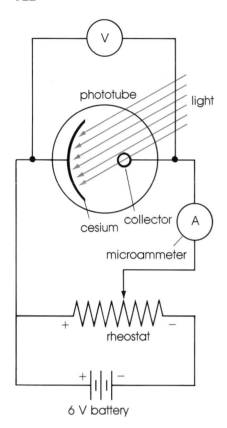

phototube

light

cesium

collector

A

microammeter

rheostat

+ WWWWW −

+ ||i|| −

6 V battery

The voltmeter above must have a very high resistance. Otherwise, a correction must be made in the measured current to allow for it.

the current in the phototube. At a certain negative potential (V_o) the current will stop. At this point, the retarding potential difference between the electrodes represents the maximum possible kinetic energy of the ejected photoelectrons (see page 701). Since the potential difference is in volts, this maximum kinetic energy of the electrons can be expressed in joules, using the relationship $E = qV_o$. Light with different colours (wavelengths) is directed at the photoelectric surface during the experiment.

Since many schools do not have access to the equipment described, data from an actual experiment is provided for analysis.

Observation Chart

Colour	Yellow	Green	Blue	Violet	
Wavelength	578 nm	546 nm	480 nm	410 nm low-intensity	410 nm high-intensity
Retarding potential (V)	Photo-current (μA)	Photo-current (μA)	Photo-current (μA)	Photo-current (μA)	Photo-current (μA)
0.00	3.2	10.4	11.2	8.5	14.8
0.05	2.3	8.7	10.1	8.1	14.0
0.10	1.3	7.1	9.0	7.6	13.3
0.15	0.6	5.5	8.0	7.2	12.6
0.20	0.2	4.0	7.0	6.7	11.9
0.25	0	2.4	6.0	6.2	11.1
0.30	0	1.0	4.9	5.7	10.4
0.35		0.2	3.8	5.3	9.6
0.40		0	2.8	4.8	8.9
0.45		0	1.7	4.4	8.2
0.50			1.2	3.9	7.0
0.55			0.7	3.4	6.7
0.60			0.4	3.0	6.0
0.65			0.1	2.5	5.2
0.70			0	2.0	4.5
0.75			0	1.6	3.7
0.80				1.1	3.0
0.85				0.9	2.3
0.90				0.7	1.7
0.95				0.5	1.2
1.00				0.3	0.8
1.05				0.2	0.4
1.10				0.1	0.1
1.15				0	0
1.20				0	0

Analysis:

1. Plot a graph of photocurrent versus retarding potential for each of the lights used. Choose the scales of the axes carefully so that all five graphs fit nicely on the same set of axes.
2. What is the relationship between the maximum electric current and the intensity of the incident light?
3. Which colour of light has the largest cut-off voltage? Analysing only the two graphs for violet light, does the intensity of the incident light affect the cut-off voltage?
4. The cut-off voltage is a measure of the maximum kinetic energy of the electrons ejected from the photoelectric surface. Using a chart similar to the following, determine the maximum kinetic energy of the photoelectrons in both electronvolts and joules. Which colour of light has the highest-energy photons? Explain your reasoning.

Colour of light	Wave-length of light (nm)	Cut-off voltage (V)	Maximum E_k of ejected electrons		Fre-quency of light (Hz)
			E(eV)	E(J)	
yellow	578				
green	546				
blue	480				
violet	410				

5. Using the relationship $c = f\lambda$, determine the frequency of each colour. Plot a graph of the maximum kinetic energy of the ejected electrons, in joules, versus frequency, in hertz. The energy axis should have a negative axis equal in magnitude to the positive axis, and the frequency should begin at zero. To simplify your graph, use scientific notation for the scales on both axes. How are the two variables related?
6. Find the slope of the graph for energy versus frequency. The accepted value for this slope is Planck's Constant (6.63×10^{-34} J·s). Calculate your experimental error.
7. As you will note in the graph of step 5, if the graph line is extrapolated, it has intercepts on both the energy and frequency axes. The magnitude of the negative intercept on the energy axis represents the work function (W), which is the energy required to release the electron from the photoelectric surface (see page 702). What is the work function for cesium? What is the significance of the negative value?

8. The intercept on the frequency axis represents the threshold frequency (f_o), or the minimum frequency of the photons of light that will cause electrons to be ejected from a cesium surface. What are the threshold frequency and the threshold wavelength for cesium?

9. Using the slope and intercept values above, write a general equation describing the graph in the mathematical form $y = mx + b$.

10. Write a conservation of energy equation using the variables E_{photon}, E_k, and W. Rearrange it so that it is in the same form as the equation in 9. You will need to recall the equation relating the energy and the frequency of a photon.

11. Below are the data collected for two other photoelectric surfaces. Make the appropriate calculations and plot the data on the graph you used in step 5.

Barium

Frequency ($\times 10^{14}$ Hz)	Cut-off voltage (V)
6.25	0.10
6.55	0.25
7.00	0.40
7.50	0.65

Calcium

Frequency ($\times 10^{14}$ Hz)	Cut-off voltage (V)
8.50	0.20
9.25	0.50
10.0	0.80
11.0	1.25

12. Using the two new graph lines, determine the threshold frequencies and work functions for both barium and calcium. Which of the three substances used in this experiment would not produce photoelectric emission for the visible range of the spectrum?

13. Compare the slopes for the three graphs. What does this indicate about Planck's Constant?

Investigation 18.3: Randomness in Radioactive Decay

Preamble:

A radioactive source emits its particles in a random manner. This behaviour is very similar to the way that photons are emitted from an incandescent source. By studying the emission rate of particles from a radioactive source, we can gain insight into the behaviour of light "particles", that is, photons.

Materials:
Geiger counter
low-power, encapsulated, radioactive source
metre rule
stopwatch

Notes: 1. The radioactive source you are using is low-power. There is minimum risk if you use this source for time intervals of less than a few hours. Store the source in a lead container when not in use.

2. It is helpful to do this investigation with two experimenters.

Procedure:
1. Set up the Geiger counter as instructed by your teacher.
2. Place the radioactive source near the Geiger tube. Adjust the volume control so that the "clicks" of arriving particles can be heard easily.
3. Move the source far away from the Geiger tube. During a 1 min interval or less, you should hear a number of clicks representing detected particles. This is known as the **background count**. The particles are arriving from natural sources of radiation in the building and from cosmic rays (high-energy rays from outer space). This background count has the same statistical qualities as the count rate of any radioactive material and can be ignored in this investigation.
4. Arrange the source and the Geiger tube so that, typically, 6-10 clicks are heard in a 10 s interval. For higher count rates it is sometimes difficult to detect closely arriving particles.
5. Count the number of particles striking the Geiger tube in two 10 s intervals, as a practice run.
6. Count the number of clicks continuously for 20 min, recording the number counted during each successive 10 s interval. Record your results in a chart, as illustrated.

Usually the average background count is subtracted from the detected radiation levels when measuring them. However, since we are more concerned in this experiment with the distribution of events in time rather than the number of events, the background count may be included in the counts.

Interval	Number of clicks (n) in the interval	Cumulative average count rate (clicks/10 s)
1	5	5.0
2	8	6.5
3	4	5.7
4		

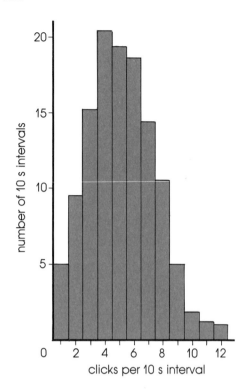

number of 10 s intervals (vertical axis)

clicks per 10 s interval (horizontal axis)

Step 8 can be done using a computer program. A sample program is provided in the Teacher's Manual for this text.

7. Draw a distribution bar graph, plotting the number of intervals with *n* clicks vertically, and the clicks per interval horizontally. A sample bar graph is illustrated in the margin. Using the graph, estimate the average count rate.

8. Add the count obtained in the second 10 s interval to the count obtained in the first, and divide by two to find the average count rate over two 10 s intervals. Then add the count found in the third interval to the sum of the counts in the first two intervals and divide by three to find the average rate over three 10 s intervals. Continue this, interval by interval, until you arrive at the average count rate over a period of 20 min. Record your results in the chart used in step 6. Compare this with your estimate in step 7.

9. What average count rate would you expect to find if you counted clicks for 2 h?

10. In any 10 s time interval, could you predict the actual count rate? What quantity can you predict? Explain your answers.

11. If you place the source nearer the Geiger tube, how will the count rate for 10 s and the average count rate change?

12. An incandescent source emits photons of light. Discuss the following:
    (a) the arrival time of individual photons at a photon detector,
    (b) the number of photons arriving at the detector per second.
    (c) If the photon detector is placed closer to the incandescent source, how would your answers to (a) and (b) change?

18.8 Review

Discussion

1. According to the electromagnetic theory, energy in the form of electromagnetic waves is emitted by all objects. Explain, using the photon theory, why our eyes cannot see in the dark.

2. How can an astronomer determine the approximate average temperature of the surface of a star by analysing its spectrum?

3. The sun's average surface temperature is 6000 K. An incandescent light has a temperature of 2500 K, and a fluorescent light can be considered to have an average temperature of 3500 K. Why do neither of these artificial sources of light provide proper light when exposing a colour film designed to be used in sunlight? Why does a xenon flash (6000 K) provide proper illumination for the same daylight film?

4. When prints are developed in a darkroom, red light may be used for some types of film. Explain, using the photon theory, why the red light does not affect the photographic film.

5. Ultraviolet light can kill skin cells, as it does when you are sunburned. Infrared light, also from the sun, only warms the same cells. Explain this phenomenon, using the photon theory.

6. The process known as photosynthesis involves the chemical change of carbon dioxide and water into sugar and oxygen, in the presence of light and chlorophyll. As shown in the graph in the margin, the rate of the reaction depends on the wavelength of the incident light. Using the photon theory and the graph, explain the following:
   (a) Why do leaves containing chlorophyll appear green in white light?
   (b) Why will green light, on its own, not produce photosynthesis?
   (c) Why will an incandescent lamp (2500 K) not provide proper light for the growing of green plants?

7. How does the pair of curves on page 699 illustrate that the maximum velocity of the photoelectrons is independent of the intensity of the light directed at the photoelectric surface?

8. Using the chart in the margin of page 701, locate sodium and copper. Does it take more energy to remove a photoelectron from sodium or from copper? Which has the higher threshold frequency, potassium or barium? Explain your answers.

9. When monochromatic (single-frequency) light illuminates a photoelectric surface, photoelectrons with many different velocities, up to the maximum value, are ejected. Explain why there is a variation in the velocities.

10. Compare and contrast a 2 eV electron and a 2 eV photon, citing at least four properties of each.

11. High-speed neutrons, in a nuclear reactor, have a velocity of approximately 4×10^6 m/s. When they approach a uranium nucleus, instead of hitting the nucleus and causing fission (splitting the atom into two relatively equal parts), they tend to diffract around it. For this reason, the neutrons are slowed down to approximately 2×10^3 m/s by a moderator, such as heavy water or graphite, so that the fission-producing collision is more likely to take place. Using your knowledge of matter waves, explain why a moderator is necessary to enhance the process of fission. Using your knowledge of elastic collisions, explain how the moderator works.

12. Describe the theory of blackbody radiation. Include Planck's Quantum Theory and Wien's Law.

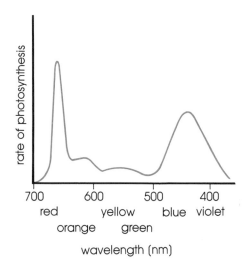

13. Write a short biography of one of the following scientists who contributed to the development of early quantum theory: Max Planck, Arthur Compton, Niels Bohr, William Henry Bragg, Louis de Broglie, and C. Davisson or L. Germer.

14. Some of the vocabulary of physics has become part of the vernacular. For example, "quantum leap" is used to describe changes outside the field of quantum mechanics, and "polarization" is used with reference to opinions, political views, and philosophies as well as optical phenomena. Describe the use of two or more other words from the world of physics that have become part of the vernacular.

Problems

15. Calculate the energy of an ultraviolet photon of light whose wavelength is 122 nm. Express your answer in both joules and electronvolts.

16. What are the energies of the photons emitted by two radio stations with the following frequencies: (a) 570 kHz, and (b) 102 MHz? Express your answers in electronvolts.

17. Show that $E = \dfrac{1.24 \times 10^3}{\lambda}$, where E is the energy of a photon in electronvolts, and λ is its wavelength in nanometres.

18. (a) What is the frequency of a photon with a wavelength of 2.0×10^{-7} m?
    (b) What is the energy of the same photon in joules and in electronvolts?
    (c) What is the momentum of the same photon?

19. The average solar power received at ground level in Toronto and Montreal is about 1.0 kW/m².
    (a) If the average wavelength of light is taken as 550 nm, how many photons strike an area of 1.0 cm² per second? (Assume that the light rays strike perpendicularly to the surface.)
    (b) How many photons would you find in a thimble with a volume of 1 cm³?

20. What is the minimum frequency of the light required to eject photoelectrons from a metallic surface whose work function is 7.2×10^{-19} J?

21. What is the threshold frequency for a calcium surface whose work function is 3.33 eV?

22. What is the longest wavelength of light that can eject electrons from a surface whose work function is 2.46 eV?

23. Light with a wavelength of 600 nm strikes a metal having a work function of 2.3×10^{-19} J. Calculate the maximum kinetic energy, in joules, of the emitted electrons and the voltage required to stop them.

24. Light with a wavelength of 430 nm falls on a photoelectric surface. The maximum kinetic energy of the photoelectrons is 1.21 eV. What is the work function of the surface?

25. What is the wavelengh of light that ejects photoelectrons from a tungsten surface ($W = 4.52$ eV), when the maximum kinetic energy of the electrons is 1.68 eV?

26. When light with a wavelength of 480 nm falls on a metallic surface, a retarding potential of 1.2 V is required to make the current passing through the phototube zero. What is the work function of the metal?

27. What is the momentum of a 410 nm photon of violet light?

28. What is the momentum and the equivalent mass of a 0.20 nm X-ray photon? (This does not imply a mass for the photon!)

29. (a) What is the momentum of an electron that has an associated de Broglie wavelength of 1.0×10^{-10} m?
    (b) What is the velocity of the same electron?
    (c) What is the kinetic energy of the same electron?

30. What is the associated de Broglie wavelength of
    (a) a neutron ($m_n = 1.67 \times 10^{-27}$ kg) travelling at 1.5×10^4 m/s?
    (b) an electron ($m_e = 9.11 \times 10^{-31}$ kg) travelling at 1.2×10^6 m/s?
    (c) a proton whose kinetic energy is 1.0×10^9 eV?
    (d) an artillery shell with a mass of 0.50 kg and a velocity of 500 m/s?

31. What is the energy, in electronvolts, required to give an electron an associated de Broglie wavelength of 0.15 nm?

32. An electron is accelerated from rest through a potential difference of 100 V. What is the associated de Broglie wavelength of the electron?

33. According to the Bohr theory of the atom (to be studied in the next chapter), the velocity of an electron in the first Bohr orbit of the hydrogen atom is 2.19×10^6 m/s.
    (a) What is the de Broglie wavelength associated with this electron?
    (b) The radius of the first Bohr orbit is 5.3×10^{-11} m. How does the de Broglie wavelength of the electron compare with the circumference of the first orbit?

Numerical Answers to Review Problems

15. 1.63×10^{-18} J, 10.2 eV
16. (a) 2.36×10^{-9} eV (b) 4.22×10^{-7} eV
18. (a) 1.5×10^{15} Hz
    (b) 9.9×10^{-19} J, 6.2 eV
    (c) 3.3×10^{-27} kg·m/s
19. (a) 2.8×10^{17} photons/cm²·s
    (b) 9.3×10^8 photons/cm³
20. 1.1×10^{15} Hz
21. 8.05×10^{14} Hz
22. 5.04×10^{-7} m
23. 1.0×10^{-19} J, -0.63 V
24. 1.67 eV
25. 200 nm
26. 1.38 eV
27. 1.61×10^{-27} kg·m/s
28. 9.9×10^{-16} J, 1.1×10^{-32} kg
29. (a) 6.6×10^{-24} kg·m/s
    (b) 7.3×10^6 m/s
    (c) 2.4×10^{-17} J or 150 eV
30. (a) 2.6×10^{-11} m (b) 6.1×10^{-10} m
    (c) 9.1×10^{-16} m (d) 2.6×10^{-36} m
31. 67 eV
32. 1.23×10^{-10} m
33. (a) 3.32×10^{-10} m (b) equal

19 Models of the Atom

As early as 400 B.C., the Greek philosopher Democritus theorized that all matter was composed of tiny, indivisible particles called atoms. His theory was based on philosophical reasoning rather than on any direct experimental evidence. Laboratory evidence for the existence of atoms was not found until much later, early in the 19th century, by an English chemist, John Dalton (1766-1844). He proposed that atoms were like tiny, solid, billiard balls, and could join together in small, whole-numbered combinations to produce various compounds. Some clue to the internal structure of the atom was provided much later by J.J. Thomson, who suggested that the atom was more like a sphere of positive charge, with negative electrons embedded throughout it, like raisins in a bun. By the turn of the 20th century, scientists were convinced that the atom did have a "discrete" internal structure, and they were busy finding ways to reveal it.

19.1 Rutherford's Model of the Atom

Our modern concept of the structure of the atom relies heavily on some astute detective work done in the early 20th century, leading to the proposal of an atomic model, in 1911, by Ernest Rutherford (1871-1937).

By the end of the 19th century, it was known that an atom's negative charge was carried by its electrons, whose mass was only a very small fraction of the atom's total mass. It followed, then, that the rest of the atom should contain an equal amount of positive charge (the atom was known to be neutral), and most of the atom's mass. The question to be answered was: "How are this mass and positive charge distributed within the atom?"

A possible answer to this question lay in a creative experiment proposed by Rutherford, when he was director of the research laboratory at England's Manchester University. It was carried out by his associates, Hans Geiger and Eric Marsden, between 1911 and 1913. The essence of their experimental technique was to show how small, high-speed particles could be scattered by the unknown internal structure of the atom.

A simple example may help us understand the principles involved in a typical scattering experiment. Suppose we have a large black box, of known size and mass, but are unable to look inside it, to see its internal structure and how its mass is distributed. The box might be completely filled with some substance of uniform

Ernest Rutherford

After a period of study at the University of New Zealand, Rutherford was awarded a scholarship at Cambridge University, and worked under J.J. Thomson. He began his work on alpha particle scattering while at McGill University in Montreal, and continued it when he returned to Manchester University in England in 1908. He received the 1908 Nobel Prize for Chemistry, for his alpha scattering experiments, and was knighted in 1914. He returned to Cambridge in 1919 as professor of physics, and was president of the Royal Society from 1925 until 1930.

density, such as wood, or it might be filled with a mixture of inflated balloons and steel ball bearings. How can we determine which model best represents the actual distribution of mass within the box?

We could shoot a stream of bullets into the box, all with the same speed and in the same direction, and see what effect the box and its contents had on them. If all of the bullets emerged going in the same direction with only a slightly reduced speed, we could assume that the box was filled with some uniform, low-density substance (like wood) which would not cause the bullets to change direction (i.e., scatter) but would just slow them down slightly. On the other hand, if we found that while most of the bullets had gone through the box undeflected (same speed, same direction), a few had emerged in drastically different directions, it would be fair to assume that the latter had bounced off some small, very dense, widely dispersed material in their paths.

Then, by studying the distribution of bullets scattered by the box (in both direction and speed), it would be possible to learn much about the distribution of mass within the box.

The Rutherford Experiment

Rutherford proposed using high-speed alpha particles from a radioactive polonium source as the "bullets", and a very thin sheet of gold foil as the "black box". The experimental set-up he used is shown in the diagram.

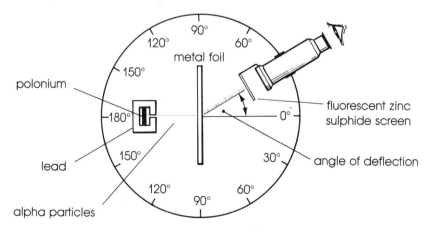

A narrow beam of alpha particles emitted spontaneously by the polonium source was selected by a hole drilled in a lead shield (called a collimator) surrounding the polonium. These alpha particles struck a very thin sheet of gold foil placed in their path. The thinnest gold foil available to Rutherford was about 10^{-7} m thick but, even so, it was composed of about 400 layers of gold atoms. After being scattered by the gold foil, the particles were detected by a scintillation counter placed at an angle θ to the particles' original direction. The scintillation counter was a screen coated with a thin zinc sulphide film. When a particle struck this screen, a tiny flash of light (called a scintillation) was given off by the zinc sulphide and observed through a microscope. This was evidence that the particle had been scattered.

The experiment consisted of moving the scintillation counter through all possible values of θ from 0° to ± 180°, and counting the number of alpha particles detected at each scattering angle θ.

Geiger and Marsden performed the laborious scattering experiments with great care for nearly two years and, in 1913, were able to report the following results:

- The great majority of alpha particles passed through the gold foil with virtually no deviation from their original path (only 1 in 10 000 was deflected by more than 10°).
- A very few alpha particles were scattered by sizable angles.
- In extremely rare cases, an alpha particle was deflected by 180°, back along its original path.
- After a period of exposure to the beam, the foil had acquired a positive charge.

In interpreting these results, Rutherford formulated a model of atomic structure that includes the following features:

- The atom has a positively charged, very small but extremely dense, central region called a nucleus, that contains all of the atom's positive charge and most of its mass.

He reasoned that a positive alpha particle was deflected by the force of electric repulsion from this small, positive nucleus only when it approached the nucleus very closely. Since so very few particles were deflected by any appreciable angle, the nucleus must be so small that most alpha particles did not approach it closely enough to be deflected.

- The greatest proportion of an atom's volume is empty space.

This would account for the observation that most alpha particles passed through this great volume of empty space and were undeflected.

- Within this empty space were a number of very light, negatively charged electrons moving in orbits around the nucleus.

Although Rutherford's experiments with gold foils were done while he was at Manchester, they were based on the knowledge he had gained about radioactive particles while working with Frederick Soddy at McGill University in Montreal. In fact, in 1908, Rutherford was awarded the Nobel Prize for Chemistry for his discovery of the basic principles underlying radioactivity.

As the alpha particles passed undeflected through the empty space of the atom, occasionally one of them would encounter an electron, "capture" it by the force of electrostatic attraction, and move on, undeflected by the very slight mass of the electron. The gold atom was thus ionized with a positive charge due to the loss of this electron. The electrons must be moving around the positive nucleus, held in orbit by the force of electric attraction to the nucleus, much like the planets moving around the sun. If the electrons were at rest, they would "fall" into the nucleus, and be captured by it, thereby neutralizing it and making it incapable of deflecting alpha particles.

As a result of these assumptions, Rutherford's model became known as the "planetary model". With a few modifications and additional features, it is roughly how we view the atom today.

"We haven't the money. So we've got to think."

Ernest Rutherford

19.2 Information from Alpha Particle Scattering Experiments

In Section 19.1 we described the principles used by Rutherford in his gold foil experiment, and some of the general findings that led to his proposal of a planetary model for the atom. Rutherford and his colleagues did, however, continue to analyse the results of alpha particle scattering very closely, and were able to derive a great deal more information about the nature of atomic structure.

1. The Trajectory of the Alpha Particles

Initially, Rutherford wondered what force was acting between the stationary gold nucleus and the incoming alpha particle, causing it to be scattered. He knew that alpha particles were positively charged. His model suggested that all of the atom's positive charge was concentrated within the nucleus, and that the scattering occurred because of an electrostatic repulsion between the alpha particle and the nucleus. He further proposed that this force obeyed Coulomb's Law, its magnitude being inversely proportional to the square of the distance between the alpha particle and the nucleus:

$$F = k \frac{q_1 q_2}{r^2}$$

It was then necessary to obtain some experimental evidence that this assumption about the Coulomb force was valid. Using mathematics beyond the scope of this book, Rutherford was able to show that the path taken by any incoming alpha particle, in the presence of a Coulomb force field, is a hyperbola, with the initial and final directions of the alpha particle representing its asymptotes, and the nucleus one of its foci. The diagram depicts some of these hyperbolic paths; notice that the eccentricity (amount of bending) of each hyperbola depends on the distance of the initial path from a direct hit. This distance, by which an alpha particle would miss the nucleus if not deflected, is called the aiming error b.

b is also called the "impact parameter".

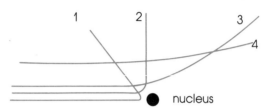

For a given value of b, an alpha particle of a given energy is deflected along a hyperbolic path, scattered by an angle θ, as shown:

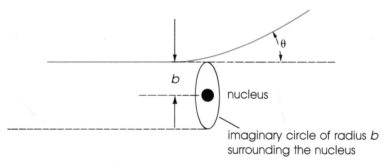

imaginary circle of radius b
surrounding the nucleus

2. Angular Distribution of Scattered Alpha Particles

If an alpha particle with an aiming error b is scattered through an angle θ, then any particle with an aiming error less than b will be scattered through an angle greater than θ. Of course, for a particle with $b = 0$ (a direct hit), $\theta = 180°$, and the particle is deflected back along its initial path. Using the mathematics mentioned previously, it is possible to determine the relationship between b and θ (assuming a Coulomb scattering force). The magnitude of θ for any aiming error b depends on the initial energy of the alpha particle and the magnitude of the charge on the scattering nucleus. A graph of the relationship is shown.

Not being able to see individual atoms, it is impossible to actually measure the aiming error for any alpha particle, in order to directly test this relationship between b and θ. An indirect measurement must be made in order to confirm Rutherford's assumption about the Coulomb scattering force.

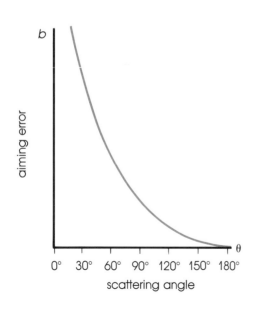

For any particle to be scattered by greater than a given angle θ, it must have an aiming error of less than the corresponding value of b. That is, it must approach the nucleus through a cylinder of radius b and cross-sectional area πb^2, as shown in the diagram on page 734.

If we assume that the incoming beam of alpha particles is distributed uniformly, then the number of particles with less than a given value of aiming error b (and hence within its cylinder, of radius b) is proportional to the area of the "target cylinder", πb^2. Therefore, the number of particles scattered by greater than any angle θ, N_θ, is proportional to b^2, where b is the aiming error for that particular value of θ. Since we already know the relationship between b and θ, as given in the graph on page 734, we can construct a graph of the expected relationship between N_θ and θ, as shown to the right.

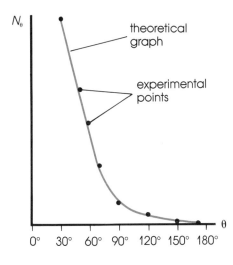

This is a graph that can be tested experimentally. In fact, that is what Geiger and Marsden did, in 1913. By counting the number of particles scattered at each angle θ, they were able to draw a graph of N_θ versus θ. The solid dots on our graph represent the data of Geiger and Marsden, which, within experimental limits, confirmed the validity of the computed curve. Of course it also validated the assumptions upon which the computed curve was based, namely, that the scattering force obeyed Coulomb's Law. It is of great importance in understanding atomic structure to know that Coulomb's Law applies to the electric force between small charged particles even at distances smaller than the size of atoms.

3. The Charge on the Nucleus

The explanation we have used to account for the scattering of alpha particles by gold nuclei could apply equally well to any other nucleus. Other nuclei would differ from gold nuclei only in the two components: mass and charge. Since we assumed that the scattering nucleus was essentially fixed in position, a nucleus of a different mass would have no significant effect on the alpha particle's trajectory. A different nuclear charge would, however, affect the magnitude of the Coulomb force experienced by the incoming alpha particle, and hence its scattering angle. The diagram on page 736 shows how two alpha particles of the same energy and aiming error are scattered by two different nuclei, of charges Z_1 and Z_2. The charge on a nucleus, represented by Z, is also referred to as its "atomic number".

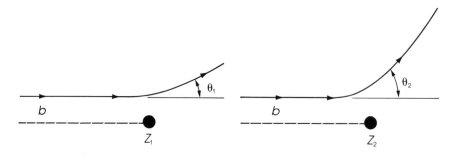

In the example shown, Z_2 is greater than Z_1, thereby exerting a stronger force on the alpha particle and causing it to be deflected by a greater amount. Again, using detailed computations based on Newton's Laws and Coulomb's Law, and taking into account the geometry of the scattering interaction, it can be shown that the number of alpha particles scattered at a given angle θ is proportional to the square of the nuclear charge, Z^2. These results can be verified experimentally by comparing the scattering data when alpha particles of the same energy are fired at foils composed of different atoms. Of course, the thickness of each foil used must be such that the alpha particles encounter about the same number of layers of atoms, in order for the scattering patterns to be compared.

4. The Size of the Nucleus

The fact that an occasional alpha particle can be stopped by a gold nucleus and returned along its initial path provides us with a way of estimating an upper limit for the size of the nucleus.

Alpha particles come closest to a nucleus when aimed directly at its centre. Any alpha particle of mass m, charge q_1, and speed v_0, a very great distance away from a stationary nucleus of mass m and charge q_2, has only kinetic energy, given by

$$E_{k_0} = \frac{1}{2} m v_0^2$$

As it approaches the nucleus, it begins to encounter the electric field of the nucleus, thereby losing kinetic energy and gaining electric potential energy, E_e, but with its total energy remaining constant, at E_{k_0}.

Thus, at any point along its hyperbolic path,

$$E_{total} = E_k + E_e = E_{k_0} \text{ (constant)}$$

An alpha particle making a direct hit will be brought to rest a distance r_0 from the nucleus, at which point all of its energy will have been converted from kinetic into electric potential energy.

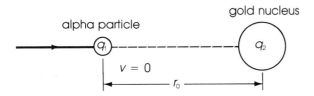

At that point,

$$E_{total} = E_e = E_{k_o} = \frac{1}{2} mv_o^2$$

But for two charges, q_1 and q_2, a distance r_o apart,

$$E_e = k \frac{q_1 q_2}{r_o}$$

so that

$$k \frac{q_1 q_2}{r_o} = \frac{1}{2} mv_o^2$$

or

$$r_o = \frac{2 k q_1 q_2}{mv_o^2}$$

Alpha particles from a polonium source have a speed of 1.6×10^7 m/s, and their charge and mass are 3.2×10^{-19} C and 6.6×10^{-27} kg, respectively. The charge on a gold nucleus, of atomic number 79, is 1.3×10^{-17} C. Therefore

$$r_o = \frac{2(9 \times 10^9 \text{ N·m}^2/\text{C}^2)(3.2 \times 10^{-19} \text{ C})(1.3 \times 10^{-17} \text{ C})}{(6.6 \times 10^{-27} \text{ kg})(1.6 \times 10^7 \text{ m/s})^2}$$

$$= 4.2 \times 10^{-14} \text{ m}$$

This represents the closest distance at which an alpha particle moving with an initial speed of 1.6×10^7 m/s can approach a gold nucleus and, as a result, it is an upper limit for the radius of the gold nucleus. If the nucleus were any larger than 4.2×10^{-14} m, the alpha particle would make a contact collision, and the scattering would not conform to the predictions based on Coulomb's Law.

Other measurements, of the distance between adjacent gold atoms, yield a value of about 2.5×10^{-10} m. This gives a value for the atomic radius of about 1.2×10^{-10} m. We can therefore calcualte the ratio of the volume of the atom to the volume of its nucleus as follows:

$$\frac{V_{atom}}{V_{nucleus}} = \frac{(r_{atom})^3}{(r_{nucleus})^3} = \frac{(1.2 \times 10^{-10} \text{ m})^3}{(4.2 \times 10^{-14} \text{ m})^3} = 2.3 \times 10^{10}$$

That is to say, in terms of volume, the atom is about 10^{10} times the size of its own nucleus. This graphic example shows just how small the nucleus in Rutherford's planetary model of the atom really is.

In everyday terms, if the nucleus were the size of the head of a straight pin (about 1 mm in diameter), the atom would be about the size of your bedroom (about 3 m wide).

Before 1925 it was generally assumed that the sun and stars contain the same elements as the Earth — iron, silicon, oxygen, carbon, nitrogen, etc. — in approximately the same ratios. This assumption was based on the fact that the absorption spectral lines corresponding to the known characteristic wavelengths of those elements were found in both solar and stellar spectra. This agreed with the accepted theory that the Earth had been made from material extracted from the sun. The British-born astronomer, Cecelia Payne-Gaposchkin, expanded this theory when she was a graduate student working in physics at Harvard, in 1925, and found that stellar atmospheres appear to be composed primarily of hydrogen and helium. Her discovery became the basis of the modern theory that heavier elements were synthesized from hydrogen and helium in the stars.

19.3 Emission and Absorption Spectra

Long before Rutherford proposed his planetary model for atomic structure, it was known that matter, when heated intensely, would give off light. Solids, liquids, and very dense gases gave off light with a continuous spectrum of wavelengths. On the other hand, the light emitted when a high voltage was applied to a rarefied gas was quite different. Though a known fact for some time before the proposal of the Rutherford model, this was to provide a valuable clue to the structure of the atom.

The **continuous spectrum** given off by a heated solid was assumed to be due to the interactions between each atom or molecule and its neighbours. By contrast, in a rarefied gas exposed to a very high voltage, the atoms are very far apart, on the average, so that any light emitted must come from individual, isolated atoms rather than from interactions between adjacent atoms. Because of this, an analysis of the light given off by a rarefied gas may provide a clue to the structure of the gas atoms themselves.

As early as the beginning of the 19th century it had been known that the radiation from electrically "excited" gases was discrete rather than continuous. That is, only specific frequencies of light are given off by an excited gas. When this light is passed through a spectroscope, a "bright line emission spectrum" is observed, containing lines of light of the various frequencies given off by that gas. Each gas emits its own specific set of characteristic frequencies,

Continuous spectrum

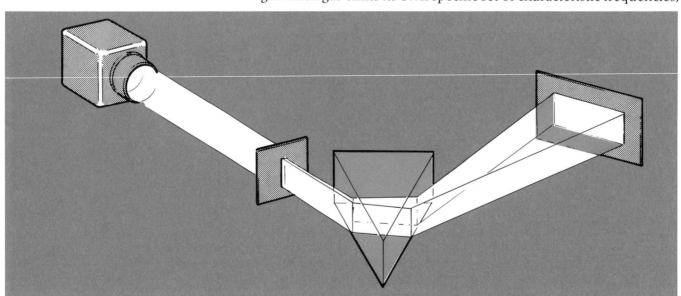

called its **emission spectrum**, making spectroscopy a particularly accurate method for identifying elements.

For example, if a sample of hydrogen gas under low pressure in a vacuum tube is excited by a high electric potential applied between electrodes at the ends of the tube, a pink glow is produced. If this light is passed through a spectroscope, it is found to consist of four lines of visible light: red, blue-green, blue, and violet. A spectroscope consists of a slit that limits the entering light to a narrow beam, a prism that disperses the light into its spectral components, and a viewing telescope for observing the lines in the dispersed spectrum. In fact, the so-called lines in the spectrum are merely images of the slit dispersed by the prism. Some spectroscopes even have a calibrated scale on the telescope, to measure the wavelengths of the lines in the spectrum. The diagram shows a typical emission spectrum and the apparatus needed to create it.

Emission spectrum

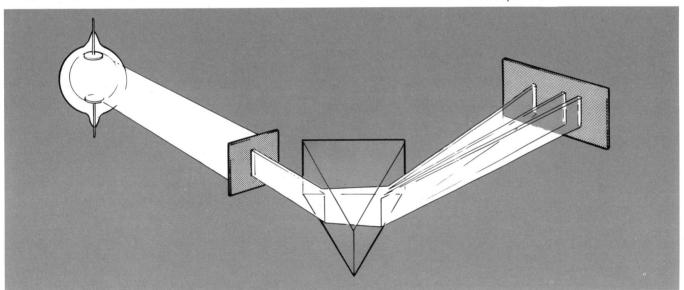

A more extensive examination of the hydrogen emission spectrum, using photographic film sensitive to infrared and ultraviolet radiation, would reveal that it also contains a number of frequencies in these regions of the electromagnetic spectrum.

It can also be shown that if white light is allowed to pass through a gas, and the transmitted light is analysed with a spectroscope, dark lines of missing light are observed in the continuous spectrum at exactly the same frequencies as the lines in the emission spectrum of that gas. This is called an **absorption spectrum**, created by light absorbed from the continuous spectrum as it passes through the gas.

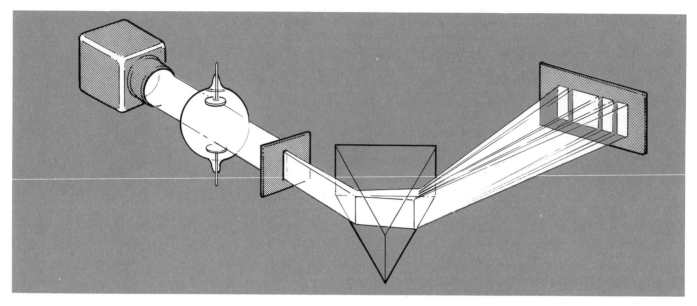

Absorption spectrum

It is evident that atoms absorb light of the same frequencies as they emit. Our model of the atom must be capable of explaining why atoms only emit and absorb certain discrete frequencies of light; it should, in fact, be able to predict what these frequencies are. Rutherford's planetary model made no attempt to account for these discrete emission and absorption spectra. Clearly, some additional modifications were needed.

19.4 The Franck-Hertz Experiment

Another significant contribution to our understanding of atomic structure was provided by a team of two German physicists, James Franck and Gustav Hertz, in 1914. Earlier studies of emission and absorption spectra had revealed that atoms emit and absorb light energy only at discrete, characteristic frequencies, and not in a continuous spectrum, as might have been anticipated. Franck and Hertz devised an experiment to investigate how atoms absorb energy in collisions with fast-moving electrons.

Franck and Hertz used an apparatus similar to that shown on the next page. Free electrons emitted from the cathode were accelerated through the low pressure mercury vapour by a positive voltage applied to the wire screen anode. Most of the electrons missed this screen, and were collected by a plate maintained at a slightly lower voltage. These collected electrons constituted an electric current, which was measured by the sensitive ammeter shown.

Franck and Hertz received the 1925 Nobel Prize for Physics for this work. When the Nazis came to power in Germany, Franck was forced to flee to the U.S.A. In order to carry his gold Nobel Prize medal with him, he dissolved it in a bottle of acid, only to precipitate the metal and recast it later.

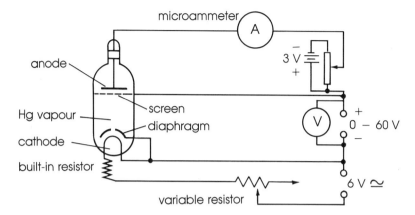

The experiment consisted of gradually increasing the accelerating voltage and, for each value, measuring the electric current passing through the mercury vapour and collected by the plate. Franck and Hertz found the following results:

- As the accelerating voltage was increased slowly from zero, the current increased gradually, as well.
- Then, at a voltage of 4.9 V, the current dropped dramatically, almost to zero.
- As the voltage was increased further, the current once again began to increase.
- Similar minor decreases in current also occurred at voltages of 6.7 V and 8.8 V.
- Another significant decrease in current occurred at a voltage of 9.8 V.

A graph of collected current transmitted through the mercury vapour versus electron accelerating voltage is shown.

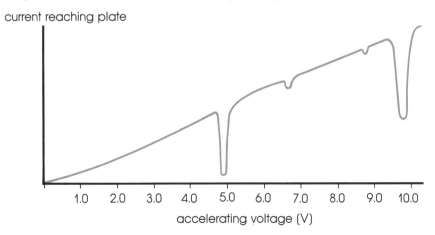

An electron accelerated by a potential difference of 4.9 V acquires a kinetic energy of 4.9 eV (1 eV = 1.6 × 10⁻¹⁹ J). Franck and Hertz found that for certain values of bombarding electron energy (4.9 eV, 6.7 eV, 8.8 eV, 9.8 eV, . . .) the electrons do not "make it" through the mercury vapour to contribute to the measured current. Their energy is lost because of collisions with mercury vapour atoms; but only at these specific values of electron energy do these collisions seem to occur. The proposed explanation was simple, yet elegant:

● Whenever the energy of the incident electrons was less than 4.9 eV, they simply bounced off any mercury vapour atoms they encountered, with no loss of energy, and continued on as part of the current. These were elastic collisions with little loss of energy from the electrons, so they still passed between the screen wires and reached the plate.

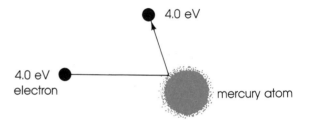

● Those electrons with an energy of 4.9 eV that collided with a mercury atom transferred all of their energy to the mercury atom and, therefore, with no energy remaining, did not reach the plate. Instead, they were drawn to the wire screen.

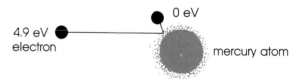

● At energies greater than 4.9 eV, electrons colliding with mercury atoms can give up 4.9 eV in the collision and still move off with the remaining energy and reach the plate.

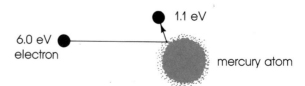

- At electron energies of 6.7 eV and 8.8 eV, collisions once again rob the bombarding electrons of all their energy, but these collisions are less likely to occur than those at 4.9 eV, so that the effect on the current is less severe.
- At 9.8 V accelerating potential, electrons are able to make a collision, losing 4.9 eV of energy, and then go on to make a second similar collision with another mercury atom, losing another 4.9 eV of energy. Since these collisions are more probable, a sharper decrease in current occurs.

In a collision between a moving and a stationary puck (Chapter 9), the target puck could absorb any amount of energy from the moving puck in the collision. When the mass of the moving puck is very small compared to that of the stationary puck (as would certainly be the case for a moving electron and a stationary mercury atom), almost no kinetic energy is transferred to the stationary puck, so that the moving puck "bounces off" with almost no loss of energy.

In the electron-mercury atom collision, the mercury atom absorbs all of the electron's energy, but only at certain values (4.9 eV, 6.7 eV, 8.8 eV, . . .). Classical mechanics would suggest that a massive object like the mercury atom would not absorb these amounts of kinetic energy from such a tiny object as an electron. This is the significance of the Franck-Hertz experiment: atoms can change their *internal* energy as a result of collisions with electrons, but only by specific, discrete amounts.

A mercury atom that has not absorbed any extra internal energy as a result of a collision with an electron is normally found in its **ground state**. When it has absorbed 4.9 eV, the smallest amount of energy it is capable of absorbing — called its **first excitation energy** — we say the atom is in its first excited state. Other, greater

Conservation of momentum tells us that the atom must acquire a velocity from the collision. However, since it is so massive compared to the electron, the kinetic energy it gains is very small and we can neglect it in this discussion.

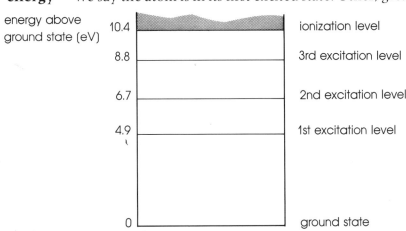

energy above
ground state (eV)

10.4	ionization level
8.8	3rd excitation level
6.7	2nd excitation level
4.9	1st excitation level
0	ground state

Although only three excitation levels are shown, there are many more above the third level, spaced progressively more closely together up to the ionization level.

amounts of internal energy are the second and third excitation energies, respectively. These successive values of internal energy that an atom can possess are called its **energy levels**, and can be depicted on an energy-level diagram, such as the one shown on the previous page for mercury.

An important difference occurs, though, when the absorbed energy is 10.4 eV or greater. The structure of the mercury atom itself changes. The 10.4 eV of internal energy is too great to be absorbed without the ejection of one of the mercury atom's electrons, leaving behind a positive mercury ion. Of course, the ejected electron can carry away with it any excess amount of kinetic energy not needed for its release. In this way, the atom can absorb any value of incident energy greater than 10.4 eV. For mercury, 10.4 eV is called its **ionization energy**, and the energy-level diagram is a continuum above this energy, rather than a series of discrete levels.

Other elements can also be studied by using electron collision experiments similar to the Franck-Hertz technique. Each different element is found to have its own unique ionization energy and set of internal energy levels.

The energy levels used for some problems are illustrative only, and do not necessarily correspond to actual elements, or the laws that govern them.

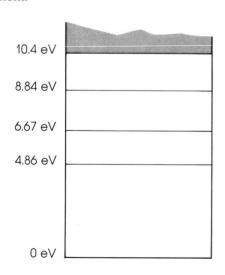

Sample problem

Electrons with kinetic energy of 12.0 eV collide with an atom of metallic element X in the gaseous state. The electrons are found to scatter with energies of 4.0 eV and 7.0 eV only. What are the first and second excitation levels of element X?

Since energy is conserved in the interaction between a free electron and one bound to an atom in its ground state,

$$E_n = E_{k \text{ initial}} - E_{k \text{ final}}$$
$$E_1 = 12.0 \text{ eV} - 7.0 \text{ eV} = 5.0 \text{ eV}$$

and
$$E_2 = 12.0 \text{ eV} - 4.0 \text{ eV} = 8.0 \text{ eV}$$

Practice

1. The energy level diagram for mercury is shown. An electron with a kinetic energy of 9.00 eV collides with a mercury atom in the ground state. With what possible energies might it scatter?
(4.14 eV, 2.33 eV, 0.16 eV)

2. When a gaseous sample of a metallic element was bombarded with electrons of increasing energy, the following data were collected:
   (i) Electrons with less than 1.4 eV of kinetic energy collided elastically with the gas atoms.
   (ii) Electrons with a kinetic energy of 1.8 eV scattered with a kinetic energy of 0.3 eV.

(iii) Electrons with a kinetic energy of 5.2 eV scattered with a kinetic energy of either 3.7 eV or 1.9 eV.

What are the most likely values for the first two energy levels of this element?   (1.5 eV, 3.3 eV)

19.5 Analysing Atomic Spectra

Another observation resulting from the Franck-Hertz experiment, but not mentioned in Section 19.4, provides further information about the internal energy levels in atoms. When bombarded with electrons whose energy is less than 4.9 eV, the mercury vapour gave off no light. But, for electron energies of just greater than 4.9 eV, light was emitted. When this light is examined using a spectrometer, it is found to consist of a single frequency of ultra-violet light of wavelength 254 nm (1 nm = 10^{-9} m).

See the colour plate for the line spectra of mercury, sodium vapour, and atomic hydrogen.

It seems that when atoms absorb energy in collisions with electrons, they quickly emit this excess energy in the form of light. Recalling from Chapter 18 Planck's hypothesis that light consists of photons whose energy and wavelength are related by the equation

$$E_p = \frac{hc}{\lambda}$$

this ultraviolet light from mercury vapour thus consists of photons of energy:

$$E_p = \frac{(6.63 \times 10^{-34}\,\text{J·s})(3.00 \times 10^8\,\text{m/s})}{2.54 \times 10^{-7}\,\text{m}}$$
$$= 7.83 \times 10^{-19}\,\text{J}$$
$$= 4.89\,\text{eV}$$

This was a significant discovery. Atoms that will only absorb energy in 4.9 eV packages re-emit the energy in the form of photons of exactly the same energy. In other words, mercury atoms raised to their first excitation level by collisions with electrons de-excite and return to their ground state by emitting a photon whose energy is equal to the difference between the energy of the first excited state and the ground state.

Suppose we were to analyse the light coming from the same mercury atoms when the energy of the bombarding electrons is increased above the second excitation level, say to 7 eV. What would we expect to find? There should be a line in the spectrum composed of photons emitted when the atom de-excites from its second excitation level, of 6.67 eV, to the ground state. Its wave-length is given by

$$\lambda = \frac{hc}{E_p}$$

$$= \frac{(6.63 \times 10^{-34}\ \text{J·s})(3.00 \times 10^8\ \text{m/s})}{(6.67\ \text{eV})(1.60 \times 10^{-19}\ \text{J/eV})}$$

$$= 1.86 \times 10^{-7}\ \text{m, or 186 nm}$$

This line is more difficult to observe in the spectrum of mercury, since its wavelength is too short to be detected on normal photographic film, or with the naked eye. Yet special film sensitive to ultraviolet radiation is able to confirm its presence.

There are, however, additional lines in the spectrum of mercury that do not correspond to de-excitations from the various excited states to the ground state. Apparently there are other photons emitted as the atom gives off its excess energy in returning from the second excited level to the ground state. A line observed at a wavelength of 697 nm provides a clue. The energy of these photons is

$$E_p = \frac{hc}{\lambda}$$

$$= \frac{(6.63 \times 10^{-34}\ \text{J·s})(3.00 \times 10^8\ \text{m/s})}{697 \times 10^{-7}\ \text{m}}$$

$$= 285 \times 10^{-19}\ \text{J, or 1.78 eV}$$

Since the first excitation level (and hence the lowest) in mercury is 4.89 eV, this photon cannot correspond to a transition from any excited state to the ground state. A careful examination of the energy levels of mercury would show that the difference between the first excitation level and the second excitation level is

$$E_2 - E_1 = 6.67\ \text{eV} - 4.89\ \text{eV}$$

$$= 1.78\ \text{eV}$$

It seems that a mercury atom can de-excite from the second excitation level in two stages — first by emitting a 1.78 eV photon to decrease its energy to the first excitation level and then by emitting a 4.89 eV photon to reach the ground state. A further examination of the complete spectrum of mercury would reveal other lines corresponding to downward transitions between higher excitation levels. In general, for the emission spectrum of any element, we can write

$$\boldsymbol{E_p = E_i - E_f}$$

where E_p is the energy of the emitted photon
        E_i is the energy of the initial (higher) level
        E_f is the energy of the final (lower) level
or, in terms of the wavelength of the spectral line,

$$\lambda = \frac{hc}{E_i - E_f}$$

Sample problem

An unknown substance has first and second excitation levels of 3.65 eV and 5.12 eV, respectively. Determine the energy and wavelength of each photon found in its emission spectrum when bombarded with electrons of energy:

(a) 3.0 eV
(b) 4.5 eV
(c) 6.0 eV

(a) Since the first excitation energy is 3.65 eV, no energy will be absorbed and there will be no emission spectrum.

(b) With incident electrons of energy 4.5 eV, excitation to the first excitation level, only, is possible. Thus, the energy of emitted photons is

$$E_p = E_1 - E_0$$
$$= 3.65 \text{ eV} - 0 \text{ eV}$$
$$= 3.65 \text{ eV}$$

and　　$$\lambda = \frac{hc}{E_p}$$

$$= \frac{(6.63 \times 10^{-34} \text{ J·s})(3.00 \times 10^8 \text{ m/s})}{(3.65 \text{ eV})(1.60 \times 10^{-19} \text{ J/eV})}$$

$$= 341 \text{ nm}$$

(c) With incident electrons of energy 6.0 eV, excitation to both the first and second excitation levels is possible. Thus, in addition to the photon emitted in (b), we can have

$$E_p = E_2 - E_0$$
$$= 5.12 \text{ eV} - 0 \text{ eV}$$
$$= 5.12 \text{ eV}$$

and　　$$E_p = E_2 - E_1$$
$$= 5.12 \text{ eV} - 3.65 \text{ eV}$$
$$= 1.47 \text{ eV}$$

whose wavelengths, calculated using the same equation as in (b), are 243 nm and 846 nm, respectively.

None of these photons would be visible to the naked eye, one being infrared and the other two being ultraviolet.

As we learned in Section 19.3, examination of emission spectra is not the only way in which the internal energy levels of an atom can be probed. Similar information is available when we pass a beam of white light through a sample of the substance. Photons, of energy absorbed by the atoms, are "missing" from the transmitted light, and appear as dark lines or gaps in the continuous spectrum.

Dr Gerhard Herzberg (1904–　) was born and educated in Germany. He studied engineering physics as an undergraduate, and later received his Ph.D. in molecular spectroscopy. He left Germany because of Nazi harassment in 1935 (his wife was Jewish), and went to work at the University of Saskatchewan.

Although Herzberg considers himself a physicist, his discoveries have been most important for the field of chemistry. Using the spectroscope and the telescope, much of his early work had to do with identifying the arrangement of the atoms that make up more complicated molecules. In 1931 he discovered the so-called "Herzberg Bands" of oxygen in the upper atmosphere, a discovery that explained such phenomena as the light in the night sky and the production of ozone in the upper atmosphere.

In his investigations of "free radicals" (bits and pieces of molecules that combine easily to form other molecules), Herzberg worked out methods for determining how atoms are arranged in two free radicals: methyl (CH_4) and methylene (CH_3). This was of great importance to chemists, since carbon compounds are the constituents of all organic compounds. Herzberg's ideas and discoveries did much to stimulate the growth of modern chemical development. For his work he was awarded the Nobel Prize for Chemistry in 1971. The National Research Council of Canada has named the Herzberg Institute of Astrophysics in his honour.

The missing photons are absorbed by the atoms, causing a transition from a lower internal energy level (normally the ground state) to some higher level (an excited state). The relationship between the energy of the photons absorbed and the internal energy levels of the atom is the same as for an emission spectrum, except that the order of the process is reversed: the initial energy level is lower and the final level is higher.

$$E_p = E_f - E_i$$

For example: in the absorption spectrum of sodium, dark gaps appear at wavelengths of 259.4 nm, 254.4 nm, and 251.2 nm. What energy difference between internal energy levels corresponds to each of these absorption bands?

For the 259.4 nm line, the energy of the absorbed photon is given by

$$E_p = \frac{hc}{\lambda}$$
$$= \frac{(6.63 \times 10^{-34} \text{ J·s})(3.00 \times 10^8 \text{ m/s})}{2.59 \times 10^{-7} \text{ m}}$$
$$= 7.68 \times 10^{-19} \text{ J, or } 4.80 \text{ eV}$$

Thus, there are two energy levels in sodium that are 4.80 eV apart. Photons of that energy would be absorbed from the incoming light, causing electrons in the sodium atoms to jump from the lower to the higher level. Similarly, for the other two lines, the energy differences are 4.89 eV and 4.95 eV, respectively.

This analysis of absorption spectra explains why most gases, mercury vapour included, are invisible to the eye at room temperature. Even the most energetic photons in visible light (they are deep violet, with energies of about 3 eV) do not have sufficient energy to excite a mercury atom from the ground state to its first excitation level (4.87 eV, as you recall), and to be absorbed from the white light. Thus, all of the photons in the visible light pass through the mercury vapour without any being absorbed, giving the vapour an invisible appearance.

The emission spectrum of any element contains more lines than its absorption spectrum does. As we saw, lines in an emission spectrum can correspond to downward transitions between two excited states, as well as from any excited state to the ground state. On the other hand, since most atoms are normally in their ground state, only absorptions from the ground state to an excited state are likely. Atoms do not remain in an excited state for a sufficiently long time to make a further absorption to an even higher excited state probable. For example, the emission and absorption spectra of sodium vapour are shown.

We have all seen emission spectra in the visible region when we look at a neon light.

The alert reader may wonder why the re-emission of photons does not act to fill in the missing spaces in the absorption spectrum. It does, but they are emitted in all directions at random, and only a few will be in the direction of the original beam. As well, for absorption to other than the first excitation level, the de-excitation mode may result in a series of photons being emitted, different from the ones absorbed.

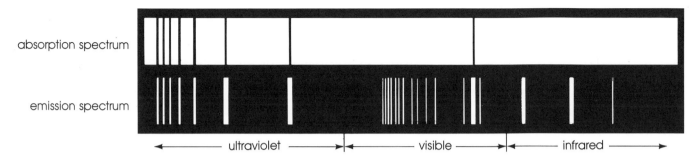

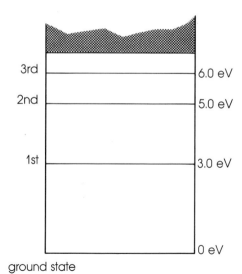

The absorption and emission spectra of sodium vapour

In summary, then, atoms can receive energy in two quite different ways:

- *By collisions with high speed particles such as electrons:* In these collisions, the atom receives only as much energy from the particle as corresponds to the energy difference between two of its internal energy levels. The particle continues on with the remaining energy.

  For example, a 5.4 eV electron colliding with a mercury atom in the ground state may give up 4.9 eV of energy to the mercury atom (the difference between its ground state and first excited state) and continue on with the remaining 0.5 eV.

- *By absorbing a photon:* In these interactions, the photon will *only* be absorbed if its energy corresponds exactly to the difference between two energy levels in the atom, the lower level being occupied by an electron. In most cases, this means the difference between the ground state, where most electrons normally reside, and any excited state.

  For example, a mercury atom in its ground state will only absorb photons of 4.9 eV, 6.7 eV, 8.8 eV, etc. Photons of energy 5.0 eV or 6.4 eV will pass through the mercury vapour with no chance of absorption.

Practice

1. The emission spectrum of an unknown substance contains lines with the following wavelengths: 172 nm, 194 nm, and 258 nm. If these all represent transitions *to the ground state*, (a) calculate the energies of the first three excited states, and (b) determine the wavelengths of three other lines in the substance's emission spectrum.

   (4.82 eV, 6.41 eV, 7.22 eV, 51.6 nm, 78.2 nm, 152 nm)

2. The energy level diagram for hypothetical atom *X* is shown.

   Determine all of the wavelengths in both its emission and absorption spectra.

   (1240 nm, 414 nm, 207 nm, 622 nm, 249 nm;
   249 nm, 414 nm, 207 nm)

19.6 The Energy Levels of Hydrogen

As early as the middle of the 19th century, it was known that hydrogen was the lightest and simplest atom, and was therefore an ideal candidate for the study of atomic structure. Its emission spectrum was of particular interest. The spectra of most substances show very little regularity. For hydrogen, the spacing of its spectral lines in the visible region of the spectrum formed a regular pattern. In 1885, this pattern attracted the attention of J.J. Balmer, a Swiss teacher who devised a simple empirical equation from which all of the lines in the visible spectrum of hydrogen could be computed. He found that the wavelengths of all of the spectral lines obeyed the equation

$$\frac{1}{\lambda} = R\left(\frac{1}{n_l^2} - \frac{1}{n_u^2}\right)$$

where R is a constant, later called the Rydberg constant, whose value Balmer found to be 1.097×10^7 m^{-1}

     n is a whole number greater than 2. Each successive value of n (i.e., 3, 4, 5, . . .) yields a value for the wavelength of the next line in the spectrum.

> This expression for R was totally empirical, in that it was derived from the spectroscopic data without any thought of what its value represented. Bohr's quantum-mechanical treatment, described later in this chapter, resulted in a theoretical value for R that was within 0.02% of the empirical value.

Further studies of the hydrogen spectrum carried out over the next 30 or 40 years, using ultraviolet and infrared detection techniques, revealed that the entire hydrogen spectrum obeyed a relationship similar to that devised by Balmer. By replacing the 2^2 term in Balmer's expression with the square of other whole numbers, the general expression below was devised, to predict the wavelengths of all possible lines in the hydrogen spectrum.

$$\frac{1}{\lambda} = R\left(\frac{1}{n_l^2} - \frac{1}{n_u^2}\right)$$

where n_l is any whole number 1, 2, 3, 4, . . .

     n_u is any whole number greater than n_l

(The choice of subscripts l (lower) and u (upper) will be obvious later.)

Thinking in terms of atomic structure, spectroscopists were tempted to rearrange the expression above into one involving the energies of photons in the emission spectrum and, as a consequence, the energies of the various levels within the hydrogen atom.

Using $E_p = \dfrac{hc}{\lambda}$ as the energy of an emitted photon, and making the assumption that n_u and n_l represent the numbers of the energy levels in the hydrogen atom involved in the transition that produced the photon, we can write

$$E_p = E_u - E_l \quad \text{and} \quad \frac{1}{\lambda} = \frac{E_p}{hc}$$

$$\frac{E_p}{hc} = R\left(\frac{1}{n_l^2} - \frac{1}{n_u^2}\right)$$

or

$$E_u - E_l = Rhc\left(\frac{1}{n_l^2} - \frac{1}{n_u^2}\right)$$

If we now assume that the highest energy level possible approaches the ionization state (E_I) when the value of n_u approaches infinity, we can write, for any energy level E_n,

$$E_I - E_n = Rhc\left(\frac{1}{n^2} - \frac{1}{\infty^2}\right)$$

or

$$E_n = E_I - \frac{Rhc}{n^2}$$

Rutherford's planetary model proposed that the hydrogen atom consists of a single proton nucleus (as the sun) and a single orbiting electron (as the planet). The electron is bound to its nucleus by the Coulomb force of attraction in much the same way that the Earth is bound to the sun by the gravitational force. When we studied such a gravitational system earlier (Chapter 10), we found it useful to choose the zero level of energy at the point where the two masses are no longer bound to each other. This zero level of energy denotes the borderline between the bound and the free condition of the system. If a mass has a total energy greater than zero, it can reach an infinite distance away, where its potential energy is zero, before coming to rest. For the hydrogen atom, this situation corresponds to ionization: the electron is no longer bound to its nucleus, as part of the atom, but is free. Thus, if we choose $E_I = 0$ when $n \rightarrow \infty$, then the expression for the energy levels of hydrogen becomes even simpler:

$$E_n = E_I - \frac{Rhc}{n^2}$$

$$= 0 - \frac{(1.097 \times 10^7 \text{ m}^{-1})(6.63 \times 10^{-34} \text{ J·s})(3.00 \times 10^8 \text{ m/s})}{n^2}$$

$$= -\frac{2.18 \times 10^{-18}}{n^2} \text{ J}$$

Then, converting from joules to electronvolts, we have

$$E_n = -\frac{13.6}{n^2} \text{ eV}$$

Just as electrons have different energy levels and orbitals, so do the protons and neutrons in the nucleus. In 1963, the Nobel Prize for Physics was shared by Marie Goeppert-Mayer, J.H.D. Jensen, and Eugene P. Wigner for explaining the properties of atomic nuclei in terms of the structure of shells (spherical layers) or orbits. Marie Goeppert-Mayer (1906–1972) was educated in Germany and, in 1939, went to the United States, where she worked on the separation of uranium isotopes for the atomic bomb project. In 1947, at the Institute for Nuclear Studies, the University of Chicago, she discovered that certain nuclei are more stable and abundant in nature than most. All of these nuclei have a particular number of neutrons (such as 50, 82, and 126) and an equal number of protons. In 1949, Mayer explained these numbers (now called the "magic numbers"), and, with J.H.D. Jensen, wrote the book *Elementary Theory of Nuclear Shell Structure* (1955). In 1960 she became professor of physics at the University of California in San Diego.

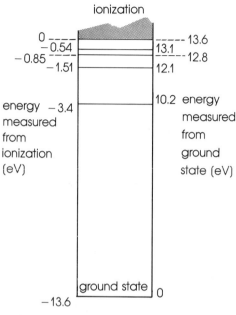

ionization

energy measured from ionization (eV)

ground state

Using this equation, we can calculate the values of all the energy levels of the hydrogen atom, which are given in the following table.

Level	Value of n	Energy	Energy above ground state
ground state	1	— 13.6 eV	0
1st excited state	2	— 3.4 eV	10.2 eV
2nd excited state	3	— 1.51 eV	12.1 eV
3rd excited state	4	— 0.85 eV	12.8 eV
4th excited state	5	— 0.54 eV	13.1 eV
⋮			
ionization state	∞	0	13.6 eV

We can represent these values graphically on an energy-level diagram, showing both the energy above the ground state (on the right), and the energy below ionization (on the left).

19.7 The Bohr Model of the Atom

The Rutherford planetary model of the atom, proposed in 1911, was very appealing, in spite of some major shortcomings. Recall that Rutherford's model had negative electrons moving in orbits around a small, dense, positive nucleus, held there by the centripetal force of the Coulomb attraction between unlike charges.

According to James Clerk Maxwell's well-established theories of electrodynamics, any accelerating electric charge would continuously emit energy in the form of electromagnetic waves. An electron orbiting a nucleus, in Rutherford's model, would be accelerating centripetally, and hence continuously giving off energy in the form of electromagnetic radiation. As its total energy decreased, the electron could be expected to spiral in towards the nucleus in an orbit of ever-decreasing radius. Eventually, with all of its energy spent, it would be captured by the nucleus, and the atom could be considered to have collapsed. Detailed calculations beyond the scope of this book suggest that this collapse would occur within 10^{-8} s. Thus, on the basis of classical mechanics and electromagnetic theory, atoms should remain stable for only an extremely short time. This is, of course, in direct contradiction to the evidence that atoms do exist on·a seemingly permanent basis and show no such tendency to collapse, a fortunate situation for us.

Niels Bohr

Secondly, under certain conditions, atoms do emit radiation in the form of visible and invisible light, and they do so with only specific, discrete frequencies. The spiralling electron described above would emit radiation in a continuous spectrum, with a gradually increasing frequency until it stopped. Furthermore, the work of Franck and Hertz, and the analysis of emission and absorption spectra, had virtually confirmed the notion of discrete, well defined internal energy levels within the atom, a feature that Rutherford's model completely lacked.

Shortly after the publication of Rutherford's model, a young Danish physicist, Niels Bohr (1885–1962), a post-doctoral student working in Rutherford's laboratory, became intrigued with these problems inherent in the model. He realized that, within the confines of the atom, the laws of classical mechanics and electrodynamics might not apply. Inspired by the work of Planck and Einstein, in introducing the particle nature of electromagnetic radiation, Bohr proposed a quantum approach to the motion of electrons within the atom.

His paper, released in 1913 after two years of formulation, sent shock waves of amazement through the scientific community. In making the following three postulates about the motion of electrons within atoms, he defied the well-established classical laws of mechanics and electromagnetism:

- Of all the possible circular and elliptic orbits for electrons around a nucleus, only a very special few orbits are "allowed": each allowed orbit is characterized by a different specific amount of electron energy.
- When moving in an allowed orbit, an electron is exempt from the classical laws of electromagnetism and does not radiate energy as it moves along its orbital path. As a result, each such orbit is called a **stationary state**.
- Electrons may "jump" from a higher energy orbit to a lower energy orbit, with the energy difference between these two stationary states being given off in the form of a single photon of electromagnetic radiation. Similarly, energy can only be absorbed by an atom if that amount of energy is equal to the difference in energy between a lower stationary state and some higher one.

Essentially, then, Bohr's idea was that atoms only exist in certain stationary states characterized by certain allowed orbits for their electrons, which move in these orbits with only certain amounts of total energy, the so-called energy levels of the atom. But what made these allowed orbits special and different from all of the other, disallowed orbits?

Bohr received his Ph.D. from the University of Copenhagen in 1911. Having obtained a grant to study abroad, he went to Cambridge University and worked there under Rutherford until, in 1916, he returned to the University of Copenhagen as professor of physics. For his development of the atomic model, he was awarded the 1922 Nobel Prize for Physics. An avid supporter of the peaceful uses of atomic energy, he organized the first Atoms for Peace Conference in Geneva, in 1955, and in 1957 he was honoured with the first Atoms for Peace Award.

The Theory of Laser Action

The laser (an acronyn for **l**ight **a**mplification by **s**timulated **e**mission of **r**adiation) was the first device made capable of directly amplifying light. The principle of the laser was first developed for microwave frequencies in the **maser** (the **m** stands for microwaves), invented by the American physicist Charles H. Townes in the 1950s. He was awarded the Nobel Prize for Physics in 1964 for his work. The first maser used ammonia gas, but other substances, such as ruby, carbon dioxide, argon, and helium-neon have subsequently been found to have "masing" or "lasing" action. There are several different types of lasers, but the general principles involved can be illustrated in the action of the helium-neon laser. It is the one most commonly used in classroom and laboratory demonstrations.

An excited atom can emit photons by two mechanisms: spontaneous emission and stimulated emission. As described in this chapter, the absorption of a quantum of energy by an atom raises an electron to a higher energy level. The electron usually descends spontaneously to a lower energy level in a relatively short time ($\sim 10^{-8}$s). There is no amplification in spontaneous emission, because the energy absorbed by the atoms is nearly equal to what is radiated. Stimulated emission can produce amplification, but only under

certain conditions. If a photon passes an excited neon atom, it could stimulate the atom to emit an identical photon in addition to the incident photon. This means that one photon approaches an atom, but two photons leave. For this to take place, the incident photon must have exactly the same frequency as the photon emitted by the atom. The two photons leaving the atom would have the same frequency and wavelength, and would travel in the same direction exactly in phase. In other words, the light is coherent.

Suppose we have a large group of atoms with more atoms in the excited state than in the ground state, and suppose that the energy-level difference for the atoms is exactly the same as the energy of the photons in the incident light beam. A first photon interacting with an excited atom could produce a second photon; these two photons could stimulate the emission of two more, and very quickly a chain reaction could occur, amplifying the light. Unfortunately, under normal conditions, the number of atoms in the ground state is greater than in the excited state.

Some substances or combinations of substances have excited states that are **metastable**, in which electrons can be excited to higher energy levels and stay there for a

relatively longer time ($\sim 10^{-4}$s) before moving back to the ground state. When more atoms are in a metastable condition than are in the ground state, we say there is a **population inversion**. For laser action to take place, both population inversion and the conditions for stimulated emission must exist in the lasing medium.

The red light of the helium-neon laser is produced in a capillary tube containing a mixture of 85% helium and 15% neon, at low pressure. There is a metal cathode outside the tube and, at one end, inside the tube, an anode. A potential difference of 8000 V creates a strong electric field that provides a continuous source of energy for the laser. Fused to the capillary tube at one end is a flat mirror that is 99.9% reflective while, at the other end, another mirror reflects 99% of the light and transmits 1%. It is this transmitted light that is the output of the laser (see diagram).

The strong electric field along the length of the laser tube causes free electrons to gain kinetic energy as they are accelerated towards the positive anode. Before reaching the electrode, there is a high probability that an energetic electron will collide with a helium atom, putting it into its excited state as one of its electrons "jumps" to a higher energy level. The thermal motions of the excited helium atoms result in collisions with neon atoms in the laser tube. During such collisions, a helium atom may revert to the ground state and the neon atom absorb the energy. It so happens that helium has exactly the same amount of energy in its excited state as the neon atom requires to raise it to its metastable state. Of course, the possibility exists that an energized electron could supply the correct amount of energy directly to the neon atom, raising it to its metastable level, but it is hardly likely, since neon has 10 orbiting electrons and many different energy levels for each. The presence of the helium atom assures that most of the neon atoms are excited to their metastable state (3S2).

When an excited neon electron makes a transition from its 3S2 level to the 2P4 level (see diagram), 1.96 eV of energy is released and a photon with a wavelength of 633 nm is created. Since there is a population

inversion in the tube, this photon stimulates the emission of an identical photon from an adjacent neon atom which, in turn, produces more stimulations along the tube. An amplified beam of red light is produced.

To further strengthen the output of coherent light, the mirrors at each end of the tube reflect the light along the axis of the tube, back and forth through

the laser medium. Further reinforcement is achieved with each transition of the tube as a multitude of neon atoms are stimulated to produce 633 nm photons. The mirrors reflect most, but not all, of the light. They transmit a small percentage of the light with each reflection, sufficient to produce the bright laser beam that comes out of the laser aperture.

Energy Absorption, Collision Transfer, and Spontaneous Emissions of Neon

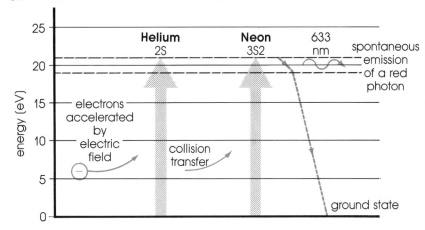

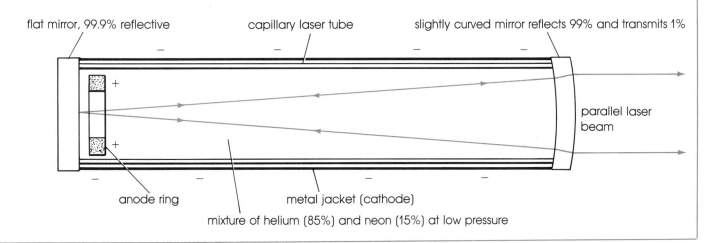

flat mirror, 99.9% reflective

capillary laser tube

slightly curved mirror reflects 99% and transmits 1%

parallel laser beam

anode ring

metal jacket (cathode)

mixture of helium (85%) and neon (15%) at low pressure

Bohr felt, drawing on the work of Planck, that something in the model of the atom must be quantized. He actually chose angular momentum, but the picture is clearer if we leap ahead a decade and borrow the concept of wave-particle duality from de Broglie. This was Bohr's ingenious quantum postulate: that electrons could only exist in stable orbits if the length of the orbital path was a whole number of de Broglie electron wavelengths. Recall that an electron of mass m and speed v has a de Broglie wavelength given by

$$\lambda = \frac{h}{mv}$$

where h is Planck's constant (6.63×10^{-34} J·s)

Then, assuming that the orbits are circular, and letting the first allowed orbit have a radius r_1 and an electron moving with a speed v_1, the length of the orbital path will be one wavelength.

$$2\pi r_1 = \lambda$$

$$2\pi r_1 = \frac{h}{mv_1}$$

Similarly, for the second allowed orbit,

$$2\pi r_2 = 2\lambda$$

$$2\pi r_2 = 2\left(\frac{h}{mv_2}\right)$$

Or, more generally, for the nth allowed orbit,

$$2\pi r_n = n\lambda = n\left(\frac{h}{mv_n}\right)$$

Thus, according to Bohr, the allowed orbits are those in which the electron can move with

$$mv_n r_n = n\left(\frac{h}{2\pi}\right)$$

The whole number n appearing in this equation, which represents the number of de Broglie wavelengths in the orbital path, is called the "quantum number" for the allowed orbit. The equation itself, called "Bohr's quantum condition", provides the key to a much more complete explanation of atomic structure.

This model was so bizarre that the young Dane kept it in his desk for two years. However, when it gave the Rydberg constant, correct to 0.02%, he knew there must be some truth in it, so he published it.

The expression "$m\,v_n\,r_n$" represents the angular momentum of a mass m, moving in a circle of radius r_n, at a constant speed v_n. $h/2\pi$ is an expression that appears frequently in quantum physics, and is often abbreviated to $\hbar$, called "h bar".

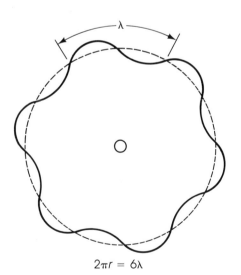

$$2\pi r = 6\lambda$$

One possible stationary electron orbit. In this example, the circumference of the orbit is six wavelengths.

19.8 The Wave-Mechanical Model of the Hydrogen Atom

With the formulation of Bohr's quantum hypothesis about the special nature of the allowed orbits, it became possible to combine classical mechanics with quantum wave mechanics to produce an elegant and satisfactory model of atomic structure. Like any model, it is a guide with which to interpret existing observations and predict new ones.

A hydrogen atom consists of a stationary proton, of mass m_p and charge e^+, and a moving electron of mass m_e and charge e^-. The electron moves in a circular orbit of radius r_n at a constant speed of v_n, such that n complete de Broglie wavelengths fit exactly in each orbital path. The centripetal force necessary to sustain the orbit is provided by the Coulomb force of electrical attraction between the proton and the electron.

$$F_c = F_e$$

$$\frac{m_e v_n^2}{r_n} = k\frac{e^2}{r_n^2}$$

or more simply
$$m_e v_n^2 = k\frac{e^2}{r_n} \tag{1}$$

But, applying Bohr's quantum hypothesis,

$$2\pi r_n = n\left(\frac{h}{m_e v_n}\right) \tag{2}$$

and, solving equation (2) for v_n, we have

$$v_n = \frac{nh}{2\pi m_e r_n} \tag{2a}$$

Substituting this value for v_n in equation (1),

$$m_e\left(\frac{nh}{2\pi m_e r_n}\right)^2 = \frac{ke^2}{r_n}$$

$$\frac{n^2 h^2}{4\pi^2 m_e r_n^2} = \frac{ke^2}{r_n}$$

$$r_n = \frac{n^2 h^2}{4\pi^2 m_e ke^2} \tag{3}$$

which is an expression for the radius of the nth circular allowed orbit in the hydrogen atom. By substituting known values for the constants, we can evaluate this radius:

$$r_n = n^2\left[\frac{(6.63 \times 10^{-34}\text{J·s})^2}{4\pi^2(9.1 \times 10^{-31}\text{ kg})(9.0 \times 10^9 \text{ N·m}^2/\text{C}^2)(1.6 \times 10^{-19}\text{ C})^2}\right]$$

$$= 5.3 \times 10^{-11}n^2 \text{ m}$$

The radius of the smallest orbit in hydrogen, when $n = 1$, is 5.3×10^{-11} m, sometimes called the Bohr radius, and is a good estimate of the normal size of a hydrogen atom. The radii of other orbits, given by the equation above, are:

$$r_2 = 2^2 r_1 = 4 r_1 = 2.1 \times 10^{-10} \text{ m}$$
$$r_3 = 3^2 r_1 = 9 r_1 = 4.8 \times 10^{-10} \text{ m} \qquad \text{(and so on)}$$

Remember that, according to Bohr, an electron can only exist in one of these allowed orbits: no other orbital radius is possible.

To find the speed, v_n, with which the electron moves in its orbit, rearrange equation (2a) to get

$$v_n = \frac{nh}{2\pi m_e \left(\dfrac{n^2 h^2}{4\pi^2 k m_e e^2} \right)}$$
$$= \frac{2\pi k e^2}{nh} \tag{4}$$

Again, substituting known values, we have

$$v_n = \frac{1}{n} \left[\frac{2\pi (9.0 \times 10^9 \text{ N·m}^2/\text{C}^2)(1.6 \times 10^{-19} \text{ C})^2}{6.63 \times 10^{-34} \text{ J·s}} \right]$$
$$= \frac{1}{n} (2.2 \times 10^6) \text{m/s}$$

so that $\quad v_1 = 2.2 \times 10^6$ m/s

$$v_2 = \frac{1}{2} v_1 = 1.1 \times 10^6 \text{ m/s}$$
$$v_3 = \frac{1}{3} v_1 = 7.3 \times 10^5 \text{ m/s} \qquad \text{(and so on)}$$

In its nth orbit, the electron has a definite, characteristic amount of energy, given by the sum of its kinetic and electrical potential energies:

$$E_n = E_k + E_e$$
$$= \frac{1}{2} m_e v_n{}^2 + \left(-\frac{k e^2}{r_n} \right)$$

Substituting values for v_n from equation (4), and for r_n from equation (3), we have

$$E_n = \frac{1}{2} m_e \left(\frac{2\pi k e^2}{nh} \right)^2 - \frac{k e^2}{n^2 h^2 / 4\pi^2 k m_e e^2}$$
$$= \frac{2\pi^2 m_e k^2 e^4}{n^2 h^2} - \frac{4\pi^2 m_e k^2 e^4}{n^2 h^2}$$

$$E_n = -\frac{2\pi^2 m_e k^2 e^4}{n^2 h^2}$$

"I THINK YOU SHOULD BE MORE EXPLICIT HERE IN STEP TWO."

Again, substituting values for the constants, we have

$$E_n = -\frac{1}{n^2}\left[\frac{2\pi^2(9.0\times10^{-31}\text{ kg})(9.0\times10^9\text{ N·m}^2/\text{C}^2)^2(1.6\times10^{-19}\text{ C})^4}{(6.63\times10^{-34}\text{ J·s})^2}\right]$$

$$= -\frac{2.17\times10^{-18}}{n^2}\text{ J}$$

$$E_n = -\frac{13.6}{n^2}\text{ eV}$$

Recall from page 751 the Rydberg expression for this same quantity

$$E_n = -\frac{Rhc}{n^2} = -\frac{13.6\text{ eV}}{n^2}$$

The Rydberg constant had been evaluated theoretically from a model; its accuracy was about 0.02%.

This was probably the most accurate theoretical prediction ever made in the history of science, up to that point.

Thus, the energy levels for the allowed orbits of hydrogen are

$$E_1 = -\frac{13.6}{1^2} = -13.6\text{ eV}$$

$$E_2 = -\frac{13.6}{2^2} = -3.4\text{ eV}$$

$$E_3 = -\frac{13.6}{3^2} = -0.85\text{ eV} \qquad \text{(and so on)}$$

Notice that this model verifies, exactly, the hydrogen atom energy levels that were established on the basis of the evidence from the atom's emission spectrum. All of the energy levels are negative, characteristic of a "bound" system, but the energy of the outer orbits is less negative, and hence greater. The orbit closest to the nucleus ($n = 1$) has the lowest energy (-13.6 eV), the smallest radius (0.53×10^{-10} m), and the greatest electron speed (2.2×10^6 m/s).

It is now possible to draw a complete and detailed energy-level diagram for the hydrogen atom on the next page.

The hydrogen atom's lone electron normally resides in the ground state ($n = 1$). However, by absorbing energy from photons, or in collisions with high speed particles, it may be boosted up to any of the excited states ($n = 2, 3, 4, \ldots$). Once in an excited state, the electron will quickly jump back down to any lower state, giving off the excess energy by creating a photon in the process. The vertical arrows on the diagram represent downward transitions giving rise to the various lines found in the hydrogen spectrum. They are grouped together in series, according to their common lower state; the series are named after famous spectroscopists whose work led to their discovery. A sample problem will illustrate how we can identify these spectral lines.

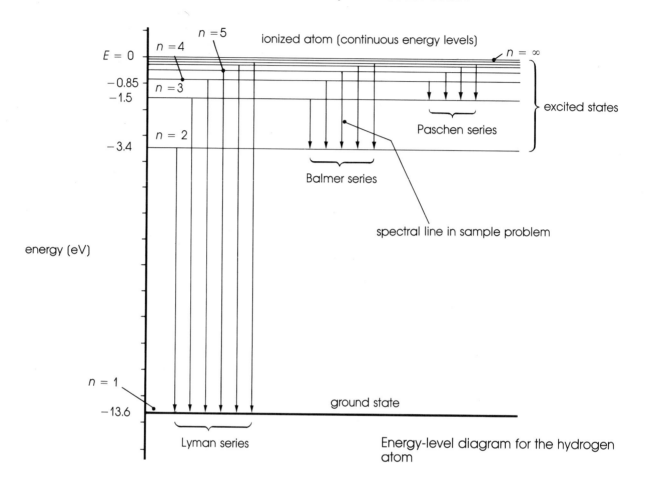

Energy-level diagram for the hydrogen atom

Sample problem

Determine the wavelength of light emitted when a hydrogen atom makes a transition from the $n = 5$ orbit to the $n = 2$ orbit.

For $n = 5$, $E_5 = -\dfrac{13.6}{5^2}$ eV $= -0.54$ eV

For $n = 2$, $E_2 = -\dfrac{13.6}{2^2}$ eV $= -3.40$ eV

$E_p = E_5 - E_2 = -0.54$ eV $- (-3.40$ eV$) = 2.86$ eV

But $\lambda = \dfrac{hc}{E_p} = \dfrac{(6.63 \times 10^{-34} \text{ J·s})(3.00 \times 10^8 \text{ m/s})}{(2.86 \text{ eV})(1.60 \times 10^{-19} \text{ J/eV})}$

$\phantom{\text{But } \lambda} = 4.35 \times 10^{-7}$ m, or 435 nm

This is a violet line in the visible spectrum and the third line in the Balmer series (see diagram above).

Practice

1. What is the wavelength of the line in the Balmer series for which $n = 4$? (488 nm)
2. Determine the wavelength of (a) the most energetic photon that can be emitted by a hydrogen atom in the $n = 7$ state; and (b) the least energetic. (93 nm, 1.2×10^4 nm)
3. What are the energy and wavelength of the least energetic photon that can be absorbed by a hydrogen atom at room temperature? (10.2 eV, 122 nm)

At room temperature, all of the atoms in a sample of atomic hydrogen can be assumed to be in the ground state.

Bohr's theory, based more on a theoretical assumption designed to fit the observations than on any empirical evidence, was quite successful, in that it:

- provided a physical model of the atom, whose internal energy levels matched those of the observed hydrogen spectrum;
- accounted for the stability of atoms. Once an electron had descended to the ground state, there was no lower energy to which it could jump. Thus, it stayed there indefinitely, and the atom was stable;
- applied equally well to other one-electron atoms, such as a singly ionized helium ion.

It was incomplete, however, and failed to stand up to closer examination, in that:

- it broke down when applied to many-electron atoms, because it took no account of the interactions between electrons in orbit but only between an electron and its nucleus;
- with the development of more precise spectroscopic techniques, it became apparent that each of the excited states was not a unique, single energy level but a group of finely separated levels, near the Bohr level. To explain this splitting of levels, it was necessary to introduce modifications to the shape of the Bohr orbits, as well as to the concept that the electron was spinning on an axis as it moved.

Even though the Bohr model had, eventually, to be enhanced, it was a triumph of original thought, and one whose basic features are still useful. It first incorporated the ideas of quantum mechanics into the inner structure of the atom, and provided a basic physical model of the atom for a time when scientific thought would extend into the less tangible realm of electron waves and probability distributions.

19.9 Heisenberg's Uncertainty Principle

Werner Heisenberg

Once scientists had abandoned the well-established realm of classical Newtonian mechanics and entered the new, uncharted world of quantum mechanics, many phenomena were discovered that were both strange and difficult to visualize. In classical mechanics, objects we identify as particles always behave like particles, and things we identify as wave phenomena always exhibit pure wave properties. But the quantum hypotheses of Planck, Einstein, Bohr, etc., created a new dilemma: light, which had traditionally been viewed as a wave phenomenon, was apparently composed of photons possessing distinct particle characteristics; and electrons, to this point thought of as tiny particles with a definite charge and mass, behaved like waves with a definite wavelength, as they moved in orbits within the atom and interacted with objects of atomic dimensions. Clearly, a new way of looking at particle and wave phenomena was needed.

The equations developed in Section 19.8 suggest that we can be very precise about the properties of an electron in the hydrogen atom. We can determine its precise location using the equation for r_n, as well as its exact speed and energy. In 1927, the German physicist Werner Heisenberg (1901-1976) proposed that there was always some inherent uncertainty in the determination of these quantities. It wasn't a question of accuracy of measurements. The uncertainty was inherent, and was due to the quantum-mechanical nature of subatomic particles. An example should illustrate.

Suppose we are measuring the temperature of a cup of hot coffee, using a laboratory thermometer. Of course, when the room temperature thermometer is immersed in the coffee, it extracts some heat from the coffee, and the temperature indicated is that of the mixture of the two, and not the original temperature of the coffee. Using a smaller thermometer will disturb the temperature of the coffee less, thereby producing a more precise reading. In the limiting situation, an infinitely small thermometer would produce an infinitely precise result. There is no inherent lower limit to the size of the thermometer that would limit the precision of the temperature determination.

Suppose, now, we are trying to determine the position of an electron within an atom. To do this, we irradiate it with light of a given wavelength. A photon of wavelength λ will have a momentum h/λ, and we know, from our understanding of the Compton Effect (Section 18.3), that this photon will transfer some of its momentum to the electron when they interact. Thus, the electron will acquire a new and unknown value of momentum just as a consequence of being located by the photon. The more accurately we try to locate the electron, by using a smaller wavelength photon, the less precisely we know its momentum. If we use a longer wavelength photon, so as to be more precise about its momentum, we must be content with being less certain of its location.

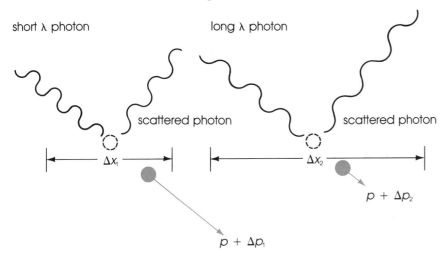

As a result, we are unable to measure both the position and the momentum of the electron with unlimited accuracy. Heisenberg was able to determine the limits of these inherent uncertainties, and to express them mathematically.

If Δx is the uncertainty in a particle's position and Δp is the uncertainty in its momentum, then

$$\Delta x \, \Delta p \geqslant \frac{h}{2\pi}$$

---

where h is Planck's Constant.

Heisenberg's Uncertainty Principle may also be expressed in terms of the uncertainty in simultaneously measuring a particle's energy over a period of time, as

$$\Delta E \, \Delta t \geqslant \frac{h}{2\pi}$$

To see just how significant the implications of Heisenberg's principle are, let us look at examples from both the macroscopic and the microscopic worlds. For a large particle, of mass 1.0 kg, whose momentum, p, is given by the equation $p = mv$,

$$\Delta x \, \Delta p = \Delta x \, m \, \Delta v \geqslant \frac{h}{2\pi}$$

$$\Delta x \, \Delta v \geqslant \frac{h}{2\pi m}$$

$$\geqslant \frac{(6.6 \times 10^{-34} \text{ J·s})}{2\pi \, (1.0 \text{ kg})}$$

$$\geqslant 1.1 \times 10^{-34} \text{ J·s/kg}$$

That is, if we can know the particle's position to within $\pm 10^{-6}$ m, we are permitted to know its velocity to within $\pm 10^{-28}$ m/s. Clearly, such small uncertainties are of no consequence when dealing with such large, macroscopic objects.

On the other hand, for an electron of mass 9.1×10^{-31} kg,

$$\Delta x \, \Delta v \geqslant \frac{h}{2\pi m}$$

$$\geqslant \frac{(6.6 \times 10^{-34} \text{ J·s})}{2\pi \, (9.1 \times 10^{-31} \text{kg})}$$

$$\geqslant 1.2 \times 10^{-4} \text{ J·s/kg}$$

Now, if we confine the uncertainty in the location of the electron to $\pm 10^{-10}$ m (about the size of an atom), we cannot know its velocity within an uncertainty of less than $\pm 10^6$ m/s. These uncertainties are significant enough to invalidate Bohr's picture of a finite electron moving in a well-defined orbit. Clearly, a new look is needed at just what an electron is, and what constitutes an orbit.

19.10 Probability and Determinism

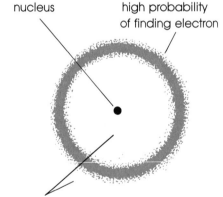

nucleus   high probability
                 of finding electron

low probability of finding electron

The electron cloud, or probability distribution, for the ground state of the hydrogen atom. The cloud is densest — indicating the highest probability — at a distance from the nucleus of 0.53×10^{-10} m, which is just what the Bohr model predicts for the radius of the first orbit. But, unlike the Bohr model, quantum mechanics tells us that the electron can be within or beyond that distance at any given time.

The Newtonian view of mechanics was a deterministic one. Knowing the position and velocity of an object at a particular time, its future position and velocity for all time could be determined by simply knowing the forces acting on it. More than two centuries of success in describing the macroscopic world had made this view of nature quite convincing. Bohr had no reason to believe that the motion of electrons within atoms would be any different.

However, because of the uncertainty in measuring an electron's position and velocity, it becomes impossible to say, for any individual electron, exactly where it is now or where it will be at any future time. Because of its inherent wave properties, an electron in an atom cannot be visualized as a Newtonian particle. Rather than saying where it is, we must be satisfied with describing its location by stating *the probability* that it will be found near any point.

One way of visualizing this concept is to think of the electron existing as a cloud of negative charge distributed around the atom, rather than as a particle moving in a circular orbit. The cloud is more dense in areas of high probability and less dense in areas where the electron is less likely to be found. For the first Bohr orbit of the hydrogen atom ($n = 1$), the cloud is most dense in a spherical shell of radius 5.3×10^{-11} m, the first Bohr radius. Even though this is where the electron is most likely to be, it does have a small statistical probability of being anywhere else.

The "probability cloud" for other allowed Bohr orbits takes on different shapes and dimensions.

The shapes and dimensions of these probability distributions can be determined mathematically. In 1925, working independently, Heisenberg and Erwin Schrödinger devised equivalent mathematical equations whose solutions gave the probability distributions for virtually any problem in quantum mechanics. The expression became known as the Schrödinger equation, and has been immensely successful in the solution of problems of atomic structure. It provides a mathematical interpretation of the physical situation, and gives the values of all measurable quantities such as momentum and energy, as well as the probability for all positions that the particle can occupy. Physicists have spent countless hours applying these techniques to a seemingly endless array of problems. One example is the whole field of solid-state physics, from which semiconductors, the backbone of modern electronics, have developed.

Erwin Schrödinger

19.11 Investigations

Investigation 19.1: The Energy Levels of Hydrogen

Problem:
(a) How can the visible spectrum of hydrogen be observed, using a spectrometer?
(b) How can the wavelengths of lines in the hydrogen spectrum be calculated, using a knowledge of diffraction?

Materials:
diffraction grating spectrometer
high voltage source (transformer or induction coil)
hydrogen gas discharge tube
metre stick

Procedure:
1. Examine the apparatus that has been set up for you. Note each part and draw a properly labelled diagram. Please do not move the collimator or telescope from their mounts; the adjustment and focus can be quite time consuming.
2. Tape a piece of paper under the telescope mount, ensuring that the mount can move freely.
3. Move the gas discharge tube so that it is lined up as closely as possible with the slit in the collimator. Place the black shield so

that light does not radiate in the direction of the telescope. Turn on the high voltage source. CAUTION: DO NOT TOUCH THE LEADS TO THE SOURCE WHILE IT IS OPERATING.

4. Turn off the room lights and adjust the telescope mount so that the telescope is in a direct line with the slit. Sight the telescope carefully so that the hairline aligns with the central maximum, a bright line. Slight adjustment of the gas discharge tube may still be necessary.

5. Move the telescope to one side and locate the three brightest lines (i.e., violet, green, and red). If you have good eyesight, the room is very dark, and the equipment is adjusted properly, you may see a fainter violet line adjacent to the bright violet line. Move the telescope to the other side of the central maximum and locate the same set of spectral lines.

6. Return to the centre line and make a mark with a sharp pencil in the notch on your paper. Move the telescope to one side and make similar marks at the positions of each of the spectral lines you locate. Repeat on the other side of the central maximum.

7. Measure the distance from the central line to the mark you have made for each spectral line. Average the distances on either side of the central maximum.

8. Turn off the power supply. The useful life of the hydrogen tube is only a few hours. After this time, lines in addition to hydrogen lines will begin to appear in the spectrum, owing to contamination of the gas by elements in the materials from which the tube is made.

Calculations:

1. Remember from your previous work on diffraction of light by a diffraction grating, that the wavelength of the light is given by

$$\lambda = \frac{d\Delta x}{L}$$

where d = separation of the slits, causing diffraction
Δx = distance from central maximum to first bright fringe in the diffraction pattern
L = distance from slits to screen on which diffraction pattern is viewed

The teacher will give values for d and L for the particular spectrometer you used.

2. Using the relationship above, calculate the wavelength of the photons in each spectral line observed.

3. Determine the energy, in electronvolts, of the photons comprising each spectral line observed.

4. Calculate the energies of the electrons in each of the first six allowed energy levels for hydrogen, using the relationship
$$E_n = -\frac{13.6}{n^2}\ eV$$

5. Determine the energy of the first four photons in the Balmer series, in which electrons descend to the $n = 2$ state from any higher state.

6. Determine the energy levels involved in the transition leading to each of the spectral lines you have observed. Compare the energy of each photon, as calculated, with its theoretical value.

7. Record all of the observed and calculated data in a table, as shown.

Colour of spectral line	Distance to centre line x		Average value of x	Wave-length $\lambda = \frac{d\Delta x}{L}$	Energy $E = \frac{h\,c}{\lambda}$	Transition involved
	left	right	m	nm	eV	
	m	m				

19.12 Review

Discussion

1. What major features must an atomic model possess, in order to account for the way in which alpha particles are scattered by a gold foil?
2. In Rutherford's planetary atom, what keeps electrons from flying off into space?
3. What are the major discrepancies between the Rutherford model's explanation of the emission of light by atoms and the actual observed emission of light?
4. Draw an energy-level diagram that represents the findings of the Franck-Hertz experiment.

The National Research Council, established by an Act of Parliament in 1916, is responsible for keeping Canada at the forefront of scientific progress. The NRC, run entirely by scientists, has made Canada a pioneer in government subsidization of scientific research. It specializes in scientific research that is not being done for industrial or corporate gain, such as space research and the invention of ingenious devices to assist the handicapped.

"WE HAVE REASON TO BELIEVE BINGLEMAN
IS AN IRRATIONAL NUMBER HIMSELF."

5. A spectroscope is used to examine the white light that has been passed through a sample of mercury vapour. Dark lines, characteristic of the absorption spectrum of mercury, are observed.
   (a) What eventually happens to the energy the mercury vapour absorbs from the white light?
   (b) Why, then, are the absorption lines dark?

6. Many substances emit visible radiation when illuminated with ultraviolet light, a phenomenon known as fluorescence. The emitted light has a wavelength that is the same as, or longer than, that of the illuminating light. Account for this result, using the Bohr theory.

7. Using a development similar to that for hydrogen, derive an expression for the energy levels of the electron in a singly ionized helium atom. (The helium nucleus has a charge of $+2e$.)

8. When a broad spectrum of light passes through a sample of hydrogen gas at room temperature, absorption lines that correspond to the Lyman series *only* are observed. Why do we not observe any of the other series?

9. Draw a scale diagram of the first five circular Bohr orbits of the hydrogen atom.

10. Discuss the difficulty in explaining Bohr's theory of electron orbits, and electron velocities in these orbits, in view of the limitations imposed by the uncertainty principle.

11. How accurately can a particle's position and velocity be known, simultaneously?

Problems

12. If the alpha particles approaching a certain nucleus with an aiming error b are scattered by 135°, through what range of angles are those particles scattered that have a smaller aiming error?

13. In a gold foil scattering experiment, 5 alpha particles out of 12 000 are scattered by an angle greater than 5°. How many particles would be scattered by greater than 5°
   (a) if the thickness of the foil were doubled?
   (b) if the foil were made 100 times as thick?

14. What is the closest distance of approach of a 4.5 MeV alpha particle, of mass 6.6×10^{-27} kg, to a fixed gold nucleus of charge $+79e$?

15. How many times as closely can an alpha particle of a given energy approach an aluminum nucleus as it can a gold nucleus? ($Z_{al} = 13$, $Z_{au} = 79$)

16. What is the energy difference between the two energy levels in a sodium atom that give rise to the emission of a 589 nm photon?

17. An electron whose kinetic energy is 3.9 eV collides with a free mercury atom. What will be the kinetic energy of the electron after the collision?

18. Electrons are accelerated in a Franck-Hertz experiment through mercury vapour, with a potential difference of 7.0 V. What are the energies of all the photons that may be emitted by the mercury vapour?

19. If an atom emits a photon of wavelength 684 nm, how much energy does the atom lose?

20. Calculate the ratio of the gravitational force between the proton and electron in the ground state of a hydrogen atom to the electrical force between them. Can either force be ignored? Explain.

21. Assuming that the hydrogen atom is spherical, by what factor is its volume greater when in its first excited state than when in its ground state?

22. Electrons are accelerated through hydrogen gas at room temperature, in a Franck-Hertz type experiment, by a potential difference of 12.3 V. What wavelengths of light can be expected to be emitted by the hydrogen?

23. What energy is needed to ionize a hydrogen atom from the $n = 2$ state? How likely is this to occur? Explain.

24. What values of n are involved in the transition that gives rise to the emission of a 388 nm photon from hydrogen gas?

25. Determine the wavelength and frequency of the fourth Balmer line ($n = 6$ to $n = 2$) for hydrogen.

26. Determine the energies of all the photons that could possibly be emitted by a large sample of hydrogen atoms, all initially excited to the $n = 5$ state.

27. What would be the value of n in order for a hydrogen atom to have a Bohr orbit of radius 1.0 mm? What would be its energy in that orbit?

Numerical Answers to Review Problems

12. $\pm 135° < \theta < \pm 180°$
13. (a) 10 (b) 500
14. 5.1×10^{-14} m
15. 6.1 times
16. 2.1 eV
17. 3.9 eV
18. 4.9 eV, 6.7 eV, 1.8 eV
19. 1.82 eV
20. 4.4×10^{-40}:1
21. 64
22. 122 nm, 103 nm, 654 nm
23. 3.4 eV
24. $n = 8$ to $n = 2$
25. 412 nm, 7.3×10^{14} Hz
26. 0.31 eV, 0.65 eV, 0.96 eV, 1.9 eV, 2.6 eV, 2.9 eV, 10.2 eV, 12.1 eV, 12.8 eV, 13.1 eV
27. $n = 4.3 \times 10^5$, -7.4×10^{-11} eV

20 Elementary Particles

Our study of physics began with the fundamental properties of matter at rest and in motion. Later we considered the basic interactions of matter and, finally, the most important relationships between matter and energy. In this chapter we discuss the properties of the fundamental, or elementary, particles that are the ultimate building blocks of matter.

By 1930, scientists had identified four subatomic particles: the electron, the proton, the neutron, and the photon. With the construction and development of particle accelerators, more subatomic (elementary) particles were discovered. Since 1970, the existence of over 200 such particles has been firmly established, and several laws governing the relations among them have been developed. Although no complete theory exists as yet, experimental and theoretical research is progressing on a large scale at high-energy research facilities around the world. Time and research should tell us which particles and interactions are truly fundamental.

20.1 Radioactive Decay

The study of elementary particles begins with the work of Rutherford. In 1898, Ernest (later Lord) Rutherford, a physicist from New Zealand working at McGill University, Montreal, took up the study of radioactivity. He discovered and named the two particles emitted in radioactive emission: alpha (α) and beta (β) particles. A year later, Paul Villard, a French physicist, discovered the third emission, gamma (γ) rays.

Properties of Radioactive Emissions

Alpha (α) Particles
- They are positively charged particles (actually the nuclei of helium ions).
- They are ejected at a high speed but have a range of only a few centimetres in air.
- They are stopped by an ordinary sheet of thin aluminum foil.

Beta (β) Particles
- They are streams of high-energy electrons.
- They are ejected with various speeds, sometimes approaching the speed of light (3.00×10^8 m/s).

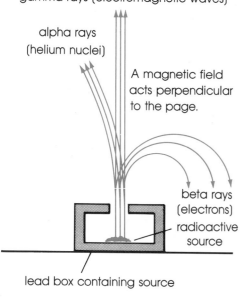

gamma rays (electromagnetic waves)

alpha rays (helium nuclei)

A magnetic field acts perpendicular to the page.

beta rays (electrons)

radioactive source

lead box containing source

This is a composite diagram: it is not possible to study all three particles at the same time in the same apparatus.

- Some beta particles are able to penetrate several millimetres of aluminum.

Gamma (γ) Rays
- They are electromagnetic radiations with very short wavelengths.
- Their wavelengths and energies can vary.
- High-energy gamma rays can penetrate at least 30 cm of lead or 2 km of air.

Based on their studies of radioactive decay, at McGill University in the period 1899-1906, Rutherford and his associate Frederick Soddy summarized the rules for alpha and beta decay.

Alpha Decay

The alpha decay of radon will serve to illustrate the general properties of alpha decay. The equation for the alpha decay of radon is stated as follows:

$$^{222}_{86}\text{Rn} \longrightarrow {}^{218}_{84}\text{Po} + {}^{4}_{2}\text{He} \text{ (α particle)}$$

The alpha particle is represented as ${}^{4}_{2}\text{He}$ since it is a helium nucleus. Note that the atomic number of the radon nucleus decreases by two, since two protons are lost, and that the mass number decreases by four, since two neutrons as well as the two protons are lost. The arrow in a nuclear equation indicates the direction of the reaction and also may be thought of as an equals sign. The sum of the atomic numbers on the right side equals the atomic number on the left side, and the sum of the mass numbers on the right equals the mass number on the left.

In general, for alpha decay:

$$^{A}_{Z}\text{X} \longrightarrow {}^{A-4}_{Z-2}\text{Y} + {}^{4}_{2}\text{He}$$

parent nucleus → daughter nucleus + α particle (helium nucleus)

Symbols for atoms are usually written as shown.
$${}^{A}_{Z}\text{X}$$
where X is the atom's symbol
Z is its atomic number
A is its atomic mass number

Beta Decay

When a beta particle is emitted by a radioactive element, the atomic number of the nucleus increases by one, but the mass number remains the same. For example, in the beta decay of sodium-24,

$$^{24}_{11}\text{Na} \longrightarrow {}^{24}_{12}\text{Mg} + {}^{0}_{-1}\text{e}$$

Beta particles are electrons with a high speed and are represented as ${}^{0}_{-1}\text{e}$, since they have a charge of -1 but negligible mass (when compared with the nucleus).

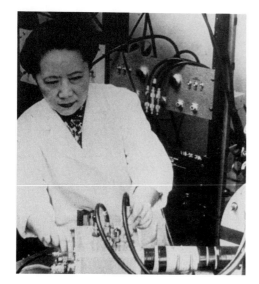

Chien-Shiung Wu (1912–   ) is an experimental physicist and professor at Columbia University. In 1956, her most celebrated experiment overturned one of the basic laws of physics — the Law of Conservation of Parity. (The law stated that a phenomenon of nature is symmetrical and looks the same whether observed directly or in a mirror, with left and right reversed.) Two Chinese-born, American theoretical physicists, the Nobel Prize winners Tsung-Dao Lee and Chen Ning Yang, had concluded in 1956 that the parity conservation principle would not apply when dealing with the weak interactions of subatomic particles. Dr. Wu, an expert on beta decay, designed and performed an experiment to test their hypothesis. She placed a radioactive cobalt-60 source in a strong magnetic field and cooled it almost to absolute zero. As the cobalt-60 decayed, most of the emitted electrons were observed to go in only one direction, opposite to the direction in which the nucleus of each atom was spinning. "This taught us a lesson," says Dr. Wu, "never to take the so-called self-evident laws for granted. With this discovery, nature gives us a new tool to pry into the phenomena of weak interactions."

In the decay process a neutron disappears, a proton appears at the same time in the nucleus, and a beta particle is emitted from the nucleus. This accounts for the fact that the atomic number increases by one though the mass number remains constant. (The total number of particles in the nucleus remains the same.)

In general, for beta decay:

$$^A_Z X \longrightarrow\ ^{\ \ A}_{Z+1} Y +\ ^{\ 0}_{-1} e$$

$$\begin{matrix} \text{parent} \\ \text{nucleus} \end{matrix} \longrightarrow \begin{matrix} \text{daughter} \\ \text{nucleus} \end{matrix} + \begin{matrix} \beta \text{ particle} \\ \text{(electron)} \end{matrix}$$

Gamma Radiation

Gamma radiation usually accompanies alpha and beta decay. It consists of photons that have no mass or electric charge. Gamma rays by themselves produce no changes in the atomic number or the atomic mass of the nucleus. Gamma rays are represented by the symbol $^0_0\gamma$.

$$^A_Z X \longrightarrow\ ^A_Z X +\ ^0_0\gamma$$

Alpha decay and beta decay may be illustrated by a series of naturally occurring transmutations called the uranium-lead **decay series**. The nuclear equations for the first five of these transmutations are:

$$\begin{aligned}
\alpha\text{-decay} \quad &^{238}_{92}U \longrightarrow\ ^{234}_{90}Th +\ ^4_2He +\ ^0_0\gamma \\
\beta\text{-decay} \quad &^{234}_{90}Th \longrightarrow\ ^{234}_{91}Pa +\ ^{\ 0}_{-1}e +\ ^0_0\gamma \\
\beta\text{-decay} \quad &^{234}_{91}Pa \longrightarrow\ ^{234}_{92}U +\ ^{\ 0}_{-1}e +\ ^0_0\gamma \\
\alpha\text{-decay} \quad &^{234}_{92}U \longrightarrow\ ^{230}_{90}Th +\ ^4_2He +\ ^0_0\gamma \\
\alpha\text{-decay} \quad &^{230}_{90}Th \longrightarrow\ ^{226}_{88}Ra +\ ^4_2He +\ ^0_0\gamma
\end{aligned}$$

20.2 Conservation Laws Applied to Alpha and Beta Decay

The old law of conservation of mass was incorporated into a broader and more effective law of conservation of energy when Einstein's mass-energy relationship ($E = mc^2$) was included (see Section 17.6). We will now apply this new conservation law to the kinetic energies of the particles emitted by radioactive substances.

The energy of an alpha particle can be determined from the mass of the original radioactive nucleus, the mass of the alpha particle, and the mass of the final nucleus. The alpha particle and the final nucleus together have a mass slightly smaller than that of the original nucleus. The energy equivalence of the missing mass is equal to the kinetic energy of the emitted alpha particle.

For example, in the decay of thorium-232, an alpha particle (helium-4) is emitted, and the final nucleus is radium-228. All the thorium-232 nuclei have identical masses, as do all radium-228 nuclei and all alpha particles. Without measuring the masses of the nuclei directly, one can predict, using the Law of Conservation of Energy, that when thorium-232 emits an alpha particle, the mass deficit should be equal to the energy of the alpha particle. In theory, the alpha particles emitted by thorium-232 should all have the same kinetic energy.

This prediction was verified in the 1920s by a series of experiments carried out to measure the energy of the emitted alpha particles. It was found that the alpha particles from thorium-232 could all penetrate 2.8 cm of air. In the case of polonium-212, the particles all penetrated 8.6 cm of air, while those from radium-222 penetrated 3.3 cm. Thus, it could be concluded that since the penetration is directly related to the energy of the particle, the alpha particles from a specific radioactive source all have the same energy.

For alpha particles, the new law of conservation of energy worked very well, as it does to the present day. But this was not so for beta particles. If the same reasoning is applied to beta decay, the particles emitted from identical radioactive nuclei should each have the same energy. It was clear, as early as 1900, that this was not the case. Beta particles could be given off with any value of kinetic energy, up to a maximum amount. In each beta decay there was a certain loss of mass, which should have been equivalent to the kinetic energy of the emitted beta particle. But it was found that the kinetic energy of the beta particle had a range of values, though never greater than the energy equivalent of the mass decrease.

According to the Law of Conservation of Energy, no beta particle should have a kinetic energy less than the energy equivalent of the mass decrease — the maximum kinetic energy of the beta particle should also be the minimum kinetic energy. However, this did not appear to be the case in the early 1900s. Beta particles were regularly given off with less kinetic energy than predicted. In fact, very few beta particles have the predicted maximum kinetic energy that the Law of Conservation of Energy requires. (On average, the most common value is one-third of the maximum.) On the surface, it appeared that the Law of Conservation of Energy failed for beta particle production. This was an alarming conclusion to the physicists of the 1920s.

$$^{232}_{90}\text{Th} \rightarrow {}^{228}_{88}\text{Ra} + {}^{4}_{2}\text{He}$$

Actually, there were some irregularities in the alpha particle penetration. Later it was found that the original radioactive nucleus, like orbiting electrons, could exist in a number of excited states. When an alpha particle is emitted from a nucleus in an excited state, the alpha particle carries away most of this extra energy. Since the normal condition of the nucleus, like that of an atom, is to be in its ground state, the vast majority of emitted alpha particles have the same energy.

The Pauli Exclusion Principle

As you may recall from studying chemistry, electrons move around a nucleus in certain "allowed" orbits. These are characterized by four quantum numbers: n, l, m and s. Electron energies are largely determined by the quantum number n, which also determines the average radius of an electron's orbit. The shape and orientation of the orbit are determined by the l and m quantum numbers, and the spin by the s quantum number. *Only two electrons having opposite spins may occupy the same orbit.* The illustration shows this for the atoms of hydrogen (H), helium (He), and sodium (Na). The principle expressing this, often called the **Pauli Exclusion Principle**, was first formulated by Wolfgang Pauli in 1925.

In the nucleus, neutrons and protons also must obey the rules of quantum physics: all known particles having half-integer, intrinsic angular momentum (or spin) obey Pauli's principle, including quarks.

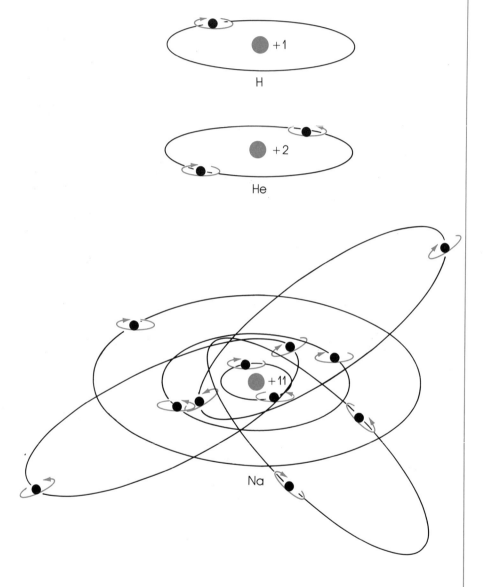

According to the Pauli Exclusion Principle, only two electrons of opposite spin may occupy the same orbit. The illustration shows how the atoms of hydrogen (H), helium (He), and sodium (Na) are constructed on this basis.

In 1931, Wolfgang Pauli (of Exclusion Principle fame) suggested an explanation. He proposed that if the beta particle did not carry off all the available energy, the remainder might be given to a second particle. But what would the properties of this mysterious second particle be?

To begin with, we should recall that when beta particles are produced, a neutron in the nucleus is converted to a proton. We can symbolize the neutron as $_0^1\text{n}$, the proton as $_{+1}^1\text{p}$, and the electron as $_{-1}^0\text{e}$. The reaction had been written as follows before Pauli's particle was predicted:

$$_0^1\text{n} \longrightarrow {}_{+1}^1\text{p} + {}_{-1}^0\text{e}$$

Since the neutron was neutral, to satisfy the Law of Conservation of Electrical Charge Pauli's particle also had to be neutral. Further, a charged particle would be easily detectable, and the new particle had not been observed.

When a neutron breaks down into a proton and an electron, the loss in mass is equivalent to approximately one-half the mass of an electron. In fact, Pauli's particle must have been considerably lighter, since the emitted electron usually gets most of the energy and sometimes all of it. As physicists recalculated their estimates of the mass of Pauli's particle, it became clear that it, like the photon, was a massless particle — it had a rest mass of zero.

Pauli's particle thus emerged as a neutral, massless particle. Enrico Fermi, the great Italian physicist, suggested that this particle be called the **neutrino**, which in Italian means "little neutral one". The name has been used ever since. The neutrino is usually given the symbol ν, which is the Greek letter "nu". Now the equation for neutron decay can be written:

$$_0^1\text{n} \longrightarrow {}_{+1}^1\text{p} + {}_{-1}^0\text{e} + \nu$$

The neutrino, proposed by Pauli and supported by the subsequent work of Fermi, received a mixed reception in the world of physics. To some it appeared to be a mythical particle created to save the Law of Conservation of Energy. But this was not the only conservation law saved by the neutrino.

When a neutron is at rest, its momentum is zero. When it breaks down, the emitted electron will have momentum, as will the recoiling proton. According to the Law of Conservation of Momentum, the electron should shoot off in one direction and the proton in exactly the opposite direction. But the proton should have a much lower velocity, because of its greater mass, very much like a bullet and a gun when the gun is fired. This is not what happens. The electron and proton are both emitted at an angle, which means that the electron-proton system has momentum after the breakdown. Momentum is apparently created out of nothing, which the Law of Conservation of Momentum does not permit. However, if

In other words, neutrons decay inside the nucleus. But if neutrons decay inside the nucleus, do individual neutrons in a free state break down and change into protons? In the 1950s, when large quantities of free neutrons were available in atomic reactors, it was found that neutron decay does occur (the half-life is 12 min).

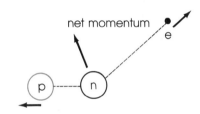

Momentum not conserved

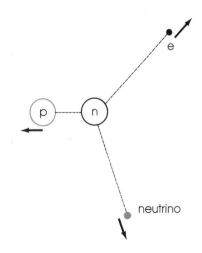

Momentum conserved by the addition of a neutrino

Cosmic Gall
John Updike

Neutrinos, they are very small.
  They have no charge and have no
    mass
And do not interact at all.
The earth is just a silly ball
  To them, through which they simply
    pass,
Like dustmaids down a drafty hall
  Or photons through a sheet of glass.
  They snub the most exquisite gas,
Ignore the most substantial wall,
  Cold-shoulder steel and sounding
    brass,
Insult the stallion in his stall,
  And, scorning barriers of class,
Infiltrate you and me! Like tall
And painless guillotines; they fall
  Down through our heads into the
    grass.
At night, they enter at Nepal
  And pierce the lover and his lass
From underneath the bed—you call
  It wonderful; I call it crass.

a neutrino is formed and comes off in a direction that will make the net momentum of the system zero, the Law of Conservation of Momentum is upheld.

Another conservation law to be considered is the Law of Conservation of Angular Momentum. As mentioned in Chapter 19, particles have energy and angular momentum because of their spin. Using the quantum scale of measurement, the proton and electron both have a spin of one-half. Angular momentum can, however, exist in two variations, clockwise and counterclockwise. The spin of an electron or proton can be either way, and can therefore be represented as $+1/2$ or $-1/2$. If angular momentum is to be conserved in a system that contains a number of particles, the total spin of the system before the interaction must be equal to the sum of the spins of the individual particles after the interaction.

In beta decay, the neutron, proton, and electron all have spins of either $+1/2$ or $-1/2$. If, for example, the neutron has a spin of $+1/2$, the spins of the proton and the electron can be $+1/2$ and $+1/2$; or $+1/2$ and $-1/2$; or $-1/2$ and $+1/2$; or $-1/2$ and $-1/2$. The net possible spins after the neutron breaks down are $+1$, 0, and -1, respectively, but never $+1/2$, the original angular momentum of the neutron. In other words, the Law of Conservation of Angular Momentum is violated. On the other hand, if a neutrino is added, with a spin of $+1/2$ or $-1/2$, the law holds. Using the example above, if the neutron has a spin of $+1/2$, the proton, electron, and neutrino can have spins of $+1/2$, $+1/2$, and $-1/2$, respectively, so that net spin of the three particles taken together is $+1/2$, the same as that of the original neutron.

In summary, it appears that the neutrino is required in order to save no less than three conservation laws, those of energy, linear momentum, and angular momentum.

The strength of these arguments slowly convinced physicists that this mysterious, ghostlike particle must be there, even though it could not be detected. In 1956, a particle with zero rest mass, travelling at the speed of light (like a photon), with linear momentum and a spin of $1/2$ was observed. The existence of the neutrino had been experimentally verified.

20.3 The Positron and Antiparticles

In 1927, Paul Dirac, an English physicist, worked out a mathematical model for the electron. He predicted that an electron should exist in two different forms, both exactly the same except that one would be positive and the other negative. While studying cosmic rays, an American physicist, Carl Anderson, found particles which had the same properties as electrons except that they curved in the opposite direction in a magnetic field. Anderson had found Dirac's positively charged electron, which he called the **positron**.

The electron and the positron are usually called the negative electron and positive electron, respectively, and are represented by the symbols e^- and e^+. The positron is also called an **antielectron**, because it is exactly the same as the electron except that its charge is "anti", or opposite. These opposite particles, the electron and the positron, are referred to as **antiparticles**. It is now the practice to represent an antiparticle by the symbol of the particle, with a horizontal line above it. For example, the symbol for a positron is $\bar{e}$.

In 1934, it was found that certain artificially created radioactive atomic nuclei produced positrons when they decayed. The first such nucleus was discovered by Frédéric and Irène Joliot-Curie, a husband-wife team of French physicists. (Irène Joliot-Curie was a daughter of Madame Curie.) When bombarding aluminum atoms with alpha particles, they found that the radioactive product, phosphorus-30, emitted positrons spontaneously as it decayed to silicon-30, as follows:

$$^{30}_{15}P \longrightarrow {}^{30}_{14}Si + {}^{0}_{+1}\bar{e}$$

In the reaction, the electric charge is conserved ($14 + 1 = 15$) and the mass number, or number of particles in the nucleus, remains constant at 30. On the other hand, the atomic number of the lighter nucleus, silicon-30 ($+14$), is one less than that of phosphorus-30 ($+15$), indicating that the silicon-30 nucleus contains one proton less. For this to occur, a proton must have been converted into a neutron when the positron was emitted, reducing the atomic number by 1 and leaving the mass number unchanged. This is exactly the reverse of normal beta decay, where a neutron is converted into a proton when an electron is emitted. To distinguish between the two types of beta decay, β^- **decay** is the name applied to the process in which an electron is ejected, and β^+ **decay** is the process in which the emitted particle is a positron.

Just as in β^- decay, another massless particle with no charge and a spin of $1/2$ must be emitted. But this particle is the antiparticle of the one that must exist if the laws of conservation are valid for electron emission. It turns out that the ghostlike particle postulated for electron emission was not the neutrino ν, but its antiparticle, the **antineutrino** $\bar{\nu}$.

Cosmic rays are an intensely energetic form of radiation bombarding Earth from outer space.

Irène Joliot-Curie (1897–1956) was the daughter of Pierre and Marie Curie. After World War I, she went to work in her mother's laboratory, where she met and later married Frédéric Joliot (1900–1958), a researcher interested in fundamental atomic and nuclear processes. In 1933 Irène and Frédéric Joliot-Curie determined the conditions necessary for the formation of electrons and positrons. A year later, they demonstrated that artificial isotopes could be produced by alpha particle bombardment. This discovery paved the way for the production of artificial radioactive elements. For their work, they shared the Nobel Prize for Chemistry in 1935.

The Joliot-Curies continued their research work during World War II, as well as taking part in the French resistance. After the war they were active in the French Atomic Energy Commission. Irène Joliot-Curie died in 1956 of leukemia, the same disease that had taken her mother's life. In both cases, the leukemia is considered to have resulted directly from their lifelong work with radioactive materials, without the benefit of adequate safety precautions.

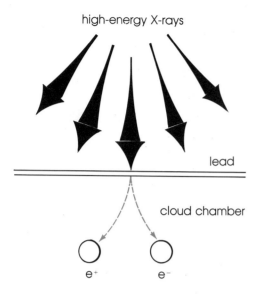

high-energy X-rays

lead

cloud chamber

e+   e−

Electromagnetic radiation causes pair production to occur in dense materials such as lead. The resulting pair of particles can then be seen as tracks in a cloud chamber or other detector.

Examples of nuclear equations for each type of decay are:

β⁻ decay

$$^{14}_{6}C \rightarrow \, ^{14}_{7}N + \, ^{0}_{-1}e + \bar{\nu}$$

electron   antineutrino

β⁺ decay

$$^{15}_{8}O \rightarrow \, ^{15}_{7}N + \, ^{0}_{+1}\bar{e} + \nu$$

positron   neutrino

As mentioned previously, Carl Anderson was the first to observe the positron. In his experiment, high-energy cosmic rays were passed through a cloud chamber, and two types of particle tracks were observed. Cosmic rays consist of highly energetic X-ray photons and charged particles from extraterrestrial sources. When these X-ray photons collided with a thin lead plate, electrons and positrons were created simultaneously in a process called **pair production**. This was not β⁺ decay. In pair production, a photon interacts with a nucleus, the photon ceases to exist, and an "electron pair" (an electron and a positron) is created.

A photon cannot spontaneously decay into an electron pair without the presence of a nucleus. The latter is required for the conservation of energy and momentum. Also, for pair production to occur, the photon must have a minimum energy of 1.022 MeV. This can be determined as follows. If energy is conserved:

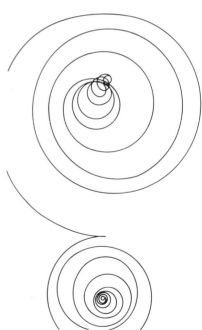

Cloud chamber photograph and sketch showing pair production of an electron and a positron. Note that since they are opposite in charge they spiral in opposite directions when acted on by the same magnetic field.

$$hv \geq m_{e^-}c^2 + m_{e^+}c^2$$

rest mass   rest mass
of electron   of position

$$hv \geq 0.511 \text{ MeV} + 0.511 \text{ MeV} \geq 1.022 \text{ MeV}$$

$$m_e c^2 = \frac{(9.1 \times 10^{-31} \text{ kg})(3.0 \times 10^8 \text{ m/s})^2}{(1.6 \times 10^{-19} \text{ J/eV})}$$
$$= 0.511 \times 10^6 \text{ eV}$$

But if positrons are formed in β^+ decay and in pair production, why are they not normally found in nature? The positron, like the electron, is a stable particle. If left on its own it will never undergo any change, as far as we know. But the positron is not alone in the universe. There are always other particles around, including electrons. Under normal conditions, a positron will collide with an electron within a millionth of a second. When particle meets antiparticle both cease to exist, and energy in the form of photons is emitted. This process is known as **pair annihilation**, the direct conversion of (rest) mass into electromagnetic energy. It is the inverse of pair production, in a manner of speaking. As noted in Section 17.6, these two processes are striking examples of the mass-energy equivalence predicted by Einstein.

As determined above, the energy equivalence of the electron is 0.511 MeV. Thus when pair annihilation occurs, 1.022 MeV of energy must be liberated. This is found to be true experimentally, but two photons, each with 0.511 MeV of energy, are usually emitted — not one photon of 1.022 MeV, as one might expect. In an electron-positron system, the conservation laws of energy, momentum, angular momentum, and charge must hold. We have already seen energy and charge to be conserved. Photons have no charge, but they do have linear momentum and angular momentum. In order that the total linear momentum and the total angular momentum of the system do not change, the two photons must be emitted in specific directions and with appropriate spins. For example, if the positron and electron have spins of $+1/2$ and $-1/2$, respectively, the angular momentum of the system will remain constant (zero) if the photons have spins of $+1/2$ and $-1/2$.

Having discovered positrons and predicted antineutrinos, physicists began to speculate about other kinds of antiparticles. In fact, it was possible to imagine a world of antimatter, where positrons moved in Bohr orbits around nuclei containing negatively charged antiprotons. It would be difficult to visibly distinguish such an antimatter world from our world, because the physical behaviour of antimatter atoms would be the same as that of ordinary atoms. However, if antimatter and ordinary matter came into contact, they would annihilate each other with an explosive release of energy, just as the positron and the electron do in pair annihilation.

Since an antielectron, or positron, exists, then in theory an antiproton should also exist. Since a proton is 1840 times as massive

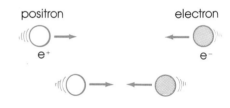

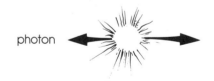

electromagnetic radiation

The annihilation process:
$e^+ + e^- \rightarrow \gamma + \gamma$
for a slowly moving
positron and electron

Lise Meitner (1878–1968) was born and educated in Vienna. She studied physics, chemistry, and philosophy at the University of Vienna where she received her doctorate in physics in 1906. Upon graduation in 1907, she attended Max Planck's lectures in Berlin and joined Otto Hahn in research into radioactivity. After a break in her scientific work, while she served as an X-ray nurse in the Austrian army during World War I, Lise Meitner was given the task of establishing a department of radioactive physics at the Kaiser Wilhelm Institute in Berlin.

Because she was Jewish, Lise Meitner left Germany in the summer of 1938 to settle in Sweden. But she continued her theoretical work in association with Otto Hahn for over thirty years. Together, they discovered and named two chemical elements: practinium and thorium C; studied the properties of alpha and gamma radiation; investigated the products of the neutron bombardment of uranium; took the first known pictures of a positron track; and were the first to observe pair-production.

After Hahn and Fritz Strassmann had identified lighter barium in neutron-bombarded uranium, Lise Meitner, with her nephew, Otto Frisch, explained the process of nuclear fission. She retired to Cambridge, England, in 1960. In 1966 she was awarded the Enrico Fermi Award, along with Hahn and Strassmann, for the joint research that led to the discovery of uranium fission, the process involved in nuclear reactors and atomic bombs.

as an electron, the energy required to produce an antiproton would have to be 1840 times greater than that of the cosmic rays that produce positrons, or about two thousand million electronvolts (2 GeV)!

Physicists had to wait until extremely high-energy particle accelerators were built before they could generate antiprotons. When these accelerators were built, the expected results occurred, and a host of other particles and antiparticles were observed. Before describing and classifying these particles, we will describe the construction and operation of various types of accelerators used in high-energy physics.

20.4 Particle Accelerators

The first scientist to use high-energy particles to explore the atom was Ernest Rutherford. In his famous alpha particle scattering experiment (Section 19.2), Rutherford began the period of exploration of the properties of nature at very small distances. All nuclear physics research prior to 1932 was performed with alpha particles originating from naturally occurring radioactive elements such as polonium. Although natural alpha particles have kinetic energies as high as 8 MeV, it is not possible to form these particles into a well-defined beam with equal energies. To do so, the quantity of alpha particles has to be reduced to the point where they are of little use. Devices were needed that would generate large electrical potential differences in order to accelerate ions to the desired energies.

A brief review of Section 15.5 is necessary before proceeding. If a negatively charged particle, such as a hydrogen ion, starting from rest at a grounded plate, accelerates towards a positive plate with an electrical potential of $+ 1$ V, the particle arrives at the plate with an energy of 1 eV. If the particle is a negative hydrogen ion, it will be travelling at 5.0×10^4 km/h (approximately 14 km/s) when it reaches the plate. If the positive plate has an electrical potential of 1 MV, the same particle will have an energy of 1 MeV and a speed of 5.0×10^7 km/h. These energies depend only on the electrical potential difference; they are independent of the nature of the path the particle traces as it moves through the electrical field.

Today there are accelerators that give particles energies of over 500 thousand million electronvolts, or 500 GeV. An accelerator called the Tevatron has been designed to force two beams of particles to smash into each other with energies of 2 trillion (two thousand thousand million) electronvolts, or 2 TeV, the root of the Tevatron's name.

The escalation of accelerator energies over the past five decades has enabled physicists to probe ever deeper into the fundamental nature of matter. So the history of particle physics is not just the domain of the theorists. It is also a history of the inventions of applied physicists and engineers who have built the accelerators and detectors, which in turn have made the discoveries and theories of particle physics possible.

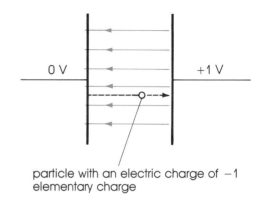

particle with an electric charge of −1 elementary charge

Constant-voltage Accelerators

The first successful experiments with accelerated ions were performed by J.D. Cockcroft and E.T.S. Walton, in 1932 at Cambridge University, England. The high-voltage source for their apparatus

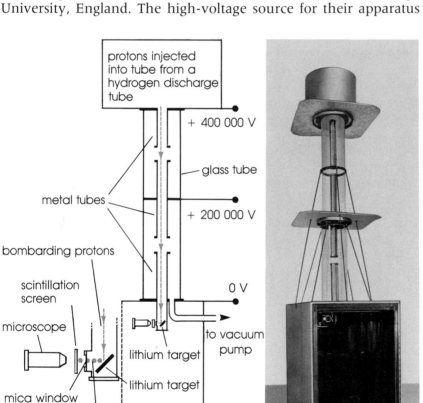

The Cockcroft-Walton proton accelerator

The large "tank" at the rear contains Atomic Energy of Canada's tandem Van de Graaff accelerator.

was a four-stage voltage multiplier powered by a 200 000 V high-voltage transformer. Using this apparatus, they were able to accelerate protons to energies of 710 keV. At these energies, protons move at extremely high speeds (800 km/s). The physicists directed a beam of high-energy protons at a lithium target, as illustrated on the previous page. A high-energy proton penetrated a lithium nucleus, causing it to disintegrate into two helium nuclei. This nuclear reaction is represented as follows:

$$\tfrac{7}{3}\text{Li} + \tfrac{1}{1}\text{H} \rightarrow \tfrac{4}{2}\text{He} + \tfrac{4}{2}\text{He} + \text{energy}$$

Their achievement, the first nuclear reaction produced by artificially accelerated particles, was recognized when they were awarded the Nobel Prize for Physics in 1951, nearly 20 years later. Cockcroft and Walton's system for producing high voltages is still used today, but the accelerators are limited to about 4 MeV.

Working at the same time at Princeton University, Robert J. Van de Graaff constructed the first belt-charged, electrostatic high-voltage generator. In this type of generator, the electric charge is transported on a rapidly moving belt made of an insulating material. Close to one end of the belt is a metallic comb of needles, charged to an electrical potential of over 10 kV. The motion of the belt carries the charges from these needles to the other end of the belt, where a second comb of needles transfers the charges to the high-voltage terminal. The high-voltage terminal is usually constructed as a metal sphere, so that the charges are equally distributed over its outside surface. As the belt moves, more and more charges are

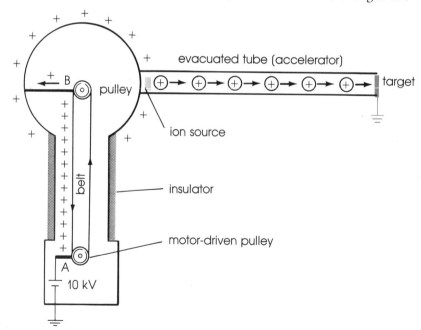

transferred to the high-voltage electrode, and the potential typically builds up to 9 MV. Because such high electrical potentials tend to cause arcing in air, the sphere is usually covered by a hood that traps pressurized, non-conducting gas over the electrode, thereby insulating it. Using this and other methods of insulation, the Van de Graaff generator can operate at up to approximately 20 MV. It should be noted that the Van de Graaff generator is only a source of electrical potential. The acceleration of charged particles occurs in a separate, evacuated tube, as illustrated on the previous page.

Today, many Van de Graaff generators are used as two-stage (**tandem**) accelerators. These devices, constructed horizontally, create a beam of protons with twice the energy produced in the original Van de Graaff design. An ion source produces protons, which are first accelerated by an outside high-voltage supply. This proton beam passes through an evacuated tube, to a point where some of the protons are converted into negative hydrogen ions by the addition of two electrons. As the mixture of protons and neg-ative hydrogen ions moves farther along the tube, it encounters a strong magnetic field at a bend in the tube. Here the negative hydrogen ions are deflected into the accelerator, and the protons are removed. The beam of negative ions is now accelerated towards the positive high-voltage electrode of the Van de Graaff. Inside this electrode, the negative hydrogen ions pass through a thin carbon foil that strips off two electrons from many of them, changing those affected back into positive ions (protons). These are now repelled by the positive electrode and accelerated through the second part of the evacuated tube. At a second bend in the tube, the protons are magnetically separated from other charged particles, and a beam of pure high-energy protons, all with the same energy, is directed at various targets by a beam-steering magnet.

To minimize electrical discharges induced by high voltages, sulphur hexafluoride (SF_6) gas is used in the area around the charged surfaces. In the tandem Van de Graaff generator, the whole device is enclosed in a steel tank containing the gas.

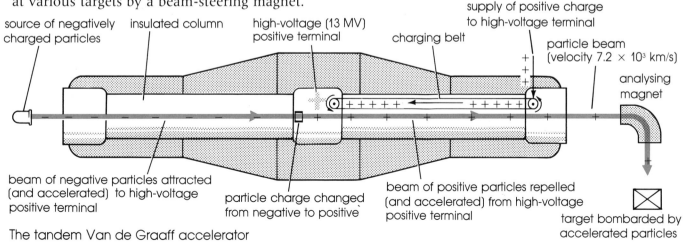

supply of positive charge to high-voltage terminal

source of negatively charged particles

insulated column

high-voltage (13 MV) positive terminal

charging belt

particle beam (velocity 7.2×10^3 km/s)

analysing magnet

beam of negative particles attracted (and accelerated) to high-voltage positive terminal

particle charge changed from negative to positive

beam of positive particles repelled (and accelerated) from high-voltage positive terminal

target bombarded by accelerated particles

The tandem Van de Graaff accelerator

Because of the high energies required in particle physics research, the tandem Van de Graaff generator is commonly used to initially accelerate protons before they are injected into other accelerators, such as those described later in this section. These generators are also used in nuclear physics to bombard atomic nuclei, in order to produce artificial nuclear reactions. Constant-voltage generators can also be used to accelerate electrons. These intense beams of electrons are used in the treatment of cancer, and for sterilization, industrial radiography, and the polymerization of plastics.

Cyclotrons

Lawrence's first cyclotron. The cover has been removed in the bottom "D" to show its construction.

The problems of working with very high voltages stimulated Ernest Lawrence, an American physicist, to consider accelerating particles by means of a large number of small increases in electrical potential rather than one large increase, as in the Van de Graaff generator. He proposed that this could be accomplished by magnetically deflecting the particles into a circular orbit. The key to the operation of such a device is the fact that the orbits of the ions in a uniform magnetic field are **isochronous**. This means that the time taken for particles with the same mass and charge to make one complete cycle is the same at any speed or energy. (The radius of the circular path will increase exactly as the speed, so that the time for any orbit stays constant.) This property makes it possible for a modest potential difference, reversing in polarity at constant frequency, to accelerate a charged particle many times.

The first magnetic resonance accelerator, or cyclotron, was built by Lawrence and his student, M.S. Livingston, at the University of California at Berkeley, in 1931. It produced 80 keV ions. By the late 1930s, cyclotron energies had reached 25 MeV.

An ion source is located in the middle of an evacuated chamber in the shape of a short cylinder, much like a pillbox (see diagram on next page). This chamber is positioned between the poles of a strong electromagnet, which creates a uniform magnetic field perpendicular to the flat surfaces of the chamber. Inside the evacuated chamber are two hollow electrodes, called **dees** because they are shaped like the letter "D". An alternating potential difference, which operates at a frequency equal to the orbital frequency of revolution of the particles in the magnetic field, is applied between the dees. The acceleration occurs only in the space between the dee electrodes, where the electric fields are concentrated, not inside the dees. Each time a particle crosses the gap between the dees it is accelerated, since the direction of the electric field reverses between

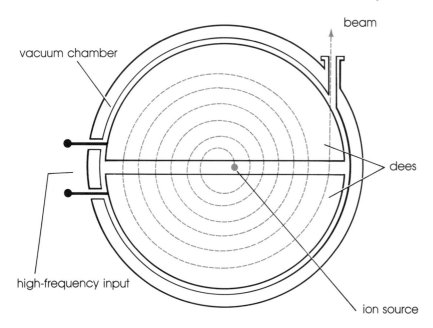

See Section 16.7 for a more detailed discussion of the motion of a charged particle in an electromagnetic field.

Plan view of the classical cyclotron

crossings. Because the speed of the particle increases with each cycle, the radius of its path increases, and the path is spiral-like until the particle reaches the outside edge of the device. Magnets are used to focus a beam of particles onto a target when the beam exits the cyclotron.

Cyclotrons are limited in energy by the relativistic effects on the mass of a particle as its velocity approaches the speed of light (see Section 17.5). As an ion approaches the speed of light, its mass increases. This in turn changes the isochronous condition, and it is no longer in step with the alternating potential difference on the electrodes. As a result, synchronization is lost for protons with energies above approximately 10 MeV. Nevertheless, cyclotrons were the primary nuclear research tool in the 1930s and early 1940s. They were used to produce many of the radioisotopes, such as Americium, Californium, Einsteinium, and Lawrencium.

Today there are many cyclotrons in operation. They are used in medical and biological research, in material science, and in a wide variety of other applications. However, nuclear physics is still the major use. Cyclotrons are often teamed with other accelerators such as the Van de Graaff. The Chalk River research facility of Atomic Energy of Canada uses such a device.

The element Lawrencium is named after Lawrence and the element Californium after the University of California, because of Lawrence's work there. Lawrence was awarded the Nobel Prize for Physics in 1939 for his work with cyclotrons and his nuclear research.

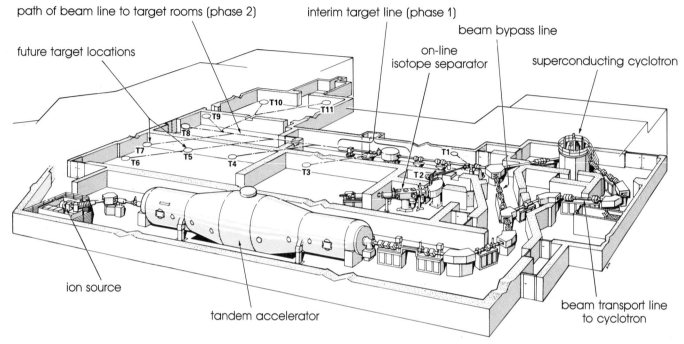

path of beam line to target rooms (phase 2)

future target locations

interim target line (phase 1)

on-line
isotope separator

beam bypass line

superconducting cyclotron

T10
T11
T9
T8
T7
T6
T5
T4
T3
T1
T2

ion source

tandem accelerator

beam transport line
to cyclotron

Tandem accelerator superconducting cyclotron (TASCC)

Synchrocyclotrons

A synchrocyclotron, or frequency modulation (F.M.) cyclotron, is
a classical cyclotron in which the frequency of the electrical potential is changed during the accelerating cycle. This permits the
particles to stay in phase with the frequency of the alternating
electrical field between the dees, even though their mass increases.
As a result, the relativistic mass increase does not impose as low a
limit on the energy of the accelerated particles as is the case with
the cyclotron.

For example, in the early part of the acceleration, when the speed
is lower, the frequency might typically be 32 MHz. By the time
the proton has acquired an energy of 400 MeV, the required frequency has fallen to 20 MHz. This change in frequency takes approximately 10 ms. As a result, the accelerated protons are delivered
in bunches, one for each time the accelerating frequency goes
through its cycle. The frequency must then return to 32 MHz in
order to pick up another batch of protons.

The intensity of the beam of protons is much lower than in a classical cyclotron, because it is not continuous but comes in bursts. To compensate, very large synchrocyclotrons, with very large and powerful magnets, have been constructed in many countries. The upper energy limit of a synchrocyclotron is set at 1 GeV by the size and cost of the large magnets. The use of superconducting magnets may increase this limit and thereby decrease the great size of these devices.

In the 1970s, several new versions of the synchrocyclotron appeared that were designed to improve both the intensity of the proton beam and the length of the duty cycle (duration of the bursts of protons). In these machines, the magnetic field is varied, rather than the frequency of the potential difference, to compensate for the relativistic mass effect. The frequency of the alternating potential difference is kept constant. Adjustments had to be made in the magnetic field as problems in focusing developed. It was found that if the electromagnets were segmented, this problem was partially resolved. The CERN machine at Zurich, Switzerland, and the TRIUMF at the University of British Columbia in Vancouver, are examples of synchrocyclotrons with segmented magnets, now called **sector-focused cyclotrons**.

The TRIUMF sector-focused cyclotron under construction. The seated workers give some concept of its size.

When a charged particle undergoes acceleration, electromagnetic radiation is produced (see Section 16.8). When an electron is confined to a circular orbit in a betatron or synchrotron, it constantly accelerates (recall that this is centripetal acceleration). The resulting radiation is called synchrotron radiation or "Bremsstrahlung". Until recently, this radiation has been a laboratory curiosity only, as well as a nuisance. (The loss in energy due to the radiation limits the energy of the accelerated electrons.)

Synchrotron radiation provides a broad range of wavelengths, from radio, through visible light, to "soft" X-rays. By filtering out unwanted wavelengths, biologists and solid-state physicists have found that synchrotron radiation can be used to reproduce very fine detail in electromicrographs.

When a biological microphotograph is taken, the sample is dead, usually frozen. The freezing of the water in the cells causes the cell walls to burst, deforming the sample. The soft X-rays of synchrotron radiation, however, let microscopists examine cells that are still alive — or almost. Another use of synchrotron radiation is in "photo-resist etching". In this process, a mask or pattern is placed between the source of light and a special light-sensitive surface. When the exposure is made, light reaches this surface, causing a molecular change, but only in the areas not covered by the shadow of the intervening pattern. This is how the small "chips" used in computers are made. It has been found that synchrotron radiation, due to its shorter wavelength, produces less diffraction around the pattern and thus a sharper image is formed. This allows smaller microcircuitry than achieved using traditional methods (down to 0.5 μm).

Betratrons

The betatron is given this name because it accelerates beta particles, another name for electrons. The electrons are accelerated in a doughnut-shaped, evacuated chamber located between the poles of a magnet. As in the cyclotron, the magnetic field is perpendicular to the plane of the vacuum chamber, so that electrons will be forced into circular paths. The strength of the magnetic field is not maintained at a constant value but increases at a uniform rate. The change in magnetic field creates an electric field that acts on the moving electron, causing the latter to speed up but remain in the same circular path. A burst of electrons is injected into the chamber; the electrons gain approximately 100 eV per revolution (in a 20 MeV betatron). When the magnetic field reaches its maximum value, the beam is deflected; the electrons strike a target, producing a beam of high-energy, intense X-rays. Electrons can also be ejected from the betatron, using electrostatic deflection, so that the beam of electrons can be used outside the machine.

The practical limit on the energy of a betatron is determined by the radiation of electromagnetic energy created by the accelerating electrons (see Section 19.7). This type of radiation is referred to as **synchrotron radiation**. The largest betatron accelerates electrons to 300 MeV. This is sufficient to produce other subatomic particles, emanating from a target struck by the electrons.

Betatrons are now commercially available, principally as sources of high-energy (hard) X-rays. They are used in the treatment of cancer and in industrial applications such as checking for flaws in metal castings.

The Stanford linear accelerator

Linear Accelerators

There are a number of disadvantages to accelerating particles in cyclotrons, synchrocyclotrons, and betatrons. Since the particles are contained by a magnetic field, the ejection of a high-energy beam is both difficult and inefficient. Internal targets are generally used, but this limits the kinds of experiments that can be performed. Also, in the case of high-energy electrons, there are severe losses of energy because of synchrotron radiation.

The linear accelerator, or **linac**, consists of a long, evacuated tube containing a large number of hollow drift tubes. Alternate drift tubes are connected to opposite sides of a high-frequency generator via transmission lines running the length of the accelerator (see diagram). If a negatively charged particle is injected

You will note in the diagram that the successive drift tubes increase in length. The length of the tube must be such that the time required for the particles to pass through the tube is exactly equal to the time for the alternating potential difference between successive tubes to reverse. Since the speed of the particle increases with each transition between drift tubes, the lengths of the drift tubes are made proportional to the speeds of the particles that pass through them. When used to accelerate electrons, the drift tubes can be essentially the same length, since the electrons quickly approach the speed of light.

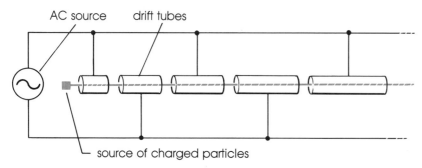

Schematic diagram of a linear accelerator. Charged particles accelerate as they are attracted by the alternately charged drift tubes.

when the potential of the first drift tube is positive, the particle will accelerate to it, acquiring kinetic energy. Once it is in the first hollow tube, it does not accelerate further, but moves at a constant velocity: it "drifts" through the tube. Inside the drift tube the electric field is zero, and the particle is unaffected by changes in the tube's electric potential. If by the time the particle reaches the end of the first drift tube the electrical potential difference between alternate drift tubes has reversed, the particle accelerates between the tubes. The particle then drifts faster through the second tube, which is longer, and is further accelerated in the space between the second and third tubes, since the potential difference has reversed again. This continues through a succession of longer drift tubes, increasing the kinetic energy of the particles with each transition.

The Stanford Linear Accelerator (SLAC), completed in 1961, is 3.2 km long and contains 240 drift tubes. It is designed to accelerate electrons to energies of approximately 20 GeV. At this energy,

Inside a linear accelerator

because of relativistic effects, an electron has a mass 40 000 times its normal mass. The highest-energy proton linac is located at Los Alamos, New Mexico. Completed in 1973, it accelerates protons to 800 MeV.

The intense pulses of high-energy protons make these devices ideal as injectors for proton synchrotrons, which will be described next. They are used on their own primarily to bombard targets, producing mesons. As a result, they are commonly called meson factories. (See page 796.)

Synchrotrons

The tremendous progress that has occurred in nuclear research was made possible by raising the energies of protons in successively larger and larger accelerators. This trend was curtailed because of the cost of making the huge magnets required — some have masses of up to 3.6×10^4 t.

Another way to accelerate protons is to combine some of the ideas used in the linear accelerator with those used in the synchrocyclotron. Instead of one large magnet, a series of smaller magnets is used to keep the accelerated beam in a circular path. Between successive electromagnets are radio-frequency accelerating devices called cavities, which work much like short sections of a linear accelerator. As illustrated in the diagram, protons are first accelerated by a linear accelerator, then directed into a circular vacuum chamber which runs through a succession of electromagnets. The electromagnets are designed so that the field increases with increasing radius, keeping the beam of protons to a relatively small cross-section. This beam may be used directly to strike targets outside the ring, or a target can be placed in the beam, and secondary particles then ejected from the target. In either case, special magnets direct the particles out of the ring.

Synchrotrons are enormous in size and cost. The Fermi National Accelerator Laboratory (Fermilab) at Batavia, Illinois, has a circumference of 6.3 km. At CERN (European Council for Nuclear Research) in Geneva, the synchrotron is 6.9 km in circumference.

In the 500 GeV Fermilab synchrotron, the energy of the protons is increased by a series of accelerators before they are injected. First a Cockcroft-Walton accelerator raises the protons to 700 keV. Next they are fed into a 200 MeV linear accelerator, which in turn injects the protons into a synchrotron that lifts them to 8 GeV as they enter the main ring. In 1983, a second ring was completed below the existing ring. The 1000 magnets in this ring are superconducting magnets with coils of niobium and titanium (at a cost

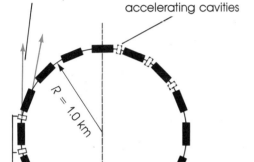

beams of particles

accelerating cavities

R = 1.0 km

electromagnets

inflector

linear accelerator

source of particles

extraction magnets

of $40 000 apiece). Cooled to $-268°C$ by liquid helium, the coils lose nearly all of their resistance, which sharply reduces power demands. The CERN proton synchrotron operates at 400 GeV; it too has a second ring adjacent to the first.

The Fermi National Accelerator has a circumference of 6.3 km.

The purpose of the second ring is to store accelerated particles, so that they can be used to collide with accelerated particles in the first ring. When a moving particle strikes a fixed target, only a small portion of the resulting energy is available for interaction with another particle. Most of the energy is lost to heat and deformation. For particles with speeds close to that of light, the effect is significant. For example, if a 400 GeV proton strikes a proton in a target at rest, only 27.4 GeV is available for the interaction. On the other hand, if the two particles are moving in opposite directions and collide, then all the energy is available for the interaction. For example, if two 31.4 GeV protons collide, 62.3 GeV is available for the interaction. (Obviously the collision is not quite head on!)

Beams of particles are accelerated in both rings at CERN, but in one beam the particles go clockwise and in the other they go counterclockwise. When the beams intersect, some of the particles interact. Using colliding beams of protons and antiprotons in the CERN accelerator, physicists, under the direction of Carlo Rubbia, confirmed the existence of three particles, the $W+$, $W-$, and Z particles, known collectively as intermediate vector bosons. This was a very important discovery in particle physics, as we will see in Section 20.9.

Plans are being made to build even larger synchrotrons. There is a proposal to build one in the American southwest, 160 km in circumference. It would have 20 times the energy levels of the Fermilab device. (It has been nicknamed the "Desertron", since only the desert has room for it.) Construction of a LEP (a Large Electron-Positron storage ring) started at CERN in 1983. It will set electrons and positrons on collision courses 27.5 km along a ring

The cost of synchrotrons is enormous. As an estimate, the cost increases as the cube of the radius. The old Fermilab machine required 60 MW of power to produce 400 GeV. The new ring should consume 20 MW when operating at 1000 GeV. The electric bill for six months in 1982 was $12 million. (Since 1000 GeV = 1 TeV the Fermilab accelerator is now referred to as the Tevatron.)

reaching from the CERN laboratory in suburban Geneva to the base of the Jura Mountains in France. The circle will all be underground. In Russia, a superconducting accelerator is being constructed at Serpukhov, 96 km south of Moscow. It is designed to reach energy levels of 3 TeV.

It is apparent that the magnitude and costs of high-energy particle research have reached levels which even large nations can no longer afford. Eventually, nationalism must be discarded and joint research must take place internationally, as the CERN facility has illustrated.

These photographs were taken at the CERN accelerator. On the left we see where the two beams intersect. On the right is a view of the circular tunnel housing the accelerator.

20.5 Particle Detectors

Subatomic particles are far too small and move too fast to be observed and measured directly. Also, most elementary particles decay into smaller particles very quickly. The particle detectors used to observe the products of high-energy accelerators are in some ways just as impressive, technologically, as the accelerators. For example, some detectors must be capable of photographing the effects of a subatomic particle that may only remain in the detector for 10^{-11} s!

In order for a detector to sense a particle, there must be an interaction between the particle and the material of which the detector is made. This interaction produces a response. The three primary responses are: the emission of light, the ionization of the medium, and a phase or chemical change in the medium. The chart summarizes the various devices used to detect subatomic particles. We will describe only two of the detectors used in high-energy research — the cloud chamber and the bubble chamber.

The cloud chamber was invented in 1911 by Charles Wilson, a Scottish physicist (1869-1959). Wilson found that in a gas supersaturated with a vapour, the vapour will condense into droplets around the trajectories of charged ions as they pass through the gas. The ions leave behind trails of droplets which can be photographed.

A simple cloud chamber can be made with a glass or plastic cylindrical container, open at one end. A piece of black cloth saturated with alcohol is placed on a block of dry ice and then covered by the glass container. The container soon fills with alcohol vapour, and a supersaturated layer of alcohol forms just above the black cloth. If a radioactive source, emitting alpha or beta particles, is put into the container, the moving particles will leave vapour trails behind them as they condense the alcohol vapour. The effect is similar to contrails left by commercial jet aircraft passing high overhead.

Some Properties of Particle Detectors				
Primary response	Type of device	Sensitive material	Time resolution	Space resolution
Ionization	solid-state detector	solid		size of detector
	ionization chamber proportional counter Geiger counter	gas	10^{-6} to 10^{-7} s	
	spark chamber			1 mm
Light emission	scintillation counter Cherenkov counter	gas, liquid, or solid	10^{-9} s	size of detector
	scintillation chamber	solid	10^{-8} s	1 mm
Phase or chemical change	cloud chamber	gas	none	0.1 mm
	bubble chamber	liquid		
	nuclear emulsion	gel		1 μm
	solid-state track detectors	solid		

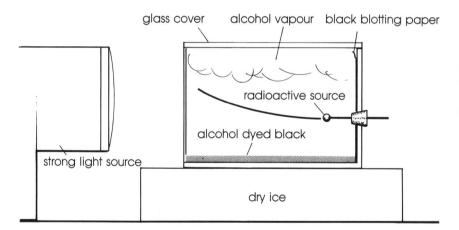

glass cover alcohol vapour black blotting paper

radioactive source

alcohol dyed black

strong light source

dry ice

Cloud chamber

In the cloud chambers for particle research, argon or ethyl alcohol are commonly used. A piston is forced forward by compressed air when valve A (next page) is opened. When valve B is opened to the atmosphere, the piston is forced backward, the pressure decreases, and the vapour expands to a supersaturated state, making droplet growth possible. When charged particles pass through the chamber they attract nearby molecules, creating tiny droplets

Alpha particle "tracks" in a cloud chamber

of liquid that form small vapour trails in the chamber. A high-speed strobe photograph, triggered by the particle passage, records the paths of the particles, including any collisions, for future study.

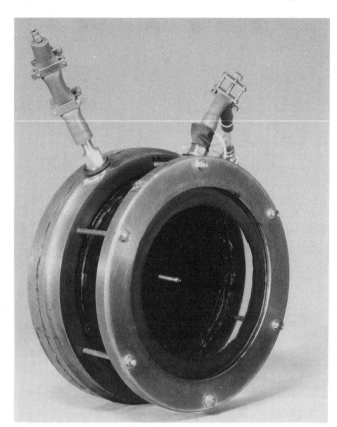

A Wilson cloud chamber

An array of photo detectors can be used instead of photography. Sequential light pulses can be stored in memory, and computer programs can scan the data for interesting occurrences.

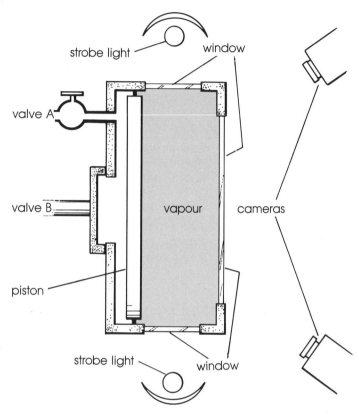

Cloud chamber, shown schematically, holds vapour at a pressure above atmospheric. The piston is forced forward by compressed air from valve A. When valve B is opened to the atmosphere, the piston is forced backward and the vapour expands. This expansion supersaturates the vapour, making droplet growth possible.

In the bubble chamber, liquid propane, hydrogen, helium, and xenon are all used. However, liquid hydrogen is used most commonly, since the hydrogen nuclei provide target protons for collisions. The liquid hydrogen must be kept below $-252.8°C$ to remain liquid. If the pressure in the liquid hydrogen is suddenly lowered, however, the hydrogen boils. If a high-speed charged particle passes through the hydrogen at exactly the same instant, hydrogen ions are formed, and the hydrogen boils a few thousandths of a second sooner around these ions than in the rest of the container. Carefully

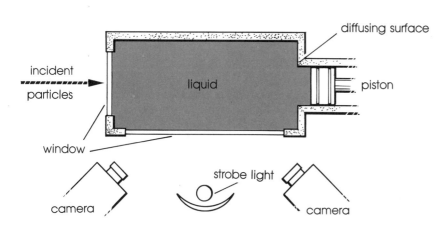

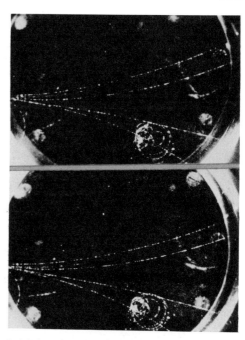

Bubble chamber, shown schematically, holds a liquid at high pressure. The liquid is superheated by allowing the chamber pressure to drop slightly. The bubbles that form are made visible on the diffusing surface and are then photographed stereoscopically.

Bubble chamber photographs

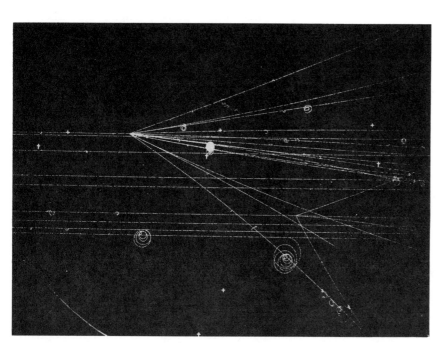

A typical bubble chamber photograph, showing particle collisions and disintegrations

A hydrogen bubble chamber

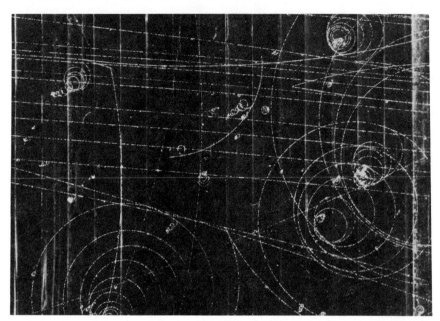

Notice that a magnetic field perpendicular to the plane of the photograph forces the charged particles into circular paths. By measuring the radius of a circular path, the mass of the particle can be determined.

timed photographs record the paths of the resulting bubble trails. Frequently a magnetic field is applied across the chamber, bending the paths of the charged particles. Positive particles are curved in one direction, negative particles in the other. By measuring the curvature of their paths and knowing the strength of the magnetic field, the masses of the particles can be determined. The interaction between particles occurs in the liquid hydrogen. Since a hydrogen atom is simply a proton and an electron, collisions between accelerated protons and the protons in the tank could occur and be recorded. One such collision can be seen clearly at the bottom left of the bubble chamber photograph in the margin. As seen in the photographs, bubble chambers are quite large and complex. Without them accelerators would be of little use since the particles themselves and their effects on other particles could not be observed.

20.6 The Meson and the Strong Nuclear Force

The concept that matter is composed of elementary building blocks originated with Democritus (circa 500 B.C.). By the early 1800s, with acceptance of Dalton's atomic theory, the atom was considered to be elementary. Indeed, the term element is still used when referring to the 103 or so different known atoms. By the early part

of this century, the discovery of the electron and the basic subatomic structure of the atom indicated that the electron, proton,
and neutron were the elementary particles. By the mid 1930s, the
photon, positron, and neutrino were also considered to be elementary. Since that time, hundreds of additional elementary particles have been discovered and are still being discovered. The question
arises then, what particles are elementary? It is this question that
challenges participants in the field of physics known as elementary
particle physics.

The basis of particle physics is the work of Paul Dirac, an English
theoretical physicist. In 1927, Dirac worked out the quantum mechanics of electromagnetic fields, giving a theoretical explanation
for the formation and absorption of photons in the atom and pos-
tulating the existence of the positron (see Section 20.3).

As we discussed earlier, it is the Coulomb force that attracts the
electron to the positive nucleus and in fact holds matter together.
In our study of objects in collision (Chapters 8 and 9), we described
certain interactions involving forces as "action-at-a-distance",
whereby two objects interact, with an interchange of energy and
momentum. For example, two magnetic air pucks repel one another because they have opposite poles, or an alpha particle is
repelled by a gold nucleus because they are both positively charged.
In neither example is there actual physical contact. How, then, is
the transfer of energy and momentum achieved?

In Chapter 18, we saw that an electromagnetic wave (light) can
also be considered as a stream of photons, each photon having
energy and momentum. This was an example of the wave-matter
duality in nature. Using the work of Dirac, this quantum approach
can be applied to the effects caused when one particle's electromagnetic field acts on the electromagnetic field of another particle.

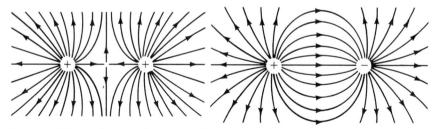

Two positive spheres close
together

Two oppositely charged spheres close
together

The electromagnetic force between two charged particles, studied
in Chapter 15, is caused by the electromagnetic field set up by one
particle acting on the electromagnetic field set up by the other (see
diagrams). Using quantum mechanics, we can consider an electro-

R.L. Feynman

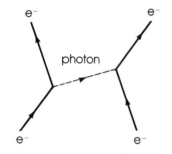

Feynman diagram, showing how a photon acts as a carrier of electromagnetic force between two electrons

magnetic field to be composed of particles. When one electromagnetic field acts on another, the two fields exchange photons with each other during the interaction. In other words, photons are the carriers or transfer agents that carry the electromagnetic force from one charged particle to another.

As an analogy, consider a girl and a boy standing facing each other on a nearly frictionless ice surface, each holding a hockey puck. If the girl throws her puck to the boy, the girl will move backward (action-reaction and impulse). The boy will also move backward when he catches the puck. Their movements demonstrate repulsive force. On the other hand, if they exchange pucks by grabbing them from each other, they will be pulled together — the equivalence of an attractive force.

To summarize: according to the quantum mechanics explanation of Dirac, when two charged particles repel or attract one another, the electromagnetic force between them is created by an exchange of one or more photons.

R.L. Feynman (1918–), an American physicist, developed the concept of a space-time diagram to illustrate such electrodynamic interactions. Examples are found on page 799. The simplest case occurs when only one photon is exchanged. Consider the interaction of two electrons. One electron may be considered to create a photon and the other may be considered to absorb the photon. Each of the electrons undergoes changes in energy and momentum because of the exchanged photon, and the electrons repel each other. This concept was applied to many other electromagnetic interactions, and it was concluded that the exchange of a photon, or photons, is responsible for all electromagnetic interactions between charged particles. The exchange photon is unobservable for a variety of reasons, and is therefore called a **virtual photon** to distinguish it from a real photon.

In the nucleus of the atom, protons and neutrons are bound together by a force that must be both different and stronger than the electromagnetic force. It is called the **strong nuclear force**. In 1935,. a Japanese physicist named Hideki Yukawa (1907-1981) proposed that, just as the photon was the particle that transferred the electromagnetic force, there should be a particle that transferred the strong nuclear force between the nucleons in the nucleus. Yukawa predicted that this new particle would have a rest mass midway between that of the electron and that of the proton. As a result, it was called the **meson**, meaning "in the middle". (Nucleon is the name given to a particle located in the nucleus of an atom. For example, protons and neutrons are nucleons.)

Yukawa calculated that this particle would have a mass 270 times that of an electron (270 m_e). He predicted that, since photons can be observed as free particles as well as being involved in an electromagnetic interaction, so a free meson should be observable. At the time, the most obvious place to look for this particle was the sky, and the method used was to examine the particles created by cosmic radiation. In 1936, a new particle was discovered whose mass was 207 m_e. It was first thought to be the elusive meson, but on closer study was found not to behave like the particle predicted by Yukawa. Aside from having a mass too small, its interactions with matter were very weak. For instance, these particles were found in deep mines, having passed through several kilometres of earth unaffected. The particles were called **mu(μ) mesons**, or **muons**. They exist in two forms, positive and negative.

Finally, in 1947, Yukawa's particle was found. It was named the **pi (π) meson**, or **pion**. Pions were found to exist in two varieties (positive and negative) and to have a rest mass of 274 m_e, as Yukawa had predicted. These particles were later produced artificially, using a particle accelerator, and a third π meson was discovered, a neutral one, with a slightly smaller mass (264 m_e).

The π mesons exhibit strong interactions with matter. It is generally accepted that mesons transit, or mediate, the strong nuclear force in much the same way that photons do the electromagnetic force. Free π mesons are unstable and quickly decay (in 10^{-8} s) into μ mesons; in fact the μ mesons observed in cosmic radiation are probably produced from the decay of π mesons. Since the discovery of the pion a number of other mesons have been discovered, and these too appear to mediate the strong nuclear force.

Hideki Yukawa

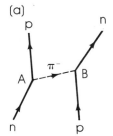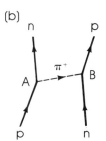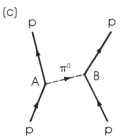

Feynman diagrams of nucleon-nucleon interactions through the exchange of virtual pions
(a) neutron-proton interaction
(b) proton-neutron interaction
(c) proton-proton interaction

20.7 The Classification of Elementary Particles

Murray Gell-Mann

More than 150 years ago, scientists recognized that elements could be arranged in groups according to their chemical properties. The periodic table of elements resulted. As more and more subatomic particles were discovered, it was found that they too could be organized into groupings according to their properties. A table of subatomic particles was first proposed by an American physicist, Murray Gell-Mann (1929–   ), and the Japanese physicist Nishijima (1912–   ), each working independently.

The main divisions in their original tables were based chiefly on mass, but as more new particles were discovered, it was found that the spin of the particle was an important factor also. To understand the system of classification, it is important to first know the definitions that distinguish one group of particles from another:

- The **photon** is in a category of its own, because it is only involved in electromagnetic interactions and has no rest mass.
- **Leptons** are particles that are involved solely with the weak nuclear force. The leptons are the electron, the muon, and the two neutrinos — the electron neutrino and the muon neutrino.
- **Hadrons** are particles that interact via the strong nuclear force. They include the neutron, the proton, the pion, and other particles with larger rest masses. Hadrons are further divided by spin into the **mesons**, the **baryons**, and the **hyperons**.

The chart on page 801 shows the classification of elementary particles. The table describes some of the subatomic particles known at the time of writing.

Elementary Particles

Name		Rest Mass (in units of electron rest mass, m_e)	Particle — Charge +	0	−	Antiparticle — Charge +	0	−	Spin quantum number
Photon	photon	0		γ			γ		1
Leptons	neutrino / antineutrino	0		ν_e			$\overline{\nu}_e$		
	μ neutrino / μ antineutrino	0		ν_μ			$\overline{\nu}_\mu$		$\frac{1}{2}$
	electron / positron	1			e^-	e^+			
	muon	207			μ^-	μ^+			
Mesons	π mesons (pions)	264	π^+	π^0			π^0	π^-	
		274	π^+					π^-	
	K mesons (kaons)	966	K^+					K^-	0
		974		K^0			$\overline{K}^0$		
	η meson (eta)	1074		η^0			η^0		
Baryons	proton / antiproton	1836	p					$\overline{p}$	
	neutron / antineutron	1839		n			$\overline{n}$		
(Hyperons)	lambda	2183		Λ^0			$\overline{\Lambda}^0$		$\frac{1}{2}$
	sigma	2327	Σ^+					$\overline{\Sigma}^+$	
		2334		Σ^0			$\overline{\Sigma}^-$		
		2343			Σ^-	$\overline{\Sigma}^-$			
	xi	2573		Ξ^0			$\overline{\overline{\Xi}}^0$		
		2586			Ξ^-	$\overline{\Xi}^+$			
	omega	3272			Ω^-	Ω^+			$\frac{3}{2}$

Note (left margin): **Hadrons** brace encompassing Mesons, Baryons and (Hyperons).

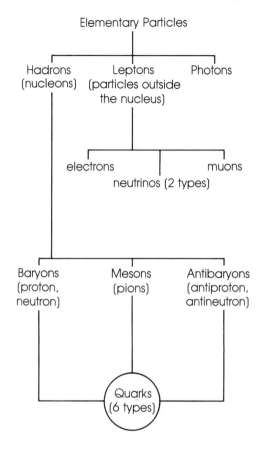

Elementary Particles

- Hadrons (nucleons)
- Leptons (particles outside the nucleus)
  - electrons
  - neutrinos (2 types)
  - muons
- Photons

- Baryons (proton, neutron)
- Mesons (pions)
- Antibaryons (antiproton, antineutron)

Quarks (6 types)

20.8 Quarks — The Stuff of Matter

As more and more particles were discovered in the 1960s and 1970s, it was found that the new particles were all hadrons. It became apparent that the four leptons (the electron, the muon, and the two neutrinos) were truly elementary particles, since they did not appear to break down into smaller particles. On the other hand, hadrons did.

In the late 1960s, using high-energy proton beams to probe nucleons, physicists noted that the nucleons appeared to have three separate centres of charge inside them. In the proton, these would combine to form a single quantum of charge. In the neutron, the charge centres would combine to balance out and create a net charge of zero. It was concluded that instead of being the fundamental particles of matter, the nucleons were made up of even smaller elementary particles.

At the same time, theoretical work was being done at the California Institute of Technology by Murray Gell-Mann. He was attempting to derive a possible general substructure of particles by listing all known particles. He saw a pattern, and proposed that hadrons were made up of six sub-particles, which he called **quarks**. He proposed the existence of three quarks and three **antiquarks**. The word quark did not have a special meaning, it simply appeared in the novel *Finnegans Wake* by James Joyce. (In fact, all the names that follow were casually and whimsically given. They have no connection with the properties of the subatomic particles. This practice is confusing, and can lead to misunderstanding if one is not careful.) Gell-Mann divided his three quarks into **flavours**, which he called **up**, **down**, and **sideways**, abbreviated **u, d**, and **s**. Later it became apparent that sideways had to do with **strangeness**, but the abbreviation remained the same. In his theory, the three quarks would have the properties listed in the chart in the margin.

Each hadron was pictured as having three quarks. For example, a neutron would consist of the three quarks, u, d, and d. The charges on the three quarks would add to zero, the baryon number would add to +1, and the strangeness would add to 0. The two half-spins would line up in opposite directions to cancel one another out, leaving the spin of the neutron as 1/2. In other words, the properties of the quarks added up to those of the neutron.

In the case of a proton, it would be made up of the quarks u, u, and d. The charges would add to +1, and all other properties would

Quark flavour	Baryon number	Charge	Strangeness	Spin
u	$1/3$	$+2/3$	0	$1/2$
d	$1/3$	$-1/3$	0	$1/2$
s	$1/3$	$-1/3$	-1	$1/2$

be the same as in the neutron, and identical with the properties of the proton.

With this system, Gell-Mann was able to show the make-up of each baryon by using its three quarks. Applying the theory to the meson, he proposed that it was composed of a quark and an antiquark, which worked out as well.

There was one problem with his scheme. According to the Pauli Exclusion Principle, two identical particles with identical sets of quantum numbers cannot occur together in the same atomic or subatomic system. But each quark has a half-spin, and quarks with identical flavours exist in the same particle. For example, the proton has two u quarks and one d quark, and an omega particle has three s quarks.

To solve this problem, Sheldon Glashow, a Danish-American physicist, suggested that quarks had another quality which he called **colour**. He proposed that every quark or antiquark was either **red**, **yellow**, or **blue**. He further proposed that the three quarks that make up baryons all have a different colour. For example, in the case of the omega particle, the three s quarks would each have a different colour, whether they came in identical flavours or not. This mix of colours results in baryons being colourless (red, yellow, and blue are the primary additive colours). If this were not true, there could be 10 different varieties of each baryon (and each antibaryon), which is not the case.

But how does colour work with mesons? They are made up of a quark and an antiquark. Since the quark and the antiquark already have different quantum states, they do not need to be of different colour. Instead, the theory proposes that they rapidly change colour from red to blue to yellow. The change in colour is so fast that colours balance out, and the meson is colourless.

So what does quark colour do aside from keeping quarks in different quantum states? Glashow believed that the quark colour had to do with the strong nuclear force and that quarks had exchange particles called **gluons**. According to the theory, the exchange of gluons (of colour) in the interactions between quarks was the real source of the strong force, not the mesons, as originally proposed.

Before completing our discussion of quarks we must return to the quark flavours. It is these flavours that cause the variety among hadrons. If there are four leptons, then by symmetry there should be four quarks. For this and other reasons, Glashow predicated the

Neutron (n)	Antineutron ($\overline{\text{n}}$)
u d d	*u d d*
Proton (p+)	Antiproton ($\overline{\text{p}}$−)
u u d	*u u d*
Omega (Ω)	Antiomega ($\overline{\Omega}$)
s s s	*s s s*
Xi minus (Ξ−)	Antixi plus ($\overline{\Xi}$+)
d s s	*d s s*
Xi zero (Ξ°)	Antixi zero ($\overline{\Xi}$°)
u s s	*u s s*
Sigma minus (Σ−)	Antisigma plus ($\overline{\Sigma}$+)
d d s	*d d s*
Sigma zero (Σ°)	Antisigma zero ($\overline{\Sigma}$°)
u d s	*u d s*
Sigma plus (Σ+)	Antisigma minus ($\overline{\Sigma}$−)
u u s	*u u s*
Lambda (Λ)	Antilambda ($\overline{\Lambda}$)
u d s	*u d s*

Sheldon Glashow

Particle Table with Four Quark Flavours

Quarks	Anti-quarks	Leptons	Anti-leptons
u	$\bar{u}$	e^-	e^+
d	$\bar{d}$	v_e	$\bar{v}_e$
s	$\bar{s}$	μ^-	μ^+
c	$\bar{c}$	v_μ	$\bar{v}_\mu$

existence of a fourth quark, called **charm** (symbolized by the letter "c") as the name of the quark and its flavour. The properties of all the quarks are summarized in the table in the margin.

Theoretical physicists had proposed a fifth and sixth quark and had given them names — **top** and **bottom** in America, and **truth** and **beauty** in Europe. Evidence for these quarks was found in 1984, using the large colliding beam accelerator at CERN, Switzerland.

In the 1970s and early 1980s, scientists found that the fundamental particles are the quarks and the leptons. Of the former fundamental triad — proton, neutron, and electron — only the electron survives as fundamental. The question arises, "What importance do quarks have to the materials we use in the everyday world?" The only leptons we need are the electron and its companion neutrino, to explain the weak interactions. The "up" and "down" quarks are needed to form the protons and neutrons in atomic nuclei. The muon and its neutrino, and the "strange" quark, only appear in the high-energy world of cosmic rays, high above the Earth; they have no role in the ordinary world at the Earth's surface. Similarly, the "charmed" and "bottom" quarks only appear in the explorations of particle accelerators. And so it seems that the quarks do not have much relevance for us. Yet these phantom particles apparently have a purpose in nature's scheme. The problem remains to determine just what this purpose is.

20.9 The Fundamental Forces of Nature

After dealing with fundamental particles, it is appropriate that we conclude this chapter by briefly discussing fundamental forces. We now recognize four of these. In addition to the force of gravity and the electromagnetic force, there are the strong nuclear force and the weak nuclear force. The strong nuclear force binds only the particles of the nucleus together, acting over a range no greater than the diameter of a proton. In contrast, gravity exerts its influence over infinite distances, affecting all forms of matter. However, the gravitational attraction between protons is 10^{39} times weaker than the attraction due to the strong nuclear force (see chart on 805). We know very little about the weak nuclear force except that it exists and is relatively weak compared to the strong nuclear force and the electromagnetic force. Even so, it is 10^{26} times stronger than the gravitational force. It is believed that the weak nuclear force is involved in beta decay, muon decay, and decay of other

Modern theoretical physics relies heavily on the language of mathematics. This is particularly true in particle physics, in which it was the abstract analysis of symmetry groups that led to predictions of new particles. One mathematical theorem crucial for constructing a single set of field equations linking gravity and electromagnetic fields was Noether's Theorem. This theorem was published in 1918 by the German mathematician Emmy Noether.

elementary particles. For example, in beta decay the neutrino interacts very weakly with matter.

The quest for a theory that would unify the forces of nature began in the 1860s with the work of the Scottish physicist, James Clerk Maxwell, when he combined the electrical and magnetic forces into one — the force of electromagnetism. For the last 30 years of his life, Albert Einstein was frustrated in his attempts to develop a theory that would unify the forces of gravity and electromagnetism. Each time he reached a dead end, he published his research "to save another fool from wasting his time on the same idea". But by the late 1960s more information was available, and a few young physicists had a new idea.

Four Fundamental Forces

	Strong nuclear	Electro-magnetic	Weak nuclear	Gravitational
Range	$10^{-10} -$ 10^{-11} m	infinity	less than 10^{-11} m	infinity
Relative strength	1	10^{-3}	10^{-14}	10^{-40}
Particles act upon	hadrons	charged particles	hadrons leptons	everything with mass
Intermediaries	gluons	photons	intermediate vector bosons	gravitons
Examples	nuclear forces	atomic forces	radioactive decay	astronomical forces

In Section 20.6, we explained how the exchange-particle concept works for electromagnetic and strong nuclear interactions. That is, the photon is the exchange particle for electromagnetic interactions, and the π meson is the particle of mediation for reactions involving the strong nuclear force. Over a period of 10 years, in the late 1960s and early 1970s, three theoretical physicists — Sheldon Glashow (American), Steven Weinberg (American), and Abdus Salam (Pakistani) — pieced together a theory that described electromagnetism and the weak nuclear force as aspects of a more fundamental force, called the **electroweak**. They postulated that there were three "heavy" photons that mediated the electroweak — a positive W particle, a negative W particle, and a neutral Z particle (symbolically W+, W−, and Z, respectively). For their important work, they shared the Nobel Prize for Physics in 1979.

Carlo Rubbia

Did these theoretical particles exist, in fact? It remained the task of other physicists to locate them.

Carlo Rubbia (1934–   ), an Italian physicist at Harvard, thought that the particles could be found, provided the giant accelerator at the European Centre for Nuclear Research (CERN) was converted into a colliding beam accelerator (see page 791). It took three years to complete the conversions. The engineering problems were enormous, and many scientists were sceptical that the converted accelerator would work. But it did, and the results were hailed as a landmark in the history of science. When the beams of protons and antiprotons collided, annihilating one another, the physicists discovered the unmistakable signature of the Ws and the Z, verifying the electroweak theory. Their discovery was announced in November 1982, and their accomplishment was recognized in 1984, when Carlo Rubbia and Dutch-born Simon van de Meer were awarded the Nobel Prize for Physics. (As shown in the diagram, the discovery of the W particle led to the discovery of the elusive top and bottom quarks.)

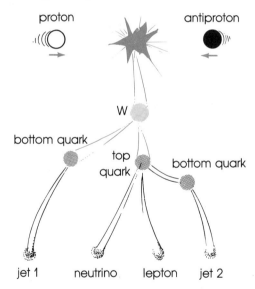

A proton and an antiproton collide, making a W particle. The top quark appears when W decays. Physicists recognize the quark by examining the records of its decay particles.

One interaction we have not yet discussed is the gravitational force. If exchange theory is applied to gravitational interactions, there should be an exchange particle to mediate interactions between two masses. The theoretical exchange particles called **gravitons** are the predicted particles of interaction. They are calculated to have zero rest mass, like the photon. Although the search is on, gravitons may never be found because of the extremely weak nature of the interaction.

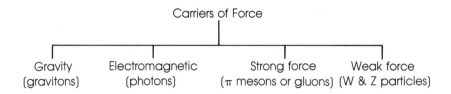

We have described the present state of our knowledge about the fundamental forces that affect the behaviour of matter, large and small. Scientists have worked for over 30 years in an effort to produce a unified field theory that would unite all four natural forces, much as Maxwell did when he united the electric and magnetic forces. Einstein spent the last 20 years of his life working on unified field theory, but was unable to develop the theory. The work of a series of physicists was responsible for significant progress in the 1970s and 1980s, and the electroweak theory was a milestone in the quest. But the search goes on to discover a single, unified field theory that will unite the four known forces of Nature.

While these developments were occurring in particle physics, cosmologists were establishing the Big Bang Theory for the creation of the universe. According to this model, the newborn universe, including space and time, was created about 15 thousand million years ago, and was very hot and dense. The developments in cosmology and in the understanding of the fundamental forces of Nature have run in parallel. On the one hand, in order to understand the early universe, one must understand the physics of extremely high energies. On the other hand, the superforce necessary to unify the four known natural forces would require energies far beyond those possible in even the most adventuresome particle accelerator. But such energies might occur in the "Big Bang". In fact, when the universe was created in its hot state, perhaps the superforce was instrumental in the process. The superforce created space, and the particles of matter that gave shape to our universe. Then, as the universe cooled, the superforce broke into the separate forces we know today. This would be a truly omnipotent force — the fountainhead of all existence. But our knowledge of how these events may have occurred is sketchy, and there is much work left for future scientists in the quest for a fundamental knowledge of our universe.

"Science . . . means unresting endeavour and continually progressing development toward an aim which the poetic intuition may apprehend but which the intellect can never fully grasp."

Max Planck

20.10 Review

Discussion

1. Particle research is very costly compared to other areas of scientific research. In 500 words or less, justify or argue against the use of government funds for particle research.
2. Listed below are some of the most important names in particle research. Using 500 words or less, write a brief biography of one of these scientists.

Ernest Lawrence	Paul Dirac
Irène Joliot-Curie	Carl Anderson
John Cockcroft	Robert Van de Graaff
Charles Wilson	Hideki Yukawa
Murray Gell-Mann	Sheldon Glashow
Steven Weinberg	Abdus Salam
Carlo Rubbia	

3. Cyclotrons and betatrons are used in some hospitals to produce radioactive isotopes with very short half-lives. Briefly explain (a) how radioactive particles are produced using a cyclotron, and (b) why cyclotron-produced isotopes are easier to manage than those produced in a nuclear reactor.
4. Why are accelerated particles and mesons useful in the treatment of cancer?
5. Why is it difficult to detect a neutrino?

Problems

particle	mass (amu)
electron	5.94×10^{-4}
proton	1.00867
neutron	1.00783
boron-12	12.01435
carbon-12	12.00000
nitrogen-12	12.01864
phosphorus-32	31.97390
sulphur-32	31.97207

$1 \text{ amu} = 1.66 \times 10^{-27} \text{ kg} \approx 931 \text{ MeV}$

6. Using the data in the margin, answer the following:
(a) What is the energy of the neutrino, if a phosphorus-32 atom beta-decays into a sulphur-32 atom, and the kinetic energy of the accompanying electron is 0.90 MeV?
(b) A boron-12 atom beta-decays into a carbon-12 atom. What is the maximum kinetic energy of the emitted electron?
(c) In the $\beta+$ decay of nitrogen-12 into carbon-12, a positron with energy of 11.0 MeV is emitted. What is the energy of the neutrino?

7. The potential difference between the dees of a cyclotron is 30 kV. How many revolutions do the protons have to make in order to reach an energy of 25 MeV?

8. Protons injected into the new Tevatron synchrotron at the Fermilab travel around a circumference of 6.4 km. When they are injected into the synchrotron, they have an energy of 8.0 GeV, but when they leave, they can have an energy of 1.0 TeV. If the protons gain 3.0 MeV in each rotation,
   (a) how many rotations are required?
   (b) how far do the protons travel?

9. Calculate the energy required to produce a neutron-antineutron pair.

10. A proton is accelerated to a kinetic energy of 1.0 GeV. What is its total energy?

11. What is the de Broglie wavelength of a 400 GeV proton? Of an 18 GeV electron?

12. An X-ray photon with a frequency of 1.8×10^{18} Hz collides with a nucleus. Will electron pair production occur? Explain your answer.

13. What is the wavelength of the photons produced in electron pair annihilation?

Numerical Answers to Review Problems

6. (a) 0.25 MeV (b) 12.8 MeV
   (c) 5.8 MeV
7. 417 revolutions
8. (a) 3.3×10^5 rotations
   (b) 2.1×10^6 km
9. 1.88 GeV
10. 1.9 GeV
11. 4.5×10^{-17} m, 2.9×10^{-15} m
13. 2.4×10^{-12} m, or 2.4 pm

"The stumbling way in which even the ablest of the scientists in every generation have had to fight through thickets of erroneous observations, misleading generalizations, inadequate formulations and unconscious prejudice is rarely appreciated by those who obtain their scientific knowledge from textbooks."

James Bryant Conant

Appendix A

Prefixes of the Metric System

Factor	Prefix	Symbol
10^{12}	tera	T
10^{9}	giga	G
10^{6}	mega	M
10^{3}	kilo	k
10^{2}	hecto	h
10	deka	da
10^{-1}	deci	d
10^{-2}	centi	c
10^{-3}	milli	m
10^{-6}	micro	μ
10^{-9}	nano	n
10^{-12}	pico	p
10^{-15}	femto	f
10^{-18}	atto	a

Some Examples

1 kilometre	=	1000 m
1 centimetre	=	0.01 m
1 megatonne	=	1.0×10^{6} T
1 milliampere	=	1.0×10^{-3} A
1 microvolt	=	1.0×10^{-6} V
1 gigahertz	=	1.0×10^{9} Hz
1 picofarad	=	1.0×10^{-12} F
1 terayear	=	1.0×10^{12} yar

Appendix B

Selected Physical Quantities and Measurement Units

Physical quantity	Quantity symbol	Measurement unit	Unit symbol	Unit dimensions
Fundamental Units				
length	l	metre	m	m
mass	m	kilogram	kg	kg
time	t	second	s	s
electric charge	Q	coulomb	C	C
temperature	T	Kelvin	K	K
Derived Units				
acceleration	a	metre per second per second	m/s²	m/s²
area	A	square metre	m²	m²
density	D	kilogram per cubic metre	kg/m³	kg/m³
electric current	I	ampere	A	C/s
electric field intensity	ε	newton per coulomb	N/C	kg·m/C·s²
electric resistance	R	ohm	Ω	kg·m²/C²·s
electric potential	V	volt	V	kg·m²/C·s²
work	W	joule	J	kg·m²/s²
energy	E	joule	J	kg·m²/s²
force	F	newton	N	kg·m/s²
frequency	f	hertz	Hz	s⁻¹
heat	Q	joule	J	kg·m²/s²
magnetic flux	ϕ	weber	Wb	kg·m²/C·s
magnetic flux density	B	weber per square metre	Wb/m²	kg/C·s
potential difference	V	volt	V	kg·m²/C·s²
power	P	watt	W	kg·m²/s³
pressure	p	newton per square metre	N/m²	kg/m·s²
velocity	v	metre per second	m/s	m/s
volume	V	cubic metre	m³	m³

Appendix C

Table of Natural Trigonometric Functions

Angle	Sine	Cosine	Tangent	Angle	Sine	Cosine	Tangent
1°	.0175	.9998	.0175	24°	.4067	.9135	.4452
2°	.0349	.9994	.0349	25°	.4226	.9063	.4663
3°	.0523	.9986	.0524				
4°	.0698	.9976	.0699	26°	.4384	.8988	.4877
5°	.0872	.9962	.0875	27°	.4540	.8910	.5095
				28°	.4695	.8829	.5317
6°	.1045	.9945	.1051	29°	.4848	.8746	.5543
7°	.1219	.9925	.1228	30°	.5000	.8660	.5774
8°	.1392	.9903	.1405				
9°	.1564	.9877	.1584	31°	.5150	.8572	.6009
10°	.1736	.9848	.1763	32°	.5299	.8480	.6249
				33°	.5446	.8387	.6494
11°	.1908	.9816	.1944	34°	.5592	.8290	.6745
12°	.2079	.9781	.2126	35°	.5736	.8192	.7002
13°	.2250	.9744	.2309				
14°	.2419	.9703	.2493	36°	.5878	.8090	.7265
15°	.2588	.9659	.2679	37°	.6018	.7986	.7536
				38°	.6157	.7880	.7813
16°	.2756	.9613	.2867	39°	.6293	.7771	.8098
17°	.2924	.9563	.3057	40°	.6428	.7660	.8391
18°	.3090	.9511	.3249				
19°	.3256	.9455	.3443	41°	.6561	.7547	.8693
20°	.3420	.9397	.3640	42°	.6691	.7431	.9004
				43°	.6820	.7314	.9325
21°	.3584	.9336	.3839	44°	.6947	.7193	.9657
22°	.3746	.9272	.4040	45°	.7071	.7071	1.0000
23°	.3907	.9205	.4245	46°	.7193	.6947	1.0355

Table of Natural Trigonometric Functions

Angle	Sine	Cosine	Tangent	Angle	Sine	Cosine	Tangent
47°	.7314	.6820	1.0724	69°	.9336	.3584	2.6051
48°	.7431	.6691	1.1106	70°	.9397	.3420	2.7475
49°	.7547	.6561	1.150.4				
50°	.7660	.6428	1.1918	71°	.9455	.3256	2.9042
				72°	.9511	.3090	3.0777
51°	.7771	.6293	1.2349	73°	.9563	.2924	3.2709
52°	.7880	.6157	1.2799	74°	.9613	.2756	3.4874
53°	.7986	.6018	1.3270	75°	.9659	.2588	3.7321
54°	.8090	.5878	1.3764				
55°	.8192	.5736	1.4281	76°	.9703	.2419	4.0108
				77°	.9744	.2250	4.3315
56°	.8290	.5592	1.4826	78°	.9781	.2079	4.7046
57°	.8387	.5446	1.5399	79°	.9816	.1908	5.1446
58°	.8480	.5299	1.6003	80°	.9848	.1736	5.6713
59°	.8572	.5150	1.6643				
60°	.8660	.5000	1.7321	81°	.9877	.1564	6.3138
				82°	.9903	.1392	7.1154
61°	.8746	.4848	1.8040	83°	.9925	.1219	8.1443
62°	.8829	.4695	1.8807	84°	.9945	.1045	9.5144
63°	.8910	.4540	1.9626	85°	.9962	.0872	11.4301
64°	.8988	.4384	2.0503				
65°	.9063	.4226	2.1445	86°	.9976	.0698	14.3007
				87°	.9986	.0523	19.0811
66°	.9135	.4067	2.2460	88°	.9994	.0349	28.6363
67°	.9205	.3907	2.3559	89°	.9998	.0175	57.2900
68°	.9272	.3746	2.4751	90°	1.0000	.0000	

Appendix D

Greek Alphabet

Greek letter	Greek name	English equiva- lent	Greek letter	Greek name	English equiva- lent
A α	alpha	ä	N ν	nu	n
B β	beta	b	Ξ ξ	xi	ks
Γ γ	gamma	g	O o	omicron	o
Δ δ	delta	d	Π π	pi	p
E ϵ	epsilon	e	P ρ	rho	r
Z ζ	zeta	z	Σ σ	sigma	s
H η	eta	ā	T τ	tau	t
Θ θ	theta	th	Υ υ	upsilon	ü,ōō
I ι	iota	ē	Φ ϕ	phi	f
K κ	kappa	k	X χ	chi	h
Λ λ	lambda	l	Ψ ψ	psi	ps
M μ	mu	m	Ω ω	omega	ō

Appendix E

Physical Constants

Constant	Symbol	Value
velocity of light	c	3.00×10^8 m/s
gravitational constant	G	6.67×10^{-11} N·m²/kg²
rest mass of electron	m_e	9.11×10^{-31} kg
rest mass of proton	m_p	1.67×10^{-27} kg
rest mass of neutron	m_n	1.67×10^{-27} kg
charge on an electron	e	1.60×10^{-19} C
Planck's constant	h	6.63×10^{-34} J·s
Coulomb's constant	k	9.0×10^9 N·m²/C²
mean radius of Earth		6.38×10^6 m
mean radius of Earth's orbit		1.49×10^{11} m
mean radius of moon		1.74×10^6 m
mean radius of moon's orbit		3.84×10^8 m
length of year		3.16×10^7 s

Appendix F

Graphing Scientific Data

You may have drawn x-y graphs in your mathematics class. Most of the graphs used in this book are different in that they involve experimental data. The following guidelines are to assist you in drawing a graph based on experimental data.

Speed-time graph for ball rolling down a slope

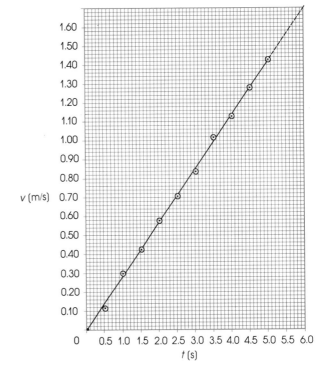

Step 1 – Choosing the Axes

Determine which of the physical quantities is the **dependent variable** and which is the **independent variable**. The independent variable is the one whose values the experimenter chooses. In the graph illustrated, time is the independent variable since the experimenter chooses at which times to measure the speed of the ball. The independent variable is plotted on the horizontal axis and the dependent variable on the vertical axis. Usually the title of the graph indicates how the axes are to be labelled. For example, in the graph of A versus B, the values of A are plotted vertically, those of B horizontally.

Step 2 – Scaling the Axes

When choosing scales, spread the measured values across the graph paper as widely as possible. The scales chosen must be easy to read and must have equal divisions. Each division must represent a small whole number of units of the variable being plotted, such as 1, 2, 5, 10, or some simple multiple of these. For example, the maximum measured reading for speed in the accompanying graph is 1.40 m/s.

The graph paper has 17 vertical divisions that could be used to plot speed. If we divided the number of divisions (17) into the maximum value to be plotted (1.40 m/s) we would obtain $\frac{1.40}{17}$ or 0.0823 m/s per division. The plotted values of speed would then take up the entire axis, but the numbers on the divisions would be very awkward. To simplify, we round up 0.0823 m/s to 0.1 m/s, thereby using only 14 divisions and having three left over.

Similarly, if the number of divisions in the horizontal scale (12) is divided into the maximum value to be plotted (5 s), we get $\frac{5}{12}$ or 0.417 s per division. We round 0.417 s up to 0.5 s, thereby using 10 divisions and having two left over. To summarize, choose the correct scale for an axis by dividing the maximum number of divisions on the axis into the maximum value to be plotted, and round the result up to the nearest 1, 2, 5, 10, or some simple multiple of these values.

Most of the graphs used in this book have an origin of zero, that is (0,0). It is not necessary to label every line on each axis, any more than it is necessary to label every division on a ruler. Each axis is labelled with the symbol for what is being plotted and the unit.

Step 3 – Plotting the Data

Find each data point and mark it with a small dot *in pencil*. Around each dot draw a small circle not exceeding two small scale divisions in diameter. With a well-sharpened pencil, lightly draw in the smooth curve that best joins the small circles. Do not try to force your line to go through all dots, since experimental error will cause some points to be slightly off the smooth curve. If the points seem to lie on a straight line, use a ruler, preferably a transparent one, so that you can see all the points while selecting the best line. You have used pencil to mark your points, and draw your smooth curve, so that you could easily make changes, if necessary. Once you are satisfied with the curve you have chosen, draw it in, in ink.

Sometimes a point obviously has no experimental error, so the line must go through it. In the example we have used, (0,0) is such a point because the speed will be zero when $t = 0$.

Step 4 – Choosing a Title

Every graph should be given a title. In this case, "Speed-time graph for a ball rolling down a slope" is the title. The title may be placed at the top of the page, or in a box in a clear area on the graph.

Step 5 – Using the Graph

The graphing of data serves at least four functions:

1. It permits easy **interpolation** (finding values between measured points) and **extrapolation** (finding values beyond measured points). If a graph is extended, a dotted line is used.
2. The scatter of the points off the smooth curve gives an indication of the errors in the measured data.
3. Where a point falls far off the smooth curve, this suggests that a serious error may have been made and that the data for that point should be remeasured. Alternatively, it may indicate that there is another variable that has not been taken into consideration in the investigation.
4. We can deduce from the slope of the graph the mathematical relationship between the variables. For example, if the graph is a straight line through the origin, the relationship is of the form y = mx: y is directly proportional to x. In some cases, the experimental values will not result in a straight line.

Appendix G

Nobel Prize Winners – Physics

Year	Winner	Country	Contribution
1901	Wilhelm Röntgen	(Ger.)	discovery of X-rays
1902	Hendrik Antoon Lorentz	(Neth.)	investigation of the influence of magnetism on radiation
	Pieter Zeeman	(Neth.)	
1903	Antoine-Henri Becquerel	(Fr.)	discovery of spontaneous radioactivity
	Pierre Curie	(Fr.)	investigations of radiation phenomena discovered by A.-H. Becquerel
	Marie Curie	(Fr.)	
1904	Lord Rayleigh	(Brit.)	discovery of argon
1905	Philipp Lenard	(Ger.)	research on cathode rays
1906	Sir J.J. Thomson	(Brit.)	research into electrical conductivity of gases
1907	A.A. Michelson	(U.S.)	spectroscopic and metrological investigations
1908	Gabriel Lippmann	(Fr.)	photographic reproduction of colours
1909	Guglielmo Marconi	(Italy)	development of wireless telegraphy
	Karl Braun	(Ger.)	
1910	J. van der Waals	(Neth.)	research concerning the equation of state of gases and liquids
1911	Wilhelm Wien	(Ger.)	discoveries regarding laws governing heat radiation
1912	Nils Gustaf Dalén	(Swed.)	invention of automatic regulators for lighting coastal beacons and light buoys
1913	H. Kamerlingh Onnes	(Neth.)	investigation into the properties of matter at low temperatures; production of liquid helium
1914	Max von Laue	(Ger.)	discovery of diffraction of X-rays by crystals
1915	Sir William Bragg	(Brit.)	analysis of crystal structure by means of X-rays
	Sir Lawrence Bragg	(Brit.)	
1917	Charles Barkla	(Brit.)	discovery of characteristic X-radiation of elements
1918	Max Planck	(Ger.)	discovery of the elemental quanta
1919	Johannes Stark	(Ger.)	discovery of Doppler effect in positive ion rays and division of spectral lines in electric field
1920	Charles Guillaume	(Switz.)	discovery of anomalies in alloys
1921	Albert Einstein	(Switz.)	services to theoretical physics
1922	Niels Bohr	(Den.)	investigation of atomic structure and radiation
1923	Robert Millikan	(U.S.)	work on elementary electric charge and the photoelectric effect
1924	Karl Siegbahn	(Swed.)	work in X-ray spectroscopy
1925	James Franck	(Ger.)	discovery of the laws governing the impact of an electron upon an atom
	Gustav Hertz	(Ger.)	
1926	Jean-Baptiste Perrin	(Fr.)	work on discontinuous structure of matter
1927	Arthur Holly Compton	(U.S.)	discovery of wavelength change in diffused X-rays
	Charles Wilson	(Brit.)	method of making visible the paths of electrically charged particles
1928	Sir Owen Richardson	(Brit.)	discovery of Richardson's law
1929	Louis de Broglie	(Fr.)	discovery of the wave nature of electrons
1930	Sir C. Raman	(India)	work on light diffusion; discovery of Raman effect
1932	Werner Heisenberg	(Ger.)	formulation of indeterminacy principle of quantum mechanics
1933	P.A.M. Dirac	(Brit.)	introduction of wave-equations in quantum mechanics
	Erwin Schrödinger	(Austria)	
1935	Sir James Chadwick	(Brit.)	discovery of the neutron
1936	Victor Hess	(Austria)	discovery of cosmic radiation
	Carl Anderson	(U.S.)	discovery of the positron
1937	Clinton Davisson	(U.S.)	experimental demonstration of the interference phenomenon in crystals irradiated by electrons
	Sir George Paget Thomson	(Brit.)	
1938	Enrico Fermi	(Italy)	disclosure of artificial radioactive elements produced by neutron irradiation
1939	Ernest Lawrence	(U.S.)	invention of the cyclotron
1943	Otto Stern	(U.S.)	discovery of the magnetic moment of the proton
1944	Isidor Rabi	(U.S.)	resonance method for registration of magnetic properties of atomic nuclei
1945	Wolfgang Pauli	(Austria)	discovery of the exclusion principle
1946	Percy Bridgman	(U.S.)	discoveries in the domain of high-pressure physics
1947	Sir Edward Appleton	(Brit.)	discovery of Appleton layer in upper atmosphere
1948	Patrick Blackett	(Brit.)	discoveries in the domain of nuclear physics and cosmic radiation
1949	Yukawa Hideki	(Japan)	prediction of the existence of mesons
1950	Cecil Powell	(Brit.)	photographic method of studying nuclear processes; discoveries about mesons
1951	Sir John Cockcroft	(Brit.)	work on transmutation of atomic nuclei by accelerated particles
	Ernest Walton	(Ire.)	
1952	Felix Bloch	(U.S.)	discovery of nuclear magnetic resonance in solids
	Edward Purcell	(U.S.)	
1953	Frits Zernike	(Neth.)	method of phase-contrast microscopy
1954	Max Born	(Brit.)	statistical studies on wave functions
	Walther Bothe	(Ger.)	invention of coincidence method
1955	Willis Lamb, Jr.	(U.S.)	discoveries in the hydrogen spectrum
	Polykarp Kusch	(U.S.)	measurement of magnetic moment of electron
1956	William Shockley	(U.S.)	investigations on semiconductors and discovery of the transistor effect
	John Bardeen	(U.S.)	
	Walter Brattain	(U.S.)	
1957	Tsung-Dao Lee	(China)	discovery of violations of the principle of parity
	Chen Ning Yang	(China)	
1958	Pavel A. Cherenkov	(U.S.S.R.)	discovery and interpretation of the Cherenkov effect
	Ilya M. Frank	(U.S.S.R.)	
	Igor Y. Tamm	(U.S.S.R.)	

1959 Emilio Segrè   (U.S.)   confirmation of the existence of the
     Owen Chamberlain   (U.S.)   antiproton
1960 Donald Glaser   (U.S.)   development of the bubble chamber
1961 Robert Hofstadter   (U.S.)   determination of shape and size of
                                          atomic nucleons
     Rudolf Mössbauer   (Ger.)   discovery of the Mössbauer effect
1962 Lev D. Landau   (U.S.S.R.)   contributions to the understanding
                                          of condensed states of matter
1963 J.H.D. Jensen   (Ger.)   development of shell model theory
     Maria Goeppert Mayer (U.S.)   of the structure of atomic nuclei
     Eugene Paul Wigner   (U.S.)   principles governing interaction of
                                          protons and neutrons in the nu-
                                          cleus
1964 Charles H. Townes   (U.S.)   work in quantum electronics leading
     Nikolay G. Basov   (U.S.S.R.)   to construction of instruments based
     Aleksandr M. Prokhorov (U.S.S.R.)   on maser-laser principles
1965 Julian S. Schwinger (U.S.)   basic principles of quantum electro-
     Richard P. Feynman   (U.S.)   dynamics
     Tomonaga Shin'ichirō (Japan)
1966 Alfred Kastler   (Fr.)   discovery of optical methods for
                                          studying Hertzian resonances in
                                          atoms
1967 Hans A. Bethe   (U.S.)   discoveries concerning the energy
                                          production of stars
1968 Luis W. Alvarez   (U.S.)   work with elementary particles, dis-
                                          covery of resonance states
1969 Murray Gell-Mann   (U.S.)   discoveries concerning classification
                                          of elementary particles and their in-
                                          teractions
1970 Hannes Alfvén   (Swed.)   work in magnetohydrodynamics and
     Louis Néel   (Fr.)   in antiferromagnetism and ferri-
                                          magnetism
1971 Dennis Gabor   (Brit.)   invention of holography
1972 John Bardeen   (U.S.)   development of the theory of super-
     Leon N. Cooper   (U.S.)   conductivity
     John R. Schrieffer   (U.S.)
1973 Leo Esaki   (Japan)   tunnelling in semiconductors and su-
     Ivar Giaever   (U.S.)   perconductors
     Brian Josephson   (Brit.)
1974 Sir Martin Ryle   (Brit.)   work in radio astronomy
     Antony Hewish   (Brit.)
1975 Aage Bohr   (Den.)   work toward understanding of the
     Ben R. Mottelson   (Den.)   atomic nucleus that paved the way
     L. James Rainwater   (U.S.)   for nuclear fusion
1976 Burton Richter   (U.S.)   discovery of new class of elementary
     Samuel C.C. Ting   (U.S.)   particles (psi, or J)
1977 Philip W. Anderson   (U.S.)   contributions to understanding of the
     Sir Nevill Mott   (Brit.)   behaviour of electrons in magnetic,
     John H. Van Vleck   (U.S.)   noncrystalline solids
1978 Pyotr L. Kapitsa   (U.S.S.R.)   invention and application of helium
                                          liquefier
     Arno A. Penzias   (U.S.)   discovery of cosmic microwave back-
     Robert W. Wilson   (U.S.)   ground radiation, providing support
                                          for the big-bang theory
1979 Sheldon Glashow   (U.S.)   establishment of analogy between
     Abdus Salam   (Pakistan)   electromagnetism and the "weak"
     Steven Weinberg   (U.S.)   interactions of subatomic particles

1980 James W. Cronin   (U.S.)   demonstration that time reversal does
     Val L. Fitch   (U.S.)   not precisely reverse the course of
                                          certain subatomic particle reactions
1981 Kai M. Seighahn   (Swed.)   analytical study of the interaction of
     Nicolaas Bloembergen (U.S.)   electromagnetic radiation with
     Arthur L. Schawlow   (U.S.)   matter
1982 Subrahmanyan Chandra-(U.S.)   provided the mathematical basis for
     sekhar   black-hole theories
     William Fowler   (U.S.)   development of a complete theory of
                                          the formation of the chemical ele-
                                          ments in our universe
1983 Kenneth G. Wilson   (U.S.)   development of a general mathe-
                                          matical procedure for theories in-
                                          volving the transformation of matter
1984 Carlo Rubbia   (U.S.)   discovery of intermediate boson par-
     Simon Van de Meer   (Dutch)   ticles — important evidence for the
                                          unified field theory
1985 Klaus von Klitzing   (Ger.)   quantized Hall Effect used in com-
                                          mercial electronics

Index

Credits

The publisher has made every effort to contact the copyright holders of material included in this text. Further information pertaining to rights on this material would be welcome.

Photographs
AIP Niels Bohr Library: 167 (E. Scott Barr Coll.), 271, 579 (Barr Coll.), 656 (W.F. Meggers Coll.), 696 (Meggers Coll.), 730, 751, 762 (Meggers Gallery of Nobel Laureates), 762 (photo by Francis Simon), 772, 777 (French Embassy Info. Div.), 798 (photo by Harvey of Pasadena), 799 (Meggers Coll.); Alfa-Laval Ltd.: 184 (bottom left); Athlete Information Bureau and Canadian Olympics Association: 74, 386; Atomic Energy of Canada Ltd.: 661 (bottom), 782; Bausch & Lomb: 544 (left); Courtesy of Bridges Magazine: 280; British Airways: 85; British Defence Liaison Staff, Canada: 97; Brookhaven National Laboratory: 778, 789, 796; Bureau International des Poids & Mesures, Sèvres, France: 3; M. Cagnet, M. Françon, J.C. Thierr, *Atlas of Optical Phenomena*, Springer-Verlag © 1962: 523 (top & middle), 530, 536 (top), 541, 543, 544 (right), 547 (upper), 559, 708; Courtesy of California Institute of Technology Archives: 800; Canadian Portland Cement Association: 242; Canapress Photo Service: 372, 535 (top right, bottom left & right), 803, 806; Courtesy of Central Scientific Company of Canada Ltd., cat. no. 74880-05: 363; CERN Photos: 792, 795 (bottom left); CNCP Telecommunications: 655; CN Tower: 572; Kathy Cox: 87, 171 (top); Defence & Civil Institute of Environmental Medicine: 186; Courtesy of Department of Communications: 396; © Eastman Kodak Co., 1981: 560; Dr. Harold Edgerton, MIT, Cambridge, MA: 17, 18, 291, 317; Irene Fedun: 73, 122; Fermi National Accelerator Laboratory: 791; Courtesy Firestone Canada Ltd.: 556 (bottom left & right); Gaertner Scientific Corporation: 545, 551; The Globe & Mail: 535 (top left); D.C. Heath & Company, Lexington, MA: 466, 483, 486, 490, 491, 493, 494, 496, 497, 508, 536 (bottom left & right); Japan Air Lines: 42; Jouan S.A.: 185 (bottom right); Karsh/Miller Services: 688, 747; Victor Last: 239, 240; Emmett N. Leith, Institute of Science and Technology, University of Michigan: 556 (top left); W. Llowarch, *Ripple Tank Studies of Wave Motion*, Oxford University Press, © 1961: 526; Ian Mackenzie: 88; Robert Macnaughton: 120, 172, 191, 422, 423; David Martindale: 184 (top), 185 (top), 226, 704; Mercedes-Benz of North America, Inc.: 184 (bottom right); Merlan Scientific Ltd.: 250; Metropolitan Toronto Library Board: 519, 597; Miller Services: 406 (R. Vroom); Minolta Canada Inc.: 445; NASA: 185 (bottom left), 195, 391, 481; Courtesy, National Bureau of Standards, Washington, D.C.: 5, 409; National Library of Medicine, Bethesda, MD: 128, 267, 269, 273, 278, 661 (top), 712, 752; North American Philips Corporation: 719 (left); Olympus Corporation of America: 426; Ontario Ministry of Energy: 659; Ontario Ministry of Tourism: 228; Ontario Ministry of Transportation and Communications: 131 (upper); Ontario Science Centre: 573; Joseph Perez: 131 (lower); Physics and Engineering Laboratory, New Zealand: 719 (right); Public Archives Canada: 204 (neg. no. C9766); Raytheon Company: 618; Albert Rose, *Vision: Human and Electronic*, © 1974. Plenum Publishing: 711; Scanada Consultants Limited: 660; The Science Museum, London: 524, 529, 634, 647, 657, 715, 781, 784, 793, 794, 795 (top & bottom right); Science Software Systems, Inc.: 19, 20, 45, 62, 132, 413, 425, 429, 446, 492, 516, 557, 558, 580, 588, 589, 623, 624, 625, 642; F.W. Sears, *Optics*, © 1949. Addison-Wesley, Reading, MA. Fig. 9-8. Reprinted with permission: 523 (bottom); Spectra-Physics: 535 (bottom middle); Stanford Linear Accelerator Center and U.S. Dept. of Energy: 685, 788; Toronto Star: 294; TRIUMF, University of British Columbia: 787; TRW Inc.: 555; University of Toronto Archives: 717; U.S. Air Force Photos: 86, 304; Courtesy of the Van Keuren Co.: 547 (lower); Volkswagen Canada Inc.: 171 (bottom); Yerkes Observatory, University of Chicago: 264.

Illustrations
Diagrams courtesy of Atomic Energy of Canada Ltd.: 783, 786; Sidney Harris: 6, 130, 176, 284, 672, 693, 714, 768; Brian Johnston: 496; National Geographic (copied with permission): 41 (original by Dale Gustafson), 555 (original by Pierre Mion); Sony Canada (copied with permission): 552, 553; Xerox Canada Inc.: 617.

Colour Plate
Side 1: Milton Roy Company, Analytical Products Division (top); M. Cagnet, M. Françon, S. Mallick, *Atlas of Optical Phenomena: Supplement*, Springer-Verlag © 1971 (bottom left); D.C. Heath & Company (bottom right).
Side 2: Atlas of Optical Phenomena: Supplement (top left); Science Software Systems, Inc. (top right, bottom left & right).